Ramsay's

Catalogue of

BRITISH DIECAST
MODEL TOYS

NINTH EDITION

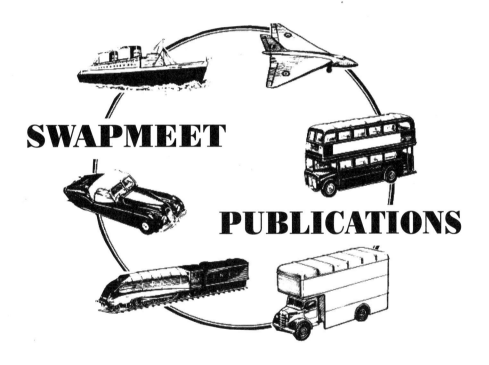

SWAPMEET

PUBLICATIONS

Swapmeet Publications
22 Foxgrove Lane, Felixstowe, Suffolk, IP11 9HE
Phone (01394) 670700, Fax: (01394) 670730
Web site: www.swapmeet.co.uk
E-mail: info@swapmeet.co.uk

Swapmeet Toys and Models Ltd., t/a Swapmeet Publications
Reg. No. 1715966. Reg. Office: 36 Rembrandt Way, Bury St Edmunds, Suffolk. Directors: E. J. Ramsay, S. E. Ramsay, Co. Sec. M. J. Ramsay, BA.

Originator and Editor
John Ramsay

Technical Editor
John King

1st Edition published 1983
2nd Edition published 1986
3rd Edition published 1988
Update published 1989
4th Edition published 1991
5th Edition published 1993
6th Edition published 1995
7th Edition published 1997
8th Edition published 1999
9th Edition published 2001

ISBN 09528352 –6– 6

Book designed by John King.
Origination by Swapmeet Publications, Felixstowe.
Printed by Page Bros. Ltd., Norwich.
Colour sections printed by Norwich Colour Print Ltd.

The front cover illustration is of a
Dinky Toys 514 Guy Van 'Weetabix' from 1952 on its original box.
(Sold by Vectis Auctions Ltd)

CONTENTS

CONTENTS continued

Contents of 'Collectable Modern Diecasts' Section (1983 - 2001)

Acknowledgements

The Editor would like to express appreciation to the following collectors, traders and manufacturers, who very kindly took the time and trouble to provide information about new entries and colour variations.

John Clark, Cambridgeshire
John Kinchen, Hampshire
David Cooke, Norwich
Dick Henrywood, Dreweatt Neate Auctioneers,
  Newbury, Berkshire
Rob Butler, Wallis and Wallis Auctions,
  Lewes, Sussex
Leigh Gotch, Bonhams Auctioneers

Paul Campbell, Sotheby's Auctions
Brian Goodall and David Nathan,
  Vectis Auctions Ltd, Stockton-on-Tees
Hugo Marsh and Nigel Mynheer of Christie's
  Model Auctions
George Beevis of Lacy Scott & Knight Model
  Auctions, Bury St Edmunds
Glen Butler of Wallis & Wallis Auctioneers
Barry Potter of Barry Potter Auctions
Chris Brierley, The Corgi Heritage Centre,
  Heywood, Lancashire
Susan Pownall, Corgi Collectors Club
  (see Club advertisement)

Adrienne Fuller, Corgi Classics Ltd., Leicester
George Hatt, Trowbridge, Wiltshire
Graham Reeves, Maldon, Essex
Mrs Joyce Peterzell, Los Angeles, USA
Stephen Beardmore, Sandbach, Cheshire
Tim Walker, Grimsby
C. J. Wigginton, London
Hans-Peter Brüggemann, Bremen
The Toy Cupboard Museum
Simon Welham, Shenfield, Essex
Andrew Rimmer, Thame, Oxon.

INTRODUCTION

Welcome to the 9th Edition of the 'British Diecast Model Toys Catalogue' which is the largest and most comprehensive edition to date.

All the previous 8th Edition listings have been carefully revised and the new listings reflect the many changes which have taken place. In addition, the design and layout of various sections of the Catalogue have been improved to make it more user-friendly. Other changes are as follows:

Dinky Toys

An exhaustive review has been undertaken and collectors will find many important price changes and new variations in the revised listings. Much of the new information has emanated from several important recent auctions such as the 'Manhattan Collection' (Vectis Model Auctions) and the 'Remy-Meeùs Collection' (Christie's, South Kensington). Dinky Toys Trade Box information has been greatly enhanced and extended by David Cooke of Norwich.

In addition, many other leading auction houses such as Bonhams of London, Wallis & Wallis of Lewes, and Lacy, Scott & Knight of Bury St Edmunds have also sold many rare boxed sets and fine models over the past couple of years. The demand for excellent quality Dinky Toys has remained constant and the prices are firm.

Corgi Toys and Classics

All the listings have been totally revised and, as a result, contain even more detailed and accurate information. This particularly applies to the Corgi Cars listing which is now in two sections and reflects the feedback received from Catalogue users. The demand for Character and Film/TV-related models has been very strong and prices have moved sharply upwards.

The major Corgi Classics section now includes all the new issues to the beginning of 2002. The Editor would like to express his thanks to Susan Pownall, Adrienne Fuller and Chris Brierly for their great assistance in updating the listings.

Matchbox Toys

The important '1-75 Series' models have been in strong demand and the revised listings reflect the high prices paid at auction for many of the rarer examples. The listings have been redesigned for greater ease of use. The Editor would like to thank Nigel Cooper for his help in preparing the listings.

The equally important 'Models of Yesteryear' and 'Matchbox Collectibles' listings have been revised and updated by Horace Dunkley and now form probably the only comprehensive listings available to collectors anywhere.

Lledo 'Days-Gone' and 'Vanguards'

The listings have been updated to include all issues to the end of 2001.

Minor Manufacturers

This very interesting area of diecast is gradually becoming more accessible despite a severe lack of manufacturers' documentation. The Editor is grateful to the many collectors who supplied information which has enabled us to list many previously unrecorded items.

Market Prices

The trend over recent years has been for model collectors to become far more concerned over the quality of the models they purchase. As a result, prices for top quality items have remained strong but models displaying faults have been available at much reduced price levels.

It cannot therefore be overstated that the Market Price Range (MPR) figures given in this Catalogue are in respect of top quality pristine models, and that anything of inferior quality will not command prices at the levels quoted.

Thanks to you

Finally, a big 'Thank You' to the many collectors who have provided new information during the past two years – do please keep it coming!

Market Price Range Grading System

Based on the findings of the Market Surveys undertaken since 1983 virtually all the models have been given a 'Market Price Range'. The price gap between the lower and higher figures indicates the likely price range a collector should expect to pay for the model.

Models qualifying for a price at the top end of the range could include:

- Boxed models where both the model and the box are in pristine condition,
- A scarce or unusual colour
- An unusual component such as special wheels
- A model with pristine decals where this is unusual
- A model in an unusual or special box
- A model priced by a trader who disagrees with the price range quoted in the Catalogue (which is only a guide).

PRICES FOR MODELS IN LESS THAN MINT BOXED CONDITION

Many boxed models seen for sale fail to match up to the exacting standards on which the Market Price Range has been based, having slight model or box damage. In these instances models may be priced at 50% to 60% of the Market Price Range shown, and this is particularly relevant when a model is common. Boxed models with considerable damage or models lacking their original box will be priced much lower.

Note: It cannot be over-emphasised that irrespective of the price guidance provided by this Catalogue, collectors should not always expect to see prices asked within the price ranges shown. Traders will ask a price based on their trading requirements and will NOT be governed by any figures shown in this Catalogue, nor could they be reasonably expected to do so.

MODELS NOT GIVEN A 'MARKET PRICE RANGE'

It has not been possible to give every model a price range and these exceptions are as follows:

NPP No Price Possible

This is shown alongside models never encountered in the survey or about which there is doubt as to their actual issue, even though a model may have been pictured in a catalogue. Readers will appreciate that unlike postage stamps or coins, no birth records are available in respect of all the die-cast models designed or issued.

NGPP No Grading Possible at Present

Price grading may not be possible at present because:

i) The model or gift set is particularly rare and has not come to market in recent times. Consequently, no price grading has been shown as the Compiler believes that to attempt one would be carrying rarity and value assessment into the realms of pure guesswork. As and when information becomes available concerning these rarities it will be included in the Catalogue.

ii) The model may have been recently introduced or announced in the model press or in a manufacturer's own literature, but a price has not yet been suggested or communicated to us.

GSP Gift Set Price

If a model forms part of a Set (and is not available separately) the price range will be shown against the entry in the relevant Gift Set section and will refer to the complete set.

DESCRIPTION OF MODEL COLOURS

The descriptions of the various colours used to describe model colour variations have been derived from the following sources:

i) Manufacturers colour descriptions.

ii) Colours commonly used and known to refer to certain models over a period of many years

iii) Colours which we in consultation with the trade or specialist collectors decide most closely describes a previously unrecorded genuine colour variation

iv) Colours given a model by an bonafide auction house. If this model is a previously unrecorded colour variation we will include the variation in future catalogue listings provided that:

a) The auctioneers are themselves satisfied that the model is genuine and not a repaint

b) Specialist dealers and collectors who view the model are satisfied that the colour variation is genuine and is not a repaint.

SCARCE COLOURS AND VARIATIONS

Collectors or traders who know of other variations which they believe warrant a separate listing are invited to forward this information to the Editor together with any supporting evidence.

AUCTION PRICE REALISATIONS

Prices of common models sold are often less than the Market Price Range figures shown. In many instances, the models have been purchased by the trade who will add their own mark-up.

Classifying the condition of models and boxes

The condition of a model and its accompanying box does of course have a direct bearing on its value which makes accurate condition grading a matter of key importance.

Unlike other collecting hobbies such as stamps or coins, no one universal grading system is used to classify the condition of models and boxes. Nevertheless, whilst several versions exist, there are really two main systems of condition classification in the UK as follows:

1. The 'Specific Condition' Grading System

The following example is fairly typical of the types of descriptions and gradings seen on Mail Order lists.

M.........Mint   AM......Almost Mint
VSC ....Very Slightly Chipped   SC ....Slightly Chipped
C ....Chipped   VC.......Very Chipped

If a model is described as Mint Boxed, the condition of its box is not normally separately described. However, it is expected to be in first class and as near original condition as is possible, bearing in mind the age of the model concerned.

If a box is damaged the flaws are usually separately described. This method has always seemed to work out quite well in practice, for all reputable dealers automatically offer a 'Sale or Return if not satisfied' deal to their clients, which provides the necessary safeguard against the misrepresentation of the model's condition. The Compiler would stress that the foregoing is only an example of a mail order condition grading system and stricter box grading definitions are known to exist.

2. The 'General Condition' Grading System

This method is often used by auctioneers although it is also to be seen used on the occasional mail order list.

(M)   Mint   (E)   Excellent
(G)   Good   (F)   Fair
(P)   Poor

Usually these gradings are separately applied to describe firstly the condition of the model and secondly the condition of the box. From our observations and purely for guidance purposes, we would suggest the following descriptions approximately represent the different grades.

MODEL CONDITION GRADINGS

1. MINT (M)
The model must be complete and as fresh, new and original in appearance as when first received from the manufacturers.

2. EXCELLENT (E)
The model is almost in mint condition and is only barred from that classification by having a few slight flaws, e.g., slight paintwork chipping in unimportant areas.

3. GOOD (G)
The model is in a complete and original condition and retains an overall collectable appearance despite having a few chips or rubbed paintwork.

4. FAIR (F)
The model may not be in its original state having, for example, a broken bumper, replacement radiator or windscreen, or it may have signs of metal fatigue. The paintwork may be faded, well chipped, retouched or repainted. There may be signs of rust. Unless the model is rare it is in a barely collectable condition.

5. POOR (P)
The model may be damaged, incomplete, repainted, altered, metal fatigued, or have a rusted baseplate or heavily chipped paintwork, etc. Unless the model is rare it has little real value to a collector other than as a candidate for a complete restoration or use as spares.

BOX CONDITION GRADINGS

1. MINT (M)
The box must be complete both inside and out and contain all the original packing materials, manufacturer's leaflet and box labels. It should look as fresh, new and original in appearance as when first received from the manufacturers.

2. EXCELLENT (E)
The box is in almost mint condition but is only barred from that classification by just the odd minor blemish, e.g., there may be slight damage to the display labels caused by bad storage. The original shop price label may have been carelessly removed and caused slight damage. The cover of a bubble pack may be cracked or there may be very slight soiling etc.

3. GOOD (G)
The box is complete both inside and out, and retains an overall attractive collectable appearance. Furthermore, despite showing a few signs of wear and tear, it does not appear 'tired'.

4. FAIR (F)
The box will have a 'tired' appearance and show definite signs of wear and tear. It may be incomplete and not contain the original packing materials or leaflets. In addition it may not display all the exterior identification labels or they may be torn or soiled or a box-end flap may be missing or otherwise be slightly damaged. In this condition, unless the model is particularly rare, it will not add much to the model's value.

5. POOR (P)
The box will show considerable signs of wear and tear. It will almost certainly be badly damaged, torn, incomplete or heavily soiled and in this condition, unless it is very rare, is of little value to a collector.

Model and Box Valuation Guidelines

The research has produced the following comparative price information concerning the values of both unboxed models and separate boxes in the various condition classifications.

The guidelines have been based on the 'General Condition' grading system as described in the previous section. The percentage value ranges are designed to reflect the relatively higher values of the rarer models and boxes.

UNBOXED MODEL CLASSIFICATION	% VALUE OF MINT BOXED MODEL
Mint	50% - 60%
Excellent	40% - 50%
Good	20% - 40%
Fair	10% - 20%
Poor	0% - 10%

BOX CLASSIFICATION	%VALUE OF MINT BOXED MODEL
Mint	40% - 50%
Excellent	30% - 40%
Good	20% - 30%
Fair	10% - 20%
Poor	0% - 10%

Note: The same model may have been issued in two or more types of box (Yesteryears for example). The model in the earlier box is usually (though not always) the more valuable.

Rare Models and Sets

The exceptions to the foregoing guidelines are in respect of rare models or boxes, or models seldom found in first class condition such as some pre-war models. In these situations rarity commands a premium and the asking price or the price realised at auction will almost certainly reflect it.

Selling models to the Trade

The model value figures produced by the Price Grading system always refer to the likely *asking prices* for models.

They have been prepared solely to give collectors an idea of the amount they might reasonably expect to pay for a particular model.

The figures given are *not* intended to represent the price which will be placed on a model when it is offered for sale to a dealer. This is hardly surprising bearing in mind that the dealer is carrying all the expense of offering his customers a collecting service which costs money to maintain.

Collectors should not therefore be surprised when selling models to the trade to receive offers which may appear somewhat low in comparison with the figures shown in the Catalogue.

Dealers are always keen to replenish their stocks with quality items and will as a result normally make perfectly fair and reasonable offers for models. Indeed, depending on the particular models offered to them, the actual offer made may well at times exceed the levels indicated in the Catalogue which are only *guidelines* and not firm figures.

One last point when selling models to the trade do get quotations from two or three dealers especially if you have rare models to be sold.

How to use the Catalogue

Identifying models from their lettering

All lettering shown in CAPITAL LETTERS indicates the actual lettering on the model itself. It may appear in either the Model Type (vehicle) or Model Features (description) column. Similarly *lettering in Italics* indicates that it is shown on the actual model.

Abbreviations

In this 9th Edition dependence on abbreviations has been reduced to a minimum but where necessary they are used to include information concisely. An Abbreviations list is included (near the back of the book) and provides additional and helpful information.

Catalogue omissions

Accurate birth records do not exist in respect of all the die-cast models issued. Therefore whilst every effort has been made to provide comprehensive information it is inevitable that collectors will have knowledge of models which have not been included. Consequently the Compiler will be pleased to receive details of these models in order that they may be included in future editions. Naturally, supporting evidence regarding authenticity will be required.

This Catalogue has been prepared solely for use as a reference book and guide to the rarity and asking prices of die-cast model toys.

Whilst every care has been taken in compiling the Catalogue, neither the Compiler nor the publishers can accept any responsibility whatsoever for any financial loss which may occur as a result of its use.

LACY SCOTT AND KNIGHT

The largest regular diecast, tinplate, lead and steam model auctions in the country

Examples of items which have successfully passed through our auctions

- Four major sales per year of 1,500 lots
- Free on-site parking

- Payments to vendors within 10 working days
- Refreshments on sale days

Auction Centre
10 Risbygate Street, Bury St Edmunds, Suffolk, IP33 3AA
Tel: 01284 748600   Fax: 01284 748620
Catalogue website: www.lsk.co.uk

WSD

How will you know if you're getting the best diecast deal until you've seen *our* prices?

free list available

Wholesale Direct
Unit 33, 24-28 St Leonards Road, Windsor, Berkshire SL4 3BB, England
Telephone: 01-173-737-873 Email: sales@wsdirect.fsnet.co.uk
International mail order specialist – most major credit cards accepted

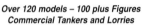
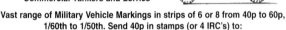

If you are really serious about buying or selling diecast models, there is only one place to visit....

Sandown Park

Europe's No.1 Toy Collectors Fair

Sandown Exhibition Centre, Sandown Park Racecourse, Esher, Surrey
10:30am – 4pm

2002 Sandown Dates
saturday 2nd March
Saturday 25th May
Saturday 10th August
Saturday 2nd November
2003 dates available later

The finest 500 Stalls in Britain

Meet all the country's Top Dealers and Collectors
and see the best of everything in Collectable Toys and Trains
Only 5 miles from junction 10 of the M25 Regular trains from Waterloo to Esher
Adult £4 Senior £3-50 Children £1 Free Parking for 6000 cars

Other leading Toy Collectors Fairs are held at
◆Bolton Reebok Stadium◆
◆Buxton◆ ◆Coventry◆
◆Dunstable◆ ◆Great Central Railway◆
◆Kettering◆ ◆Market Harborough◆
◆Northampton◆ ◆Peterborough◆
◆Rugby◆ ◆Stoneleigh◆
◆Sutton Coldfield◆

Call us for a free detailed calendar of events
on 01604 770025 or 01858 468459

Or visit our website at
www.barrypotterfairs.com

BARRY POTTER
..... *Fairs* .....

When replying to advertisements, please mention 'John Ramsay's Catalogue'.

15

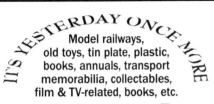

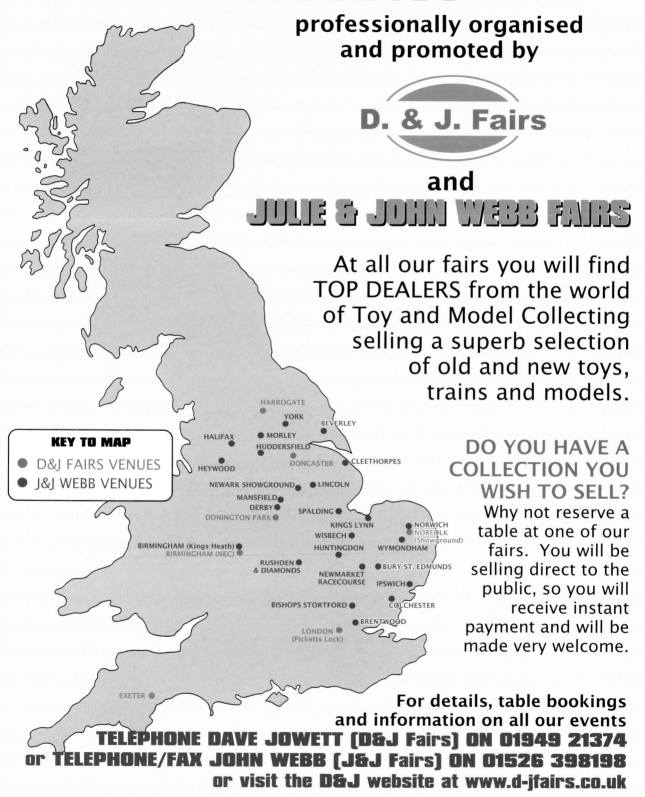

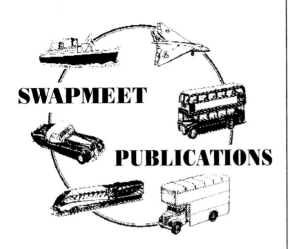

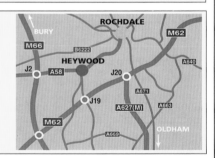

When replying to advertisements, please mention 'John Ramsay's Catalogue'.

Benbros and Zebra Toys

The following history and listings of Benbros and Zebra models have been provided by Robert Newson.

Benbros was started in the late 1940s by brothers Jack and Nathan Benenson, at Walthamstow in north-east London. They first called themselves 'Benson Bros.' and made diecast toys and lead figures (some of which are marked 'Benson'). The name Benbros was adopted in 1951. One of their best known die-cast toys was a miniature coronation coach, copied from the Moko-Lesney coach. Their range of large die-cast toys was expanded during the 1950s with re-issues of various Timpo Toys, for which Benbros had acquired the dies. The miniature

'T.V. Series' was introduced in late 1954, packed in individual boxes which resembled a 1950s television set. By 1956 there were 24 models in the T.V. Series, and soon after this the packaging was changed to red and yellow 'Mighty Midget' boxes. The Mighty Midgets were available up to 1965.

The Zebra Series was introduced in the 1960s in an attempt to update the range with better features and more accurate models. However, toy production was discontinued when Benbros was taken over in 1965.

NB See the 'Miscellaneous Models' colour section for pictures.

Benbros 'T.V. Series' and 'Mighty Midgets'

Ref	Year(s)	Model name	Colours, features, details	Market Price Range

Most models came in a very wide range of colours, so these have not been listed, but full details of colours and other variations are given in the illustrated booklet 'Benbros T.V. Series & Mighty Midgets' by Robert Newson.

Ref	Model name	Colours, features, details	Market Price Range
1	Horse Drawn Hay Cart	With man and raves. Later models marked 'BENBROS'	£20-25
2	Horse Drawn Log Cart	With man and 'log', 'Made in England' under horse	£20-25
3	A.A. Motorcycle and Sidecar	With rider and separate windscreen. 'Made in England' under sidecar	£20-30
4	Stage Coach with four horses	'KANSAS STAGE' cast in, separate driver on some, 'BENBROS' on later models	£20-25
5	Horse Drawn Gipsy Caravan	No maker's name on model	£75-100
6	Horse Drawn Milk Cart	Milkman and horse, two separate or cast-in churns, 'BENBROS' on later models	£20-25
7	Three-wheeled Electric Milk Trolley	With milkman, 'EXPRESS DAIRY' cast in	£20-25
8	Foden Tractor and Log Trailer	With log (wood dowel)	£20-25
9	Dennis Fire Escape	Separate wheeled escape ladder	£20-25
10	Crawler Bulldozer	with rubber tracks	£15-20
11	Crawler Tractor with Hay Rake	Rubber tracks. Same basic casting as no. 10. No maker's name on model	£15-20
12	Army Scout Car	Separate or cast-in driver	£15-20
13	Austin Champ	Separate or cast-in driver	£15-20
14	Centurion Tank	with rubber tracks	£15-20
15	Vespa Scooter	With rider	£25-30
16	Streamlined Express Loco	('TV Series' only). Runs on four concealed wheels	£15-20
16	Chevrolet Nomad Station Wagon	('Mighty Midget' only). Most models have silver painted flash	£15-20
17	Crawler Tractor with Disc Harrow	Rubber tracks. Same tractor as no. 11. No maker's name on model	£15-20
18	Hudson Tourer	Same chassis as no. 16	£15-20
19	Crawler Tractor and Trailer	Rubber tracks. Same tractor as nos. 11 and 17. No maker's name on model	£15-20
20	Foden 8-wheel Flat Lorry	Early models in two-tone colours	£30-40
21	Foden 8-wheel Open Lorry	Early models in two-tone colours	£30-40
22	ERF Petrol Tanker	Similar to Matchbox 11a. No adverts or with 'Esso' transfer on one side	£30-40
23	AEC Box Van	No transfers. Open rear end	£20-25
23	Bedford Box Van	Without adverts or with 'Dunlop' transfers. Open rear end	£20-25
24	Field Gun	Solid wheels. No maker's name on model. Working firing mechanism	£10-15
25	Spyker	Similar to Charbens no. 2. Both models are marked with the maker's name	£10-15
26	1904 Vauxhall 5 h.p.	Same chassis as no.25	£10-15
27	1906 Rolls-Royce	Same chassis as no.25	£10-15
28	Foden 8-w Flat Lorry with Chains	'Chains' are cast with the body	£20-25
29	RAC Motorcycle and Sidecar	With rider and separate windscreen. 'Made in England' under sidecar	£20-30
30	AEC Army Box Van	Same casting as no. 23 in Military Green paint	£20-25
30	Bedford Army Box Van	Same casting as no. 23 in Military Green paint	£20-25
31	AEC Lorry with Tilt	Cast metal 'canvas' tilt, riveted in place	£20-25
31	Bedford Lorry with Tilt	Cast metal 'canvas' tilt, riveted in place	£20-25
32	AEC Compressor Lorry	Usually painted Yellow	£20-25
32	Bedford Compressor Lorry	Usually painted Yellow	£20-25
33	AEC Crane Lorry	No hook cast	£20-25
33	Bedford Crane Lorry	No hook cast	£20-25
34	A.A. Land Rover	'AA ROAD SERVICE' cast in, open rear end	£30-40
35	Army Land Rover	No lettering on sides, open rear end	£15-20
36	Royal Mail Land Rover	'ROYAL MAIL E-II-R' cast in, open rear end	£20-30
37	Wolseley Six-Eighty Police Car	A little smaller than Morestone / Budgie no. 5	£30-40
38	Daimler Ambulance	Similar to Matchbox no. 14b. Civilian or military	£20-25
39	Bedford Milk Float	Similar to Matchbox no. 29a	£15-20
40	American Ford Convertible	Windscreen frame and seats cast with body	£20-25
41	Army Hudson Tourer	No. 18 in Military-Green paint	£20-25

42	**Army Motorcycle and Sidecar**	Castings as nos. 3 and 29, 'Made in England' and 'AA' or 'RAC' cast on sidecar	£20-30
43	**Bedford Articulated Box Van**	Without adverts or with 'Dunlop' transfers, open rear end	£20-25
44	**Bedford Articulated Lowside Lorry**	First version has hinged tailboard, later fixed	£20-25
45	**Bedford Articulated Low Loader**	With log (wood dowel)	£20-25
46	**Bedford Articulated Petrol Tanker**	Without adverts or with 'Esso' transfer on one side	£20-30
47?	**Bedford Articulated Crane Lorry**	No hook cast	£20-25
48	**Bedford Articulated Lorry with Chains**	'Chains' are cast with the model	£20-25
49	**Karrier Bantam Bottle Lorry**	Similar to Matchbox 37a. 'Drink Coca-Cola' transfers. No maker's name	£30-40
50?	**RAC Land Rover**	'RAC ROAD SERVICE' cast in, open rear	£20-30

Benbros 'Zebra Toys'

Ref	Year(s)	Model name	Colours, features, details	Market Price Range

Zebra Toys were introduced in the early 1960s and were manufactured along with the existing production of large scale Benbros vehicles. Zebra Toys were packaged in distinctive black and white striped boxes. Most of the models had jewelled headlights and some also had windows and plastic interiors.

The AA and RAC Mini Vans apparently had not been introduced when toy production by Benbros came to an end in 1965. They do not appear on a trade price list dated January 1965 but a small number of these models (probably a trial run) were sold off with the remaining toy stocks and are now in the hands of collectors.

In the following list, numbers in brackets are those shown on Zebra boxes. The other numbers are cast on the models themselves. There seems to be no connection between the two numbering systems! Original retail prices (quoted in shillings and pre-decimal pence) are those given in 1964 and 1965 trade price lists. These models are rare in today's market.

100 (16)	**Foden Concrete Mixer**	Red cab and chassis, Beige or Yellow barrel, 70 mm. (3s 1d)	£70-90
101 (36)	**Scammell Scarab Articulated**		
	Van 'BRITISH RAILWAYS'	Maroon cab and trailer, Pale Orange or Mustard-Yellow tilt, 105 mm. (4s. 4d.)	£70-90
103 (10)	**Jaguar 'E'-type**	Metallic Light Green, Metallic Light Blue or Metallic Light Brown, 90 mm. (3s 0d)	£75-100
104 (30)	**Routemaster Bus**	Red, *'Fina Petrol goes a long way'* adverts, 111 mm. (4s. 11d.)	£100-150
106 (34)	**Heinkel Bubble Car**	Red or Blue body, 100 mm. (4s 4d)	£75-100
107 (27)	**Daimler Ambulance**	Cream body, 101 mm. (4s 1d)	£75-100
--- (20)	**Bedford Cattle Transporter**	Red cab and chassis, Light Brown body, 101 mm. (4s. 4d.)	£70-90
---	**Lansing Bagnall Rapide 2000**	Fork Lift Truck, Red body, 89 mm. (3s. 6d.)	£70-90
---	**Field Gun**	Dark Green, 'BENBROS' cast on model, 102 mm. (2s. 0d.)	£15-20
--- (1)	**Police Patrol Motorcycle**	(Triumph) 'Silver' plated, plastic rider, 'ENT 303' cast, 84 mm. (2s. 6d.)	£30-40
---	**Rally Motorcycle**	(Triumph) 'Silver' plated, plastic rider, 'ENT 303' cast, 84 mm. (2s. 6d.)	£30-40
--- (3)	**Army Despatch Motorcycle**	(Triumph) 'Silver' plated, plastic rider, 'ENT 303' cast, 84 mm. (2s. 6d.)	£30-40
--- (4)	**Telegraph Boy Motorcycle**	(Triumph) 'Silver' plated, plastic rider, 'ENT 303' cast, 84 mm. (2s. 6d.)	£30-40
---	**'RAC' Triumph Motorcycle and Sidecar**	Black bike, Blue sidecar, White fairing, plastic rider, 'ENT 303', 84 mm. (3s. 5d.)	£75-100
--- (6)	**'A.A.' Triumph Motorcycle and Sidecar**	Black bike, Yellow sidecar and fairing, plastic rider, 'ENT 303', 84 mm. (3s. 5d.)	£75-100
--- (60)	**Austin Mini Van**	'AA PATROL SERVICE', Yellow body. Opening side and rear doors	£150-200
---	**Austin Mini Van**	'RAC', Blue body. Opening side and rear doors	£150-200

'Qualitoys' and other Benbros model vehicles

Ref	Year(s)	Model name	Colours, features, details	Market Price Range

This list includes all the other vehicles in the Benbros range, mostly large scale items. Many carried the name 'Qualitoy' as well as 'Benbros', and most were individually boxed. Dating of these models is quite difficult, since there were few contemporary adverts, and the only catalogues known are trade price lists for 1964 and 1965. The Timpo re-issues were probably no earlier than 1952, and the various motorcycles were introduced in late 1955. Where a retail price is shown (in shillings and pence) the model was still available on the 1964 and 1965 price lists.

Coronation Coach with 8 horses	'ER' cast on doors, 'MADE IN ENGLAND' on drawbar. Later boxes marked 'Zebra Toys', 116 mm (3s 7d)	£30-40
State Landau with 4 horses	Two separate footmen. 'MADE IN ENGLAND' under coach. 105 mm. (3s 7d)	£30-40
Father Christmas Sleigh	With four reindeer. Metallic green or metallic blue. 110 mm. (2s 6d)	£60-80
Covered Wagon with 4 Bullocks	Re-issue of a model by L. Brooks (Toys) Ltd. (1958). Hollow-cast lead bullocks (diecast on the Brooks model). 'MADE IN ENGLAND' lengthwise under, Cloth canopy, Green wagon, Yellow wheels, cowboy. 186 mm	£60-80
Covered Wagon with 4 Horses	Same wagon as above. Canopy plain or with 'BUFFALO BILL'S COVERED WAGON' or 'CALGARY STAMPEDE COVERED WAGON' printed. Red or Green wagon (Yellow shaft) or Metallic Green or Metallic Blue (Red shaft). Yellow wheels, two barrels, metal or plastic cowboy holding whip. 186 mm. (4s 8d)	£60-80
Rickshaw with two Passengers	Pulled by Ostrich or Zulu. Shown in the Joplin book* as Crescent, but believed to be Benbros. 150 mm	£125-175
Roman Chariot with two horses	With figure. Metallic Green or Yellow with Red wheels. About 135 mm	£60-80
Horse Drawn Farm Cart and man	Re-issue of Timpo model. Light Green or Yellow cart, Brown horse	£60-80
Horse Drawn Water Wagon	Re-issue of Timpo model. Light Green wagon, Brown horse	£80-100
Horse Drawn Log Wagon with Log	Yellow with Red wheels, or Red with Yellow wheels, or Orange with Red wheels, Brown horse. 225 mm	£80-100
Stephenson's Rocket		
Loco and Tender	Metallic Brown or Silver plated loco. Tender metallic Green, Metallic Blue, Orange or Red. 105 mm	£30-40
Caterpillar Tractor	Copy of early Lesney model. Red or Yellow or metallic Blue, rubber tracks, 97 mm. (3s 6d)	£30-40

Caterpillar Bulldozer	Copy of early Lesney model. Red tractor with Black blade, or metallic Blue with Red or Yellow blade. Rubber tracks. 118 mm. (4s 11d)	**£30-40**
Caterpillar Excavator with driver	Orange (Green shovel) or metallic Blue (Red shovel), rubber tracks, Red or Green driver, 138 mm. (4s. 11d.)	**£30-40**
Ferguson Tractor with driver	No name on model. Yellow or Red with unpainted wheels, metallic Green or Yellow with Red wheels, Orange with Black or Blue wheels. Driver Green, Brown, Blue, Metallic Blue or Grey. 73 mm. (2s 6d)	**£70-80**
Ferguson Tractor with Cab and Shovel	No name on model. Red, Yellow or dark Green, unpainted wheels, Green or Brown driver. 100 mm	**£70-80**
Ferguson Tractor and Log Trailer	With driver and log. Tractor details as above. Red trailer (179mm) with yellow wheels. (4s 3d)	**£70-80**
Ferguson Tractor with Roller	With driver. No name on model. Former Timpo horse-drawn roller plus drawbar. Tractor as above, Red trailer with Yellow rollers. Trailer length 109 mm. (3s 6d)	**£70-80**
Ferguson Tractor with Harrow	With driver. No name on model. Former Timpo horse-drawn harrow plus drawbar. Tractor as above, Red or Yellow trailer, length about 110 mm. (3s 6d)	**£70-80**
Euclid Dumper Lorry	Copy of Dinky 965. Metallic Blue cab and chassis, Yellow or Orange tipper. 145mm. (5s 10d)	**£50-60**
Muir Hill Dumper with Driver	Orange (Green tipper, Blue wheels), Yellow (Red or Orange tipper, Blue wheels), Metallic Green (Orange tipper, Blue wheels), or Red with Yellow tipper, Black wheels, 105 mm. (3s 11d)	**£40-50**
A101 Army Land Rover and Field Gun	Open Land Rover has two figures cast, separate windscreen, metal wheels with rubber tyres. Field gun marked 'BENBROS', solid rubber wheels. Matt Dark Green. 111 mm. and 102 mm	**£60-80**
A102 Lorry with Anti-Aircraft Gun ..	Matt dark Green, Silver gun. 117 mm	**£25-30**
A103 Lorry with Radar Scanner	Matt dark Green, Silver radar dish. 117 mm	**£25-30**
A104 Lorry with Searchlight	Matt dark Green. 117 mm	**£25-30**
A105 Armoured Car and Field Gun ..	Dark Brownish-Green or matt dark Green. Field gun same as A101. 96 mm and 102 mm	**£30-40**
A106 Army AEC Lorry with Tilt	'SUNDERLAND' cast on cab sides. Dark Brownish-Green or matt dark Green, Green cloth tilt. 132 mm	**£100-125**
A107 Army Closed Land Rover	Casting as A101. Matt dark Green, Black roof. Opening side and rear doors. 111 mm	**£40-50**
A110 Army Articulated Low-Loader with Field Gun	Matt Dark Green Low-loader as no. 221, Field Gun as no. A101 but with metal hubs and rubber tyres	**£30-40**
220 AEC Flat Lorry with chains	'SUNDERLAND' cast on cab sides. Red cab and chassis, light Green, Blue, Beige or Metallic Green body. 130 mm. (3s 6d)	**£100-125**
221 Articulated Low Loader	Re-issue of Timpo model. Red or Green cab with Red, Yellow or metallic Green trailer. No name on model. 166 mm	**£25-30**
223 Land Rover 'Royal Mail'	Red (Black roof). 'ROYAL MAIL E-II-R' cast on sides. Opening side and rear doors, 2 figures cast inside. 111mm .	**£100-120**
224 Articulated Tanker	Re-issue of Timpo model, no maker's name on model, 146mm (3s 6d). Red or Orange cab, Green or metallic Green or Yellow trailer, 'MOTOR OIL ESSO PETROL' transfer	**£60-75**
	Green cab, Red trailer, 'SHELL PETROL' label	**£60-75**
	Light Green cab, Red trailer, 'UNITED DAIRIES' transfer	**£60-75**
225 AEC Dropside Lorry	'SUNDERLAND' cast on cab sides. Red cab and chassis, light Green or Blue body. 132 mm. (3s 6d)	**£75-100**
226 Petrol Tanker	Re-issue of Timpo model. Red cab / chassis with Red or Yellow tank, light Green cab / chassis with Yellow tank. 'Motor Oil Esso Petrol' or 'Fina Petrol Goes a Long Way' transfer. No name on model. 117 mm. (3s 1d)	**£80-100**
227 AEC Flat Lorry	Re-issue of Timpo model. 'SUNDERLAND' cast on cab sides. Red cab and chassis, light Green, Blue or Cream body. 130 mm. (3s 1d)	**£80-100**
228 AEC Lorry with Tilt	As no.225 with plain cloth tilt. 132 mm	**£75-100**
Forward Control Box Van	Re-issue of Timpo model, no maker's name on model. 99 mm. Green cab and chassis with light Green or Red body with 'Pickfords Removals' labels	**£80-100**
	Red cab, chassis and body, plain	**£25-30**
	Red cab and chassis, Green body, 'CHIVERS JELLIES' transfers	**£80-100**
Articulated Box Van	Re-issue of Timpo model, no maker's name on model. 145 mm. Red or Green cab with Green, Red or Cream trailer. 'LYONS TEA' transfers.	**£100-150**
	Red cab with Green trailer. 'UNITED DAIRIES' transfers.	**£100-150**
	Light Green cab with Red or Orange trailer. 'BISHOP & SONS DEPOSITORIES LTD.' transfers	**£100-150**
A.A. Land Rover	Casting as A107 and 223. 'AA ROAD SERVICE' cast on sides and roof sign. Opening side and rear doors, two figures inside. Yellow with Black roof or all Yellow. 111 mm. (5s 10d)	**£100-125**
310 Ruston-Bucyrus 10-RB Crane	Maroon and Yellow body, dark Green chassis and jib, rubber tracks. 'BENBROS' cast underneath. (3s 6d)	**£70-80**
311 Ruston-Bucyrus 10-RB Excavator	Maroon and Yellow body, dark Green chassis and arms, rubber tracks. 'BENBROS' cast underneath. (3s 6d)	**£70-80**
AEC Lorry and Ruston-Bucyrus Crane	'SUNDERLAND' cast on cab sides. Red cab and chassis, Yellow body. Crane as no.310 with Maroon and Yellow body, dark green jib. 128 mm. (5s 10d)	**£100-125**
AEC Lorry with Ruston-Bucyrus Excavator	'SUNDERLAND' cast on cab sides. Red cab and chassis, Yellow body. Excavator as no.311 with Maroon and Yellow body, dark Green arms. 128 mm. (5s 10d)	**£100-125**
A.A. Motorcycle and Sidecar	Black cycle, AA badge cast on Yellow sidecar and windscreen, 'TTC147' cast on number plates. 84 mm.	
	(i) Fixed front forks, windscreen with plastic glazing, dark Brownish-Green metal rider	**£75-100**
	(ii) Steering front forks, windscreen with curved frame cast in place of glazing, plastic rider	**£75-100**
RAC Motorcycle and Sidecar	Black cycle, RAC badge cast on Blue sidecar and windscreen. 'TTC147' cast on number plates. Steerable front forks, windscreen with curved frame, plastic rider. 84 mm	**£75-100**
Solo Motorcycle with Rider	Fixed front forks, 'TTC147' cast on number plates. 84 mm.	
	(i) Police Patrol - Maroon cycle, Black metal rider	**£30-40**
	(ii) Telegraph Boy - Red cycle, Red metal rider	**£30-40**
	(iii) Army Despatch Rider - Dark Brownish-Green cycle and metal rider	**£30-40**
	(iv) Rally Rider - Green cycle, Blue metal rider	**£30-40**
Solo Motorcycle with Rider	Steerable front forks, 'TTC147' cast on number plates. Silver plated cycles with plastic riders in four versions - Police Patrol, Telegraph Boy, Army Despatch Rider and Rally. 84 mm	**£30-40**

* Reference: 'The Great Book of Hollow-Cast Figures' by Norman Joplin (New Cavendish Books).

Britains Model Vehicles

BRITAINS MOTOR VEHICLES

by Mike Richardson

Most people are aware of the military vehicles made by Britains both before the War and after in 1/32 scale to go with their soldiers, but not so many are acquainted with the contemporary civilian models. Some of these models are only colour variations of the military versions, for example the 59F 'Four-wheeled Lorry with Driver' in the farm series is the same as 1335 'Lorry, Army, Four-wheeled type' but painted in a smart duotone colour scheme instead of khaki. Other models are only available in the civilian type, usually for the good reason that the army could not possibly have a use for a militarised version. A good example of this would be 1656 'John Cobbs Railton Wonder Car' (or 'Railton Mobil Special' as we know it!).

Britains are our oldest toy company which is still in business having been started in 1860 although the first of the famous soldiers did not appear until 1890. This still means over a hundred years continuous toy manufacture, surely a record. The motor lorry models appeared in late 1932 and were based on the Albion army lorries of the time with the familiar 'square' cab design which was to be a hallmark of the Britains lorries until the end of the decade. The range of 4, 6 and 10-wheel farm lorries are still illustrated in the 1940 catalogue. After the War the cab was brought up to date by a change to a more rounded Fordson type, not nearly so attractive.

The military ambulance was also used in civilian versions, a cream 'Corporation' and a blue 'Volunteer Corps' as alternative liveries to the khaki army one. The rarest version of this model is the red and black 'Royal Mail' van which was sold for a short time towards the end of the production run.

There are three civilian cars, a 'Two-seater Coupé' and two 'Sports Model Open Tourers' in the pre-war production. The coupé and the open sports car without driver and passenger do not have military equivalents, but when the open sports car has people in it then it is either a 'Mobile Police Car with 2 Officers' (finished in green with black wings), or a 'Staff Car with 2 Officers'

as the military offering. The occupants of the car are legless and their lower regions are covered with a tartan rug - how nice for them on cold days! After the War there was a one-piece casting version of the staff car and police car without the separate grilles of the pre-war models and these were rather plain by comparison.

The final group of models consists of the superb record cars 'Bluebird' and 'Railton Special'. These came out in the late 1930s and each is over 6 inches long. The Bluebird was produced in three versions; a) with fully detailed removable chassis, b) without this part, and c) a slightly smaller one (just over 5 inches), without underside detail. The Railton Mobil Special always had the removable chassis and was available painted silver for 1s.6d. or chrome plated for 2s.6d.

After the War two new farm tractor models appeared, a couple of Fordson Majors produced with the active co-operation of the Ford Motor Company. These are excellent models both finished in the correct shade of dark blue and with the name 'Fordson' applied to the front and sides of the radiator. One version has standard wheels but the other (rarer) one had the spiked or 'spud' wheels used on heavy ground.

All these models are to the same scale as the soldiers (1/32), but there is also a similar range in '00' gauge (1/76 scale) to go with model railways. The smaller models date mainly from the post-war era although a sports car and a fastback saloon were seen pre-war. The small scale trucks have a Fordson cab similar to the later large scale farm and army lorries.

The large scale pre-war models are very collectable and prices are consequently very high for rare items in excellent condition and with original lovely boxes. Some few years ago a batch of replicas of the coupé were made here in England so exercise care when buying this model. Spare parts are, or have been available for most of these toys to enable repairs to be carried out.

NB See the 'Miscellaneous Models' colour section for pictures.

ARMY VEHICLES

1876   Bren Gun Carrier, Carden Vickers type suspension, with Driver, Bren Gun and Gunner, and 2nd Guard.
Measures 3½″ long.

1448   Staff Car, with General and Driver.
Measures 4″ long.

1334   Four-wheeled Army Lorry, with Driver, Tipping body.   Measures 6″ long.

1335   Six-wheeled Army Lorry, with Driver, Tipping body.   Measures 6″ long.

MANUFACTURED BY *W Britain* IN LONDON, ENGLAND
TRADE   REGD. No. 459993.   MARK.

An illustration from the January 1955 Britains Ltd. catalogue.

Britains Motor Vehicles (pre-war issues)

The models were constructed of a lead based alloy and the main body parts were hollow cast. However, parts such as wings and running boards were die-cast individually by hand. The Market Price Range figures refer to boxed models in excellent condition.

Civilian Vehicles

Ref	Model name	Colours, features, details	Market Price Range
59 F	Four-wheeled Lorry with Driver	Back and doors open, rubber tyres, 6"	£150-200
60 F	Six-wheeled Lorry with Driver	Two-tone Blue body, White cab roof, Silver radiator surround, back and doors open, White rubber tyres, 6"	£150-200
61 F	Ten-wheeled Lorry with Driver	Back and doors open, rubber tyres	£200-250
90 F	Builders Lorry	As 59 F plus builders name on side. *'DAVIS ESTATES LTD BUILDERS OF HOMES'*	£2,000-3,000
91 F	Builders Lorry	As 60 F plus builders name on side. Never seen.	NPP
92 F	Builders Lorry	As 61 F plus builders name on side. Never seen.	NPP
1398	Sports Model Open Tourer	Cream body, Black chassis and wheels, White rubber tyres, 4.25"	£750-1,000
1399	Two-Seater Coupé (fitted bumpers)	Cream body, Tan roof, wings and running-boards, Black hubs, White tyres, 4.5". (Also in other colours)	£1,000-1,250
1413	Mobile Police Car with two Officers	2-piece casting, Green body, Black wings, White tyres, 4.75". (Also in other colours)	£500-600
1470	The Royal Household Set	Coronation State Coach, King George VI plus the Queen with twelve attendants	£300-500
1513	Volunteer Corps Ambulance with Driver, Wounded Man and Stretcher	Blue body, 'AMBULANCE', Red/White cross, White tyres	£600-700
1514	Corporation Type Motor Ambulance with Driver, Wounded Man and Stretcher	Cream body, 'AMBULANCE', Red/White cross, White tyres	£700-900
1552	'ROYAL MAIL' Van with Driver	Post-Office Red body, Black bonnet, 'GR' plus crown design, White tyres	£1,600-2,000
	1924 Wembley Exhibition Locomotive	Bronze finished diecast locomotive on plinth with '1924 Wembley Exhibition' '240 tons - largest locomotive in the world'	NGPP

Military Vehicles

Early issues of lorry and truck models in the ranges 1333 - 1433 and 1641 - 1643 had 'square' cabs, (post-war issues had 'rounded' cabs).

Ref	Model name	Colours, features, details	Market Price Range
1321	**Armoured Car with Gun**	Military Green, solid metal wheels	£100-125
1333	**Lorry, Army, Caterpillar Type with Driver**	Military Green finish, rubber tyres, 6"	£150-200
1334	**Four-wheeled Tipper Lorry**	with Driver	£150-200
1335	**Lorry, Army, Six-wheeled Type with Driver**	Military Green finish, rubber tyres, 6"	£150-200
1392	**Autogiro**	Military Green finish, RAF roundels, pilot, three detachable rotor blades	£750-950
1432	**Tender, Army, Covered, Ten-wheeled (with Driver)**	Military Green finish, White rubber tyres, 6"	£150-200
1433	**Tender, Army, Covered, Ten-wheeled Caterpillar Type (with Driver)**	Military Green finish, White rubber tyres, 6"	£150-200
1448	**Car, Staff**	Military Green car with 2 Staff Officers, White rubber tyres, 4"	£350-450
1641	**Underslung Heavy Duty Lorry (18 wheels) with Driver**	Military Green finish, 10"	£350-450
1641	**Underslung Heavy Duty Lorry (18 wheels) with Driver**	with 1749 Mounted Barrage Balloon Winch	£900-1,100
1642	**Underslung Heavy Duty Lorry (18 wheels) with Driver**	with Mounted Searchlight, Military Green finish, 10"	£350-450
1643	**Underslung Heavy Duty Lorry (18 wheels) with Driver**	with Mounted Anti-Aircraft Gun (small)	£350-450
1643	**Underslung Heavy Duty Lorry (18 wheels) with Driver**	with Mounted Anti-Aircraft Gun (large)	£600-800

Autogiro and Record Cars (1:43 scale)

Ref	Model name	Colours, features, details	Market Price Range
1392	**Autogiro**	Blue body, (other colours are known) including Military Green with pilot and three detachable rotor blades	£750-950
1936	**Bluebird Record Car**	(Napier-Campbell) Malcolm Campbell's car, lift-off body, detailed engine, White tyres	£150-175
1939	**Napier Railton**	John Cobb's car, '350.20 mph World Land Speed Record'	£250-300

'Circus' Series

'Mammoth Circus Roundabout'
Six horses (Black, Brown, White) plus riders, Green, Red and Yellow Carousel canopy.
Lead and card construction. Circa 1910 .... £2,000-3,000
'The Flying Trapeze' Set (No. 1141)
High wire act with balancing clown and suspended girl trapeze artiste, twirling paper parasol, wire
and card winder, marbled patterned box. 1936-39 .... £2,000-3,000

'Motor and Road' Series

Ref	Model name	Colours, features, details	Market Price Range
1313	**Volunteer Corps 'AMBULANCE'**	Finished in Blue, with wounded man and stretcher	£300-400
2024	**Light Goods Van with Driver**	Various colours, 'BRITAINS LTD' logo	£400-500
2045	**Clockwork Van** (c1938)	Various colours, driver, opening rear doors. In Red box with Dark Yellow picture label	£900-1,200
	NB	A boxed example of 2045 with red cab and green van body, Black 'BRITAINS' logo on White background, with driver and original clockwork key sold at the Lacy, Scott & Knight 11/97 auction for	£1,050

23

Britains Motor Vehicles (post-war issues)

Ref	Year(s)	Model name	Colours, features, details	Market Price Range

'Farm' series

59 F		Farm Tipping Lorry	with Driver Light Green or Blue	£150-250
127 F		Fordson 'MAJOR' Tractor	with Driver and spade-end wheels	£200-250
128 F		Fordson 'MAJOR' Tractor	with Driver and rubber-tyred wheels	£175-225

'Clockwork' series

2041		Clockwork Unit (2-wheeled trailer)	..'Will last 1 1/2 minutes when fully wound and capable of driving any other vehicle 20-30 feet'	£45-55
2045		Clockwork Van	Finished in various colours with 'BRITAINS LTD' logo	£500-700

Military issues

Post-war issues of lorry and truck models in the ranges 1333 - 1433 and 1641 - 1643 had 'rounded' cabs, (pre-war issues had 'square' cabs).

1334		Four-wheeled Tipper Lorry	('rounded' cab) with Driver	£150-200
1335		Six-wheeled Tipper Lorry	('rounded' cab) with Driver	£150-200
1433		Covered Army Truck	('rounded' cab) Caterpillar type with Driver	£150-200
1448		Staff Car	with General and Driver	£350-450
1512		Army 'AMBULANCE'	('rounded' cab) with wounded man and stretcher	£150-200
1791		Motorcycle Dispatch Rider	sold unboxed	£25-35
1876		Bren Gun Carrier with Driver, Gunner and 2nd Guard	Carden-Vickers type suspension cast-in, separate Bren gun, 3½ "	£75-125
1877		Beetle Lorry and Driver		£65-75
2150		Centurion Tank	Military Green	£300-400
2156		Centurion Tank	Desert Warfare finish	£400-500
2048		Military Set	1877, 2041 and 2026 Gun	£150-175

'Lilliput' Series (1:76 scale)

LV 601	Open Sports Car	2.25" long	£60-70
LV 602	Saloon Car	2.25" long	£60-70
LV 603	Articulated Lorry	4" long	£60-70
LV 604	Fordson Tractor with Driver	1.5" long	£35-45
LV 605	Milk Float and Horse with Milkman. 2.25" long		£45-55
LV 606	Tumbrel Cart and Horse with Hay Racks and Carter	2.75" long	£35-45
LV 607	Austin 3-ton Covered Military Truck		£35-45
LV 608	Austin 3-ton Farm Truck		£35-45
LV 609	Austin Military Champ		£65-75
LV 610	Centurion Tank		£35-45
LV 611	Self-propelled 25-pounder Gun		£25-35

LV 612	Humber 1-1/2 ton Military Truck		£35-45
LV 613	Humber 1-1/2 ton Military Truck	Covered version	£35-45
LV 614	Farm Trailer		£15-25
LV 615	Saracen Armoured Vehicle		£15-25
LV 616	1½ ton Truck		£35-45
LV 617	Civilian Ambulance. Cream body with 'AMBULANCE' on sides, 'BRITAINS' on rubber tyres, Red plastic hubs		£100-125
LV 618	Army Ambulance		NGPP
LV 619	'ROYAL MAIL' Van		NGPP
LV 620	3 ton Open Truck		NGPP

Motor Cycle Combination

9699		BMW Racing Combination	Red and Yellow with Black rider with White helmet	NGPP

Illustration of Mechanical Unit driving No. 127F
" Fordson Major " Tractor.

Illustration of Mechanical Unit driving No. 128F
" Fordson Major " Tractor.

MANUFACTURED BY *W Britain* IN LONDON ENGLAND

TRADE   REGD No. 459993.   MARK

An illustration from the January 1951 Britains Ltd. catalogue.

Chad Valley

The Chad Valley company (makers of board games and wooden toys) produced tinplate toy vehicles from 1932 incorporating the year of manufacture in the registration number on the number plates.

Their first 'Wee-Kin' diecast toy vehicles were produced around 1949 and had 'CV 1949' as the registration number. They were fitted with a key-wound clockwork motor and were designed more as toys than models having generic titles like 'Open Lorry' or 'Fire Engine'. The cars issued between 1951 and 1954 as Rootes Group promotionals are much better attempts at models and were sold at Rootes Group garages as well as normal toy shops. The tractors produced from 1952 are particularly fine and well detailed models.

The years shown below indicate the periods in which Chad Valley offered them for sale though not all the toys were available for the whole of the period and some were still in the shops well after production ceased in 1956.

Ref	Year(s)	Model name	Colours, features, details	Market Price Range

Chad Valley diecast clockwork toys and model vehicles

Ref	Year(s)	Model name	Colours, features, details	Market Price Range
220	1949-53	Razor Edge Saloon	Various colours, number plates 'CV 1949', approximate scale 1:43	£140-180
221	1949-53	Traffic Control Car	Casting as 220 plus loudspeaker, 'CV 1949', approximate scale 1:43	£140-180
222	1949-53	Police Car	Casting as 220 plus loudspeaker and 'POLICE' sign, 'CV 1949', scale 1:43	£140-180
223	1949-53	Track Racer	'CV 1949' on number plates, no other details	£140-180
224	1949-53	Double Decker Bus	Red body, number plates 'CV 1949', Approximate scale 1:76	£140-180
225	1949-53	Open Lorry	Various colours, 'CV 1949' on number plates	£140-180
226	1949-53	Low-Loader	Green / Red body, 'CV 1949' on number plates, three cream-coloured packing cases	£140-180
227	1949-53	Timber Wagon	'CV 1949', body has round bosses to fit milk churns or other 'loads'	£140-180
228	1949-53	Cable Layer	Red cab, Green body, silver trim, number plates 'CV 1949'	£150-180
229	1949-53	Breakdown Lorry	Number plates 'CV 1949', no other details	£150-180
230	1949-53	Milk Float	Number plates 'CV 1949', load of eight milk churns	£150-180
231	1949-53	Fire Engine	Red body, number plates 'CV 1949'	£150-175
232	1949-53	Tower Repair Wagon	Number plates 'CV 1949', Green body and hubs	£200-250
233	1949-53	Milk Tanker	Blue body and logo, White tank, number plates 'CV 1949'	£150-175
234	1949-53	Petrol Tanker	Number plates 'CV 1949', no other details	£150-175
236	1949-53	The Hillman Minx	Grey or Metallic Dark Blue body, Rootes Group promotional, 1:43 scale	£140-180
237	1949-53	The Humber Super Snipe	Metallic Dark Green or Red body, Rootes Group promotional, 1:43 scale	£140-180
238	1949-53	The Sunbeam-Talbot	Light Blue or Metallic Dark Green, Rootes Group promotional, 1:43 scale. Base has the wording 'A Rootes Group Product' plus usual Chad Valley marks	£140-180
239	1949-53	Dust Cart	Body has tinplate sliding side panels, number plates 'CV 1949'	£140-180
240	1949-53	Commer Avenger Coach	Blue or Red body marked 'A Rootes Group Product', 1:76 scale, promotional	£200-250
242	1949-53	The Commer Hands	(6-wheel artic.), 'A Rootes Group Product', Red body with 'Commer Hands' sticker, promotional	£150-175
507	1951-54	The Humber Hawk	Metallic Dark Blue, Metallic Dark Green, or mid-Green body, Rootes Group promotional, 1:43 scale	£140-180
	1951-54	Guy Van	Dark Blue / Cream, tinplate doors, *Lyons Ice Cream Cadby Hall London W11*	£150-200
-	1951-54	Guy Van	Red body, Blue hubs, tinplate doors, Red *'CHAD VALLEY'* logo	£150-200
-	1951-54	Guy Van	Green body, tinplate doors, Yellow *'Guy Motors Ltd, Commercial Vehicle Manufacturers'*	£150-200

Other issues (with or without motor)

Ref	Year(s)	Model name	Market Price Range	Ref	Year(s)	Model name	Market Price Range
--	1950-55	Massey Ferguson Tractor	£100-125	--	1950-55	Guy Truck 'LYONS ICE CREAM'	£100-125
--	1950-55	Ford Tractor	£100-125	--	1950-55	Sunbeam-Talbot Saloon, metallic pale brown	£75-95
--	1950-55	Hillman Minx Saloon	£100-125	--	1950-55	Guy Milk Tanker, blue /cream, 'MILK'	£75-95
--	1950-55	Humber Super Snipe, blue / grey body	£90-120	--	1950-55	Guy Cable Lorry	£75-95
--	1950-55	Guy Truck	£75-95	--	1950-55	Guy Petrol Tanker 'REGENT PETROL'	£100-125
--	1950-55	Sunbeam Racer	£100-125	--	1950-55	Guy 'FIRE' Engine	£100-125
--	1950-55	Humber Hawk	£75-95	--	1950-55	Guy Container Lorry	£75-95
--	1950-55	Rolls-Royce Razor Edge Saloon	£75-95		1950-55	Guy Refuse Lorry	£75-95
--	1950-55	Routemaster London Bus	£100-125				
--	1950-55	Commer Avenger Coach	£100-125				

Chad Valley model Tractors

Ref	Year	Model name	Colours, features, details	Market Price Range
--	1952	Fordson Major E27N	Dark Blue body, Orange wheels, rubber tyres (2 types of tread on rear), steering, towbar with pin, clockwork wound by starting handle. Scale 1:16. Illustrated box or plain box with small label	£150-200
--	1954	Fordson Major DDN	Mid-Blue body, Orange wheels, rubber tyres, working steering, lifting bonnet, towbar/pin, hydraulic lift at rear (detachable centre arm), clockwork wound through rear hub. Scale 1:16. Illustrated box or plain box with small label	£150-200
	Static version:		As previous model but without clockwork but without clockwork operation. Illustrated box or plain box plus small label. The word 'working' is deleted from all sides of box	£150-200
	Chrome version:		Static (non-clockwork) version in chrome plate, with or without wooden plinth. Thought to be a ploughing trophy or Ford presentation model	£250-400
--	1955	Ford Dexta	Mid-Blue, Orange wheels, radiator panels and 'Fordson Dexta', not steerable, rubber tyres, hook, 1:16. Illustrated box	£400-600
--	1955	Ferguson	Green, Red wheels, 'Ferguson' on sides, steering, hook, scale 1:16. Illustrated box inscribed 'Ferguson'. Promotional	£500-700
			Grey body, Grey wheels, hydraulic lift at rear	£600-800
--	1955	Fordson Major E27N	Red and Yellow with driver, clockwork, scale 1:43, boxed. Made under licence by 'Raybro & Sturdy Products S.A.', Johannesburg, South Africa (model marked 'Chad Valley GB')	£50-100

The introduction to the Chad Valley section was written by Sue Richardson who also provided the basic listing.
Additional listing information came from the Cecil Gibson archives and John G. Butler of Berkhampstead, Herts.

Charbens Toys

The following history and listings have been researched by Robert Newson and Swapmeet Publications.

The firm of Charbens & Co. was started around 1928 by Charles and Benjamin Reid and was based at Hornsey Road, Holloway, London N7. They made hollow-cast lead figures, and a few lead vehicles were also produced in the 1930s. After the war zinc die-casting was introduced, and some items exist in both lead and zinc versions (the latter from new dies). Zinc castings by Charbens very often have metal failure as a result of contamination from the lead that was still used extensively in the factory.

The 'Old Crocks' series of miniatures was introduced in 1955. After 1967 all vehicle models were deleted from the catalogue except for a few items included in sets with plastic figures. Production of figures was discontinued in 1973.

Model numbers were allocated around 1954, so items which had already been withdrawn are not numbered. Dates of issue have been taken from catalogues or adverts, but inevitably are incomplete. Most pre-war items have 'RD' cast in, most post-war items have 'CHARBENS' cast underneath.

NB See the 1st colour section for pictures.

Ref	Year(s)	Model name	Colours, features, details	Market Price Range

Pre-war issues (part hollow-cast, part diecast construction)

-	-	Motorcycle Policeman	Solid cast machine with green petrol tank	£30-40
-	-	Police Motor Cycle and Sidecar	Solid cast machine, rider and passenger in black / white uniforms, black sidecar	£30-40
-	-	Soap Box Racer	Solid cast brown base, four red wheels (six spokes), Cub Scout pushing,Cub Scout rider	£70-90
-	-	Goat Cart with Girl	Blue cart and girl, brown goat, yellow 6-spoke wheels	£30-40
-	-	Goat Cart with Girl	Red cart and girl, white goat, 6-spoke wheels	£30-40
-	-	Road Workers Set	Contains Horse Roller (green / orange / brown), orange / black tar boiler truck with 6-spoke wheels, plus 4 workmen, a nightwatchman, hut, brazier, 'Road up' sign, pipe and 2 barriers	£150-180
-	-	Gypsy Caravan	Blue / white caravan with white horse, yellow wheels (smaller at front) plus orange / black seated Gypsy woman with baby, standing man, linen line with washing, cooking pot	£200-250
-	-	The Farm Wagon	Green / yellow four-wheel wagon with two hay racks, brown carthorse, cream / black carter figure. In red card box with cream label	£70-90
-	-	Tumbril Cart (two wheels)	Green / yellow cart with two hay racks, brown horse, cream / black carter, cream card box	£40-50
-	-	Coster Cart with Donkey	Green / yellow cart, solid sides, grey donkey, costermonger figure (see 24 below)	£40-50
-	-	Organ Grinder's Cart (two wheels)	Brown / yellow organ, grey donkey, red monkey with mug, brown / green organ-grinder	£70-80
-	-	Governor's Cart (two wheels)	Yellow / black, cream / red or brown / black cart, 2 children, donkey, zoo-keeper figure	£40-50
-	-	Milk Float (two wheels)	Yellow / red cart with 'PURE MILK' cast in. Brown horse, milkman figure (see 25)	£35-45
-	-	Milk Float (four wheels)	Orange / white body with 'UNITED DAIRIES', 'PASTEURISED MILK' and 'CREAM' logo. 8-spoke wheels with rubber tyres, brown horse, white / blue milkman with bottle	£150-200
-	-	Milk Handcart	with 'MILK' logo and Milkman	£150-200
-	-	Bread Handcart	with 'HOVIS' logo and Delivery-man	£150-200
-	-	Cape Cart (two wheels)	Enclosed dark blue body and roof, brown horse, mid-blue figure	£25-35
-	-	Tree Wagon (four wheels)	Yellow / red log carrier, 12-spoke wheels, 4 horses, 2 white figures with poles, (see also 1)	£70-80
-	-	Dairy Float (four wheels)	Mid-blue, 'EXPRESS DAIRY', 'PURE MILK', 'BUTTER & EGGS' shafts, brown horse, 8-spoke wheels, rubber tyres, white / blue milkman holding bottle	£150-200
-	-	Coal Cart (four wheels)	Black cart, coalman and coal sack, white / orange horse, 12-spoke wheels, 6 spare sacks	£200-250
-	-	Coffee Stall (four wheels)	Orange / yellow stall, silver chimney, brown / white horse, tea urn and crockery	£70-90
-	-	Railway Wagon (four wheels)	Grey / red open wagon, 'London Midland Scottish Railway' cast in, driver, white horse	£200-150
-	-	Horse-Drawn Grass Cutter	Yellow / red cutter, brown driver and horse (see also 3)	£60-75
-	-	Horse-Drawn Roller	Green / yellow roller, brown driver and horse (see also 2)	£60-75
-	-	Horse-Drawn Delivery Van	See picture in 1st colour section	£200-250

Pre-war Motor Vehicles (all cast in lead)

6	**Petrol Tanker**. Red, blue, yellow	£200-300
524	**Fire Engine**. Cast-in driver, separate ladder, rubber tyres	£150-200
525	**Car and Caravan**. Six-light saloon car (red, green or yellow); Caravan copied from Dinky Toys 30g, yellow with orange lower half	£200-300
526	**Motor Van**. No details	£100-150
728	**Ambulance**. Man cast on rear step. Green or brown	£150-200
864	**Racing Car**. Pale blue, green or yellow	£50-60
865	**Breakdown Lorry**. No details	£100-120
---	**Bentley Ambulance**. Copy of Dinky Toys 24a in off-white	£100-120
---	**1935 Bluebird**. Blue body	£200-300
---	**Armoured Car**. Six wheels, brown	£40-50

---	**Caterpillar Tractor**. Copy of Tootsietoy but larger. 'MIMIC TOY' cast underneath	£100-200
---	**Tank**. Copy of Tootsietoy. 'MIMIC TOY' cast underneath. Very dark blue	£40-50
---	**Mack Stake Lorry**. Copy of Tootsietoy. Green and red	£80-100
---	**Mack Lorry with AA Gun**. Copy of Tootsietoy. Light brown, black and silver	£100-150
---	**Mack Searchlight Lorry**. Copy of Tootsietoy. Light brown and black	£100-150
---	**Mack Barrage Balloon Set**. No details. Johillco made a similar set	£150-200

Circus Figures

Circus Clown Set: Clowns on Stilts, Clown on Unicycle, Clown climbing Ladder, Clown standing, Policeman clown ... £50-75
Single Figures: Liberty Horses, Performing Elephants, Seal with Balls, Strongman, Boxing Midgets, Acrobats, Parrot, Dog, Ringmaster ... each: £15-20

Post-war issues (Boxed models, mostly all-diecast construction)

-	late 1940s	**Packard Saloon**. 'JAVELIN' cast under. Red or green	£30-40
-	late 1940s	**Petrol Tanker**. Different from the pre-war tanker. Red, Green or Blue	£30-40
-	late 1940s	**Station Wagon**. Tan with dark brown bonnet and wings, spare wheel at rear	£30-40
1	1940s-60	**Horse-Drawn Log Wagon**. Yellow, red wheels, with man, two tandem horses, wooden log, cream card box	£60-75
2	1940s-67	**Horse-Drawn Roller**. Yellow with green or red roller, with horse and man (seated)	£60-75
3	1940s-67	**Horse-drawn Grass Cutter**. Yellow, red wheels, unpainted cutter, with horse and man (seated)	£60-75

4	1940s-67	**Horse-drawn Two-wheel Farm Wagon with Raves**. Green wagon, yellow shafts and wheels	£60-75
5	1940s-67	**Horse-drawn Four-wheel Farm Wagon with Raves**. Green wagon, yellow shafts and wheels	£60-75
6	1940s-67	**Tractor with Driver**. Red or orange with metal wheels or blue with rubber wheels	£60-75
7	1940s-62	**Horse-drawn Van with Man**. Blue with cream upper half, metal wheels, 'HOVIS BREAD' or 'PURE MILK' labels; or Orange with light brown upper half, rubber wheels, 'HOVIS BREAD' labels	£100-150
8	1940s-62	**Tipper Lorry**. Cab/tipper colours include: red/cream, blue/cream, dark green/yellow, orange/yellow	£30-40

9	1940s-62	**Motor Coach**. Yellow with red flash, dark red with cream flash, dark blue with green flash, light green with blue flash, beige with green flash **£100-120**
10 to 14		**Light Vans**. Two castings known. The first was a small boxy van with no rear windows. The second (from the early 1950s) was larger and more rounded, resembling a Ford E83W, with two rear windows.
10	1940s-60	**Royal Mail Van**. Red, second casting with black bonnet, 'ROYAL MAIL', 'G-VI-R' paper labels **£75-90**
11	1940s-62	**'AMBULANCE'**. Cream, Red Cross on paper labels ...**£75-90**
12	1940s-62	**'Carter Paterson' Van**. Dark green, 'CARTER PATERSON' on paper labels.......................**£75-90**
13	1940s-60	**'Police' Van**. Dark blue, 'POLICE GR' paper labels....**£75-90**
14	1940s-62	**Post Office Telephones Van**. Green, 'POST OFFICE TELEPHONES' on paper labels **£75-90**
15	1940s-62	**Fire Engine and Wheeled Escape**. Red or orange-red, unpainted ladders, three firemen and hose **£50-60**
16	1940s-67	**Covered Wagon with Four Horses and Driver**. Green wagon, yellow wheels, cloth canopy, metal shaft and horses **£50-60**
		Same, but Orange wagon, plastic shaft and horses **£50-60**
17	1940s-67	**Tractor and Log Trailer with Driver**. Tractor as No.6, Trailer as No.1 but with drawbar in place of shafts **£100-150**
18	1940s-62	**Tractor and Grass Cutter with two Drivers**. Tractor as No.6, Trailer modified from No.3 ....**£100-150**
19	1940s-67	**Tractor and Reaper with two Drivers**. Tractor as No.6, green reaper (yellow metal blades) or light blue reaper (red plastic blades), or all plastic **£100-150**
20	1954-67	**Mobile Crane**. Red body, green chassis, unpainted or yellow jib **£30-40**
		Orange body, light blue chassis, yellow jib....................**£30-40**
21	1954-67	**Muir-Hill Dumper with Driver**. Beige or Orange with Green dumper, Orange with Yellow dumper....................**£30-40**
		Red with Yellow plastic dumper **£30-40**
22	1954-67	**Travelling Zoo**. Elephant between two cages with two lions, two polar bears, man. Red chassis, unpainted cages, yellow roofs, metal or plastic animals.......................**£70-90**
		Same but orange chassis, lt. blue cages, yellow roofs **£70-90**
23	1955-58	**Water Pistol**. no details **£5-10**
24	1954-55	**Costermonger's Cart**. Dark green cart, red or yellow wheels, donkey, man and basket......................................**£25-35**
25	1955-?	**Horse-drawn Milk Cart**. Yellow with red wheels, 'PURE MILK' labels. With man and churn...................**£70-80**

26	1954-62	**Armoured Car**. Green or beige, metal or rubber wheels ..**£25-35**
27	1955-67	**Large Tractor**. Cast in two halves. Red with yellow wheels or orange with light blue wheels **£100-120**
28	1954-67	**Diesel Road Roller**. Green or pale green, red wheels, unpainted flywheel......................................**£25-35**
29	1954-62	**Mincer**. Toy kitchen equipment, Yellow **£5-10**
30	1955	**Scammell Mechanical Horse and Trailer**. Blue with 'LNER' labels, or dark brown cab with beige trailer and 'GWR' labels...........................**£35-45**
31	1955-62	**Articulated Low-loader with Cable Drum**. Red or green cab, yellow trailer **£35-45**
32	1955-62	**Alfa-Romeo Racing Car**. Hollow-cast lead, red with rubber wheels **£50-75**
33	1955-62	**Cooper-Bristol Racing Car**. Hollow-cast lead, green with rubber wheels **£50-75**
34	1955-62	**Ferrari Racing Car**. Hollow-cast lead, blue (yellow) nose, rubber wheels **£50-75**
35	1954-67	**Horse-drawn Log Wagon**. As No.1 but single horse....**£50-75**
36	1940s-55	**3-wheel Pedestrian Electric Van**. Dark blue, 'DAIRY MILK' printed on sides; milkman, crate and bottles ..**£100-120**
		Orange, 'HOVIS' on sides, man, tray of loaves **£100-120**
36	1957-62	**Maudslay Horse Box**. Dark red, 'HORSE TRANSPORT' printed on sides, with horse and driver **£100-120**
		Green/Red body, 'NEWMARKET HORSEBOX' **£100-120**
36	1967	**Steam Roller Large scale**. Green body, red 12-spoke wheels, unpainted roller, black chimney **£200-300**
37	1960-62	**Articulated Low-loader with Rocket Missile**. Dark green cab / trailer, orange / black missile launcher. No makers name on model....................................**£70-90**
38	1955-60	**'Shoot and Save' Money Box** Savings bank, with gun to fire coin into bank **£70-90**
39	1955	**Telephone Kiosk** Red kiosk with opening door, unpainted telephone **£15-20**
40	1940s-55	**Fire Engine with Ladder and Firemen**. Different from No.15. Red body, unpainted 2-part ladder.............**£70-90**
41	1955	**Fireplace**. Dolls house item **£5-10**
445	c1955	**'Auto Race Set'** 'Andover series'. Made only for the Flare Import Corporation, 230 Fifth Ave., New York. Contains 3 (Dinky style) racing cars, 6 mechanics, man with chequered flag. 43mm scale, hollow-cast. Card box has Formula I race scene on colour label...................**£300-400**

Salco series

i)	---	**Mickey Mouse Fire Brigade**...............Red fire engine with unpainted ladder, 3 painted Mickey Mouse figures. All card picture box **£1,000-1,250**
ii)	---	**Mickey and Minnies' Piano** ....Cream piano with operating handle, Mickey and Minnie Mouse figures. ....Black/Blue/Yellow/White all card picture box **£1,000-1,250**
iii)	---	**Mickey and Minnies' Barrel Organ**..Red organ with Yellow wheels, Mickey and Minnie Mouse figures. All card picture box **£500-750**
iv)	---	**Horse-drawn Brewer's Dray**..............Light Blue dray with Yellow detachable brewery sign marked 'TOY TOWN BREWERS', ...six unpainted barrels, black bowler-hatted driver and brown horse...**£150-200**

'Old Crocks', Military models and 'Miniature Lorries'

'OLD CROCKS' series

1	**1904 Darracq**. Dark Blue, Red or Orange, open 2-seater...............**£10-25**
2	**1904 Spyker**. Yellow 4-seater open car **£10-25**
3	**1914 'Old Bill' Bus**. 2-piece casting, or single casting plus separate top deck, Red or Orange **£10-25**
4	**1907 Ford Model T**. 2-piece casting, tin chassis, Dark Blue **£10-25**
	Single casting, no separate chassis, Dark Blue.........**£10-25**
5	**1907 Vauxhall**. Green open 2-seater **£10-25**
6	**1906 De Dion Bouton**. Light Green or Violet open 2-seater **£10-25**
7	**1898 Panhard**. Light Green or Brown 2-seater.......................**£10-25**
8	**1906 Rolls-Royce Silver Ghost**. Silver 4-seater open car **£10-25**
9	**1903 Standard 6hp**. Dark Red or Maroon with Beige roof...........**£10-25**
10	**1902 Wolseley**. Light Blue 4-seater open car **£10-25**
11	**1908 Packard Runabout**. Light Green open 2-str.........................**£10-25**
12	**1905 Vauxhall Hansom Cab**, Orange / Beige.........................**£10-25**
13	**1900 Straker Flat Steam Lorry**. Light Green, packing case........**£10-25**
	1900 Straker Lowside Steam Lorry. Light Blue, three barrels ..**£10-25**
14	**Stephenson's 'Rocket' Locomotive**. Yellow / Black **£10-25**
15	**Tender for 'Rocket'**, colours as 14 ....**£10-25**
16	**1909 Albion**. Dark or Light Blue open truck...............................**£10-25**
17	**1912 Rover**. Orange 2-seater open sports car **£10-25**
18	**1911 Mercedes-Benz**. Dark Green open 2-seater **£10-25**
19	**Bedford Horse-Box**. Brown, *'HORSE TRANSPORT'* cast on sides, 'H.G. IVORY' on tailgate........................**£15-25**

20	**1910 Lanchester**. Light Blue 4-seater sports tourer.......................**£10-25**
21	**1922 Morris Cowley**. Beige 2-seater open car...............................**£10-25**
22	**1900 Daimler**. Maroon 2-seater **£10-25**
23	**1904 Autocar**. Dark Blue, open 3-wheeler.....................................**£10-25**
24	**1870/80 Grenville Steam Carriage**. Green or Light Green **£10-25**
25	**1905 Napier**. Violet or Purple 2-seater racer **£10-25**
26	**Fire Engine and Escape**. Red or Orange......................................**£10-25**
27	**Articulated Breakdown Lorry**. Dark Green cab, Light Blue trailer, Orange crane **£10-25**
28	**Mercer Runabout**. Dark Blue or Green 2-seater sports **£10-25**

MILITARY MODELS

30	**Searchlight on 4-wheel Trailer**. Green and Silver **£10-25**
31	**Twin Bofors Gun on Trailer**. Green and Silver **£10-25**
32	**Radar Scanner on Trailer**. Green and Silver **£10-25**
33	**Field Gun on Trailer**. Green and Silver **£10-25**
34	**Rocket Gun on Trailer**. Green and Silver **£10-25**
35	**Armoured Car**. Green **£10-25**

'MINIATURE LORRIES' (not issued)

40	**Articulated Tanker**. Listed in 1960 catalogue ....NPP
41	**Articulated Lorry**. Listed in 1960 catalogue...............................NPP
42	**Six-wheeled Lorry**. Listed in 1960 catalogue................................NPP
43	**Six-wheeled Tanker**. Listed in 1960 catalogue.............................NPP

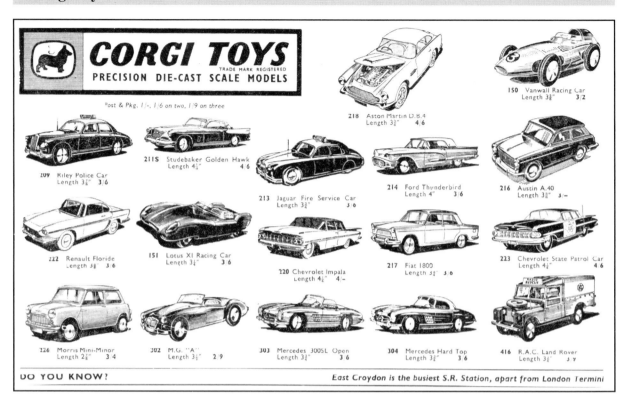

CORGI TOYS
PRECISION DIE-CAST SCALE MODELS

Post & Pkg. 1/-, 1/6 on two, 1/9 on three

218 Aston Martin D.B.4
Length 3⅜" **4/6**

150 Vanwall Racing Car
Length 3⅜" **3/2**

209 Riley Police Car
Length 3¾" **3/6**

211S Studebaker Golden Hawk
Length 4¼" **4/6**

213 Jaguar Fire Service Car
Length 3¾" **3/6**

214 Ford Thunderbird
Length 4" **3/6**

216 Austin A.40
Length 3⅜" **3/-**

222 Renault Floride
Length 3⅝" **3/6**

151 Lotus XI Racing Car
Length 3¼" **3/6**

220 Chevrolet Impala
Length 4¼" **4/-**

217 Fiat 1800
Length 3½" **3/6**

223 Chevrolet State Patrol Car
Length 4¼" **4/6**

226 Morris Mini-Minor
Length 2⅜" **3/4**

302 M.G. "A"
Length 3¼" **2/9**

303 Mercedes 300SL Open
Length 3¾" **3/6**

304 Mercedes Hard Top
Length 3¾" **3/6**

416 R.A.C. Land Rover
Length 3¼" **3/9**

DO YOU KNOW?   *East Croydon is the busiest S.R. Station, apart from London Termini*

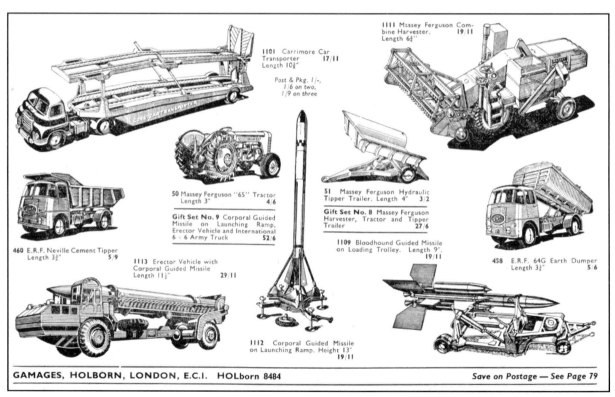

1101 Carrimore Car Transporter **17/11**
Length 10⅜"

Post & Pkg. 1/-, 1/6 on two, 1/9 on three

1111 Massey Ferguson Combine Harvester. **19/11**
Length 6½"

50 Massey Ferguson "65" Tractor
Length 3" **4/6**

Gift Set No. 9 Corporal Guided Missile on Launching Ramp, Erector Vehicle and International 6 × 6 Army Truck **52/6**

51 Massey Ferguson Hydraulic Tipper Trailer. Length 4" **3/2**

Gift Set No. 8 Massey Ferguson Harvester, Tractor and Tipper Trailer **27/6**

460 E.R.F. Neville Cement Tipper
Length 3¾" **5/9**

1113 Erector Vehicle with Corporal Guided Missile
Length 11½" **29/11**

1109 Bloodhound Guided Missile on Loading Trolley. Length 9" **19/11**

1112 Corporal Guided Missile on Launching Ramp. Height 13" **19/11**

458 E.R.F. 64G Earth Dumper
Length 3¾" **5/6**

GAMAGES, HOLBORN, LONDON, E.C.I.   HOLborn 8484

Save on Postage — See Page 79

Pages from Gamages of Holborn 1961 'Model Book'

Corgi Toys were launched in 1956 by the Mettoy Company which had itself been founded in Northampton by Phillip Ullmann in 1933. The 'Mettoy' name was derived from the first three letters of 'Metal' plus 'toy' - the company's main product range being composed of lithographed metal toys. In 1948 Mettoy produced their first cast metal toys and called them 'Castoys'. The Castoys models contained a clockwork motor and when the first Corgi Toys models were introduced they also contained a mechanism. This plus the introduction of windows gave Corgi a competitive edge against their great rivals Dinky Toys.

The development of the Corgi Toys product range was largely instigated by Howard Fairbairn, a Mettoy Company Director.Prior to his director appointment, he had been Head of Development at the Birmingham Aluminium Casting Co. and had considerable diecasting experience. The first truly Corgi Toys product was No.200 Ford Consul in 1956.

In 1983, the Mettoy Company went into receivership and Corgi Toys became the subject of a management buyout.

From 1985, the new company shifted emphasis from the mass production of toy vehicles to the development of authentic, limited edition models aimed at adult collectors - hence the superb 'Corgi Classics' range was introduced.

Since the takeover of the company by toy giant Mattel in 1995, the company, now known as Corgi Classics, has moved ahead strongly. In 1996, the 40th anniversary of the Corgi brand, the company launched a new roadshow which visits exhibitions, shows and events all over the country to spread the word about diecast collecting and give enthusiasts the chance to preview forthcoming releases. New Corgi Regional Retail Centres have also been introduced which stock the widest range of models. Increasingly, model production has moved to the Far East. Another page in the history of Corgi has now been turned with the acquisition in 2000 of Corgi (and Lledo) by the Hong-Kong based diecasting supremo Zindart.

The Corgi Collector Club, led by Susan Pownall, continues to build on its past success and now has over 10,000 members worldwide. Members receive a regular magazine, discounts on models and many other benefits. For a unique showcase of Corgi past and present, all diecast collectors should visit the Corgi Heritage Centre in Heywood, near Rochdale.

The Corgi Classics range goes from strength to strength with four main sections. Firstly, the Corgi Classics Collectables range of classic commercial vehicles and cars. Secondly, the Original Omnibus issues for bus lovers. Thirdly, the Aviation Archive now offers a tremendous range of model civilian and military aircraft. Finally, the Corgi Classics range now includes a superb new collection of vintage steam vehicles. Truly a comprehensive range of collectable models for the collectors of the new century. Corgi Classics listings are now included in the new 'Collectable Modern Diecasts' section of the Catalogue.

The Editor wishes to thank all who have contributed to the greatly revised listings.

Corgi Toys Identification

Often referred to as 'the ones with windows', Corgi Toys were the first manufacturer to produce models with that refinement. Some of their first models also had a mechanical motor. Spring suspension was introduced from 1959 and in 1960 the first die-cast model to have an opening bonnet. The first models were based on real cars of the period. Similarly, with the launch of the 'Corgi Major Toys' in 1959, models of real commercial vehicles were available and competed with the Dinky 'Supertoys' range.

In the 1960s Corgi produced many successful film and TV-related models. Probably the best remembered was the 'James Bond' Aston Martin which sold in huge quantities in the autumn of 1965. Indeed, such was the popularity of the model that a version was still available in 1992!

Corgi introduced many new features in the 1960s such as: jewelled headlights, opening bonnet revealing detailed engine, opening boot revealing spare, self-centering steering, ruby rear lights, etc. One particularly attractive model was the Midland Red Motorway Express Coach. The detailed interior even incorporated a toilet! Needless to say good examples of this model are highly sought after by bus collectors. Similarly the 'Chipperfields Circus' collection of models were beautifully produced and are highly prized today.

Innovations were frequent and imaginative in the 1960s. 'Golden Jacks' for instance, a built-in jacking system which enabled models to have 'Take-Off' wheels. And 'Trans-O-Lites' whereby light rays were captured and fed through prisms to illuminate the headlights. 'WhizzWheels' and the slightly larger scale of 1:42 were introduced in the 1970s.

A market strategy unique to Corgi was the launching a replica model car simultaneously with the real car. To date simultaneous launches have occurred with Austin Metro, Ford Escort, Triumph Acclaim, Ford Sierra and the MG Maestro 1600, which is a unique record. Corgi were the first die-cast manufacturers to introduce the dimensions of light, sound and movement into their models by using the micro-chip in their 'Corgitronic' range. The models 'come alive', for example by just pushing down on the rear axle or, in the case of the Road Repair Unit, by pressing the workman to activate the pneumatic drill sound. Others (like the Sonic Corgi Truck) can be operated from a remote control handset.

Mechanical. Some early Corgi Toys were produced in either the normal form or with a friction type flywheel motor. Exceptions were the sports cars and trucks which could not be converted to take the flywheel. The mechanisms were not robust and were phased out in 1959.

Boxes. July 1956 - Blue box, January 1959 - Yellow/Blue box (Two-tone cars were first to use them) December 1966 - Window box (2 square window ends) May 1973 - Angled window box (one square window end, coloured lines around box) 1980 - Yellow window box, 1987 New style Corgi logo box.

Box contents. Model boxes often contain much more than just the basic model. Prices shown in the Catalogue assume that not only is the model in pristine condition, but that it is accompanied by all the original additional contents. These can include: extra card packing, inner card or polystyrene trays, pictorial stands, plastic protectors, transit card protection intended for removal by the retailer, instruction and information leaflets, catalogues, consumables (such as unopened packets of rockets, decals, etc.). This particularly applies to some Novelty and Film/TV models, e.g., Nos. 268, 277, 497, 511, 1123, 1139, 1144 and Gift Sets 3, 10, 20 and 21. A further example relates to the early 'Blue box' models each of which should contain a concertina catalogue leaflet plus a 'Join the Corgi Club' leaflet. If original items are missing, e.g., the plastic dome protector included with 511 Chipperfields Poodle Truck or card protectors with other models, it will affect the price that a model will achieve.

Whilst every effort has been made to describe models and, where known, their accompanying contents, any further information would be welcomed.

Mettoy Diecast Toys – The 'Castoys' series

Castoys were produced by the Mettoy Company between 1948 and 1958 and were instigated by a request from Marks and Spencers for a robust, long lasting toy. The models were made of zinc alloy and were initially advertised as 'Heavy Cast Mechanical Toys'.

Generally, they had windows, a clockwork motor and brake, plus black rubber tyres on cast hubs. Of the original issues, only two models, No. 840, the 'Eight Wheel Lorry' and 870 'Delivery Van' remained in production after 1951 and these

were packaged in attractive Yellow/Red boxes which displayed a picture of the model inside. The later issues of the Delivery Van with their various attractive body designs are now rare and sought after items.

The following listing contains all the information available at present. The Editor would welcome any additional information on body colours and variations.

NB See the 'Miscellaneous Models' colour section for pictures.

Ref	Year(s)	Model name	Colours, features, details	Market Price Range

Large Scale Models 1:35

Presented in Yellow/Red endflap boxes each displaying an excellent picture of the model contained within.

Ref	Year(s)	Model name	Colours, features, details	Market Price Range
-	-	Milk Handcart	with 'MILK' logo and Milkman	£150-170810
718	1956-58	Luxury Observation Coach	Metallic Blue and Gold body with Silver raised roof section and base, Red door with Brown plastic male passenger Destination board shows 'PRIVATE' and registration 'MTY 718'	£250-350
			Metallic Brown and Pink body with Silver raised roof section and radiator, with Green female passenger	£200-300
810	1948-51	Limousine	Cream, Red or Green body, 'MTY 810'	NGPP
820	1948-51	Streamline Bus	Cream, Green or Red body, clockwork mechanism, Red pressed tin seating, solid rubber wheels, unpainted chassis. Registration No 'MTY 820'	£100-200
			As previous model but with opening door and registration No 'MTY 720'	£100-200
830	1948-51	Racing Car	Light Green, 6˝ long approx, 'METTOY' cast in base, tinplate hollow printed wheels with motor and brake	£100-200
840	1948-58	8 Wheel Lorry	Metallic Blue cab with Grey rear body, Silver radiator and hubs	£100-200
850	1948-51	Fire Engine	Red body, Silver ladder and crank	£100-200
			Red body, Silver extending ladder, no crank	£100-200
860	1948-51	Tractor	No models seen but shown in 1951 catalogue with Yellow/Red body	£100-200
863		Ferguson TE20 Tractor and Trailer	Red/Blue tractor, Yellow trailer, Red hubs, painted plastic driver	£100-125
870	1948-51	Delivery Van	No models seen but shown in 1948 catalogue with plain Dark Blue body	£100-150
	1952-55	'EXPRESS DELIVERY'	Yellow or Blue body with Red logo and design on sides	£150-200
	1955-58	'POST OFFICE TELEPHONES'	Green body, White logo, Royal crest in Gold, Silver two part extending ladder	£200-300
	1955-58	'ROYAL MAIL'	Red body, Silver trim, Yellow logo and Royal crest, 'MTY 870'	£200-300
	1955-58	'AMBULANCE'	Cream body with Black logo on sides	£100-200
	1956-58	'BOAC'	Blue body, Silver trim, White 'Fly By BOAC' on roof	£250-350

Small Scale Models 1:45

Ref	Year(s)	Model name	Colours, features, details	Market Price Range
---	1955-57	Soft Drinks Van	Dark red body, number plate 'CWS 300', Silver wheels, Logo on rear: 'CWS SOFT DRINKS - THIRST COME - THIRST SERVED'	£75-95

Special 1:18 scale issue for Marks and Spencer

Ref	Year(s)	Model name	Colours, features, details	Market Price Range
---	1958	'VANWALL' Racing Car	Diecast body, perspex screen, driver, 'VANWALL' transfers, 'push and go' motor in some. 'Vanwall the famous British Grand Prix Winner' cast in base.	
		i)	Green body, racing number '7' or '18', no Mettoy logo on base	£200-300
		ii)	French Blue body, racing number '20', no Mettoy logo on base	£200-300

The 'Miniature Numbers' series

The range of models produced between 1951 an 1954 was based on just two vehicles - the Standard Vanguard and the Rolls Royce. Models were issued in two sizes and featured a clockwork motor plus brake, adjustable steering (controlled by moving the central fog lamp sideways) and moulded grey plastic wheels. Both diecast and plastic bodies have been observed on some examples. They were packaged in attractive window boxes. The following listing has been taken from the 1951 Mettoy Catalogue and the Editor would welcome any additional information.

Ref	Year(s)	Model name	Colours, features, details	Market Price Range
502	1951	Standard Vanguard Saloon	Shown with Green body in catalogue (2 7/8 inches long)	£50-75
505	1951	Rolls-Royce Saloon	Red or Blue body, Silver trim (3 inches long)	£50-75
510	1951	Standard Vanguard Police Car	Black with White 'POLICE' logo on doors; roof siren and bell	£50-75
511	1951	Standard Vanguard Taxi	Shown in 1951 catalogue with Yellow body and Red roof rack	£50-75
512	1951	Standard Vanguard Fire Chief	Red, White 'FIRE CHIEF' on doors; single Silver ladder on roof	£50-75
602	1951	Standard Vanguard Saloon	Blue body shown in catalogue (large scale version of 502, 4¼ inches long)	£50-75
603	1951	Standard Vanguard Saloon	As 602 but with automatic to and fro bump feature	£50-75
605	1951	Rolls-Royce Saloon	Yellow body shown in catalogue (large scale version of 505, 4½ inches long)	£50-75
606	1951	Rolls-Royce Saloon	As 605 but with automatic to and fro bump feature	£50-75

Mettoy Castoys
718 Luxury Observation Coach
(see previous page)

Join today

CORGI *collector club*

The Corgi Collector Club is a must for all Corgi diecast model enthusiasts. Through the pages of our regular A4, full colour magazine, we bring you news of the latest releases from Corgi, fascinating features and background stories on the vehicles from which they are modelled, competitions, reader offers and much more.

Club benefits include:

- 10 issues of the Corgi magazine - Corgi Collector - for a year from the date your subscription is processed, with an automatic reminder when you need to renew.
- Free Retail Directory detailing your nearest Corgi stockists
- A Free annual Limited Edition Corgi Collector Club model - exclusive to Club subscribers - sent to you separately and automatically when available during the year.
- Club membership card giving discount on Corgi purchases at selected Corgi Gold Star stockists.
- Family membership discount - 1 magazine per family - for one additional adult and up to 3 children - all living at the same address.
- Free gifts when you introduce new members   ■ Competitive insurance facilities
- Invitations to selected Corgi previews in your area
- The opportunity to buy Club merchandise and catalogues through the Club.

Original Omnibus Company Club

We have lots of variety on offer for all 1:76 scale bus collectors.

Your annual subscription entitles you to:

- 6 bi-monthly copies of Bus Route, our full colour newsletter.
- The opportunity to buy the exclusive, Limited Edition annual Club model as well as special models made available to Club members, many of which are not generally available through normal retail channels
- Your membership card which gives you discount from selected Corgi stockists on your Original Omnibus purchases
- A free copy of the Corgi Retail Directory listing your local Corgi dealer
- A free Original Omnibus Company catalogue
- A free bi-annual Fleet List keeping you up to date on all OOC models produced by Corgi, past and present.

Aviation Archive Collectors Club

Welcome to the new Corgi Aviation Archive Collectors Club.

Your annual subscription includes:

- Your membership card, giving you discount from selected Corgi stockists on your Aviation Archive purchases.
- A free copy of the Corgi Retail Directory listing the Aviation Archive stockists in your locality
- 6 copies of Flight Recorder, the full colour bi-monthly Aviation Archive newsletter
- A free Aviation Archive catalogue
- The opportunity to buy the exclusive Limited Edition Aviation Archive Club model, to be announced in Flight Recorder when available.

Auction Results – Miscellaneous Models

Crescent Wild Animals set – £80;　　　　Crescent Model Farm set – £130;

All models and boxes pictured are in very good condition for their age.

Britains Army Ambulance (No. 1512) – £280;
Mettoy 'BOAC' Van – £270;
Mettoy 'Post Office' Telephones Van – £270;
Morestone Gipsy Caravan – £320;
Charbens Horse Delivery Van – £250;
Benbros 'United Dairies' Van – £120;
Morestone 'Breakdown' Van – £140;
Morestone 'AA' Land Rover – £160;

Chad Valley Cable Lorry – £95;
Chad Valley Milk Tanker – £120;
Chad Valley 'Lyons' Guy Van – £230;
*Charbens Van – £85;
*1950's Timpo 'Smiths' Van – £85;
*Kemlows 'Pickfords' Van – £90;
*Timpo 'Pickfords' Van – £90;
*All unboxed.

Gift Set 38 Rallye Monte-Carlo
Vehicles very good conditon, minor chipping
Good original box – £350;

Corgi Garage 1962-64 *(not including the models)*
Good to very good condition for age. Includes 'SHELL' sign and petrol pumps plus battery powered 'GARAGE' sign – £460;

Models sold by Wallis & Wallis, West Street Auction Galleries, Lewes, Sussex BN7 2NJ. Pictures reproduced by their kind permission.

Auction Results – Corgi Toys

Horse Transporter No.1130
complete with horses, display insert
and packing.
Minor wear and chips – £115
Performing Poodles No.511
Mint, boxed – £260

Circus Crane No.1144
Boxed, some wear – £170
Circus Menagerie No.1139
Boxed with packing
Model excellent – £270

Gift Set 23
Box with minor wear
Contents with minor chips – £260

N.B. All models shown are in excellent to mint condition unless shown differently.

(No.435) – £110; (No.1110) – £110;
(No.1141) – £200; (No.1140) – £210;
(No.462) – £100; 416 (441) – £90; 417 (413) – £110;
(453 some wear) – £60; (411 some wear) – £85;
(459 box damage, model wear) – £65;

(471 'POTATES FRITES') – £170;
(426 minor chips) – £125; (508) – £100;
(471) – £70; (428) – £160;
(474) – £170;

Auction Results – Corgi Toys

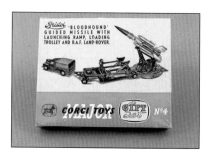

Gift Set No 4
Good to 'E' with
Inner packing – £220

GS 10 Marlin Rambler Set
Near mint in 'E' box – £240

Gift Set 12
Grand Prix Racing Set
Models 'E', box fair+ – £130

Gift Set 20
Scammell Tri-decker Set
Models good - 'E', box fair – £280

Gift Set 36
"Lotus" Racing Team Set
Near mint in 'E' box – £250

Gift Set 48 Scammell Transporter Set
Models near mint,
Box outer good+ – £600

Gift Set 48 Ford Transporter Set
Models excellent, in good+
Outer box – £500

Shop Display Stand
With picture of Gift Set No 8
Excellent – £170

Gift Set No 1
Models excellent in fair
Outer box (estimate £250 - 300)

Gift Set No 16
Ecurie Ecosse
Models 'E' in good+ box – £200

Gift Set 20
Scammell Transporter Set
Models 'E' in fair outer box – £190

Gift Set 21
"Chipperfields" Set
Near mint in good window box – £490

Models sold by Vectis Auctions Ltd., Fleck Way, Thornaby, Stockton-on-Tees, TS17 9JZ. Pictures reproduced by their kind permission.

Auction Results – Corgi Toys

GS No 3 1st type
Super example – £1,300

Gift Set 3 "Batman"
Models mint, Batboat is early issue
with tin back, box is 'E' – £720

Gift Set 40 "Batman"
All mint in excellent box – £480

Gift Set 38 "Monte-Carlo Rally"
Models good to 'E'
Good outer box – £400

Gift Set 15 "Silverstone"
Models 'E' to mint in similar
boxes, outer box fair– £1,150

Gift Set 40 "The Avengers"
Models and stand 'E'
In good+ box – £250

Batmobile (1st issue)
Excellent model in similar
Box (no instructions) – £180

Batboat & Trailer
(1st issue with tin back)
Near mint in good+ box – £170

Green Hornet
Mint in 'E' box – £260

"Saints" Volvo P1800
Near mint in 'E' box – £150

Rolls Royce Silver Ghost
"Hardy Boys", Mint in 'E' box
£190

Juniors "James Bond"
Ford Escort O.H.M.S.S.
Mint on near bubble pack – £750

Auction Results – Corgi Toys

201 M Austin Cambridge
Orange body, mint, in Excellent
Box with leaflet– £240

203 M Vauxhall Velox orange
Mint in near mint box – £360

204 M Rover 90
Metallic green,
Mint boxed – £180

200 Ford Consul
Green/cream
Mint in 'E' box – £150

201 Austin Cambridge
Silver over metallic green
Mint in 'E' box – £170

202 Morris Cowley
Pale green/blue
Mint in 'E' box – £130

214 M Ford Thunderbird
Pink/black, yellow
Interior near mint in 'E' box – £290

225 Austin 7 "Jensons"
Dutch Promotional issue
Mint, in near mint box – £700

225 Austin 7 Mini
Primrose yellow, red interior
Mint boxed – £410

227 Morris Mini Cooper
"Competition" blue/white RN '1'
Mint, in 'E' box – £180

227 Morris Mini Cooper
"Competition" pale yellow/white RN '3'
Near mint, boxed – £240

321 Mini Cooper-S
With roof signatures
Mint boxed – £300

Auction Results – Corgi Toys

Bentley Continental Sports Saloon
Black over silver
Mint boxed – £150

240 Ghia Fiat 600 "Jolly"
Blue, 2 figures
Mint in near mint box – £100

242 Ghia Fiat 600
Yellow, 2 figures
Near mint in good+ box – £210

328 Hillman Imp "Monte Carlo Rally"
Complete with rare advertising card
Near mint, boxed – £130

335 Jaguar 'E' Type
Mint including all
Packing and box – £140

349 Morris Mini Minor "Popart Mostest"
Red body, lemon interior cast wheels
Near mint, boxed – £1,550

Canadian issue catalogues
1. 1961 racing cars scene, 2. 1963-64 boy in blue,
3. 1963-64 boy in red
All mint – £130

256 VW 1200
'East African Safari'
Mint in near mint box – £200

304 Mercedes Benz 300SL
Hardtop Roadster
Mint in 'E' box – £260

320 Ford Mustang Fastback 2+2
Metallic deep yellow and black
Near mint in 'E' box – £900

322 Rover 2000 "Monte Carlo"
Mint in 'E' box – £120

322 Rover 2000 "International Rally
Finish", mint boxed (box has
international rally label on side) – £290

Auction Results – Corgi Toys

270 "James Bond" Silver Aston Martin
DB5 with tyre slashers
Mint in rare issue box – £600

Group of three "James Bond"
1:36 scale. Model nos 2 x 94060, C271/1
Mint boxed – £140

270 "James Bond" with tyre slashers
1st issue wing flapped bubble pack
Excellent in good box– £160

270 "James Bond" Aston Martin DB5
Silver with tyre slashers. Near mint in
Good+ striped windows box – £200

"James Bond" Toyota 200 GT
Near mint model and stand
Box good+ – £180

391 "James Bond" Ford Mustang
Mach 1, mint in near mint
Box with correct flash – £210

Gold plated No 272
"James Bond" Citroen 2cv.
No 8 of only 12 produced in 1981 for a special promotion.
Strada authentication certificate must be present.
Estimate – £3,500-4,500

Gold plated Corgi Classic 96445
"James Bond" Aston Martin DB5.
This being "0007" and signed by Shirley Eaton
from "Goldfinger".
Mint – £900

Models sold by Vectis Auctions Ltd., Fleck Way, Thornaby, Stockton-on-Tees, TS17 9JZ. Pictures reproduced by their kind permission.

Auction Results – Corgi Toys

416 S Land Rover Radio Rescue "TS
Radio" (Touring Secours) Belgian issue
Mint in 'E' box – £910

421 Bedford Van "Evening Standard"
Black body, silver roof
Near mint, boxed – £130

421 Bedford Van "Evening Standard"
Black lower body, silver upper body
Near mint, boxed – £130

422 Bedford Van "Corgi Toys"
Yellow with blue roof
Near mint, boxed – £210

422 Bedford Van "Corgi Toys"
Blue lower body, yellow upper body
Near mint, boxed – £700

428 Smiths "Mr Softie"
Ice Cream van
Mint, boxed – £230

438 Land Rover
"Lepra" variant
Mint on near mint box – £580

447 Ford Thames
"Walls Ice Cream"
Mint, boxed – £310

Meltoy "Castoys"
Luxury Observation coach
'E' in good+ box – £260

433 VW Delivery Van
"Vroom & Dreesman"
Near mint in 'E' box – £520

Window display sign
27" long x 8" high, illuminated probably Belgian issue
Excellent condition – £750

Models sold by Vectis Auctions Ltd., Fleck Way, Thornaby, Stockton-on-Tees, TS17 9JZ. Pictures reproduced by their kind permission.

Auction Results – Corgi Toys

281 Rover 2000 TC
Metallic purple, yellow interior
Whizzwheels – £70

266 Chitty Chitty Bang Bang
Good in fair outer box – £120

803 Beatles Submarine
Yellow/red hatches
Near mint in fair box – £220

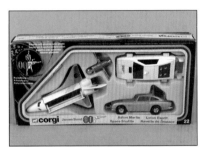

Gift Set 22
"James Bond", models excellent
Tray and box 'E' – £320

1121 Chipperfields Circus Crane Truck
Near mint, boxed – £110

1139 Chipperfields Menagerie Truck
Near mint, boxed – £240

8102 Marks & Spencer issue
Motorway breakdown set
Near mint, boxed – £100

452 Commer Lorry, 468 "Naturally Corgi
Toys" Routemaster, 1120 Midland Red Coach
All near mint in good boxes – £160

513 Citroen Safari
Near mint in excellent box – £160

Tinplate hanging shop sign
Good condition – £170

652 Concorde Japan Airlines
Mint in good+ box – £100

448 Mini "Police" Van
Near mint in good box – £105

For car models introduced from 1980, see separate listing that follows this main listing. See also 'Novelty, Film and TV-related' section.

Ref	Year(s)	Model name	Colours, features, details	Market Price Range
150	1957-61	Vanwall Racing Car	Green body, Silver trim, Yellow seat, flat spun hubs, racing number '3' on nose, Blue tinted screen, Blue box with leaflet	£80-90
			Same as previous model but with racing number '20' on nose and cockpit sides....................................	£80-90
			Mid-Green body, Silver seat, 'VANWALL' logo, clear screen, RN '1'	£80-90
			Mid-Green body, Yellow seat, small 'VANWALL' logo, clear screen, RN '1'	£80-90
	Blue/Yellow box:		Red body, Yellow seat, large 'VANWALL' logo, Blue tinted screen, RN '1'	£80-90
			Red body, Silver seat, small 'VANWALL' logo, clear screen, RN '1'	£80-90
150 S	1961-65	Vanwall Racing Car	Red body, Silver trim, Blue/White bonnet design plus Black number '25', White driver	£80-90
150	1972-74	Surtees TS9 Formula 1	Metallic Purple or Metallic Blue body, 'BROOKE BOND OXO' logo, 8-spoke WhizzWheels...............	£20-25
			Metallic Turquoise body with cast 8-stud WhizzWheels..	£15-20
	1975-76	..........................Gift Set model:	Blue/Yellow body with 'DUCKHAMS', (in GS 29 only)..	GSP
151	1958-61	Lotus XI Le Mans Racing Car .	Dull Blue body, Red seats, clear or Blue-tinted windscreen, racing numbers '1', or '3'	£80-100
			Silver body, Red seats, racing numbers '3'. Blue tinted windscreen	£100-120
			Red body, Cream seats, racing numbers '1'. Blue tinted windscreen	£125-175
151 A	1961-65	Lotus XI Le Mans Racing Car .	Blue body, Red/White bonnet stripe, White driver, Black racing number '7'	£60-70
			Lemon body, racing number '3', driver	£50-60
151	1974-76	Yardley Mclaren M19A	White body, 'YARDLEY', RN '55', 8-spoke or stud WhizzWheels	£20-25
		Gift Set model:	Same but Blue stripe on White helmet, 8-stud WhizzWheels, (GS30 only)	GSP
152	1958-61	B.R.M. Racing Car...................	Light or Dark Green body, Yellow seat, no driver, racing numbers '1', '3' or '7'. Blue box with leaflet...	£50-60
	1961-65		Turquoise body, Silver trim, Union Jack on bonnet, RN's '1', '3' or '7'. Blue/Yellow box, no leaflet......	£50-60
152 S	1961-65	B.R.M. Racing Car...................	Turquoise body, Silver trim, Union Jack on bonnet, racing numbers '1', '3' or '7', White driver, Blue/Yellow box, no leaflet	£50-60
152	1974-75	Ferrari 312 B2	Red body, 'Ferrari/Shell' logo, RN '5', White driver, Orange/Blue helmet, 8-spoke or 8-stud cast hubs...	£20-25
153	1960-61	Bluebird Record Car...............	Blue body, UK and US flags on nose, metal hubs	£65-75
153 A	1961-65	Bluebird Record Car...............	Blue body, UK and US flags on nose, plastic hubs	£65-75
		variant:	Blue body with two Union Jacks on nose, Black plastic hubs	£65-75
153	1972-74	Team Surtees TS 9B	Red body, RN '26', Blue or Blue/White driver (Rob Walker), 8-spoke hubs	£20-25
		Gift Set issue:	Red body, 'NORRIS' logo, (GS30 only)	GSP
154	1963-72	Ferrari Formula 1	Red body, Ferrari badge on bonnet, White driver, racing number '36'	£30-35
154	1974-79	'JOHN PLAYER SPECIAL' Lotus.....................	Black body, Gold trim, racing number '1' or '4', drivers Emerson Fittipaldi or Ronnie Petersen.	
			'JPS' logo, Black/Red helmet, 8-stud hubs, 'Fittipaldi' on box	£15-20
			'JPS' logo, Black or Blue helmet, 'Petersen' on box	£15-20
			'JPS TEXACO' logo, Red helmet	£15-20
		Gift Set issue:	'JPS TEXACO' logo, Black helmet, 12-spoke hubs, (GS32 only)	GSP
		Gift Set issue:	'JPS SHELL' logo, Black/Red helmet, (GS30 only)	GSP
		Marks & Spencers issue:	No 'Corgi' on base, 'TEXACO' logo, Orange (?) helmet	GSP
155	1964-69	Lotus Climax Racing Car........	British Racing Green body, Yellow stripe on bonnet, White driver, Blue helmet, racing number '1'	£45-55
155	1974-76	'SHADOW' Formula 1	Black body, 'UOP', racing number '17', driver (Jackie Collins) White/Maroon helmet	£20-25
156	1967-68	Cooper-Maserati......................	Dark Blue body, racing number '7', windscreen, White driver, Blue helmet	£40-50
156	1974-76	Graham Hill's Shadow..............	White/Red body, racing number '12', driver, 'EMBASSY RACING'	£20-25
		Special issue:	Model in box with outer sleeve as presented at the National Sporting Club showing name 'MENU'	£300-500
158	1969-73	Lotus Climax Racing Car........	Orange and White body, Blue driver, White helmet, Black number '8' and bonnet stripe	£30-35
158	1975-78	Elf Tyrrell Ford F1	Blue body, racing number '1', 'ELF', Jackie Stewart driving	£25-30
159	1969-72	Cooper-Maserati......................	Yellow and White body with high wing, Black bonnet stripe, Blue driver, White helmet, cast wheels, Yellow racing number '3'..	£30-35
159	1974-76	Indianapolis Racing Car............	Red body, racing number '20', Patrick Eagle driving	£25-30
160	1975-78	'HESKETH' 308 F1	White body, 'HESKETH', Black helmet, 4-spoke or 8-stud hubs	£20-25
		Marks & Spencers issue:	White body, no 'CORGI' on some, White driver, Orange helmet	GSP
		Gift Set issue:	Yellow body, 'CORGI TEAM' logo, Orange driver (James Hunt), Black helmet, Blue belts, (GS26 only)	GSP
161	1971-73	Santa Pod 'COMMUTER'	Red 'Dragster' body, Chrome engine, racing number '2', WhizzWheels..............................	£20-25
161	1977-78	'ELF-TYRRELL' P34...............	Blue and Yellow body, 'ELF' logo, Red or Blue helmet, 8-stud hubs, Yellow racing number '4'........	£20-25
162	1978-79	'ELF-TYRRELL' P34...............	Blue and White body, 'FIRST NATIONAL BANK' logo, Red or Orange helmet	£20-25
		Marks & Spencers issue:	As previous model but no 'Corgi' on base, 8-stud hubs	GSP
162	1971-72	'Quartermaster' Dragster	Green and White body, aerofoil, driver, plastic hubs	£25-30
163	1971-73	Santa Pod Dragster	White body, Blue trim, Red chassis, 'GLOWORM', driver, plastic hubs	£25-30
164	1972-73	Ison Bros Dragster	Yellow/Red body, 'WILD HONEY', 'JAGUAR', WhizzWheels	£25-30
165	1972-74	Adams Brothers 'Drag-star'	Red/Yellow body, 4 x V-8 engines, WhizzWheels	£25-30
166	1971-74	Ford Mustang	Yellow/Green body, 'ORGAN GRINDER', racing number '39', driver	£25-30
167	1973-74	USA Racing Buggy	White/Red body, racing number '7', driver, US flag	£25-30
169	1974-77	'Starfighter Jet' Dragster	Blue/Silver/Red body, 'FIRESTONE'	£25-30
170	1974-77	John Woolfe's Dragster	Blue/Yellow body, 'RADIO LUXEMBOURG', '208'	£25-30
190	1974-77	'JOHN PLAYER' Lotus	1:18 scale, Black/Gold, RN '1', driver, removable wheels, tools included in box	£35-40
191	1975-80	'TEXACO MARLBORO' F1 Mclaren..........................	1:18 scale, White/Red, RN '5', removable wheels, tools included in box	£35-40

200	1956-61	**Ford Consul**	Cream, Dark or Pale Green, Tan or Dark Tan body, no suspension, leaflet with early issues...............£100-140
		(First Corgi Toys model)	Blue, Light Greyish-Brown or Bright Green body, flat spun hubs £100-140
200M	1956-59	**Ford Consul**	Leaflet with early issues.
		(with flywheel motor)	Two-tone Green £130-160
			Green/Cream £130-160
			Silver/Cream £130-160
			Pale Grey over Green £130-160
			Blue body £125-150
			Dark Green or Bright Green £100-140
200	1976-78	**BLMC Mini 1000**..................	Metallic Blue body, Silver roof, Red and White interior.............................£20-25
200A	1978-83	**BLMC Mini 1000**..................	Metallic Blue or Silver body, White or Red interior, Union Jack stripe on roof, WhizzWheels...............£25-35
201	1956-61	**Austin Cambridge**	Pale Blue, Turquoise or Mid-Grey body, no suspension, leaflet with early issues £100-140
			Light Grey body £100-140
			Green/Cream £150-200
			Two-tone Green £100-140
			Silver over Metallic Green £120-160
201M	1956-59	**Austin Cambridge**	Cream, Red, Slate Grey or Medium Grey body with motor, leaflet with early issues.............£100-140
			Silver or Metallic Blue £120-150
			Orange body, spun hubs, leaflet £150-200
201	1970-72	**The Saint's Volvo**...............	White body, White 'Saint' logo on red label, WhizzWheels, driver, Red/Yellow 'window' box £140-160
201	1979-82	**BLMC Mini 1000**..................	Silver body, Red interior, with or without 'TEAM CORGI' and '8' £15-25
			As previous model but with Orange body £15-25
			Dark Blue body without 'TEAM CORGI' £15-25
			Dark Blue body with 'ESSO' and 'MICHELIN' labels.......................£15-25
202	1956-61	**Morris Cowley**	Bright Green or Grey body, smooth hubs, no suspension, leaflet with early issues £100-140
			Blue body, no suspension £100-140
			Grey/Blue or Blue/Cream body £100-140
			Pale Green/Blue or White/Blue body £100-140
202 M	1956-59	**Morris Cowley**	Pale Green, Medium Green or Off-White body, flywheel motor, leaflet £140-150
			Dark Green body, spun hubs, flywheel motor, leaflet £140-180
202	1970-72	**Renault 16TS**	Blue/Silver body, Yellow interior, no suspension, WhizzWheels £20-25
203	1970-72	**De Tomaso Mangusta**	Metallic Dark Green, Gold stripes, racing number '1' £20-25
203	1956-61	**Vauxhall Velox**	Red, Cream or Yellow body, no suspension, leaflet with early issues £100-140
			Yellow/Red body £140-170
203 M	1956-59	**Vauxhall Velox**	Red body, flywheel motor, leaflet with early issues £130-160
			Orange body, spun hubs, flywheel motor, leaflet £200-300
203	1971-72	**De Tomaso Mangusta**..........	Green/Gold body, White interior, WhizzWheels, aerial £20-25
204	1956-61	**Rover 90**	Cream or Off-White body, smooth hubs, leaflet with early issues £100-140
			Light or Dark Grey body, smooth hubs £100-140
			Mid or Dark Green body, smooth hubs £100-140
			Metallic Green body, smooth hubs £140-180
			Metallic Red lower body, with Cream upper body, smooth hubs £120-150
204 M	1956-59	**Rover 90**	Bright Mid-Green or Grey body, smooth hubs, flywheel motor, leaflet £120-160
			Mid or Dark Green body, smooth hubs, flywheel motor, leaflet................£140-180
204	1972-73	**Morris Mini-Minor**	Dark Blue body with WhizzWheels £80-100
			Deep Blue body, WhizzWheels £200-250
			Metallic Blue body, WhizzWheels £50-60
			All-Orange body, WhizzWheels £40-50
			Orange body, Black roof, WhizzWheels £90-120
205	1956-62	**Riley Pathfinder**...................	Red or Blue body, no suspension, smooth hubs, leaflet with early issues £100-140
205 M	1956-59	**Riley Pathfinder**...................	Red body, smooth hubs, flywheel motor, leaflet £130-160
			Mid Blue body, leaflet..£100-140
			Dark Blue body, leaflet..£140-180
206	1956-59	**Hillman Husky Estate**..............	Tan or Greyish Light-Brown body, no suspension, leaflet with early issues £70-90
			Metallic Blue and Silver body £100-130
206 M	1956-59	**Hillman Husky Estate**..............	Cream, Mid-Blue, Dark Blue or Grey body, flywheel motor, leaflet £100-130
			Turquoise body, spun hubs, leaflet £250-350
207	1957-62	**Standard Vanguard III**	White body (Red roof) or Grey body (Red roof), smooth or shaped hubs, leaflet £80-100
			Red over Green body, spun hubs £100-140
207 M	1957-59	**Standard Vanguard III**	Primrose Yellow body, flywheel motor, leaflet................................£150-200
			Pale Green body, Red roof pillars, leaflet £100-140
208	1957-60	**Jaguar 2.4 litre**....................	White body, no suspension, leaflet with early issues.....................£100-140
208 M	1957-60	**Jaguar 2.4 litre**....................	Metallic Dark Blue body, flywheel motor, leaflet £100-140
208 S	1960-63	**Jaguar 2.4 litre**....................	Lemon body, with spring suspension, smooth spun hubs.................£75-85
			Pale Lemon body, shaped spun hubs £85-95
210	1957-60	**Citroën DS19**.....................	Yellow body, Red roof, Grey baseplate, smooth hubs, leaflet with early issues...............£100-140
			Yellow body, Red roof, Silver baseplate with detailed drive shaft..............£100-140
			Metallic Dark Green body, Black roof, Grey or Silver baseplate............£90-110
			As previous but with bulge to take flywheel motor. A '210M' was not produced...............£120-150
210 S	1960-65	**Citroën DS19**.....................	Red body, Grey baseplate, spring suspension £60-70

211	1958-60	**Studebaker Golden Hawk**	Blue body, Gold rear wing flashes, no suspension, smooth hubs, leaflet..	**£90-110**
			White body, Gold rear wing flashes, leaflet..	**£90-110**
211 M	1958-59	**Studebaker Golden Hawk**	White/Gold body, flywheel motor, no suspension, smooth hubs, leaflet..................................	**£150-175**
211 S	1960-65	**Studebaker Golden Hawk**	Gold ('plated') body, White flash, suspension, shaped hubs..	**£90-110**
			Gold (painted) body, shaped hubs..	**£100-125**
212	1958	**Road Racer**..............................	Not released, one example known to exist	**NPP**
214	1959-65	**Ford Thunderbird Hardtop**	Pale Green (Cream roof) or Grey with Red roof, '1959' on rear number plate..........................	**£90-110**
			Pale Green body, Cream roof, blank rear number plate..	**£90-110**
214 M	1959-60	**Ford Thunderbird Hardtop**	Pink body, Black roof, flywheel motor, '1959' on rear number plate, leaflet..........................	**£200-250**
			Pale Green body, Cream roof, flywheel motor	**£170-200**
214 S	1962-64	**Ford Thunderbird Hardtop**	Metallic Grey/Red or Black/Red body, Lemon interior, with suspension	**£90-110**
215	1959-62	**Thunderbird Open Sports**.......	White body, Blue interior or Blue body, White interior, no suspension	**£90-110**
215 S	1962-64	**Thunderbird Open Sports**.......	Red body with Yellow interior and driver, with spring suspension	**£90-110**
216	1959-62	**Austin A40**..............................	Two-tone Blue body, no suspension, smooth hubs, leaflet with early issues	**£80-100**
			Red body, Black roof, smooth hubs..	**£80-100**
216 M	1959-60	**Austin A40**..............................	Red body, Black roof, flat hubs, flywheel motor, no suspension, leaflet	**£120-140**
			All-Red body, leaflet..	**£120-140**
217	1960-63	**Fiat 1800 Saloon**	Light Blue or Two tone Blue body, smooth or shaped hubs	**£30-35**
			Light Tan body	**£30-35**
			Pale Yellow/Brown or Mustard Yellow body, Yellow interior	**£40-50**
218	1960-62	**Aston Martin DB4**	Red body, Yellow interior, smooth or shaped hubs	**£65-75**
	1961-62		Red body, Red interior, cast 'spoked' hubs	**£75-85**
219	1959-63	**Plymouth Suburban Sports**	Cream with Fawn roof	**£40-50**
220	1960-65	**Chevrolet Impala**	Metallic Red body, Red or Yellow interior, spun hubs, leaflet	**£40-50**
			Powder Blue body, Red or Yellow interior, spun hubs, leaflet	**£40-50**
			Pink body, Yellow interior, spun hubs	**£55-65**
221	1960-63	**Chevrolet Impala Cab**..............	Yellow body, *'YELLOW TAXIS'*, smooth/shaped spun wheels	**£55-65**
222	1959-65	**Renault Floride**.........................	Dark Red, Maroon or Lime Green body, Red, White or Yellow vac-formed interior, smooth or shaped hubs, suspension..	**£60-70**
			Metallic Blue body, Red interior, shaped hubs..	**£60-70**
224	1961-65	**Bentley Continental**..................	Seats, opening boot with removable spare, steering, special lights.	
			White over Metallic Apple Green, Red interior, spun hubs	**£100-125**
			Black over Silver body, Red interior, spun hubs	**£100-125**
			Two-tone Green or Gold body	**£100-125**
			Metallic Green and White body	**£100-125**
225	1961-65	**Austin 7 (Mini) Saloon**.............	Red body, windows, suspension, seats, steering wheel	**£75-85**
			Primrose-Yellow body, Red interior, smooth spun hubs..	**£250-350**
		Danish promotional:	'JENSONS', Red body, Yellow interior	**£500-750**
226	1960-68	**Morris Mini Minor**....................	Pale Blue body, Cream or Yellow interior, smooth or shaped hubs	**£50-60**
			Red body, smooth or shaped hubs..	**£50-60**
			Sky Blue body, Red interior, hubs..	**£200-250**
			Metallic Maroon body, suspension, detailed cast hubs..	**£50-60**
			Yellow body	**£200-250**
		Gift Set issue:	Deep Blue body, only in GS11..	**GSP**
		NB	The Light Blue version of 226 was also supplied for a short time by a games manufacturer as part of a table-top racing game. This version has a large drive-pin hole in the base and has 'rally' stickers on the bonnet. Not separately boxed	**NGPP**
227	1962-65	**Mini Cooper Rally**....................	Bright Blue body, White roof and bonnet, Red interior, spun hubs, Union Jack and chequered bonnet flags, racing numbers '1', 3' or '7'	**£175-225**
			As above but Bright Blue body and bonnet, White roof	**£175-225**
			Primrose Yellow body, White roof and bonnet, with flags and racing number '7'..........................	**£225-275**
			Primrose Yellow body and bonnet, with flags and racing number '1'..........................	**£225-275**
			Green body, White roof. Not seen..	**NGPP**
228	1962-65	**Volvo P-1800**	Beige body, (Red interior) or Dark Red (Lemon interior),spun hubs	**£45-55**
			Pink or Dark Pink body..	**£55-65**
229	1961-66	**Chevrolet Corvair**	Mid-Blue body, Bright Yellow interior, spun hubs	**£45-55**
			Pale Blue body, Pale Yellow interior, shaped hubs	**£45-55**
		Gift Set issue:	Gold body, (in 'Golden Guinea' set)..	**GSP**
230	1962-64	**Mercedes-Benz 220 SE**.............	Cream (Red interior) shaped spun hubs, spare wheel in boot	**£60-70**
			Metallic Red body, Lemon interior, shaped spun hubs, spare wheel in boot	**£60-70**
			Black body, Lemon interior, shaped spun hubs, spare wheel in boot..........................	**£70-80**
			Dark Blue body, Lemon interior	**£60-70**
231	1961-65	**Triumph Herald**........................	Gold top and bottom, White in centre, spun hubs, red seats	**£70-80**
			Mid Blue top and bottom, White in centre, red seats	**£60-70**
			All Pale Blue (other details required please)	**NGPP**
232	1961-63	**Fiat 2100**	Pale Pink with Mauve roof, Lemon interior, spun hubs	**£45-55**
233	1962-72	**Heinkel Trojan**	Red, Orange, Pink or Lilac body, Lemon interior, spun hubs or detailed cast hubs	**£40-50**
			Metallic Blue, Fawn or Turquoise body, smooth spun hubs	**£80-90**
234	1961-65	**Ford Consul Classic**	Beige body, Pink roof, Lemon interior, or Gold body	**£50-60**
235	1962-66	**Oldsmobile Super 88**.................	Black body, White side flash, spun hubs	**£50-60**
			Metallic Steel Blue, White side flash, Red interior	**£40-50**

			Light Blue body, Red interior, White side flash, spun hubs	£50-60
236	1964-68	**Motor School Austin A60**	Light Blue body, 2 figures, steering control on roof, 'Highway Code' leaflet, right-hand drive	£60-70
			As previous model but left-hand drive, leaflet	£100-120
238	1962-67	**Jaguar Mk10**	All issues have spun hubs, luggage in boot. Blue/Yellow box with leaflet.	
			Pale Blue body, Red interior	£70-90
			Mid-Green body, Red interior	£70-90
			Deep Blue body, Red interior	£90-110
			Kingfisher Blue body, Lemon interior	£100-120
			Sea-Green body, Red interior	£125-150
			Metallic Steel (Blue-Grey) body, Red interior	£70-90
			Metallic Deep Blue body, Red or Lemon interior	£125-150
			Metallic Sea-Blue body, Red interior	£125-150
			Metallic Cerise body, Lemon interior	£70-90
			Metallic Silver body, Red interior	£125-150
			Metallic Green body, Red interior	£70-90
239	1963-68	**VW 1500 Karmann Ghia**	Cream (Red interior) or Red (Yellow interior) spare wheel/suitcase in boot	£50-65
			Gold body, Red or Yellow interior, spare wheel/suitcase in boot	£60-75
240	1963-64	**Fiat 600 Jolly**	Light Blue body, Silver/Red canopy, Red interior, spun hubs, 2 figures	£75-85
			Dark Metallic Blue body, Red seats	£75-85
241	1963-69	**Chrysler Ghia L64**	Shaped spun or detailed cast hubs, Corgi dog on rear shelf.	
			Metallic Blue/White or Metallic Green body, White interior	£30-40
			Metallic Gold, Metallic Silver Blue (Red interior), or Metallic Copper	£40-50
242	1965-66	**Ghia Fiat 600**	Orange-Yellow body, Red interior, two figures in swim gear, windscreen but no canopy	£250-350
245	1964-68	**Buick Riviera**	Metallic Gold body, Red interior, 'Trans-O-Lites', spoked hubs, towbar	£45-55
			Metallic Steel Blue (Red interior) or Metallic Greenish Blue body, towbar	£45-55
			Pale Blue body, spun or cast hubs	£55-65
246	1965-68	**Chrysler Imperial Convertible** .	All issue should include driver/passenger, golf trolley in boot, Blue/Yellow box with inner packing.	
			Metallic Deep Red body, Pale Blue interior, shaped spun or detailed cast hubs	£70-80
			Metallic Turquoise body, Green interior, shaped spun or detailed cast hubs	£70-80
			Metallic Blue body, Pale Blue interior, cast hubs	£110-130
			Metallic Kingfisher Blue body, Green interior, cast hubs	£175-225
247	1964-69	**Mercedes-Benz Pullman**	Metallic Maroon body, windscreen wipers, instruction sheet	£40-50
248	1965-67	**Chevrolet Impala**	Brown body, Cream roof/interior, Chrome side stripe, shaped spun hubs	£45-55
249	1965-69	**Morris Mini-Cooper**	Black body, Red roof, Lemon interior, wickerwork panels, spun or cast hubs	£75-85
251	1963-66	**Hillman Imp**	Metallic Blue body, Yellow interior, luggage	£40-45
			Metallic Bronze body with White side stripe or Metallic Red body, luggage	£70-80
		Danish promotional:	Light Blue body, Yellow interior, 'JENSON'S' logo, spun hubs	£300-500
252	1963-66	**Rover 2000**	Metallic Light Blue or Steel Blue body, Red interior	£55-65
			Metallic Maroon body, Red or Yellow interior	£65-75
253	1964-68	**Mercedes-Benz 220 SE**	Metallic Maroon, or Metallic Blue, luggage, spare wheel	£40-50
255	1964-68	**Motor School A60**	Dark Blue body, left-hand drive, 5 language leaflet, (USA issue of 236)	£100-125
256	1965-68	**Volkswagen 1200 Rally**	Red body, rally number '18', 'EAST AFRICAN RALLY', steering wheel on roof, rhinoceros	£150-175
258	1965-70	**The Saint's Volvo P1800**	See 'Novelty, Film and TV-related' section.	
259	1966-69	**Citroën 'Le Dandy'**	Metallic Dark Red body with Yellow interior, wire wheels	£90-110
			Metallic Blue body, White roof and boot	£110-130
260	1969	**Renault 16 TS**	Metallic Red, opening bonnet and hatchback, adjustable seats	£35-45
261	1965-69	**James Bond's Aston-Martin**	Bright Gold body (metal roof), Red interior, wire wheels. With James Bond at the wheel, passenger seat ejector (with bandit figure). Accessories: envelope with 'secret instructions', spare bandit figure, self-adhesive '007' badge, (plus 'Model Car Makers to James Bond' Corgi Catalogue in earlier boxes). Blue/Yellow picture box has inner pictorial stand. From the film 'Goldfinger'	£400-500
		variant:	As previous model but the opening roof component is made of plastic	NGPP
262	1967-69	**Lincoln Continental Executive Limousine**		
			Metallic Gold/Black body, with picture strip for onboard 'TV set'	£125-150
			Light Blue/Tan body, with picture strip for onboard 'TV set'	£150-175
263	1966-69	**Rambler Marlin Sports**	Red body, Black roof White interior, spun or cast hubs	£45-50
		Gift Set issue:	White body, Blue roof, (in Gift Set 10)	GSP
264	1966-69	**Oldsmobile Toronado**	Metallic Medium or Dark Blue body, smooth or cast spoked hubs, retractable headlights	£45-55
269	1977-83	**James Bond Lotus Esprit**	See 'Novelty, Film and TV-related' section.	
270	1968-78	**James Bond Aston-Martin**	See 'Novelty, Film and TV-related' section.	
271	1978-92	**James Bond Aston-Martin**	See 'Novelty, Film and TV-related' section.	
271	1969-69	**Ghia Mangusta De Tomaso**	Blue/White body with Gold stripes, or Orange-Red body	£55-65
273	1970	**Rolls-Royce Silver Shadow**	Metallic Silver/Blue, Golden Jacks, Take-Off wheels, spare	£65-75
			Metallic White over Metallic Blue	£55-65
274	1970-72	**Bentley 'T' Series**	Bright Pink body, Cream interior, special lights, WhizzWheels	£45-55
275	1968-70	**Rover 2000 TC**	Metallic Olive Green body, Brown or Red interior, Amber roof panel, 'Golden Jacks', spare on bootlid ..	£50-60
			Same as above but with White interior	£80-90
			White body, Red interior, Amber roof panel, 'Golden Jacks' wheels, spare wheel on bootlid	£130-160
			Metallic Maroon body, 'Golden Jacks' wheels, spare wheel on bootlid	£50-60
			Gold plated version	£125-150
276	1968-72	**Oldsmobile Toronado**	Metallic Blue or Red body, Golden Jacks, cast 'Take-Off wheels'	£40-50
			Metallic Gold body	£40-45
			Metallic Green body	NGPP
280	1970-78	**Rolls-Royce Silver Shadow**	Metallic Silver upper body, Blue lower body, Brown interior, WhizzWheels	£35-40

			Metallic Blue body, Brown interior, WhizzWheels	£30-35
281	1971-72	**Rover 2000 TC**	Metallic Red body, Yellow interior, amber or clear roof, WhizzWheels	£60-75
			Lacquered Purple body, Amber roof	£70-90
282	1971-74	**Mini Cooper Rally**	White/Black/Yellow, rally number '177', special lights, WhizzWheels	£55-65
283	1971-74	**DAF 'City' Car**	Red/Black body, White interior, opening doors/bonnet, WhizzWheels	£25-30
284	1970-76	**Citroën SM**	Metallic Gold or Metallic Mauve, opening doors, WhizzWheels	£25-30
285	1975-81	**Mercedes-Benz 240 D**	Silver, Blue, Bronze or Beige (all Metallic), WhizzWheels	£15-20
286	1975-79	**Jaguar XJC V-12**	Blue/Black, Red/Black, Red, Pearl, Blue or Orange (all Metallic), WhizzWheels	£15-20
287	1975-78	**Citroën Dyane**	Metallic Yellow/Black, Metallic Green or Bronze, duck decal, WhizzWheels	£15-20
288	1975-79	**Minissima**	Beige/Black/Yellow body	£15-20
289	1976-80	**VW Polo 'DBP'**	Yellow/White body, left-hand drive, WhizzWheels, (German issue)	£35-45
289	1977-81	**Volkswagen Polo**	Lime Green or Orange body	£15-20
289	1977-81	**VW Polo 'ADAC'**	As previous model but Yellow body, German issue	£25-35
290	1976-77	**Kojak Buick**	See 'Novelty, Film and TV-related' section.	
291	1977-80	**AMC Pacer**	Metallic Red body, opening doors and hatchback	£10-12
290	1977-82	**Starsky & Hutch Ford Torino**	See 'Novelty, Film and TV-related' section.	
293	1977-80	**Renault 5 TS**	Orange, Silver or Silver/Blue body, WhizzWheels	£10-15
		French issue:	Light Blue body, Dark Blue roof, 'SOS MEDICINS'	£75-85
294	1980-84	**Renault 5 TS Alpine**	Black body with White stripe, opening doors and hatchback	£10-15
300	1956-65	**Austin Healey 100-4**	Red with Cream seats, leaflet supplied with early issues	£130-160
			Cream with Red seats, leaflet supplied with early issues	£130-160
			Blue body with Cream seats	£175-225
300	1970-70	**Chevrolet Corvette Stingray**	Lacquered-finish Bright Green, Dark Red or Green body, Golden Jacks, luggage	£75-85
	NB		Models without box header cards contained instructions.	
300	1979-82	**Ferrari 'DAYTONA'**	Green, multicoloured flash, racing number '5', opening doors, 120 mm	£15-20
301	1956-61	**Triumph TR2**	Cream body with Red seats	£125-150
			Red body with Cream seats	£125-150
			Deep Green body with Cream seats	£125-150
301	1970-73	**Iso Grifo 7 litre**	Metallic Blue body, Black bonnet, White interior, Silver or Black roll-bar, WhizzWheels	£30-35
301	1979-82	**Lotus Elite Racing Car**	Yellow/Red body, racing number '7', 'FERODO'	£10-15
302	1957-65	**MG 'MGA'**	Red (Cream seats) smooth or chrome spun hubs, (paint shades exist)	£100-125
			Cream with Red seats	£100-125
			Mid or Dark Metallic Green body (Cream or Yellow seats), smooth or shaped spun hubs	£100-125
302	1969-72	**Hillman Hunter Rally**	Blue body, White roof, Matt-Black bonnet, RN '75', equipment, kangaroo, 'Golden Jacks', transfers, toolbox, leaflet, instructions	£100-125
302	1979-82	**VW Polo**	Metallic Brown/Red body, racing number '4', various adverts	£15-20
303	1958-60	**Mercedes-Benz 300 SL** (Open Roadster)	White body, Blue seats, smooth hubs, Blue box	£80-100
			Blue body, White seats, smooth hubs, Blue box	£80-100
			Cream body, Blue seats, smooth hubs, Blue box	£80-100
	NB		Models in rare plain overprinted box, add **£20-30**.	
303 S	1961-63	**Mercedes-Benz 300 SL** (Open Sports)	White body, Yellow interior, Red bonnet stripe, racing numbers '1' to '12'	£90-120
			Mid-Blue body, Yellow interior, Red bonnet stripe, racing numbers '1' to '12'	£90-120
	NB		'Open Sports' models housed in 303S 'Open Roadster' boxes.	
303 S2	1963-64	**Mercedes-Benz 300 SL** (Open Sports with Driver)	With driver dressed in Grey Suit, White shirt and Red bow-tie.	
			White body, Yellow interior, Red bonnet stripe, racing numbers '1' to '12'	£90-120
			Blue body, Yellow interior, Red bonnet stripe, racing numbers '1' to '12'	£90-120
			Chrome plated body, Lemon/Brown interior, Red bonnet stripe, spoked or cast hubs, RNs '1' to '12'	£125-150
303	1970-72	**Roger Clark's Ford Capri**	White body, Black bonnet, RN '73', decal sheet, WhizzWheels	£40-45
			As previous model but with Red spot hubs. Yellow/Red box with '9 transfers for you to apply!'	£80-100
304	1959-61	**Mercedes-Benz 300 SL Hardtop**	Yellow body, Red hardtop, spun hubs, no suspension	£70-90
			Yellow body and hardtop, flat spun hubs	£175-225
304 S	1961-63	**Mercedes-Benz 300 SL Hardtop**	Chrome body, Red hardtop, stripe, smooth/shaped/spoked hubs, RN '3' or '7'	£70-90
			White body, Red hardtop, shaped hubs	£200-300
304	1971-72	**Chevrolet Camaro SS350**	Dark Blue body, White bonnet band and detachable roof, special lights	£30-40
305	1960-63	**Triumph TR3**	Metallic Olive Green or Cream body, Red seats, smooth or shaped hubs	£90-110
305 S	1962-63	**Triumph TR3**	Light Green or Cream body, spring suspension, shaped spun hubs	£150-175
305	1972-73	**Mini Marcos GT 850**	White body, Red interior, Blue/White stripes, racing number '7', WhizzWheels	£30-35
306	1971-73	**Morris Marina 1.8 Coupé**	Metallic Red body, Cream interior, WhizzWheels	£40-45
			Metallic Lime Green body, Cream interior, WhizzWheels	£40-45
307	1962-64	**Jaguar 'E' type**	Metallic Grey body with Red removable hard-top, inner packing	£80-90
			Red body and hard-top, inner packing	£80-90
308	1972-76	**Mini Cooper 'S' 'MONTE CARLO'**	Yellow body, RN '177', two spare wheels on roof-rack, WhizzWheels, (339 update)	£65-75
			Gold (vacuum plated) body. Only 144 thought to exist	£1,000-1,500
309	1962-65	**Aston Martin DB4 Competition**	Turquoise/White body, Yellow interior, flags, spun hubs, RN '1', '3' or '7'	£80-100
			Variation with spoked hubs	£90-110
310	1963-67	**Chevrolet Corvette Stingray**	Metallic Red, Yellow interior, shaped hubs	£30-40
			Metallic Silver body, Yellow interior, wire wheels	£40-50
			Metallic Bronze body, Yellow interior	£80-100
311	1970-72	**Ford Capri V6 3-litre**	Orange body, Gold wheels with Red hubs, Black interior	£80-90
			Fluorescent Orange body, WhizzWheels	£50-60
			Fluorescent Orange body, Red spot WhizzWheels	£100-150

			Red body, Black bonnet, Red spot WhizzWheels	£50-60
312	1964-68	'E' type Jaguar	Silver (vacuum plated) body, racing number '2', driver, suspension, spoked hubs	£90-110
312	1971-74	Marcos Mantis	Metallic Red body with opening doors, spoked hubs	£20-30
313	1970-73	Ford Cortina GXL	Metallic Blue body, Black roof, Black/White interior, Graham Hill figure, WhizzWheels	£60-70
			Bronze body, Black roof	£60-70
			Yellow body, Black roof	£150-175
			Metallic Pale Green body, Black roof	£100-120
		Promotional:	Tan body, Black roof, Red interior, left-hand drive, 'CORTINA' number plate	£250-350
314	1965-72	Ferrari Berlinetta 250 LM	Red body, racing number '4', wire wheels, suspension	£45-55
314	1976-79	Fiat X1-9	Metallic Lime Green/Black or Silver/Black body, suspension, hook	£25-35
315	1964-66	Simca 1000 Sports	Plated Silver, Red interior, RN '8', Red/White/Blue racing stripes	£35-40
			Metallic Blue body, racing number '8', Red/White/Blue stripes	£100-120
315	1976-79	Lotus Elite	Red or Yellow with White seats, opening doors, suspension	£20-25
316	1963-66	NSU Sport Prinz	Metallic Red body, Yellow seats, spun hubs	£40-50
316	1971-73	Ford GT 70	Lime Green and Black body, White interior, racing number '32', flag design	£30-40
317	1964-65	Mini Cooper 'S' 'MONTE CARLO 1964'	Red body, White roof, Yellow interior, racing number '37', roof spotlight	£125-150
			Red body, Pink roof variation	£175-200
318	1965	Mini Cooper 'S' 'MONTE CARLO 1965'	Red body, White roof, 'AJB 44 B', racing number '52', no roof spotlight	£150-175
318	1965-67	Lotus Elan S2 Open Top	Metallic Steel Blue, racing number '6' or '8', driver, opening bonnet, tilt seats, 'tiger' decal, *I'VE GOT A TIGER IN MY TANK* logo on boot lid, Blue/Yellow box, unapplied decals	£80-90
318	1965-68	Lotus Elan S2 Open Top	Dark Green body, Yellow stripe with Black or Red interior (GS37)	GSP
			White body, Black interior (GS40), 'tiger' label, unapplied decals	£200-250
			Metallic Copper body, unapplied decals	£150-200
		Colour trial?:	Yellow body, Green stripe, Black interior, spun hubs	£300-500
319	1967-69	Lotus Elan S2 Hardtop	Dark Green body (Yellow top), or Blue body (White top), shaped hubs	£85-95
			Red body, White top, cast hubs	£75-85
			Red body, Red top, cast hubs	£75-85
			Blue body, White top, cast hubs	£65-75
			Green and Yellow lift-off body	£80-90
			Red body with White top, WhizzWheels	£50-60
		NB	1967-69 issues include a sheet of self-adhesive racing numbers '1' to '12'.	
319	1973-74	Lamborghini P400GT	Metallic Silver body with Purple/Yellow stripes design, racing number '7', WhizzWheels	£25-30
319	1978-81	Jaguar XJS	Metallic Red body, Black roof, opening doors, suspension	£15-20
320	1965-67	Ford Mustang Fastback 2+2	Opening doors, suspension, Corgi dog, half-open window.	
			Silver (Red interior) or Metallic Deep Blue (White interior) detailed cast hubs	£60-70
			Metallic Deep Blue body (Cream interior) or Light Green body (Cream interior), spoked hubs	£60-70
			Metallic Lilac body, Cream interior, spoked hubs	£60-70
			Metallic Deep Yellow body, Black bonnet and interior, cast hubs	£500-750
320	1978-81	The Saint's Jaguar XJS	See 'Novelty, Film and TV-related' section.	
321	1965-66	Mini Cooper 'S' 'MONTE CARLO 1965'	Red body, White roof, spotlight, rally number '52'.	
			317 picture box with 'No. 321' and 'MONTE CARLO WINNER' flash	£350-450
			Red body, White roof with spotlight, rally number '52'	£200-250
321	1966-67	Mini Cooper 'S' 'MONTE CARLO 1966'	Red body, White roof with rally number'2' and *TIMO MAKINEN* and *PAUL EASTER* signatures, no spotlight. Box flashed with white sticker with '1966 MONTE CARLO RALLY AUTOGRAPHED MINI-COOPER 'S' in Red capital letters	£250-350
		variant:	As previous issue but in 321 pictorial box with 'RALLY' text printed in Red panel	£350-450
321	1978-81	Porsche 924 Saloon	Metallic Green body with hook	£40-45
			Red body	£20-25
			Metallic Light Brown body, Red interior	£60-70
322	1967-67	Rover 2000 'MONTE CARLO'	Metallic Maroon body, White roof, Red interior, rally number'136', rally plaques	£120-150
			As previous model but with Green interior	NGPP
			Model boxed in rare 252 box with 322 labels over the box ends	£150-200
	1967	'INTERNATIONAL RALLY FINISH'	White body, Black bonnet, Red interior, White/Orange label on doors with Black RN '21', cast hubs. 322 box with Red 'ROVER 2000 INTERNATIONAL RALLY FINISH' and box flash. Paint shade differences are known	£200-250
323	1965-66	Citroën DS19 'MONTE CARLO 1965'	Pale Blue with White roof, rally plaques and number '75', suspension	£100-125
323	1974-78	Ferrari Daytona 365 GTB/4	White/Red/Blue body, racing number '81', opening doors	£10-15
324	1966-69	Marcos Volvo 1800 GT	White body with two Green stripes	£35-40
			Blue body with two White stripes	£40-50
324	1973-75	Ferrari Daytona Le Mans	Yellow body, racing number '33', *A.BAMFORD*, 122 mm	£25-35
325	1965-69	Ford Mustang Competition	White body with double Red stripe (Blue interior), shaped spun hubs, detailed cast hubs, wire wheels or cast 'alloy' wheels	£50-60
			White body, double Red stripes, Gold 'alloy' wheels	£60-70
		NB	A sheet of four racing numbers enclosed with each model.	
327	1967-69	MGB GT	Dark Red body, Blue or Yellow interior, spoked wheels, luggage	£70-85
328	1966-67	Hillman Imp 'MONTE CARLO 1966'	Metallic Dark Blue/White, 'FRW 306 C', rally plaques and number '107', spun hubs	£100-125
		NB	If 'HILLMAN IMP 328' Yellow/Red advertising card is with model, add **20%** to price.	
329	1973-76	Ford Mustang Rally Car	Metallic Green body, White roof, rally number '69', (391 special)	£25-30
330	1967-69	Porsche Carrera 6	White body, Red bonnet and doors, racing number '60', cast hubs, Blue engine cover	£45-50

331	1974-76	**Ford Capri GT Rally**	White body, Dark Blue bonnet and doors, racing number '60', cast hubs, Orange engine cover	**£80-100**
			White body, Black bonnet, 'TEXACO', racing number '5'	**£45-55**
332	1967-69	**Lancia Fulvia Zagato**	Metallic Green, Metallic Blue, or Orange, suspension, tilt seats	**£50-60**
			Yellow/Black body	**£100-125**
333	1966	**Mini Cooper 'S'**		
		'SUN - RAC Rally'	Red body, White roof, RN '21' and *'SUN RAC INTERNATIONAL RALLY'* decals,	
			225 box with White label '1966 RAC INTERNATIONAL RALLY' in Blue	**£175-225**
334	1968-70	**Mini Cooper 'Magnifique'**	Metallic Dark Blue or Green, jewelled lights, sunshine roof, 73 mm	**£50-60**
335	1968-70	**Jaguar 4.2 litre 'E' type**	Metallic Dark Red body, spoked wheels, wing flap bubble pack	**£80-90**
			Metallic Blue body, Black interior, wing flap bubble pack	**£80-90**
			Orange body, Black roof, wing flap bubble pack	**NGPP**
336	1967-69	**James Bond Toyota 2000GI**	See 'Novelty, Film and TV-related' section.	
337	1967-69	**Chevrolet Stock Car**	Yellow body, racing number '13', *'STINGRAY'*, suspension	**£35-40**
338	1968-71	**Chevrolet SS 350 Camaro**	Metallic Green/Black, Gold/Black or Bronze/Black, 'Golden Jacks' and 'Take-Off' wheels	**£35-45**
339	1967-71	**Mini Cooper 'S'**		
		'MONTE CARLO 1967' ......(i)	Red body, White roof, RN '177', 2 spare wheels, shaped spun hubs, Austin grille, in	
			227 box with White flash label with '1967 MONTE-CARLO WINNER B.M.C.	
			MINI-COOPER 'S' in Red capital letters, Red '339' flash on box end	**£150-200**
		(ii)	As (i) but with cast detailed hubs and slight Silver detail	**£150-200**
		(iii)	As (i) but with shaped spun hubs and slight Silver detail	**£150-200**
		(iv)	As (i) but with cast detailed hubs and Morris grille	**£150-200**
		(v)	As (i) but in 339 picture box with winner's text in Red lettering on box front.	
			Special leaflet enclosed with each model	**£150-200**
		(vi)	As (i) but in 339 box with the winners text in Red panel	**£150-200**
340	1967-69	**Sunbeam Imp**		
		'MONTE CARLO 1967' .....(i)	Metallic Blue, RN '77', spun hubs, flashed 328 box with '1967 MONTE CARLO SUNBEAM IMP	
			WINNER PRODUCTION CARS UP TO 1000cc' text in Blue capitals plus model no. '340'	**£100-125**
		(ii)	As (i) but in 340 pictorial box with 'winner' text printed in Red on the	
			box front plus cast detailed hubs.	**£100-125**
		(iii)	As (i) but Metallic Dark Blue body, cast detailed hubs, 'winner' text printed in	
			Red panel on box front.	**£125-175**
341	1968-70	**Mini Marcos GT 850**	Metallic Crimson (Cream seats) or Metallic Maroon body, 'Golden Jacks' and 'Take-off' wheels	**£30-40**
342	1970-72	**Lamborghini P400 Miura**	Red body, White interior, Black plastic rampant bull figure, WhizzWheels.	
			1st type box: Blue/Yellow box has 'Revised specification' label regarding 'Take-off' wheels	**£75-85**
			2nd type box: Red/Yellow box with 'Revised specification' label	**£40-50**
			Lime Green body, Red interior, with bull figure	**£40-50**
343	1969-73	**Pontiac Firebird**	Metallic Silver/Black, Red seats, Gold/Red Take-Off wheels, Golden Jacks	**£25-35**
			With Red-spot WhizzWheels	**£50-60**
344	1969-73	**Ferrari Dino Sports**	Yellow with Black doors (number '23') or Red (number '30') WhizzWheels	**£30-40**
			With Red-spot WhizzWheels	**£40-50**
345	1969	**MGC GT Competition**	Yellow body, Black bonnet, tailgate and interior, spoked wheels.	
			'MGB GT' on box overprinted 'NEW MGC' Self-adhesive numbers enclosed	**£80-90**
		Gift Set version:	Orange body (Car Transporter Gift Set 41)	**£150-200**
347	1969-74	**Chevrolet Astro Experimental** .	Metallic Dark Blue or Green body, Red-spot WhizzWheels	**£40-50**
			As previous model but with plain WhizzWheels	**£30-40**
348	1968-69	**Mustang 'Pop Art' Stock Car** ..	Light Blue with Red/Orange 'Flower-Power' labels, racing number '20'	**£65-75**
			Light Blue body without labels	**£50-60**
349	1967-67	**'POP ART' Morris Mini**	Red body, Yellow interior, 4 psychedelic labels, *MOSTEST* logo, few only produced	**£1,500-2,000**
371	1970-73	**Porsche Carrera 6**	White/Red, racing number '60', plated Blue engine cover, WhizzWheels, (330 update)	**£20-25**
372	1970-72	**Lancia Fulvia Zagato**	Orange body, Black bonnet, WhizzWheels	**£30-35**
374	1970-76	**Jaguar 'E' type 4.2 litre**	Red or Yellow body, WhizzWheels, (2+2), (335 update)	**£30-40**
374	1973	**Jaguar 'E' type 5.3 litre**	Yellow or Metallic Yellow body 'New' on box label	**£40-50**
375	1970-72	**Toyota 2000 GT**	Metallic translucent 'candy' Blue body, White interior, WhizzWheels, (modified 336), leaflet	**£40-50**
			Metallic Purple body, White interior, WhizzWheels	**£45-55**
376	1970-72	**Chevrolet Corvette Stock Car** ..	Silver body, racing number '13', *'GO-GO-GO'*, WhizzWheels, (337 update)	**£25-35**
			Metallic Blue body, Red interior, racing number '13', WhizzWheels	**£25-35**
377	1970-72	**Marcos 3 litre**	Yellow body, Black bonnet, WhizzWheels, (324 conversion)	**£40-45**
			White body, Grey sunroof, Whizzwheels	**£70-80**
			Metallic Blue-Green body, Black interior, bonnet decal, WhizzWheels	**£30-40**
378	1970-72	**MGC GT**	Red body, Black bonnet and interior, WhizzWheels, (345 update)	**£60-70**
		Gift Set issue:	Orange body, (this version in Gift Set 20)	**GSP**
380	1970-74	**Alfa Romeo P33**	White body, Gold roll bar, Red seats, WhizzWheels, (Pininfarina)	**£25-30**
381	1970-76	**VW Beach Buggy**	Metallic Red/White, Blue/White, Orange/White or Red/White, 2 surfboards, WhizzWheels	**£15-20**
382	1970-75	**Porsche Targa 911S**	Metallic Silver-Blue body, Black roof with Gold stripe, WhizzWheels	**£30-40**
			Metallic Olive-Green body, Black roof with or without Gold stripe, WhizzWheels	**£30-40**
383	1970-76	**VW 1200 'Flower Power'**	Red body with psychedelic Grenadine and Green daisy labels on bonnet and doors	**£75-85**
383	1970-73	**Volkswagen 1200 'ADAC'**	Yellow/Black body, 'ADAC' logo (German equivalent of 'AA')	**£70-80**
		Volkswagen 1200 'PTT'	Yellow/Black body, Red interior, 'PTT' logo, Swiss issue	**£70-80**
383	1977-78	**Volkswagen 1200 Rally**	Blue body, rally number '5', chequered roof and sides	**£10-15**
384	1978	**Volkswagen 1200 Rally**	Blue body, rally number '5', chequered stripes	**£35-45**
			As previous model but with *'CALEDONIAN AUTOMINOLOGISTS'* logo	**£80-90**

			Blue body, Cream interior, WhizzWheels, '40th Anniversary 1938 - 1978'	£140-160
384	1970-73	**Adams Brothers Probe**	Green or Red body (White interior), or Metallic Gold body, WhizzWheels	£20-25
385	1970-76	**Porsche 917**	Metallic Blue or Red body, racing number '3', cast or WhizzWheels, with leaflet	£30-35
386	1971-74	**Bertone Barchetta**	Yellow/Black 'RUNABOUT', aerofoil, WhizzWheels	£20-25
387	1970-73	**Corvette Stingray**	Metallic Blue body, Black bonnet, roof emblem, WhizzWheels	£35-45
			Metallic Pink body, Black bonnet	£50-60
388	1970-74	**Mercedes-Benz C111**	Orange/Black body, WhizzWheels	£20-25
389	1971-74	**Reliant Bond 'BUG' 700 ES**	Orange body, Orange/Black 'BUG' labels, Cream interior, WhizzWheels	£35-45
			Lime Green body, WhizzWheels	£65-75
391	1972-72	**James Bond Ford Mustang**	See 'Novelty, Film and TV-related' section.	
392	1973-76	**Bertone Shake Buggy**	Pink and Green body, detailed engine, flag, WhizzWheels	£25-30
			Yellow body, Black or Green interior	£25-30
393	1972-79	**Mercedes-Benz 350 SL**	White body, Pale Blue interior with chrome, spoked wheels	£25-30
			Metallic Blue or Dark Blue body with chrome solid disc wheels	£25-30
			Metallic Green body, Brown interior	£55-65
394	1972-77	**Datsun 240 Z 'Safari Rally'**	'East African Safari Rally' finish: Red body, rally number '11', *CASTROL* and *JAPAN* logos	£40-50
396	1973-76	**Datsun 240 Z 'US Rally'**	'US Rally' finish: Red/White body, rally number '46', *JOHN MORTON* and *DATSUN* logos	£40-50
397	1974-76	**Porsche-Audi 917-10**	White/Red body, White 'L&M' logo, racing number '6', *CORGI*, racing driver	£25-30
400	1974-75	**Volkswagen 1300**	Metallic Red body, 'CORGI MOTOR SCHOOL', roof steering wheel, cones	£70-80
			Metallic Blue body version	£40-50
			Metallic Blue with 'CORGI FAHR SCHULE', German issue	£100-120
401	1975-77	**Volkswagen 1300**	Same as C400 but supplied with 24 'bollards' and diorama for miniature driving practice	£45-55
406	1957-62	**Land Rover '109 WB'**	Yellow body, Black roof, smooth hubs, thin tyres	£70-90
			Metallic Dark Blue body, Cream roof, smooth or shaped hubs, thin or thick tyres	£60-70
			Green body with Tan tinplate cover, smooth hubs, thin or thick tyres	£60-70
		'ETENDARD' variant:	As previous issue but with 'ETENDARD' decals, plus Red/White/Green roundels on front wings	NGPP
406s	1963	**Land Rover '109 WB'**	Yellow body, Red seats, shaped hubs, suspension	£60-70
411	1976-79	**Mercedes Benz 240 D**	Orange/Black or Cream body, *'TAXI'* on roof	£10-15
		German issue:	Black body, Red *'TAXI'* roof sign, *'TAXI'* on doors	£35-45
418	1960-65	**Austin FX4 Taxi**	Black body, *'TAXI'* sign, smooth or shaped hubs, no driver	£40-50
			Black body, *'TAXI'* sign, smooth or shaped hubs, 'younger' driver figure	£35-45
			Black body, *'TAXI'* sign, smooth or shaped hubs, 'older' driver figure	£30-40
425	1978	**London Taxi**	FX4 type taxi with Black body, *'TAXI'*, WhizzWheels	£10-15
			Maroon body, Red interior, WhizzWheels	£80-100
415	1976-78	**Mazda Camper**	Red body with drop-down tailboard, White caravan	£25-30
417	1960-62	**Land Rover Breakdown**	Red body, Yellow tinplate canopy, smooth hubs, *'BREAKDOWN SERVICE'*	£55-65
417s	1963-65	**Land Rover Breakdown**	Red body, Yellow tinplate canopy, shaped hubs, suspension, *'BREAKDOWN SERVICE'*	£45-55
419	1978-79	**AMC Jeep CJ-5**	Metallic Green body with White plastic top, or Metallic Dark Green body	£25-35
420	1962-66	**Ford 'Airborne' Caravan**	Ford Thames in Two-tone Green, Brown interior or Blue/Pale Grey,	
			Red interior or Blue/Green, Brown interior	£40-50
			Two-tone Lilac, Beige interior	£70-80
421	1977-80	**Land Rover Safari**	Orange body, Black roof rack with ladder, spare wheel	£20-25
			Red body, White roof rack with ladder, *'FOREST FIRE WARDEN'* logo	£20-25
		Land Rover Workman's Bus	Yellow/Red body, no roof rack or ladder	NGPP
424	1961-65	**Ford Zephyr Estate**	Pale Blue body, Dark Blue bonnet and side flash, suspension, luggage, smooth or shaped spun hubs	£65-75
430	1962-64	**Ford Bermuda 'TAXI'**	White body, Yellow and Red canopy	£60-75
		(Ford Thunderbird)	White body, Lime Green and Red canopy	£60-75
			White body, Blue and Red canopy	£60-75
			Metallic Blue body, Red canopy	£150-200
436	1963-65	**Citroën ID19 'SAFARI'**	Yellow body, driver and passenger, detailed interior, roof luggage, 'Wild Life Reservation' logo	£70-80
438	1963-77	**Land Rover 109 WB**	Model has plastic canopy. Earlier issues have metal towhooks (plastic later), suspension.	
			Dark Green body Grey or Tan canopy, Yellow interior, shaped hubs	£100-125
			Dark Brown body, Light Brown canopy, Red interior, shaped hubs	£100-125
			Metallic Green body, Olive-Green canopy, Yellow interior, shaped hubs	£60-80
			Metallic Green body, Olive-Green canopy, Chrome hubs	£60-80
			Metallic Green body, Olive-Green canopy, WhizzWheels	£40-60
			Red body, Brown tilt, Red interior, shaped hubs	£40-60
		'LEPRA' variant:	Metallic Green body, Tan canopy with 'LEPRA' logo, Yellow interior, shaped hubs,	
			Silver steering wheel	£400-500
			Red body, Blue canopy, (in Gift Set 19)	GSP
		Promotional:	with '10 MILLIONTH CORGI LAND ROVER' label	£50-75
440	1966-69	**Ford Consul Cortina Estate**	Metallic Dark Blue with Brown side panels, plastic golfer, caddie and trolley	£100-125
440	1979-	**Mazda Custom Pick-Up**	Orange/Yellow/Red, US flag	£15-20
443	1963-65	**Plymouth Suburban US Mail**	Blue/White body, *'ADDRESS YOUR MAIL CAREFULLY'*	£65-75
445	1963-66	**Plymouth Suburban Sports Station Wagon**	Pale Blue body, Red roof, Lemon interior, Silver side stripe	£65-75
			Beige body, Tan roof	£55-65
477	1966-68	**Land Rover Breakdown**	Red/Yellow/Silver, spare wheel on some, hook, WhizzWheels	£30-35
480	1965-66	**Chevrolet Impala Taxi**	Yellow body, Red roof, Chrome stripe, shaped spun wheels	£50-55
			As previous model but with detailed cast wheels	£50-55

485	1965-69	Mini Countryman with Surfer	Sea-Green body, Lemon interior, 2 surfboards on roof-rack, male figure, special leaflet	£125-150
			As previous model but with unpainted grille	£140-170
491	1966-69	Ford Consul Cortina Estate	Metallic Red body, Brown/Cream side/rear panels	£65-75
			Metallic Blue body, Brown/Cream side/rear panels	£65-75
			Metallic Dark Grey body, Brown/Cream side/rear panels	£65-75
	NB		No golf equipment issued with this model (see 440).	
497	1966-69	'The Man From UNCLE' Car	See 'Novelty, Film and TV-related' section.	
507	1969	Chrysler Bermuda Taxi	Shown in catalogue but not issued	NPP

Corgi Toys Cars, 1980 onwards

IMPORTANT NOTES:
The main focus of interest for collectors of Corgi Toys model cars is the earlier listing seen above. Therefore, post-1980 cars have been separated out into the listing below. While most of these command only low prices, there are notable exceptions (Film/TV issues and promotionals, for example). Most model references from 1980 (particularly 're-used' ones) were preceded with the letter 'C', some with 'D'. These prefixes have been omitted from this list. See also: 'Novelty, Film and TV-related' section.

Ref	Year(s)	Model name	Colours, features, details	Market Price Range
46	1983-	Super Kart	Blue or Orange main body, Red/Silver racing driver	£5-10
100	1985	'PORSCHE' 956	Yellow/Black body, racing number '7', 'CASTROL'	£7-10
100/2	1986		Yellow body, racing number '7', 'TAKA-Q'	£7-10
100/3	1988		Black body, racing number '1', 'BLAUPUNKT'	£7-10
101	1985	Porsche 956	Red/White body, racing number '14', 'CANON'	£7-10
101/2	1985	Porsche 956	White body, 'Clipper' logo plus 4 Red stripes on bonnet and tail, 'ADMIRAL ENERGY GROUP Ltd' logo	£15-20
102	1985	Opel Manta 400	Red body, racing number '43', 'SHELL'	£7-10
	1988		Black body, racing number '18', 'SHELL'	£7-10
102	1985		Yellow body, racing number '12', 'BRITISH TELECOM'	£7-10
			White body, racing number '1', 'OPEL'	£7-10
102/4	1990	'VAUXHALL OPEL' Manta	White body, racing number '6', 'MOBIL' on bonnet	£7-10
103	1985	Opel Manta 400	White body, racing number '15', 'CASTROL'	£7-10
104	1985	Toyota Corolla 1600	White/Red body, Yellow racing number '16', 'LAING'	£7-10
	1986		White/Red body, racing number '2', 'TOTAL'	£7-10
105	1985	Toyota Corolla 1600	Red body, Yellow design, racing number '8', 'DUNLOP'	£7-10
	1986		Red body, Yellow design, racing number '5', 'TOTAL'	£7-10
			Red body, Yellow/Black/Pink stripes, racing number '6', 'BRITAX WEBER'	£7-10
106	1985	Saab 9000 Turbo	White body, Red/Yellow design, racing number '3'	£7-10
106/1	1987		Red body, White design 'FLY VIRGIN'	£7-10
106/3	1988		Black body, racing number '7', 'MOBIL'	£7-10
106/9	1990	Saab Turbo	White/Maroon body, racing number '4', 'FEDERAL EXPRESS'	£7-10
			Red body, White stripes, racing number '7', 'DUCKHAMS', 'DUNLOP'	£7-10
107	1985	Saab 9000	Red body, Yellow design, racing number '41', 'BRITAX'	£7-10
108	1985	Chevrolet Z-28	Red body, Yellow design, racing number '52', 'WEBER'	£7-10
			Red body, Black stripe, racing number '8', 'BOSCH'	£7-10
109	1985	Chevrolet Z-28	White body, Black/Yellow bands, Red racing number '84'	£7-10
110	1985	BMW 635	White body with Union Jacks and racing number '6'	£7-10
110/1	1986		Red body, racing number '25', 'FERODO'	£7-10
110/2	1987		White body, racing number '2', 'MOTUL'	£7-10
110/3	1988		White body, racing number '46', 'WARSTEINER'	£7-10
			White body, Grey/Black stripes, racing number '41', 'GOODYEAR'	£7-10
111	1985	BMW 635	White/Blue body, racing number '18', 'BRITAX'	£7-10
	1986		White body, racing number '8', 'PIRELLI'	£7-10
113	1987	Saab 9000	Red body, C7PM (Swedish)	£7-10
139/2	1987	Porsche 911	Orange body, racing number '24', 'JAGERMEISTER'	£7-10
139/4	1988		Red/Blue body, racing number '91', 'DENVER'	£7-10
150/4	1990	Chevrolet Camaro	Blue body, Orange/Black design, racing number '77'	£7-10
257	1985	Mercedes-Benz 500 SEC	White body, 'Magic Top' (fold-away roof)	£10-15
258	1985	Toyota Celica Supra	Brown body, Black base, opening doors and tailgate	£10-15
			Blue body or Blue and Cream body with Red line	£10-15
275	1981-84	Mini Metro	Blue, Purple or Red body, Yellow interior, opening doors and hatchback	£10-15
			Gold body	£45-50
		'Royal Wedding' Metro	Mauve body with Silver 'Charles & Diana' crest, special Mauve box	£20-25
272	1981-83	James Bond Citroën 2cv	See 'Novelty, Film and TV-related' section.	
273	1982-83	Honda Ballade 'BSM' Driving School Car	Yellow body with Red side stripes	£25-35
276	1982-83	Triumph Acclaim	Metallic Blue, Metallic Blue or Cream body, steering control	£7-10
277	1982-	Triumph Acclaim	'BSM' Driving School car with Yellow body, Black 'wheel' steering control on roof	£15-20
278	1982	Triumph Acclaim Driving School Car	Yellow body, with steering control, 'CORGI MOTOR SCHOOL' logo	£25-35

279	1980	Rolls-Royce Corniche................	Metallic Dark Red body, opening doors/bonnet/boot, tilt seats........................	£20-25
	1985		Metallic Blue, Bright Red, Off-White/Cream, Cream or Silver/Grey body................	£20-25
	1987		Silver/Black body with chrome trim....................................	£20-25
279/3	1990	Rolls-Royce........................	Gold body with White seats....................................	£5-8
			Royal Blue body with White seats....................................	£5-8
			Light and Dark Brown body....................................	£5-8
281	1982-	'DATAPOST' Metro................	Blue/White body, rally number '77', various adverts................	£9-12
291	1982	Mercedes Benz 240 Rally........	Muddy Cream body, RN '5', 'EAST AFRICAN RALLY' or 'E.A.R.' logos............	£20-25
294	1980-84	Renault 5 TS Alpine................	Black body with White stripe, opening doors and hatchback................	£10-15
298	1982-83	Magnum P.I. Ferrari 308GTS..	See 'Novelty, Film and TV-related' section.	
299	1982	Ford Sierra 2.3 Ghia................	Metallic Light Brown/Black stripe, Dark Brown or Grey interior, Brown or	
			Dark Grey base. Issued in a special two-tone Blue 'Ford' box........................	£20-25
			As previous model but Metallic Light Brown, Metallic Blue, Red or Yellow	
			body, packed in White/Red 'Ford' box or normal Black/Yellow/Red box................	£15-20
	1985	....	Metallic Silver or Yellow body....................................	£15-20
	1985		Red body, White broken ground....................................	£15-20
299	1987	Sierra Rally........................	Black body, rally number '7', 'TEXACO'....................................	£10-12
299/4	1990	Ford Sierra........................	Pink body, 'MR TOMKINSON'S CARPETS' logo....................................	£10-12
303	1980-	Porsche 924 Racer..................	Orange body, racing number '2', 'PIRELLI'....................................	£9-12
			Yellow body with 'HELLA' logo....................................	£35-45
306	1980-81	Fiat X1/9S........................	Metallic Blue body with Red/Yellow bands, racing number '3' or '6'................	£15-20
307	1981-82	Renault Turbo........................	Yellow/Red body, racing number '8', 'CIBIE', other adverts................	£10-15
308	1982-82	BMW M1........................	Yellow and Black body, racing number '25', 'TEAM BMW', detailed engine................	£10-15
309	1982-	VW 'TURBO'........................	White and Orange body, racing number '14', Red decals....................................	£10-15
310	1982-	'PORSCHE' 924 Turbo..........	Black/Gold, opening doors and hatchback, 'GOODYEAR'....................................	£10-15
310	1984	Porsche 924 Turbo..................	Black body (Gold design, Red seats) or Red body with Porsche badge................	£10-15
312	1983-	Ford Capri 'S'........................	White, racing number '6', hinged parcel shelf, various adverts................	£10-15
314	1982-	Supercat Jaguar XJS-HE........	Black body, Red or Tan interior, opening doors....................................	£10-15
318	1981	Jaguar XJS........................	Blue/Cream body with Red line....................................	£15-20
318	1983	....	Black/Red/White body, racing number '4', 'MOTUL', 'JAGUAR'................	£15-20
	1985	........................Export issue:	Green body, racing number '12' and 'DEUTCHSLAND' logo................	NGPP
318	1985	....	British Racing Green body with White band, racing number '12'................	£10-15
	1988		Pale Blue body, Beige seats....................................	£10-15
318/8	1990	....	Blue body with White seats....................................	£10-15
325	1981-	Chevrolet Caprice..................	Metallic Light Green or Dark Green body, White-wall tyres................	£20-25
			Metallic Silver over Dark Blue (US market)....................................	£70-80
327	1980-81	Chevrolet Caprice Taxi..........	Yellow body, 'THINK TWA', fare table on door....................................	£15-20
329	1980-82	Opel Senator........................	Dark Blue or Bronze body, opening doors....................................	£15-18
			Silver body....................................	£25-30
Q330/1	1989	Mini 30th Anniversary............	Pearlescent Cherry Red, Austin-Rover mail-order model (17,500)................	£8-10
(Q24/1)	1989	Mini 30th Anniversary............	Q330/1 Mini specially packaged with 'MINI' book................	£45-55
330/10	1990	Mini 'AFTER EIGHT'............	Dark Blue with Gold stripe, French export model (5,000)................	£10-15
334	1981-	Ford Escort 1.3 GL..................	Blue, Green or Yellow body....................................	£12-15
			Red body with 'AVIS' logo on roof....................................	£25-35
338	1980-83	Rover 3500........................	Metallic Blue, Red/Black or Bronze/Brown body................	£15-20
340	1981-84	Rover 'TRIPLEX'....................	White/Red/Blue body, racing number '1', hinged parcel shelf................	£15-20
341	1981-82	Chevrolet Caprice..................	Red/White/Blue body, racing number '43', 'STP', White tyres................	£10-15
342	1980-82	'The Professionals' Ford Capri	See 'Novelty, Film and TV-related' section.	
343	1980-81	Ford Capri 3 litre....................	Yellow or Silver body, Black designs, opening doors/hatchback................	£30-35
345	1981-82	Honda Prelude........................	Metallic Blue, Cream/Green or Metallic Yellow body, sunshine roof................	£10-15
346	1982-84	Citroën 2cv........................	Yellow/Black, Burgundy/Black, Red/White or Grey/Red body................	£10-15
		German promotional:	Yellow body, Black roof, 'REISGOLD' label....................................	£100-120
348	1980-81	'Vegas' Ford Thunderbird........	See 'Novelty, Film and TV-related' section.	
350	1985	Toyota Celica Supra................	Red/White body, racing number '14', 'HUGHES', racing tyres................	£7-10
351	1985	Ford Sierra Pace Car..............	White body, Green/Yellow tampo-print design, warning lights, flags................	£7-10
352	1986	BMW 325........................	White with Black logo Swiss export model....................................	NGPP
353/1	1986	BMW 325........................	Red body, Black trim, opening features....................................	£7-10
353/9	1990	BMW 325i........................	Black body with Red seats....................................	£7-10
353	1987	BMW 325i Rally....................	White body, Green logo 'CASTROL'....................................	£7-10
354	1986	BMW 325........................	White body, racing number '33', 'FAVRAUD' logo....................................	£7-10
370	1982	Ford Cobra Mustang..............	White/Black/Red/Blue, 'MUSTANG', with or without tailgate stripe................	£10-15
370	1982	Ford Cobra Mustang..............	White body, Red interior, Blue/Red design....................................	£10-15
373	1981-	Peugeot 505........................	Red body, Silver or Black lining, opening doors, suspension................	£10-15
373/3	1987	Peugeot 'POLITI'....................	Black/White body, warning lights, Norwegian export model................	£15-20
378	1982-	Ferrari 308 GTS....................	Red or Black body, pop-up headlights, opening engine cover................	£20-30
380	1983-	'BASF' BMW M1....................	Red/White body, '80', aerofoil, opening engine cover................	£7-10
381	1983-	'ELF' Renault Turbo..............	Red/White/Blue, racing number '5', 'FACOM'....................................	£10-15
			Blue/White, racing number '13', 'ELF'....................................	£10-15
382	1983-	Lotus Elite 22........................	Metallic Blue body, 'Elite 22', opening doors, number plates................	£10-15
384	1983-84	Renault 11 GTL....................	Dark Cream body, Red interior, opening doors and boot, (export issue)................	£25-30
			Maroon or Metallic Mauve body....................................	£25-30
385	1984	Mercedes 190 E....................	Silver/Black body, White seats, number plates, chrome trim................	£9-12
	1985		All-Silver body....................................	£9-12
386	1987	Mercedes 23/16....................	White body, Black racing number '17', 'SERVIS'....................................	£5-8
386/4	1988	....	As previous model but racing number '17', 'BURLINGTON AIR EXPRESS'................	£5-8
386/8	1990	....	Red body with Beige seats....................................	£5-8
388	1987	Mercedes 190 Taxi................	White or Beige body, Yellow/Black 'TAXI' logo, export model................	£5-10

399	1985	Peugeot 205	Silver body, racing number '205', multi-coloured tampo-print design	£7-10
399/5	1988	Peugeot 205 T16	Yellow body, racing number '2', 'VATENEN'	£7-10
402	1985	BMW M1	Red/White body, racing number '101', 'CASTROL'	£7-10
403	1985	Ford Escort	White body, racing number '84', multicoloured print, 'TOTAL'	£7-10
404	1985	Rover 3500	Red body, racing number '13', 'DAILY MIRROR'	£7-10
	1986		Red body, racing number '1', 'TEXACO'	£7-10
420	1984	'BMW M1'	Blue/White body, racing number '11', 'LIGIER'S'	£7-10
	1985		White body, racing number '17', 'ESSO'	£7-10
422	1984	'RENAULT 5' TBA	Blue body, racing number '25', 'BOSCH' and 'ELF'	£7-10
	1985		Dark Blue body, multicoloured print, racing number '18'	£7-10
423	1984	Ford Escort	Blue/White body, 'BROOKLYN', Red seats, racing number '69', 'SHELL'	£7-10
424	1984	'FORD MUSTANG'	Black body, Yellow/Red print, racing number '77', 'ESSO'	£8-10
425/1	1986	London Taxi	FX4 type taxi with Black body, 'RADIO CAB', Yellow design on door	£5-10
426	1984	'HEPOLITE' Rover	Yellow/Red, racing number '4', 'FERODO'	£8-10
	1988		Yellow/Red body, 'DAILY EXPRESS'	£8-10
434	1985	Mercedes 'TAXI'	Yellow body, Red taxi sign, chrome trim	£10-15
435	1986	Volvo 760 Turbo	Dark Blue or Silver body or Metallic Dark Brown body	£8-10
435/2	1987	Volvo 760 Turbo	White body, Blue/Yellow print, 'GILLANDERS'	£8-10
435/12	1990	Volvo 760 Turbo	Green body with White seats	£8-10
440	1988	Porsche 944 Saloon	Red body	£8-10
440	1988	'PORSCHE 944' Rally	White body, Red design	£8-10
440/6	1990	Porsche 944 Rally	White body, Pink/Blue design, 'PIRELLI', rally number '44'	£8-10
441	1979-83	'GOLDEN EAGLE' Jeep	Brown/Tan or Gold/White, detachable roof, spare wheel on some	£15-20
447	1983	'RENEGADE' 4x4 Jeep	Yellow body, racing number '5' (As 448 but without hood). In GS 36	GSP
448	1983	'RENEGADE' 4x4 Jeep	Yellow body, Red hood, racing number '5'	£8-10
448	1985	'RENEGADE' 4x4 Jeep	Red/White body, roll bar	£5-10
450	1983	Peugeot Taxi	Beige with Blue label, '739:33:33', (French issue)	£30-35
451		Ford Sierra Taxi	Cream body	NGPP
453	1984	Ford Escort RS 1600 i	White body, Red seats, Black design	£10-15
457	1981-83	Talbot Matra Rancho	Red/Black or Green/Black, opening doors and boot, tilt seats	£10-15
457	1984	Talbot Matra Rancho	Orange/Black or White/Blue body, Brown seats	£20-25
501	1984	Range Rover	Beige and Dark Brown body	£5-10
507	1987-?	Range Rover Rally	Navy Blue body, White roof, 'PARIS-DAKAR' logo	£20-30
522		Range Rover	Red/White/Blue, 'STIMOROL'	NGPP
522/2	1986-	Ruby Anniversary Land Rover	Maroon body with '40th ANNIVERSARY' on bonnet. Special box (Major Pack)	NGPP
567	1984	Range Rover	White body, 'PARIS MATCH', and 'VSD'	£7-10
580/6	1999	London Taxi	Blue, with 'ENGLAND 2006' decals. (Football Association promotional)	£100-150
600	1984	Ford Escort	All Red or Red/Black or Red/White body, opening doors	£8-10
601	1984	Fiat N-9	Red or Silver/Red body, opening doors	£8-10
602	1984	BL Mini 1000	Yellow body, with or without 'CITY', opening doors	£8-10
	1984		Chrome plated model, wooden plinth, in black 'Austin-Rover' box, 'Austin-Rover Mini 25th Celebration Donington Park - August 1984'	£70-80
	1984		Metallic Dark Blue, racing number '8'	£20-25
603	1984	Volkswagen Polo	Green/White or White body, opening doors	£8-10
604	1984	Renault 5	Dark Blue or Black or Yellow body, with or without 'Le Car TL'	£8-10
605	1984	Austin Mini Metro	Blue body, with or without 'TURBO'	£8-10
611	1985-86	Ford Escort	Red body, 'DATAPOST 66'	£8-10
612	1985-86	Ford Escort	Red body, 'DATAPOST 77'	£8-10
613	1985-86	Metro Saloon	Red body, 'DATAPOST 66'	£8-10
614	1985-86	Metro Saloon	Red, body 'DATAPOST 77'	£8-10
619	1986	Range Rover	Dark Beige body, Black ladder, roof-rack, luggage	£5-10
			Red body with 'ROYAL MAIL' logo	£10-15
			Red or Metallic Blue body, Brown 'wood' panels, shaped spun hubs	£50-60
Q619/3	1990	'NORWEB' Land Rover	White with 3 Black side stripes, spare wheel	£15-20
675/14	1990	BMW 635	Red/Black body, White-wall tyres	£8-10
1009	1984	MG Maestro	Yellow body, White flash, 'AA SERVICE'	£8-10
60317	1992	F1 Racing Car	Green/White body, 'FUJI FILM' logo, Boots promotional (35,000)	NGPP
?	?	Jaguar XJR9	White body, 'Martin Brundle', 'J. Nielsen' and 'R. Bosel' roof signatures 'CASTROL' logos, rally number '60', Petrol Co promotional	£8-10
91812	1992	Taxi	Cream body, 'FINANCIAL TIMES' logo	NGPP

Collectors notes

Corgi Classics - Cars (original issues)

A factory fire ended production in 1969 of this original series of 'Classics' cars. Boxes are of two types: one with separate lid with coloured line-drawings printed on it and containing a separate picture of the model; and type two which has the model attached to a sliding-drawer style base in an outer box with half-flaps (similar printing to 1st type). Early issues have reference numbers '901' onwards which were changed to '9001' etc. just before release.

9001	1964-69	1927 3-litre Bentley.................	British Racing Green, racing number '3', detachable hood, driver..£30-40
9002	1964-68	1927 3-litre Bentley.................	Red body, civilian driver, no racing number, detachable hood £50-60
9004	1967-69	'WORLD OF WOOSTER'	
		Bentley	As previous model but in Green or Red and with Jeeves and Wooster figures £100-150
9011	1964-68	1915 Model 'T' Ford	Black body, driver, passenger, spoked wheels, brass radiator £30-40
9012	1965-68	Model 'T' Ford	Version with Yellow/Black body, Black or Yellow wheels £30-40
9013	1964-69	1915 Model 'T' Ford	Blue/Black body, detachable hood, spare wheel, driver cranks £30-40
9014		1915 'LYONS TEA' Van	Appeared in 1967/68 catalogue but was not issued ....NPP
9021	1964-69	1910 38 hp Daimler	Red body, driver and 3 passengers, folded hood, detailed chassis £30-40
9022		1910 38 hp Daimler	Appeared in the 1966 catalogue but not issued ....NPP
9031	1965-68	1910 Renault 12/16	Lavender/Black body with carriage lamps, spoked wheels £30-40
9032	1965-69	1910 Renault 12/16	Same as previous model but Primrose Yellow and Black body £30-40
9041	1966-70	1912 Rolls-Royce Silver Ghost .	Silver and Black body, carriage lamps, spoked wheels £30-40
		variant:	Maroon body, Silver roof and bonnet ....NGPP

Corgi Classics - Cars (re-introduced issues)

Some of the 'Classics' were re-introduced in 1985 when original tools were discovered. These later models are distinct from the originals as they have 'SPECIAL EDITION' on their baseplates and are packed in Grey/Red boxes which do not contain a picture of the model. The model numbers are different and 13,500 of each colour were made.

C860	(9041)	1985	1912 Rolls-Royce Silver Ghost...................Silver, Black or Ruby Red body £10-15
C861	(9002)	1985	1927 3-litre Bentley open top ....British Racing Green, Black or Ruby Red body £10-15
C862	(9031)	1985	1910 Renault 12/16..Yellow, Pale Blue, Cream or Brown body £10-15
C863	(9012)	1985	1915 Model 'T' Ford ....Black, Red or Blue body...£10-15

317 'Monte Carlo Rally' BMC Mini-Cooper 'S'

318 Lotus Elan S2 with driver

328 Hillman Imp in 'Monte Carlo Rally' trim

Another version of 318 Lotus Elan S2 with driver

275 Rover 2000 TC
with 'Golden Jacks' and 'Take-off Wheels'

303 Roger Clark's Ford Capri
fitted with WhizzWheels

302 Hillman Hunter Rally Car with 'Golden Jacks', a
kangaroo and 18 additional transfers

513 Citroën Safari 'Alpine Rescue Car'
with St Bernard dog and handler

499 'Winter Olympics' Citroën
with tobogganist

497 'The Man From U.N.C.L.E.'s 'Thrush-Buster'
Oldsmobile in white, with
diorama packing and 'Waverley' ring

Photo's on this and the previous page are of Corgi Toys models sold by Vectis Auctions Ltd. Photo's reproduced by their kind permission.

Corgi Toys Major Gift Set No.1 with No. 1101 Bedford 'S' type Carrimore Transporter and 4 Cars
(Picture supplied by Christie's South Kensington and used by their kind permission)

Commercial Vehicles

Excluding models issued from 1987 as 'Corgi Classics' (see 'Collectable Modern Diecasts' section).

Ref	Year(s)	Model name	Colours, features, details	Market Price Range
100	1957-65	Dropside Trailer	Cream/Red or Yellow body, drawbar	£10-15
101	1958-63	Platform Trailer	Grey/Yellow body, drawbar and axle swivel	£10-15
109	1968-69	'PENNYBURN' Trailer	Blue body, Yellow chassis	£30-35
403	1956-60	Bedford 12 cwt Van	'DAILY EXPRESS' on Dark Blue body	£80-100
			As previous model but Deep Blue body	£100-120
403M	1956-60	Bedford 12 cwt Van	'KLG PLUGS' on Bright Red body, flywheel motor	£125-150
403	1974-79	Thwaites Skip Dumper	Yellow/Green tipping body, driver, WhizzWheels	£25-35
404	1956-62	Bedford Dormobile	Cream (Blue roof on some), Turquoise, Blue, Red or Metallic Red, smooth or ribbed roof, smooth or shaped hubs. Early issues have divided windscreen	£65-75
			Yellow body with Blue roof	£80-90
			Yellow lower half, Blue upper half	£150-200
			All-Yellow body, with suspension	£75-85
404M	1956-60	Bedford Dormobile	Red, Metallic Red, Turquoise or Blue body, flywheel motor	£85-95
409	1959-65	Forward Control Jeep	Light Blue body, Red grille, smooth or shaped hubs	£25-35
405	1981	Ford Transit Milk Float	'DAIRY CREST' logo on cab doors, 'MILK MARKETING BOARD' logo on each side and 'MILK' on rear	£20-30
405	1982	Ford Transit Milk Float	'LOTTA BOTTLE' on Blue/White body, opening doors	£10-15
406	1971-75	Mercedes-Benz Unimog	Yellow/Green or Yellow/Red body, detachable top, suspension, hook	£25-35
407	1957-62	Smiths Karrier Bantam	'HOME SERVICES HYGIENIC MOBILE SHOP', Pale Green/Red	£75-85
408	1957-59	Bedford 'AA' Service Van	Yellow/Black, divided windscreen, smooth hubs, Blue box, leaflet	£100-120
	1958-59		Yellow/Black, undivided windscreen, smooth or shaped hubs, Blue box, leaflet	£70-80
	1959-63		Yellow/Black, undivided windscreen, shaped hubs, Blue/Yellow box, no leaflet	£60-70
	late issue:		Yellow/Black, single windscreen, ridged roof, flat spun hubs	£70-80
409	1976-77	Unimog Dumper	White/Red or Blue/Yellow body, suspension, hook	£20-30
409	1981	'ALLIS CHALMERS' Forklift	Yellow body, pallets/load/driver	£15-20
411	1958-62	Karrier Bantam Van	Yellow body, Grey plastic shutter, opening doors, 'LUCOZADE', Blue box	£100-120
			As previous model but with shaped wheels, Blue/Yellow box	£100-120
413	1960-64	Smiths Karrier Bantam Mobile Butchers	White/Blue van, 'FAMILY BUTCHERS', meaty decals. Blue box	£85-95
			As previous model but with suspension	£120-140
413	1976-78	Mazda Motorway Maintenance	Yellow/Black body, figure, road signs, bollards, decal sheet enclosed, (modified 478/493)	£25-35
416	1959-61	R.A.C. Land Rover	Blue body, 'RADIO RESCUE' on cab roof sign, metal canopy, smooth hubs, Blue/Yellow box	£90-110
			Blue body, no cab roof sign, 'RADIO RESCUE' on canopy, shaped hubs	£150-175
	Belgian issue:		Yellow body, Green metal canopy, 'TS RADIO' decals on doors	£250-300
416s	1962-64	R.A.C. Land Rover	Blue body, Lemon interior, suspension, 'RADIO RESCUE' on plastic canopy	£65-75
	Belgian issue:		Yellow body, Grey plastic canopy, suspension, 'TS RADIO' decals on doors	£250-300
421	1960-63	Bedford 12 cwt Van	'EVENING STANDARD', Black body, Silver ridged roof, undivided windscreen, smooth hubs	£100-120
			'EVENING STANDARD', Black lower body, Silver upper body and ridged roof, undivided windscreen, smooth hubs	£100-120
			Medium Blue body, 'AVRO BODE' logo	£250-300
422	1960-62	Bedford 12 cwt Van	'CORGI TOYS', Yellow body, Blue roof, smooth or shaped hubs	£140-160
	reversed colours:		Blue body, 'CORGI TOYS', Yellow roof, smooth wheels	£250-350
	variation:		Blue lower half with Yellow upper body, 'CORGI TOYS'	£250-350
424	1977-79	Security Van	Black/Yellow/White body, 'SECURITY', windows with grilles	£10-15
426	1962-64	Karrier Bantam Van Circus Booking Office	Red/Blue body, smooth hubs, 'Chipperflelds Booking Office'	£175-200
			As previous model but with shaped hubs	£150-175
426	1978-81	Chevrolet Booking Office Van	Yellow/Red/Blue body, 'PINDER-JEAN RICHARD', two loudspeakers	£25-35
428	1963-66	Karrier Ice-Cream Van	Blue/White body, detailed chassis, salesman swivels, 'MR SOFTEE'	£125-150
431	1964-66	Volkswagen Pick-Up	Yellow body, Red or Olive-Green canopy, Red 'VW' emblem	£55-65
			Metallic Gold body, Red 'VW' emblem	£140-160
431	1978-79	'VANATIC'	White Chevrolet van, psychedelic 'VANATIC' side labels	£15-20
432	1978-79	'VANTASTIC'	Black Chevrolet van, Orange/Red 'VANTASTIC' design	£15-20
433	1978	'VANISHING POINT'	Golden Yellow Chevrolet van with Red 'sunrise' design. Shown in 1978 catalogue but not issued	NPP
434	1963-66	Volkswagen Kombi	Two-tone Green, Red or Yellow seats	£60-70
433	1962-64	Volkswagen Delivery Van	Red/White body, Red or Yellow interior	£60-70
	Dutch issue:		'VROOM & DREESMAN', Grey body, shaped spun wheels, promotional	£400-500
434	1962	Volkswagen Kombi	Metallic Pale Grey over Green body, Red interior, spun hubs	£65-75
435	1962-63	Karrier Bantam Van	Blue/White/Yellow body, 'DRIVE SAFELY ON MILK',	£65-75
437	1979-80	Chevrolet Van 'COCA-COLA'	Red body, White logo, tinted roof windows, crates	£20-25
440	1979-80	Mazda Custom Pick-up	Yellow body, Red roof	£15-20
441	1963-67	Volkswagen Van	Blue body, Lemon interior, 'Trans-o-lite' headlamps, 'CHOCOLATE TOBLERONE',	£75-85
443	1963-66	Plymouth Suburban US Mail	Blue/White body, 'ADDRESS YOUR MAIL CAREFULLY'	£65-75
447	1965-66	'WALLS ICE CREAM' Van	Ford Thames van in Blue/Cream, salesman, boy, spare transfers. Blue/Yellow card box, inner base, leaflet	£180-230

Commercial vehicles

450	1964-67	Austin Mini Van	Green body with unpainted grille, Red interior	£55-65
			Green body with painted grille, Red interior	£90-110
			Green body with Austin Countryman grille, Red interior	£90-110
		Promotional:	Metallic Green body, Grey base, Red interior, White 'FDR1.2009/17' logo. Housed in original 450 box with club slip. Thought to be a Dutch promotional	NGPP
452	1956-63	Commer Dropside Lorry	Red and Cream body, (raised ridge on some cab roofs), smooth or shaped hubs	£65-75
			Blue body, Cream back	£75-85
453	1956-60	Commer Refrigerated Van 'WALLS ICE CREAM'	Dark Blue cab, Cream back, smooth roof, flat spun hubs	£125-175
			Light Blue cab, Cream back, cast roof, flat spun hubs	£100-125
454	1957-63	Commer Platform Lorry	Metallic Blue cab and chassis, Silver-Grey platform	£70-80
			Yellow cab and chassis, Silver platform	£70-80
455	1957-61	Karrier Bantam 2-ton	Blue, Red or Grey body, Red platform floor, smooth hubs	£70-80
		variant:	Early Mettoy issue, Red body with 'C.W.S. SOFT DRINKS' logo on rear	£100-125
456	1960-63	ERF 44G Dropside Lorry	Yellow/Metallic Blue, smooth/shaped wheels	£65-75
457	1957-65	ERF 44G Platform Lorry	Two-tone Blue or Yellow/Blue body, smooth hubs	£65-75
458	1958-66	E.R.F. Earth Dumper	Red and Yellow body, 'ERF' cast-in, smooth or shaped hubs	£40-50
459	1958-60	ERF 44G Van	Yellow/Red, 'MOORHOUSES LEMON CHEESE'	£150-200
459	1973-78	Raygu Rascal Roller	Yellow/Green body, 'Road Roller'	£15-20
460	1959-61	E.R.F. Neville Cement Tipper	Pale Yellow with Silver tipper, metal or plastic fillers, smooth or shaped hubs	£45-55
462	1970	Commer Van 'CO-OP'	White/Blue promotional model	£75-85
462	1971	Commer Van 'HAMMONDS'	Green/Blue/White promotional model, cast hubs	£100-120
465	1963-66	Commer Pick-Up Truck	Red/Yellow, Yellow/Red or Green/Grey, 'Trans-O-Lites'	£50-60
466		Commer Milk Float	White cab, chassis and load; Blue rear roof and sides	£50-60
			As previous model but with 'CO-OP' labels	£70-80
470	1965-72	Forward Control Jeep	Blue/Grey, Mustard Yellow or Light Blue body, suspension, left-hand drive	£30-35
471	1965-66	Karrier Bantam Snack Bar	Blue/White, 'JOE'S DINER' with figure and opening hatch	£70-85
		Belgian issue:	Blue/White, 'PATATES FRITES'	£160-200
474	1965-68	Musical 'WALLS ICE CREAM' Van	Ford Thames van in Blue/Cream, musical movement (must function), diorama but no figures. Blue/Yellow card box	£160-200
478	1965-68	Jeep Tower Wagon	Green, Yellow and Silver body, figure, (Forward Control)	£25-35
479	1968-71	Commer Mobile Camera Van	Blue/White body, shaped hubs, 'SAMUELSON FILM COMPANY LTD', camera and operator	£80-90
			As previous model but with cast hubs	£80-90
483	1968-72	Dodge Tipper Truck	White cab, Blue tipper, 'KEW FARGO', cast wheels	£25-35
484	1967-69	Dodge Livestock Transporter	Beige/Green body, 'KEW FARGO', 5 pigs	£30-40
486	1967-69	'KENNEL CLUB' Truck	White/Orange Chevrolet Impala with 'Vari-View' dachshund picture, 4 dogs	£50-60
493	1975-78	Mazda B 1600 Pick-Up	Blue/White or Silver/Blue body	£20-25
495	1983-	4x4 Mazda 'OB TRUCK'	Blue/Black, 'Corgi Cruiser', drop-down tailboard	£5-10
495	1985	4x4 Mazda	As previous model but Blue/White body, 'SURF RIDER'	£5-10
494	1967-72	Bedford Tipper	Red cab/chassis, Yellow tipper	£40-50
			Red cab/chassis, Silver tipper	£90-110
			Yellow cab/chassis, Blue tipper	£110-130
			Blue cab/chassis, Yellow tipper	£130-150

Major Packs

1100	1958-63	Bedford 'S' Carrimore	Yellow cab, Metallic Blue low-loader trailer, smooth or shaped hubs	£100-125
			Red cab, Metallic Blue low-loader trailer	£100-125
1100	1971-73	Mack Truck	Orange cab, Black/Orange/Silver trailer, sliding doors, jockey wheel, 'TRANS-CONTINENTAL'	£40-50
			Orange and Metallic Lime Green version	£70-80
1101	1957-62	Bedford 'S' Carrimore	Blue cab, Yellow transporter body, 'CORGI CAR TRANSPORTER'	£125-150
			Red cab, Blue transporter body, smooth hubs	£100-125
1101	1976-81	Mobile Crane	Yellow/Blue body, 'Warner & Swasey'	£25-30
1102	1958-62	'EUCLID' TC-12 Bulldozer	Yellow body, Pale Grey tracks. Box has inner lining	£100-125
			As previous model but with Black tracks	£60-70
			Pale Lime-Green body	£80-100
1102	1974-76	Crane Freuhauf	Yellow cab, Orange dumper body, 'Road Maker Construction' logo, (Berliet Dumper)	£30-35
1103	1960-65	'EUCLID' Crawler Tractor	Yellow or Pale Lime-Green body, Pale Grey tracks	£80-90
			As previous model but with Black tracks	£60-70
1104	1958-63	Bedford 'S' Carrimore	Red cab, Silver trailer, smooth hubs, operable winch, (Machinery Carrier)	£100-125
			Blue cab, Silver trailer, smooth hubs	£100-125
1104	1974-77	Bedford 'TK' type	Green or Metallic Green Horse Transporter, 'NEWMARKET', four horses and boy	£50-60
1105	1962-66	Bedford 'TK' type	Red cab, Blue/White trailer, collapsible decks, 'Corgi Car Transporter'	£100-125
1105	1976-80	Berliet Racehorse Transporter	Brown/White, 'NATIONAL RACING STABLES', four horses	£40-50
1106	1972-77	Mack Container Truck 'ACL'	Yellow/Black/White body, two Red containers with White logo	£40-50
			Promotional issue for '3M'	£120-140
1106	1984	'CORGI' Loadlugger	Yellow body and chassis, Red 'BIG BIN'	£10-15
1107	1963-66	'EUCLID' with Dozer	Yellow body, Black or Grey tracks, driver	£150-175
			Red body	£150-175
			Lime-Green body	£70-80
1107	1978-79	Berliet Container Lorry	Blue cab, White chassis, 2 Grey containers, 'UNITED STATES LINES'	£30-40
1108	1982	Ford Truck 'MICHELIN'	Blue/White articulated body, two containers	£40-50
1109	1979	Ford Truck 'MICHELIN'	Blue/Yellow articulated body, two containers	£40-50
1110	1959-64	Bedford 'S' Tanker	Red/White articulated body, detachable cab, 'MOBILGAS'	£120-140
			As previous model but with shaped spun hubs	£140-160
1110	1965-67	Bedford 'TK' Tanker	Blue/White articulated tanker, 'SHELL BENZEEN', Dutch model	£1,500-2,000

1110	1976-80	'JCB' Crawler Loader	Yellow/White body, Red working bucket, Black tracks, driver	£30-40
1110	1976-80	'JCB' Crawler	Yellow and White body, driver	£30-40
			Light Blue/Orange with Light Blue chassis, driver	£30-40
			Yellow body, Light Blue cab, Red bucket	£30-40
			Red body, Light Blue cab and bucket	£30-40
			Orange body, 'BLOCK CONSTRUCTION' logo	£30-40
1113	1981-86	'HYSTER' Handler	Yellow or Black/White main body, 'US Lines', hoist	£30-40
	1986-87		Yellow or Black/White main body, 'SEALINK', container, export model	£50-70
	1986-87		White/Dark Blue/Yellow, 'MICHELIN', container	£30-40
1114	1984	Mercedes Gritter	Yellow/Black body and plough, ladder	£10-15
			Yellow/Black body with Red stripes, 'MOTORWAY MAINTENANCE'	£10-15
1115	1985	Parisienne Refuse Truck	Green body, 'PARIS' logo, export model	£10-15
1116	1979	Refuse Lorry	Shelvoke and Drewry Revopak. Orange/Silver or Red/Silver body	£15-20
	1988		Blue cab, White tipper, 'BOROUGH COUNCIL'	£5-10
1117	1980-85	'FAUN' Street-sweeper	Orange and Yellow or All-Yellow, with operator	£15-20
1119	1983	Mercedes Load Lugger	Yellow/Red body, 'CORGI'	£15-20
1121	1983	Ford Transit Tipper	Orange/Beige body, 'CORGI', (Corgimatic)	£15-20
1122	1984	Mercedes Mixer	Orange body, Black stripes	£10-15
1122	1985		Orange body, White revolving drum, Black/Yellow design	£10-15
1126	1961-65	Racing Car Transporter	Metallic Dark Blue body with 'ECURIE ECOSSE' in Yellow lettering	£150-200
	later version:		with logo in Orange lettering	£90-110
			with logo in White lettering	£90-110
			with logo and raised ridges in Light Blue	£90-110
	colour variant:		Metallic Light Blue body with 'ECURIE ECOSSE' in Red lettering	£90-110
1128	1963-76	'PRIESTMAN' Cub Shovel	Red/Yellow body, driver	£30-35
1128	1984	Mercedes Tipper	Yellow cab, Red tipper, 6 wheels, 'BLOCK' logo	£10-15
1128	1985	Mercedes Tipper	Black body, White logo 'TARMAC'	£10-15
1129	1962-65	Bedford 'S' Tanker	Blue/White articulated body, detachable cab, 'MILK' logo	£150-175
1131	1963-66	Bedford 'TK' Carrimore	Blue cab, Silver trailer, Yellow detachable rear axle unit, spun hubs, (Machinery Low Loader)	£80-100
			Blue cab, Silver trailer, Black detachable rear axle unit, spun hubs	£70-80
1132	1963-65	Bedford 'TK' Carrimore	Yellow cab, Red low loader trailer, spare wheels, no winch	£100-125
1137	1966-69	Ford Articulated Truck	Blue/Silver/Red body, 'H' series tilt-cab, 'EXPRESS SERVICES'	£75-85
1138	1966-69	Ford Articulated Transporter	Red body, Silver tilt cab, two-tone Blue transporter body, 'CORGI CARS'	£85-95
1140	1965-67	Bedford 'TK' Petrol Tanker	Red/Silver/White articulated body, tilting cab, 'MOBILGAS'. Box includes inner packing	£140-160
1141	1965-67	Bedford 'TK' Milk Tanker	Blue/White articulated body, tilting cab, 'MILK'	£175-200
1142	1967-74	Holmes Wrecker Recovery Truck	White/Red/Gold body, 2 mechanics	£70-80
1145	1969-76	Unimog Goose Dumper	Yellow/Red body, '406'	£30-35
1146	1970-73	Scammell Carrimore Mk.V	Orange/White/Blue Tri-deck Transporter articulated transporter with 3 collapsible decks	£80-100
1147	1969-72	Scammell Truck	Yellow/White body, 'FERRYMASTERS INTERNATIONAL HAULIERS'	£50-60
1148	1969-72	Scammell Carrimore Mk.IV	Red/White car transporter body with Yellow chucks	£80-100
1150	1971-77	Mercedes Snowplough	Unimog 406 in Green/Black, 2 Red flags, Orange/Silver plough	£30-35
			Unimog 406, Yellow cab and back, Red chassis, Silver plough, 2 Red flags	£30-35
1151	1970	Scammell Truck	Blue/White body, 'Co-operative Society', promotional	£120-140
1151		Mack Tanker 'EXXON'	Red/White body, striped window box	£60-70
1152	1971-76	Mack Tanker 'ESSO'	White/Red/Blue articulated body, Gloster Saro Petrol Tanker (detachable)	£40-50
			As previous model but with 'EXXON' logo	£70-80
1152	1983-	'BARRATT' Tipper	Green/White body, tipper section tips	£5-10
1153	1973-74	'PRIESTMAN' Crane	Red/Orange body, 'Higrab'	£45-55
1153	1983-84	'WIMPEY' Tipper Truck	Green/Silver body, tipping section tips, (Scania)	£5-10
1153	1984		Yellow body	£5-10
1153	1985	'LAING' Tipper Truck	As previous model but with Yellow body and Black logo	£5-10
1154	1974-76	Priestman Crane Truck	Yellow/Red body, Silver boom, hook	£45-55
1154	1979	Giant Tower Crane	Orange/Yellow crane, White body, 'BLOCK CONSTRUCTION' logo	£35-45
1155	1975-79	'Skyscraper' Tower Crane	Yellow/Red body, Black tracks	£35-40
1156	1977-79	Volvo Concrete Mixer	Yellow/Red/Orange body, 'RAPIER'	£30-35
1156	1980		Orange/White body, 'BLOCK CONSTRUCTION'	£30-35
1157	1976-81	Ford Tanker 'ESSO'	White/Red articulated body	£25-35
1158	1976	Ford Tanker 'EXXON'	White/Black articulated body, US issue only	£50-60
1159	1976-79	Ford Car Transporter	Metallic Blue/White or Metallic Green articulated body	£40-50
1160	1976-78	Ford Tanker 'GULF'	White/Orange articulated body	£30-40
1161	1976-78	Ford Tanker 'ARAL'	Blue/White/Black articulated body, German export model	£50-60
1169	1982	Ford Tanker 'GUINNESS'	Red/Cream/Black articulated body	£40-50
1170	1982	Ford Car Transporter	Red/White/Yellow articulated body	£50-60
1191	1985	Ford Articulated Truck	White cab, chassis and tampo print, two Blue containers, 'FORD QUALITY' logo	£15-20
	1985	Ford Articulated Truck	'BALLANTINES SCOTCH'. Container holds 6 miniatures. Available from duty-free shops (20,000)	£65-75
	1985	Ford Truck 'KAYS'	Red/White articulated body, Cerise/Black tampo print, Mail-order model (4,000)	£10-15

Ref	Year(s)	Model name	Colours, features, details	Market Price Range
50	1959-66	Massey-Ferguson 65 Tractor....	Red bonnet, Pale Grey or Cream chassis, Red metal or plastic hubs, metal or plastic steering wheel	£70-80
50	1974-77	Massey Ferguson 50B Tractor .	Yellow/Black/Red body, windows	£25-35
51	1959-64	Massey-Ferguson Tipper Trailer	Red chassis, Yellow or Grey body, Red metal or plastic wheels	£15-20
53	1960-66	Massey-Ferguson 65 Tractor with Shovel	Red bonnet, Beige or Light Grey chassis, Red metal or Orange plastic hubs, operable shovel, painted or unpainted arms	£70-80
54	1974	Massey-Ferguson Tractor with Shovel	Yellow/Red or White/Red body	£30-35
54	1962-64	Fordson Power Major Tractor. (Roadless Half-Tracks)	Blue body, Orange rollers and wheels, Black rubber tracks, lights in radiator grille. Plain 'early' box ..	£140-160
			Same but with Grey rubber tracks, lights at sides of grille, picture box	£120-140
55	1961-63	Fordson Power Major Tractor.	Blue/Grey/Red body	£80-120
55	1977	David Brown Tractor	Black/Red/White body, steering wheel	£25-35
56	1961-63	Four-Furrow Plough	Red/Brown/Yellow body	£15-20
56	1977	Farm Tipper Trailer................	Red/Yellow or Red/White body with drop-down tailboard	£10-15
57	1963-66	Massey Ferguson Tractor with Fork	Red/Silver/Cream body, driver, steering wheel	£75-85
58	1965-72	Beast Carrier	Red, Cream and Blue body, four calves	£20-25
60	1964-71	Fordson Power Major Tractor.	Blue body, plough lifts	£70-80
61	1964-71	Four-Furrow Plough	Blue/Silver body	£5-10
62	1965-72	Ford Tipper Trailer	Red/Yellow body with two raves	£10-15
64	1965-69	Forward Control Jeep	Red, Yellow/White working conveyor, farmhand figure	£60-75
66	1966-72	Massey-Ferguson '165' Tractor..	Red/Blue/White body, engine sound	£45-55
67	1967-72	Ford Super Major Tractor	Blue/White/Silver body, 'FORD 5000'	£75-100
69	1967-72	Massey-Ferguson '165' Tractor and Shovel	Red/Blue body, Silver shovel, figure	£75-85
71	1967-72	Fordson Disc Harrow...............	Yellow/Red/Silver body	£15-20
72	1971-73	Ford 5000 Tractor and Towbar	As Corgi 67 but with frame, bucket and pipes	£90-120
73	1970-73	Massey-Ferguson Tractor and Saw.................	As Corgi 66 plus Yellow rotating saw	£75-85
74	1969-72	Ford 5000 Tractor and Scoop ..	As Corgi 67 plus Yellow/Silver scoop	£75-85
100	1957-61	Dropside Trailer	Yellow/Red/Grey body	£10-15
101	1958-61	Platform Trailer	Yellow/Grey or Blue/Grey body	£10-15
102	1958-59	Rice's Pony Trailer	Red body, Brown chassis, wire drawbar, smooth hubs, plastic pony	£50-60
			Red body, Silver chassis, wire drawbar, smooth hubs, plastic pony	£40-50
	1959-65		Red body, Black chassis, wire or cast drawbar, smooth or shaped hubs	£30-40
			Red body, Silver chassis, wire or cast drawbar, smooth or shaped hubs	£30-40
			Cream body, Red chassis, wire or cast drawbar, smooth or shaped hubs	£30-40
	1961-68		Tan/Cream body, Silver chassis, cast drawbar, shaped hubs	£30-40
112	1969-72	Rice Beaufort Horse-Box.........	Blue/White horse-box with mare and foal	£25-30
484	1967-69	Dodge Livestock Transporter...	Beige/Green body, 'KEW FARGO', 5 pigs	£30-40

Major Packs (and large Agricultural Models)

Ref	Year(s)	Model name	Colours, features, details	Market Price Range
1111	1959-60	M-F Combine Harvester...........	Red/Yellow, Yellow metal wheels, metal tines, box has internal packing	£80-100
1111	1960-61	M-F '780' Combine Harvester .	Red/Yellow, Yellow metal wheels, plastic tines, box has internal packing	£75-85
	1961-64		Red/Yellow, Red plastic wheels, Yellow plastic tines, box has internal packing	£65-75
1112	1977-78	David Brown Tractor and Combine Harvester	Corgi 55 Tractor with Red/White/Black combine harvester	£60-70

Duo Packs

These packs combine standard models with (mainly) similar 'Junior' models. Launched early in 1982 in France with the name 'Les Plus de Corgi', the packs later became available in the UK in Woolworths as 'Little and Large; the Little One Free'.
See also 'Novelty, Film and TV-related' section for additional details.
All NGPP except where shown.

No.53 **Triple Pack** (1982), **'Stunt Bikes'**:
171 Street Bike, 172 Police Bike, 173 Café Racer.... **NGPP**

'Les Plus de Corgi' Duo Pack range:

1352	Renault 5 (307) Metro (C275)	£15-25
1353	Austin Metro	£15-25
1354	Texaco Lotus (C154) Junior 53	£15-25
1355	Talbot Matra Rancho (457)	£15-25
1356	Fiat XI/9 (306)	£15-25
1357	Golden Eagle Jeep (C441)	£15-25
1358	Citroën 2cv	£15-25
1359	Ford Escort (334), Junior 105	£15-25

F.W. Woolworth's 'Little & Large' Promotional Duo Pack selection:

1352	Renault 5 (307) Metro (C275)	£15-25
1353	Austin Metro	£15-25
1355	Talbot Matra Rancho (457)	£15-25
1356	Fiat XI/9 (306)	£15-25
1359	Ford Escort (334), Junior 105	£15-25
1363	Buck Rogers (607)	£50-60
1364	Space Shuttle 'NASA' (648)	£20-30
1365	469 Routemaster Bus, E71 Taxi	£20-30
1371	Volkswagen Turbo (309)	£15-25

Other Duo Packs (most available in UK).

1360	Batmobile (267)	£150-175
1361	James Bond Aston Martin, Silver	£125-150
1362	James Bond Lotus Esprit (269)	£125-150
1363	Buck Rogers (607)	£50-60
1364	Space Shuttle 'NASA' (648)	£20-30
1365	469 Routemaster Bus, E71 Taxi	£15-25

1372	Jaguar XJS (319)	£15-25
1373	Ford Capri (312) Junior 61	£15-25
1376	Starsky & Hutch Ford Torino	£70-80
1378	Porsche 924, Yellow	£15-25
1380	Mercedes 240D, Metallic Grey	£15-25
1381	Ferrari 308GTS, Red	£15-25
1382	Ford Mustang (320)	£15-25
1383	Mack Fire Pumper	£15-25
1384	Ford Thunderbird, Cream/Orange	£15-25
	Ford Thunderbird, Cream/Black	£15-25
1385	Austin Metro 'DATAPOST'	£15-25
1389	Ford Sierra (299) Junior 129	£15-25
1390	Porsche 924, Black	£15-25
1393	447 Jeep and E182 Jeep	£15-25
1394	448 Jeep and E183 Jeep	£15-25
1395	495 Mazda, E184 Range Rover	£15-25
1396	Space Shuttle	£15-25
1397	BMW M1 'BASF' (380)	£15-25
1401	Lotus Elite and E10 TR7	£15-25
1402	1133 Tipper plus E85 Skip Truck	£15-25
1403	Mercedes Tanker, E185 Van	£15-25
1405	Jaguar	£15-25

Emergency Vehicles

Police, Fire, Ambulance and Breakdown Vehicles, etc.

See also under 'Corgi Commercial Vehicles', and in the 'Corgi Classics' section for other references to emergency vehicle models.

Ref	Year(s)	Model name	Colours, features, details	Market Price Range
106/13	1990	Saab 'BRANDWEER'	Red body, White side panels, 'ALARM', (Dutch export model)	£15-20
209	1958-61	Riley Pathfinder Police Car	Black and Silver body, bell, 'POLICE'	£65-75
213	1959-61	Jaguar Fire Chief's Car	Red body, bell, Grey aerial, roof sign, smooth spun wheels	£80-90
213s	1961-62	Jaguar Fire Chief's Car	As previous model but with suspension and shaped spun wheels	£100-120
223	1959-61	Chevrolet Impala 'State Patrol'	Black body, Silver stripe, 'STATE PATROL', Grey aerial. Box also contains internal packing	£55-65
237	1962-66	Oldsmobile Sheriff's Car	Black body, White roof, 'COUNTY SHERIFF', clear or Blue light. Box also contains internal packing	£55-65
260	1979-81	Buick 'POLICE' Car	Metallic Blue/White body, 'CITY OF METROPOLIS', 2 flashing light bars	£30-40
284	1982-83	Mercedes-Benz 240 D	Red body, 'NOTRUF 112', flashing lights, German export model	£20-25
292	1985	Sapeurs Pompiers	Pale Blue or Dark Blue body	£20-25
			Dark Blue body, 'POLICIA'	£25-30
293	1977-80	Renault 5 TS	Metallic Orange or Two-tone Blue body, WhizzWheels	£15-25
293	1980-81	Renault 5 TS	Two-tone Blue body, roof light, 'S.O.S. MEDICINS'	£25-35
295	1982-83	Renault 5 TS Fire Chief	Red/White 'SAPEURS POMPIERS', warning lights, French export model	£15-20
297	1982-86	Ford Escort 'Panda' Car	Light or Dark Blue, White doors, Blue warning lights, 'POLICE'	£15-20
299	1985	Ford Sierra 'POLIS' Car	Blue/Yellow/Black body, warning lights, Swedish export model	£30-40
299/7	1985	Sierra Ghia 2.3 'POLIS'	White/Black body with White logo, (Sweden)	£30-40
317	1986	Peugeot 'POLITI'	Black/White body, warning lights, Norwegian export model	£30-40
326	1980-81	Chevrolet Caprice Police Car	Black/White body, 'POLICE', suspension	£20-30
332	1980-81	Opel Doctors Car	White/Red body, 'NOTARTZ', opening doors	£30-40
339	1980	Rover 3500 Police Car	White and Red body, 'POLICE'	£20-25
353	1987	BMW 'NOTARTZ'	Red/White body, 2 Blue warning lights, German export model	£15-20
357	1987	Ford Sierra 'BRANDCHEFF'	Red body, door badge, warning lights	£15-20
358/1	1987	Ford Sierra 'POLICE'	White body, Yellow/Black stripe, warning lights unit on roof	£15-20
358	1987	Ford Sierra 'POLITI'	White body, Red/Blue logo, warning lights, export model	£30-40
358	1987	Ford Sierra 'POLICE'	White body, Red logo, warning lights, Dutch export model	£30-40
358/3	1986	'RIJKSPOLITIE'	White body, White/Red bonnet, crest, roof beacon, (Holland)	£30-40
358/4	1986	'LEGIBIL'	White/Black body, 'LEGE', twin roof beacons, (West Germany)	£30-40
361	1987	Volvo 'POLIS'	White body, Black/Yellow logo, Swedish export model	£20-30
373	1970-76	VW 1200 Police Car	Black/White/Blue body, 'POLIZEI', WhizzWheels	£40-50
			Black/White/Blue body, 'POLITIE', WhizzWheels	£80-90
			White body, Black bonnet and boot, Blue dome light, phosphorescent 'POLICE' labels, WhizzWheels	£55-65
373/3	1987	Peugeot 'POLITI'	Black/White body, warning lights, Norwegian export model	£15-20
383	1970-73	VW 1200 'ADAC'	Yellow body, Black roof with '1341', 'ADAC STRASSENWACHT' logo on doors	£75-85
386	1987	Mercedes 'POLIZEI'	Green/White body, two Blue warning lights, German export model	£30-40
395	1972/73	Fire Bug	Orange body, Whizzwheels, Red/Black or Pink/Black stripe, (381 Beach Buggy)	£20-30
402	1972-77	Ford Cortina GXL Police Car	White/Red body, 'POLICE' labels, (updated 313)	£35-45
			White/Red body, 'POLIZEI', German issue	£75-85
405	1956-60	Bedford Fire Tender	Bright or Dark Green body, divided windscreen, Silver or Black ladder, 'A.F.S.', smooth or shaped hubs. (Utilicon)	£80-100
405 M	1956-59	Bedford Fire Tender	Red body, divided windscreen, Silver or Black ladder, 'FIRE DEPT', smooth or shaped hubs, friction motor. (Utilicon)	£120-140
405	1978-80	Chevrolet Ambulance	White/Orange, patient on stretcher and two attendants	£20-25
406	1980-81	Mercedes Bonna Ambulance	White body, Red/Black design, opening doors, stretcher, ambulancemen, 'AMBULANCE'	£15-20
		German issue:	Cream body, 'KRANKENWAGEN'	£30-40
		Danish issue:	Red/White/body, 'FALCK'	£30-40
		Swedish issue:	White/Red/Black body, 'SDL 951'	£30-40
406/2	1990	Mercedes Bonna Ambulance	White/Red stripes, 'FALCK', (Danish export model)	£5-10
407	1980	Mercedes Bonna Ambulance	White body, Red/Black design, opening doors, stretcher, ambulancemen, 'AMBULANCE'	£15-20
408	1957-59	Bedford 'AA' Service Van	Yellow/Black, divided windscreen, smooth hubs, Blue box, leaflet	£100-120
	1958-59		Yellow/Black, undivided windscreen, smooth or shaped hubs, Blue box, leaflet	£70-80
	1959-63		Yellow/Black, undivided windscreen, shaped hubs, Blue/Yellow box, no leaflet	£60-70
	late issue:		Yellow/Black, single windscreen, ridged roof, flat spun hubs	£70-80
412	1957-60	Bedford 'AMBULANCE'	Cream 'Utilicon' body, divided windscreen, smooth hubs	£65-75
			As previous model but with one-piece windscreen	£150-175
	Factory error:		A few examples of 412 were issued with 'HOME SERVICES' front labels	NGPP
412	1976-79	Mercedes Police Car	White/Black body, 'POLICE' logo, Blue roof lamp	£25-30
			Green/White body, 'POLIZEI' logo, Blue roof lamp, German issue	£35-45
414	1975-77	Jaguar XJ12-C	White/Blue body, 'COASTGUARD'	£10-15

416	1959-61	R.A.C. Land Rover...................	Blue body, *'RADIO RESCUE'* on cab roof sign, metal canopy, smooth hubs, Blue/Yellow box............**£90-110**
			Blue body, no cab roof sign, *'RADIO RESCUE'* on canopy, shaped hubs **£150-175**
		Belgian issue:	Yellow body, Green metal canopy, 'TS RADIO' decals on doors...**£250-300**
416s	1962-64	R.A.C. Land Rover...................	Blue body, Lemon interior, suspension, *'RADIO RESCUE'* on plastic canopy...............................**£65-75**
		Belgian issue:	Yellow body, Grey plastic canopy, suspension, 'TS RADIO' decals on doors................................**£250-300**
416	1977-79	Buick Police Car......................	Blue body or Metallic Blue body, *'POLICE'*, two policemen **£25-30**
419	1960-65	Ford Zephyr Motorway Car	White or Cream body, smooth or shaped hubs, *'POLICE'*, aerial, large or small roof light.................**£55-65**
		Export issues:	with *'POLITIE'* or *'RIJKS POLITIE'* logo (Dutch) **£150-200**
421	1977-79	Land Rover Station Wagon......	Red body, White roof-rack, 'FOREST WARDEN' **£20-25**
422	1977-80	Riot Police Wagon	Red/White body, number '6' and *'RIOT POLICE'* on doors, water cannon **£15-20**
423	1960-62	Bedford 12cwt. Tender............	Red body, Black ladder, undivided windscreen, smooth or shaped hubs, 'FIRE DEPT.'....................**£90-110**
			Red body, unpainted ladder, undivided windscreen, shaped hubs..**£100-120**
424	1976-79	'SECURITY' Van......................	Black/Yellow/White body, mesh windows, WhizzWheels..**£10-15**
428	1978-80	Renault Police Car	Black/White body, *'POLICE'*, aerial, warning lights, (export isssue) **£55-65**
429	1978-80	Police Jaguar XJ12-C	White/Red/Blue body, *'POLICE'*, aerial, warning lights **£25-35**
430	1978-80	Porsche 924 'Police'	Black/White body, *'POLICE'*, warning light...**£15-20**
430	1978-80	Porsche 924 'Polizei'	White/Green body, *'POLIZEI'*, warning light, (export isssue)...**£55-65**
435/13	1990	Volvo 'POLIS'.........................	White with Blue panels front and rear, flashing lights bar, (export isssue)....................................**£30-40**
437	1962-65	Cadillac Superior Ambulance ..	Cream over Red body, 'AMBULANCE' on side windows **£65-75**
	1965-68		Light Blue over White body, 'AMBULANCE' on sides, Red cross on bonnet **£65-75**
			Metallic Red over Metallic Silver body..**£65-75**
438	1987	Rover Sterling 800..................	White body, Red stripe, *'POLICE'*, flashing lights bar **£15-20**
439	1963-65	Chevrolet Impala.....................	Red body, 'FIRE CHIEF', White stripe, aerial, Orange roof light, firemen,
			with White painted door labels with *'FIRE DEPT'*..**£60-70**
			with White rectangular label on front doors *'FIRE DEPT'*..**£60-70**
			with round Red label on front doors *'FIRE DEPT'*...**£60-70**
448	1964-69	Austin Police Mini Van	Dark Blue body, Red interior, shaped or cast hubs, aerial, White *'POLICE'* logo,
			policeman and dog, pictorial stand and internal support packaging...**£125-150**
454	1984	Ford Sierra 'POLIZEI'	Green/White body, Swiss export model..**£30-40**
456	1986	Ford Sierra 'POLIZEI'	Green/White body, German export model..**£30-40**
461	1972-79	'Police' Vigilant Range Rover ..	White/Blue, warning lights, policemen, 8 *'POLICE'* emergency signs + bollards **£25-35**
			White/Red body, *'LANGZAAM'*, policemen, emergency signs, Dutch model................................**£50-60**
463	1964-66	Commer 'AMBULANCE'........	Cream or White body, Red interior, Blue tinted windows and roof light **£65-75**
464	1967-68	Commer 'POLICE' Van...........	Dark Blue, *'COUNTY POLICE'*, window bars, clear roof light, leaflet **£65-75**
			As previous model but Metallic Light Blue, with Blue roof light **£60-70**
			Dark Blue, window bars, Red roof light, *'CITY POLICE'*, instruction leaflet **£175-200**
			Dark Blue, 'open' windows, Blue roof light, White *'POLICE'* cast into sides, with instructions.............**£70-90**
			Deep Green body, *'POLICE'*, export model, opaque rear/side windows......................................**£400-500**
			Metallic Green body, *'POLIZEI'*, German issue...**£150-175**
			Metallic Blue body, *'SECOURS'*, French issue...**£150-175**
			Metallic Blue body, window bars, *'RIJKSPOLITIE'*, Dutch issue...**£150-175**
477	1966-67	Land Rover Breakdown	Red body, Yellow canopy with spotlight and 'BREAKDOWN SERVICE' logo
			rubber (or later plastic) 'tyre' crank, shaped or cast hubs..**£45-55**
			As previous model but with large or small Silver crank, WhizzWheels.......................................**£35-40**
481	1965-69	Chevrolet Police Car	White/Black body, *'POLICE PATROL'*, Red roof lights, two policemen **£55-65**
482	1966-69	Chevrolet Impala......................	Red over White body, Chrome stripe, bonnet logo, Blue light, Grey aerial.
			with rectangular *'FIRE CHIEF'* label on front doors, shaped spun wheels..................................**£55-65**
			with round label on front doors *'FIRE CHIEF'*, shaped spun wheels.......................................**£65-75**
			with round label on front doors *'FIRE CHIEF'*, detailed cast wheels.......................................**£55-65**
482	1974-77	Vigilant Range Rover..............	Red and White body with *'AMBULANCE'* logo...**£25-30**
			White body with Blue side stripe and *'AMBULANCE'* logo, stretcher and 2 ambulancemen **£25-30**
483	1979	Belgian Police Range Rover	White body, Red stripes, warning lights, policemen, emergency signs **£55-65**
484	1978-80	AMC Pacer 'RESCUE'............	White/Orange/Black body, number '35', *'RESCUE'* **£10-15**
			As previous issue but with *'SECOURS'* logo..**£40-50**
489	1980	Volkswagen Polo	White/Green body, *'POLIZEI'*, opening doors and hatchback, (export issue)................................**£50-55**
			Variation with 'ADAC' logo, (export issue)..**£50-55**
490	1967-69	Volkswagen Breakdown..........	Unpainted fittings, Chrome tools, Red 'VW' emblem, Red/Yellow stripe label, two spare wheels.
			Tan body, shaped hubs, 'BREAKDOWN SERVICE' labels..**£45-55**
	1968-72		As previous issue but with 'RACING CLUB' labels (in GS 12)...**GSP**
492	1966-70	VW 1200 Car	Green body, White roof, White *'POLIZEI'* on bonnet, No '18' logo **£75-85**
492	1966-69	VW European Police Car	White body with Black *'POLIZEI'* on doors and bonnet, (Germany)..**£200-250**
			Dark Green body, White roof and wings, Red *'POLIZEI'*, Blue lamp.......................................**£50-60**
	NB		Box should contain 'True Scale Steering' Red/Yellow cardboard roof fitting.
			All-White body, Light Brown interior, driver, crest on doors, *'POLITIE'*, Blue lamp, Dutch model......**£175-225**
			All-White body, Light Brown interior, driver, crest on doors, *'POLITZIE'*, Blue lamp, Swiss model **£175-225**
506	1968-69	Sunbeam Imp 'Panda' Car	White body, Black bonnet and roof, Blue roof light **£50-60**
			White body, Black roof, 'luminous' door panels, Blue roof light...**£50-60**
			Light Blue body, White roof, 'luminous' door panels, Blue roof light..**£50-60**

509	1970-75	Porsche 911s Targa Police Car	White/Red body, Black roof, 'POLICE' logo	£55-65
			White/Red body, 'POLIZEI', siren, warning lights	£55-65
			'RIJKSPOLITIE' export issue	£100-125
541	1986	Ford Sierra 'POLICE'	Black/White body, Norwegian/Danish export model	£10-15
541	1987	'POLITI'	White with Blue/Yellow side stripes, (Norway)	£10-15
541/2	1988	Ford Sierra 'NOTRUF'	Red body, warning lights, German export model	£10-15
542	1987	Bonna 'AMBULANCE'	Red/White body, 2 warning lights, Norwegian export model	£10-15
576	1988	Mercedes 207 D Van	Red body, White 'POMPIERS', French export model	£10-15
597	1986	Ford Sierra 'POLICE' Car	White body, Yellow/Black logo, two warning lights	£9-12
598	1986	Range Rover 'POLICE'	White body, Yellow/Black print, two warning lights	£9-12
619	1988	Land Rover	Red/White body, 'SAPEUR POMPIERS', export model	£9-12
621	1986	Ford Escort 'POLICE' Van	White body, Red/Black side flash, Blue logo	£9-12
656	1987	Ford Transit Van	White/Red body, flashing lights bar, Red Cross, 'AMBULANCE'	£9-12
656	1987	Ford Transit Van 'POLICE'	Black body, White logo, Finnish export model	£9-12
656	1987	Ford Transit Van 'FALCK'	White body, two Red stripes, warning lights, export model	£10-15
656	1987	Ford Transit Van	White/Red, 'AMBULANSE', flashing lights bar, Norwegian export model	£10-15
656/28	1990	Ford Transit	White/Yellow stripe, 'NOTTINGHAM AMBULANCE SERVICE'	£9-12
674/1	1988	'AA' Ford Transit	Breakdown truck with Yellow body, White stripe, Black rear lifting gear	£9-12
674/2	1988	'RAC' Ford Transit	Breakdown truck with White body, Red/Blue stripe, Black lifting gear	£9-12
674/3	1988	'POLICE' Ford Transit	Breakdown truck with White body, Red stripe, roof lights, Black lifting gear	£9-12
674/4	1988	'BARNINGSKAREN'	Red/Yellow Transit breakdown truck, Black lifting gear, export model	£10-12
700	1974-79	Motorway Ambulance	White/Red body, 'ACCIDENT', Red Cross	£15-20
702	1975-79	Breakdown Truck	Red/Black, single bumper, hook, 'ACCIDENT'	£10-15
703	1976-78	Hi-Speed Fire Engine	Red body, Yellow ladder, warning lights	£10-15
911	1976-80	Air-Sea Rescue Helicopter	Blue/Yellow body, Black 'flick-spin' rotor, 'N 428', operable winch	£15-20
921	1975-81	Hughes OH-6A Helicopter	White/Red, 'POLICE', 'RESCUE', warning lights	£15-20
921/1	1975-80	'POLIZEI' Helicopter	White/Blue, 'POLIZEI', Black 'flick-spin' rotor, operable winch, German issue	£40-50
921/2	1975-80	'POLITIE' Helicopter	White/Blue, 'POLITIE', Black 'flick-spin' rotor, operable winch, Dutch issue	£40-50
921/4	1975-80	'ADAC' Helicopter	Yellow body, 'D-HFFM', Black 'flick-spin' rotor, operable winch	£40-50
921/6	1975-80	Swiss Red Cross	Red helicopter body, Black blades, 'flick-spin' rotor, operable winch	£30-40
922	1975-78	Casualty Helicopter	Sikorsky Skycrane with Red/White body	£15-20
923	1975-78	Casualty Helicopter	Army Sikorsky Skycrane with Olive/Yellow body	£15-20
924	1977-81	Air-Sea Rescue Helicopter	Orange/Yellow/Black body, 'RESCUE'	£15-20
927	1978-79	Surf Rescue Helicopter	Blue/White body, 'SURF RESCUE'	£15-20
931	1979-80	Jet Ranger Helicopter	White/Red body, 'POLICE RESCUE', 'flick-spin' rotor, operable winch	£15-20

Major Packs (Emergency Vehicles)

1001	1980-82	HCB Angus Firestreak	Red body, Yellow ladder, 2 firemen plus equipment	£30-35
1103	1976-81	Chubb Pathfinder	Red/Silver, 'AIRPORT CRASH TRUCK', operable pump and siren, orange logo	£45-55
			As previous model but non-working siren, Brick-Red logo	£35-45
			Red/Silver, operable pump and siren, 'NEW YORK AIRPORT' logo	£55-65
1118	1981-83	Chubb Pathfinder	Red body, 'AIRPORT FIRE SERVICE', operable water pump	£35-45
1120	1984	Dennis Fire Engine	Red body, turntable, warning lights, Yellow plastic ladder, crest design	£10-15
1126	1977-81	Dennis Fire Engine	Red/White/Yellow, turntable, ladder, 6 firemen, 'SIMON SNORKEL'	£55-65
1127	1964-74	Bedford Fire Engine	Red/Yellow/Silver, turntable, ladder, 6 fireman, 'SIMON SNORKEL'	£50-60
1140	1982	Ford Transit Wrecker	White/Red, '24 Hour Service', operable winch, hook,	£10-15
			As previous model but logo changed to 'RELAY'	£10-15
	1982		Red/Yellow body, 'ABSCHLEPPDEENST', export model	£10-15
	1987		Red body, Gold 'FALCK' logo, Danish export model	£10-15
	1987		Red body, Yellow side panels, 'VIKING', export model	£10-15
1142	1967-74	'HOLMES WRECKER'	Red/White/Blue, Grey or Gold twin booms, ladder, 2 spare wheels	£70-80
1143	1968-80	'AMERICAN LA FRANCE'	Articulated Fire Engine in Red/White/Yellow, shaped spun or detailed cast wheels, 4-part extending ladder, 5 firemen, plain early box	£70-80
			As previous model but in later striped window box	£50-60
1144	1975-78	Berliet Wrecker Recovery	Red/White/Gold body, with Gold or Grey hoists,	£40-50
2029	1980-83	Mack Fire Engine	Red body, warning light, detachable ladder, 'HAMMOND FIRE DEPT'	£10-15
91822	1992	'FALKEN' Ford Transit	White body, Blue/Gold stripes, Black lifting gear, export model	£9-11

Military and R.A.F. models

Unless described otherwise, all models in this listing are finished in Military-Green or Olive-Drab camouflage.

Ref	Year(s)	Model name	Colours, features, details	Market Price Range
290	1977-80	Bell Army Helicopter	Red crosses, Black rotor, 'ARMY' markings	£20-30
350	1958-62	Thunderbird Missile	Blue or Silver missile, Air Force Blue loading trolley	£40-50
351	1958-62	RAF Land Rover	Blue body, RAF roundel, spare wheel, windows	£75-85
			As previous model but with suspension	£90-120
352	1958-62	RAF Vanguard Staff Car	Blue bodied Standard Vanguard with RAF roundel	£75-85
353	1959-61	Decca Radar Scanner	Blue/Orange, scanner rotates	£35-45
354	1964-66	Commer Military Ambulance	Military Green body, Red cross, driver	£80-90
355	1964-65	Commer Van 'MILITARY POLICE'	Military Green body, driver, Blue roof light	£80-90
356	1964-66	VW Personnel Carrier	Military Green body, Red interior, driver, Blue roof light, 'US Personnel'	£90-120
357	1964-66	Land Rover	Military Green body, Red interior, driver, White star, aerial, 'Weapons Carrier'	£120-140
358	1964-68	Oldsmobile Staff Car	Military Green body, Red interior, White star, 'HQ STAFF', driver, 3 passengers, aerial	£80-90
359	1964-66	Commer Army 'FIELD KITCHEN'	Military Green, Blue interior, US star on roof, driver/attendant	£100-125
414	1961-63	Bedford Dormobile Military Ambulance	Olive drab body, Red crosses, smooth hubs	£75-85
			As previous model but with shaped hubs and suspension	£75-85
500	1963-64	US Army Land Rover	Rare version of model 357	£200-250
900	1974-78	German Tiger MkI Tank	Brown/Green, Rubber tracks, fires shells (12 supplied) aerial, '144'	£20-30
901	1974-78	Centurion Mk.I Tank	Rubber tracks, fires shells (12 supplied) aerial, Union Jacks	£20-30
902	1974-80	American M60 A1 Tank	Rubber tracks, fires shells (12 supplied)	£20-30
903	1974-80	British Chieftain Tank	Fires shells (12 supplied) rubber tracks	£20-30
904	1974-78	German King-Tiger Tank	Rubber tracks, fires shells (12 supplied) Black crosses, 'B 34'	£20-30
905	1975-76	Russian SU100 Tank Destroyer	Grey, Fires shells (12 supplied) rubber tracks, Red Star	£20-30
906	1975-76	Saladin Armoured Car	Rubber tracks, fires shells (12 supplied) elevating gun	£20-30
907	1976-80	German Rocket Launcher	Steel Blue/Red, half-track, detachable limber, fires rockets (12)	£20-30
908	1977-80	French AMX Recovery Tank	Crane, lifting dozer blade, equipment, 3 figures	£40-50
909	1977-80	Tractor Gun and Trailer	Sand-coloured British gun and trailer, fires shells (12 supplied)	£40-50
920	1975-78	Bell Army Helicopter	Military-Green helicopter with Army markings, Black or Green rotor	£15-20
922	1975-78	Casualty Helicopter	Red/White/Yellow Sikorsky helicopter, number '3', Red crosses	£15-20
923	1975-78	Sikorsky Sky Crane	Military-Green helicopter, Red cross, 'ARMY' marking	£15-20

MAJOR PACKS - (Military and R.A.F. models)

Ref	Year(s)	Model name	Colours, features, details	Market Price Range
1106	1959-61	Karrier Decca Radar Van	Cream body, 4 Orange bands, rotating scanner, aerials, box has interior packing	£100-125
			Cream body, 5 Orange bands, rotating scanner, aerials, box has interior packing	£100-125
1108	1958-60	Bristol Bloodhound Guided Missile & Launching Ramp	Green ramp, Yellow/Red/White Guided Missile, RAF markings	£70-80
1109	1959-61	Bristol Bloodhound Guided Missile & Loading Trolley	Green ramp, Yellow/Red/White Guided Missile, RAF markings	£70-80
1112	1959-62	Corporal Guided Missile on Launching Ramp	Military-Green mechanical base, White missile, Red rubber nose cone, instruction sheet in box	£75-85
	1960-62		Same but with separately boxed 1408 Percussion head and instructions	£100-120
1113	1959-62	Corporal Guided Missile Erector Vehicle	with lifting mechanism and Guided Missile, spare wheel	£200-250
1115	1958-61	Bristol Ferranti Bloodhound	Yellow/Red/White Guided Missile with RAF markings	£55-65
1116	1959-61	Bloodhound Launching Ramp	Military-Green launching ramp for 1115. Rotates, has lifting mechanism	£45-55
1117	1959-61	Bloodhound Loading Trolley	for use with model 1115 Military-Green, spare wheel, drawbar pivots	£45-55
1118	1959-64	International Tow Truck	Military-Green with British markings (US markings on box picture)	£100-150
			Dutch issue with Silver grille and sidelights	£100-150
			US Army issues	£100-150
1124	1960-61	Launching Ramp for Corporal Guided Missile	Military-Green, operable mechanisms, in plain 'Temporary Pack' box	£35-45
1133	1965-66	Troop Transporter	Olive International six wheeled truck, 'US 7811332', hook	£125-150
1134	1965-66	'US ARMY' Fuel Tanker	Olive Bedford 'S' Type Artic, US Army star, 'NO SMOKING'	£200-250
1135	1965	Heavy Equipment Transporter	Bedford Carrimore, Military Green, US Army star, driver, Red interior	£250-300

Miscellaneous models

Ref	Year(s)	Model name	Colours, features, details	Market Price Range
171	1982-	Street Bike	Red, Silver and Black body, multicoloured swirl	£5-10
172	1982-	'POLICE' Bike	White/Black/Silver body	£5-10
173	1982-	Cafe Racer	Silver and Black racing number '26', '750 cc Class'	£5-10
490	1976-79	Touring Caravan	White and Blue body, opening doors, drawbar	£10-15

Novelty, Film and TV-related models

Ref	Year(s)	Model name	Colours, features, details	Market Price Range
107	1967-70	Batboat on Trailer	Black boat (tinplate fin cover) with Batman and Robin figures, gold trailer (suspension, cast wheels). Blue/yellow pictorial box also contains black accessory towing hook for attachment to Batmobile	£140-170
	1974-81		Black boat (plastic fin) with Batman and Robin figures, gold trailer (no suspension, Whizzwheels), striped window box	£60-80
201	1970-72	The Saint's Volvo	White body, White 'Saint' logo on red label, WhizzWheels, driver, Red/Yellow 'window' box	£140-160
246	1965-68	Chrysler Imperial Convertible.	All issue should include driver/passenger, golf trolley in boot, Blue/Yellow box with inner packing.	
			Metallic Deep Red body, Pale Blue interior, shaped spun or detailed cast hubs	£70-80
			Metallic Turquoise body, Green interior, shaped spun or detailed cast hubs	£70-80
			Metallic Blue body, Pale Blue interior, cast hubs	£110-130
			Metallic Kingfisher Blue body, Green interior, cast hubs	£175-225
256	1965-68	Volkswagen 1200 Rally	Red body, rally number '18', 'EAST AFRICAN RALLY', steering wheel on roof, rhinoceros	£150-175
258	1965-68	The Saint's Volvo P1800	White body, Black 'Saint' logo (transfer), Red interior, driver, spun hubs, Blue/Yellow card box	£150-175
258	1968-70	The Saint's Volvo P1800	White body, white 'Saint' logo on Red label, Red interior, driver, cast hubs, Blue/Yellow card box	£140-160
258	1968-70	The Saint's Volvo P1800	As previous version but white 'Saint' logo on blue label	NGPP
259	1979-80	Penguinmobile	White car with 'Penguin' and Red/Yellow parasol, Black/Yellow 'window' box	£35-40
260	1979-81	Superman Police Car	Blue/White body, 'CITY of METROPOLIS', Black/Yellow pictorial window box	£35-40
261	1965-69	James Bond's Aston-Martin	Bright Gold body (metal roof), Red interior, wire wheels. With James Bond at the wheel, passenger seat ejector (with bandit figure). Accessories: envelope with 'secret instructions', spare bandit figure, self-adhesive '007' badge, (plus 'Model Car Makers to James Bond' Corgi Catalogue in earlier boxes). Blue/Yellow picture box has inner pictorial stand. From the film 'Goldfinger'	£400-500
	variant:		As previous model but the opening roof component is made of plastic	NGPP
261	1979-81	Spiderbuggy	Red/Blue jeep body with crane, Spiderman and Green Goblin figures. Black/Yellow pictorial window box	£75-100
262	1967-69	Lincoln Continental Executive Limousine	Metallic Gold/Black body, with picture strip for onboard 'TV set'	£125-150
			Light Blue/Tan body, with picture strip for onboard 'TV set'	£150-175
262	1979-80	Captain Marvel's Porsche	White with flames and stars, driver, Black/Yellow 'window' box	£35-40
263	1979-81	Captain America's Jetmobile	White/Red/Blue body, Red wheels, Black/Yellow 'window' box	£25-30
264	1979-82	Incredible Hulk Truck	Bronze Hulk in Red cage on Mazda pick-up, Black/Yellow 'window' box	£45-55
			As previous model but Hulk in Grey cage.	£55-65
	NB		Dark Bronze Hulk is rare – add **£10** to price.	
265	1979-82	Supermobile	Blue/Red/Silver body, Superman at the controls, moving fists'. Black/Yellow pictorial 'window' box has 10 spare rockets / instruction leaflet	£40-50
266	1968-72	Chitty Chitty Bang Bang	Chrome, Brown and Red body (162 m), Red/Yellow retractable 'wings', figures of Caractacus Potts, Truly Scrumptious, a boy and a girl Pictorial Blue/Yellow 'window' box comes in two sizes	£250-300
	1992	25th Anniversary replica:	model on 'mahogany' display stand. Direct mail offer from Corgi	£60-70
266	1979-83	Spider Bike	Red/Blue motorcycle, Spiderman rider, Black wheels, Black or Red handlebars forks, Black or Blue seat and fairing, amber or clear windshield, rocket launchers.	
		Box 1:	Black/Yellow pictorial 'window' box with header card, 10 spare rockets	£50-60
		Box 2:	Black/Yellow 'window' box without header card, 10 spare rockets	£50-60
		Box 3:	Black/Red/Yellow striped 'window' box without header card, 10 spare rockets.	£50-60
266	1980-82	Spider Bike	As previous model but with White wheels.	£70-80
267	1966-67	Batmobile	Gloss Black body, Red 'Bat' logo on doors and on gold cast hubs, Batman and Robin figures, 'pulsating exhaust flame', sealed secret instructions concealed in box base. 12 spare rockets (Red or Yellow) attached to sprue, self-adhesive 'Batman' badge. Pictorial card box with diorama, earliest versions had 'features' leaflet within	£400-500
			As previous model but with Matt Black body	£600-800
	1967-72		Same (Gloss Black body) but with brass towing hook cast into base. Blue/Yellow 'window' box	£200-250
	1967-72		Same but with cast Silver wheels. Black/Blue/Yellow 'window' box	£250-300
	1973		As previous model but with Red WhizzWheels (with Chrome hubs) and without pulsating 'flame' effect. Blue/Yellow 'window' box with missiles and instructions	£300-400
	1974-77		As previous model but with Black WhizzWheels and without pulsating 'flame' effect. Copyright information cast in base Dark Blue/Yellow 'window' box (header card on some), spare rockets, no instruction sheet	£125-175
	1977-79		As previous casting but wider WhizzWheels, no Robin figure. Black/Red/Yellow 'window' box	£100-150
268	1978-80	Batman's Batbike	Black/Red rocket-firing motorcycle with Red or Grey Batman figure. Black and Yellow 'window' box (header card on some), spare rockets	£60-80
	1980-83		As previous versions but in Black/Red/Yellow striped 'window' box	£50-70
268	1967-72	The Green Hornet's 'Black Beauty'	Black body, Green interior, driver and Green Hornet figures, transfer on roof, spun or cast detailed hubs. Fires missile from front, radar scanner from rear. Four of each, plus 'secret instructions' are in Blue/Yellow pictorial card box which should include a greaseproof paper roof decal protector, and inner pictorial card	£350-450

55

269   1977-83   **James Bond Lotus Esprit** .... White body, Black windows, operable fins and rocket mechanism. From the
film 'The Spy Who Loved Me'. Early Black/Yellow pictorial 'window' box with plain base
must contain instruction sheet and 10 spare rockets attached to sprue **£100-130**

     1977   .... Later pictorial 'window' box has instructions printed on base, 10 spare rockets **£90-110**

10 gold-plated versions of 269 were presented to VIPs at the film's launch.
The models had special mountings and boxes **£3,000-5,000**

270   1968-76   **James Bond's**
         Aston-Martin DB5 .... Silver body (slightly larger than 261). Features as 261, plus revolving number-plates and extending
tyre slashers. Box must contain inner pictorial stand, James Bond leaflet, sealed 'secret instructions'
packet, unused '007' lapel badge (different from 261), set of unapplied number plates and bandit
figure. Variations include Gold or Silver coloured bumpers, metal or plastic spoked rear wheels.

       Box 1:   Pictorial wing-flap box. Model sits on card platform under vac-formed bubble (fragile, few made) **£300-500**

       Box 2:   Blue/Yellow 'window' box (some with card 'upstand' till 1973, few made) **£500-750**

       Box 3:   Black/Blue/Yellow striped 'window' box (1973-76) **£140-175**

270   1977-78   .... As previous version but with fixed number plates, 'solid' chrome WhizzWheels, no tyre-slashers,
no 'secret instructions'. Striped window box, ejectable passenger lodged in box inner **£125-150**

271   1978-81   **James Bond Aston-Martin** ...... Silver body (1:36 scale), Red interior, Gold radiator/bumpers, WhizzWheels ('spoked' detail or
'alloy racing'). Early Black/Yellow boxes had '1:36' printed on window tag, plus header card **£70-80**
Later Black/Yellow boxes did not have the window tag **£50-60**
Final issues were in Black/Red/Yellow striped window boxes **£40-50**

271   1990   ...'MODELAUTO' promotional: Silver body, Red interior with 2 figures, Blue logo 'National Motor Museum Holland' **£180-220**

?   1991-92   **James Bond Aston-Martin** ...... Reissue of C271 in clear plastic display box with plastic '007' badge **£20-30**

271/1   **James Bond Aston-Martin** ...... Silver body (1:36 scale), small 4-spoked wheels **£80-100**

272   1981-83   **James Bond Citroën 2cv** .... Yellow body, opening bonnet, WhizzWheels From film 'For Your Eyes Only'.

       Box (1):   Black/Red/Yellow 'window' box with pictorial header card **£30-40**

       Box (2):   Black/Red/Yellow 'compact' box with pictorial top flap **£30-40**

272   1981   ....Gold plated version: (12 only produced). Strada Jewellry Certificate should be with model **£2,000-3,000**

277   1968-72   **'MONKEES' Monkeemobile** ... Red body, White roof, Yellow logo, cast detailed wheels, plus figures of Mike,
Mickey, Davy and Pete. Blue/Yellow 'window' box **£200-300**

            In Blue/Yellow 'window' box with clip-in cardboard header as used for shop display purposes **£500-600**

           NB   Pre-production model with plastic engine exists.

278   1981-   **Dan Dare's Car** .... Red/Yellow space vehicle. Planned but not produced .... NPP

290   1976-77   **Kojak Buick** .... Bronze body (various shades), 4-spoke or disc type wheel hubs, 'gunfire' sound,
self-adhesive 'Lieutenant' badge, figures of Kojak (no hat) and Crocker (blue jacket).
Black/Yellow pictorial 'window' box **£80-100**

     1977-80   .... Same but Kojak figure has a hat and Crocker has a Black jacket. 'New' tag on some boxes **£40-50**

292   1977-82   **Starsky & Hutch Ford Torino**.. Red/White body, figures of Starsky, Hutch, and a suspect. Black/Yellow pictorial 'window' box **£100-150**

     1986   .... Reissued as an export model (20,000) **£10-15**

298   1982-83   **Magnum P.I. Ferrari** .... Red Ferrari 308GTS with 4-spoke or disc wheels. Black/Red/Yellow pictorial 'window' box **£20-30**

302   1969   **Hillman Hunter Rally** .... Blue body, White roof, Matt-Black bonnet, RN '75', equipment, kangaroo,
'Golden Jacks', transfers, toolbox, leaflet, instructions **£100-125**

320   1978-81   **The Saint's Jaguar XJS** .... White body, standard or 'dished' WhizzWheels. Black/Yellow 'window' box (yellow or black inner) **£30-35**

336   1967-69   **James Bond's Toyota 2000 GT**.. White body, Red aerial, 2 figures, rocket launchers in boot. From film 'You Only Live Twice'.
Diorama box must have card reinforcements to protect aerial, 8 spare rockets on sprue, sealed
envelope marked 'secret instructions' which also contains self-adhesive '007' badge **£400-500**

342   1980-82   **'The Professionals' Ford Capri** Silver/Black body, tinted windows, tinted windows, dished or disc
hubs, figures of Cowley, Bodie, Doyle Black/Yellow pictorial 'window' box **£100-125**
Version with chrome wheel hubs **£125-150**

348   1968-69   **Ford Mustang**
         'POP ART' Stock Car .... Blue body and interior, 5 psychedelic labels '20'. Not shown in catalogues **£70-80**

348   1980-81   **'Vegas' Thunderbird** .... Red body with Dan Tanner figure Black/Yellow pictorial 'window' box **£35-45**

349   1967-67   **'POP ART' Morris Mini** .... Red body, Yellow interior, 4 psychedelic labels, *MOSTEST* logo. Model not
generally released or shown in catalogues, few only produced **£1,500-2,000**

383   1970-76   **VW 1200 'Flower Power'** .... Red body with psychedelic Grenadine and Green daisy labels on bonnet and doors **£75-85**

391   1972-72   **James Bond**
         Ford Mustang Mach I .... Red body, White interior and base, WhizzWheels (2 types known). From film
'Diamonds Are Forever'. Red/Yellow 'window' box has '007' Red sticker **£225-285**
As previous model but with 'CORGI TOYS' shop display stand **£250-350**

391   1972-73   **'FIREBUG'** .... Orange body, Yellow ladder, *FIREBUG*, WhizzWheels **£15-25**

423   1978-78   **'ROUGH RIDER'** .... Yellow Chevrolet van, motorcycle side labels **£20-25**

426   1962-64   **'CHIPPERFIELDS CIRCUS'**
         Mobile Booking Office .... Karrier Bantam in red and blue, with clown and circus posters, spun hubs. Blue/yellow card box........ **£150-175**

426   1978-80   **Circus Booking Office** .... Yellow/Red Chevrolet van, 'JEAN RICHARD PINDER', WhizzWheels **£40-60**

           NB   The 'clown's face' poster may be at the front or the rear on the nearside of the model.

428   1963-66   **'Mr SOFTEE' Ice Cream Van** . Karrier van, Blue/White body, salesman swivels **£125-150**

431   1978-79   **'VANATIC'** .... White Chevrolet van, polychromatic side labels **£15-20**

432   1978-79   **'VANTASTIC'** .... Black Chevrolet, Yellow/Red design **£15-20**

433   1978   **'VANISHING POINT'** .... Chevrolet van shown in 1978 catalogue but not issued .... NPP

434   1978-80   **'CHARLIE'S ANGELS' Van** ... Pink Chevrolet Custom van, Yellow or Brown interior, 4-spoke or disc wheels.
Black/Yellow pictorial 'window' box **£20-30**

435   1979-80   **'SUPERMAN' Van** .... Metallic Silver Chevrolet 'SuperVan'. Black/Yellow pictorial 'window' box (printing variations seen) **£30-35**

436   1979-80   **'SPIDERVAN'** .... Blue Chevrolet van, 'Spiderman' design, 4-spoke or disc wheels. Black/Yellow pictorial 'window' box .. **£30-35**

437	1979-80	'COCA COLA'	Red Chevrolet van, White design, tinted roof windows, crates	£30-35
	NB		Various other labels were designed for the Chevrolet 'van' series. Some prototype labels were printed but not officially used. Some of these may have found their way on to repainted van castings – they are NOT official Corgi issues. Logos include: 'Apache Patrol', 'Light Vantastic', 'Vanilla Treat', 'Cosmos', 'Columbia', 'Aquarius', 'Centaur', 'Colorama', 'Rocket Van', 'Centaur', plus four other unlettered 'psychedelic' designs.	
436	1963-65	Citroën 'WILDLIFE SAFARI'	Yellow Citroën ID19, driver and passenger, detailed interior, roof luggage, 'Wild Life Reservation' logo	£70-80
440	1966-69	Ford Consul Cortina Estate	Metallic Dark Blue with Brown side panels, plastic golfer, caddie and trolley	£100-125
447	1965-66	'Walls Ice Cream' Van	Ford Thames van in Blue/Cream, salesman, boy, spare transfers. Blue/Yellow card box, inner base, leaflet	£175-225
448	1964-69	Austin Police Mini Van	Dark Blue body, Red interior, shaped or cast hubs, aerial, White 'POLICE' logo, policeman and dog, pictorial stand and internal support packaging	£115-130
472	1964-66	'VOTE FOR CORGI'	Corgi 438 Land Rover in Green/Yellow, Blue/Yellow card box	£75-85
474	1965-68	Musical 'Walls Ice Cream' Van	Ford Thames van in Blue/Cream, musical movement (must function), diorama but no figures. Blue/Yellow card box with packing ring and packing piece, plus unused sticker sheet	£175-250
475	1964-65	'Olympic Winter Sport'	White/Yellow Citroën Safari, '1964', roof-rack, skier, skis. Diorama 'By Special Request' box	£90-110
475	1965-68	'CORGI SKI CLUB'	Citroën with Off-White body, Red roof-rack, 4 Yellow skis and 2 poles, bonnet transfer, Brown dashboard/rear seats, Green front seats	£90-110
475	1965-68	'CORGI SKI CLUB'	Citroën with White body, Yellow Roof-rack, 4 Red skis and 2 poles, Green dashboard/rear seats, Brown front seats	£90-110
479	1967-71	Mobile Camera Van	Blue/White Commer van, spun hubs, camera/operator, 'Samuelson Film Services', equipment case	£100-125
479	1967-71		As previous model but with detailed cast hubs	£80-90
485	1965-69	Mini Countryman with Surfer	Sea-Green body, Lemon interior, 2 surfboards on roof-rack, male figure, special leaflet	£125-150
			As previous model but with unpainted grille	£140-170
486	1967-69	'KENNEL CLUB' Truck	White/Orange Chevrolet Impala with 'Vari-View' dachshund picture, 4 dogs	£50-60
487	1965-69	'CHIPPERFIELDS' Parade Vehicle	472 Land Rover in Red/Blue, 'CIRCUS IS HERE' label, chimpanzee, clown, Blue/yellow card box	£150-175
497	1966-66	'The Man From UNCLE's 'Thrush Buster'	Oldsmobile (235) with White body, cast wheels, cast spotlights, 'UNCLE' logo, gun sound, figures of Napoleon Solo and Ilya Kuriakin. Blue/Yellow pictorial card box (which must include internal packaging, roof packing, and 3-D 'Waverley' ring)	£500-750
497	1966-69		Same as previous model but Metallic Purplish-Blue body, cast or plastic spotlights	£150-200
499	1967-69	'1968 Winter Olympics'	White/Blue Citroën, 'Grenoble Olympiade', Red or Yellow roof rack, Yellow or Red skis/poles, male tobogganist, female skier. Blue/Yellow 'window' box	£125-150
503	1964-70	'CHIPPERFIELDS' Giraffe Transporter	Red/Blue Bedford 'TK', cast or spun wheels, 2 giraffes. Blue/Yellow card box	£100-150
	1970-71		As previous model but larger 'stepped' front wheels	£130-170
			Window box variation	£150-200
510	1970-73	Team Manager's Car	Red Citroën, 'Tour De France', figures, spare wheels, 'Paramount'	£70-80
511	1970-71	'CHIPPERFIELDS' Poodle Truck	Blue/Red Chevrolet Pick-Up, 'PERFORMING POODLES' labels, female trainer, 4 White and 2 Black poodles, Blue/Yellow 'window' box (should include a plastic dome over dogs)	£350-450
513	1970-72	Citroën 'Alpine Rescue'	White/Red car, Yellow roof-rack, St Bernard, sled, skis, male figure. Blue/Yellow 'window' box	£250-350
607	1963-68	'CHIPPERFIELDS' Elephant Cage	A Corgi Kit with Brown plastic cage and elephant parts, instruction leaflet. Blue/Yellow card box	£50-75
647	1980-83	Buck Rogers Starfighter	White/Black, White retractable wings, Wilma Dearing and Tweaky figures, Black/Yellow pictorial 'window' box, 10 spare rockets	£40-45
648	1981-82	NASA Space Shuttle	White/Black body, 'USA Satellite', opening hatch	£20-25
649	1979-82	James Bond Space Shuttle	White body (C468 casting), separate satellite (early versions retained by nylon strap). From film 'Moonraker' Larger pictorial Black/Yellow box	£50-75
681	1972	Stunt Bike	Gold body, Blue and Yellow rider, Red trolley, 'window' box, (19,000 made)	£125-150
700	1974-80	Motorway Service Ambulance	White/Red futuristic vehicle, WhizzWheels	£8-12
701	1974-80	Inter-City Mini-Bus	Orange body, Yellow labels, WhizzWheels	£8-12
801	1969-69	Noddy's Car	Yellow/Red car with dickey-seat, cast hubs, chrome bumpers. Figures of Noddy, Big-Ears, and black-faced Golly Pictorial Blue/Yellow, 'window' box	£1,000-1,500
			As previous model but Golly has Light Tan face	£750-1,000
			As previous model but Golly has Grey face	£350-500
	1969-73		As previous model but Master Tubby (light or dark brown) instead of Golly	£200-300
802	1969-72	Popeye's Paddle-Wagon	Yellow/White body, Red wings, Blue paddle covers, White or Yellow rear wheels, anchors, moving figures of Popeye, Olive Oyl, Swee'Pea, Bluto and Wimpey. Blue/Yellow pictorial 'window' box	£300-400
803	1969-72	The Beatles Submarine	Yellow/White, psychedelic design, hatches (Yellow rear, White front) open to show John, Paul, George and Ringo, pictorial window box with Blue-Green inner lining	£250-350
	1970-71		As previous model but with Red hatch covers	£350-450
	1970-71		With one red hatch and one white hatch	£500-600
804	1975-78	Noddy's Car	Red/Yellow car, no dickey-seat, no rear bumper. Figure of Noddy only. Dark Blue/Yellow pictorial 'window' box	£175-225
805	1970-71	Hardy Boys Rolls-Royce	9041 Silver Ghost casting in Red, Blue and Yellow, plated wheels. Bubble-pack of five Hardy Boys figures also contained in the Blue/Yellow 'window' box	£150-200
806	1970-72	Lunar Bug	Red/White/Blue, 'Lunar Bug', windows, drop-down ramps	£65-75
807	1971-73	Dougal's Magic Roundabout Car (based on 510 Citroën)	Yellow/Red, with Brian, Dougal and Dylan. Yellow/Blue 'window' box with decal sheet	£180-225
807	1973-74	Dougal's Car	As previous model but in Black/Yellow 'window' box, with decal sheet	£140-170
808	1971-73	Basil Brush's Car	Red/Yellow car with hand-painted Basil figure, 'Laugh tapes' and soundbox are in separate printed box within pictorial Blue/Yellow 'window' box	£175-200
809	1973-73	Dick Dastardly's Car	Blue/Red/Yellow racing car with Dick and Muttley figures. Dark Blue/Yellow 'window' box	£150-175
811	1972-74	James Bond Moon Buggy	Blue/White body, Yellow WhizzWheels, Red scanner. Roof opening mechanism should be working. Blue/Yellow pictorial window box	£300-400

Novelty, Film and TV-related models

H851	1972-74	**Magic Roundabout Train**	Red/Blue, Mr Rusty and Basil in the locomotive (engine sound), Rosalie and Paul in the carriage and Dougal in the van. Blue/Yellow pictorial 'window' box with Blue nylon tow-rope	**£250-300**
H852	1972-74	**Magic Roundabout Carousel**	Red/Yellow/Blue working roundabout with Swiss musical movement playing the TV theme. Dylan, Paul, Rosalie, Florence and Basil figures. Blue/Yellow pictorial card box	**£350-450**
H853	1972-74	**Magic Roundabout Playground**	Contains a modified H852, H851 (with the figures), plus Zebedee, Dylan, four kids, see saw, park bench, 3 Blue and 3 Orange shrubs and 2 flowers. Operating carousel and track. Theme music plays when Dylan is wound up	**£1,000-1,500**
H859	1972-74	**Mr McHenry's Trike**	Red/Yellow trike and trailer, Mr McHenry and pop-up Zebedee figures, Blue and Yellow pictorial 'window' box with blue towing cord and instruction sheet	**£175-225**
H860-H868	1972-74	**Magic Roundabout figures**	Figures packed in individual clear plastic tubs: 860 Dougal, 861 Florence, 862 Zebedee, 863 Mr Rusty, 864 Brian Snail, 865 Basil, 866 Ermintrude the Cow, 868 Dylan the Rabbit	Each: **£20-30**
925	1976-81	**Batcopter**	Black body, Red 'Bat' rotors, Batman figure, operable winch, 143 mm	**£65-75**
926	1978-80	**Stromberg Helicopter**	Black body/rotors, ten spare rockets. From 'The Spy Who Loved Me'. Black/Yellow 'window' box	**£60-70**
927	1978-80	**Chopper Squad Helicopter**	White/metallic Blue Jet Ranger helicopter, operating winch. Black/Yellow pictorial 'window' box	**£35-45**
928	1981-82	**Spidercopter**	Blue/Red body, 'spider legs', retractable tongue. Black/Yellow pictorial 'window' box	**£40-50**
929	1979-80	**'DAILY PLANET' Jetcopter**	Red/White body, rocket launchers, Black/Yellow pictorial 'window' box contains 10 spare rockets	**£50-60**
930	1972-80	**'Drax' Helicopter**	White body, 'Drax' logo, ten spare rockets. From the film 'Moonraker'. Black/Yellow 'window' box	**£60-70**
9004	1967-69	**'The World of Wooster' Bentley**	Green 9002 Bentley with figures of Jeeves and Wooster, plated wheels. Bubble-packed in display base	**£70-90**

Marks & Spencer issues

In 1978 a series of special sets and single models were produced for sale through selected M & S stores. They were packed in attractive non-standard boxes and had unique liveries. They were not issued in great quantities.

SINGLE MODELS

8800	1979	Custom Van	No details available	**£25-35**
8801	1979	Spindrift Helicopter	Black body with Yellow chassis, floats and rotor blades	**£25-35**
8802	1979	Massey Ferguson Tractor	Red/Black body with White arms and Red shovel	**£40-50**
8803	1979	Buick 'FIRE CHIEF' Car	Red body with 'City Fire Department' logo on bonnet	**£50-75**

SMALL SETS

8000	1978	F1 Racing Set	Includes 162 'ELF' Tyrrell (Dark Blue) and 160 Hesketh F1 (White)	**£75-100**
8001	1978	Wings Flying Team	Includes 301 Lotus Elite (Green) and Nipper aircraft (White) on Grey trailer	**£100-150**
8002	1978	Motorway Police Patrol	C429 'POLICE' Jaguar (Green) and Blue Fiat X1-9	**£60-80**
8003	1979	Spindrift Power Boat Team	301 Ferrari Daytona (Yellow) and Yellow power boat on trailer	**£60-80**

MEDIUM SETS

8100	1978	Racing Team	C421 Land Rover (White with 'FORMULA' logo), 338 Rover, and 301 Lotus on trailer	**£150-200**
8101	1978	Wings Flying School	C421 Land Rover (Grey with 'WINGS' logo) Grey helicopter and Nipper aircraft on Grey trailer	**£150-200**
8102	1978	Motorway Breakdown	C429 'POLICE' Jaguar, 293 Renault 5 (Yellow) plus Berliet Wrecker with 'RESCUE BREAKDOWN SERVICES'	**£100-150**
8103	1979	Spindrift Power Boat Team	Includes Spindrift 301 Ferrari, Helicopter and Dinghy	**£150-200**

LARGE SETS

8400	1978	Grand Prix Racing	Includes 160 Hesketh (White) 162 'ELF' Tyrrell (Dark Blue) Fiat X1-9 (Blue) and Land Rover (White with 'FORMULA 1 RACING TEAM' logo)	**£250-350**
8401	1978	Wings Flying Club	Land Rover, Helicopter, Tipsy Nipper aircraft on trailer plus Lotus Elite	**£250-300**
8402	1978	Motorway Rescue	Includes 'POLICE' Jaguar, Berliet Wrecker, Renault 5 and Fiat X1-9	**£250-300**
8403	1979	Spindrift Power Boat Team	Includes Ferrari Daytona (Yellow) Yellow power boat on trailer, Yellow/Black helicopter, plus MF Tractor and 'RESCUE' dinghy	**£250-300**

Trophy Models

(Marks & Spencer special 'plated' issues)

The models were specially produced in 1961 to be sold by Marks & Spencer. The set consisted of five vacuum-plated 'gold' models taken from the existing Corgi product range, each mounted on a detachable black moulded base with a gold name label. The models were packaged in white boxes with red/grey design plus 'St Michael Trophy Models' in red. They did not sell well at the time of issue but are keenly sought after by present day collectors.

150 S	1961	**Vanwall Racing Car**	Gold vacuum-plated body, Red wheels and radiator grille	**£100-200**
152	1961	**BRM Racing Car**	Gold vacuum-plated body, Red wheels and radiator grille	**£100-200**
300	1961	**Austin-Healey Sports Car**	Gold vacuum-plated body, plastic windscreen, Red wheels and grille	**£100-200**
301	1961	**Triumph TR2 Sports Car**	Gold vacuum-plated body, plastic windscreen, Red wheels and grille	**£100-200**
302	1961	**MG 'MGA' Sports Car**	Gold vacuum-plated body, plastic windscreen, Red wheels and grille	**£100-200**

The 'Exploration' Range

D2022	1980	**'SCANOTRON'**	Green/Black/Yellow	**£15-25**
D22023	1980	**'ROCKETRON'**	Blue/Yellow, Black tracks	**£15-25**
D2024	1980	**'LASERTRON'**	Orange/Black/Yellow	**£15-25**
D2025	1980	**'MAGNETRON'**	Red/Black	**£15-25**

'The Muppets Show' models

D2030	1979-80	**Kermit's Car**	Yellow car with a famous Green frog, bubble-packed	**£40-45**
	1980-82		Same model but in Red/Yellow pictorial 'window' box	**£35-40**
D2031	1979-80	**Fozzie Bear's Truck**	Red/Brown/White truck, Silver or Black hooter, bubble-packed	**£35-40**
	1980-82		Same model but in Red/Yellow pictorial 'window' box	**£30-35**
D2032	1979-80	**Miss Piggy's Sport Coupé**	Pink sports car, Red or Pink dress, bubble-packed	**£40-45**
	1980-82		Same model but in Red/Yellow pictorial 'window' box	**£35-40**
D2033	1979-80	**Animal's Percussionmobile**	Red traction-engine, Yellow or Red wheels, Yellow or Black chimney, Yellow or Silver cymbal. Bubble-packed	**£35-40**
	1980-82		Same model but in Red/Yellow pictorial 'window' box	**£30-35**

Major Packs

Original internal packaging for securing model and accessories must all be present before model can be considered complete and therefore to achieve the best price. See Corgi model identification page.

1121	1960-62	'CHIPPERFIELDS' Crane Truck	Red body, Raised Blue log and wheels, operable grey tinplate jib and hook, instruction leaflet. Blue/Yellow lidded box with packing	£150-200
	1963-69		Red body, raised Blue logo and wheels, operable chrome tinplate jib and hook, instruction leaflet. Blue/Yellow card box with end flaps	£150-200
1123	1961-62	'CHIPPERFIELDS' Circus Cage	Red body, Yellow chassis, smooth hubs, red diecast end and middle sliding doors, 2 plastic lions (in stapled bags), animal name decals, instruction sheet. Blue/Yellow lidded box with packing	£75-100
	1963-68		Red body, Yellow chassis, smooth or spun hubs, Blue plastic end and middle sliding doors, 4 animals (lions, tigers or polar bears in stapled bags), animal name decals. Blue/Yellow card box with end flaps	£75-100
1130	1962-70	'CHIPPERFIELDS' Horse Transporter	Bedford TK truck, Red/Blue, Green or Red 'horse-head' design at rear, cast or spun hubs, 6 Brown or Grey horses, Blue/Yellow card box with card packing around horses	£175-225
	1970-72		As previous model but with larger 'truck' wheels	£150-175
1139	1968-72	'CHIPPERFIELDS' Menagerie Transporter	Scammell Handyman MkIII, Blue/Red cab, Blue trailer with 3 plastic cages, 2 lions, 2 tigers and 2 bears. Blue/Yellow pictorial 'window' box with packing to hold animals, plus spare self-adhesive securing tape for animals	£300-400
1144	1969-72	'CHIPPERFIELDS' Crane and Cage with Rhino	Red/Blue Scammell Handyman MkIII, 'COME TO THE CIRCUS' on n/s, silver jib and hook, stepped 'truck' front wheels on some, Grey rhinoceros in plastic cage. Blue/Yellow 'window' box with pre-formed blister-pack around animals	£500-600
1163	1978-82	Human Cannon Truck	Red and Blue body, 'MARVO' figure	£30-40
1164	1980-83	Berliet 'DOLPHINARIUM'	Yellow cab, Blue trailer, Clear plastic tank, 2 dolphins, girl trainer. Black/Yellow 'window' box with header card on some	£100-150
			Yellow cab, Yellow trailer, 'window' box with header card on some	£100-150

Duo Packs (Film and TV-related models)

1360	1982-?	Batmobile	267 plus a Corgi juniors version, Black/Red/Yellow 'window' box	£150-175
1361	197?-?	James Bond Aston-Martin	271 plus a Corgi Juniors version, Black/Red/Yellow 'window' box	£125-150
1362	197?-?	James Bond Lotus Esprit	269 plus a Corgi Juniors version, Black/Red/Yellow 'window' box	£125-150
1363	1982-83	Buck Rogers Set	647 plus a smaller version Black/Yellow pictorial 'window' box	£50-60
1376	1982-83	Starsky & Hutch Ford Torino	292 plus a Corgi Juniors version	£70-80

Aircraft

Helicopters and Space Vehicles are also listed in the Emergency Vehicles, Novelty and Military Sections.

Ref	Year(s)	Model name	Colours, features, details	Market Price Range
650	1973-80	'BOAC' Concorde	White/Blue with Gold tail design, all-card box with 'BRITISH AIRWAYS', box has inner packing	£70-80
			White/Blue with Red/White/Blue tail, display stand, 'G-BBDG'	£50-60
			Version with White stripes on tail	£15-25
			Version with crown design on tail	£15-25
651	1973-81	'AIR FRANCE' Concorde	White/Blue with Gold tail design, all-card box	£70-80
			White/Blue, Red/White/Blue tail, display stand	£40-50
652	1973-81	'JAPAN AIRLINES' Concorde	White/Red/Blue/Black, all-card box, box has inner packing	£150-200
653	1973-81	'AIR CANADA' Concorde	White/Red/Blue/Black, all-card box, box has inner packing	£150-200
1119	1960-62	HDL Hovercraft 'SR-N1'	Blue/Grey/White body, Yellow rudders and wheels (Major Pack)	£30-35
1301	1973-77	Piper Cherokee Arrow	Yellow/Black with White wings, or White/Blue, 'N 286 4 A'	£35-45
1302	1973-77	Piper Navajo	Red/White or Yellow/White, 'N 9219 Y'	£35-45
1303	1973-77	Lockheed F104A Starfighter	Silver or Camouflage with Black crosses	£35-45
1304	1973-77	Mig-21 PF	Blue or Silver, number '57', Red stars, retractable undercarriage	£25-35
1305	1973	Grumman F-11a Tiger	Blue 'NAVY', or Silver with US stars	£25-35
1306	1973-77	North American P51-D Mustang	Silver or Camouflage, Black props, US stars, moveable control surfaces	£25-35
1307	1973-77	Saab 35 X Draken	Silver or Camouflage, retractable undercarriage, Swedish markings	£35-45
1308	1973-77	BAC (or SEPCAT) Jaguar	Silver or Camouflage, retractable wheels, moveable control surfaces	£35-45
1309	1973-77	'BOAC' Concorde	Dark Blue/White, retractable wheels	£45-55
1310	1973-77	'AIR FRANCE' 'BOEING 707B'	White/Blue body, Silver wings, retractable wheels	£35-45
1311	1973-77	Messerschmitt ME410	All Silver body, Black Iron Crosses on wings and fuselage	£35-45
1312	1973-77	Boeing 727 'TWA'	White body, Silver wings, retractable wheels	£35-45
1313	1973-77	Japanese Zero-Sen A6M5	Green or Silver with Red circles, retractable wheels	£35-45
1315	1973-77	'PAN-AM' Boeing 747	White body, Silver wings, hinged nose, retractable wheels	£35-45
1315/1		'BRITISH AIRWAYS' Jumbo Boeing 747	White/Silver, Blue logo, hinged nose, retractable wheels	£45-55
1316	1973-77	McDonnell Douglas F-4c5	Phantom II in Silver or Camouflage with retractable undercarriage	£35-45
1320	1978-80	'BRITISH AIRWAYS' VC-10	White/Silver with Red tail, Blue logo, retractable wheels	£35-45
1325	1978-80	'SWISSAIR' DC-10	White/Silver with Red stripe and tail, retractable wheels	£35-45

These models have 'Battery-operated Micro-Chip Action'.

Ref	Year(s)	Model name	Colours, features, details	Market Price Range
1001	1982	HCB Angus Firestreak............	Red/Yellow/White, *'RESCUE'*, electronic siren, on/off switch	£40-50
1002	1981	Sonic Corgi Truck Set..............	Yellow/White/Black/Red, *'SHELL SUPER OIL'*, *'BP OIL'*, remote control.................................	£25-30
1002	1981	'YORKIE' Truck Set	White/Yellow/Blue/Orange, *'MILK CHOCOLATE YORKIE'*, remote control........................	£25-30
1003	1981	Ford Road Hog	Black, Yellow/White twirls, 2-tone horn, press-down start	£15-20
1004	1981	'Beep Beep Bus'.......................	Red, *'BTA WELCOME TO BRITAIN'*, 2-tone horn, press-down start	£20-25
	1983		Red body with *'WELCOME TO HAMLEYS'* logo	£20-25
1005	1982	Police Land Rover	White/Red/Blue, *'POLICE'*, electronic siren, press-down start	£15-20
1006	1982	'RADIO WEST' Roadshow	*'Your Local Radio 605'*, AM radio, advertised but not issued	NPP
1006	1982	'RADIO LUXEMBOURG'	Red/White, *'RTL 208'*, AM radio, 3 loudspeakers...	£25-30
1007	1982	Road Repair Unit		
		Land Rover and Trailer	Yellow/Red/Silver, *'ROADWORKS'*, press start, road drill and sound..........................	£25-35
1008	1982	Fire Chief's Car.....................	Red/White/Yellow/Silver, *'FIRE DEPARTMENT'*, press-down start, siren......................	£15-20
1009	1983	MG Maestro 1600...................	Yellow/Black, press start, working front and rear lights	£15-20
			Red/Black body. Sold in Austin-Rover Group box	£20-25
1024	1983	'Beep Beep Bus'.......................	Red, *'BTA'*, supplied exclusively to Mothercare shops	£20-25
1121	1983	Ford Transit Tipper Lorry	Orange/Black, Flashing light and working tipper...	£20-25

This illustration of the **Corgi Constructor Set** is taken from the 1966 Corgi catalogue.

Corgi Gift Sets

Original internal packaging for securing models and accessories must all be present before sets can be considered complete and therefore to achieve the best price. See Corgi Toys model identification page.

Ref	Year(s)	Set name	Contents, features, details	Market Price Range
1	1957-62	Transporter and 4 Cars	1101 Blue/Yellow Bedford Carrimore Transporter plus 201 Austin Cambridge, 208 Jaguar 24, 301 Triumph TR2 (or 300 Austin-Healey) and 302 MGA, plus 2 Yellow/Black 'Corgi Toys' dummy boxes	£400-500
1a	1957-62	Transporter and 4 Cars	1101 Red/Two-tone Blue Transporter, 200 Ford Consul, 201 Austin Cambridge, 204 Rover 90, 205 Riley Pathfinder, 2 Yellow 'Corgi Toys' dummy boxes	£300-400
1b	1959-62	Transporter and 4 Cars	1101 Red/Two-tone Blue Transporter, 214 Ford Thunderbird Hardtop, 215 Ford Thunderbird Convertible, 219 Plymouth Suburban Sport, 220 Chevrolet Impala. (US issue set)	£350-450
1c	1961-62	Transporter and 4 Cars	1101 Red/Two-tone Blue Transporter, 210s Citroën (or 217 Fiat 1800), 219 Plymouth Suburban Sport, 226 Mini, 305 Triumph TR3. (US issue set)	£350-450
1	1966-72	Farm Set	Ford 5000 Tractor plus 58 Beast Carrier, pictorial stand	£100-120
1	1983	Ford Sierra Set	Ford Sierra 299 with Blue body and Blue/Cream Caravan	£20-30
1/2	1985	'London Scene'	469 'LONDON STANDARD', Sierra Police Car and 425/1 Taxi	£15-20
2	1958-68	Land Rover and Pony Trailer	438 Land Rover (Green, Beige tin tilt) and 102 Pony Trailer (Red/Black)	£150-175
			As previous but with All Red Land Rover	£175-200
			with Light Brown Land Rover (Cream plastic tilt), Light Brown/Cream trailer	£70-80
2	1971-73	Unimog Dumper and Shovel	1128 Mercedes Tipper and 1145 Unimog Goose Dumper	£60-70
2	1980-81	Construction Set	Contains 54 Tractor, 440 Mazda, tool-box and cement mixer	£30-35
	1980-80	Construction Set	French export set containing 1110 and 1156 plus cement mixer	£30-40
3	1959-63	Thunderbird Missile Set	Contains 350 Thunderbird Missile and 351 Land Rover	£150-175
3	1967-69	Batmobile and Batboat		
		1st issue:	267 Batmobile with 'Bat' wheels, plus 107 Batboat (cast wheels), in plain or pictorial window box with inner tray and 4 figures, 12 rockets in unopened packet	£500-600
3	1980	2nd issue:	267 Batmobile (plain cast wheels), and 107 Batboat (WhizzWheels), pictorial window box, 2 figures, 12 rockets in unopened packet	£200-300
3	1986-88	'British Gas' Set	Contains Blue/White Ford Cargo Van, Ford Escort Van (2nd), plus compressor	£20-25
4	1958-60	Bristol Ferranti Bloodhound Guided Missile Set	Contains: 351, 1115, 1116, 1117 (see 'Military Vehicles' section)	£200-300
4	1974-75	Country Farm Set	Models 50 and 62 plus hay load, boy and girl	£60-70
5	1959-60	Racing Car Set	150 (Red) 151 (Blue) 152 (Green). All have flat spun wheels. Bubble-packed on inner card tray	£150-200
5	1960-61	Racing Car Set	150 (Red) 151 (Blue) 152 (Green). All have cast spoked wheels. Bubble-packed on inner card tray	£150-200
5s	1962-63	Racing Car Set	150s (Red) 151a (Blue) 152s (Turquoise). 'Gift Set 5s' stickers on box which contains an inner polystyrene packing tray	£250-350
5	1976-77	Country Farm Set	Same as Set 4 above, but minus boy, girl and hay load	£40-50
5	1967-72	Agricultural Set	484 Livestock Transporter and pigs, 438 Land Rover (no hood) 62, 69, 71, accessories 1490 skip and churns, 4 calves, farmhand and dog, 6 sacks. Box has inner pictorial stand	£150-200
6	1959-60	'Rocket Age' Set	Contains: 350, 351, 352, 353, 1106, 1108, 1117 (see 'Military' section)	£600-800
6	1967-69	Cooper-Maserati Set	Contains 490 VW Breakdown Truck plus 156 on trailer	£150-175
7	1959-64	Tractor and Trailer Set	Contains 50 and 51	£75-95
7	1968-76	'DAKTARI' Set	438 Land Rover in Green with Black Zebra stripes, spun or cast hubs. 5 figures: Paula, Dr Marsh Tracy with chimp Judy on his lap, a Tiger on the bonnet, and Clarence The Short-Sighted Lion (with spectacles!)	£100-125
			Version with WhizzWheels	£55-65
8	1959-62	Combine Harvester, Tractor and Trailer Set	Contains 1111, 50 and 51	£200-250
8	1968-74	'Lions of Longleat' Set	Land Rover with shaped hubs, keeper, 3 lions, plastic den, 3 joints of meat. Box has inner packing	£125-150
			As above but with WhizzWheels	£70-80
8/2	1987	Police Set	Ford Sierra Police Car, 674/3 Ford Transit Breakdown Truck and 621 Ford Escort Van	£20-25
9	1959-62	Corporal Guided Missile Set	Contains: 1112, 1113, 1118 (see 'Military Vehicles' section)	£300-400
9	1968-72	Tractor, Trailer and Shovel Set	Contains 66, 69 and 62	£100-125
9		3 Racing Minis Set	Yellow, White and Blue, numbers/stripes/adverts, special Red 'Hamleys' box	£90-110
10	1968-69	Rambler Marlin Set	Blue/White 319 with Trailer and 2 canoes (1 with figure). Box has inner packing and pictorial tray	£200-250
10	1973-78	Tank Transporter Set	Contains 901 Centurion Mk.I Tank and 1100 Mack articulated transporter	£70-80
10	1982	Jeep Set	Red 441 plus motorcycle on trailer	£20-25
10	1985	Sierra and Caravan Set	C299 Sierra plus Pale Brown caravan with Blue/Grey strip	£25-35
11	1960-64	ERF Dropside and Trailer	456 and 101 with cement and planks load	£125-150
			As above but with WhizzWheels	£60-70
11	1971-72	London Transport Set	Contains 418 Taxi, 468 'OUTSPAN' Bus, 226 Mini (Deep Blue), policeman on stand, inner tray	£100-120
11	1980-82	London Transport Set	C425 Taxi with C469 Bus 'B.T.A.' and policeman	£35-45
11/2	1986	'NOTRUF' Gift Set	Contains Ford Sierra, Mercedes Bonna Ambulance, 'FIRE' Range Rover	£20-30
12	1961-64	'Chipperfields Circus' Set	1121 Circus Crane Truck 'CHIPPERFIELDS' and 1123 Circus Cage, plus instructions	£150-175
12	1968-71	Grand Prix Racing Set	155, 156 and 330 with 490 Volkswagen tender, 3 mechanics, 16 bollards and hay bales	£200-250
12	1971-72	Grand Prix Racing Set	158, 159 and 330 (or 371) with 490 Volkswagen tender, 3 mechanics, 16 bollards and hay bales. The artwork on the box and the vac-formed base are different from previous issue	£250-300
12	1981-	Glider and Trailer Set	345 with Trailer and Glider	£40-50
13	1964-66	Fordson Tractor and Plough Set	Contains 60 and 61	£80-100

13	1968-72	**Renault 16 Film Unit**..............	White/Black, *'TOUR DE FRANCE'* , 'PARAMOUNT', cameraman, cyclist.	
			Inner tray plus plain orange card backdrop **£140-160**
13	1981-82	**Tour de France**		
		'RALEIGH' Team Car	373 Peugeot, White body, Red/Yellow 'RALEIGH' and 'TOTAL' logos,	
			racing cycles and Manager with loudhailer **£60-70**
13	1985	**'RAC' Ford Escort and**		
		Caravan Set	Blue and White van and caravan, 'INFORMATION CENTRE'....................................**£45-55**
14	1961-64	**Tower Wagon Set**....................	409 Jeep, Yellow cradle, lamp standard and electrician **£60-70**
14	1969-73	**Giant 'DAKTARI' Set**	Gift Set and items plus 503 and 484 transporters (spun hubs) with large and small elephants.	
			Blue/Yellow window box with pictorial card and inner tray...**£250-300**
			Version with WhizzWheels. Pictorial card and inner tray **£200-250**
14	1985	**'AA' Ford Escort and**		
		Caravan Set	Yellow and White van and caravan, 'INFORMATION CENTRE'..................................**£45-55**
15	1963-64	**Silverstone Set**..........................	150s, 151a, 152s, 215s, 304s, 309, 417s, 3 buildings, plain box (no picture)...................**£1250-1500**
15	1964-66	**Silverstone Set**..........................	150s, 154, 152s, 215s, 304s, 309, 417s, 3 buildings, layout shown on box..................**£1250-1500**
15	1968-77	**Land Rover and Horsebox Set**.	Contains 438, 112, spun hubs, mare and foal. Box contains inner polystyrene tray **£75-95**
			Version with WhizzWheels. Box contains inner card packing..**£55-75**
15	1986	**'TARMAC' Motorway Set**	'Motorway Maintenance' Green/Black 1128 Mercedes Tipper, Mazda Pickup and a compressor **£20-30**
16	1961-65	**'ECURIE ECOSSE' Set**	1126 Transporter with 3 racing cars with instruction leaflet and internal packing.	
		i)	Metallic Dark Blue 1126 Transporter (with Orange lettering), 150 Vanwall (Red,	
			no '25'), 151 Lotus XI (Blue, number '3'), 152 BRM (Turquoise, no '3') **£200-250**
		ii)	Metallic Dark Blue 1126 Transporter (with Yellow lettering), 150s Vanwall,	
			151a Lotus XI (Blue, no '7'), 152s BRM **£250-300**
	1965	....iii)	Metallic Light Blue 1126 Transporter (with Red lettering), 150s Vanwall,	
			152s BRM, 154 Ferrari (Red, no'36') **£200-250**
		iv)	Metallic Dark Blue 1126 Transporter (with Light Blue lettering and ridges),	
			150s Vanwall, 152s BRM, 154 Ferrari **£200-250**
17	1963-67	**Ferrari Racing Set**....................	438 Land Rover in Red with Green top, Red 154 Ferrari F1 on Yellow trailer, box has inner tray........**£125-150**
17	1977-80	**Military Set**	Contains 904, 906, 920 (see 'Military Vehicles' section)..**£40-50**
17	1986	**'BRITISH TELECOM'**	Ford Cargo Box Van, Ford Escort Van and a Compressor **£20-30**
18	1961-63	**Ford Tractor and Plough Set** ...	Contains 55 and 56..**£80-100**
18	1975-80	**Emergency Gift Set**	Contains 402, 481, C921 (see 'Emergency Vehicles' section)...**£60-70**
18/1	?	**3 Mini Racers Set**	with *'CHELSEA'*, *'PARK LANE'* and *'PICADILLY'* logos **£20-30**
18/2	?	**Mini Special Editions Set**..........	with *'RED HOT'*, *'RITZ'* and *'JET BLACK'* logos...**£20-30**
		Note:	C18/1 and C18/2 were sold (in long 'window' boxes) exclusively by Woolworths.	
19	1962-68	**'CHIPPERFIELDS' Cage Set**..	438 Land Rover (plastic tilt) and 607 Elephant and cage on trailer.	
			Blue/Yellow window box has inner card tray and additional packing **£175-225**
19		**'RNLI' Set**	438 Land Rover plus Orange dinghy on trailer with *'Mumbles Lifeboat'* logo....................**£60-70**
19	1972-77	**Land Rover and**		
		Nipper Aircraft	438 Land Rover (Blue/Orange) Yellow/Red or All-Orange plane '23' on trailer **£60-70**
19	1973-77	**'CORGI FLYING CLUB'**	Blue/Orange Land Rover (438) with aircraft..**£60-70**
19	1979-82	**Emergency Gift Set**	Contains C339 and C921 ....**£30-40**
19	1980-82	**Emergency Gift Set**	Contains C339 and C931 in Red/White liveries..**£35-45**
19/7	1990	**'AMBULANSE' Set**	White Ford Transit Van and Saab 9000 'POLITI' (Norwegian) **£30-40**
19/8	1990	**'AMBULANS' Set**	White/Red Ford Transit & White/Blue Saab 9000 'POLIS' (Swedish)...................................**£30-40**
19/9	1990	**Swedish Breakdown Set**...........	Red/Yellow Ford Transit *'Bjarnings'*, Black Saab 9000 *'BRANDCHEF'* **£30-40**
20	1961-64	**'Golden Guinea' Set**.................	Gold-plated 224 Bentley Continental, 234 Ford Consul, 229 Chevrolet Corvair, Catalogue,	
			2 Accessory Packs. Inner card tray with lower card packing, outer Dark Green sleeve with window **£150-175**
20	1970-73	**Tri-Deck Transporter Set**	1st issue contains 1146 Transporter with 210 'Saint's' Volvo, 311 Ford Capri, 343 Pontiac,	
		(Scammell Handyman Mk.III)	372 Lancia, 377 Marcos, 378 MGC GT (rare Orange version).	
			Instruction sheet, 'Mr Retailer' transit card protector **£500-600**
		Harrods set:	Late issue with WhizzWheels: 1146 Transporter, 382 Porsche Targa (Silver Blue),	
			313 Ford Cortina GXL (Bronze/Black), 201 Volvo (Orange 'Saint' label), 334 Mini (Orange) and	
			377 Marcos (Silver Green). Box also has instruction sheet and 'Mr Retailer' transit card protector **£500-600**
20	1978-80	**Emergency Gift Set**	Contains C429, C482, C921 (see 'Emergency Vehicles' section). Box has inner tray **£35-45**
20/2	1986	**'AA' Services Set**	Ford Escort and Transit Vans, Ford Transit Breakdown **£25-30**
20/3	1986	**'AA' Services Set**	Range Rover plus caravan 'Information Centre'..**£25-30**
21	1962-66	**ERF Dropside and Trailer**.......	456 and 101 with milk churns and self-adhesive accessories **£175-225**
21	1969-71	**'Chipperfields' Circus Set**	Contains 1144 Crane and Cage, and 1139 Menagerie Transporter,	
			internal packaging and 'Mr Dealer' box protector card **£750-1,000**
21	1980-82	**Superman Set**............................	Contains 260, 265 and 925, plus inner tray and plastic rockets on sprue **£100-125**
21/2	1986	**RAC Set**....................................	Range Rover, Ford Escort Van and Ford Transit Breakdown **£25-30**
22	1962-65	**Agricultural Set**........................	1111, 406, 51, 101, 53, 1487, 1490, accessories and GS18...**£300-400**
22	1980-82	**James Bond Set**........................	Contains 269 Lotus Esprit, 271 Aston-Martin DB5 and 649 Space Shuttle plus rockets and	
			2 spare bandit figures. Box has inner tray **£250-300**

22	1986	**'ROYAL MAIL' Set**	Ford Cargo and Escort Vans, Austin Mini Metro *'DATAPOST'*	**£25-30**
23	1962-66	**'CHIPPERFIELDS' Set**		
		1st issue:	1121 Crane Truck, 2 x 1123 Animal Cages (2 lions, 2 polar bears), plus Gift Set 19 and 426 Booking Office, (items contained in inner polystyrene tray)	**£500-750**
	1964	2nd issue:	as 1st issue but 503 'TK Giraffe Truck' replaces 426 Booking Office, inner polystyrene tray	**£400-600**
23	1980-82	**Spiderman Set**	Contains 261, 266 and 928	**£90-110**
24	1963-68	**Commer Constructor Set**	2 cab/chassis units, 4 interchangeable bodies, milkman, accessories	**£80-95**
24	1976-78	**Mercedes and Caravan**	Contains 285 in Metallic Blue plus 490 Caravan in White	**£35-45**
	1979	colour change:	285 in Metallic Brown plus 490 Caravan in Bronze	**£30-40**
25	1963-66	**BP or Shell Garage Set**	224, 225, 229, 234 and 419 all in Blue/Yellow boxes plus: 601 Batley Garage, 602 'AA' and 'RAC' Boxes, 606 Lamp Standards (2), 608 Filling Station, 609 accessories, 1505 Figures	**£1,000-1250**
25	1969-71	**Racing Car and Tender**	159 and VW Tender, 2 sets of decals in stapled bags. Blue/Yellow window box, inner plastic tray	**£120-140**
25	1980-81	**Talbot Rancho Set**	457 plus two motorcycles on trailer	**£15-20**
26	1971-76	**Beach Buggy Set**	381 plus Red Sailing Boat with Blue sail	**£30-40**
26	1981-83	**Corgi Racing Set**	457 Talbot Matra Rancho, 160 Hesketh (Yellow), 'Corgi Racing Team' trailer	**£35-45**
27	1963-72	**Priestman Shovel on Machinery Carrier**	1128 and 1131 (Bedford Machinery Carrier)	**£100-125**
27		**Emergency Set**	no details	**£15-20**
28	1963-65	**Transporter and 4 Cars**	1105 Bedford TK Transporter with 222 Renault Floride, 230 Mercedes-Benz, 232 Fiat, 234 Ford Classic, 2 dummy 'Corgi Toys' boxes, instructions. Pictorial box	**£400-500**
28	1975-78	**Mazda B1600 Dinghy Set**	493 Mazda plus dinghy and trailer	**£30-35**
28	1987	**Post Set**	Contains 656/2, Red Sierra (racing number '63') or Brown Saab 9000	**£20-25**
29	1963-66	**Massey-Ferguson Set**	Contains 50 Massey-Ferguson Tractor with driver and 51 Tipper Trailer	**£90-110**
29	1981-82	**'CORGI' Pony Club**	Contains 441 Jeep, 112 trailer, girl on pony, 3 jumps, 3 hay bales	**£55-65**
29	1975-76	**'DUCKHAMS' FI Racing Set**	Surtees Racing Set with 323 Ferrari Daytona and 150 Ferrari in Blue/Yellow *'DUCKHAMS RACING TEAM'* livery	**£75-85**
30	1973-73	**Grand Prix Gift Set**	'Kit' versions of 151 Yardley (1501), 154 JPS (1504), 152 Surtees (1502) plus 153 Surtees (1503)? in unique Norris livery. Mail order only	**£150-200**
30	1979-80	**Circus Gift Set**	Land Rover and Trailer	**£60-75**
31	1964-68	**Buick Riviera Boat Set**	245 Buick, Red boat trailer, and Dolphin Cabin Cruiser towing lady water-skier. Pictorial sleeve box with internal packing display tray around models	**£125-150**
31	1976-80	**Safari Land Rover Set**	C341 Land Rover with animal trailer, Warden and Lion. Box has inner polystyrene tray	**£55-65**
32	1965-68	**Tractor, Shovel and Trailer Set**	Contains 54 and 62	**£100-125**
32	1976-79	**Lotus Racing Set**	Black/Gold C301 Lotus Elite, and C154 JPS Lotus on trailer	**£80-100**
32	1979-83	**Lotus Racing Set**	Black/Gold C301 Lotus Elite, and C154 Texaco Lotus on trailer	**£70-85**
32	1989-90	**3 Model Set**	Contains Concorde, Taxi and Routemaster Bus 'STANDARD'	**£30-40**
33	1965-68	**Tractor and Beast Carrier**	Contains 55 and 58	**£100-125**
	1968-72		Contains 67 and 58	**£70-80**
33	1980-82	**'DLRG' Rescue Set**	White/Red 421 Land Rover and boat on trailer	**£25-30**
34	1976-79	**Tractor & Tipping Trailer**	Contains 55 and 56	**£55-65**
35	1964-68	**London Traffic Set**	418 Taxi with 468 *'Corgi Toys'* or *'Outspan'* Bus and policeman on stand. Box has inner tray	**£150-175**
35	1978-79	**'CHOPPER SQUAD' Surf Boat**	Contains 927, 419, trailer, rescue boat	**£30-40**
36	1967-70	**Marlin Rambler Set**	Contains 263 and Boat	**£45-65**
36	1967-71	**Oldsmobile Toronado Set**	Contains 276 (Greenish-Blue) Chrome trailer, Yellow/Blue boat, 3 figures	**£120-140**
36	1983	**Off-Road Set**	447 (Dark Blue/Cream, racing number '5') plus power-boat on trailer	**£25-35**
36	1976-78	**Tarzan Set**	Light Green 421 Land Rover and trailer, paler Green 'zebra' stripes, Tarzan, Jane, Cheetah (chimp), boy, dinghy with hunter, elephant, snake, vines, etc	**£140-160**
37	1966-69	**'Lotus Racing Team'**	490 VW Breakdown Truck, Red trailer with cars 318, 319, 155, plus 2 sets of spare racing numbers ('5' and '9' or '4' and '8'), a 1966 illustrated checklist, a sealed pack of cones, set of bollards and a spare Lotus chassis unit	**£250-300**
37	1979-80	**Fiat X-19 Set**	Fiat X-19 and Boat 'Carlsberg'	**£30-40**
38	1977-78	**Mini 1000 Camping Set**	Cream Mini with 2 figures, tent, barbecue in inner display stand	**£90-110**
38	1965-67	**'1965 Monte Carlo Rally'**	318 Mini Cooper 'S', 322 Rover 2000, and 326 Citroën DS19. Monte Carlo Rally emblem on each bonnet. Box contains pictorial stand and inner card packing	**£400-500**
38	1980-	**Jaguar XJS Set**	319 with Powerboat on Trailer	**£20-30**
40	1966-69	**The Avengers Set**	John Steed's Bentley (Green body, Red wire wheels), Emma Peel's Lotus Elan (Black/White body), John Steed and Emma Peel figures, 3 Black umbrellas. Inner pictorial stand	**£500-600**
			As previous set but Bentley in Red/Black livery with Silver wire wheels	**£400-500**
40	1976-82	**Batman Gift Set**	Contains modified 107 Trailer plus 267 Batmobile (WhizzWheels) and 925 Helicopter, box has inner tray with card packing	**£200-300**
41	1966-68	**Carrimore Car Transporter with Ford Tilt Cab**	1138 Transporter (Red/Two-tone Blue), 252 Rover 2000 (Metallic Plum), 251 Hillman Imp (Metallic Bronze), 440 Ford Cortina Estate (Metallic Blue), 204 Morris Mini-Minor (Light Blue), 321 Austin Mini Cooper 'S' (Red, RN '2', '1966 Monte Carlo Rally', with roof signatures), 249 Morris Mini Cooper 'S' (Black/Red, 'wickerwork' panels). Only sold by mail order	**£500-750**
41	1977-81	**Silver Jubilee Set**	The State Landau with HRH Queen Elizabeth and Prince Phillip (and a Corgi!)	**£15-20**
42	1978-79	**Agricultural Set**	Contains 55 David Brown Tractor plus 56 Trailer, Silo and Elevator	**£45-55**
43	1979-80	**Silo and Conveyor Set**	Silo and Conveyor *'CORGI HARVESTING COMPANY LTD'*	**£40-50**

43	1985	'TOYMASTER' Set	C496 *'ROYAL MAIL'*, C515 'BMX' and Volvo 'TOYMASTER' truck	£20-25
44	1978-80	Metropolitan Police Set	421 Land Rover, 112 Horsebox plus Policeman on horse	£55-65
45	1966	'All Winners' Set	261 James Bond's Aston-Martin, 310 Chevrolet Stingray, 324 Marcos Volvo, 325 Ford Mustang Competition, 314 Ferrari Berlinetta 9,000 sets sold	£300-400
45	1978-79	Royal Canadian Police Set	RCMP Land Rover (421), Trailer (102) and 'Mountie' on horse	£85-95
46	1966-69	'All Winners' Set	264 Oldsmobile Toronado (Metallic Blue), 307 Jaguar 'E'-type (Chrome finish, RN '2', driver), 314 Ferrari Berlinetta (Red, RN '4'), 337 Chevrolet Stingray (Yellow, RN '13'), 327 MGB GT (Red/Black, suitcase). Box should contain unopened bag of cones and unused decal sheets	£225-275
46	1982	Super Karts Set	Two Karts: one Red, one Purple, with Silver/Red driver in each	NGPP
47	1966-71	Ford 5000 Tractor and Conveyor Set	Contains 67, trailer with conveyor belt, figure, accessories plus inner display card	£140-160
47	1978-80	Pony Club Set	421 Land Rover and Horsebox in Metallic Bronze, girl on pony figure	£25-30
48	1967-68	Carrimore Car Transporter with Ford Tilt Cab	1138 Transporter (Orange/Silver/Two-tone Blue) with 252 Rover 2000 (Metallic Maroon), 251 Hillman Imp, 440 Ford Cortina Estate, 180 Morris Mini Cooper 'S' (with 'wickerwork' panels), 204 Morris Mini-Minor (Metallic Maroon), 321 Mini Cooper 'S' ('1966 Monte Carlo Rally'), Red/White, RN '2'	£250-300
	1968	'SUN/RAC' variation	As previous set but 321 Mini Cooper is replaced by 333 SUN/RAC Rally Mini. Also 251 Hillman Imp is changed to Metallic Gold with White stripe and the 204 Mini Minor is now Metallic Blue with RN '21'	£350-450
48	1969	Carrimore Car Transporter with Scammell Cab	1148 Transporter (Red/White) with 378 MGB (Yellow/Black), 340 Sunbeam Imp (1967 Monte Carlo, Metallic Blue, RN '77'), 201 Saint's Volvo P1800 (White with Orange label), 180 Morris Mini Cooper 'S' (with 'wickerwork' panels), 339 Mini Cooper 'S' ('1967 Monte Carlo Rally', RN '177'), 204 Morris Mini-Minor (Metallic Maroon), plus sealed bag of cones and leaflet	£500-600
48	1978-80	'PINDER' Circus Set	Contains C426, C1163, C30, ringmaster, artistes, animals, seating, and cardboard cut-out 'Big-Top' circus tent	£100-125
48/1	1986	Racing Set	C100/2 plus 576/2	£20-25
49	1978-80	'CORGI FLYING CLUB'	Metallic Green/White Jeep (419) with Blue/White Tipsy Nipper Aircraft	£50-60
51		'100 Years of the Car' Set	3 Mercedes: C805 (White) C806 (Black) C811 (Red) (Originally for Germany)	£20-25
?	1978-80	'The Jaguar Collection'	C804 (Cream), C816 (Red), C318 (Mobil Green/White). ('UNIPART' stores)	£30-35
54	1978-80	Swiss Rega Set	Bonna Ambulance and Helicopter	£30-35
55	1978-80	Norway Emergency Set	Police Car, Breakdown Truck, Ford Transit Ambulance, 'UTRYKKNINGUSSETT'	£20-30
56	1978-80	Swedish Set	Ford Sierra 'POLIS', Bonna Ambulance	£12-18
57	1978-80	Swedish Set	Contains Volvo and Caravan	£12-18
57	1978-80	Volvo 740 and Caravan	Red Volvo, White/Red/Blue Caravan Swedish export set	£15-20
61	1978-80	Swiss 'FEUERWEHR' Set	1120 Dennis Fire Engine, Sierra 'POLITZEI', Escort Van 'NOTRUF'	£30-35
62	1986	Swiss Services Set	C564 *'PTT'*, Box Van *'DOMICILE'*, VW Polo *'PTT'* Export Set	£20-25
63	1986	French Set	Bonna Ambulance, Peugeot 505, Renault 5 'POLICE', 'INTERVENTION'	£30-35
63	1986	Emergency Set	Mercedes Ambulance (White body, Blue designs and roof lights, Fire Chief Car (*'Sapeurs Pompiers'*) 'POLICE' Car (White body, Black doors, Blue roof light)	NGPP
64	1965-69	FC Jeep 150 and Conveyor Belt	Jeep (409) Yellow/White Conveyor	£40-45
65	1978-80	Norway Set	Ford Transit Ambulance plus Helicopter	£20-30
67 /n	1978-80	Cyclists Sets	Sold in France, 2 Cars, 2 Bicycles. Three sets: 67/1, 67/2, 67/3	Each set: £20-30
70	1978-80	Danish 'FALCK' Set	Bonna Ambulance and Ford Breakdown Truck	£20-30
72	1978-80	Norway Set	Contains C542 plus Helicopter *'LN OSH'*	£20-30
73/1	1990	Swedish 'POLIS' Set	White/Blue Volvo 740 and Red/White Jet Ranger Helicopter	£20-30
330/2-5		Mini 30th Anniversary	4 Minis (*'ROSE'*, *'SKY'*, *'FLAME'* and *'RACING'*), interior colours vary	£40-50
?		Mini 30th Anniversary	Model of a Mini with Anniversary Book	£35-45
330/6-9		Four Mini Set	Silver (*'CITY'*), Blue (*'MAYFAIR'*), Maroon (*'MAYFAIR'*), Yellow (*'CITY'*)	£20-30
1151	1970	Scammell 'Co-op' Set	Contains 1147, 466 & 462 in Blue/White livery Promotional in brown box	£150-175
1412	?	Swiss Police Set	Range Rover and Helicopter *'POLITZEI'*	£18-22
?	1967	Monte Carlo Game	Fernel Developments game with two Lavender 226 Minis, '1967 Rallye Monte Carlo' bonnet labels, RNs 1 and 4, plastic/paper winding roads, cards, dice shakers, Blue/White/Red box. Set made for the Scandinavian market	£250-350
?	1985	Wiltshire Fire Brigade	Dennis Fire Escape plus Escort Van both in red (650)	£45-55
?	1985	Race Team Set	'ADMIRAL ENERGY GROUP Ltd' logos on 501 Range Rover (White), Porsche 956 (White) on trailer	£35-45
?	1980	Construction Site Set	Contains 54 with 440 (Mazda Pick-Up)	£30-35
?	1988	'ROYAL MAIL' Set	Post Office Display Set not sold to the public includes 611, 612 and 496 Escort Vans, 613, 614 and 615 Metro Vans, 616 General Motors (Chevrolet) Van, 421/1 Land Rover and 618 Mercedes-Benz Artic, plus Juniors 39, 90/1/2/3/4	£500-750
?	1992	Set of 4 Minis	Black ('Check'), White ('Designer'), Red ('Cooper'), Metallic Blue ('Neon')	£12-14

NB See also Marks & Spencers Gift Set issues at the end of the Cars section.

Buses, Minibuses and Coaches

(Excluding models issued as 'CORGI CLASSICS')
Only models thought to have been 100% produced by Corgi have been included in the listings.

Identification of Routemaster Double-Decker Bus models

1ST CASTING, 1964 - 1975
MODEL No. 468 ONLY – CLOSED TOP MODEL
Length 114 mm, die-cast body comprised of two separate castings which make up the lower and upper decks. The castings are separated by a white plastic joint.

The baseplate is die-cast, painted grey and stamped 'Corgi Toys', 'LONDON TRANSPORT', 'ROUTEMASTER', 'MADE IN ENGLAND' plus the Patent No. 904525. The early issues had turned metal wheels with rubber tyres. These lasted until 1973 when cast metal wheels were introduced with plastic tyres and in 1974/75 WhizzWheels were seen.

Early issues also had jewelled headlights which were replaced in 1973 by the cast-in type painted silver. The decals are of the transfer printed variety and there is a board at the front only. The model has spring suspension, windows, a metal platform handrail and a driver and clippie. The interior seats are white or cream.

2ND CASTING, 1975 ONWARDS
CLOSED TOP AND OPEN TOP MODELS
MODEL Nos: C460, C463, C464, C467, C469, C470, C471, C473, C475, C476, C477, C479, C480, 1004 and all the numbers allocated to the 'Specials'. Length 123 mm, die-cast body comprised of two separate castings which make up the lower and upper decks. The castings are separated by a cream plastic joint for normal issues and very often by a coloured joint for 'Specials'. Until Model No. 480 was issued as an AEC Renown in 1983 the plastic baseplates were stamped 'CORGI', 'LONDON TRANSPORT', 'ROUTEMASTER' and 'MADE IN ENGLAND'. However 'LONDON TRANSPORT' and 'ROUTEMASTER' were removed from this time onwards.

The logos were originally stick-on labels followed by tampo printing in the mid-eighties. The seats were normally white or cream but other colours are used for the 'Specials' (eg. Red in the 'BRITISH DIE-CAST MODEL TOYS CATALOGUE' Special). The model has silver painted cast-in headlights, spring suspension, windows, a metal platform handrail but apart from the very early issues does not have a driver or clippie. The wheels are of the WhizzWheel type. The early issues were of a close fitting type e.g. 'BTA', 'SWAN & EDGAR', 'DISNEYLAND'. However by the time the model was issued they had become protruding. The wheel hubs are either chrome (earlier models) or painted with plastic tyres.

Ref	Year(s)	Model name	Colours, fleetnames, details	Market Price Range

Routemaster Buses, 1964-1975, (1st casting)

Ref	Year(s)	Model name	Colours, fleetnames, details	Market Price Range
468	1964-66	'NATURALLY CORGI'	Red, London Transport, *CORGI CLASSICS*	£60-70
468	1964	'NATURALLY CORGI'	Green/Cream/Brown, (Australian) 'NEW SOUTH WALES', *CORGI CLASSICS*	£500-750
468	1966	'RED ROSE TEA & COFFEE'	Red body, driver and clippie, 1st type box, Canadian promotional	£150-200
468	1967	'OUTSPAN ORANGES'	Green/Cream/Brown body, Australian issue	£150-200
468	1967-75	'OUTSPAN ORANGES'	Red, London Transport, 10, (diecast or WhizzWheels)	£40-50
468	1968	'GAMAGES'	Red, London Transport, '10'	£150-175
468	1969	'CHURCH'S SHOES'	Red, London Transport, '10', Union Jacks	£110-130
468	1970	'MADAME TUSSAUDS'	Red, London Transport, '10'	£90-110
468	1975	'THE DESIGN CENTRE'	Red, London Transport, '10'	£50-60
468	?	'cokerchu', '2d'	Red, London Transport, promotional	£110-130

Routemaster Buses, 1975 – 1983, (2nd casting)

Ref	Year(s)	Model name	Colours, fleetnames, details	Market Price Range
C467	1977	'SELFRIDGES'	Red, London Transport, '12'. Box 1 – standard; Box 2 – 'SELFRIDGES' own	£20-25
C469	1975-76	'BTA WELCOME TO BRITAIN'	Red, London Transport, '11', driver, clippie	£15-20
C469	1976	'THE DESIGN CENTRE'	Red, London Transport, '11', driver, clippie, *Visit The Design Centre* in black or red	£110-130
C469	1977	'CADBURYS'	Orange, *Cadburys Double Decker*, on-pack offer, special box	£12-18
C469	1979	'SELFRIDGES'	Red, London Transport, '12'. Re-issue of C467 (see above)	£20-25
C469	1979	'LEEDS PERMANENT BUILDING SOCIETY'	'LEEDS', '22'	£15-20
C469	1979	'SWAN & EDGAR'	Red, London Transport, '11'	£25-35
C469	1979	'HAMLEYS'	Red, London Transport, '11'	£15-20
C469	1980	'HAMLEYS'	Five clowns advert., '6'	£10-15
C469	1978-80	'BTA'	Red, London Transport, ('7', '11' or '12')	£10-15
C469	1982	'BLACKPOOL'	Cream/Green, 'Blackpool Illuminations', '21'	£30-40
C469	1983	'GAMLEYS'	Red, *Toyshop Of The South*	£10-15
C469	1983	'EAGLE STAR'	White/Black, '1 Threadneedle Street'	£10-15
C469	1983	'REDGATES'	Cream/Brown (Red seats) '25'	£30-40
C469	1983	'L.T. GOLDEN JUBILEE'	Red/White/Silver, 21, *1933-1983*, (1,000)	£30-40
C469	1983	'BLACKPOOL PLEASURE BEACH'	Cream/Green, Blackpool Transport, '23', *Britain's No.1 Tourist Attraction*	£35-45
C469	1983	Open-top version:	As previous model but with open top	£50-55
C469	1983	'NORBROOK MOTORS'	Dark Blue (White seats) route '57'	£12-18
C469	1983	colour change:	As previous model but Red version	£12-18
C469	1983	'DION DION'	Dark Blue, *Saves You More* in Orange	£10-15
		South African issue:	has incorrect label *Saves You Money*	£15-20
C469	1983	'THORNTONS'	Brown/Cream, route '14'	£10-15
C469	1983	'MANCHESTER LIONS'	Cream, route '105BN Manchester'	£15-20
C469	1984	'NEW CORGI COMPANY'	Red, '29th March 1984', *South Wales - De Cymru*, (2,000)	£15-20
C469	?	'COBHAM BUS MUSEUM'	no details	£25-35
C470	1977	'DISNEYLAND'	Yellow Open Top, Disney characters	£10-15
C471	1977	'SEE MORE LONDON'	Silver, '25', *The Queens Silver Jubilee London Celebrations 1977*	£10-15
C471	1977	'WOOLWORTHS'	Silver, '25', *Woolworths Welcome The World* & *Queens Silver Jubilee 1977*	£20-30
C638	1989	'Great Book of CORGI'	Yellow/Blue, '1956-1983'. Originally only available with book	£25-35

Other 2nd casting Routemaster Buses, (1975 onwards)

C460 'BOLTON EVENING NEWS'	C469 'OLD SMUGGLER'	C527 'TIMBERCRAFT CABINETS'
C463 'BRITISH MEAT'	C469 'BTA'	C529 '1985 CALENDAR BUS'
C464 'BRITISH MOTOR SHOW'	C469 'LONDON STANDARD'	C530 'YORKSHIRE POST'
C469 'DIECAST and TINPLATE'	C469 'ANDREX'	C558 'RADIO VICTORY'
C469 'JOLLY GIANT'	C469 'TAYLOR & McKINNA'	C566 'GELCO EXPRESS'
C469 'GLOUCESTER TOY SALE'	C469 'TDK CASSETTES'	C567 'LINCOLN CITY'
C469 'ARMY AND NAVY'	C469 'WORLD AIRWAYS'	C567 'SEE MORE LONDON'
C469 'MANCHESTER UNITED'	C469 'LINCOLN CITY'	C570 'BUS COLLECTORS SOCIETY'
C469 'LLANDINDROD'	C473 'GAMLEYS'	C571 'The TIMES'
C469 'TROWBRIDGE TOYS'	C475 'TAKE OFF FROM BRISTOL'	C572 'The TIMES'
C469 'MANCHESTER EVENING NEWS'	C476 'BRITISH TELECOM'	C574 'BLACKPOOL CENTENARY'
C469 'ROUND LONDON'	C476 'CULTURE BUS'	C580 'GUIDE DOGS'
C469 'BTA WELCOME'	C476 'WHITE LABEL WHISKY'	C583 'MANCHESTER EVENING NEWS'
C469 'BRITISH TOY'	C477 'THE BUZBY BUS'	C589 'AUTOSPARES'
C469 'JOHN WEBB'	C478 'SUNDECKER'	C590 'MEDIC ALERT'
C469 'TWINNINGS'	C479 'LONDON CRUSADER'	C591 'MEDIC ALERT'
C469 'STRETTON SPRING WATER'	C480 'WHITE LABEL WHISKY'	C591 'ROLAND FRIDAY'
C469 'READING EXPRESS'	C481 'BEA'	C596 'HARRODS'
C469 'LIVERPOOL GARDEN FESTIVAL'	C482 'LEEDS PERMANENT	C625 'CITYRAMA'
C469 'HAMLEYS'	BUILDING SOCIETY'	C627 'MODEL MOTORING'
C469 'GEMINI DIECAST'	C483 'HMV SHOP'	C628 'POLCO PLUS'
C469 'BTA'	C485 'I. O. W. COUNTY PRESS'	C633 'HOSPITAL RADIO'
C469 'MIDLAND BUS MUSEUM'	C485 'ML ELECTRICS'	C638 'WEETABIX'
C469 'GREAT WESTERN RAILWAY'	C486 'THE CULTURE BUS'	32401
C469 'ESSEX ORGAN STUDIOS'	C488 'NEW CORGI COMPANY'	32402
C469 'FAREWELL TO ROE'	C488 'BEATTIES'	32403
C469 'HAMLEYS'	C492 'GLOBAL SALES'	32705
C469 'HAMLEYS' (Open Top)	C521 'HAIG WHISKY'	91765 'CROSVILLE'
C469 'UNDERWOODS'	C523 'BRITISH DIE-CAST	91766
C469 'JUST A SECOND'	MODEL TOYS CATALOGUE'	
C469 'COWES STAMP and MODEL SHOP'	C524 'STEVENSONS'	

Routemasters difficult to catalogue

Shortly before and after Mettoy ceased trading during the period 1982-84 the following models were all given a '469' number and were issued in rapid succession in many different colour variations

The models were normally issued as a closed-top version but some will also be found as open-tops as well. These (open-tops) were issued in either an orange or yellow livery with often a 'BOURNEMOUTH' fleetname. The Route numbers seen were usually '14' or '24'. Corgi have referred to this period as the 'oddball patch'.

The models are: 'OLD HOLBORN', 'OXO', 'AERO', 'TDK', 'LION BAR', 'BARRATT', 'WORLD AIRWAYS', 'PENTEL', 'BUY BEFORE YOU FLY - DUTY FREE'.

The colours seen: Brown/Cream, Blue/Cream, Green/Yellow, Blue, Green, Black, Cream, White.

Fleetnames were not used on the majority of these issues with the following exceptions:
'TAYSIDE' ('Barratt', 'Oxo', 'Aero')
'TRANSCLYDE' ('World Airways', 'Buy Before You Fly')
'SOUTH YORKS' ('TDK', 'World Airways')
'LONDON TRANSPORT' ('Lion Bar', 'Oxo', 'Aero').

Model No 470 was issued bearing the 'LONDON COUNTRY' fleetname in respect of 'Barratt', 'Pentel', 'Buy Before You Fly', 'TDK', and no doubt others. It is known that at the time of Mettoy going into receivership batches of labels were sold off to the trade which no doubt accounts for many of the different variations to be found.

Therefore with this background it is not possible to provide meaningful price and rarity guidance.

Customer-Exclusive models

These models are listed for the sake of completeness but there is little real opportunity of collectors obtaining them as very few were issued (usually 50 or less).

C468 'RED ROSE COFFEE'	C469 'VEDES VISIT TO SWANSEA'	C469 'MARRIOT HOTELS'
C469 'METTOY SALES CONFERENCE'	C469 'MARKS & SPENCER VISIT SWANSEA'	C469 'CHARLIE'S ANGELS'
C469 'MGMW DINNER'	C469 'HAROLD LYCHES VISIT'	C469 'CORGI COLLECTORS VISIT'
C469 'QUALITOYS VISIT'	C469 'METTOY WELCOMES SWISS	C469 'REDDITCH'
	BUYERS to SWANSEA'	C469 'SKYRIDER BUS COLLECTORS'
	(Sold for **£450** by Vectis, 10/96)	C469 'WHATMAN PAPER'
	C469 'FINNISH VISIT to SWANSEA'	C469 'COLT 45 CONFERENCE'
	C469 'MGMW DINNER'	C469 'SKYRIDER'
	C469 'OCTOPUSSY'	C461 'MANNHEIM VISIT 1986'

Electronic issues

1004 1981 **'CORGITRONICS'** .... 'FIRST in ELECTRONIC DIE-CAST', Red, London Transport, '11' **£15-20**
Other issues will be found combining 'BTA', 'HAMLEYS', 'OXO', etc with the 'CORGITRONICS' logo. See that section for details.

Metrobus Mk.2 Double-Decker Bus issued 1988-96

Market Price Range as shown,
otherwise under £15

C675/1	'WEST MIDLANDS TIMESAVER'	**£15-20**	
C675/2	'READING TRANSPORT GOLDLINE'	**£15-20**	
C675/3	'WEST MIDLANDS TRAVEL'	**£15-20**	
C675/4	'BEATTIES'		
C675/5	'THE BEE LINE'		
C675/6	'YORKSHIRE TRACTION'		
C675/7	'WEST MIDLANDS'		
C675/9	'NEWCASTLE BUSWAYS'		
C675/10	'LONDON TRANSPORT'		
Q675/12	'MAIDSTONE'		
Q675/13	'EAST KENT'		
Q675/14	'GM BUSES'		
Q675/15	'NATIONAL GARDEN FESTIVAL'		
C676/16	'STRATHCLYDE'		
91702	'AIRBUS'		
91848	'YORKSHIRE RIDER'		
91851	'READING'		
91852	'STEVENSONS'		
91853	'BRADFORD'		
91854	'HALIFAX'		
91855	'WEST YORKS'		
91856	'SUNDERLAND'		
91857	'NEWCASTLE'		
91858	'LEEDS'		
91859	'WY PTE'		
91860	'HUDDERSFIELD TRAMWAYS'		
91861	'TODMORDEN'		
91862	'BRADFORD CENTENARY'		
91863	'HUDDERSFIELD'		
91864	'GREY & GREEN'		
91865	'YORKS RIDER'		
97051	'INVICTAWAY'	GSP	
97064	'ROLLER COASTER'	GSP	
97065	'STAGECOACH'	GSP	
97802	'TRANSIT' (Sunbeam Models)		

Plaxton Paramount Coaches issued 1985-96

Market Price Range as shown,
otherwise under £15

C769	'NATIONAL EXPRESS'	**£20-30**
C769	'CLUB CANTABRICA'	**£60-70**
C769/4	'SAS'	**£15-20**
C769/5	'GLOBAL'	**£15-20**
C769/6	'POHJOLAN LIIKENNE'	**£50-75**
C769/7	'SCOTTISH CITYLINK'	
C769/8	'BLUEBIRD EXPRESS'	
C770	'HOLIDAY TOURS'	**£20-25**
C771	'AIR FRANCE'	**£20-25**
C771	'SAS'	
C773	'GREEN LINE'	
C774	'RAILAIR LINK'	**£25-30**
C774	'ALDER VALLEY'	
C775	'CITY LINK'	
C776	'SKILLS SCENICRUISERS'	
C777	'TAYLORS TRAVEL'	**£25-30**
C791	'SWISS PTT'	**£25-30**
C792	'GATWICK FLIGHTLINE'	**£15-20**
C793/1	'INTASUN EXPRESS'	**£20-25**
C1223	'PHILIPS'	
91908	'SAS'	
91909	'FINNAIR'	
91911	'APPLEBY'	
91913	'VOYAGER PLAXTON'	
91914	'SPEEDLINK'	
91915	'TELLUS'	
91916	'EAST YORKS'	
91917	'HIGHWAYMAN'	**£20-25**
91918	'SOUTHEND'	
91919	'SHEARINGS'	
91920	'NOTTINGHAM'	
97051	'INVICTAWAY'	GSP
97064	'SEAGULL'	GSP
97065	'STAGECOACH'	GSP

Ford Transit Minibus issued 1988-89

Market Price Range **£5-10**

C676/1	'BLUEBIRD'	
C676/2	'SOUTH WALES TRANSPORT'	
C676/3	'BADGERLINE'	
C676/4	'FALCK SYGETRANSPORT'	
C676/5	'ROYAL MAIL'	
C676/6	'CHASERIDER'	
C676/7	'BRITISH AIRWAYS'	
C676/10	'AMBULANS'	
C676/11	'POLIS'	
C676/12	'OXFORD'	
701	'INTER-CITY'	

Major Models – Coaches

1120	1961-62	'MIDLAND RED COACH'	Mid-Red body, Black roof, Lemon interior, flat spun hubs	**£55-65**
			Dark Red body, Black roof, Lemon interior, spun hubs	**£65-75**
C1168	1983	'GREYHOUND'	Red/White/Blue, 'Americruiser'	**£15-20**
C1168	1983	'MOTORWAY EXPRESS'	White/Brown/Yellow/Red, Limited Edition	**£10-15**
C1168	1983	'EURO EXPRESS'	White/Red/Blue, Limited Edition	**£15-20**
C1168	1983	'ROVER BUS'	Blue, 'Chesham Toy and Model Fair', LE	**£10-15**
			As previous model but Cream body	**£20-25**
C1168	1983	SWISS 'PTT'	Confirmation required - was this issued?	NGPP

Miscellaneous

508	1968-69	Commer 2500 Minibus	Orange/White/Green body, 'HOLIDAY CAMP' logo	**£45-55**

Collectors notes

Corgi Kits

601	1961-68	Batley 'LEOFRIC' Garage	£20-25
602	1961-66	'A.A.' and 'RAC' Telephone Boxes	£50-60
603	1961-66	Silverstone Pits	£30-40
604	1961-66	Silverstone Press Box	£50-60
605	1963-67	Silverstone Club House and Timekeepers Box	£60-70
606	1961-66	Lamp Standards (2)	£5-10
607	1963-67	Circus Elephant and Cage	£45-55
608	1963-66	'SHELL' Filling Station Building	£35-45
609	1963-66	'SHELL' Filling Station Forecourt Accessories	£25-35
610	1963-66	Metropolitan Police Box and Public Telephone Kiosk	£60-70
611	1963-66	Motel Chalet	£25-35

Spare wheels for 'Take-off Wheels' models; bubble-packed on card.

1341	1970	for 344 Ferrari Dino Sport. Shown in 1969 catalogue but model issued with WhizzWheels	£10-15
1342	1968	for 300 Chevrolet Corvette	£10-15
1351	1968	for 275 Rover 2000 TC	£10-15
1352	1968	for 276 Oldsmobile Toronado	£10-15
		for 338 Chevrolet Camaro	£10-15
		for 343 Pontiac Firebird. Shown in 1969 catalogue but model not issued with 'Take-off Wheels'	£10-15
1353	1970	for 342 Lamborghini P400	£10-15
		for 302 Hillman Hunter Rally	£10-15
1354	1970	for 273 Rolls Royce Silver Shadow	£10-15
1361	1968	for 341 Mini Marcos GT 850. (This was the first 'Take-Off Wheels' model)	£10-15

Corgi 'Cargoes' Bubble-packed on card.

1485	1960	Lorry Load - Planks	£10-15
1486	1960	Lorry Load - Bricks	£10-15
1487	1960	Lorry Load - Milk Churns	£10-15
1488	1960	Lorry Load - Cement	£10-15
1490	1960	Skip and 3 Churns	£10-15

Figures

1501	1963-69	Racing Drivers and Pit Mechanics (6)	£10-15
1502	1963-69	Silverstone Spectators (6)	£10-15
1503	1963-69	Race Track Officials (6)	£10-15
1504	1963-69	Press Officials (6)	£10-15
1505	1963-69	Garage Attendants (6)	£10-15

Self-adhesive accessories

1460	1959	'A' Pack (66 items) including Tax Discs, Number Plates, 'GB' and 'Running-In' labels, etc	£10-15
1461	1959	'B' Pack (36 items) including White-wall tyre trim, 'Styla Sportsdiscs', Number Plates, etc	£10-15
1462	1959	'C' Pack (69 items) including Number Plates, Commercial & Road Fund Licences (A, B and C), 20 and 30mph Speed Limit and Trailer Plates, etc	£10-15
1463	1959	'D' Pack (100 items) including Number Plates, 'Corps Diplomatique' and 'L' Plates, Touring Pennants, etc	£10-15
1464	1961	'E' Pack (86 items) including Assorted Badges, Take-Off Wheels, Trade and Licence Plates, etc	£10-15

Spare tyre packs

1449	1970-71	New Standard 15 mm	£10-15
1450	1958-70	Standard 15 mm	£10-15
1451	1961-70	Utility Vehicles 17 mm	£10-15
1452	1961-70	Major Models 19 mm	£10-15
1453	1965-70	Mini Cars 13 mm	£10-15
1454	1967-70	Tractor wheels (Rear) 33 mm	£10-15
1455	1967-70	Tractor wheels (Front) 19 mm	£10-15
1456	1967-70	Racing wheels (Rear) 16 mm	£10-15
1457	1967-70	Racing wheels (Front) 14 mm	£10-15
1458	1967-70	Commercial (Large) 24 mm	£10-15
1459	1967-70	Commercial (Medium) 19 mm	£10-15

Miscellaneous

1401	1958-60	Service Ramp (operable)	£15-20
1445	1962	Spare Red bulb for 437 Ambulance	£2-3
1441	1963	Spare Blue bulb for 464 Police Van	£2-3
1443	1967	Red flashing bulb for 437 Ambulance	£2-3
1444	1967	Blue flashing bulb for 464 Police Van	£2-3
1445	1967	Spare bulb for 'TV' in 262 Lincoln	£2-3
1446	1970	Spare tyres for 1150 Snowplough	£2-3
1480	1959	Spare nose cone for Corporal Missile	£2-3
1497	1967	James Bond Spares (2 Bandits and lapel badge for 261)	£15-25
1498	1967	James Bond Spares (Pack of missiles for 336 Toyota)	£10-15
1499	1967	Green Hornet Spares (Pack of missiles and scanners for 268)	£10-15
?	1960s	Corgi Club Badge. Gold Corgi dog on Red background	£20-25
?	1962-64	Corgi Garage in Bright Blue, Yellow, Red and White livery, 'SKYPARK' and 'CENTRAL PARK GARAGE' logos	£300-400

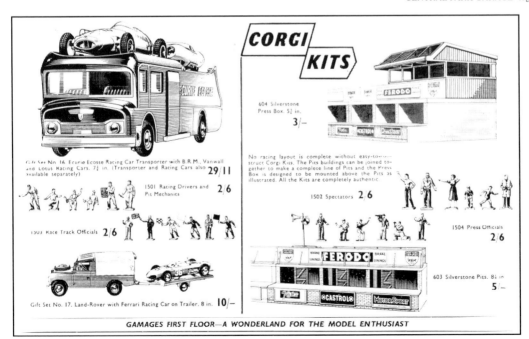

A page from an early 1960s Gamages catalogue illustrating some of the Corgi accessories that were available.

'Husky' models were introduced by Mettoy Playcraft in 1965 to compete with the Matchbox 1-75 range. These small-scale models have plenty of detail and action-features and the range includes cars, commercials, military and Film/TV specials.

The models have either a plastic or die-cast chassis together with various types of regular wheels and WhizzWheels. Models could only be obtained from 'Woolworths' stores and were only sold in blister packs. Production under the 'Husky' trade name ceased in 1969 and the range was reissued in 1970 as 'Corgi Juniors'. To facilitate this change, 'HUSKY' was removed from the baseplates which were then re-engraved 'CORGI JUNIORS'.

The models were mostly fitted with 'WhizzWheels' to enable them to be used on the 'Rocket Track' and to compete against the new Matchbox 'Superfast' range. Corgi Juniors were blister packed on blue/white card for the 'regular' issues and red/white card for the 'specials'. Each pack incorporated a 'Collectors Card' picture of the real vehicle and these could be cut out and pasted into a special collectors album.

The Market Price Range shown for 'Husky' and 'Corgi Juniors' refers only to mint condition models in unopened blister packs.

Ref	Year	Model name	Colours, features, details	Market Price Range

Husky models issued 1965-1969

Ref	Year	Model name	Colours, features, details	Market Price Range
1-a1	1965-66	Jaguar Mk.10 (small casting)	Metallic Blue, Yellow interior, Grey plastic wheels	£20-25
1-a2	1966	Jaguar Mk.10 (small casting)	Red, Yellow interior, Grey plastic wheels	£40-45
1-b1	1967	Jaguar Mk.10	Light Metallic Blue, Yellow interior, Grey plastic wheels	£20-25
1-b2	1967	Jaguar Mk.10	Blue, Yellow interior, Grey plastic wheels	£25-30
1-b3	1968	Jaguar Mk.10	Light Metallic Blue, Yellow interior, tyres	£25-30
1-b4	1968	Jaguar Mk.10	Cream, Yellow interior, tyres	£45-55
1-b5	1969	Jaguar Mk.10	Dark Blue, Yellow interior, tyres	£25-30
1-b6	1969	Jaguar Mk.10	Dark Maroon, Yellow interior, tyres	£30-35
2-a1	1965-66	Citroën Safari with Boat (small casting)	Pale Yellow, Tan boat, Grey plastic wheels	£20-25
2-b1	1967	Citroën Safari with Boat	Metallic Green, Brown boat, Yellow interior, Grey plastic wheels	£45-50
2-b2	1967	Citroën Safari with Boat	Metallic Gold, Blue boat, Yellow interior, Grey plastic wheels	£40-45
2-b3	1968-69	Citroën Safari with Boat	Metallic Gold, Blue boat, tyres	£20-25
3-a1	1965-67	Mercedes 220	Pale Blue, Yellow interior, Grey plastic wheels	£15-20
3-bt	1967-68	Volkswagen Police Car	White/Black doors, smooth hubs with tyres	£25-30
3-b2	1969	Volkswagen Police Car	White/Black doors, detailed hubs with tyres	£25-30
4-a1	1965-66	Jaguar Fire Chief (small casting)	Red, chrome siren, 'Fire' labels on doors, Yellow interior, Grey plastic wheels	£25-30
4-b1	1967	Jaguar Fire Chief	Red, chrome siren, 'Fire' labels on doors, Yellow interior, Grey plastic wheels	£25-30
4-b2	1968-69	Jaguar Fire Chief	Red, chrome siren, 'Fire' labels on doors, Yellow interior, tyres	£30-35
5-a1	1965	Lancia Flaminia	Red, Yellow interior, Grey plastic wheels	£40-45
5-a2	1965-66	Lancia Flaminia	Blue, Yellow interior, Grey plastic wheels	£15-20
5-b1	1967-69	Willys Jeep	Metallic Green, Grey windshield	£15-20
5-b2	1967-69	Willys Jeep	Metallic Green, Yellow windshield, tyres	£25-30
6-a1	1965-67	Citroën Safari Ambulance	White, Red Cross, Blue warning lights, Grey plastic wheels	£20-25
6-b1	1968-69	Ferrari Berlinetta	Red, Red interior, chrome engine, tyres	£25-30
6-b2	1968-69	Ferrari Berlinetta	Maroon, Red interior, chrome engine, tyres	£25-30
7-a1	1965-66	Buick Electra	Orange-Red, Yellow interior, Grey plastic wheels	£15-20
7-b1	1967	Duple Vista 25 Coach	Green/White, tinted windows, Yellow interior, Grey plastic wheels	£20-25
7-b2	1968-69	Duple Vista 25 Coach	Green/White, tinted windows, Yellow interior, tyres	£20-25
8-a1	1965-66	Ford Thunderbird	Pink, Black open body, Yellow interior, Grey plastic wheels	£20-25
8-b1	1967	Ford Thunderbird Hardtop	Yellow, Blue detachable hard top, Yellow interior, Grey plastic wheels	£30-35
8-c1	1967-69	Tipping Farm Trailer	Yellow, Red back, tyres	£10-15
9-a1	1965-67	Buick Police Patrol	Dark Blue, Yellow interior, Red warning light, 'Police' on doors, Grey plastic wheels	£20-25
9-b1	1968-69	Cadillac Eldorado	Light Blue, Red interior, tyres	£20-25
10-a1	1965-67	Guy Warrior Coal Truck	Red, tinted windows, Grey plastic wheels	£15-20
10-a2	1968-69	Guy Warrior Coal Truck	Red, tinted windows, tyres	£20-25
11-a1	1965-67	Forward Control Land Rover	Green, Brown removable tilt, rear corner windows, Grey plastic wheels	£15-20
11-a2	1968-69	Forward Control Land Rover	Metallic Green, Brown removable tilt, no rear corner windows, Grey plastic wheels	£15-20
12-a1	1965-66	Volkswagen Tower Wagon	Yellow, Red tower, Grey plastic wheels	£20-25
12-b1	1967	Ford Tower Wagon	Yellow, Red tower, Grey plastic wheels	£30-35
12-b2	1967	Ford Tower Wagon	White, Red tower, Grey plastic wheels	£15-20
12-b3	1968-69	Ford Tower Wagon	White, Red tower, tyres	£20-25
13-a1	1965-66	Guy Warrior Sand Truck	Yellow, tinted windows, Grey plastic wheels	£15-20
13-a2	1967-68	Guy Warrior Sand Truck	Blue, tinted windows, Grey plastic wheels	£15-20
13-a3	1969	Guy Warrior Sand Truck	Blue, tinted windows, tyres	£20-25
14-a1	1965-66	Guy Warrior Tanker (round tank)	Yellow, 'Shell' decals, Grey plastic wheels	£20-25
14-b1	1967	Guy Warrior Tanker (square tank)	Yellow, 'Shell' decals, Grey plastic wheels	£20-25
14-b2	1967	Guy Warrior Tanker (square tank)	White, 'Esso' decals, Grey plastic wheels	£20-25
14-b3	1968-69	Guy Warrior Tanker (square tank)	White, 'Esso' decals, tyres	£20-25
15-a1	1965-66	Volkswagen Pick Up	Turquoise, Brown removable canopy, Grey plastic wheels	£15-20
15-b1	1967-68	Studebaker Wagonaire TV Car	Yellow, tinted windows, Grey plastic wheels	£20-25
15-b2	1968	Studebaker Wagonaire TV Car	Metallic Blue, Blue tinted windows, Grey plastic wheels	£25-30
15-b3	1969	Studebaker Wagonaire TV Car	Metallic Blue, Blue tinted windows, tyres	£25-30
16-a1	1965-66	Dump Truck/Dozer	Yellow, Red back, chrome dozer, Grey plastic wheels	£15-20
16-a2	1966	Dump Truck/Dozer	Red, Grey back, chrome dozer, Grey plastic wheels	£20-25

17-a1	1965-66	**Guy Warrior Milk Tanker**	White, 'Milk' decals, round tank, Grey plastic wheels	£20-25
17-b1	1967	**Guy Warrior Milk Tanker**	White, 'Milk' decals, square tank, Grey plastic wheels	£20-25
17-b2	1968	**Guy Warrior Milk Tanker**	Cream, 'Milk' decals, round tank, Grey plastic wheels	£20-25
17-b3	1969	**Guy Warrior Milk Tanker**	Cream, 'Milk' decals, round tank, tyres	£20-25
18-a1	1965-66	**Plated Jaguar** (small casting)	Chrome, Yellow interior, Grey plastic wheels	£20-25
18-bi	1967-68	**Plated Jaguar**	Chrome, Yellow interior, Grey plastic wheels	£20-25
18-b2	1969	**Plated Jaguar**	Chrome, Yellow interior, tyres	£30-35
19-a1	1966	**Commer Walk Thro' Van**	Red, sliding Red door, Grey plastic wheels	£40-45
19-a2	1966-67	**Commer Walk Thro' Van**	Green, sliding Red door, Grey plastic wheels	£25-30
19-b1	1968-69	**Speedboat on Trailer**	Gold trailer, Red, White and Blue boat, tyres	£15-20
20-a1	1965-66	**Ford Thames Van**	Red, Yellow interior, Yellow ladder and aerial, Grey plastic wheels	£20-25
20-b1	1967	**Volkswagen 1300 with Luggage**	Tan, Yellow interior, tyres	£30-35
20-b2	1967-69	**Volkswagen 1300 with Luggage**	Blue, Yellow interior, tyres	£20-25
21-a1	1966-67	**Military Land Rover**	Military Green, 'star' decal on roof, Grey plastic windows	£15-20
21-b1	1968-69	**Jaguar 'E'-type 2+2**	Maroon, Yellow interior, tyres	£20-25
22-a1	1965-66	**Citroën Safari Military Ambulance**	Khaki, Red Cross on roof, Blue roof lights, Grey plastic wheels	£20-25
22-b1	1967-68	**Aston-Martin DB6**	Metallic Gold, Yellow interior, Grey plastic wheels	£25-30
22-b2	1968-69	**Aston-Martin DB6**	Purple, Yellow interior, tyres	£30-35
23-a1	1966-67	**Guy Army Tanker**	Khaki, US Army decals on tank, Grey plastic wheels	£15-20
23-b1	1968	**Loadmaster Shovel**	Orange, chrome shovel, Black plastic wheels	£25-30
23-b2	1968-69	**Loadmaster Shovel**	Yellow, chrome shovel, Black plastic wheels	£15-20
24-a1	1966-67	**Ford Zephyr Estate**	Blue, Yellow interior, Grey plastic wheels	£20-25
24-a2	1968-69	**Ford Zephyr Estate**	Red, Yellow interior, Grey plastic wheels	£25-30
25-a1	1966-67	**SD Refuse Van**	Light Blue, chrome back, Grey plastic wheels	£15-20
25-a2	1968	**SD Refuse Van**	Red, chrome back, Grey plastic wheels	£30-35
25-a3	1968-69	**SD Refuse Van**	Red, chrome back, tyres	£40-45
26-a1	1966-67	**Sunbeam Alpine**	Metallic Bronze, Blue removable hard top, Yellow interior, Grey plastic wheels	£25-30
26-a2	1967	**Sunbeam Alpine**	Red, Blue removable hard top, Yellow interior, Grey plastic wheels	£40-45
26-a3	1968-69	**Sunbeam Alpine**	Red, Blue removable hard top, Yellow interior, tyres	£50-55
27-a1	1966-67	**Bedford Skip Lorry**	Maroon, Grey plastic wheels	£20-25
27-a2	1967	**Bedford Skip Lorry**	Dark Green, Grey plastic wheels	£50-60
27-a3	1967	**Bedford Skip Lorry**	Orange, Grey plastic wheels	£20-25
27-a4	1968-69	**Bedford Skip Lorry**	Orange, tyres	£20-25
28-a1	1966-67	**Ford Breakdown Truck**	Blue, chrome hoist, metal jib, Grey plastic wheels	£15-20
28-a2	1968-69	**Ford Breakdown Truck**	Blue, chrome hoist, Gold jib, tyres	£20-25
29-a1	1966-67	**ERF Cement Mixer**	Yellow, Red barrel, metal chute, Grey plastic wheels	£15-20
29-a2	1968-69	**ERF Cement Mixer**	Yellow, Red barrel, metal chute, tyres	£20-25
30-a1	1966-67	**Studebaker Wagonaire Ambulance**	White, Red Cross decals, stretcher, Grey plastic Wheels	£25-30
30-a2	1968-69	**Studebaker Wagonaire Ambulance**	White, Red Cross decals, stretcher, tyres	£25-30
30-a3	1969	**Studebaker Wagonaire**	Pale Green, Green tinted windows, tyres	£35-40
31-a1	1966-67	**Oldsmobile Starfire Coupé**	Olive Green, Yellow interior, Grey plastic wheels	£15-20
31-a2	1968-69	**Oldsmobile Starfire Coupé**	Olive Green, Yellow interior, tyres	£20-25
32-a1	1966-67	**Volkswagen Luggage Elevator**	White, Yellow conveyor, Grey plastic wheels	£25-30
32-a2	1967	**Volkswagen Luggage Elevator**	White, Blue conveyor, Red belt, Grey plastic wheels	£30-35
32-a3	1968-69	**Volkswagen Luggage Elevator**	Red, Blue conveyor, Red belt, Grey plastic wheels	£35-40
33-a1	1967	**Farm Trailer and Calves**	Olive Green, tyres	£10-15
33-a2	1968-69	**Farm Trailer and Calves**	Turquoise, tyres	£10-15
34-a1	1967	**Tractor**	Red, Red exhaust, tyres	£20-25
34-a2	1968-69	**Tractor**	Red, Black exhaust, tyres	£20-25
35-a1	1967	**Ford Camper**	Yellow, chrome back, Grey plastic wheels	£20-25
35-a2	1967	**Ford Camper**	Metallic Blue, chrome back, Grey plastic wheels	£25-30
35-a3	1968-69	**Ford Camper**	Metallic Blue, chrome back, tyres	£25-30
36-a1	1967	**Simon Snorkel Fire Engine**	Red, chrome snorkel, Grey plastic wheels	£20-25
36-a2	1968-69	**Simon Snorkel Fire Engine**	Red, chrome snorkel, tyres	£20-25
37-a1	1968-69	**NSU RO80**	Metallic Blue, tyres	£25-30
38-a1	1968	**Rices Beaufort Single Horse Box**	Turquoise, tyres	£10-15
38-a2	1969	**Rices Beaufort Single Horse Box**	Metallic Green, tyres	£20-25
39-a1	1969	**Jaguar XJ6 4.2**	Yellow, Red interior, tyres	£45-55
40-a1	1969	**Ford Transit Caravan**	Red, Cream interior, White rear door, tyres	£25-35
40-a2	1969	**Ford Transit Caravan**	Lime green, Cream interior, White rear door, tyres	£25-35
41-a1	?	**Porsche Carrera 6**	Shown in catalogue but not issued	NPP
42-a	1969	**Euclid Truck**	Yellow body, Red dumper	£40-45
43-a	?	**Massey-Ferguson 3003**	no details	£40-45

Novelty, Film and TV-related models   *See also following section and 'Corgi Rockets'.*

1001-a1	1967	**James Bond Aston Martin DB6**	Silver, Red interior, 2 ejector figures, Grey plastic wheels	£180-200
1001-a2	1968-69	**James Bond Aston Martin DB6**	Silver, Red interior, 2 ejector figures, tyres	£180-200
1002-a1	1967-69	**Batmobile**	Black, Batman and Robin figures, tow hook, Grey plastic wheels	£150-160
1003-a1	1967-69	**Batboat**	Black boat, Red fin, Batman and Robin figures, Grey plastic wheels	£150-160
1004-a1	1968-69	**Monkeemobile**	Red, White roof, 4 figures, 'Monkees' on doors, tyres	£160-180
1005-a1	1968-69	**Man From UNCLE Car**	Blue, 3 Missiles on sprue, 2 figures, tyres	£160-175
1006-a1	1969	**Chitty Chitty Bang Bang**	Chrome, Dark Grey base, Red wings, Yellow fins, 4 figures, tyres	£120-140

Corgi Juniors 1970 - 1972

Ref	Year	Model name	Colours, features, details	Market Price Range

Note: The models in this list were each accompanied by a colourful Picture Card, the lack of which could adversely affect the model's potential price.

Ref	Year	Model name	Colours, features, details	Market Price Range
1-a1	1970	Reliant TW9 Pick Up	Beige, Green tinted windows, removabte plastic front bumper, Black WhizzWheels	£20-25
1-a2	1970-72	Reliant TW9 Pick Up	Orange, Green tinted windows, removable plastic front bumper, Black WhizzWheels	£15-20
2-a1	1970	Citroën Safari with Boat	Blue, White boat, Yellow interior, tyres	£25-30
2-a2	1970	Citroën Safari with Boat	Blue, White boat, Yellow interior, Black WhizzWheels	£20-25
2-a3	1971-2	Citroën Safari with Boat	Yellow, White boat, Yellow interior, Black WhizzWheels	£15-20
2-a4	1971-2	Citroën Safari with Boat	Purple, White boat, Yellow interior, Black WhizzWheels	£15-20
3-a1	1970	Volkswagen 1300 Police Car	White, Black 'Police' sign on doors, Red interior, Blue light, tyres	£30-35
3-a2	1970	Volkswagen 1300 Police Car	White, Black 'Police' sign on doors, Red interior, Blue light, Black WhizzWheels	£20-25
3-a3	1971-72	Volkswagen 1300 Police Car	White, Black 'Police' sign on doors, Red interior, Blue light, chrome WhizzWheels	£20-25
3-a4	1971-72	Volkswagen 1300 Police Car	White, Black 'Police' sign on doors, Yellow interior, Blue tinted windows, chrome WhizzWheels	£15-20
4-a1	1970-72	Zeteor 5511 Tractor	Orange, Red base, Black chimney, Black plastic wheels	£10-15
5-a1	1970	Willys Jeep	Tan, Brown interior, Grey windshield, tyres	£15-20
5-a2	1970	Willys Jeep	Tan, Brown interior, Grey windshield, Black WhizzWheels	£10-15
5-a3	1971	Willys Jeep	Tan, Brown interior, Grey windshield, chrome WhizzWheels	£10-15
5-a4	1970	Willys Jeep	Orange, Brown interior, Grey windshield, Black WhizzWheels	£10-15
5-a5	1971	Willys Jeep	Orange, Brown interior, Grey windshield, chrome Whizzwheels	£10-15
5-a6	1971-72	Willys Jeep	Red, Yellow interior, Grey windshield, chrome WhizzWheels	£10-15
6-a1	1970	De Tomaso Mangusta	Lime Green, Green tinted windows, Black WhizzWheels	£10-15
6-a2	1970	De Tomaso Mangusta	Metallic Purple, Green tinted windows, Black WhizzWheels	£10-15
6-a3	1971-2	De Tomaso Mangusta	Metallic Purple, Green tinted windows, chrome WhizzWheels	£10-15
7-a1	1970	Duple Vista 25 Coach	Red, White, Yellow interior, Green tinted windows, tyres	£20-25
7-a2	1970	Duple Vista 25 Coach	Yellow, White, Yellow interior, Green tinted windows, Black WhizzWheels	£12-15
7-a3	1971-2	Duple Vista 25 Coach	Purple, White, Yellow interior, Green tinted windows, chrome WhizzWheels	£12-15
7-a4	1971-2	Duple Vista 25 Coach	Orange, White, Yellow interior, Green tinted windows, chrome WhizzWheels	£12-15
8-a1	1970	Tipping Farm Trailer	Blue, Orange back, tyres	£10-15
9-a1	1970	Cadillac Eldorado	Metallic Green, Red interior, Red tow hook, tyres	£25-30
9-a2	1970	Cadillac Eldorado	Metallic Green, Red interior, Red tow hook, Black WhizzWheels	£15-20
9-a3	1970	Cadillac Eldorado	White, Black bonnet, Red interior, Red tow hook, Black WhizzWheels	£15-20
9-a4	1971	Cadillac Eldorado	White, Black bonnet, Red interior, Red tow hook, chrome WhizzWheels	£15-20
9-b1	1971-72	Vigilant Range Rover	White, 'Police' decals on doors, Blue tinted windows, chrome WhizzWheels	£12-15
10-a1	1970	Guy Warrior Coal Truck	Orange, Green tinted windows, tyres	£15-20
10-b1	1971-2	Ford GT7O	Orange, Green tinted windows, Silver engine cover, chrome WhizzWheels	£10-12
11-af	1970	Austin Healey Sprite Le Mans	Red, Blue interior, Amber windows, Grey base, RN '50', sticker pack, Black WhizzWheels	£30-35
11-a2	1971	Austin Healey Sprite Le Mans	Red, Yellow interior, Amber windows, Grey base, RN '50', sticker pack, chrome WhizzWheels	£30-35
11-a3	1971-2	Austin Healey Sprite Le Mans	Red, Yellow interior, Amber windows, Black base, RN '50', sticker pack, chrome Whizzwheels	£30-35
12-a1	1970	Reliant-Ogle Scimitar GTE	White, Amber tinted windows, Yellow interior, Black WhizzWheels	£20-25
12-a2	1970	Reliant-Ogle Scimitar GTE	Metallic Blue, Amber tinted windows, Yellow interior, chrome WhizzWheels	£20-25
12-a3	1971-2	Reliant-Ogle Scimitar GTE	Matt Blue, Amber tinted windows, Yellow interior, chrome WhizzWheels	£20-25
13-a1	1970	Guy Warrior Sand Truck	Blue, Green tinted windows, tyres	£15-20
13-a2	1971-72	Guy Warrior Sand Truck	Red, Green tinted windows, chrome WhizzWheels	£12-15
14-a1	1970	Guy Warrior Tanker (square tank)	White, Green tinted windows, 'Esso' decals, tyres	£15-20
14-a2	1971-2	Guy Warrior Tanker (square tank)	White, Green tinted windows, 'Esso' decals, Black plastic base, chrome WhizzWheels	£12-15
15-a1	1970	Studebaker Wagonaire TV Car	Metallic Turquoise, Blue tinted windows, tyres	£35-40
15-a2	1970	Studebaker Wagonaire TV Car	Yellow, Blue tinted windows, Black WhizzWheels	£25-30
15-a3	1970	Studebaker Wagonaire TV Car	Metallic Lime Green, Blue tinted windows, Black WhizzWheels	£25-30
15-a4	1971-2	Studebaker Wagonaire TV Car	Metallic Lime Green, Blue tinted windows, chrome WhizzWheels	£25-30
16-a	1970-2	Land Rover Pick Up	Metallic Green, Orange tinted windows, chrome WhizzWheels	£10-12
17-af	1970	Volkswagen 1300 Beetle	Metallic Blue, Yellow interior, 'flower' decals	£45-50
17-a2	1970-72	Volkswagen 1300 Beetle	Metallic Green, Yellow interior, 'flower' decals	£20-25
18-a1			nothing issued	
19-a1	1970	Speedboat on Trailer	Blue trailer, Red,White and Blue boat, tyres	£15-20
19-a2	1970	Speedboat on Trailer	Blue trailer, Red,White and Blue boat, Black WhizzWheels	£10-15
19-a3	1971-2	Speedboat on Trailer	Blue trailer, Red,White and Blue boat, chrome WhizzWheels	£10-15
20-a1	1967	Volkswagen 1300 with Luggage	Mustard Yellow, Yellow interior, tyres	£25-30
20-a2	1967-69	Volkswagen 1300 with Luggage	Red, Yellow interior, Black WhizzWheels	£20-25
21-a1	1971-72	BVRT Vita-Min Mini Cooper S	Metallic Purple, chrome interior, Blue tinted windows, chrome WhizzWheels	£25-30
22-a1	1970	Aston-Martin DB6	Purple, Yellow interior, tyres	£45-50
22-a2	1970	Aston-Martin DB6	Metallic Olive, Yellow interior, tyres	£45-50

22-b1	1971-72	**Formula 1 Grand Prix Racing Car**	Yellow, Union Jack on front, White driver, chrome WhizzWheels	£12-15
23-a1	1970-2	**Loadmaster Shovel**	Yellow, chrome shovel, Black plastic wheels	£10-12
24-a1	1971-2	**Aston-Martin DBS**	Green, Black bonnet, Cream interior, chrome WhizzWheels	£20-25
25-a1	1970-72	**SD Refuse Van**	Orange, chrome back, Green tinted windows, tyres	£15-20
26-a1	1971-72	**ERF Fire Engine Water Tender**	Red, Green tinted windows and roof lights, Yellow ladder, chrome WhizzWheels	£12-15
27-a1	1970	**Bedford Skip Lorry**	Orange, Silver skip, tyres	£20-25
28-a1	1970	**Ford Breakdown Truck**	Blue, chrome hoist, Gold jib, Green tinted windows, tyres	£20-25
28-a2	1970	**Ford Breakdown Truck**	Blue, chrome hoist, Gold jib, Green tinted windows, Black WhizzWheels	£15-20
28-a3	1970	**Ford Breakdown Truck**	Turquoise, chrome hoist, Gold jib, Green tinted windows, Black WhizzWheels	£15-20
29-a1	1971-72	**Simon Snorkel Fire Engine**	Red, Yellow snorkel, Green tinted windows, chrome WhizzWheels	£12-15
30-a1	1970	**Studebaker Wagonaire Ambulance**	White, Red Cross decals, Blue windows, removable stretcher, tyres	£25-30
30-a2	1970	**Studebaker Wagonaire Ambulance**	White, Red Cross decals, Blue windows, removable stretcher, Black WhizzWheels	£20-25
30-a3	1970	**Studebaker Wagonaire Ambulance**	White, Red Cross decals, Blue windows, non-removable stretcher, Black WhizzWheels	£15-20
30-a4	1971	**Studebaker Wagonaire Ambulance**	White, Red Cross decals, Blue windows, non-removable stretcher, small chrome WhizzWheels	£15-20
30-a5	1971-72	**Studebaker Wagonaire Ambulance**	White, Red Cross decals, Blue windows, non-removable stretcher, chrome WhizzWheels	£15-20
31-a1	1970-71	**Land Rover Breakdown**	Purple, 'Wrecker Truck' labels, Gold hook, Amber windows	£12-15
31-a2	1972	**Land Rover Breakdown**	Red, 'Wrecker Truck' labels, Gold hook, Amber windows	£12-15
32-a1	1970-71	**Lotus Europa**	Metallic Green, Yellow interior and engine cover, chrome WhizzWheels	£15-20
32-a2	1972	**Lotus Europa**	Green, Yellow interior and engine cover, chrome WhizzWheels	£15-20
33-a1	1970	**Farm Trailer and Calves**	Orange, tyres	£10-15
33-b1	1970-72	**Jaguar 'E'-type Series 2**	Yellow, Red interior, chrome WhizzWheels	£12-15
34-a1	1970-72	**B.M. Volvo 400 Tractor**	Red, Yellow plastic Wheels, tyres	£15-20
35-a1	1970	**Ford Camper**	Turquoise, chrome back, Green tinted windows, tyres	£25-30
35-a2	1970-2	**Ford Camper**	Turquoise, chrome back, Green tinted windows, Black WhizzWheels	£25-30
35-a3	1970-2	**Ford Camper**	Red, Cream back, Green tinted windows, Black WhizzWheels	£20-25
36-a1	1970	**Simon Snorkel Fire Engine**	Red, chrome Snorkel, tyres	£20-25
37-a1	1970	**NSU RO80**	Metallic Blue, Silver interior, Green tinted windows, tyres	£25-30
37-a2	1970	**NSU RO80**	Metallic Mauve, Silver interior, Green tinted windows, Black WhizzWheels	£15-20
37-a3	1970	**NSU RO80**	Purple, Black bonnet, Silver interior, Green tinted windows, Black WhizzWheels	£15-20
37-a4	1971-2	**NSU RO80**	Purple, Black bonnet, Silver interior, Green tinted windows, chrome WhizzWheels	£15-20
37-a5	1971-2	**NSU RO80**	Metallic Copper, Black bonnet, Silver interior, Amber tinted windows, chrome WhizzWheels	£15-20
38-a1	1970	**Rices Beaufort Single Horse Box**	Metallic Green, horse, tyres	£15-20
38-a2	1970	**Rices Beaufort Single Horse Box**	Red, White horse, tyres	£15-20
38-a3	1970	**Rices Beaufort Single Horse Box**	Red, White horse, Black WhizzWheels	£10-15
38-a4	1971-72	**Rices Beaufort Single Horse Box**	Metallic Copper, White horse, chrome WhizzWheels	£10-15
39-a1	1970	**Jaguar XJ6 4.2**	Yellow, Red interior, tyres	£30-35
39-a2	1970	**Jaguar XJ6 4.2**	Silver, Red interior, Black Whizzwheels	£20-25
39-a3	1971-72	**Jaguar XJ6 4.2**	Silver, Red interior, chrome Whizzwheels	£20-25
39-a4	1971-72	**Jaguar XJ6 4.2**	Metallic Red, Yellow interior, chrome WhizzWheels	£20-25
39-a5	1971-72	**Jaguar XJ6 4.2**	Red, Yellow interior, chrome WhizzWheels	NGPP
4d-a1	1970	**Ford Transit Caravan**	Yellow, Blue interior, Silver rear door, tyres	£25-30
40-a2	1970	**Ford Transit Caravan**	Yellow, Cream interior, Silver rear door, Black WhizzWheels	£20-25
40-a3	1970	**Ford Transit Caravan**	Blue, Cream interior, Silver rear door, Black WhizzWheels	£20-25
40-a4	1971-72	**Ford Transit Caravan**	Blue, Cream interior, Silver rear door, chrome WhizzWheels	£20-25
40-a5	1971-72	**Ford Transit Caravan**	Metallic Pale Blue, Cream interior, Silver rear door, chrome WhizzWheels	£15-20
40-a6	1972	**Ford Transit Caravan**	Metallic Pale Blue, Cream interior, Silver rear door, Black plastic base, chrome WhizzWheels	£15-20
41-a1	1970	**Porsche Carrera 6**	White, clear canopy, RN '19', tyres	£20-25
41-a2	1970	**Porsche Carrera 6**	White, Blue tinted canopy, RN '19', Black WhizzWheels	£15-20
41-a3	1971-72	**Porsche Carrera 6**	White, Blue tinted canopy, RN '19', chrome WhizzWheels	£15-20
42-a1	1970	**Euclid Dumper**	Yellow cab, Red back, Dark Grey base, Black wheels	£15-20
42-a2	1970	**Euclid Dumper**	Red cab, Yellow back, unpainted Base, chrome WhizzWheels	£10-15
42-a3	1971-72	**Euclid Dumper**	Yellow cab, Red back, Dark Grey base, Black WhizzWheels	£10-15
42-a4	1971-72	**Euclid Dumper**	Blue cab, Silver back, Dark Grey base, chrome WhizzWheels	£10-15
42-a5	1971-72	**Euclid Dumper**	Blue Cab, Yellow back, Dark Grey base, chrome WhizzWheels	£10-15
43-a1	1970	**Massey Ferguson Tractor Shovel**	Yellow, Red interior, Black plastic wheels	£12-15
43-a2	1971-72	**Massey Ferguson Tractor Shovel**	Yellow, Red shovel and interior, Black plastic wheels	£10-15
44-a1	1970-72	**Raygo Rascal Road Roller**	Blue, Orange front, Grey roller, Grey seat and engine, Black plastic wheels	£10-12
45-a1	1970	**Mercedes 280SL**	Metallic Silver, Red interior, tyres	£30-35
45-a2	1970	**Mercedes 280SL**	Metallic Blue, Red interior, Black Whizzwheels	£20-25
45-a3	1970	**Mercedes 280SL**	Yellow, Red interior, unpainted base, Black Whizzwheels	£15-20
45-a4	1970	**Mercedes 280SL**	Yellow, Red interior, White base, Black Whizzwheels	£15-20
45-a5	1970	**Mercedes 280SL**	Red, Cream interior, Black WhizzWheels	£25-30
45-a6	1971-72	**Mercedes 280SL**	Red, Cream interior, chrome WhizzWheels	£25-30
45-a7	1971-72	**Mercedes 280SL**	Blue, Cream interior, unpainted base, chrome WhizzWheels	£20-25

46-a1	1970	**Jensen Interceptor**............................Maroon, Yellow interior, Green tinted windows, unpainted base, tyres..........................**£35-40**
46-a2	1970	**Jensen Interceptor**............................Maroon, Yellow interior, Green tinted windows, unpainted base, Black WhizzWheels.....................**£25-30**
46-a3	1971	**Jensen Interceptor**............................Orange, Yellow interior, Green tinted windows, unpainted base, chrome WhizzWheels.................**£25-30**
46-a4	1972	**Jensen Interceptor**............................Metallic Green, Yellow interior, Green tinted windows, unpainted base, chrome WhizzWheels **£25-30**
47-a1	1971-72	**Scammell Concrete Mixer**.................White cab, Blue base, Red mixer, Amber windows, chrome WhizzWheels....................................**£10-15**
48-a1	1971-72	**ERF Tipper Truck** ....Red cab, Silver back, unpainted base, Amber windows, chrome WhizzWheels **£10-15**
48-a1	1971-72	**ERF Tipper Truck** ....Blue cab, Orange back, unpainted base, Amber windows, chrome Whizzwheels.............................**£10-15**
48-a1	1971-72	**ERF Tipper Truck** ....Blue cab, Orange back, Dark Grey base, Amber windows, chrome WhizzWheels........................**£10-15**
48-a1	1971-72	**ERF Tipper Truck** ....Blue cab, Yellow back, Dark Grey base, Amber windows, chrome WhizzWheels........................**£10-15**
49-a1	1971-72	**Pininfarina Modulo**...........................Yellow, Red stripe, Red interior, chrome WhizzWheels..**£10-12**
50-a1	1971-72	**Ferrari 512s**......................................Metallic Red, Cream interior, unpainted base, chrome WhizzWheels......................................**£10-12**
51-a1	1971-72	**Porsche 917**......................................Gold, RN '23', chrome interior, Red base, chrome WhizzWheels..**£10-12**
52-a1	1971-72	**Adams Probe 16** ....Metallic Pink,White interior, Green tinted windows, Black plastic base, chrome WhizzWheels.......**£10-12**
54-a1	1971-72	**Ford Container Wagon**......................Red, Yellow skip, Yellow plastic base, chrome WhizzWheels..**£10-12**
55-a1	1970-72	**Daimler Fleetline Bus** ....Red, Yellow interior, 'Uniflo' adverts, chrome WhizzWheels...**£10-12**
56-a1	1970-72	**Ford Capri Fire Chief**......................Red, White bonnet, 'Fire' decal on door, White interior, Blue windows, chrome WhizzWheels **£25-30**
56-a2	1970-72	**Ford Capri Fire Chief**......................As previous model but with 'Fire Chief' decal on door...**£25-30**
56-a3	1970-72	**Ford Capri Fire Chief**......................All-Red, 'Fire Chief' decal on door, Yellow interior, Blue windows, chrome WhizzWheels...........**£25-30**
57-a1	1970-72	**Caddy Hot Rodder**............................Metallic Blue, Red interior, 'Caddy Hot Roddy' on doors, sticker pack, chrome WhizzWheels......**£12-15**
57-a2	1970-72	**Caddy Hot Rodder**............................Metallic Pink, Red interior, 'Caddy Hot Roddy' on doors, sticker pack, chrome WhizzWheels......**£12-15**
58-a1	1971-72	**G.P. Beach Buggy**............................Metallic Red, Cream interior, chrome WhizzWheels **£10-12**
58-a2	1971-72	**G.P. Beach Buggy**............................Metallic Red, Yellow interior, chrome WhizzWheels..**£10-12**
59-a1	1971-72	**The Futura**.......................................Orange, Blue windows, 'Futura' on sides, Black plastic base, sheet of stickers, chrome WhizzWheels.**£10-12**
60-a1	1971-72	**VW Double Trouble Hot Rod** ....Metallic Pink, chrome interior, Green tinted windows, chrome WhizzWheels **£12-15**
61-a1	1970-72	**Mercury Cougar Police Car**.............White, Black roof, 'Sheriff', Yellow interior, Blue windows and lights, chrome WhizzWheels **£12-15**
62-a1	1970	**Volvo P1800** ....Red, Black bonnet, Yellow interior, chrome WhizzWheels...**£35-40**
62-a2	1971-72	**Volvo P1800** ....Red, Black Bonnet, Blue interior, chrome WhizzWheels..**£25-30**
62-a3	1972	**Volvo P1800** ....Red, Black Bonnet, Cream interior, chrome WhizzWheels..**£45-50**
63-a1	1970-72	**Ford Escort Monte Carlo Rally Car**.Metallic Blue, RN '32', Red interior, sheet of stickers, chrome WhizzWheels.............................**£35-40**
63-a2	1972	**Ford Escort Monte Carlo Rally Car**.Metallic Blue, RN '32', Yellow interior, sheet of stickers, chrome WhizzWheels..........................**£45-50**
63-a3	1972	**Ford Escort Monte Carlo Rally Car**.Metallic Blue, RN '32', Cream interior, , sheet of stickers, chrome WhizzWheels..........................**£45-50**
64-a1	1971-72	**Morgan Plus 8** ....Yellow, Black interior, chrome WhizzWheels **£20-25**
64-a2	1971-72	**Morgan Plus 8** ....Red, RN '20' on doors, Black interior, chrome WhizzWheels..**£20-25**
65-a1	1971-72	**Bertone Carabo** ....Metallic Purple, Pale Green base, White interior, Amber tinted windows, chrome WhizzWheels ...**£12-15**
65-a2	1971-72	**Bertone Carabo** ....Metallic Purple, Pale Green base, Orange interior, Amber tinted windows, chrome WhizzWheels ..**£10-12**
67-a1	1971-72	**Ford Capri Hot Pants Dragster**.........Yellow, 'Hot Pants' decal on roof, opening body, Red interior, chrome WhizzWheels **£35-40**
70-a1	1971-72	**US Racing Buggy** ....Blue, 'Stars and Stripes' on roof, White driver, chrome WhizzWheels.....................................**£10-12**
71-a1	1971-72	**Marcos XP** ....Orange, chrome interior, Amber tinted windows, chrome WhizzWheels **£12-15**
72-a1	1971-72	**Mercedes-Benz C111** ....Red, Amber tinted windows, chrome Interior, Black plastic base, chrome WhizzWheels **£10-12**
73-a1	1971-72	**Pininfarina Alfa Romeo P33** ....Blue, White interior and base, chrome WhizzWheels...**£10-12**
74-a1	1971-72	**Bertone Barchetta** ....Orange, Red interior, White base, chrome WhizzWheels..**£10-12**
75-a1	1971-72	**Superstock Car**.................................Silver, Blue base, Union Jack on bonnet, Red interior, sticker pack, chrome WhizzWheels **£20-25**
76-a1	1971-72	**Chevrolet Astro** ....Metallic Red,Cream interior, chrome WhizzWheels **£12-15**
77-a1	1971-72	**Bizzarrini Manta** ....Pink, Cream interior, Black base, chrome WhizzWheels...**£10-12**
78-a1	1971-72	**Old MacDonalds Truck** ....Red, Brown back, chrome WhizzWheels..**£25-30**
1017-a1	1971-72	**Holmes Wrecker & Towing Cradle**...Yellow cab, Red back, Amber glass, 'Auto Rescue' decals, Gold booms, Red cradle and hooks .**£100-120**

Collectors notes

Novelty, Film and TV-related models   See also preceding section and 'Corgi Rockets'.

1001-a1	1970	**James Bond Aston-Martin DB6**	Silver, Red interior, 2 ejector figures, tyres	**£180-200**
1001-a2	1970	**James Bond Aston-Martin DB6**	Silver, Red interior, 2 ejector figures, Black WhizzWheels	**£160-180**
1001-a3	1971-72	**James Bond Aston-Martin DB6**	Silver, Red interior, 2 ejector figures, chrome WhizzWheels	**£160-180**
1002-a1	1970	**Batmobile**	Black, Batman and Robin figures, tow hook, Grey plastic wheels, 'Corgi Junior' label on base	**£150-160**
1002-a2	1970	**Batmobile**	Black, Batman and Robin figures, tow hook, Black WhizzWheels	**£150-160**
1002-a3	1971-72	**Batmobile**	Black, Batman and Robin figures, tow hook, chrome WhizzWheels	**£150-160**
1003-a1	1970	**Batboat**	Black boat, Red fin, Batman and Robin figures, GPW, 'Corgi Junior' label on base	**£140-150**
1003-a2	1970	**Batboat**	Black boat, Red fin, Batman and Robin figures, Black WhizzWheels	**£130-140**
1003-a3	1971-72	**Batboat**	Black boat, Red fin, Batman and Robin figures, chrome WhizzWheels	**£140-150**
1004-a1	1970	**Monkeemobile**	Red, White roof, 4 figures, 'Monkees' on doors, tyres, 'Corgi Junior' label on base	**£160-180**
1004-a2	1970	**Monkeemobile**	Red, White roof,4 figures, 'Monkees' on doors, tyres, 'Corgi Junior' base	**£160-180**
1004-a3	1971	**Monkeemobile**	Red, White roof, 4 figures, 'Monkees' on doors, tyres, Black WhizzWheels	**£150-160**
1005-a1	1970	**Man From UNCLE Car**	Blue, 3 missiles on sprue, 2 figures, tyres, 'Corgi Junior' label on base	**£160-175**
1006-a1	1970	**Chitty Chitty Bang Bang**	Chrome, Dark Grey base, Red wings, Yellow fins, 4 figures, tyres	**£130-140**
1006-a2	1971	**Chitty Chitty Bang Bang**	Chrome, Dark Grey base, Red wings, Yellow fins, 4 figures, Black WhizzWheels	**£120-130**
1007-a1	1971-72	**Ironsides Police Van**	Blue, 'San Francisco' logo, Ironside in back, chrome WhizzWheels	**£160-180**
1008-a1	1971-72	**Popeye's Paddle Wagon**	Yellow, Blue, Popeye with Olive and Sweet Pea, chrome WhizzWheels	**£120-130**
1010-a1	1972	**James Bond Volkswagen**	Orange, Green stripe and 'Corgi Toys' on roof, RN '5', Yellow interior, chrome WhizzWheels	**£600-800**
1011-a1	1971-72	**James Bond Bobsleigh**	Yellow, '007' decal, Grey plastic bumper, George Lazenby figure, Black WhizzWheels	**£400-450**
1012-a1	1971-72	**S.P.E.C.T.R.E. Bobsleigh**	Orange, 'Boars Head' decal, Grey plastic bumper, Blofleld figure, Black WhizzWheels	**£400-450**
1013-a1	1971-72	**Tom's Go Cart**	Yellow, Tom figure, chrome WhizzWheels	**£50-60**
1014-a1	1971-72	**Jerry's Banger**	Red, Jerry figure, chrome WhizzWheels	**£50-60**

Major Models

2001	1968-69	**'HUSKY' Multi Garage**	A set of four garages (no cars), 'Husky' on base	**£15-20**
	1970-75	Corgi Juniors issue:	As previous model but with 'CORGI' logo, 'Juniors' on base	**£10-15**
2002	1967-69	**'HUSKY' Car Transporter**	Hoynor MkII, White/Blue/Orange, detachable cab, 'Husky' on base	**£30-40**
	1970-72	Corgi Juniors issue:	As previous model but with 'CORGI' logo, 'Juniors' on base	**£25-35**
2003a	1968-69	**Machinery Low-Loader**	Red/Blue/Yellow, detachable cab, drop-down ramp, 'Husky' on base	**£25-35**
2003b	1970-73	Corgi Juniors issue:	As previous model with metal wheels or WhizzWheels, 'Juniors' on base	**£25-35**
2004a	1968-69	**Removals Delivery Van**	Red or Blue cab, plated box, *'HUSKY REMOVALS'*, metal wheels, 'Husky' on base	**£45-55**
2004b	1970-72	Corgi Juniors issue:	As previous model but *'CORGI REMOVALS'*, WhizzWheels, 'Juniors' base	**£20-30**
2006	1970-79	**Mack 'ESSO' Tanker**	White body and tank, WhizzWheels, 'Juniors' on base	**£10-15**

Husky and Corgi Juniors Gift Sets 1968 - 1970

3001	1968-69	**4 Garage Set**	Contains 23, 27, 29, or 9, 30 or 36	**£75-100**
3002	1968-69	**Batmobile Set**	1002 Batmobile and 1003 Batboat on trailer	**£150-200**
3002	1970	**'Club Racing' Set**	Juniors set of 8 racing cars inc Mini Cooper 'S' (Metallic Mauve), Ford Capri, Morgan, etc	**£150-250**
3003	1968-69	**Car Transporter Set**	2002 Husky Car Transporter plus 16, 26, 6-2, 21-2, 22-2, 26	**£150-200**
3004	1968-69	**4 Garage Set**	Contains 23-2, 29	**£60-80**
3004		**James Bond 'OHMSS' Set**	Contains 1004, 1001, 1011, 1012 plus un-numbered VW Beetle in Red with Black No'5' on White circle on sides. (From film 'On Her Majesty's Secret Service')	**£2000-2500**
3005	1968-69	**Holiday Time / Leisure Time**	Contains 2-2, 5-2, 7-2, 15-2, 19-2, 20-2, 21-2, 35-1	**£150-200**
3006	1968-69	**Service Station**	Contains 14-c, 22-2, 28	**£60-80**
3007	1968-69	**'HUSKY MULTIPARK'**	In 1968 catalogue but not issued	**NPP**
3008	1968-69	**Crime Busters Set**	Contains 1001, 1002, 1003, 1005	**£450-550**
	1970	Corgi Juniors issue:	As previous set	**£350-450**
3011		**Road Construction Set**	Gift Set containing seven models	**£120-140**

Husky Accessories

1561/2	1968-69	**Traffic Signs**	**£20-30**
1571	1968-69	**Pedestrians**	**£10-15**
1572	1968-69	**Workmen**	**£10-15**
1573	1968-69	**Garage Personnel**	**£10-15**
1574	1968-69	**Public Servants**	**£10-15**
1580	1968-69	**Husky Collector Case** storage for 48 models	**£15-25**

1585	1968-69	**Husky Traveller Case** opens to form Service Station (this item never seen)	**NPP**
2001	1968-69	**'HUSKY' Multi Garage** A set of four garages, (no cars) 'Husky' on base	**£20-25**
	1970-75	Corgi Juniors issue: As previous model but with 'CORGI' logo, 'Juniors' on base	**£10-15**

Husky and Corgi Juniors Catalogues and listings

HUSKY CATALOGUES
Mettoy Playcraft (Sales) Ltd 1966

1966	**Leaflet (single fold)**..................	Red, illustrating No.1 Jaguar Mk.10 on cover and Nos.1-29 inside. '1/9 each' **£20-25**	

same ref.   1966 ......**Leaflet (Belgian issue)** ....As previous leaflet but Nos.1-32 shown, printed in French **£20-25**

same ref.   1966 ....**Booklet (10 pages)** ....Front/rear covers feature a row of garages and cars. Good pictures of 1002 Batmobile and 1001 James Bond's Aston-Martin, plus Nos.1-36..NGPP

no ref.   1967   **Catalogue (24 pages)** .... Cover features boy with Husky vehicles and sets. Good pictures of all the rare models and Gift Sets plus accessories and models 1-41 ....**£30-40**

CORGI JUNIORS CATALOGUES
Mettoy Playcraft 1970

              Catalogue (16 pages) .... Blue cover with 10 models featured. Contains excellent pictures of all the rare early models including GS 3004 James Bond 'O.H.M.S.S.' Set etc. **£30-40**

Qualitoys

A range of sturdy toys made up from the same basic parts. First issued in 1969 they were aimed at the pre school age group.

They were publicized as being from the 'makers of Corgi Toys' and did not form part of the Corgi range as such. They have little collectable value at the present time.

Q701 **Pick Up Truck** ....
Q702 **Side Tipper** ....
Q703 **Breakdown Truck** ....
Q704 **Tower Wagon** ....
Q705 **Horse Box** ....
Q706 **Giraffe Transporter**.....................................
Q707 **Fire Engine** ....
Q708 **Pick Up Trailer** ....

Corgi Rockets Stock Cars and Sports Cars (see page 79)

The following listing represents the best information available to us.
The listing is not complete and the Editor would welcome further details on other variations/issues and price levels.
Market Price Range - Scarcer items as shown, otherwise under £15. These models are fitted with WhizzWheels.

E1	1977-83	**Mercedes 220D Ambulance**, White or Cream............
E2	1980-81	**Blake's Seven Liberator** **£75-100**
E3	1977-81	**Stromberg's Helicopter** **£25-35**
E4	1975-79	**Zetor Farm Tractor** **£15-20**
E5	1980-82	**NASA Space Shuttle**....................................
E6	1979-80	**'Daily Planet' Helicopter** **£15-20**
E7	1976-80	**Dumper Truck**, Red/Yellow or Blue/Yellow...............
E7	1976-80	**Dumper Truck**, Yellow/Red or Yellow/Black...........
E8	1979-83	**Rover 3500** ....
E9	1975-80	**'POLICE' Range Rover** ....
E10	1977-81	**Triumph TR7**, White/Blue **£20-25**
		Triumph TR7, Silver/Red body **£20-25**
		Triumph TR7, Orange body...........................**£15-20**
E11	1979-85	**Supermobile** **£20-30**
E12	1980-82	**Jeep** ....
E13-1	1976-78	**Rough Terrain Truck**, Red or Blue body ....
E13-2	1980-81	**Buck Rogers Starfighter**............................**£30-40**
E14	1975-76	**(14d) 'ESSO' Tanker**...............................**£20-25**
E14-2	1977-80	**Buick Royal 'TAXI'** ....
E15	1975-84	**(15-3) Mercedes 'SCHOOL BUS'**, Yellow or Red body ....
E16-1	1975-77	**Land Rover Pick-Up** ....
E16-2	1980-82	**Rover 3500 'POLICE' Car**.............................
E17-1	1975-77	**(17-2) Volkswagen 1300 Beetle**.................**£15-20**
E17-2	1979-81	**Metropolis 3500 'POLICE' Car** **£25-35**
E18	1977	**'AMF' 'Ski-Daddler' Snowmobile**, (see Twin-Packs)
E19	1980-82	**Pink Panther Motorcycle** **£15-20**
E20-1	1976-78	**Site Cement Mixer** ....
E20-2	1979-81	**Penguinmobile** **£20-30**
E21	1977-80	**Charlie's Angels Chevrolet Van**................**£15-20**
E22-1	1975-77	**(22-3) Formula 1 Racer** ....
E22-2	1981-82	**'PARAMEDIC' Van** ....
E23	1979-81	**Batbike** **£75-100**
E24	1979-80	**'SHAZAM' Thunderbolt**............................**£40-50**
E25	1979-80	**'CAPTAIN AMERICA' Porsche** **£40-50**
E26	1977-90	**ERF Fire Tender**, Yellow body ....
E27	1976-80	**(27/2) Formula 5000 Racing Car** ....
E28-1	1975-76	**Hot Rodder** ....
E28-2	1977-80	**Buick Regal 'POLICE' Car**, White or Black body ....
E29	1975-80	**Simon Snorkel Fire Engine** ....
E30	1976-83	**Mobile Cement Mixer**, Green/Yellow, Blue/White or Red/Silver ....
E31	1975-79	**Land Rover Breakdown**, Red body, 'WRECKER TRUCK' ....
		Land Rover Breakdown, Blue body, 'CRASH SERVICE' ....
E32	1970-74	**The Saint's Jaguar XJS**.................**£65-85**
E33	1979-80	**'WONDERWOMAN's Car**.................**£30-40**
E34-1	1975-78	**Sting Army Helicopter** ....
E34-2	1980	**'HERTZ' Chevrolet Van** ....
E35-1	1975-79	**Air Bus Helicopter** ....
E35-2	1983-87	**Tipper Truck**, Silver/Blue or Red/Brown ....
E36-1	1975-77	**Healer-Wheeler 'AMBULANCE'**.................
E36-2	1979-80	**'COCA-COLA' Chevrolet Van** ....
E37	1976-79	**Porsche Carrera 'POLICE' Car**...................
E38	1980-83	**Jerry's Banger** **£15-20**
E39	1975-77	**Jaguar 'E' Type** **£35-45**
E40-1	1977-80	**Army Red Cross Helicopter** ....
E40-2	1979-81	**James Bond's Aston-Martin** **£75-125**
E41	1979-81	**James Bond Space Shuttle** **£15-20**
E42	1977-81	**'RESCUE' Range Rover**.............................
E43	1976-80	**Massey-Ferguson 3303 Farm Tractor with Blade**, Orange/Black, Yellow/Red or all Yellow.....................**£20-30**
E44-1	1976-78	**Raygo Rascal 600 Road Roller** ....
E44-2	1979-80	**Starship Liberator** **£50-75**
E45	1977-81	**Starsky and Hutch Ford Gran Torino**..........**£15-20**
E46	1976-80	**'POLICE' Helicopter**, White or Metallic blue body ....
E47	1978-80	**'SUPERVAN' (Chevrolet)**...........................
E48	1975-79	**Shovel Loader**, red ....
E49-1	1977-79	**Tipping Lorry** ....
E49-2	1981-83	**Woody Woodpecker's Car**...........................
E50	1979-80	**'Daily Planet' (Leyland) Van**, Red or Silver.................................**£15-20**
E51	1976-78	**Volvo 245 Estate Car**, Metallic green, White or Blue tailgate ....
E52-1	1976-79	**Mercedes Benz 240D 'TAXI'**.......................
E52-2	1982-83	**Scooby Doo's Vehicle** **£20-25**
E53	1977-79	**'FIRE' Launch**...
E54-1	1980-82	**'CORGI' Formula 1 Racer**, Black car, Yellow or White driver................................
E54-2	1976-78	**(54) Ford D1000 Container Truck**, Red/Yellow or Red/Orange ....
E55	1976-80	**Refuse Truck**, Blue/Yellow, Bronze/Blue or Green/White ....
E56	1979-80	**Chevrolet 'SPIDERVAN'** **£20-25**
E57-1	1975-77	**Ferrari 512s**, Blue body, number '6' ....
E57-2	1979-80	**Spiderbike** **£20-25**
E58	1976-78	**Beach Buggy** ....
E59-1	1980-83	**Tom's Cart** **£15-20**
E59-2	1977-79	**Mercedes 240D 'POLIZEI' Car** **£15-20**
E59-3	1982-84	**Mercedes 240D**, Blue, Red or White ....
E60	1977-79	**James Bond Lotus Esprit** **£50-75**
E61-1	1979-81	**Buick Regal 'SHERIFF' Car**................**£15-20**
E61-2	1980-82	**Ford Capri 3-litre** **£15-20**
E62	1977-80	**AMC Pacer**, Metallic Blue or Red ....
E63	1977-80	**'SURF RESCUE' Helicopter** ....
E64	1980-82	**'The Professionals' Ford Capri** **£15-20**
E65	1976-81	**Caravan Trailer** ....
E66-1	1976-79	**Centurion Tank** ....
E66-2	1980	**Ice Cream Van** ....
E67-1	1976-80	**Road Roller** ....
E67-2	1980-83	**Popeye's Tugboat** **£15-20**
E68	1977-79	**Kojak's Buick Regal** **£20-25**
E69	1976-80	**Batmobile** **£50-75**
E70-1	1975-77	**Cougar 'FIRE CHIEF'** ....
E70-2	1977-81	**Ford Torino 'FIRE CHIEF'** ....
E71	1980-85	**London Austin 'TAXI'** ....
E72-1	1975-77	**(72) Mercedes C111** ....
E72-2	1979-83	**Jaguar XJS**, Blue or Red body ....
		Jaguar XJS, Red body, White 'MOTOR SHOW' logo.................**£20-30**
E73	1980	**'DRAX' Helicopter** **£20-25**
E74	1978-80	**'RYDER TRUCK RENTAL' Leyland Van** ......
E75	1977-80	**Spidercopter** **£20-30**
E76	1976-78	**(76) Military Jeep** ....
E77	1977-80	**Poclain Digger**, Yellow/Red or White/Red...............
E78	1976-81	**Batcopter** **£30-40**
E79-1	1975-76	**Land Rover Military Ambulance** ....
E79-2	1980-83	**Olive Oyl's Aeroplane** **£15-20**
E80	1979-80	**'MARVEL COMICS' Van** **£20-25**
E81	1975-83	**Daimler Fleetline London Bus**, various logos, with or without faces at windows ....
E82-1	1975-78	**Can-Am Racer**, Metallic Blue ....
E82-2	1981-82	**Yogi Bear's Jeep** **£20-30**
E83-1	1975-77	**'COMMANDO' Armoured Car** ....
E83-2	1980-81	**'GOODYEAR' Blimp** ....
E84-1	1975-78	**Daimler Scout Car**....................................
E84-2	1980-83	**Bugs Bunny Vehicle** **£15-20**
E85	1975-78	**Skip Truck** ....
E86	1974-80	**Fiat X1-9**, Green body **£25-35**
		Fiat X1-9, Gold body, RN '4' **£15-20**
		Fiat X1-9, Gold body, RN '9', 'FIAT' ....
E87	1975-80	**Leyland Truck, 'COCA-COLA'** ....
		Leyland Truck, 'PEPSI-COLA' ....
		Leyland Truck, 'WEETABIX' ....
		Leyland Truck, 'W.H. SMITH' ....
E88	1975-80	**Mobile Crane** ....
E89	1975-82	**Citroën Dyane**, dark Yellow,Gold or Purple.........
E90	1977-79	**'FIREBALL' Chevrolet Van** ....
E91a	1977-79	**'GOLDEN EAGLE' Chevrolet Van** ....
E91b	1980-81	**'VANTASTIC' Chevrolet Van** (new casting) ....
E92	1977-81	**Volkswagen Polo**, Metallic Lime or darker Green body ....
E93-1	1977-78	**Tugboat**..
E93-2	1980-81	**Dodge Magnum** **£15-20**
E94-1	1975-77	**Porsche 917** ....
E94-2	1978-80	**'ADIDAS' Chevrolet Van** ....

95	1977-82	'COCA-COLA' Leyland Van ....
96-1	1975-78	**Field Gun**, military Green ....
96-2	1980-83	**Ford Thunderbird**, Red, Cream or Green ....
97-1	1977-78	**'EXXON' Petrol Tanker**..........................**£25-35**
97-2	1977-80	**'TEXACO' Petrol Tanker** ....
		'SHELL' Petrol Tanker ....
		'BP OIL' Petrol Tanker ....
98-1	1975-77	**Marcos** ....
98-2	1977-79	**Mercedes-Benz Mobile Shop** ....
98-3	1980-81	**'POLICE' Helicopter** ....
99	1979-81	**Jokermobile** **£30-40**
100	1981-83	**Hulk Cycle** **£30-40**
102	1981-83	**Renault 5 Turbo** ....
103	1981-83	**Ford Transit Wrecker** ....
104	1981-83	**Ford Mustang Cobra** ....
105	1981-83	**Ford Escort 1.3GL**, Metallic Green or Blue ....
E107	1981-83	**Austin Metro**, Metallic Dark Mid Blue ....
E108	1981-83	**Locomotive** ....
E111	1981-83	**Passenger Coach** ....
E112	1981-83	**Goods Wagon** ....
E113	1982-83	**Paddle Steamer** ....
E114	1981-83	**Stage Coach** ....
E115	1981-83	**James Bond 2cv Citroën** **£40-50**
E116	1982	**Mercedes-Benz 'ESPANA 82'** ....
J89	1988	**Mercedes 23/16 Racer**, White, 'Servis' ....
J90	1988	**Mercedes 23/16 Saloon**, Red ....
J91	1988	**Jaguar XJ40**, White, 'Police' ....
J93	1988	**Jaguar XJ40**, White, 'Jaguar' ....
J94	1988	**Mercedes 300E Estate**, Red ....
J95	1988	**Mercedes 300E Estate Taxi**, Yellow ....
J97	1988	**Land-Rover 110**, Red, 'Fire Salvage' ....
J98	1988	**Porsche Targa**, Red ....
J99	1988	**Porsche Targa**, White, 'Turbo' ....
E117	1982	**Chevrolet 'ESPANA 82' Custom Van** ....
E119	1983	**'FLUGHAFEN-FEURWEHR'**
		Fire Engine (German Issue) **£15-20**
120	?	**Leyland Van, 'Eiszeit'**
		(German Issue) **£15-20**
120	1983	**Ice Cream Van, 'FRESHLICHE'**
		(German Issue) **£15-20**
121	1983	**Chevrolet Van, 'TECHNISCHER'**
		(German Issue) **£15-20**
E123	1982-83	**'AIRPORT RESCUE' Tender** ....
124	1982-83	**Mercedes-Benz 500SL** ....
125	1982-83	**Ford Transit Lorry** ....
E125	1983	**Ford Dropside Truck** ....
126	1982-83	**Ford Transit Breakdown,**
		'ABSCHIEPPDIENST',
		(German Issue) **£15-20**
127	1982-83	**'ADAC' Car**, (German Issue) **£20-25**
128	1982-83	**Fred's Flyer** **£25-35**
129	1982-83	**Ford Sierra 2.3 Ghia,**
		Blue, Red or Silver body..................
131	1982-83	**Ferrari 308GTS, 'Magnum PI'** **£25-35**
133	1982-83	**Buick Regal 'POLICE' Car,**
		'Magnum PI' **£25-35**
134	1982-83	**Barney's Buggy**, Red/Orange,
		(The Flintstones') **£25-35**
135	1982-83	**Austin Metro 'DATAPOST'** ....
E136	1982-82	**Ferrari 308GTS**, Red or Black..................
E137	1982-84	**VW Turbo** ....
E138	1982-84	**Rover 3500** ....
E139	1982-84	**Porsche 911 Turbo** ....

E140	1982-84	**Ford Mustang Cobra** ....
E141	1982-84	**Ford Capri S 'ALITALIA'** ....
E143	1983-84	**Leyland 'ROYAL MAIL' Van**......................
E144	1983-84	**'BRITISH GAS' Van** ....
E145	1983-84	**'BRITISH TELECOM' Van** ....
E146	1983-84	**Ford Transit Pick-Up, 'Wimpey'** ....
E147	1983-84	**Leyland 'ROADLINE' Lorry** ....
E148	1983-84	**USS Enterprise** **£15-20**
E149	1983	**Klingon Warship** **£15-20**
E150	1983	**'Simon and Simon' Police Car**......................
E151	1983	**Wilma's Coupé** **£25-35**
E152	1983	**'Simon and Simon' 1957 Chevy** ....
E156	1983	**1957 Chevy** ....
E160	1983	**VW Hot Rod** ....
E161	1983	**Opel Corsa 13SR** ....
E170	?	**Vauxhall Nova** ....
E174	1983	**Quarry Truck** ....
175	?	**Ford Escort** ....
E175	1983	**Pipe Truck** ....
176	?	**Ford Capri 'S'** ....
E177	1983	**'Corgi Chemco' Tanker** ....
E178	1983	**'Corgi' Container Truck** ....
E179	1983	**Chevy Corvette**, Yellow or Aqua Blue ....
E180	1983	**Pontiac Firebird SE** ....
181	?	**Mercedes 300sl** ....
E182	1983	**4x4 Renegade Jeep** ....
E183	1983	**Renegade Jeep with Hood** ....
E184	1983	**Range Rover** ....
E185	1983	**Baja Off Road Van** ....
190	1983	**Austin Metro** ....
190	1983	**Buick Regal** ....
191	1983	**Rover 3500** ....
192	1983	**Triumph TR7**, 'British Airways' ....
192	1983	**Mercedes 'Arabic' Ambulance** ....
193	1983	**Chubb 'Arabic' Fire Truck** ....
195	1983	**Leyland Van 'Arabic Miranda'** **£15-25**
E196	1983	**'Police Tactical Force' Van** ....
198	1983	**James Bond Citroën 2cv** **£25-35**
E200	1983	**Rover SDI** with pencil sharpener in boot ..**£30-40**
201	1983	**Chevrolet Van 'Arabic Team'** **£15-25**
E203	1983	**Fiat X19**, Orange/Red or Yellow **£30-40**
E204	1983	**Renault 5 Turbo**......................
E205	1983	**Porsche 911**......................
E206	1983	**Buick Regal** ....
208	1983	**Ford Sierra 'Notartz'** **£15-25**
209	1983	**Leyland Van 'DBP'** ....
210	1983	**Matra Rancho 'Safari Park'** ....
211	1983	**Ford Escort 'Fahrschule'** **£15-25**
212	1983	**VW Polo 'Siemens'** ....
219	1983	**Ford Sierra 'Polizei'** **£15-25**
222	1983	**Chevrolet Van 'Swissair'** ....
223	1983	**Matra Rancho 'Safari Park'** ....
224	1983	**Chevrolet Van 'Rivella'** **£15-25**
226	1983	**Ford Wrecker 'Abschleppdienst'** **£15-25**
228	1983	**Leyland Van 'Waser Papeterie'** **£15-25**
250	1983	**Simon Snorkel 'Brandbil'** **£15-25**
251	1983	**ERF Fire Tender** **£15-20**
252	1983	**Ford Transit Wrecker 'Falck'** **£15-25**
253	1983	**Mercedes Ambulance 'Falck'** **£15-25**
254	1983	**Mercedes 240D 'Falck'** **£15-25**
?	?	**Leyland Van 'Geest'**, special card **£20-30**
?	?	**Chevrolet Van 'Unichem'** **£15-25**
E2209	?	**James Bond 'Aerocar'**. ('The Man With the
		Golden Gun'). Inner tray packaging..............**£200-300**

2601	**Batman Triple-Pack** **£175-225**
E2001	**Multi Garage Complex**. 4-garage complex (plastic)............**£30-35**
E3001	**Multi Garage and three cars** **£45-55**
E3005	**Leisure Time Set**...........................**£100-125**
E3013	**Emergency Rescue Set** (Rescue Station + 3 models)...........**£70-85**
E3109	**Agricultural Set**. Contains: 2 Tractors, Land-Rover,
	3 Trailers, 2 Huts **£90-110**
3019/1	**James Bond 'Octopussy' Set**, 1983-84 ....**£200-300**
E3021	**Crimefighters Gift Set** (E45, E60, E68, E69, E75, E78) .**£200-300**
E3023	**Mercedes Transporter plus 4 cars** **£75-100**
E3024	**Construction Gift Set** (6 vehicles)...........................**£75-100**
E3026	**Emergency Gift Set** (6 vehicles)...........................**£75-100**
E3030	**James Bond 'The Spy Who Loved Me' Gift Set**, 1976-77
	(E3, E60, 'Jaws' Van, Mercedes, Speedboat)..................**£300-400**

E3071	**'Growlers' 6-Car Speed Set**. Ford GT70, Ferrari 312s,
	Marcos XP, CanAm Racer, Jaguar 'E'-type, Porsche 917 .**£100-150**
E3080	**Batman Gift Set**, 1980-82
	(E20, E23, E69, E78, E99) **£300-400**
E3081	**Superman Gift Set** (E6, E11, E17, E47, E50) **£125-150**
E3082	**James Bond 'Goldfinger' Gift Set**, 1980-82,
	(E40, E41, E60, E73, plus 'Jaws' van)...........................**£300-400**
E3084	**Cartoon Characters Set** (E19, E38, E58, E67, E79) **£100-125**
E3100	**Construction Gift Set** (7 items)...........................**£75-100**
E3101	**Fire Gift Set** (6 items)...........................**£75-100**
E3103	**Emergency Gift Set** (6 items) **£75-100**
E3105	**Transporter Gift Set** (Mercedes Transporter + 4 cars)......**£75-100**
E3108	**'Scoobie and His Friends' Set** Contains 5 items...............**£75-100**
E3184	**'Data Post' Set** Contains 6 items...........................**£40-50**

'J' Series

J1	1984	NASA Space Shuttle	**£15-25**	J16	1984	Ford Capri, White, Silver or Blue	**£15-25**
J1	1988	Ford Capri, 'Duckhams'	**£15-25**	J16	1988	BMW 3251 Saloon, Red	**£15-25**
J2	1984-85	Dump Truck	**£10-15**	J17	1984	London FX4 Taxi	**£10-15**
J2	1988	Iveco Tanker, 'Esso'	**£15-25**	J18	1984-85	Jaguar XJS, White, Silver or Green	**£15-25**
J3	1984-85	Triumph TR7, Black or Red/Blue	**£15-25**	J19	1984	Matra Rancho, Green/Black or Blue	**£15-25**
J4	1984	Starfighter, (Buck Rogers)	**£15-25**	J20	1984-88	London Bus, Red	**£10-15**
J4	1988	Ford Transit Van, 'Kremer Racing'	**£15-25**	J39	1988	Chevrolet 'ROYAL MAIL' Van	**£15-25**
J5	1984-85	'Holiday Inn' Bus, Green or White	**£15-25**	J62	1985	Mobile Shop	**£15-25**
J6	1984	Rover 'Police' Car	**£15-25**	J63	1988	Ford Transit Van, 'Royal Mail'	**£10-15**
J7	1984	ERF Fire Engine	**£15-25**	J64	1988	Land-Rover 110, Yellow, 'AA'	**£15-25**
J8	1984-85	Simon Snorkel Fire Engine	**£15-25**	J66	1988	Land-Rover 110, White, 'Police'	**£15-25**
J9	1984-85	Mobile Cement Mixer	**£10-15**	J73	1988	Ford Escort XR3i	**£15-25**
J9	1988	Iveco Container, 'Mars'	**£15-25**	J74	1988	Land-Rover 110, White, 'Safari Rally'	**£15-25**
J10	1984	Aston-Martin DB5, Red	**£15-25**	J77	1988	Ferrari Testarossa, White	**£15-25**
J10	1985	Aston-Martin DB5, Yellow, 'DB6'	**£15-25**	J79	1988	Mercedes 300E Ambulance	**£15-25**
J11	1984	Volvo Estate Car, White	**£15-25**	J81	1988	Buick, Blue, 'Police NYPD'	**£15-25**
J11	1985	Volvo Support Car, White, 'Castrol'	**£15-25**	J85	1988	Porsche 935 Racer	**£15-25**
J12	1984	Skip Truck, Red/White	**£15-25**	J86	1988	Porsche 935 Racer	**£15-25**
J12	1988	Iveco Tanker, 'BP Oil'	**£15-25**	J87	1988	Porsche 935, Red, no markings	**£10-15**
J13	1984	Refuse Truck, Yellow/Grey	**£10-15**	J90	1988	Escort 'DATAPOST', '66'	**£15-25**
J13	1988	Iveco Truck, 'Pepsi'	**£15-25**	J91	1989	Escort 'DATAPOST', '77'	**£15-25**
J14	1984	Mercedes 240D	**£10-15**	J92	1988	Metro 'DATAPOST', '66'	**£15-25**
J14	1985	Mercedes 240D Rally Car	**£15-25**	J93	1989	Metro 'DATAPOST', '77'	**£15-25**
J15	1984	Lotus Esprit	**£15-25**	J94	1989	Metro Van 'ROYAL MAIL'	**£15-25**
J15	1988	Ford Transit Van, 'Police'	**£10-15**				

900 Series Issues

90010	1991	Ford Transit Van 'Kremer Racing'	**£10-15**	90390	1991	Mercedes Ambulance, White, red crosses	**£10-15**
90013	1991	Ford Transit Van 'Police', Dark Blue	**£10-15**	90420	1991	Buick 'Police' Car, Black/White	**£10-15**
90015	1991	Ford Transit Van 'RAC', White	**£10-15**	90421	1991	Buick 'Fire Chief' Car, Red/White	**£10-15**
90030	1991	ERF Fire Engine, Red/Silver	**£10-15**	90430	1991	Volvo 760 Saloon, Metallic Grey	**£10-15**
90035	1991	Simon Snorkel Fire Engine, Red/White	**£10-20**	90440	1991	Porsche 935 Racer, Red, '33'	**£10-15**
90040	1991	Iveco Container Truck 'Wispa'	**£10-15**	90460	1991	Mercedes 23/16, Blue, 'Mobil', 'Koni'	**£10-15**
90065	1991	Iveco Tanker 'Shell'	**£10-15**	90461	1991	Mercedes 23, Red	**£10-15**
90076	1991	BMW 325i, Metallic Silver-Blue	**£10-15**	90470	1991	Jaguar XJ40, 'Police', White	**£10-15**
90100	1991	Matra Rancho, Yellow, 'M'	**£10-15**	90471	1991	Jaguar XJ40, Metallic Bronze	**£15-20**
90125	1991	Ford Transit Wrecker 'Police'	**£10-15**	90500	1991	Helicopter, 'Police', White/Black	**£10-15**
90126	1991	Ford Transit Wrecker 'Kremer Racing'	**£10-15**	90520	1991	Ford Thunderbird, Black	**£10-15**
90145	1991	BMW M3, Black/White	**£10-15**	90540	1991	Ford Mustang, Blue, 'Goodyear', '77'	**£10-15**
90160	1991	Ford Sierra, Metallic Blue	**£10-15**	90541	1991	Ford Mustang, White, Red stripes, '7'	**£10-15**
90190	1991	Ferrari Testarossa, Red, 'Ferrari'	**£10-15**	90550	1991	BMW 850i, Black	**£10-15**
90200	1991	Corvette, Black/Red, 'Flame' design	**£10-15**	90560	1991	Ferrari 348 TB, Red	**£10-15**
90201	1991	Corvette, Red/White, 'Vette'	**£10-15**	90570	1991	Mercedes 500sl, Red	**£10-15**
90300	1991	Pontiac Firebird, Silver, Red bodyline	**£10-15**	90580	1991	Jaguar XJR9, White/Purple, 'Jaguar'	**£10-15**
90301	1991	Pontiac Firebird, Yellow/Black, 'Fire Bird'	**£10-15**	91000	1991	MAN Container Truck 'Perrier', Green	**£10-15**
90310	1991	Military Jeep, Olive body, Brown top	**£10-15**	91020	1991	MAN Tanker 'Texaco', White	**£10-15**
90360	1991	US Custom Van, Black/Red, 'Team Racing'	**£10-15**	91040	1991	MAN Open Back Tipper, Yellow	**£10-15**
90371	91	Land-Rover, 'Coastguard', Blue/Yellow	**£10-15**				
90374	1991	Land-Rover, 'Emergency - Fire', Red	**£10-15**				

Corgi Juniors Twin-Packs

Corgi Juniors bubble-packed in pairs from 1977 approximately.

2501	London Bus and Taxi	**£20-30**	2518	Mercedes and Caravan	**£25-35**
2502	Land Rover Breakdown and Jaguar XJS	**£30-40**	2519	Batmobile and Batboat	**£100-150**
2503	Land Rover and Horse Box	**£20-30**	2520	Rescue Set	**£30-40**
2504	Land Rover Breakdown and AMC Pace Car	**£30-40**	2521	James Bond Lotus and Aston-Martin DB5	**£70-80**
2505	'DAILY PLANET' Van and Helicopter	**£20-30**	2522	Army Attack Set	**£30-40**
2506	Supermobile and Superman Van	**£50-60**	2523	Police Car and Helicopter	**£25-35**
2507	Tom's Cart and Jerry's Banger	**£20-30**	2524	Custom Van Twin	**£25-35**
2508	Popeye's Tugboat and Olive Oyl's Aeroplane	**£20-30**	2525	Triumph TR7 and Dinghy on Trailer	**£40-50**
2510	Formula 1 and Formula 5000 Racing Cars	**£30-40**	2526	Dumper Truck and Shovel Loader	**£25-35**
2511	Sting Helicopter and Scout Car	**£20-30**	2527	'Kojak' and New York Police Helicopter	**£50-60**
2512	Space Shuttle and Star Ship 'Liberator'	**£40-50**	2528	Starsky and Hutch Twin Pack	**£50-60**
2513	Fire Tender and Ambulance	**£20-30**	2529	James Bond Lotus and Helicopter	**£80-100**
2514	Building Set	**£25-35**	2530	Rescue Range Rover and Helicopter	**£30-40**
2515	Citroën and Speedboat	**£25-35**	?	AMF 'Ski-daddler' Snowmobile and trailer	**£100-150**
2516	Tractor and Tipping Trailer	**£25-35**			

Corgi Super Juniors and Super Haulers

Corgi Super Juniors and Super Haulers were introduced in 1970.
See the 'Modern Diecasts' section for details.

Corgi Rockets

This model range was issued between 1970 and 1972 to compete against Mattel 'Hot Wheels' and similar products. The models had 'WhizzWheels' and featured a special 'Tune-Up' system which increased the play value and speed of the virtually frictionless wheels. In addition they were very robust, being advertised as 'four times stronger' than most other diecast racers. To begin with seven Corgi Juniors were adapted as Rockets and five of those received a superb vacuum metallised finish. A range of accessories was also issued in the form of 'Speed Circuits' etc, and each car was issued with a special 'Golden Tune-Up Key' which released the base. The bubble-packed models are difficult to find in top condition and the prices reflect their scarcity.

Ref	Year	Model name	Colours, features, details	Market Price Range
D 901	1970-72	Aston-Martin DB-6	Metallic Deep Gold body, Green interior	£60-70
D 902	1970-72	Jaguar XJ-6	Metallic Green body, Cream interior	£80-100
D 903	1970-72	Mercedes-Benz 280 SL	Metallic Orange body, White interior	£60-70
D 904	1970-72	Porsche Carrera 6	Orange-Yellow body, Black number '19'	£60-70
D 905	1970-72	'The Saint's Volvo P1800	White body, Blue/White 'Saint' label on bonnet	£80-100
D 906	1970-72	Jensen Interceptor	Metallic Red body, Yellow interior	£60-70
			Pink / Cream body	£80-100
D 907	1970-72	Cadillac Eldorado	Metallic Copper body, White interior	£60-70
D 908	1970-72	Chevrolet Astro	Metallic Red/Black body	£40-50
D 909	1970-72	Mercedes-Benz C111	Red or Blue body, White interior	£40-50
D 910	1970-72	Beach Buggy	Orange body, Black interior	£30-40
D 911	1970-72	Marcos XP	Gold body, Chrome interior	£30-40
?	1970-72	Ford Capri	Purple body	£40-50
D 913	1970-72	Aston-Martin DBS	Metallic Blue, Yellow interior	£70-90
D 916	1970-72	Carabo Bertone	Metallic Green/Blue, Orange interior	£20-30
D 917	1970-72	Pininfarina Alfa-Romeo	Metallic Purple/White	£20-30
D 918	1970-72	Bitzzarini Manta	Metallic Dark Blue, White interior	£20-30
D 919	1970-72	'Todd Sweeney' Stock Car	Red/Purple, Yellow/Black front, RN '531'	£100-125
D 920	1970-72	'Derek Fiske' Stock Car	White/Red, Silver bonnet, Red logo, RN '304'	£100-125
D 921	1970-72	Morgan Open Sports	Metallic Red body, Black seats	£60-75
D 922	1970-72	Rally Ford Capri	Yellow body, Orange/Black stripe, RN '8'	£100-125
			Green body, Black bonnet, (GS 2 model)	£60-75
D 923	1970-72	'James Bond' Ford Escort	White body, Pale Blue stripes, 'JAMES BOND', White '007' and 'SPECIAL AGENT' logos (From film 'On Her Majesty's Secret Service')	£500-700
D 924	1970-72	Mercury Cougar XR7	Red body with Black roof, Yellow interior	£30-40
		'James Bond' issue:	Red/Black with Yellow side flash, interior and skis on roof rack (From film 'On Her Majesty's Secret Service')	£300-400
D 925	1970-72	'James Bond' Ford Capri	White body with Black/White check design, 2 bonnet stripes and RN '6' (From film 'On Her Majesty's Secret Service')	£300-400
D 926	1970-72	Jaguar 'Control Car'	Metallic Brown body, Red roof blade, Blue/White figures	£200-250
D 927	1970-72	Ford Escort Rally	White body, Red RN '18', 'DAILY MIRROR' labels on doors, '1970 Mexico World Cup Rally Winner'	£300-400
D 928	1970-72	Mercedes 280 SL 'SPECTRE'	Black body with Red 'SPECTRE', plus boars head design	£300-400
D 930	1970-72	Bertone Barchetta	Metallic Green over White body, Red interior	£40-50
D 931	1970-72	'Old MacDonalds Truck'	Yellow cab, Brown rear, Silver engine	£100-125
D 933	1970-72	'Holmes Wrecker'	White or Blue cab, White back, 'AUTO RESCUE'	£100-125
D 937	1970-72	Mercury Cougar	Metallic Dark Green body, Yellow interior and spoiler	£20-30

Corgi Rockets Gift Sets

D 975	1970	Super Stock Gift Set 1	Contains D 905, D 919, Trailer and 3 figures	£250-350
D 976	1970	Super Stock Gift Set 2	Contains Green/Black D 922, D 920, Trailer and 3 figures	£250-350
D 977	1970	Super Stock Gift Set 3	Contains D 926, D 919, D 920 and 5 figures	£600-800

The listing above has been prepared from a Corgi Rockets 1970 catalogue. The sets themselves have not been seen and further information is required.

D 978		'OHMSS' Gift Set	Models of cars in the James Bond film 'On Her Majesty's Secret Service': D 923 and D 925 (as driven in the ice-racing scene), D 924 (as driven by 'Tracey'), D 928 (as driven by the Chief of 'SPECTRE')	£2,000-2,500
			NB Male skier has red metal base, red/yellow skis and yellow poles.	

Corgi Rockets Accessories

D 2051	1970	Action Speedset	One car, 'Autostart', 12 ft of track	NGPP
D 2052	1970	Super Autobatics Speedset	One car, 'Autostart', 16 ft of track plus 'leaps' etc	NGPP
D 2053	1970	Clover Leaf Special Speedset	One car, 'Autostart', track plus 'clover-leaf leaps' etc	NGPP
D 2058	1970	Race-Abatic Speedset	Two cars, 'Autostart', 2 x 16 ft of track plus 'leaps' etc	NGPP
D 2071	1970	Jetspeed Circuit	One car, 'Superbooster', 16 ft of track plus 'leaps' etc	NGPP
D 2074	1970	Triple-Leap Speed Circuit	One car, 19 ft, 6 in of track plus 'leaps' etc	NGPP
D 2075	1970	Grand Canyon Speed Circuit	One car, 12 ft of track	NGPP
D 2079	1970	World Champion Speedset	Two cars, 2 x 16 ft of track, 2 Boosters	NGPP

D 1928 **Rocketlube Tune-up Kit** ...	D 1936 **Space Leap** ...	D 1963 **Track** (16ft) ...	D 1977 **Lap Counter** ...
D 1931 **Superleap** ...	D 1937 **Autostart** ...	D 1970 **Super Booster** ...	D 1978 **Pitstop** ...
D 1934 **Autofinish** ...	D 1938 **Super Crossover** ...	D 1971 **Hairpin Tunnel** ...	D 1979 **Spacehanger Bend** ...
D 1935 **Connections** (3) ...	D 1945 **Adaptors** (3) ...	D 1976 **Quickfire Start** ...	

Corgi Rockets Catalogues

no ref	1969	8-page booklet	listing the first 7 issues, Green model on cover	£20-25
no ref	1970	16-page booklet	listing most issues, good pictures of rare models, sets and accessories	£30-35

Catalogues (UK Editions)

Information taken from the Cecil Gibson Archives and this Catalogue compiler's own collection of reference material.
Note: 'Concertina' leaflets were issued with models sold in the early Blue boxes.

Ref	Year	Publication	Cover features, details	Market Price Range
no ref	1956	Concertina leaflet	Blue cover, famous Corgi dog, shows first 14 models, no prices	£15-20
no ref	1956	Concertina leaflet	Blue cover with Red/Gold Corgi dog. Depicts first 14 models and shows prices of both normal and mechanical models	£20-25
50/157/K1	1957	Concertina leaflet	Blue cover with Red/Gold Corgi dog. Depicts ten models and lists the mechanical models in red	£5-10
40/257/K1	1957	Concertina leaflet	Blue cover with Red/Gold Corgi dog. Depicts ten models but does not list mechanical models	£5-10
40/257/K2	1957	Concertina leaflet	As previous leaflet but with the addition of 208	£5-10
50/557/K3	1957	Concertina leaflet	As 40/257/K2 plus 100,150, 408, 454, 'WOW! CORGI TOYS' logo	£5-10
100/1057/K3	1957	Concertina leaflet	Blue cover showing 100, 150, 207, 208, 302, 405, 408, 453, 455	£5-10
50/1057/K4	1958	Concertina leaflet	Blue cover, 'WOW! CORGI TOYS' logo. Listings include models 102, 406/7, and first 'MAJOR' toy (1101)	£15-20
50/1157/K4	1957	Concertina leaflet	Cover shows 102, 210, 406, 407, 412, 1101, 'WOW! CORGI TOYS' logo	£5-10
52/258/K5	1958	Concertina leaflet	Cover shows GS 1 and 2, 101, 211, 302, 457, 459, 1100, 1401, 1450	£5-10
52/258/K6	1958	Concertina leaflet	As previous leaflet plus 350, 351	£5-10
300/658/K7	1958	Concertina leaflet	Shows GS 3, 151, 209, 458, 'NEW CORGI TOYS' logo and prices	£5-10
25/257/C1/UK	1957	Four-fold leaflet	'Blue box' 208 Jaguar on cover, 15 model pictures inside	£50-75
25/257/C2/UK	1957	Four-fold leaflet	As previous leaflet but with 24 model pictures	£50-75
50/1057/C3/UK	1957	Four-fold leaflet	Shows GS 1 Bedford Transporter and 6 cars on Blue/Yellow cover with details of 100, 150, 200-8, 210, 300-2, 403-8, 412, 452-5, 1101	£25-30
25/1157/C4/UK	1957	Four-fold leaflet	As previous leaflet plus 101 and 102	£25-30
no ref	1958	Four-fold leaflet	As previous leaflet plus 211 No prices, car listing or ref no	NGPP
650/858/C8	1958	Catalogue	First 'book' catalogue Cover depicts boy playing with Bloodhound Missile, many other vehicles	NGPP
no ref	1959	Four-fold leaflet	Blue cover with 'THE ROCKET AGE WITH CORGI TOYS' (issued with Rocket Age models)	£15-20
no ref	9/59	Interim leaflet	Lists 152, 50 Tractor, 350 Thunderbird, new TT van and accessories	NGPP
UK 9/59	1959	16 page Catalogue	Cover features Massey Ferguson Tractor No. 50 and BRM Racer No. 152. Agricultural and 'MAJOR' issues (No.1100 etc) are listed	£30-40
no ref	1959	Single page leaflet	Features Renault Floride plus 'STRAIGHT FROM THE MOTOR SHOW' logo	£10-15
no ref	1959	Two fold leaflet	Features 'AUTHENTIC ROCKET AGE MODELS' logo and models plus 1102 Tractor Dozer	£10-15
no ref	1960	Interim leaflet	Depicts M1 Motorway scene	£5-10
UK 9/60	1960	20 page Catalogue	Cover has motorway bridge scene and Corgi models. This catalogue was the first with listings of 'CHIPPERFIELDS' issues	£30-40
UK 9/61	1961	24 page Catalogue	Racetrack scene on cover. Listings and pictures include new Sports Cars, Express Coach and Kits	£20-25
no ref	1961	Price List	Single double-sided sheet (size as catalogue), 'Revised price list as from August 1961'. 'UK' on back	£1-2
no ref	1962	Two-fold Checklist	Leaflet front cover depicts Blue/Yellow 'CORGI TOYS' plus seven models and their features Red/Grey interior plus first check list	£15-20
C/100/62	1963	32 page Catalogue	Cover depicts schoolboy (in red cap and blazer) crossing road with Corgi dog. No catalogue date is shown on front cover	£50-75
no ref	1963	32 page Catalogue	Same cover as C/100/62 but boy's cap and blazer are Blue. '1963-64' is shown on front cover	£15-20
Playcraft Toys Ltd 1964	1964	Two-fold Checklist	Leaflet with Blue/Yellow 'Corgi Toys' design on cover featuring 241 Ghia	£15-20
Playcraft Toys Ltd 1964	1965	40 page Catalogue	Cover logos: 'CORGI TOYS', 'CORGI CLASSICS', '1965'. Contains Classics and first Routemaster in the listings	£15-20
Mettoy Playcraft (Sales) Ltd 1965	1965	Two-fold Checklist	Leaflet with six model cars from six different nations featured on the cover	£5-10
Playcraft Toys Ltd 1965	1966	40 page Catalogue	Cover depicts model 261 James Bond's Aston Martin DB5. Contents give details of special Rallye Monte Carlo issues. 'Price 3d'	£15-20
C2038/66	1966	Leaflet	Cover proudly states 'MODEL CAR MAKERS TO JAMES BOND'	£8-12
C2039/4/66	1966	Four-fold Checklist	Leaflet similar to previous with 'MODEL CAR MAKERS TO JAMES BOND'. The contents feature 1127 Simon Snorkel etc	£10-15
C2017/9/66	1967	48 page Catalogue	The cover and contents are dominated by Film and TV-related models of 'BATMAN' and 'THE AVENGERS' etc. Also contains details of a model never issued – 498 Mini Countryman	£15-20
Mettoy Playcraft (Sales) 1967	1967	Three-fold Checklist	Leaflet cover shows 'NEW' in 5 languages plus 1142 Holmes Wrecker. Listings include 1967 Monte Carlo Rally winners	£15-20
C/2017/7/67	67-68	48 page Catalogue	Model 262 Lincoln Continental makes up the covers. 'Price 6d'. 2 models shown but not issued: 9022 Daimler 38 with Hood, and 9014 Model 'T' Van 'Lyons Tea' (eventually issued as Corgi Classic C865 in Feb 1986)	£10-15
C2017/9/68	1968	48 page Catalogue	Cover features 268 'Chitty Chitty Bang Bang'. Listings include 803 'Yellow Submarine' and 'Take-off Wheels' issues	£15-20
Mettoy Playcraft (Sales) Ltd 1969	1969	Seven-fold Checklist	Leaflet has 'Concorde' model on cover plus 302 Hillman Hunter. Listings include 'Corgi Comics', 'CHIPPERFIELD' and Scammell Transporter Set No.48	£5-10
The Mettoy Co Ltd 1970	1970	48 page Catalogue	Cover depicts 388 Mercedes-Benz C111, first 'WhizzWheels' models listed	£5-10
no ref	1970	Corgi Juniors Collectors Album	28 pages. To hold cards cut from Corgi Junior bubble packs. Has details of featured models below space for card. Centre two pages have 'Corgi Toys' adverts plus articles, etc.	

1970 Mettoy Co Ltd ..1971 C2017 Petty	**Two-fold Checklist**	....Leaflet with 6 WhizzWheels models on the cover. The final 'Take-Off Wheels' issues are listed	**£5-10**
7/71/LOI7b ....1972 C2017 Petty	**48 page Catalogue**	.....Cover shows 1972 Car models. Excellent 'CORGI COMICS' pictures inside	**£5-10**
7/71/LOI7B (2nd)......1972	**48 page Catalogue**	....Cars across both covers	**£5-10**
no ref.........................1972	**'Corgi Juniors with WhizzWheels'**	...........'© 1972 The Mettoy Company' on rear. 4 pages (A4). Includes 'Juniors Extra' section of TV models	**£5-10**
1973 Mettoy Co Ltd ..1973	**40 page Catalogue**	....F1 Racing Cars featured on the cover. Good Racing/Rally pictures within	**£5-10**
1974 Mettoy Co Ltd ..1974	**40 page Catalogue**	.....'John Player' Lotus on cover, good Military and Aircraft pictures	**£5-10**
1975 Mettoy Co Ltd ..1975	**Three-fold leaflet**	......Helicopters, Noddy's Car, etc on the cover. Numbers given 'C' prefix	**£5-10**
1976 Mettoy Co Ltd ..1976	**Three-fold leaflet**	......First page features 'KOJAK'. Good Roadmaking and Public Services listings	**£5-10**
C2210 1977	**48 page Catalogue**	....Silver Jubilee Coach on cover. Large section listing Corgi 'Juniors'	**£5-10**
The Mettoy Co Ltd....1978	**48 page Catalogue**	.....James Bond's Lotus on cover, 'JEAN RICHARD PINDER' models within	**£5-10**
C2250 1979	**48 page Catalogue**	.....James Bond's Space Shuttle C649 'MOONRAKER' is featured on the cover, and 'SUPERMAN' and 'THE MUPPETS' are listed inside	**£5-10**
C2270 1980	**48 page Catalogue**	.....Rover 3500 'POLICE' C339 and C1001 HCB ANGUS are the cover features. Good listings of Emergency vehicles includes foreign 'POLICE' issues	**£5-10**
C2285 1981	**32 page Catalogue**	.....'CORGI' container on cover. Listings feature Film/TV models	**£5-10**
C2337 1982	**32 page Catalogue**	....Cover features 'Gull-wing' Mercedes (C802), 'Corgitronics' within	**£5-10**
Mettoy Co PLC 1983	**36 page Catalogue**	....Boxed models on cover, new Mercedes and Scania trucks inside	**£5-10**
no ref.........................1984	**32 page Catalogue**	.....'CORGI `84' and boxed models on cover. Large scale '800' series cars listed. This was the last catalogue to display Corgi Dog emblem	**£3-5**
no ref.........................1985	**48 page Catalogue**	....Cover shows new 'CORGI' trade name logo. The new 'CLASSICS' Commercials range is listed	**£3-5**

Trade Catalogues

Catalogues for trade purposes have been produced for some years and occasionally are offered for sale to collectors. No information is available on catalogues issued before 1980 but those from the 1980-90 decade tend to be in the **£5** to **£15** range.

An imaginative illustration features on the cover of this **1966 Corgi catalogue**.

Overseas Editions of Corgi Catalogues, Leaflets and Box Inserts

The overseas editions are comprised of specially amended U.K. editions and there are many versions. They may be identified by:

- All the text being in the relevant language.
- A special reference number (but not always)
  e.g. 52/258/K5 AUSTRALIA.
- An adapted checklist/pricelist in the language/currency of the country concerned.
- The name of the country either on the cover, on page two, or on the checklist.
- Some complete catalogues were issued with all the text being in the language concerned, e.g. French, German, etc.
- Normally overseas editions, unlike U.K. editions, do not display the catalogue price on the cover. The exception to this rule being those issued with all the text in the language concerned.

Identifying Overseas Catalogues/Leaflets/Box Inserts

As stated in the introduction, the overseas editions are the same as the U.K. editions. Similarly the catalogues, leaflets and box inserts issued in any one particular year were the same for all overseas countries. The only basic differences being the reference numbers, the type of language and currency shown.

The following listing of overseas editions correspond with the country by country listings and will assist collectors identify the various editions. The reference codes shown, e.g. 52/258/K5 are common to all countries with a country reference being added as required, e.g. 52/258/K5 EAST AFRICA. The '258' refers to the month and year of issue, i.e. Feb. 1958.

Types of Catalogues Listed

Box Inserts - These were inserted in the early blue box issues circa 1957-1959. They have a single fold and contain a checklist with prices in the local currency, plus a few pictures of the latest models.

Catalogue Leaflets - These are large, full colour leaflets, usually listing the full range available, together with pictures plus a checklist with prices.

Catalogues - These may contain 16, 20, 32, 40 or 48 pages and are full colour booklets containing the complete current range.

Interim Leaflets - Usually a double folded leaflet issued to supplement the main catalogues. These contain six pages, plus a checklist of the latest issues.

The information contained in these listings has been obtained from Corgi archive material. Whilst many issues have been listed, we believe others exist and we would welcome any such information.

Overseas catalogues were produced in much smaller numbers than were the U.K. editions. Consequently as they seldom appear for sale, it is not possible to give their individual market prices. For guidance purposes however, some have been known to sell for prices in excess of **£100**. As a result the extremely rare issues such as British East Africa, West Africa, Malta, Hong Kong, etc. may be expected to attract a premium. In the circumstances all the editions have been categorised **NGPP**.

Ref	Year	Publication	Cover features, details

Leaflets, Box Inserts and Catalogues 1957 - 1982

Ref	Year	Publication	Cover features, details
20/657/C2	1957	**Catalogue Leaflet**	Unfolded size (11" x 8 3/4"). Cover shows 1st type blue box for 208 Jaguar.
15/158/C4	1958	**Catalogue Leaflet**	Unfolded size (1' x 11"). 1101 Car Transporter on cover.
10/258/C5	1958	**Catalogue Leaflet**	Unfolded size (1' x 11"). 1101 Car Transporter on cover.
40/258/C5	1958	**Catalogue Leaflet**	Same as previous.
52/258/K5	1958	**Box Insert**	1401 Corgi Service Ramp on cover.
52/258/K6	1958	**Box Insert**	350 'Thunderbird' Guided Missile on cover.
3.350/658/K7	1958	**Box Insert**	1401 Corgi Service Ramp on cover.
5/658/K7	1958	**Box Insert**	458 E.R.F. Truck & 209 Police Car on cover.
10/658/K7	1958	**Box Insert**	Same cover as previous issue.
120/1058/K8	1958	**Box Insert**	Same cover as previous issue.
40/1058/C8	1958	**16 page Catalogue**	Boy with large collection on cover.
---	1959	**20 page Catalogue**	Racing Car and Tractor design on cover.
---	1960	**20 page Catalogue**	Motorway picture on cover.
---	1960/61	**Interim Leaflet**	1119 H.D.L. Hovercraft, etc. on cover.
---	1961	**24 page Catalogue**	Formula 1 Racing Cars on cover.
---	1961/62	**Interim Leaflet**	231 Triumph Herald, etc. on cover.
C/100/62	1962/63	**32 page Catalogue**	Red boy with Corgi dog on cover.
---	1962/63	**Interim Leaflet**	224 Bentley and 304s Mercedes, etc. on cover.
C/100/62	1963/64	**32 page Catalogue**	Red boy with Corgi dog on cover.
---	1962/63	**Interim Leaflet**	224 Bentley & 304s Mercedes, etc. on cover.
---	1963/64	**40 page Catalogue**	Blue boy with Corgi on cover.
---	1964	**Interim Leaflet**	251 Hillman Imp, etc. on cover. 'Playcraft Toys Ltd. 1964' on checklist.
---	1964/65	**40 page Catalogue**	9001 1927 Bentley, etc. on cover. 'Playcraft Toys Ltd. 1964' on rear cover.
---	1965	**Interim Leaflet**	155 Lotus Climax Racing Car, etc. Mettoy playcraft (Sales) Ltd. 1965 on cover.
---	1965/66	**40 page Catalogue**	261 Aston Martin and with or without '1966' and 'Playcraft Toys Ltd. 1965' on cover.
C2017/9/66	1966	**48 page Catalogue**	Batman, Avengers, 007, Man from U.N.C.L.E. on cover.
C2017/7/67	1967/68	**48 page Catalogue**	262 Lincoln continental on cover. 'Mettoy Playcraft (Sales) Ltd. 1967' rear cover.
---	1967	**Interim Leaflet**	1142 'Holmes' Wrecker Recovery Vehicle on cover.
C2017/9/68	1969	**48 page Catalogue**	266 Chitty Chitty Bang Bang on cover.
---	1969	**Catalogue Leaflet**	Unfolded size 2'6" x 83/4" Concorde on cover. 'Mettoy Playcraft (Sales) Ltd. 1969' on rear cover.
---	1970	**48 page Catalogue**	388 Mercedes Benz C111 on cover.
---	1973	**40 page Catalogue**	152 Ferrari 312 B2 Racing Car, etc. on cover.
C2107	1974	**40 page Catalogue**	'Corgi '74' on cover.
C2111	1974	**40 page Catalogue**	'Corgi '74' on cover.
---	1975	**Catalogue Leaflet**	Unfolded. Size 2' x 8½", 'Corgi 75' on cover.
C2211	1977	**48 page Catalogue**	'Corgi 77' on cover.
C2222	1977	**32 page Catalogue**	'Corgi 77' on cover.

C2275	1980/81	**48 page Catalogue**	Fire 'RESCUE' Vehicle plus 1980/81 on cover.
C2282	1980/81	**32 page Catalogue**	Same as previous, but no Juniors included.
C2283	1980/81	**32 page Catalogue**	Same as previous.
C2290	1981/82	**32 page Catalogue**	'Corgi' Container on cover.
C2292	1981/82	**32 page Catalogue**	'Corgi' Container on cover.

African issues
English text - local currency

BRITISH EAST AFRICA

8/59	1959	**16 page Catalogue**	'British East Africa 8/59' on cover, along with a tractor and racing car.
9/60	1960	**20 page Catalogue**	'British East Africa 9/60' on cover.
---	1962/63	**Interim Leaflet**	'British East Africa' on checklist.
---	1961/62	**Interim Leaflet**	'British East Africa' on top of page two.

EAST AFRICA

52/258/K5 East Africa	Feb. 1958	**Box Insert**	'East Africa' on checklist.
---	1965	**Interim Leaflet**	'East Africa' plus 'Mettoy 1965' on checklist.
---	1964/65	**40 page Catalogue**	'East Africa 8/64' on checklist.

KENYA, UGANDA & TANGANYIKA

| 15/158/C3 KUT | Jan. 1958 | **Catalogue Leaflet** | 'Kenya, Uganda and Tanganyika' on checklist. |
| 3.350/658/K7/KEN.
-UG.-TAN | June 1958 | **Box Insert** | 'Ken.-Ug.-Tan' on checklist. |

RHODESIA Early Distributors: Coombe & Dewar Pty Ltd. P.O. Box 1572, Bulawayo and P.O. Box 663, Salisbury.

---	1961/2	**Interim Leaflet**	'Rhodesia' top of page two.
---	1962/3	**Interim Leaflet**	'Rhodesia' on checklist.
C/100/62	1962	**32 page Catalogue**	'Rhodesia 1/63' on checklist. Red boy on cover.
---	1964	**Interim Leaflet**	'Rhodesia' and 'Playcraft 1964' on checklist.
---	1965	**Interim Leaflet**	'Rhodesia' and 'Mettoy 1965' on checklist.

RHODESIA, ZAMBIA & MALAWI

| --- | 1965/66 | **40 page Catalogue** | 'Rhodesia/Zambia/Malawi 8/65' on checklist, plus '1965' on cover. |

SOUTH AFRICA & RHODESIA

| 52/258/K5
South Africa/Rhodesia | Feb 1958 | **Box Insert** | 'South Africa/Rhodesia' on checklist. |
| 52/258/K6
South Africa/Rhodesia | Feb 1958 | **Box Insert** | 'South Africa/Rhodesia' on checklist. |

SOUTH AFRICA

10/658/K7/S. Africa	June 1958	**Box Insert**	'S. Africa' on checklist page.
40/1058/C8/S. Africa	1958/59	**16 page Catalogue**	'S. Africa' on rear page.
---	1961/62	**Interim Leaflet**	'South Africa on page two.
---	1962/63	**Interim Leaflet**	'South Africa' on checklist.
---	1964	**Interim Leaflet**	'S. Africa' and 'Playcraft Toys Ltd. 1964' on checklist.
---	1965	**Interim Leaflet**	'South Africa' and 'Mettoy 1965' on checklist.
C/2017/9/66	1966	**48 page Catalogue**	'South Africa' on checklist and cover.
---	1967	**Interim Leaflet**	'South Africa' on cover, plus 'Mettoy, etc. 1967' on last page.
© 1970 Mettoy Co Ltd	1971	**2-fold checklist**	'Corgi Toys with WhizzWheels' plus 'Australia', 'S.Africa' and 'USA' on cover. Checklist has prices in all three currencies

NB As listed under CANADA a catalogue was issued in 1970 with a combined CANADA and SOUTH AFRICAN checklist.

Australia
Address of Corgi Club in 1959: The Secretary, Corgi Model Club (Australian Section),
P.O. Box 1607, M. Melbourne C1.

20/657/C2/AUS	June 1957	**Catalogue Leaflet**	Checklist dated 1.6.57. Cover shows early 'Blue Box' with Model 208.
52/258/K5/Australia	1958	**Box Insert**	Cover shows Model 350.
52/258/K6/Australia	1958	**Box Insert**	Cover shows 1401 Corgi Service Ramp.
10/658/K7/Aus	1958	**Box Insert**	Cover shows Models 209 & 458.
---	1959	**16 page Catalogue**	Australia 8/59 on cover.
---	1961/62	**Leaflet**	'Australia' on top of page two.
---	1962/63	**Leaflet**	'Australia' on checklist.
---	1967	**Leaflet**	'Australia' on cover. Page two.
© 1970 Mettoy Co Ltd	1971	**2-fold Checklist**	'Corgi Toys with WhizzWheels' plus 'Australia', 'S.Africa' and 'USA' on cover. Checklist has prices in all three currencies

Austria
German Text. "Kontrolliste fur den sammler"

20/657/C2/A	June 1957	**Leaflet**	'Austria' on checklist.
---	1964	**Interim Leaflet**	'Austria' on checklist.
---	1961/62	**Interim Leaflet**	'Austria' on top of page two.
---	1964/65	**40 page Catalogue**	'Austria 9/64' on checklist.
---	1965	**Interim Leaflet**	'Austria' on checklist.

Belgium

Early distribution: Joets Eisenmann, S.A., 111/113 Rui Masui, Bruxelles, Teleph: (02) 15.48.50.

English Text - (French Checklist). "Liste de Contrôlle pour le Collectionneur"
52/258/K6/Belgium	1958	**Box Insert**	'Belgium' on checklist.
5/658/K7/Belg.	1958	**Box Insert**	'Belg' on checklist.
---	1967	**Leaflet**	'Belgium' on cover.

English Text (Flemish Checklist). "Kontroleer zo de Verzameling"
C/2017/9/66	1966	**48 page Catalogue**	'Belgium' on cover and on checklist.
---	1967	**Leaflet**	Belgium (Flemish) on cover.

English Text (separate French and Flemish checklists)
---	1974	**40 page Catalogue**	'C2103 Belgium' on Flemish checklist plus 2107 on French checklist.
C2017/7/67	1967/68	**48 page Catalogue**	'Belgium 8/67' on Flemish checklist and 'Belgium' (French) '8/67' on French checklist.
---	1961/62	**Interim Leaflet**	'Belgium' on top of page two.
---	1962/63	**Interim Leaflet**	'Belgium' on checklist.
---	1963/4	**40 page Catalogue**	'Belgium 8/63' on checklist.
---	1964	**Interim Leaflet**	'Belgium' and 'Playcraft 1964' on checklist.
---	1965	**Interim Leaflet**	'Belgium' and 'Mettoy 1965' on checklist.
---	1967	**Leaflet**	'Belgium' on cover.
C/2017/7/67	1967/68	**48 page Catalogue**	'Belgium (French) 1967' on checklist.

English Text (French/Flemish combined checklist)
20/657/C2/B	1957	**Catalogue Leaflet**	'Belgium' on checklist.
20/258/C5/B	1958	**Catalogue Leaflet**	'Belgium' on checklist.

French Text - French checklist
120/1058/K8/Belg	1958	**Box Insert**	No. 458 E.R.F. on cover.
---	1960	**20 page Catalogue**	'Belgium 9/60' and Frs.3. - on cover.
---	1961	**24 page Catalogue**	'Belgium 9/61' and Frs.3. - on cover.
---	1965/66	**40 page Catalogue**	'Belgium 8/65' on checklist.

1958 Belgian Corgi Club: M. Le Secretaire du Club Corgi, Jouets Eisenmann, 20 BD M. Lemonnier, Bruxelles.

Canada

English text - local currency

40/258/C5/CA	1958	**Catalogue Leaflet**	'Canada' on checklist.
52/258/K5/Canada	1958	**Box Insert**	'Canada' on checklist.
52/258/K6/Canada	1958	**Box Insert**	'Canada' on checklist.
5/658/K7/CAN	1958	**Box Insert**	'CAN' on checklist.
Canada 9/60	1960	**20 page Catalogue**	'Canada 9/60' on cover.
Canada	1960/61	**Interim Leaflet**	'Canada' on checklist.
Canada 9/61	1961/62	**24 page Catalogue**	'Canada 9/61' on cover.
Canada	1961/62	**Interim Leaflet**	'Canada' on checklist.
C/100/62	1963	**32 page Catalogue**	'Canada 1/63' on checklist.
Canada	1964	**Interim Leaflet**	'Canada' and 'Playcraft Toys Ltd. 1964' on checklist.
Canada	1965	**Interim Leaflet**	'Canada' and 'Mettoy etc. 1965' on checklist.
Canada 9/64	1964/65	**40 page Catalogue**	'Canada 9/64' on checklist plus '1965' on cover.
Canada 8/65	1965/66	**40 page Catalogue**	'Canada 8/65' on checklist plus '1966' on cover.
C2017/9/60	1966	**48 page Catalogue**	'Canada' on cover and checklist.
Canada	1967	**Interim Leaflet**	'Canada' on cover plus 'Mettoy 1967' on last page.
Canada	1969	**7-fold Leaflet**	Concorde featured on cover; '8/69' on checklist.

French Text Issue
C/2017/9/66	1966	**48 page Catalogue**	'Canadian (French)' on cover.

Combined Canadian and South African checklist
---	1970	**48 page Catalogue**	'Canada, South Africa' on checklist. 'The Mettoy Co. Ltd. 1970' on rear cover.

Denmark

All the text in Danish
---	1960	**20 page Catalogue**	'Denmark 9/60' and '25 re' on cover.
---	1961/62	**24 page Catalogue**	'Denmark 9/61' and '25 re' on cover.
C2214	1977	**48 page Catalogue**	'Katalog' and 'Corgi '77' on cover.

English text - Danish checklist. 'Samlerers Kontrolliste'
---	1960/61	**Interim Leaflet**	'Denmark' on checklist.
---	1961/62	**Interim Leaflet**	'Denmark' on page two.
---	1963/64	**40 page Catalogue**	'Denmark 8/63' on checklist plus '1963-64' on cover.
---	1964	**Interim Leaflet**	'Denmark' and 'Playcraft 1964' on checklist.
---	1964/65	**40 page Catalogue**	'Denmark 9/64' on checklist plus 1965 on cover.
---	1965/66	**40 page Catalogue**	'Denmark 8/65' on checklist plus 1966 on cover.
C2017/9/66	1966	**48 page Catalogue**	'Denmark' on cover and checklist.
C2105 1974	1974	**40 page Catalogue**	Danish checklist plus 'Corgi '74' on cover.
C2271	1980/81	**48 page Catalogue**	Danish checklist plus 1980/81 on cover.
C2292	1981/82	**30 page Catalogue**	Danish checklist plus 1981-82 on cover.

Eire

52/258/K6/EIRE	1958	**Box Insert**	'Eire' on checklist.
5/658/K7/EIRE	1958	**Box Insert**	'Eire' on checklist.
---	1960/61	**Interim Leaflet**	'Eire' on checklist.
---	1962/63	**Interim Leaflet**	'Eire' on checklist.
---	1964/65	**Interim Leaflet**	'Eire' plus 'Playcraft 1964' on checklist.

Finland

English Text - local currency

---	1963/64	**40 page Catalogue**	'Finland 8/63' on checklist plus '1963-64' on cover.
---	1965	**Interim Leaflet**	'Finland 6/65' and 'Mettoy 1965' on checklist.

France

English Text - French checklist

---	1961/62	**Interim Leaflet**	'France' on page two.
---	1962/63	**Interim Leaflet**	'France' on checklist.
---	1963/64	**40 page Catalogue**	'France 8/63' on checklist plus 1963-64 on cover.
---	1964/65	**Interim Leaflet**	'France' & 'Playcraft 1964' on checklist.
---	1965	**Interim Leaflet**	'France' and 'Mettoy 1965' on checklist.

French Text and checklist   "Liste de Controle pour le Collectioneur".

---	1965	**40 page Catalogue**	'France 8/65' on checklist plus 'Playcraft Toys Ltd. 1965' on rear cover.
C2017/8/67	1968	**48 page Catalogue**	French text - 1968 on cover.
C2017/9/68	1969	**48 page Catalogue**	French text - 1969 on cover.
---	1973	**40 page Catalogue**	French text - 1973 on cover.
C2107 1974	1974	**40 page Catalogue**	French text - 1974 on cover.
---	1975	**Catalogue Leaflet**	French text - 'Corgi '75' on cover.
C2222	1977	**16 page Catalogue**	French text plus 'Corgi '77' on cover.
C2275	1980/81	**48 page Catalogue**	French text plus 1980/81 on cover (includes Juniors).
C2282	1980/81	**32 page Catalogue**	French text plus 1980/81 on cover.
C2290	1981/82	**32 page Catalogue**	French text plus '1981 Mettoy' on rear cover.

Holland / Netherlands

Agent for Holland: N.V.S/O, Herengracht 25, Amsterdam.

Dutch Text throughout

---	1959	**20 page Catalogue**	'Holland 8/59' plus 'FL.O.10' on cover plus Dutch text.
---	1961	**24 page Catalogue**	'Holland 9/61' plus 'F.O.10' on cover plus Dutch text.

French Text - Dutch checklist. "Kontroleer zo de Verzameling".

C2281	1980/81	**48 page Catalogue**	French text, Dutch checklist, plus '1980 Mettoy' on rear cover.
C2291	1981/82	**30 page Catalogue**	French text, Dutch checklist, plus '1981 Mettoy' on rear cover.

English Text with French and Dutch checklists

---	1974	**40 page Catalogue**	'C2107 1974' on French checklist. 'C2103 1974' on Dutch checklist.

English text - Dutch checklist

20/657C2/NL	1957	**Catalogue Leaflet**	'Holland' on checklist.
15/158/C4/H	1958	**Catalogue Leaflet**	'Holland' on checklist.
52/258/K5/HOLLAND	1958	**Box Insert**	'Holland' on checklist.
52/258/K6/HOLLAND	1958	**Box Insert**	'Holland' on checklist.
5/658/K7/HOL	1958	**Box Insert**	'HOL' on checklist.
---	1960/61	**Interim Leaflet**	'Holland' on checklist.
---	1961/62	**Interim Leaflet**	'Holland' top of page two.
---	1962/63	**Interim Leaflet**	'Holland' on checklist.
---	1963/64	**40 page Catalogue**	'Holland 8/63' on checklist.
---	1964	**Interim Leaflet**	'Holland' on checklist.
---	1964/65	**40 page Catalogue**	'Holland 9/64' on checklist.
---	1965	**Interim Leaflet**	'Holland' on checklist.
C2017/9/66	1966	**48 page Catalogue**	'Holland' on cover and checklist.
---	1967	**Interim Leaflet**	'Holland' on cover.
C2017/7/67	1967/68	**48 page Catalogue**	'Holland 8/67' on checklist.
C2017/9/68	1969	**48 page Catalogue**	'Holland 10/68' on checklist.
C2211 1974	1974	**40 page Catalogue**	Dutch text in checklist.
---	1974	**40 page Catalogue**	C2107 on French checklist plus C2103 on Dutch checklist.

Hong Kong

---	1961	**24 pages**	'Hong Kong 9/61' on cover.
---	1961/62	**Interim Leaflet**	'Hong Kong' on page two.
C/100/62	1963	**24 pages**	'Hong Kong 3/63' on checklist.
---	1963	**Interim Leaflet**	'Hong Kong' on checklist.
---	1964	**Interim Leaflet**	'Hong Kong' on checklist.
---	1965/66	**40 pages**	'Hong Kong 8/65' on checklist.
C2017/9/66	1966	**48 pages**	'Hong Kong' on cover and checklist.

Corgi Toys Overseas Catalogues

Italy

1963 Concessionairia per l'Italia: Ditta "Guimar" via Disciplini 7, Milano (303).
'Distinta di Controllo per l'Collezzionisti".

52/258/K5 ITALY	1958	**Box Insert**	'Italy' on checklist.
52/258/K6ITALY	1958	**Box Insert**	'Italy' on checklist.
5/658/K7ITALY	1958	**Box Insert**	'Italy' on checklist.
---	1959	**20 pages**	'Italy 8/59' on cover.
---	1960/61	**Interim Leaflet**	'Italy' on checklist.
---	1961	**24 pages**	'Italy 9/61' on cover.
---	1961/62	**Interim Leaflet**	'Italy' on page two.
---	1962/63	**Interim Leaflet**	'Italy' on checklist.
---	1963/64	**40 pages**	'Italy 8/63' on checklist.
---	1964	**Interim Leaflet**	'Italy' on checklist.
---	1964/65	**40 pages**	'Italy 9/64' on checklist.
---	1965	**Interim Leaflet**	'Italy' on checklist.
---	1967	**Interim Leaflet**	'Italy' on cover. 'ATTENDETE OGNIMESE LE NOVITA 'CORGI'

1974 concessionaria per l'Italia: Toyuro s.n.c., Via S. Vittore 45, Milano (20123).

C2112 1974	1974	**40 pages**	'Italia' reference on checklist.
C2278	1980/81	**48 pages**	Italian text throughout.
C2293	1981/82	**32 pages**	Italian text throughout.

Japan

---	1973	**40 pages**	Japanese text throughout.

Malta

---	1964	**Leaflet**	'Malta' on checklist.
---	1964/65	**40 pages**	'Malta 8/64' on checklist.
---	1965	**Leaflet**	'Malta' in checklist.

New Zealand

---	1964/65	**40 pages**	'New Zealand 8/64' on checklist.
---	1965	**Leaflet**	'New Zealand' on checklist.
---	1965/66	**40 pages**	'New Zealand 8/65' on checklist.

Sweden

'Kontrollista för Samlaren'.

English text - Swedish checklist

52/258/K5/SWEDEN	1958	**Box Insert**	'Sweden' on checklist.
52/258/K6/SWEDEN	1958	**Box Insert**	'Sweden' on checklist.
5/658/K7/SWEDEN	1958	**Box Insert**	'Sweden' on checklist.
---	1959	**16 pages**	'Sweden 8/59' on cover.
---	1960/61	**Leaflet**	'Sweden' on checklist.
---	1961	**24 pages**	'Sweden 9/61' on cover.
---	1961/62	**Leaflet**	'Sweden' on page two.
---	1962/63	**Leaflet**	'Sweden' on checklist.
---	1963/64	**40 pages**	'Sweden 8/63' on checklist.
---	1964/65	**40 pages**	'Sweden 9/64' on checklist.
---	1965	**Leaflet**	'Sweden' on checklist.
---	1966	**40 pages**	'Sweden 6/65' on checklist.
C2017/9/66	1966	**40 pages**	'Sweden' on cover and checklist.
---	1967	**Leaflet**	'Sweden' on cover.
C2106 1974	1974	**40 pages**	Swedish text on checklist.
---	1975	**Leaflet**	Swedish text throughout.
C2277	1980/81	**48 pages**	Swedish text throughout.

Swedish text - Norwegian checklist

C2287	1981/82	**32 pages**	Swedish text with Norwegian checklist.

Switzerland

English Text - English/Swiss checklist

20/657/C2/CH	1957	**Catalogue Leaflet**	'Switzerland' on checklist.
52/258/K5/Switzerland	1958	**Box Insert**	Reference on checklist.
52/258/K6/Switzerland	1958	**Box Insert**	Reference on checklist.
5/658/K7/SWITZ	1958	**Box Insert**	Reference on checklist.
25/1058/C8/SWITZ	1958	**16 pages**	'Switz' on checklist. New issues in French.
5/658/C5/CH	1958	**Catalogue Leaflet**	'Switzerland' on checklist.
---	1960/61	**Leaflet**	'Switzerland' on checklist.
---	1961	**24 pages**	'Switzerland 9/61' on cover.
---	1961/62	**Leaflet**	'Switzerland' on page two.
C100/62	1962/63	**32 pages**	'Switzerland 1/63' on checklist.
---	1962/63	**Leaflet**	'Switzerland' on checklist.
---	1964	**Leaflet**	'Switzerland' on checklist.
---	1964/65	**40 pages**	'Switzerland?' on checklist.
---	1965	**Leaflet**	'Switzerland' on checklist.
---	1966	**40 pages**	'Switzerland 8/65' on checklist.
C/2017/9/66	1966	**48 pages**	'Switzerland' on cover and checklist.
---	1967	**Leaflet**	'Switzerland' on cover.
C2017/9/68	1969	**48 pages**	'Switzerland 10/68' on checklist.

United States of America

1958 Sole Distributor for U.S.A.: Reeves International Incorp., 1107 Broadway, New York 10, N.Y.

20/458/C5/U.S.A.	1958	**Catalogue Leaflet**	'U.S.A.' on checklist
20/658/K7/U.S.A.	1958	**Box Insert**	'U.S.A.' on checklist
USA 8/59	1959	**16 page Catalogue**	'U.S.A. 8/59' on cover, plus pictures of tractor and racing car
USA 9/61	1961	**24 page Catalogue**	'U.S.A. 9/61' on cover.
USA	1961/62	**Leaflet**	'U.S.A.' on page two.
C/100/62	1962/63	**32 page Catalogue**	Cover shows boy in red with corgi dog. 'U.S.A. 5/63' on checklist
USA 8/65	1962/63	**Leaflet**	'U.S.A.' on checklist.
	1964	**2-fold Checklist**	Ghia L 6.4 featured on cover. 'USA' and '© Playcraft Toys 1964'.
	1964/65	**40 page Catalogue**	Green 9001 Bentley and Ghia L6.4 on cover. 'USA 8/64' on checklist.
	1965/66	**40 page Catalogue**	'U.S.A. 8/65' on checklist
USA	1967	**Leaflet**	'U.S.A.' on cover.
C2017/9/68	1968/69	**48 page Catalogue**	Chitty-Chitty-Bang-Bang on cover. 'USA 10/68' on checklist
© 1970 Mettoy Co Ltd	1971	**2-fold Checklist**	'Corgi Toys with WhizzWheels' plus 'Australia', 'S.Africa' and 'USA' on cover. Checklist has prices in all three currencies

Norway

'Se dem alle 1 den nye Katalogen, Samlers Liste'

English Text - Norwegian checklist

---	1961/62	**Leaflet**	'Norway' on page two.
---	1962/63	**Leaflet**	'Norway' on checklist.
---	1964	**Leaflet**	'Norway' on checklist.
---	1964/65	**40 pages**	'Norway 9/64' on checklist.
---	1965	**Leaflet**	'Norway' on checklist.
---	1966	**40 pages**	'Norway 8/65' on checklist.
C2017/9/66	1966	**48 pages**	'Norway' on cover and checklist.
C2017/7/67	1967/68	**48 pages**	'Norway 8/67' on checklist.
---	1970	**48 pages**	'Norway' on checklist.
C2113	1974	**40 pages**	Norwegian checklist.
C2272	1980/81	**48 pages**	Norwegian checklist.

Norwegian text throughout

---	1975	**Catalogue Leaflet**	Text plus '1975 Mettoy'.

Portugal

'Lista de controle para o colecionador'

English Text - Portuguese checklist.

25/257/C2/P	1957	**Catalogue Leaflet**	'Portugal' on checklist.
---	1960	**Leaflet**	'Portugal' on checklist.
---	1961/62	**Leaflet**	'Portugal' on page two.
---	1962/63	**Leaflet**	'Portugal' on checklist.
---	1963/64	**40 pages**	'Portugal 8/63' on checklist.
---	1964	**Leaflet**	'Portugal' on checklist.
C2017/7/67	1967/68	**48 pages**	'Portugal 8/67' on checklist.

Singapore and Malaya

52/258/K5 SINGAPORE/MALAYA	1958	**Box Insert**	'Singapore/Malaya' on checklist.
10/258/C5/SM	1958	**Catalogue Leaflet**	'Singapore/Malaya' on checklist.
3.350/658/K7 SING.-MAL	1958	**Box Insert**	'Sing.-Mal' on checklist.
---	1960	**20 pages**	'Singapore Malaya 9/60' on cover.
---	1960	**Leaflet**	'Singapore/Malaya' on checklist.
---	1961	**24 pages**	'Singapore/Malaya 9/61' on checklist.
---	1962/63	**Leaflet**	'Singapore/Malaya' on checklist.
C/100/62	1962/63	**32 pages**	'Singapore/Malaya 2/63' on checklist
---	1965	**Leaflet**	'Singapore/Malaya' on checklist.

Spain

"Lista de Coleccionistas"

Spanish Text and checklist

---	1961	**24 pages**	'Spanish 9/61' on cover.

English Text - Spanish checklist "Lista de Precios para Coleccionistas"

C/100/62	1962	**Checklist**	'Spanish' on checklist.
C2273	1980/81	**Checklist**	Spanish text in checklist.

International Issues 1981 - 1985

The catalogue listings are printed in English, French and German. Catalogue C2293 was issued as a miniature booklet.

1965 Corgi Club addresses

Canada: Kleinberg Agencies 1085 St. Alexander St., Montreal'Can, Quebec, Canada.
South Africa: PO Box 6024, Johannesburg,
U..S.A.: 1107 Broadway, New York 10, N.Y.

Shop display and 'point-of-sale' items

Ref	Year	Item	Details	
no ref	1957-59	Display stand, wooden	Ten cream 'corrugated' hardboard shelves, pale blue display background with yellow/blue plastic 'CORGI TOYS' sign screwed to top of display, (30 x 29 x 12 inches)	£200-300
no ref	1957-59	Display card/sign	Tin/cardboard, yellow/blue with gold 'dog' logo, 'Wow! Corgi Toys - The Ones With Windows'	£75-100
no ref	1957-59	Display card/sign	As previous item but with 'new Corgi Major Toys - The Ones With Windows'	£75-100
no ref	1957-59	Counter display unit	Two shelf stand with Blue backing logo 'CORGI TOYS', 'THE ONES WITH WINDOWS', 'MODEL PERFECTION' and 'NEW' plus the early gold Corgi dog on red background	£300-400
no ref	1957-59	Counter display unit	Cardboard, single model display card, 'new - CORGI TOYS' logo	£75-100
no ref	1957-59	Counter display unit	Cardboard, 2 tier unit with 'new - CORGI MAJOR TOYS' yellow/blue design	£200-300
no ref	1957-59	Counter display unit	Cardboard, 2 tier unit, 'COLLECT CORGI TOYS' and 'new MODELS EVERY MONTH' logos in yellow/blue design	£200-300
no ref	1957-59	Counter display unit	Cardboard, Renault Floride (222) pictorial display card with '1959 MOTOR SHOW' and 'EARLS COURT' logos	£200-300
no ref	1957-59	Counter display unit	Cardboard, Citroën (475) pictorial display card with 'new - THE CITROEN' and 'OLYMPIC WINTER SPORTS' logos	£200-300
no ref	c.1959	Display unit	Shows picture of Gift Set 8 'Combine Harvester Set'. 'At work in the field' logo	£150-175
no ref	1957-67	Metal display stand	Tiered stand 75cm x 3 cm x 45cm high, three 'CORGI TOYS' and Black logos, plus three early gold Corgi dog emblems	£175-200
no ref	c.1960	Window display sign	Yellow background with 'Naturally Corgi Toys' in Red and Blue, illuminated. 27" long x 8" high. (Possibly Belgian market)	£500-700
no ref	1960-61	Window sticker	'NEW MODELS EVERY MONTH'	£15-20
C2034	mid 1960s	Metal display stand	Stand has 'Corgi Display C2034' on the back. No other details at present	NGPP
no ref	1966-69	Window sticker	Window bills advertising new releases	£15-20
no ref	1960-69	Oblong window sign	Glass or plastic with 'CORGI TOYS' and 'PRECISION DIE-CAST SCALE MODELS' logos plus gold Corgi 'dog' logo in blue/yellow/red design	£150-175
no ref	1960s	Tinplate stand	5 Grey tiers topped by 'CORGI TOYS'/Gold dog header	£200-300
no ref.	1960-69	Glass display sign	Square sign, gold corgi dog on Red panel within Blue lined glass surround.	£150-175
no ref	1961	Corgi Dog	Moulded dog standing on hind feet holding a 'CORGI CHRISTMAS CARD'	£200-300
no ref	1968-83	Metal display stand	Tiered stand 75 cm x 3.5 cm c 45 cm high, with three 'CORGI TOYS' Black/Yellow logos, plus three White/Red late Corgi dog emblems	£145-175
no ref	1971-73	Oblong sign	Plastic, with 'CORGI' and 'TESTED BY THE CORGI TECHNOCRATS' logos plus white Corgi 'dog' logo on red square, yellow background plus 3 'Technocrats' faces	£75-100
C2001/2	1963-65	Display stand, rotary	For self-selection, 7 tray unit, large 'CORGI TOYS' header sign	£200-300
C2003	1963-65	Display stand, rotary	Self-selection, 4 columns, 4 compartments (45 x 30 in.), large 'CORGI TOYS' header boards	£200-300
C2004	1963-65	Display stand, rotary	Self-selection, 4 column, 72 compartments (72 x 30 in.)	£200-300
C2005	1963-65	Display stand, rotary	Self-selection, 2 column, 36 compartments (72 x 30 in.)	£150-200
C2006	1963-65	Display stand, rotary	Self-selection, 2 column, 36 compartments (55 x 30 in.)	£100-150
C2007	1963-65	Display stand, plastic	Large moulded plastic counter display to house up to 50 models, large black header display board with 'NATURALLY CORGI TOYS' on yellow/blue background, and 'JOIN THE CORGI MODEL CLUB' on display front	£200-300
C2008	1960s	Display stand, revolving	Glass fronted large electric display to house 100-120 models with light and dark simulated wood panels with four 'CORGI' logos, (38 x 24 x 24 in.)	£400-600
C2009	1957-66	Showcase, glass	Three glass shelves, three 'CORGI TOYS' logos (black/blue) plus gold Corgi 'dog' logo on red background, (20 x 15 x 9 in.)	£200-300
E9051	1970s	Corgi Juniors unit	Yellow plastic (21.75 x 21.75 in.), displays 48 models, logo 'LOOK FOR WHIZZWHEELS MODELS'	£100-150
---	1975	Army diorama	Plastic unit for displaying tank models	£140-160
---	1976	Kojak's Buick	Card counter-display unit	£80-90
---	?	Window poster	Advertising new model 428 'MR SOFTEE' Ice Cream Van	£60-80

NB The Editor would welcome any further information on Corgi display material.

Collectors notes

Corgi Toys Numerical Index

Refer first to the Contents List (page 3) for quick guidance to main sections. Sets, for example, are not listed here since that section is easily found and items in it are listed numerically. Corgi Classics are not included in this index (see the 'Modern Diecasts' section of the book).

A quick check through this general (alphabetical) list may also prove helpful.

Collectors notes

Crescent Toys

The Crescent Toy Company was founded in July 1922 by Henry G. Eagles and Arthur A. Schneider in a workshop 30 feet square at the rear of a private house at 67 De Beauvoir Crescent, Kingsland Road, London N1.

They manufactured model soldiers, cowboys, kitchen sets, etc. from lead alloy. These were hollow castings, hand painted, packed one dozen to a box, and sold to wholesalers at six shillings per dozen boxes. The small firm prospered and eventually opened up a factory in Tottenham. With the second World War came a ban on metal toys and production was changed to munitions. After the War the firm resumed making metal hollow-cast toys and in addition marketed the diecast products of a firm called DCMT (Die Casting Machine Tools Ltd).

As a consequence early post-war models had 'DCMT' cast into the underside of the body. In 1948 the firm opened a modern factory on a four-acre site at Cymcarn, a Welsh mining village near Newport, Monmouth (now Gwent) and two years later transferred all production there, maintaining only an office in

London. From this time Crescent toys made their own diecast products without 'DCMT' on them. Hence it is possible to find the same models with or without 'DCMT' cast in. Die Casting Machine Tools went their own way and from 1950 produced models under the name of 'Lone Star'.

Crescent Toys will be best remembered for their excellent ranges of military models and farm equipment but probably most of all for their superb reproductions of the racing cars of the 1950s.

The following post-war model listings have been extracted from a unique collection of original trade catalogues (1947-80) most kindly provided by Mr. J. D. Schneider, the former Managing Director of Crescent Toys Ltd. All of the original research and actual compiling of the lists was undertaken by Ray Strutt.

The Editor would also like to thank Les Perry of Rochdale for additional information.

Ref.	Year(s)	Details	MPR

EARLY POST-WAR MODELS (various colours)

Ref.	Year(s)	Details	MPR
223	1948	**Racing Car**	£25-35
422	1949	**Sports Car**	£30-40
423	1949	**Oil Lorry**	£30-40
424	1949	**Truck Lorry**	£30-40
425	1949	**Saloon Car**	£30-40
800	1947-49	**Jaguar**	£35-45
802	1947-49	**Locomotive**	£25-35
803	1947-48	**Locomotive**, Silver	£25-35
804	1948-49	**Police Car**, Black	£35-45
1221	1949	**Fire Engine**, Red body	£40-50
-		**Garages**, retailing at 1/-, 1/6, 2/6 and 4/-. Complete with Modern Pumps, Motor Cars and Garage Attendants, *CRESCENT GARAGES* logo	NGPP
FC 330		**Domestic Iron and Stand**	£10-15
-		**Zulu-drawn Rickshaw**. Red/Green rickshaw, 'Zulu' with wheel attached to foot, colonial couple in tropical dress/pith helmets in rickshaw	£125-175

FARM EQUIPMENT (various colours)

Ref.	Year(s)	Details	MPR
1802	1949-60	**Tractor and Hayrake**	£65-75
1803	1967-74	**Dexta Tractor and Trailer**	£45-55
1804	1950-59	**Tractor and Disc Harrow**	£55-65
1805	1950-61	**Tractor**	£55-65
1806	1950-60	**Hayrake**	£5-10
1807	1950	**Disc Harrow**	£5-10
1808	1950-56	**Platform Trailer**	£5-10
1809	1950-56	**Ricklift Trailer**	£5-10
1809	1962-80	**Dexta Tractor**	£25-35
1810	1950-80	**Box Trailer / Farm Trailer**, (No.148 1968-74)	£15-20
1811	1950-67	**Animal Trailer / Cattle Trailer**, (No.148 1968-71)	£10-15
1811	1975-81	**Dexta Tractor and Trailer**	£15-20
1813	1950	**Timber Wagon** (Horse Drawn)	£75-95
1814	1950-60	**Plough Trailer**, (No.150 1968-71)	£10-15
1815	1950	**Hayloader**	£10-15
1816	1950	**Roller Harrow**	£5-10
1817	1950-56	**Timber Trailer**	£10-15
1818	1954-60	**Tipping Farm Wagon**	£10-15
1819	1954-55	**Large Farm Wagon**	£25-35

DIECAST ACTION TOYS (various colours)

Ref.	Year(s)	Details	MPR
1219	1954-59	**'Milking Time' Set**. 2 Milkmaids, 2 cows, calf. Card box with picture on lid	£75-95
1222	1954-59	**Builders & Decorators Truck** (red handcart), unpainted ladder and bucket, beige figure on green base. Grey card box with drawing of set	£80-100
1268	1954-59	**Mobile Space Rocket**	NGPP
1269	1954-59	**Mobile Crane**	£30-40

Ref.	Year(s)	Details	MPR
1272	1954-59	**Scammell Scarab and Box Trailer**	£70-80
1274	1954-59	**Scammell Scarab and Low Loader**	£70-80
1276	1955-59	**Scammell Scarab and Oil Tanker**	£70-80
2700	1956-60	**Western Stage Coach**	£70-80
2705	1955	**Western Stage Coach**	NGPP
-		**Scammell Scarab Set**, Mechanical Horse, Box Trailer and Low Loader	NGPP

MILITARY MODELS (All in military colours)

Ref.	Year(s)	Details	MPR
155	1960-68	**'Long Tom' Artillery Gun**	£15-20
235	1946	**Cannon**, operable	NGPP
F 355	1938	**Tank and Cannon Set**	NGPP
650	1954-59	**Military Set**: two 696 British Tanks, one 698 Scout Car, one 699 Russian Tank	NGPP
NN656/2	1938-40	**Field Gun and Gunner**	NGPP
NN692	1938-40	**Deep Sea Diver**, with equipment	NGPP
NN693	1938-40	**A.R.P. Searchlight Unit**, 3 personnel, boxed	£60-80
NN694	1938-40	**A.R.P. Rangefinder Unit**, 2 personnel, boxed	£60-80
695	1938-40	**A.R.P. First Aid Post**: a tent, two stretcher bearers and patient, Red Cross nurse	£100-125
F 695	1946	**Howitzer**, unpainted, with spring and plunger, *CRESCENT* cast-in	£10-12
696	1954-59	**British Tank**	£30-40
698	1954-56	**Scout Car**	£20-30
699	1954-56	**Russian Tank**	£30-40
NN700	1938-40	**Royal Engineers Field Set**: Engineers (2 standing, 2 kneeling), telegraph pole, transmitter, aerial. Box has colour picture of set on lid	£100-125
701	-	**GPO Telephone Engineers Set**: 4 men, telegraph pole, hut, cart, accessories. Box has colour picture of set on lid	£120-150
702	-	**Sound Locator Unit**, operator figure, boxed	£60-80
K 703	1938-40	**Field Wireless Unit** with two Soldiers	NGPP
K 704	1938-40	**R.A.M.C. Stretcher Party**, 2 Soldiers and Patient	NGPP
1248	1957	**Field Gun**	£5-10
1249	1958-79	**18-pounder Quick-Firing Gun**	£10-15
1250	1958-80	**25-pounder Light Artillery Gun**	£10-15
1251	1958-80	**5.5" Medium Heavy Howitzer**	£10-15
1260	1976-79	**Supply Truck**	£30-40
1263	1962-80	**Saladin Armoured Scout Car**	£20-30
1264	1975-80	**Scorpion Tank**	£12-16
1265	1977-80	**M109 Self-Propelled Gun**	£12-15
1266	1978-79	**Recovery Vehicle**	£12-15
1267	1958-63	**'Corporal' Rocket and Lorry**	£50-60
1270	1958-60	**Heavy Rescue Crane**	£40-50
1271	1958-60	**Long Range Mobile Gun**	£20-30
1271	1976-80	**Artillery Force**	£15-20
2154	1962-74	**Saladin Armoured Patrol** (No.1270 1975-80)	£10-15

HISTORICAL MODELS (in Regal colours)

1300	1975-76	**Royal State Coach**	**£20-30**
1301	1977-79	**Royal State Coach**, (Commemorative box)	**£20-30**
1302	1977	**Royal State Coach and Figures**	**£20-30**
1450	1956-60	**Medieval Catapult**	**£20-30**
1953	1954-60	**Coronation State Coach**	**£30-40**

Miniature 'WILD WEST' Transport

906	1956	**Stage Coach**, various colours	**£30-40**
907	1956	**Covered Wagon**, various colours	**£30-40**

GRAND PRIX RACING and SPORTS CARS

1284	1956-60	**Mercedes-Benz**, all-enveloping silver body	**£90-120**
1285	1956-60	**B.R.M. Mk.II**, bright green	**£90-120**
1286	1956-60	**Ferrari**, orange-red	**£90-120**
1287	1956-60	**Connaught**, dark green, racing number '8'	**£90-120**
1288	1956-60	**Cooper-Bristol**, light blue, racing number '2'	**£90-120**
1289	1956-60	**Gordini**, French blue, racing number '14'	**£90-120**
1290	1956-60	**Maserati**, cherry red, racing number '3'	**£90-120**
1291	1957-60	**Aston-Martin DB3s**, white/light blue	**£100-150**
1292	1957-60	**Jaguar 'D' type**, dark green	**£100-150**
1293	1958-60	**Vanwall**, dark green, racing number '10'	**£150-200**
6300	1957	**Racing Cars Set**, 1284 - 1289 in display box	NGPP
	1958-60	Same set but 1290 replaces 1284	NGPP

LONG VEHICLES (various colours)

1350	1975-80	**Container Truck**	**£20-25**
1351	1975-80	**Petrol Tanker**	**£20-25**
1352	1975-80	**Girder Carrying Truck**	**£20-25**
1353	1975-80	**Flat Platform Truck**	**£20-25**

'TRUKKERS' (various colours)

1360	1976-81	**Cement Mixer**	**£5-20**
1361	1976-81	**Covered Truck**	**£5-20**
1362	1976-81	**Tipper Truck**	**£5-20**
1363	1976-81	**Recovery Vehicle**	**£5-20**
1364	1976-81	**Super Karrier**	**£5-20**

CRESCENT AIRCRAFT

O 2	1940	**Spitfire Set**. Two Spitfires with two Pilots and two Mechanics	**£50-75**
Q 2	1940	**Spitfire Set**. As O 2 but new ref. no.	**£50-75**
U 2	1940	**Aircraft Set**. Five Aircraft plus three Pilots and six Groundcrew	**£75-100**
FC 38	1946	**Aeroplane**, Spitfire	**£5-10**
FC 89	1946	**Aeroplane**, Mosquito	**£5-10**
FC 90	1946	**Aeroplane**, Lightning, 3" x 2", US markings	**£5-10**
FC 179	1946	**Khaki Bomber**	**£5-10**
FC 372	1946	**Aeroplane**, Lightning, 4.75" x 3", US markings	**£5-10**
FC 663	1946	**North Sea Patrol**. Aeroplane with pilot and one other crew member	**£20-25**

CRESCENT SHIPS

BATTLESHIPS

---		**HMS 'King George V'**. Grey hollow-cast, with main armament only, boxed	**£15-20**
---		Same but additional separately cast secondary armament	**£15-20**
---		**HMS 'Vanguard'**. Grey / black / white, solid, *'CRESCENT'* cast-in	**£5-7**
Q 3	1940	**Battleship Set**, Battleship plus four Sailors	NGPP
S 3	1940	**Warships Set**, Battleship and Destroyer plus eight Sailors	NGPP
NN 691		**HMS 'Malaya'**, grey hollow-cast, black funnels, boxed	**£15-20**

AIRCRAFT CARRIERS

-	**HMS 'Victorious'**, grey hollow-cast body, separate unpainted aircraft, boxed	**£20-25**
NN 667	**HMS 'Eagle'**, grey hollow-cast body, unpainted aircraft, Union Jack sticker attached to box	**£10-15**

OTHER WARSHIPS

---	**'H' or 'I' Class Destroyer**. Unpainted solid cast body, *'CRESCENT'* cast into bow	**£15-20**
---	**'H' or 'I' Class Destroyer**. As previous model plus three lead figures of naval personnel	**£20-25**
---	**'V' and 'W' Class Destroyer**. Grey hollow-cast body	**£2-3**
A 34	**Gunboat**. Grey hollow cast body	**£2-3**
234	**Submarine**. Unpainted, conning tower and deck gun, 4"	**£10-15**
C 310	**'County' Class Cruiser, 'Cumberland'**, grey hollow-cast	**£7-9**
K 664	**'County' Class Cruiser**, grey hollow-cast body	**£7-9**
K 665	**War Transport Ship**, grey hollow-cast body, boxed	**£15-20**

PASSENGER SHIPS

---	**'Queen Mary'**. Black / white / red, hollow-cast body, boxed	**£15-20**
---	**'Dunnottar Castle'**. Mauve / white / red, hollow-cast, boxed	**£25-30**
---	**'Athlone Castle'**. Mauve / white / red, hollow-cast, boxed	**£25-30**

'Dunnottar Castle' and 'Athlone Castle' were part of the 'Union Castle' fleet and the models were sold in souvenir boxes, probably on board.

SHIP MODEL IDENTIFICATION. Crescent Ships are of rather crude manufacture and have virtually no identifying features. Only the HMS 'Vanguard' and the 'H' or 'I' Class Destroyer are known to have *'CRESCENT'* cast in. A few of the early models had a little paper 'Crescent' half-moon label. Ship models were packed in cream cardboard boxes of varying quality.

MISCELLANEOUS models and sets

'Tower Bridge' Solid cast model of the famous landmark, in various colours **£5-10**

'Dial 999' Police and Robbers Set. Contains black police car with loudhailer on roof and four semi-flat action figures (policeman running, policeman and dog, two fleeing villains, one with swag). Packed in card box with black and white label **£150-175**

'Dan Dare' Set. Complete with five figures and rocket launcher, Packed in card box **£150-200**

'Wild Animals' Set. See picture in first colour section.
'Model Farm' Set. See picture in first colour section.

Meccano
Dinky Toys

During the course of the period 1999-2001, some fine collections have been sold at auction and many of the amounts realised have been included in the Auction Results section. These have included collections containing examples of almost every vehicle, set and accessory produced, plus previously unrecorded variants as well as rare colours and export issues. The impact of all this information on the catalogue listings has been considerable, particularly in respect of the post-war car listings which have been greatly enhanced; the 40 Series is an example.

The importance of a model's condition cannot be overstated, with pristine examples often commanding a premium. Similarly, the condition of a model's accompanying box is of equal importance. It must be as near pristine as is possible and display, where relevant, the correct colour spot. In addition, it must also contain any original packing pieces and instructions, etc. Much new information on original packing material has been included in this new edition.

All pre-war issues must be considered rare and market prices reflect this. Similarly the demand for top-quality post-war Dinky Toys remains very strong.

HISTORY OF DINKY TOYS

In 1931, Meccano Ltd introduced a series of railway station and trackside accessories to accompany their famous 'HORNBY' train sets. These 'Modelled Miniatures' were in sets numbered 1 – 22 and included railwaymen, station staff, passengers and trains. Set number 22 was comprised of six vehicles which were representative rather than replicas of actual vehicles. It was first advertised in the Meccano Magazine of December 1933.

At about this time 'Tootsie Toys' of America were introducing model vehicles into the United Kingdom and they were proving to be very popular. Consequently Meccano Ltd decided to widen their range of products and issue a comprehensive series of models to include vehicles, ships and aircraft. 'Modelled Miniatures' therefore became 'Meccano Dinky Toys' and set number 22 the first set of 'Dinky Cars'. The first 'Dinky Toys' advertisement appeared in the April 1934 edition of the Meccano Magazine. The first Dinky car produced after the change of name was 23a in April 1934. It was probably based on an early MG but was again generally representative rather than an accurate model. Set 22 cost 4/- and consisted of: 22a Sports Car, 22b Sports Coupé, 22c Motor Truck, 22d Delivery Van, 22e Tractor and 22f Tank and is today highly sought after.

The range of models produced grew quickly so that the Meccano Magazine of December 1935 was claiming that there were 200 varieties to choose from! Although the phrase 'Dinky Toys' became a household name, the actual range was of course far greater and was not limited to cars; it even included dolls house furniture. Indeed, by the time the famous Binns Road factory in Liverpool finally closed its doors in November 1979 over 1,000 different designs had been produced. Pre-war models are rare today and fetch high prices, which reflects how difficult it is to find a model in really good condition. This is because so many 1930s models were made from an unstable alloy which has tended to crystallise and disintegrate. Fortunately the post-war models do not suffer from the same problem and much of today's collecting interest is centred around the delightful models produced in the fifties and sixties with Gift Sets being particularly sought after. Most Dinky Toys boxes were made by McCorquodale in Northern Ireland.

In 1987 the Dinky trade name was bought by Matchbox who were at the time part of the Universal International Co. of Hong Kong. They introduced the 'Dinky Collection' in 1988 with some very fine models in a constant scale of 1:43. On the 7th May 1992 it was announced in the 'New York Times' that 'Tyco Toys Inc.' had acquired by merger the 'Universal Matchbox Group' and with it the famous 'Dinky Toys' brand name.

In 1998, Mattel bought the Matchbox brand and in 1999 disclosed that all new car models will be classified as 'Dinky Toys', including those previously included in their Matchbox Models of Yesteryear range. At the beginning of 2001 however, both of those famous names have been all but buried in favour of Mattel's 'Hot Wheels' brand since most of their products have been aimed at the US toy market.

Market Price Range
Please note that the prices shown refer to pristine models and boxes.
Items failing to match this standard will sell for less.
Note also that boxes must still contain all their original packing pieces
and additional contents where appropriate.

Common Features. There are several features common to various groups of models and to avoid unnecessary repetition in the listings they are shown below. Exceptions to these general indications are noted in the listings.

'Dinky Toys', 'Meccano Ltd', or 'Meccano Dinky Toys'.
These wordings are to be found cast or stamped on the base-plate or chassis or in the case of early models without a base they are cast into the model itself. Some very early models have 'HORNBY SERIES' cast-in (e.g, those in the 22 series).

Wheel hubs. Solid one-piece wheel/tyre castings were fitted to the 'Modelled Miniatures' and first pre-war 'Dinky Toys'. They had 'Hornby' or 'Meccano' cast onto their rims and were covered in a thin colour wash or silver-plated. This casting was soon replaced with more realistic cast hubs (having a smooth convex face) fitted with white (sometimes coloured) rubber tyres. Pre-war hubs may be black, coloured or sometimes silver-plated. Post-war hubs were of the 'ridged' type having a discernible ridge simulating a hub cap. They were painted and usually fitted with black rubber tyres.

Supertoys hubs and tyres. When Supertoys were introduced in 1947 the ridged type of hub was used on the Fodens with black 'herringbone pattern' tyres, and on the Guys with smooth black tyres. Fodens graduated to the use of 'fine radial-tread' tyres first in black, later in grey, then to black again but with a more chunky 'block' tread. Supertoys later acquired plastic hubs and plastic tyres.

Hub materials. Lead was used originally for a short time, the majority of models from the mid-1930s to the early 1960s having diecast mazak hubs. Small models like motor-cycles or the 35b Racer were fitted with solid one-piece wheel/tyre moulding (white or black rubber pre-war, black post-war). In 1958/9 aluminium hubs were introduced and some models (such as 131, 178, 179, 180, 181, 182 and 290 Bus) appeared fitted with either type. Plastic hubs replaced the diecast versions on racing cars numbered 230-235 while the Austin A30 and Fiat 600 were given solid one-piece wheel/tyre plastic injection mouldings. **Speedwheels** were introduced in the 1970s and some model can be found fitted with metal wheels or Speedwheels. The former are more collectable.

Baseplates are tinplate or diecast unless described otherwise. Plastic moulded baseplates are generally restricted to a few models made after 1970. **Model Numbers** appear on many Dinky Toys baseplates but not all. The **Model Name** however appears on virtually every post-war Dinky Toy. Pre-war models usually had neither (the 38 and 39 series are exceptions having the model name on their baseplates).

Construction Materials. All models assumed to be constructed at least in part of a diecast alloy. Some pre-war models were made of a lead alloy like the 22 and 28 series plus the few odd models such as 23 a Racing Car and 23m Thunderbolt. The Blaw-Knox Bulldozer was one of the very few produced (right at the end of its production) in plastic.

Windows. Pre-war and early post-war models had tinplate or celluloid windscreens. Moulded plastic windscreens appeared in the 1950s on open car models. The first Dinky to be fitted with all-round plastic window glazing was the Austin A105 Saloon. Some models in production at the time were fitted with glazing later and may therefore be found with or without it.

Hooks were not fitted to the first Supertoys Foden models (1947). Small hooks were fitted in early 1948, the usual (larger) hook appearing in mid-1948.

Axles were all 'crimped' pre-war and on these series of models post-war: 23, 25, 29, 30, 34, 35, 36, 37, 38, 39, 40 and 280. Otherwise models had rivet-ended axles until the advent of Speedwheels. Early Guy models had tinplate clips to retain the front axles. Pre-war axles are generally thinner than post-war at 0.062mm diameter while post-war axles are 0.078mm in diameter.

Size of models (where shown) is in millimetres and refers to the longest overall measurement (usually the length). In the case of pre-war models slight inaccuracies may occur from expansion of the casting as it ages in the course of time.

The Scale of Dinky Toys was originally 1:43 (with a few exceptions). Supertoys Foden and Guy vehicles (introduced in 1947) were in a scale of 1:48 while military models issued from 1953 were smaller at 1:60. Most aircraft models before 1965 were around 1:200 and ships 1:1800. In the late 1960s and early 1970s the 1:36 scale was introduced, mostly for cars.

Dinky Numbering System. The dual/triple reference numbers used on some Dinky Toys and Supertoys (for example 409 / 521 / 921 Bedford Articulated Lorry) refers to the basic model type and casting and not to model colours. The renumbering by Meccano was an administration process to re-catalogue production of existing lines and introduce new models. New colours on existing castings which arise at about the time of renumbering are therefore coincidental with it rather than a consequence of it.

Identification of early post-war Dinky Toys cars.
Note that pre-war wheel hubs may be smooth diecast or the rare chrome ('Tootsie-Toy' type) hubs which attract a premium.

Post-war 30 Series
Circa 1946.........Open chassis with smooth black wheel hubs.
Circa 1948.........Plain chassis with ridged black wheel hubs.

36 Series
Circa 1946.........Moulded chassis with smooth black wheel hubs.
Circa 1948.........Moulded chassis with ridged black wheel hubs.

38 Series
Circa 1946........With pre-war lacquered metal base, silvered sidelights, smooth black hubs, spread spigots not rivets.
Circa 1946.........Solid steering wheels, smooth black hubs, silvered sidelights, black painted baseplate.
Circa 1947........As above but with silver-edged windscreen.
Circa 1948-49....Open or solid steering wheel, ridged hubs, black painted baseplate.
Circa 1950.........As above but with coloured wheel hubs.

39 Series
Circa 1946.........'Gold' pre-war baseplate, smooth black wheel hubs, silver door handles.
Circa 1948.........Black painted baseplate, ridged black wheel hubs.
Circa 1950.........As above but with coloured wheel hubs.

Box Types Introduction

A mint condition model car without its correct box is worth but a fraction of its mint boxed equivalent. Furthermore, as model boxes made from card do not survive as well as their die-cast contents, pristine box examples are scarce and becoming scarcer. The condition of a box is of paramount importance and attention is drawn to the section in the catalogue introduction, namely: 'Classifying the Condition of Models and Boxes'.

The following listing provides collectors with a working knowledge of the range of box types issued. In addition details are given of their dates of issue, their design and of the models which used them. See also the colour sections for examples of many types of boxes.

Whilst every care has been taken in preparing the listing, other variations may exist and information on them is welcomed. Similarly, with no 'dates of birth' available the dates of issues shown are approximate and again any further information is welcomed.

Box Identification

Model colour identification marks - colour spots

These are shown on the box lid end flap and take the form of a circular colour spot. This may be either a single colour or, in the case of the later two-tone car issues, a two-tone colour spot. Colour spots were used until the early 1960s.

NB The dual numbered 234/23H box displays the **Ferrari** model name against a blue panel which matches the main body colour.

Dual numbered boxes 1953 - 1954

A new numbering system was introduced which resulted in models being issued displaying both the old and new reference numbers. The information was shown on the box end flaps as follows:

Old model number shown in red letters on either side of a larger white number set on a black oval background, e.g. 40J **161** 40J. Dual numbered boxes were only issued for a short period and may attract a premium. The numbers may be large or small.

Pre-war issues

Apart from special issues such as 23m Thunderbolt Speed Car and 23p Gardner's M.G. Record Car, individual models were sold unboxed. They were usually packaged in half-dozen retailers trade packs (see the section on Trade Packs). Models were also sold in boxed sets (see the Gift Set Section).

Post-war After the second world war models continued to be sold unboxed from trade boxes until 1953/54 when the first individual boxes were introduced. The boxes have been catalogued into three types as follows:

    Type 1: Card boxes with tuck-in flaps
    Type 2: Display boxes -Blister packs, rigid plastic packs,
            vacuform packs and card window boxes.
    Type 3: Export Issue boxes.

Type 1 1953 – 1975 All card box with tuck-in end flaps

(i) 1953- 1954 Deep yellow box with 'DINKY TOYS' in red plus the model's name and type in black. A white reference number on a black oval background is on the box end flaps but no reference number is shown on the box face. The model is pictured on the box sides but without a white shaded background. Colour spots shown on box-end flaps as applicable. Foreign language information is shown on one of the end flaps of the early issue boxes. Box in

general use during the model renumbering period. Consequently, dual numbered boxes will be found. It would appear that only models 23f, g, h, j, k and n, and 40j were housed in individual boxes prior to renumbering. Please supply details of any other models housed in boxes displaying just their old reference number.

(ii) 1955 - 1956 Same as (i) but a white reference number on a black oval background is shown on the face of the box to the left of the model picture. Also as (i) but with a white reference number on a red oval background and placed either to the left or the right of the model picture. Box in general use for all issues.

(iii) 1956 - 1960 Same as (ii) but model pictures are displayed against a white shadow background. In some instances only one picture. had a shadow; e.g. 171 Hudson Commodore and in others both pictures were given a shadow; e.g. 152 Austin Devon. Box in general use for all issues. Later issues display 'WITH WINDOWS', caption in a red line features box.

(iv) c1960 Deep yellow plain box with no model picture, 'DINKY TOYS' and text in red; rarely used. Colour spots shown as applicable. We believe these boxes may have been used for mail-order or possibly export purposes. The Editor would welcome any new information. Known examples: 103, 108, l09, 163 and 191.

(v) 1959–1961 Plain lighter yellow box with no model picture. It has two yellow and two red sides. 'DINKY TOYS' is shown in yellow on red sides. Colour spots shown as applicable. Models recorded: 105, 109, 131, 150, 157, 165, 169, 173. 174, 176, 178, 187, 189, 191, 192 and 230 to 235. The special issue 189 Triumph Heralds used this box. (vi) 1960 - 1966 Yellow box with a separate red line features box placed to the right of the model picture. Colour spots still in use on early 1960s issues. Foreign language text on one box end flap and 'WITH WINDOWS' captions on box face. Models recorded: 105, 112, 113, 131, 144, 148, 155, 157, 164–167, 176–178, 181/2, 184, 186, 191-195, 197, 199, 230-235, 237, 239 and 449. Later issues without colour spots. Boxes used for some South African issues display both English and Afrikaans text.

(vii) c.1962 – 1963 Lighter yellow box similar to (v) but colour spots not in use. A scarce issue box which may attract a premium. Model recorded: 166.
(viii) 1962 – 1963 Yellow box with a red end features panel around the left side of the box. Recorded models: 113, 147 and 198.

(ix) 1963 – 1970 Yellow box with a red end features panel around the right side. The panel is bisected by the model picture and is with or without a large or small white arrow design. Models recorded: 112-114. 120, 127-130, 133-139, 140-148, 198, 240-243, 268, 273 and 274. Some South African issues used this box, e.g. 141 Vauxhall Victor Estate Car. They display both English and Afrikaans text. The rare Triumph 2000 Saloon promotional issues will be found in this box. Some have an applied white label on the box face showing the colour of the model, e.g. Olive-Cactus.

(x) 1966 – 1969 Detailed full colour picture box with pictorial scene on two sides with 'DINKY TOYS' in red letters. Recorded issues: 133, 136, 183, 212, 214, 225 plus Hong Kong issues 57/001-57/006.

(xi) 1968 –1974 White-fronted box with a thin yellow band across the box face. A yellow laurel leaf design on a black background is a main box feature. The white face of the box may contain features information such as '1st AGAIN' and 'SPEEDWHEELS'. Variation exists with a semi-pictorial box face (probably an export special) e.g. 176 NSU R80. Models recorded: 157, 159 165/6, 169, 174/5, 179, 183, 192, 205 and 212. NB. A variation of this box exists with a large red 'DINKY TOYS' and number to the left of the picture and no yellow band across the face, e.g. 138 Hillman Imp.

Dinky Toys No. 100 Lady Penelope's 'FAB 1' provides an example of a pictorial box containing an inner card base (on which the the model is securely mounted) plus a folding pictorial upstand for an impressive display.

Photo:
Swapmeet Publications

Type 2 1962 – 1980 Display boxes, Blister packs, Rigid plastic and Vacuform packs, Window boxes

(i) 1962 – 1964 Blister Card Packs used for racing cars nos. 205210. Red/yellow display card with chequered flag design.

(ii) 1967 – 1971 Rigid plastic 'see-through' case with lift-off lid. models displayed on a card base with a black 'roadway' surface. The base sides are yellow with 'DINKY TOYS' in red. Recorded issues: 110, 116, 127, 129, 131/2, 142, 152-154, 158, 161, 163/4, 168, 175, 187-189, 190, 208, 210, 213, 215, 216, 220/1 and 223/4.

(iii) 1972 – 1976 Vacuform Packs. Models displayed on a black base with a blue surface with 'DINKY TOYS' in red/white letters. The model is covered by a close fitting plastic cover. Known issues: 129, 131, 149, 168, 178 and 192 plus 1:25 issues 2214, 3162 and 2253.

(iv) 1976 – 1979 Window Box with 'see-through' cellophane front and blue and red header card with a 'DINKY DIECAST TOYS' in yellow letters. Variations exist with a model picture on the header card e.g. 112 'Purdey's TR7'. Known issues: 113, 120, 122/3/4, 128. 180, 192, 207/8, 211, 221/2/3 and 226/7.

(v) 1968 – 1969 Plastic see-through red box made in a garage shape to house 'Mini Dinky' issues.

(vi) 1979 Bubble Pack 219 'Big Cat' Jaguar.

Type 3   1966 – 1980   Export issue boxes

(i) 1966 – 1980 An all yellow card and cellophane 'see-through' display box with outward-folding ends. 'DINKY TOYS' and four diagonal stripes plus 'A MECCANO PRODUCT MADE IN ENGLAND' are in red on the box f~ace. The box display base may be either yellow or have a black 'roadway' design. Whilst generally used for export issues it was specifically used for the U.S. export series 'MARVELS IN MINIATURE - which appeared in red letters on the box front. Later issues listed the models on the base of the box.

A box variation exists with just 'DINKY' and 'A MECCANO PRODUCT' on the face of the box plus the model name and number. The base of the box is yellow. The box was issued with a card protection strip which stated: 'Mr DEALER PLEASE REMOVE THIS STRIP'. Models known to have been issued in this box include: 110-115, 120, 127/8, 133-138, l41/2. 151, 161, 170-172, 190, 192, 196, 215, 237, 240-243, 257/8, 57/006. **NB** We believe this box was probably used in the UK but would be grateful for confirmation.

(ii) 1966 – 1968 All gold card and cellophane 'see-through' display box with just 'DINKY' in gold letters set in a red panel on the box front plus red and black diagonal stripes. 'A MECCANO PRODUCT MADE IN ENGLAND' in black is also on the front of the box. Only used for a short time so models in these boxes often sell at a premium. The known issues are: 112, 113, 148, 193, 215, 238, 240-243, 340 and 448.

(iii) 1979 – 1980 A flat yellow box with blue end flaps. Used to house the Swiss promotional issue No. 223 Hesketh F1 Racing Car 'OLYMPUS CAMERAS'.
Export issue: 449 has been observed in an 'all gold' box.

40 Series issues distribution, renumbering and packing

Models in the 40 Series were initially sold unboxed from retailers' trade boxes of 6 models as follows:

i)   1947-50   Plain Brown card box with lift-off lid. On the end of the lid was a Yellow label displaying the quantity, the model's name and its reference number, e.g., '6 RILEY SALOON   40a'.

ii)   1950-54   All Yellow card box with lift-off lid. The contents were printed in Black on the end of the box lid.

iii)   1954   Models renumbered. When the 40 Series models were renumbered, the final all-Yellow card boxes for six displayed both the original number and its new number, for example: '158 RILEY SALOON 40a'.

iv)   1954-60   The renumbered models were individually boxed in the first type of Yellow end-flap boxes as follows:
a) Displaying the dual numbers for a short time, e.g., '40a 158 40a' on the end flap.
b) Displaying just the model's new number, e.g., '158' plus the correct colour spot for the model.

Dublo Dinky Toys usually came in yellow boxes with a distinctive red band around each end. Exceptions include the 071 VW Delivery Van and 070 AEC Mercury Tanker 'SHELL-BP' shown in this picture.

Also illustrated here is the box for Dinky Toys 772 British Road Signs.

Photo:
Barry Potter Auctions

Chassis types 1934 – 1950

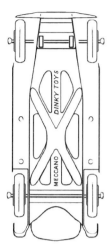 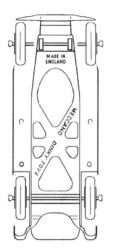  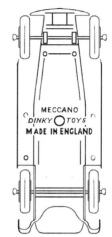 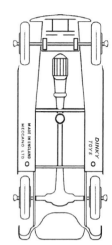

1934 - 1935
'Criss-cross' chassis
1st type
with or without
slot for spare wheel

1935 - 1936
'Criss-cross' chassis
2nd type
with or without
slot for spare wheel

1936 - 1940
Open chassis
with or without
slots for figures

1946 - 1947
Plain chassis
no slots for
figures

1948 - 1950
'Moulded'
(detailed) chassis

24 Series radiator grille types 1934 – 1940

1st type
1934 - 1938
With diamond shape
in centre of bumper
No radiator badge
No over-riders

2nd type
1934 - 1938
No diamond shape in
centre of bumper
No radiator badge
No over-riders

3rd type
1938 - 1940
'Bentley' style
with radiator badge
and over-riders

The first and second type grilles will be found on the both the first and second type chassis.
The later third type grille will be found with the second type chassis.

40 Series – casting and base identification

40e / 158 Standard Vanguard 1948 - 60

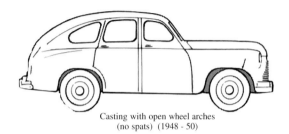

Casting with open wheel arches
(no spats) (1948 - 50)

Tinplate clip secures rear axle (1948 - 49)
Small lettering on baseplate (1948 - 53)
Baseplate has raised rails (1948 - 53)

Baseplate tabs secure rear axle (1949 - 60)
Large lettering on baseplate (1954 - 60)
No raised rails on baseplate (1954 - 60)
Body casting includes rear wheel spats (1951 - 60)

40b / 151 Triumph 1800 Saloon 1948 - 60

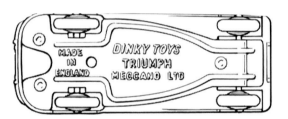

Casting with rear axle pillars (1948 - 50)
Small lettering on baseplate, as illustrated (1948 - 53)
Large lettering on baseplate (not illustrated) (1954 - 60)
Two raised rails on baseplate, as illustrated (1948 - 53)
No raised rails on baseplate (not illustrated) (1954 - 60)

40f / 154 Hillman Minx 1951 - 59

1951 - 54
Small lettering on baseplate
Two raised rails on baseplate
Rear axle secured by baseplate tabs

1954 - 59
Large lettering on baseplate
No raised rails on baseplate
Rear axle secured by baseplate tabs

Dinky Toys Cars

Market Price Range (MPR) for pre-1954 unboxed car models.

Prior to 1954, virtually all the cars were sold unboxed from retailer's trade boxes of either 6, 4 or 3 models. Consequently, all pre-1954 issues (except for 23m and 23s) have been priced as being unboxed. Post-1954 models were all boxed and have been priced accordingly. As a consequence, models which have

been renumbered will be found to have two differing prices – one for the pre-1954 unboxed version and another for its boxed and renumbered successor. See also the Trade Box section for details of individual boxes and packs that were used to supply shops.

Ref	Year(s)	Model name	Colours, features, details	Market Price Range

22 Series

Ref	Year(s)	Model name	Colours, features, details	Market Price Range
22a	1933-35	Open Sports Car	'Modelled Miniature' with 'HORNBY SERIES' cast into lead body, solid metal wheel/tyre castings (thinly painted in metallic blue, purple, green, yellow or red, or not painted at all) lead windscreen surround, tinplate radiator (grille may be same colour as body, or overpainted with the colour of the mudguards).	
			Blue body, Yellow seats and mudguards	£300-400
			Blue body, Red seats and mudguards	£300-400
			Cream body, Red seats and mudguards	£300-400
			Cream body, Green seats and mudguards	£300-400
			Cream body, Blue seats and mudguards	£300-400
			Red body, Cream or Blue seats and mudguards	£300-400
			Yellow body, Green seats and mudguards or reversed colours	£300-400
			Orange-Brown body, Cream seats and mudguards	£300-400
22b	1933-35	Closed Sports Coupé...................	'Modelled Miniature' with 'HORNBY SERIES' cast into lead body, solid metal wheel/tyre castings (coloured or plain, as 22a) tinplate radiator (painted in main body colour).	
			Cream body, Red roof and mudguards or Green roof and mudguards	£600-900
			Red body, Blue roof and mudguards or reversed colours	£600-900
			Red body, Cream roof and mudguards	£600-900
			Yellow body, Green roof and mudguards	£600-900
			Orange body, Green roof and mudguards, Gold washed wheels	£600-900
			Blue body, Yellow roof and mudguards	£600-900
22g	1935-41	Streamline Tourer	Model has cast steering wheel and windscreen, smooth diecast hubs which may be painted as body colour or a contrasting colour. Some have chrome hubs.	
			Body colours: Green, Maroon, Red, Light or Dark Blue, Cream, Buff or Black	£300-400
			Turquoise body, Blue hubs, White tyres	£500-750
22h	1935-41	Streamlined Saloon	Red, Maroon, Blue or Cream saloon version of 22g (no steering wheel). Wheels may be painted as body colour or a contrasting colour	£300-400

23 Series

Ref	Year(s)	Model name	Colours, features, details	Market Price Range
23	1934-35	Racing Car ....1st casting:	Lead body, no racing number, no driver, 0, 2, 3 or 4 exhausts stubs (without pipe), coloured tyres on some.	
		variations:	Cream or White body with either Blue, Cream, Green, Orange or Red top and nose flash	£200-300
			Yellow body with Blue upper body flash, 3 exhaust stubs	£200-300
23a	1935-41	Racing Car............(23 re-issued)	As 1st casting but diecast body, no driver, no number, Black or White tyres, 4 exhausts.	
		variations:	White body and hubs, Blue top flash and circle on nose	£200-300
			Cream body and hubs, Red top flash and circle on nose	£200-300
			Blue body, White top flash and circle on nose	£200-300
			Orange body, Green top flash and circle on nose	£200-300
			Yellow body, Dark Blue top flash and circle on nose	£200-300
			Brown body, Cream top flash	£200-300
			Silver body, Green racing number '8'	£200-300
23a		Racing Car ....2nd casting:	With driver plus raised circles for racing numbers, 6 exhausts in fishtail.	
		colour type 1:	With minor colour sidestripes and perhaps coloured tyres,	
		colour type 2:	Broad nose flash, even width top rear flash,	
		colour type 3:	Broad flash at cockpit and pointed ends top flash, cast circle on nose.	
		variations:	(type 1) Cream body, Red stripes, number '9', ('Humbug' version)	£300-400
			(type 2) Blue with White stripes and driver, racing number '11'	£300-400
			(type 2) Yellow body, Dark Blue top flash, racing number '7' or '1'	£200-300
			(type 2) Blue body, White top flash, racing number '11', '4' or '5'	£200-300
		'Humbug' version:	(type 2) Yellow with Blue stripes, racing number '7', Silvered 'Tootsie Toy' type hubs	£750-1,000
		'Humbug' version:	(type 2) Orange with Green stripes, racing number '10'	£500-750
			(type 3) White body, Blue nose/circle/top flash, number '2'	£200-300
			(type 3) Cream body, Red nose/circle/top flash, number '3'	£200-300
			(type 3) Red body, Cream nose/top flash, no number, no transverse ribs	£200-300
			(type 3) White body, Green nose/circle/top flash, number '6'	£200-300
			(type 3) Orange body, Green nose/circle/top flash, number '4'	£200-300
		casting variation:	With driver, raised racing number circle on nearside only, no detailed exhaust,	
			Orange body, Green nose circle, Green racing number '4'	£200-300
			Orange body, long Green upper body flash, 3 exhaust stubs, Green RN '4' or '10'	£200-300
			Yellow body, long Dark Blue upper body flash, chrome hubs	£200-300
23a	1946-52	Racing Car ....3rd casting:	With transverse body ribs, no raised circle for racing numbers, and only issued in colour type 3, with or without racing numbers. (Re-introduced in 1954 as 220).	
			Red or Red/Green body, Silver nose circle, top flash and side circle (Red RN '4'), Red hubs	£50-75
			Silver body, Red nose circle, top flash and side circle (Silver RN '4'), Red hubs	£50-75
			Red body, Cream flashes, Black hubs	£50-75

101

23b	1935-41	**Hotchkiss Racing Car**...............	Blue body, Dark Blue, Red or Silver flash and RN '2' or '5'; or Cream (Red flash and RN '1') **£200-300**
	1935-41	....	Yellow (Blue flash and RN '3'), Orange (Green flash and RN '6'),
			Green (Yellow flash and RN '5') or Turquoise (Blue flash and RN '4')..............................**£200-300**
	1946-48	....	Red with Silver flash and RN '5', or Silver with Red flash and RN '5'...............................**£65-85**
23c	1936-38	**Mercedes Benz Racing Car**.......	Red, Light Blue, Silver, Yellow or Green body with contrasting body flashes, with or without racing
			numbers, driver cast-in, Black hubs, treaded tyres...**£200-300**
	1938-40	....	As previous model but with rivetted baseplate bearing information.......................................**£200-300**
	1946-50	('Large Open Racing Car')...........	Re-issued 23c in Blue or Silver, various racing numbers...**£65-85**
23d	1936-38	**Auto-Union Racing Car**	Early pre-war issues without driver: Red, Blue, Pale Green, Yellow or Silver body,
			with or without racing numbers, clipped-in tinplate base..**£150-200**
	1938-41	....	Later pre-war issue with driver, rivetted baseplate..**£150-200**
	1946-50	....	Early post-war issue with driver: Red or Silver body **£50-60**
			Later post-war issue without driver **£40-50**
23e	1936-38	**'Speed Of The Wind'**	
		Racing Car..................................	Red, Blue, Light Blue, Green, Yellow or Silver body, plain clipped-in tinplate base, driver,
			with or without racing numbers, Black hubs and herringbone tyres, lead versions exist **£150-200**
	1938-41	....	As previous model but with rivetted baseplate bearing information.......................................**£100-125**
	1946-49	....	Red or Silver, rivetted informative baseplate, Red hubs, Grey tyres.................................**£75-100**
	1950-54	(Renumbered 221)	Silver body and hubs, plain base **£40-45**
23f	1952-54	**Alfa-Romeo Racing Car**	Red body, White racing number '8', Red diecast hubs. (Renumered 232)...........................**£85-95**
23g	1952-54	**Cooper-Bristol Racing Car**	Green body, White racing number '6', Green diecast hubs. (Renumbered 233) **£75-85**
23h	1953-54	**Ferrari Racing Car**	Blue body, Yellow nose, racing number '5' and diecast hubs. (Renumbered 234) **£85-95**
23j	1953-54	**H.W.M. Racing Car**	Light Green body, Yellow racing number '7', Green diecast hubs. (Renumbered 235)...........**£85-95**
23k	1953-54	**Talbot-Lago Racing Car**............	Blue body, Yellow racing number '4', Blue diecast hubs. (Renumbered 230) **£85-95**
23m	1938-41	**'Thunderbolt' Speed Car**	Silver body (Black detailing), Union Jacks on tail, Silver baseplate. In
			original Blue box dated '2-38', code: 'A2247' **£150-175**
23n	1953-54	**Maserati Racing Car**	Red, White flash and racing number '9', Red diecast hubs. (Renumbered 231) **£85-95**
23p	1939-40	**Gardner's MG Record Car**.......	Dark Green, White flash and 'MG' logo, Union Jacks, 'MG Magnette' on lacquered
			unpainted tinplate baseplate, Yellow box, dated '9-39', 104 mm **£150-200**
	1946-47	....	Dark Green, Union Jacks, no flash, 'MG Record Car' on base, not boxed **£80-100**
23s	1938-40	**Streamlined Racing Car**............	Light Green (Dark Green detailing), lead, 126 mm **£100-125**
			Light Blue (Dark Blue or Silver detailing), lead **£100-125**
			Orange body, lead...**£100-125**
			Light Green, Light Blue, Red or Orange body, mazak **£75-100**
23s	1948-54	(Renumbered 222)	Light, Mid or Dark Green, or Dark Blue, Silver flashes **£60-70**
			Silver body with Red, Green or Blue flashes **£60-70**
			Red body with Silver or Black flashes, Black base **£100-125**

24 Series

Note: The rarest of the 24 Series have coloured tyres matching the body colour and a higher value can be expected.

24a	1934-40	**Ambulance**	See 'Fire, Police and Ambulance Vehicles' Section.
24b	1934-38	**Limousine**..................................	Types 1 or 2: criss-cross chassis. Types 1, 2 or 3: grille, no sidelights, no spare wheel, 3 side
			windows, 3 'stacked' parallel horizontal bonnet louvres. Plated, Blue or Black hubs.
		..................body/chassis colours:	Maroon/Dark Maroon, Maroon/Grey, Maroon/Black,
			Blue/Yellow, Dark Blue/Black, Yellow/Brown...**£750-1,000**
	1937-40	............................casting change:	Same colours but no spare wheel slot, 3 parallel bonnet louvres, open chassis,
			'Bentley' grille and bumper **£300-400**
24c	1934-38	**Town Sedan**................................	Types 1 or 2: criss-cross chassis. Types 1, 2 or 3: grille, spare wheel, no sidelights, separate
			windscreen/steering wheel casting, smooth Blue, Black or plated hubs.
		body/chassis colours:	Green/Black, Green/Yellow, Pale Green/Red, Dark Blue/Dark Blue,
			Cream/Dark Blue, Cream/Black, Dark Blue/Black **£750-1,000**
	1937-40	............................casting change:	Same colours but open chassis, no spare wheel slot, narrower boot, shorter door handles..................**£400-600**
24d	1934-38	**Vogue Saloon**	Types 1 or 2: criss-cross chassis. Types 1, 2 or 3: grille, with nearside spare wheel, no sidelights.
			Smooth Blue, Black or plated hubs with White tyres.
		body/chassis colours:	Blue/Dark Blue, Blue/Black, Blue/Maroon, Cream/Blue, Brown/Green,
			Pink/Green, Green/Blue, Red/Grey, Green/Black, Maroon/Black **£750-1,000**
	1937-40	............................casting change:	Same colours but open chassis, higher 'domed' roofline **£400-600**
24e	1934-38	**Super Streamlined Saloon**........	Types 1 or 2: criss-cross chassis. Types 1, 2 or 3: grille, no spare or sidelights,
			12 bonnet louvres. Smooth Blue, Black or plated 'Tootsie-Toy' type hubs.
		body/chassis colours:	Maroon/Black, Red/Maroon, Red/Black, Green/Maroon, Green/Blue, Red/Brown, All Maroon..........**£300-400**
	1937-40	............................casting change:	As previous model but with 13 bonnet louvres **£300-400**
24f	1934-38	**Sportsmans Coupé**	Criss-cross chassis, with spare wheel, no sidelights, smooth hubs.
			Blue/Blue, Blue/Black, Yellow/Brown, Cream/Dark Blue, Brown/Buff **£300-400**
	1937-40	............................casting change:	Open chassis, higher 'domed' roofline, no spare wheel **£300-400**
24g	1934-38	**Sports Tourer Four-seater**	Types 1 or 2: criss-cross chassis. Types 1, 2 or 3: grille, spare wheel hub cast-in,
			no sidelights, open tinplate windscreen, separate dashboard/steering wheel casting.
			Plated, Blue or Black smooth hubs.
		body/chassis colours:	Yellow/Black, Yellow/Blue, Blue/Brown, Cream/Green, Cream/Brown,
			Black/Cream, Blue/Maroon **£300-400**
	1937-40	............................casting change:	Open chassis, filled-in windscreen, cast impression of spare...**£300-400**
24h	1934-38	**Sports Tourer Two-seater**..........	Types 1 or 2: criss-cross chassis. Types 1, 2 or 3: grille, spare wheel hub cast-in, no sidelights,
			tinplate windscreen, separate dashboard/steering wheel casting. Plated, Blue or Black smooth hubs.
		body/chassis colours:	Red/Red, Green/Dark Green, Yellow/Green, Yellow/Blue, Yellow/Black, Yellow/Brown,
			Black/Cream, Cream/Green, Red/Green, Blue/Brown, Yellow/Purple **£300-400**
	1937-40	............................casting change:	Open chassis, filled-in windscreen, cast impression of spare...**£300-400**

25j	1947-48	Jeep	Red body, Red or Blue hubs	£80-100
			Green body, Black or Red hubs	£80-100
			Aqua Blue or Sky Blue body, Black or Yellow hubs	£100-150
25y	1952-54	**Universal Jeep**	Green or Red body with hook, Maroon hubs, spare wheel on side	£80-90
		(Renumbered 405)	Red body with hook, Blue hubs, spare wheel on side	£80-90
27d	1950-54	**Land Rover**	Green, Dark Blue or Orange body, tinplate windscreen frame, driver	£50-60
		(Renumbered 340)	As previous model but with Red body	£50-60
	1952-53	Gift Set model:	Dark Brown body. Only in Gift Set No.2, Commercial Vehicles Set.	GSP
27f	1950-54	**Estate Car**	Pale Brown body with Dark Brown panels, rear axle pillars, Fawn hubs,	
		(Renumbered 344)	small lettering on matt or gloss baseplate	£50-60
27m	1950-54	**Land-Rover Trailer**	Orange body (Beige hubs), Green body (Green hubs), Blue (Blue hubs), Red (Red hubs). (See 341)	£25-35

30 Series

30a	1935-40	**Chrysler 'Airflow' Saloon**	No chassis, separate bumper units, lead versions exist, smooth plain or silvered hubs.	
		(Renumbered 32)	Turquoise, Maroon, Cream, Green, Purplish Blue, Red, (hubs may be any colour)	£300-400
			Rare issues with plated chrome hubs	£300-400
	1946		Cream or Green body, smooth hubs, White tyres	£150-200
	1946-48		As previous model but Blue, Cream or Green body (ridged hubs usually Black)	£130-160
30b	1935-40	**Rolls-Royce**	Open chassis, no sidelights, authentic radiator, smooth Black or coloured hubs.	
	1935-40		Cream/Black, Red and Maroon, Blue/Black, Dark Blue/Black, Fawn/Black, Tan/Dark Brown,	
			Red/Black, All Black	£300-400
			Yellow/Brown, Red/Red, Grey/Grey, Green/Light Green, Pale Green/Black	£250-350
			Light Blue body, smooth black wheel hubs, open chassis	£250-350
	1946		Fawn body, smooth hubs, open chassis	£100-125
	1946-50		Plain (closed) chassis, Violet-Blue/Black, Mid-Blue/Black, Dark Blue/Black, Light Blue/Black,	
			Fawn/Black or Greyish-Brown/Black; all with ridged hubs	£100-150
30c	1935-40	**Daimler**	Open chassis, no sidelights, authentic radiator, smooth hubs.	
	1935-40		Cream/Black, Blue/Black, Dark Blue/Black, Yellow/Black, Fawn/Black	£200-300
			Turquoise/Black, Fawn/Black, Light Green/Black	£200-300
			Pink/Maroon, Red/Red	£175-250
			Two-tone Grey or two-tone Green	£300-500
	1945-46		Tan body, smooth black wheel hubs, open chassis	£300-400
			Green or Fawn body, open chassis, smooth or ridged hubs	£100-125
	1946-50		Plain (closed) chassis, Dark Green/Black, Cream/Black, Fawn/Black, Beige/Black,	
			Grey/Black, Light Green/Black; all with ridged hubs	£100-125
			Medium Green body with Pale Green ridged hubs	£125-150
30d	1935-40	**Vauxhall**	Open chassis, no sidelights, spare wheel, 'egg box' or 'shield' grille.	
	1935-38		Green/Black, Blue/Black, Grey/Black, Yellow/Black, Brown/Black	£200-300
			Yellow/Brown, Cream/Brown, Tan/Brown, Red/Maroon	£200-300
			Two-tone Grey or two-tone Green	£300-500
	1938-40	radiator change:	As previous model but with 'shield' grille, Black chassis	£200-300
			With 'shield' radiator and coloured chassis	£200-300
	1946		Dark Olive Green body, open chassis, smooth black hubs, White tyres	£100-125
	1946-50		Plain (closed) chassis, no spare wheel, 'shield' radiator,	
			Green/Black, Dark Brown/Black, Maroon/Black, Yellow/Black,	
			Grey/Black, Olive-Green/Black, Blue/Black	£100-125
		Variation:	with Silver cast ridged hubs, thick axles, with Dark Olive Green body, black chassis	£200-250
30e	1935-48	**Breakdown Car**	See 'Commercial Vehicles' section.	
30f	1936-41	**Ambulance**	See 'Emergency Vehicles' section.	
30g	1936-50	**Caravan**	See 'Accessories (Pre-War)' section.	
32	1934-35	**Chrysler 'Airflow' Saloon**	Maroon (lead) body, no chassis, separate bumper units	£200-250
		(Previously 30a)	Maroon (diecast) body, no chassis, separate bumper units	£200-250
34a	1935-40	**'Royal Air Mail' Service Car**	See 'Commercial Vehicles and Vans' section.	

35 Series

35a	1936-40	**Saloon Car**	Some versions may have spare wheel cover in darker shade of main colour.	
			Blue, Maroon, Grey, Yellow, Red, Turquoise, Black or White solid rubber wheels	£90-120
	1946-48		Grey or Blue body (spare wheel cover not enhanced), Black rubber wheels	£60-70
35az	1939-40	**Fiat 2-seater Saloon**	Red, Blue or Green, White rubber wheels, 'Simca 5' cast inside. French issue	£80-100
35b	1936-39	**Racer**	Red, Silver, Yellow or Blue body, with or without driver, White solid rubber wheels,	
			Red grille and steering wheel	£65-75
35b	1939-54	**Midget Racer**	Silver body, Red grille, Brown driver, solid Black rubber wheels only	£65-75
		(Renumbered 200)	Silver body, Red grille, Silver driver, solid Black rubber wheels only	£65-75
			Green body, Black tyres	£150-175
35c	1936-40	**MG Sports Car**	Red, Pale or Dark Green, Turquoise, Blue or Maroon, Silver detailing,	
			White solid rubber wheels	£100-125
	1946-48		Red or Green body, Silver on radiator only, Black rubber wheels only	£70-80
35d	1938-40	**Austin 7 Car** (open tourer)	Wire windscreen frame, Black or White rubber wheels, Silver radiator and steering wheel,	
			hole for driver, 50 mm. Blue, Turquoise, Grey, Lime Green, Maroon or Yellow,	
			(Yellow may have Orange spare wheel cover)	£100-125
	1946-48		Blue, Grey or Yellow body, Silver on radiator only, Black rubber wheels only	£50-70
			Fawn body, Silver on radiator only, Black rubber wheels only	£70-90

36 Series

36a	1937-41	**Armstrong-Siddeley Limousine**	
		with Driver and Footman	Detailed chassis with slots, tinplate figures, sidelights, Black smooth hubs.
			Red/Dark Red, Grey/Dark Grey, Maroon/Dark Maroon, all-Maroon **£1,250-1,750**
	1946		Grey body, Black smooth wheel hubs, Moulded chassis with or without slots, no figures...........**£100-130**
36a	1947-50	**Armstrong-Siddeley**	(no slots or figures), moulded chassis, ridged hubs (black or coloured), plated radiator.
			Mid-Blue/Black, Grey/Black, Maroon/Black, Red/Maroon, Light Blue/Black,
			Powder Blue/Black, Saxe-Blue/Black, Olive-Green/Black **£150-250**
			Turquoise body, moulded chassis, ridged hubs...**£140-170**
36b	1937-41	**Bentley 2 seat Sports Coupé**	
		with Driver and Footman	Detailed chassis with slots, tinplate figures, sidelights, smooth black hubs.
			Cream/Black, Yellow/Maroon, Grey/Grey **£1,000-1,500**
	1946		Light Green or Saxe Blue body, smooth black hubs, moulded chassis (slots on some), no figures.........**£200-300**
36b	1947-50	**Bentley**	(no slots/figures). Moulded chassis, ridged hubs, plated radiator.
			Green/Black, Blue/Black, Grey/Black, Fawn/Black, Light Fawn/Black **£100-130**
			Light Blue, moulded chassis, ridged Black hubs..**£125-150**
36c	1937-41	**Humber Vogue Saloon**	
		with Driver and Footman	Detailed chassis with slots, tinplate figures, sidelights, plated radiator.
			Green/Dark Green, Blue/Dark Blue, all Royal Blue, smooth Black hubs **£1,000-1,500**
	1946		Early post war issues with smooth Black hubs, moulded chassis with or without slots, no figures **£100-150**
36c	1947-50	**Humber Vogue**	Dark Brown/Black, Blue/Black, Grey/Black, Maroon/Black, no slots or figures, ridged hubs **£90-120**
			Light Blue and Black, moulded chassis, ridged Black hubs, plated radiator **£175-225**
36d	1937-41	**Rover Streamlined Saloon**	
		with Driver and Footman	Detailed cast chassis with slots, tinplate driver and passenger, sidelights, Black smooth hubs.
			Light Green body, mid-Green wings, White tyres...**£400-600**
			Red Green body, Maroon wings, White tyres...**£400-600**
	1946		Early post war issues with smooth Black hubs and moulded chassis with or without slots............**£100-150**
36d	1947-50	**Rover**	Dark, Saxe, Mid or Bright Blue/Black, Light or Mid-Green/Black, no slots or figures..............**£90-120**
			Green body with Light Green hubs...**£100-125**
			Dark Blue body, Black wings, Light Blue hubs..**£150-200**
			Navy Blue body, Black wings, Black hubs...**£750-1,000**
36e	1937-41	**British Salmson Two-seater**	
		Sports Car with Driver	Detailed chassis, hole in seat for driver, cast Red or Green driver, Black hubs, solid windscreen,
			sidelights, spare wheel on some.
			Royal Blue/Black, Blue/Dark Blue, Black/Red, Grey/Dark Grey, Silver/Grey, Red/Maroon **£500-750**
	1946	**British Salmson**	Early post war issues with smooth Black hubs, moulded chassis, no driver **£100-125**
			Rare Brown issues..**£100-125**
36e	1947-50	**British Salmson Two-seater**	
		Sports Car	Red/Black, Light, Mid or Dark Green/Black, Fawn/Black, Mid-Blue/Black, Sky-Blue/Black or
			Saxe-Blue/Black, no hole in seat, tinplate windscreen, ridged hubs.................**£90-120**
			Red or Brown body, moulded chassis, ridged hubs.......................................**£250-300**
36f	1937-41	**British Salmson Four-seater**	
		Sports Car with Driver	Detailed chassis, hole in seat for driver, cast driver, sidelights, Black smooth hubs and solid
			windscreen, cast-in spare wheel. Red/Maroon, Green/Dark Green, Grey/mid-Grey **£500-700**
36f	1947-50	**British Salmson Four-seater**	
		Sports Car	Light or Mid-Green/Black, Brown/Black, Grey/Black, Fawn/Black, no hole or driver.
			Brownish-Grey/Black or Light Grey/Black, tinplate windscreen, ridged hubs...........**£90-120**

38 Series

NB Early Post War Issues 38 and 39 Series - see the Model Identification section for details.

38a	1940-41	**Frazer Nash BMW Sports**	Red body and smooth Black hubs with Red or Maroon seats, or Light Green with Dark Green seats....**£200-300**
			Dark Blue body and smooth hubs, Fawn seats **£200-300**
			Light Grey body, Brown seats **£200-300**
	1946	Special issue:	Dark Blue body, Light Blue seats, spread spigot not rivet, 'Hornby Series' tinplate sheet base.........**£100-150**
	1947-50	Regular issues:	with Black base, Black ridged hubs, celluloid windscreen:
			Light or Dark Blue (Fawn or Grey seats) **£75-95**
			Grey (Fawn, Khaki or Blue seats), Grey (Red seats and hubs) or Blue (Blue hubs).............**£150-200**
			Light Grey (Blue seats, Black hubs), Blue with Putty seats.............................**£150-200**
38a	1950-55		Same as previous models but made for export only (renumbered 100) ....NGPP
38b	1940-41	**Sunbeam Talbot Sports**	Red (Maroon tonneau), Red or Black smooth hubs, lacquered metal base............**£150-200**
	1946		Grey body, Fawn seats or Green with Dark Green tonneau, Black smooth hubs **£300-400**
	1947-49		Red/Maroon or Maroon/Grey, Black baseplate, Black ridged hubs **£75-95**
			Light Green/Green, Brown/Blue, Green/Dark Yellow, Black baseplate, Black ridged hubs............**£75-95**
			Light Grey (Grey or Dark Blue tonneau), Black ridged hubs, Black baseplate...........**£75-95**
			Dark Grey (Grey or Light Blue tonneau), Black ridged hubs, Black baseplate...........**£75-95**
			Yellow body and ridged hubs with matt Fawn tonneau, Black painted baseplate **£125-150**
			Deep Yellow body and ridged hubs with Dark Green tonneau, Black base, Silver edged screen...........**£125-150**
			Dark Blue body, Light Grey tonneau, Black ridged hubs and baseplate...............**£75-95**
			Light Blue body, Dark Grey tonneau, Black ridged hubs and baseplate...............**£75-95**
			Mid-Blue body, Grey tonneau, Black ridged hubs and baseplate **£75-95**
			Brown body, Blue tonneau, Silver edged screen **£150-175**
		NB	All issues may have a silver-edged windscreen.
	1950		Late post war issues with coloured hubs, e.g. Yellow body, Green tonneau, Yellow ridged hubs or
			Red body, Maroon tonneau, Red ridged hubs, plain screen **£100-150**
			Red body, Dark Green tonneau, Red ridged hubs, Black baseplate **£100-150**
38b	1950-55		As previous models but made for export only (renumbered 101)........................NGPP

38c	1946	**Lagonda Sports Coupé**	Early post war issues with Black smooth hubs...£200-300
	1947-50	....	Green body, Black or Dark Green seats, ridged Black hubs, Black baseplate £75-95
			Grey body, Fawn or Maroon seats, ridged Black hubs £75-95
			Maroon body, Dark Blue or Grey seats, ridged Black hubs, Black baseplate £75-95
			Light Grey Mid or Dark Grey seats, ridged Black hubs £75-95
38c	1950-55		As previous models but made for export only (renumbered 102)...NGPP
	1950		Late post war issues with coloured hubs, eg. Green body with Light Green hubs £100-150
38d	1940-41	**Alvis Sports Tourer**	Green body, Black seats and hubs or Maroon body, Red seats, lacquered base £150-175
	1946	....	Early post war issues £200-300
	1947-50	....	Green/Dark Green, Green/Brown, Black painted baseplate £75-95
			Green body, Black seats and hubs, Black painted baseplate £75-95
			Green body, Black seats, Green hubs, Black painted baseplate £75-95
			Maroon/Grey, Red hubs, Maroon/Red, Light Blue/Dark Blue, Black base £100-150
			Blue/Grey, Grey/Blue, Black painted base £75-95
	1950	....	Late post war issues with coloured hubs, eg. Maroon body with Red hubs £100-150
38d	1950-55		As previous models but made for export only (renumbered 103)...NGPP
38e	1940 ?	**Triumph Dolomite**.....................	Planned and catalogued but not issued ....NPP
38e	1946	**Armstrong Siddeley Coupé**	('Hurricane'). Early post war issues with Black smooth wheel hubs......................................£200-300
	1947-50		Grey/Deep Blue, Light Grey/Blue, Black painted baseplate £75-95
			Light Grey/Green, Light Green/Grey or Grey/Dark Green £75-95
			Bright Green/Grey, Red/Maroon, Cream/Blue, Black painted baseplate £75-95
			Dark Green body and interior £75-95
			Royal Blue body, Dark Green interior £75-95
			Apple Green body, Dark Grey interior £75-95
	1950		Light Green body, Apple Green hubs £200-250
			Light Green body, Grey interior, Mid-Green hubs £200-250
			Light Grey body, Dark Green interior, Grey hubs £200-250
			Grey body, Dark Blue interior, Red hubs £200-250
			Grey body, Dark Blue interior, Pale or Mid-Blue hubs £200-250
38e	1950-55	....	As previous models but made for export only (renumbered 104)...NGPP
38f	1940-41	**Jaguar (SS100) Sports Car**	Khaki/Blue, Blue/Grey, Light Blue/Grey, Grey/Blue, Grey/Black,
			Red/Maroon, Dark Brown/Black, 2 celluloid windscreens, clear lacquered baseplate...........£150-175
	1946	....	Early post-war issues with Black smooth hubs (later issues are ridged).................................£75-95
	1947-50	....	Light, Mid- or Dark Blue body, Grey or Putty seats, Black painted baseplate £75-95
			Light Brown body, Blue seats, Black painted baseplate or Red body, Maroon seats £75-95
			Brownish-Grey body, Black seats and ridged hubs £100-150
			Grey body, Red interior and ridged hubs £100-150
	1950		Late post-war issues with coloured hubs, e.g. Light Blue body, Putty seats (Blue hubs) or
			Red body, Maroon seats and tonneau (Red hubs) £100-150
38f	1950-55	....	As previous models but made for export only (renumbered 105)...NGPP

39 Series			See the 'Model Identification' and 'Wooden Prototypes' sections for more details.
39a	1939-41	**Packard Super 8 Tourer**	Light Green, Grey, Black, Yellow, Blue, Silver baseplate...£200-300
	1946	....	Early post-war issues with Black smooth wheel hubs..£90-120
	1947-50	....	Dark Brown, Green or Olive-Green body, Black painted baseplate, ridged hubs £75-95
	1950	....	Late post-war issues with coloured ridged hubs £200-250
39b	1939-41	**Oldsmobile 6 Sedan**	Black, Maroon, Yellow, Mid Blue, Light or Mid-Grey or Green, Silver base £200-300
	1946	....	Early post-war issues with Black smooth wheel hubs...£100-150
	1947-50	....	Grey, Brown, Green or Fawn body, oval baseplate supports,
			Black painted baseplate open at rear, ridged hubs £90-120
			Cream body, ridged hubs £125-150
			Violet-Blue, Black chassis, ridged hubs £150-200
	1947-50	.................................US issue:	Light Blue body, Black ridged hubs, oval baseplate support, open rear baseplate, ridged hubs £200-250
	1950		Late post-war issues with coloured ridged hubs £200-250
	1952	.............................Export issue:	Beige body and hubs, oval front supports, closed rear baseplate £200-300
39bu	1950-52	**Oldsmobile Sedan (US issue)**	Cream with Dark Blue wings, Black painted baseplate £600-800
			Cream body, Tan wings, Black painted baseplate (closed at rear), blued axles, oval studs....£600-800
			Tan body and hubs, oval studs, baseplate closed at rear £600-800
			Light Blue body, Dark Blue wings, Light Blue hubs £600-800
39c	1939-41	**Lincoln Zephyr Coupé**	Grey/Black, Yellow Red or Green body, lacquered baseplate, smooth Black hubs..............£150-175
	1946	....	Early post-war issues with Black smooth wheel hubs...£100-150
	1947-50	....	Light Grey, Brown, Maroon or Red body, Black painted baseplate, ridged hubs....................£90-120
	1950		Late post-war issues with coloured ridged hubs e.g. Light 'Riley' Green with darker Green hubs
			or Red body with Red hubs £200-250
39cu	1950-52	.................................US issue:	Red body and ridged hubs, Maroon wings, Black painted baseplate.................................£1,500-2,000
39cu	1950-52	.................................US issue:	Cream body and ridged hubs, Brown wings, Black painted baseplate £600-800
39cu	1950-52	.................................US issue:	Tan with Brown wings, Black painted baseplate, ridged hubs £600-800
39d	1939-41	**Buick Viceroy Saloon**.................	Grey, Green, Maroon, Cream or Blue, lacquered baseplate, smooth Black hubs £200-250
	1946	....	Early post-war issues with Black smooth wheel hubs...£100-150
	1946	....	Olive body, smooth hubs..£100-150
	1947-50	....	Light or Dark Green, Maroon, Fawn, Blue, Beige or Grey body, Black base, ridged hubs £90-120
			Mustard body, Black painted baseplate, ridged hubs £150-200
			Greyish-Brown body, Light Brown ridged hubs, Black painted baseplate £140-160
			Apple Green body and ridged hubs £150-200
	1950		Late post-war issues with coloured ridged hubs, eg. Light 'Riley' Green body with darker green
			hubs or Brown body with Green or Yellow hubs £150-200

Cars

39e	1939-41	**Chrysler Royal**	Yellow, Black, Green, Royal Blue or Grey body, lacquered baseplate, smooth Black hubs	£200-250
	1946	....	Early post-war issues with Black smooth wheel hubs..	£100-150
	1947-50	....	Light Blue, Mid-Blue, Dark Blue, Light Green, Mid-Green, Dark Green or	
			Dark Grey body, Black ridged hubs and baseplate	£110-140
			As previous models but with Silvered baseplate	£250-350
			Cream body, Green ridged hubs, Black painted baseplate	£100-150
	1950	....	Late post-war issues with coloured ridged hubs, eg. Light 'Triumph 1800' Blue with blue hubs	£200-250
39eu	1950-52	**Chrysler Royal** ....(US issues)	Yellow with Red wings, Yellow hubs, Black baseplate, Blued axles...................................	£1,500-2,000
			Two-tone Green body, Light Green hubs, Black baseplate, Blued axles	£1,000-1,400
39f	1939-41	**Studebaker State Commander** ..	Yellow, Green or Dark Grey body, lacquered baseplate	£200-250
	1946	....	Early post-war issues with Black smooth wheel hubs..	£100-150
	1947-50	....	Yellow body, Black smooth hubs	£250-350
			Green, Olive or Maroon body, Black baseplate, ridged hubs..	£90-120
			Dark Grey or Light Grey body, Black ridged hubs	£90-120
			Dark Maroon body, Black ridged hubs...	£90-120
			Very Dark Blue or Navy Blue body, Black ridged hubs..	£90-120
			Tan body, Black ridged hubs	£120-150
			Mid-Blue body, Black baseplate, Mid-Blue ridged hubs..	£200-250
			Dark Green body, Black baseplate, ridged hubs..	£120-140
	1950	....	Late post-war issues with coloured ridged hubs...	£200-250

40 Series

See also the 'Dinky Toys Cars - Box Types' and 'Model Identification' information pages.

40a	1947-50	**Riley Saloon**	Tinplate baseplate '40A' has small print and the rear wheels are retained by cast pillars.	
			Light, Mid or Dark Grey body, Black hubs	£70-80
			Light Grey body, Tan hubs	£70-80
			Mid-Green body, Black hubs	£80-100
	1950-53	.............................2nd baseplate:	Baseplate with '40A' and large print. With tow-hook aperture.	
			Dark Blue or Mid-Blue body, Black hubs	£80-100
			Grey body, Black hubs	£150-175
			Dark Green body, Black hubs	£80-100
			Cream body, Mid-Green hubs	£75-85
	1954	40a renumbered 158	Baseplate '158' has large print. No tow-hook aperture.	
158	1954-55	**Riley Saloon**	Cream body, Mid-Green hubs	£100-120
			Mid-Green body with Green hubs, or Light Green body and hubs......................................	£100-120
			Pale Green body, Mid-Green hubs	£100-120
			Dark Blue body, Mid-Blue hubs	£100-120
			Light Grey body and hubs	£100-120
40b	1948-49	**Triumph 1800 Saloon**.................	Small baseplate print, rear axles held by cast pillars (see diagram).	
			Light, Mid or Dark Grey body, Black or Grey hubs	£70-80
			Mid-Blue body and hubs	£100-130
			Light Blue body, Blue or Fawn hubs	£90-110
			Fawn body, Black or Fawn hubs	£80-90
			Black body, Black hubs	£500-700
	1949-54	.............................2nd baseplate:	Small print on baseplate, rear axle retained by baseplate tabs.	
			Mid or Dark Blue body, Fawn hubs, or Light Blue body and hubs...................................	£80-90
			Fawn body, Green hubs	£100-120
	1954	40b renumbered 151	Large baseplate print.	
151	1954-59	**Triumph 1800 Saloon**.................	Beige body, Green hubs, or Dark Blue with Light Blue hubs..	£100-120
			Light Blue body with Mid-Blue, Fawn or Grey hubs, or Mid-Blue body with Light Blue hubs...........	£100-120
40c	1940	**Jowett Javelin**............................	Factory drawing exists but model not issued...	NPP
40d	1949-54	**Austin (A40) Devon**....................	Small baseplate print, rear axle retained by the baseplate.	
			Maroon body and hubs	£80-90
			Red body, Maroon hubs	£400-600
			Light Grey-Green body and hubs	£100-120
			Light Blue body, Mid-Blue hubs, or Mid-Blue body with Light Blue hubs..........................	£100-120
			Dark Green body, Cream hubs..	£80-90
			Luminous Blue body, Mid-Blue hubs, Black baseplate..	£120-140
	1954	40d renumbered 152	'DEVON' cast into underside of roof.	
152	1954-59	**Austin (A40) Devon**....................	Large baseplate print (see example diagrams).	
			Suede Green body and hubs, or Dark Blue body with Light Blue hubs...............................	£120-140
			Tan body, Suede Green hubs..	£500-700
			Maroon body, Red hubs	£175-200
			Light Blue body and hubs	£400-500
			Light Green body, Mid-Green hubs, or Dark Green body with Fawn hubs...........................	£100-120
	1956-59	........................Two-tone issue:	Blue upper body and hubs, Yellow lower body	£175-200
	1956-59	........................Two-tone issue:	Pink lower body, Green upper body, Cream hubs	£175-200
40e	1948	**Standard Vanguard**	1st casting: Open rear wheel arches, small baseplate print, rear axle secured by tinplate clip.	
			Fawn body and hubs	£100-120
			Fawn body, Red hubs	£140-170
	1949-50	........................baseplate change:	Open rear wheel arches, small baseplate print, rear axle secured by baseplate tabs.	
			Fawn body and hubs	£70-80
			Mid-Blue body and hubs	£80-90
			Dark Blue body, Fawn hubs...	£500-600
	1950-54	...............................2nd casting:	Closed rear wheel arches, small baseplate print.	
			Light Blue body, Fawn hubs, or Fawn body with Fawn hubs...	£80-90
	1954	40e renumbered 153	'VANGUARD' cast into underside of roof, large baseplate print.	

106

153	1954-59	**Standard Vanguard**	Mid-Blue body, Cream hubs, or Blue body with Blue or Fawn hubs **£100-125**
			Fawn body with Cream hubs, Cream body with Cream hubs, or Maroon body with Fawn hubs..........**£100-125**
			Maroon body with Maroon hubs...**£750-1,000**
		NB	The ridge which appears on the boot of some Vanguard models is the result of worn die replacement.

40f	1951-54	**Hillman Minx**.........1st baseplate:	Small baseplate print (see diagram).
			Light Tan body with Fawn hubs, or Dark Tan body with Grey hubs..**£70-80**
			Mid-Green body with Light Green hubs, or Green body with Mid-Green or Cream hubs **£70-80**
	1955	40f renumbered 154	'HILLMAN MINX' cast into underside of roof.
154	1955	**Hillman Minx** ....2nd baseplate:	Large baseplate print (see diagram).
			Dark Tan body with Cream or Green hubs, or Pale Tan body with Blue or Yellow hubs **£100-120**
			Light Green body and hubs, or Dark Green body with Light Green hubs...**£175-200**
			Pale Blue body with Light Green hubs, or Light Green body with Mid-Green hubs...........................**£175-225**
			Pale Blue lower body and hubs, Pink upper body **£175-225**
			Cream upper body and hubs, Lime Green lower body..**£175-225**

40g	1950-54	**Morris Oxford**	Small baseplate print.
			Light Grey body and hubs..**£80-100**
			Mid-Green body and hubs..**£80-100**
			Dark Green body and hubs **£80-100**
	1954	40g renumbered 159	Small baseplate print, 'MORRIS OXFORD' cast into underside of roof.
159	1954	**Morris Oxford**	Dark Green body and hubs, or Green body with Light Green hubs...**£100-120**
		Export issue:	Beige body and hubs...**£500-800**
			Blue body, Grey hubs **£1,500-2,000**
			Fawn body, Grey or Stone hubs **£120-140**
		Two-tone issue:	Green upper body and hubs, Cream lower body **£150-175**
		Two-tone issue:	Cream upper body and hubs, Deep Pink lower body..**£150-175**
		Two-tone issue:	Turquoise upper body, Cream lower body, Turquoise-Green hubs...**£300-400**

40j	1953-54	**Austin (A40) Somerset**...............	Large print on baseplate.
			Pale Blue body and hubs..**£80-90**
			Red body and hubs...**£80-90**
			Mid-Blue body and hubs..**£80-90**
			Dark Blue body, Mid-Blue hubs..**£80-90**
	1954	40j renumbered 161	Large baseplate print, 'AUSTIN SOMERSET' cast into underside of roof.
161	1954	**Austin (A40) Somerset**...............	Pale Blue body, Mid or Dark Blue hubs...**£80-100**
			Red body and hubs...**£80-100**
	1956-59	Two-tone issue:	Red lower body and hubs, Yellow upper body **£150-175**
	1956-59	Two-tone issue:	Cream lower body and hubs, Black lower body..**£150-175**

40h	1952-54	**Austin Taxi (FX3)**..........Chassis:	Diecast chassis with cast-in driver and model number.
			All-Yellow body and hubs, Black chassis ('40H'), interior and driver...**£90-120**
			All-Yellow body and hubs, Brown chassis ('40H'), interior and driver **£150-250**
			Dark Blue body, Light Blue hubs, Black chassis ('40H'), interior and driver.....................................**£90-120**
			Mid-Blue body and hubs, Black chassis ('40H'), interior and driver **£200-250**
	1954	40h renumbered 254	
254	1956-59	**Austin Taxi (FX3)** ....Two-tone:	Yellow upper body and hubs, Dark Green lower body, Black chassis ('254'), interior and driver **£90-120**
		Spun hubs:	Black body, spun hubs, Grey chassis ('254'), interior and driver...**£110-130**
			Blue body, Light Blue hubs **£500-750**

Models 101 onwards

101	1957-60	**Sunbeam Alpine**	Pink body, Cream interior, Beige diecast hubs, Grey driver **£120-140**
		(touring finish)	Pink body, Cream interior, spun hubs, Grey driver **£200-300**
			Light Turquoise body, Dark Blue interior, Light Blue diecast hubs, Grey driver................................**£120-140**
			Light Turquoise body, Dark Blue interior, spun hubs, Grey driver...**£150-200**
102	1957-60	**MG Midget**	Orange body, Red seats and diecast hubs, Grey driver **£150-200**
		(touring finish)	Light Green body, Cream seats, Cream diecast hubs, Grey driver..**£150-200**
			Late issues with spun aluminium hubs, in plain or lighter yellow boxes..**£250-350**
103	1957-60	**Austin Healey 100**	Red body, Grey seats, diecast hubs and driver **£180-220**
		(touring finish)	Cream body, Red seats and diecast hubs, Grey driver...**£180-220**
104	1957-60	**Aston-Martin DB3S**	Light Blue body, Dark Blue interior, Mid-Blue hubs, Grey driver **£125-150**
		(touring finish)	Salmon-Pink body, Red seats and diecast hubs, Grey driver **£125-150**
105	1957-60	**Triumph TR2**..............................	Grey body, Red seats and diecast hubs..**£130-160**
		(touring finish)	As previous issue but with spun hubs in 'plain' printed box or late lighter yellow box **£250-350**
			Yellow body, Light Green seats, Mid-Green hubs, Grey driver **£180-220**
	1959-60	....	As before but with spun hubs, in 'plain' printed box with Yellow spot, or in late lighter Yellow box ...**£250-350**
106	1954-58	**Austin A90 Atlantic**	Light Blue body, Cream seats, Cream hubs...**£100-120**
		(Renumbered from 140a)	Light Blue body, Red seats, Red or Cream hubs...**£100-120**
			Light Blue body, Dark Blue seats, Cream or Dark Blue hubs...**£100-120**
			Black body, Red seats and hubs, White tyres...**£100-120**
			Pink body, Cream interior, Cream hubs, '106' on baseplate **£100-120**
		NB	Interiors may have a gloss or matt finish.
107	1955-59	**Sunbeam Alpine**	
		(competition finish).....................	Light Blue, Tan or Cream seats, Beige hubs, '26', racing driver **£120-140**
			Deep Pink body, Grey seats, Beige hubs, RN '34', racing driver..**£120-140**
		NB	See also 'Factory samples' listing at the end of this section.
108	1955-59	**MG Midget**	
		(competition finish).....................	Red body, Tan seats, Red hubs, RN '24', racing driver **£130-160**
			White body, Maroon seats, Red hubs, RN '28', racing driver **£130-160**
		NB	The version of 108 issued in the US is numbered 129.

109	1955-59	**Austin-Healey 100**		
		(competition finish)......................	Cream body, Red seats and hubs, racing driver and racing number '23'..	£100-120
			Yellow body, Blue seats and hubs, racing driver and racing number '21' or '28'........................	£100-120
110	1956-59	**Aston-Martin DB3S**		
		(competition finish)......................	Grey body, Blue seats and hubs, racing driver and number '20'..	£110-130
			Mid-Green body, Red interior, Red ridged hubs, RN '22'..	£110-130
			Light Green body, Red interior, Red ridged hubs, RN '22'..	£200-250
110	1966-67	**Aston-Martin DB5**	Metallic Red, Cream or Black seats, '110' on base, spoked wheels.......................................	£75-95
	1967-71		Metallic Red or Blue, Cream or Black seats, plain base, spoked wheels...............................	£75-95
		NB	See also 'Factory samples' listing at the end of this section.	
111	1956-59	**Triumph TR2 Sports Car**		
		(competition finish)	Salmon-Pink body, Blue seats and hubs, racing driver and RN '29'	£125-150
			Turquoise body, Red seats and hubs, racing driver and racing number '25'	£125-150
112	1961-66	**Austin-Healey Sprite Mk.II**	Red body, Cream interior, spun hubs..	£100-125
		South African issues:	Turquoise, Pink, Light Blue or Dark Blue body, spun hubs...	£500-750
113	1962-69	**MG 'MGB'**	White body, Red interior, Grey plastic driver, spun hubs...	£70-90
	1966	South African issue:	Mid-Blue body (Red interior), or Red body (Cream interior), spun hubs..............................	£500-750
114	1963-71	**Triumph Spitfire**	Sports car with Blue lady driver (plastic), spun hubs, jewelled headlamps.	
	1963-66	....	Metallic Silver-Grey body (Red seats), or Red body (Cream seats)	£90-110
	1966-70	....	Metallic Gold body with Red seats and 'Tiger In Tank' on bootlid	£90-110
	1966-70	....	Metallic Gold body, without bootlid logo	£90-110
	1970-71	....	Metallic Purple body, Gold interior	£120-140
115	1965-69	**Plymouth Fury Sports**	White open body, Red interior, cast wheels, driver and passenger	£75-85
116	1966-71	**Volvo P 1800 S**	Red body, White interior, wire wheels...	£60-75
			Metallic Red body, Light Blue interior, wire wheels...	£80-100
120	1962-67	**Jaguar 'E' type**	Red, detachable Black or Grey hardtop/optional Cream or Grey folded soft-top, spun hubs ...	£70-90
			Metallic Blue and White, Black, Grey or Cream body, spun hubs......................................	£70-90
			Metallic Light Blue and Black body, Cream seats, spun hubs	£600-800
122	1977-78	**Volvo 265 DL Estate**	Metallic Blue (Brown interior), or Cream with '265DL' wing badges, cast hubs.....................	£30-35
	1979-80		Orange version without '265 DL' (made in Italy by Polistil), Brown box	£40-50
		NB	See also 'Factory samples' listing at the end of this section.	
123	1977-80	**Princess 2200 HL**	Metallic Bronze with black roof side panels, plastic wheels...	£30-35
			All White	£30-35
			White body, Blue roof	£30-35
			White body, Blue side panels	£30-35
124	1977-79	**Rolls-Royce Phantom V**	Metallic Light Blue, boot opens - bonnet does not (see 152)..	£35-45
127	1964-66	**Rolls-Royce Silver Cloud Mk.3** .	Metallic Blue or Metallic Green, suspension and steering, spun hubs.................................	£65-75
	1966-69	....	Metallic Gold, Light Blue interior, cast wheels	£55-65
	1969-72	....	Metallic Red	£55-65
128	1964-67	**Mercedes-Benz 600**	Metallic Red body, white interior, spun hubs, three figures/luggage	£45-55
	1967-75		Metallic Red body, White interior, spun hubs or Speedwheels, driver only	£30-40
	1975-79		Metallic Blue body, White interior, driver, Speedwheels	£30-35
129	? - ?	**MG Midget** (US issue)	White body, Maroon or Red interior and tonneau, Red hubs, no driver or	
			racing number (see 108), Yellow box with '129'..	£300-400
			Red body, Tan interior and tonneau, Red hubs, no driver or	
			racing number (see 108), Yellow box with '129'..	£300-400
129	1965 -72	**Volkswagen 1300 Sedan**............	Metallic Blue body, White interior, spun hubs, registration plate 'K.HK 454'.....................	£45-55
	1972-76	....	Metallic Blue body, plastic Speedwheels..	£30-35
130	1964-66	**Ford Consul Corsair**..................	Red or Metallic Wine Red body, Off-White interior, spun hubs..	£55-65
	1966-69		Pale Blue, Metallic Dark Grey base, Off-White interior, spun hubs...................................	£45-55
		NB	Baseplates on 130 may have rounded or dimpled rivets.	
131	1956-61	**Cadillac Eldorado**	Yellow body, Red interior, Grey driver, Grey or Cream diecast hubs, packing piece also in box............	£90-110
			Salmon-Pink body, Grey interior, Grey driver, Cream diecast hubs, packing piece also in box	£90-110
	1962-63		As previous models but with spun aluminium hubs...	£110-130
131	1968-70	**Jaguar 'E'-type 2+2**	White body, Light Blue interior, cast spoked wheels, Gold base	£80-90
	1970-75	....	Metallic Bronze body, Blue interior, cast spoked wheels or plastic wheels.........................	£65-75
	1975-76	....	Metallic Mauve body, Light Blue interior, cast spoked wheels or Speedwheels...................	£100-125
	1976-77	....	Bronze body, Speedwheels..	£65-75
	1977-77	....	Metallic Red or Post Office Red body, Blue interior, Speedwheels.....................................	£70-80
132	1955-61	**Packard Convertible**.................	Light Green body, Red interior and hubs, Grey driver	£90-110
			Pale Tan body, Red interior and hubs, Grey driver...	£90-110
	1962-63		As previous models but with spun aluminium hubs...	£110-125
132	1967-74	**Ford 40 RV**	Metallic Silver or Blue body, wire wheels...	£30-40
			Red/Yellow body, White interior, wire wheels...	£30-40
		NB	Early models have red headlight recesses.	
133	1955-60	**Cunningham C5R**	White body, Dark Blue stripes, Brown interior, RN '31', Blue hubs, Light Blue driver............	£65-75
			Off-White body, Blue interior and driver...	£65-75
			As previous models but with spun aluminium hubs...	£70-80
133	1964-66	**Ford Cortina**............................	Metallic Gold/White body, Red interior, spun hubs, (issued to replace 139)........................	£55-65
	1966-68		Pale Lime body, Red interior, spun hubs..	£65-75
134	1964-68	**Triumph Vitesse**	Metallic Aqua Blue body, White side stripe, Red interior, spun hubs	£70-85

135	1963-69	**Triumph 2000 Saloon**	Red interior, Grey base, spun hubs, wipers, luggage.	
		normal colours:	Metallic Green with White roof or Metallic Blue with White roof, spun hubs	**£60-70**
		Gift Set 118 colour:	White body, Blue roof, Red interior, spun hubs, individually boxed	**£110-140**
		promotional colours:	Each promotional issue was packed in a standard Yellow/Red card picture box.	
			Black body, Cactus-Green or White roof	**£300-500**
			Blue Grey body, Black roof	**£300-500**
			Light Green body with Lilac roof, or Metallic Green with White roof	**£300-500**
			Brown body, Light Green roof	**£300-500**
			British Racing Green, White roof	**£300-500**
			Red or Cherry Red body, White roof, Blue interior	**£300-500**
			White body, Black or Light Green or Light Grey roof, Blue interior	**£300-500**
			Dark Green body, Cactus-Green roof	**£300-500**
			Gunmetal body, Black roof, with 'Gunmetal/WD' label on box	**£300-500**
136	1964-65	**Vauxhall Viva**	White-Grey body, Red interior, spun hubs	**£50-60**
	1965-68		Metallic Bright Blue body, Red interior, spun hubs	**£45-55**
	1969-73		Pale Metallic Blue body, Red interior, spun hubs	**£40-50**
137	1963-66	**Plymouth Fury Convertible**	Green, Pink, Blue or Metallic Grey body, Cream hood, spun hubs	**£70-85**
138	1963-66	**Hillman Imp**	Metallic Silver-Green body, Red interior, luggage, spun hubs, cast headlamps	**£65-75**
	1966-68		Metallic Red body, luggage, spun hubs, jewelled or plastic headlamps	**£65-75**
	1968-73		Metallic mid-Blue body, Red interior, luggage, spun hubs, jewelled headlamps	**£45-55**
			As previous issue but with Blue interior, in picture box with white background	**£125-150**
		Late issue:	Metallic Deep Blue body, Red interior, bare metal baseplate, spun hubs	**£140-160**
139	1963-64	**Ford Consul Cortina**	Pale Blue body, Off-White interior, spun hubs, cast headlamps	**£55-65**
	1964-65		Metallic Blue body, Fawn interior, spun hubs	**£65-75**
	1966	South African issue:	Bright Green body, spun hubs, Fawn interior	**£400-600**
		NB	South African issues – The boxes are printed in both English and Afrikaans, and with the distributors name.	
139a	1949-54	**Ford Fordor Sedan**	All have small lettering on the black baseplates which may be gloss or matt.	
		(Renumbered 170)	Yellow, Red, Green or Tan body, (all with matching hubs)	**£70-80**
			Brown body, Red hubs	**£70-80**
			Tan body, Maroon hubs	**£70-80**
			Red body, Maroon hubs	**£70-80**
139am	1950-54	**US Army Staff Car**	Ford Fordor in Olive drab with White stars on roof and doors, (renumbered 170m)	**£175-250**
		Canadian issue:	As previous model but without stars	NGPP
139b	1950-54	**Hudson Commodore**	Dark Blue body, Light Tan roof and hubs	**£70-80**
		(Renumbered 171)	Dark Blue body, Tan roof and hubs	**£70-80**
			Cream body, Maroon roof and hubs	**£70-80**
			Royal Blue body, Pale Tan roof and hubs	**£90-110**
			Fawn lower body, Light Blue roof (as per 151 (40b) Triumph Renown Blue)	NGPP
			Dark Blue body, Grey roof and hubs	NGPP
140a	1951-53	**Austin A90 Atlantic**	Mid-Blue body, Red or Blue seats, Cream hubs	**£65-75**
		(Renumbered 106)	Mid-Blue body, Dark Blue seats, Mid-Blue hubs	**£300-500**
			Mid-Blue body, Maroon seats, Cream hubs	**£300-500**
			Deep Blue body, Red seats and hubs	**£75-85**
			Red body, Maroon seats and hubs	**£400-600**
			Light Blue body, Red seats, Cream hubs	**£250-350**
			Red body with Cream seats and hubs, or Pink body with Cream hubs	**£100-120**
		NB	Interiors may have a gloss or matt finish.	
140b	1951-54	**Rover 75 Saloon**	Maroon body with Maroon or Red hubs	**£90-110**
		(Renumbered 156)	Cream body with Cream or Blue hubs	**£90-110**
			Turquoise lower body, Light Green upper body, Mid-Green hubs	NGPP
140	1963-69	**Morris 1100**	Light Blue or Dark Blue, spun hubs	**£40-50**
	1966	South African issue:	White body, Blue roof, Red interior, spun hubs	**£400-600**
	1966	South African issue:	Light Caramel body, Red interior, spun hubs	**£400-600**
	1966	South African issue:	Sky Blue body	**£400-600**
141	1963-67	**Vauxhall Victor Estate Car**	Yellow body, Blue interior, spun hubs	**£45-55**
	1966	South African issues:	Pink, Ivory or Yellow body, all with Blue interior, spun hubs	**£400-600**
		US promotional:	Dark Red body, Blue interior, spun hubs. Paper labels with Yellow wording: 'LIGHTNING FASTENERS LTD', 'TECHNICAL SERVICES'	**£500-750**
142	1962-68	**Jaguar Mk.10**	Metallic Light Blue or Mid-Blue, Red interior, spun aluminium hubs	**£40-50**
	1966	South African issue:	Green body with White roof, spun hubs	**£400-600**
		NB	Gold, US export issue 'see-through' window boxes. Model nos. 134, 138 and 142 housed in these boxes may attract a premium of 50%. See 'Cars - Box Types' for a complete listing.	
143	1962-67	**Ford Capri**	Turquoise body, White roof, Red interior, spun hubs	**£50-60**
144	1963-67	**Volkswagen 1500**	Off-White body, Red interior, luggage, spun hubs	**£45-55**
			Metallic Gold body, Blue interior, luggage, spun hubs	**£45-55**
			Metallic Gold body, Red interior, luggage, spun hubs	**£100-125**
		South African issue:	Metallic Green body, spun hubs	**£400-600**
		South African issue:	Bronze or Caramel body	**£400-600**

145	1962-67	**Singer Vogue**	Metallic Light Green body, Red interior, spun hubs	£60-75
			Yellow body, Red interior, spun hubs, Yellow steering wheel, Silver trim	£1,500-2,000
146	1963-67	**Daimler 2.5 litre V8**	Metallic Pale Green body, Red interior, spun hubs	£60-70
147	1962-69	**Cadillac '62**	Metallic Green body, Red or White interior, spun hubs	£60-75
148	1962-65	**Ford Fairlane**	(Non-metallic) Pea Green body, Cream interior, open or closed windows, spun hubs	£65-75
			As previous model but with Red interior	NGPP
	1965-67		Light Metallic Green, Pale Cream interior, open windows, spun hubs	£125-150
		US issue:	Metallic Emerald Green body, spun hubs, US issue Gold 'see-through' window box	£300-400
	1966	South African issue:	Bright Blue body, closed windows, spun hubs, White tyres	£400-600
	1966	South African issue:	Dark Blue body, spun hubs, no base number, White tyres	£400-600
149	1971-75	**Citroën Dyane**	Metallic Bronze body, Black roof and interior, Speedwheels	£30-35
	1971-75		Light Grey body, Dark Grey or Black roof, suspension, Speedwheels	£25-30
150	1959-64	**Rolls-Royce Silver Wraith**	Two-tone Grey body, suspension, spun hubs, Chromed metal bumpers	£55-65
			Later issues with plastic bumpers	£50-60
		NB	The French version of 150 (French reference 551) was cast from English-made dies, was assembled in France, and has 'Made in France' on the baseplate.	
151	1954-59	**Triumph 1800 Saloon**	Beige body, Green hubs, or Dark Blue with Light Blue hubs	£100-120
		(renumbered from 40b)	Light Blue body with Mid-Blue, Fawn or Grey hubs, or Mid-Blue body with Light Blue hubs	£100-120
151	1965-69	**Vauxhall Victor 101**	Yellow or Metallic Red body, White interior, spun hubs	£65-75
152	1954-59	**Austin (A40) Devon**	Large baseplate print (see example diagrams).	
		(renumbered from 40d)	Suede Green body and hubs, or Dark Blue body with Light Blue hubs	£120-140
			Tan body, Suede Green hubs	£500-700
			Maroon body, Red hubs	£175-200
			Light Blue body and hubs	£400-500
			Light Green body, Mid-Green hubs, or Dark Green body with Fawn hubs	£100-120
	1956-59	Two-tone issue:	Blue upper body and hubs, Yellow lower body	£175-200
	1956-59	Two-tone issue:	Pink lower body, Green upper body, Cream hubs	£175-200
152	1965-67	**Rolls-Royce Phantom V**	Navy Blue body, Beige interior, chauffeur and two passengers, spun hubs or cast wheels	£40-50
	1967-77	design change:	Dark Blue or Black body with Chauffeur but no passengers	£30-40
153	1954-59	**Standard Vanguard**	Mid-Blue body, Cream hubs, or Blue body with Blue or Fawn hubs	£100-125
		(renumbered from 40e)	Fawn body with Cream hubs, Cream body with Cream hubs, or Maroon body with Fawn hubs	£100-125
			Maroon body with Maroon hubs	£750-1,000
		NB	The ridge which appears on the boot of some Vanguard models is the result of worn die replacement.	
153	1967-71	**Aston-Martin DB6**	Metallic Silver Blue body, Red interior, wire wheels	£60-70
			Metallic Green body	£70-80
154	1955	**Hillman Minx** 2nd baseplate:	Large baseplate print (see diagram).	
		(Renumbered from 40f)	Dark Tan body with Cream or Green hubs, or Pale Tan body with Blue or Yellow hubs	£100-120
			Light Green body and hubs, or Dark Green body with Light Green hubs	£175-200
			Pale Green body with Light Green hubs, or Light Green body with Mid-Green hubs	£175-225
			Pale Blue lower body and hubs, Pink upper body	£175-225
			Cream upper body and hubs, Lime Green lower body	£175-225
154	1966-69	**Ford Taunus 17M**	Yellow body, White roof, Red interior, rounded spun hubs or cast wheels	£40-50
155	1961-66	**Ford Anglia 105E**	Turquoise or Green body, Red interior, suspension, windows, spun hubs	£50-70
			Turquoise body, Pale Blue interior, spun hubs	£100-150
			Very Pale Green body, Red interior, spun hubs. In mail-order box with correct spot	£350-450
		NB	Meccano issued a batch to Ford to mark the first Ford made on Merseyside on 8th March 1963. Some were fixed on plinths and given as souvenirs.	
	1966	South African issue:	Deep Cream body, Red interior, spun hubs	£500-750
	1966	South African issue:	Light Blue body	£500-750
156	1954-56	**Rover 75**	Cream body, Cream or Light Blue hubs	£130-150
		(Renumbered from 140b)	Red body, Maroon hubs	£750-1,000
			Maroon body, Cream hubs	£130-150
	1956-59	Two-tone issues:	Light Green upper body, Mid-Green lower body and hubs	£150-175
			Light Green upper body, Turquoise lower body, Mid-Green hubs	£750-1,000
			Mid-Blue upper body, Cream lower body and hubs	£150-175
			Dark Blue upper body, Cream lower body and hubs	£250-350
			Violet-Blue upper body, Cream lower body and hubs	£300-500
156	1968-71	**Saab 96**	Metallic Red or Metallic Blue body, suspension, spun hubs	£65-75
157	1954-57	**Jaguar XK120**	Yellow body, Light Yellow hubs	£150-190
			Red body, Red diecast hubs	£175-225
			White body, Fawn hubs	£150-190
			Grey-Green body, Cream or Fawn hubs	£175-225
	1957-59	Two-tone issue:	Turquoise lower body, Deep Pink upper body and hubs	£200-250
	1957-59	Two-tone issue:	Yellow lower body, Light Grey upper body and hubs	£200-250
	1959-62		Red body, spun hubs	£200-250
			Grey-Green body, spun hubs	£200-250
157	1968-73	**BMW 2000 Tilux**	Blue/White, Red interior, cast hubs, box has inner pictorial stand	£55-65
			Metallic Blue with Gold upper half, pictorial box inner	£90-120
			Pale Blue body, Red interior, spun hubs	NGPP

158	1954-55	**Riley Saloon**	Cream body, Mid-Green hubs	**£100-120**
		(Renumbered from 40a)	Mid-Green body with Green hubs, or Light Green body and hubs	**£100-120**
			Pale Green body, Mid-Green hubs	**£100-120**
			Dark Blue body, Mid-Blue hubs	**£100-120**
			Light Grey body and hubs	**£100-120**
		NB	All the 158 Riley issues have large lettering on their baseplates.	
158	1967-70	**Rolls-Royce Silver Shadow**	Metallic Red, suspension, spun hubs	**£45-55**
	1970-73		Metallic Blue, suspension, opening doors/bonnet/boot	**£55-65**
159	1954	**Morris Oxford**	Dark Green body and hubs, or Green body with Light Green hubs	**£100-120**
		(Renumbered from 40g)	Blue body, Grey hubs	**£1,500-2,000**
			Fawn body, Grey or Stone hubs	**£120-140**
		Export issue:	Beige body and hubs	**£500-800**
		Two-tone issue:	Green upper body and hubs, Cream lower body	**£150-175**
		Two-tone issue:	Cream upper body and hubs, Deep Pink lower body	**£150-175**
		Two-tone issue:	Turquoise upper body, Cream lower body, Turquoise-Green hubs	**£300-400**
160	1958-62	**Austin A30**	Turquoise body, smooth or treaded solid grey plastic wheels	**£80-100**
			Light Brown body, smooth or treaded solid grey plastic wheels	**£80-100**
		NB	A version of the Austin A30 has been reported with spun hubs, but is not confirmed.	
160	1967-74	**Mercedes-Benz 250 SE**	Metallic Blue body, suspension, steering, working stop-lights	**£25-35**
161	1954	**Austin (A40) Somerset**	Pale Blue body, Mid or Dark Blue hubs	**£80-100**
		(Renumbered from 40j)	Red body and hubs	**£80-100**
	1956-59	Two-tone issue:	Red lower body and hubs, Yellow upper body	**£150-175**
	1956-59	Two-tone issue:	Cream lower body and hubs, Black lower body	**£150-175**
161	1965-69	**Ford Mustang Fastback**	White (Red seats), 'MUSTANG' decal badge on wings, chrome detailed wheels	**£60-70**
	1969-73		Yellow body, Blue seats, cast-in logo replaces decal badge	**£50-60**
			Orange body (without decal), Speedwheels	**£30-40**
162	1956-60	**Ford Zephyr Mk.I**	Cream upper body, Green lower body, Beige hubs	**£80-90**
			Cream upper body, Lime Green lower body, Beige hubs	**£150-200**
			Two-tone Blue body, Grey hubs	**£80-90**
162	1966-70	**Triumph 1300**	Light Blue body, Red interior, fingertip steering, spun aluminium hubs	**£65-75**
163	1956-60	**Bristol 450 Coupé**	British Racing Green body, Light Green hubs, RN '27'	**£70-90**
163	1966-70	**Volkswagen 1600 TL**	Red or Dark Metallic Red, suspension, cast detailed hubs	**£40-50**
			Metallic Blue body, Speedwheels	**£60-70**
164	1957-60	**Vauxhall Cresta**	Maroon lower body, Cream upper body, Cream hubs	**£80-100**
	1957-60		Green lower body, Grey upper body, Grey hubs	**£80-100**
164	1966-71	**Ford Zodiac Mk.IV**	Metallic Silver body, Red interior, Yellow or Black chassis, cast wheels	**£50-60**
			Pale Metallic Blue body, Yellow chassis, cast wheels	**£75-85**
			Metallic Bronze body, Red interior, Yellow chassis, cast wheels, rigid plastic case	**£100-125**
165	1959-60	**Humber Hawk**	Black and Green lower body, Black roof, spun hubs	**£80-100**
			Maroon and Cream lower body, Maroon roof, spun hubs	**£125-150**
		NB	Both versions available with or without a front number plate casting.	
	1959-63		Black lower body, all Green upper body, spun hubs, with front number plate casting, in late issue lighter Yellow box with Green spot	**£150-200**
165	1969-76	**Ford Capri**	Metallic Green body, Yellow interior, Speedwheels	**£50-60**
			Metallic Purple body, Yellow interior, Speedwheels	**£50-60**
			Metallic Blue body, Yellow interior, Speedwheels	**£50-60**
166	1958-63	**Sunbeam Rapier**	Orange lower body, Deep Cream upper body, Beige hubs	**£80-100**
			Orange lower body, Deep Cream upper body, spun hubs	**£80-90**
			Mid-Blue lower body and hubs, Light Blue upper body	**£80-90**
166	1967-70	**Renault R16**	Metallic Blue, suspension and fingertip steering, spun hubs	**£40-50**
167	1958-63	**A.C. Aceca Sports Coupé**	Grey body, Red roof, Red hubs	**£80-100**
			Cream body, Reddish-Maroon roof, Silver cast hubs	**£160-190**
			Deep Cream body, Dark Brown roof, Cream hubs	**£70-90**
			All Cream body, spun aluminium hubs. (Lighter Yellow box with Cream spot)	**£160-190**
			Cream body, Maroon roof, spun hubs	**£160-190**
			Grey body, Red roof, spun hubs	**£160-190**
168	1959-63	**Singer Gazelle Saloon**	Deep Brown lower, Cream upper body, spun aluminium hubs	**£70-90**
			Dark Green lower, Grey upper body, spun aluminium hubs	**£70-90**
			Black body, spun aluminium hubs, Silver trim	**NGPP**
168	1968-70	**Ford Escort**	Pale Blue or White, cast detailed hubs	**£40-50**
	1970-74		Metallic Red body, spun aluminium hubs	**£67-75**
	1974-75		Metallic Blue body, Speedwheels	**£67-75**
169	1958-63	**Studebaker Golden Hawk**	Light Brown body, Red rear side panel and hubs, White tyres, plain Yellow/Red box	**£100-120**
			As previous issue but with spun aluminium hubs, White tyres	**£80-100**
			Light Green body, Cream rear side panel and hubs, White tyres	**£70-90**
			As previous issue but with spun aluminium hubs, White tyres	**£80-100**
169	1967-69	**Ford Corsair 2000 E**	Silver body, Black textured roof, suspension and steering	**£65-75**

Models 170, 171 and 172

> **Two paint schemes exist for two-colour issues on models 170, 171 and 172:**
> **1**: Lower colour covers wing tops and doors up to windows (generally known as 'Highline') and
> **2**: Lower colour extends only up to ridge on wings/doors ('Lowline').

170	1954-56	**Ford Fordor**	Brown body, Red hubs	£140-160
		(Renumbered from 139a)	Yellow body, Red hubs	£140-160
			Green body, Red hubs	£140-160
			Red body, Red hubs	£140-160
	1956-58	('Highline')	Red lower body, Cream upper body, Red hubs	£250-300
	1956-58	('Highline')	Blue lower body, Pink upper body, Blue hubs	£250-300
	1958-59	('Lowline')	Red lower body, Cream upper body, Red hubs	£175-225
	1958-59	('Lowline')	Blue lower body, Pink upper body, Blue hubs	£175-225
170m	1954-54	**Ford US Army Staff Car**	(was 139am) Military Green, US issue, renumbered 675	£200-250
	NB		See also 'Factory samples' listing at the end of this section.	
170	1964-70	**Lincoln Continental**	Metallic Bronze body, White roof, Blue interior, cast wheels	£75-85
			Light Blue body, White roof, Mid-Blue interior, cast wheels	£75-85
170	1979	**Ford Granada Ghia**	Not issued, but a Metallic Silver factory publicity sample was sold by Vectis Auctions in 1999 for £470.	
171	1954-56	**Hudson Commodore Sedan**	Dark Blue body, Pale Tan roof and hubs	£90-110
		(Renumbered from 139b)	Royal Blue body, Pale Tan roof and hubs	£150-200
			Light Blue body, Pale Tan roof, Fawn hubs	£300-500
			Cream body, Dark Maroon roof and hubs	£90-110
			Cream body, Dark Maroon roof, Red hubs, large lettering on baseplate	£90-110
	1956-58	('Highline')	Turquoise lower body with Red upper body, Red hubs	£250-300
		('Highline')	Blue lower body, Red upper body, Red hubs	£250-300
		('Highline')	Blue lower body, Maroon upper body, Red hubs	NGPP
		('Highline')	Grey lower body with Blue upper body, Blue hubs	£250-300
	1958-59	('Lowline')	Turquoise lower body with Red upper body, Red hubs	£250-300
		('Lowline')	Grey lower body with Blue upper body, Blue hubs	£250-300
171	1965-68	**Austin 1800**	Metallic Blue or Light Blue body, Red interior, spun hubs	£50-60
172	1954-56	**Studebaker Land Cruiser**	Light Green body, Mid-Green or Mid-Blue hubs	£90-110
			Blue body, Brown or Beige hubs	£90-110
	1956-58	('Highline')	Cream lower body, Maroon upper body, Beige hubs	£150-175
		('Highline')	Cream lower body, Tan upper body, Beige hubs	£150-175
	1958-59	('Lowline')	Cream lower body, Maroon upper body, Beige hubs	£160-180
		('Lowline')	Cream lower body, Tan upper body, Beige hubs	£130-150
172	1965-69	**Fiat 2300 Station Wagon**	Two-tone Blue body, Red interior, spun hubs	£50-60
173	1958-62	**Nash Rambler Station Wagon**	Turquoise body with Cerise flash, Grey hubs, no number on later baseplates	£55-65
			Pink body with Blue flash, Cream hubs, no number on later baseplates	£55-65
			As previous issues but with spun hubs, in plain Yellow/Red box without picture	£70-80
173	1969-72	**Pontiac Parisienne**	Metallic Maroon body, Lemon interior, retractable aerials, cast wheels	£55-65
			Metallic Blue body	£55-65
174	1958-63	**Hudson Hornet**	Red lower body, Cream roof and side flash, Beige hubs, White tyres	£90-110
			Yellow lower body, Dark Grey roof and flash, Cream hubs, White tyres	£90-110
			Later issues with spun aluminium hubs	£90-110
174	1969-72	**Ford Mercury Cougar**	Red body, cast or Speedwheels, retractable aerial	£35-45
			Blue or Metallic Dark Blue body, cast or Speedwheels	£35-45
175	1958-61	**Hillman Minx**	Grey lower body, Mid-Blue upper body and hubs	£80-100
			Light Brown body, Green roof and boot, Beige hubs	£80-100
			Light Brown body, Green roof and boot, spun hubs	£90-120
175	1969-73	**Cadillac Eldorado**	Metallic Purple body, Black roof, Yellow interior, cast or Speedwheels	£50-60
			Metallic Blue body, Black roof, Yellow interior, cast or Speedwheels	£50-60
176	1958-63	**Austin A105 Saloon**	First Dinky Toys car to have full window glazing. Body sides have a contrasting side flash. Treaded tyres may be Black or White.	
	1958-59		Cream body, Dark Blue side flash, Cream hubs	£80-95
			Light Grey body, Red side flash, Red hubs	£130-160
	1959-63		Cream body, Dark Blue roof and side flash, Cream hubs	£90-120
			Cream body, Mid-Blue roof and side flash, Cream hubs	£175-225
	1959-63		Cream body, Mid-Blue roof and side flash, spun aluminium hubs	£175-225
			Light Grey body, Red roof and side flash, Light Grey hubs	£175-225
176	1969-74	**N.S.U. Ro80**	Metallic Red body, spun hubs, luminous seats, working lights	£40-50
			Metallic Blue body	£100-150
177	1961-66	**Opel Kapitan**	Light Greyish-Blue body, Red interior, spun hubs	£60-75
	1963	South African issues:	Mid or Dark Blue, Caramel or Dark Cream body, all with Red interiors	£300-400
	NB		South African models should be housed in boxes with both English and Afrikaans text.	
178	1959-63	**Plymouth Plaza**	Light Blue body, Dark Blue roof and side flash, spun hubs	£90-110
			Pink body, Green roof and side flash, spun hubs	£90-110
			Light Tan body, Light Green roof and side flash, matt-Black base, spun hubs	£175-200
			Light Blue body, White roof and flash, spun hubs, Lighter Yellow box	£200-250
			Pale Blue body, White roof and flash, spun hubs, late issue – no number on baseplate	£150-200
178	1975-79	**Mini Clubman**	Bronze body, opening doors, jewelled headlights on some, Speedwheels	£40-50
			Red body version, Speedwheels	£100-125
179	1958-63	**Studebaker President**	Light Blue body, Dark Blue flash, Cream hubs, White tyres	£80-95
			Yellow body, Blue flash and hubs, White tyres	£80-95
			Late issues with spun hubs	£80-95

179	1971-75	**Opel Commodore**	Metallic Blue body, Black roof, suspension, Speedwheels	£45-55
180	1958-63	**Packard Clipper**	Cerise upper body, Cream lower body and hubs, White tyres	£80-95
			Orange lower body, Light Grey upper body and hubs, White tyres	£80-95
			Late issues with spun hubs	£80-95
180	1979-80	**Rover 3500**	White body, plastic chassis and wheels. Made in Hong Kong, scale 1:35	£20-25
181	1956-70	**Volkswagen Saloon**	Light Grey body, Mid-Blue hubs	£70-90
			Blue-Grey body, Mid-Blue hubs	£70-90
			Dark Blue body, Mid-Blue hubs	£120-150
			R.A.F. Blue body, Mid-Blue hubs	£70-90
			Lime Green body, Mid-Green hubs	£70-90
		Spun hubs issues:	Light Grey body, spun hubs	£90-110
			Blue-Grey body, spun hubs	£90-110
			Light Blue body, spun hubs	£90-110
			R.A.F. Blue body, spun hubs	£90-110
		Plastic hubs issue:	Light Blue body, Blue plastic hubs	£150-200
		NB	See also 'Factory samples' listing at the end of this section.	
		South African issues:	Lime Green, Pale Yellow, Pale Blue, Metallic Blue or Grey body	£400-600
182	1958-66	**Porsche 356a Coupé**	Light Blue body, Cream or spun hubs	£70-90
			Cerise (pinkish maroon) body, Cream or spun hubs	£70-90
			Red body and hubs, in standard Yellow box (no coloured spot)	£100-120
			Cream body, Mid-Blue or spun hubs, with window glazing	£100-120
			Red body and hubs. In late issue lighter Yellow box with Red spot	£200-250
			Red body, spun hubs. In lighter Yellow box	£200-250
183	1958-60	**Fiat 600**	Red body, smooth or treaded solid Grey plastic wheels	£60-70
			Light Green body, smooth or treaded solid Grey plastic wheels	£60-70
183	1966-74	**Morris Mini Minor (Automatic)**	Metallic Red body, matt or gloss Black roof, White interior, spun hubs. Box should contain 'Meccano Automatic Transmission' leaflet	£75-85
			Metallic Red body, Speedwheels	£60-70
			Metallic Blue body, White interior, spun hubs	£90-110
		NB	Late issues with 'Austin Cooper S' cast on boot (model 250 casting) will be found	NGPP
			Various registration numbers will also be found, e.g., 'UVR 576D', 'MTB 21G', 'HTB 21H'.	
184	1961-65	**Volvo 122 S**	Red body, Off-White interior, spun hubs	£70-80
			White body, Off-White interior, spun hubs	£175-200
			Cream body, Cream interior, spun hubs	£200-225
	1966	....................South African issue:	Grey-Blue body, White interior (in box with both English and Afrikaans text)	£250-350
	1966	....................South African issue:	Sage Green (White interior) or Pale Green (Fawn interior). (English and Afrikaans box text)	£250-350
185	1961-63	**Alfa Romeo 1900 Sprint**	Red or Yellow body, Red interior, spun hubs	£65-75
186	1961-67	**Mercedes-Benz 220 SE**	Light Blue or RAF Blue body, White interior, spun hubs	£35-45
	1966	....................South African issue:	Sky Blue or Grey body, (in box with both English and Afrikaans text)	£250-350
187	1959-64	**VW Karmann Ghia Coupé**	Red body, Black roof, spun hubs, White tyres, 'plain' box	£80-100
			Green body, Cream roof, spun hubs, White tyres, 'plain' box	£80-100
			As previous issue but in rare late issue picture box	£150-200
187	1968-77	**De Tomaso Mangusta 5000**	Red body, White panels front/rear, Black interior, cast wheels, racing number '7'	£35-40
188	1968-74	**Jensen FF**	Yellow body, Black interior, cast wheels	£45-55
189	1959-64	**Triumph Herald Saloon**	Blue roof and sides with White centre, spun aluminium hubs	£65-75
			Green roof and sides with White centre, spun aluminium hubs	£65-75
		special issue:	Lilac body, spun hubs, standard box	£200-300
		special issue:	Magenta body, spun hubs, standard box	£200-300
		special issue:	Red lower, White upper body, spun hubs, plain printed box with Red spot	£200-300
		special issue:	Greyish-Green, Pale Whitish-Green roof, spun hubs, plain box with correct colour spot	£200-300
		special issue:	Pinkish-Brown body with Pale Grey roof, spun hubs, standard box	£200-300
		special issue:	Dark Grey body and roof, Pale Grey bonnet and boot, spun hubs, standard box ...	£200-300
		special issue:	All Red body, spun hubs, in 'plain' standard box with Red spot	£200-300
		special issue:	Very Dark Blue body, Pale Blue hubs, standard box	£200-300
		special issue:	Very Dark Blue lower body and roof, Pale Blue mid-section, spun hubs	£200-300
		special issue:	Deep Grey and White body, spun hubs	£200-300
		special issue:	Pale Lilac body, Bluish White roof, spun hubs, in box with Blue and White spot ...	£200-300
		special issue:	Black and Pale Grey body, spun hubs	£200-300
189	1969-76	**Lamborghini Marzal**	Green/White or Red/White, cast detailed hubs	£25-45
			Yellow/White body, cast detailed hubs	£40-45
	1976-78	....	Metallic Blue/White or Dark Metallic Green/White, Speedwheels	£35-45
190	1970-74	**Monteverdi 375 L**	Metallic Red body, White interior, cast wheels or Speedwheels	£35-45
		NB	See also 'Factory samples' listing at the end of this section.	
191	1959-64	**Dodge Royal Sedan**	Cream body with Brown flash, spun hubs, White tyres	£80-95
			Cream body, Blue flash, spun hubs, lighter Yellow box, late issue – no number on base	£150-200
			Light Green body with Black flash, spun hubs, White tyres	£80-95
		NB	Casting used for 258 'USA Police Car'.	
192	1959-64	**De Soto Fireflite**	Grey body, Red roof and flash, spun aluminium hubs, White tyres	£80-95
			Turquoise body, Light Tan roof and flash, spun aluminium hubs, White tyres	£80-95
192	1970-80	**Range Rover**	Metallic Bronze (Pale Blue interior), Yellow body (Red interior), or Black body (? interior), cast detailed or Speedwheels	£25-35
		NB	See also 'Factory samples' listing at the end of this section.	

193	1961-69	**Rambler Station Wagon**	Lemon Yellow body, White roof, Black plastic roof-rack, spun hubs, standard box	**£70-80**
			As previous issue but in Gold 'see-through' export window-box	**£150-175**
	1966	South African issue:	Pink/Mauve, All Mauve, or Sage Green body	**£400-600**
	1966	South African issue:	Pale Lilac body (Black roof), Pale Blue body (Cream roof), or Dark Blue body (White roof)	**£400-600**
	1966	South African issue:	Light Greyish-Green body, Black roof, Red interior	**£400-600**
194	1961-67	**Bentley 'S' Coupé**	Grey body, Maroon seats, Tan tonneau, Grey male driver, spun hubs, gloss black baseplate	**£70-90**
			Metallic Gold body, Cream interior, Dark Blue tonneau, driver, spun hubs	**£100-125**
		NB	Late issues have plated plastic parts.	
	1966	South African issue:	Avocado Green body, Red interior, Black tonneau, spun hubs	**£500-700**
	1966	South African issue:	Cream body, Red interior, Dark Cream tonneau, spun hubs	**£400-600**
195	1961-71	**Jaguar 3.4 Mk.II**	Maroon body, White interior, spun hubs	**£70-90**
			Cream body, Red interior, spun hubs	**£70-90**
			Light Grey body, Red interior, spun hubs	**£70-90**
	1963	South African issues:	Light or Sky-Blue body, Cream or Red interior	**£400-600**
	1963	South African issues:	Red or Off-White body, Cream or Red interior	**£400-600**
196	1963-70	**Holden Special Sedan**	Metallic Gold body, White roof, spun hubs. (First Dinky Toys model to have jewelled headlights)	**£55-65**
			Turquoise body, White roof, spun hubs, Grey baseplate, Off-White interior	**£55-65**
			Turquoise body, White roof, spun hubs, Silver baseplate, Red interior	**£55-65**
			Turquoise body, White roof, spun hubs, Dark Grey baseplate, Red interior	**£55-65**
	1966	South African issue:	White body, Turquoise roof	**£400-600**
197	1961-71	**Morris Mini Traveller**	White body, Yellow interior, spun hubs	**£600-800**
			White body, Red interior, spun hubs	**£75-85**
			Dark Green body, Yellow interior, spun hubs	**£500-700**
			Fluorescent Green body, Red interior, spun hubs, with front number plate	**£160-190**
			Fluorescent Green body, spun hubs, without front number plate	**£160-190**
			Fluorescent Pink body, Red interior, spun hubs	**£200-250**
		NB	Unlike 199, there is no 'colour change' label on the 197 box.	
198	1962-69	**Rolls-Royce Phantom V**	Metallic Cream lower body, Metallic Light Green upper body, Off-White or Light Blue interior, glossy baseplate, spun hubs, chauffeur. (First Dinky Toys model with metallic paint and opening windows)	**£75-85**
			Metallic Cream upper body, Grey lower body, Red interior, glossy baseplate, chauffeur, spun hubs	**£75-85**
			Two tone Grey body, Red interior, matt baseplate, chauffeur, spun hubs	**£75-85**
	1966	South African issues:	Dark Grey over Metallic Cream body, Red interior	**£500-750**
			Sage Green or Two-Tone Grey	**£500-750**
			Pale Grey body, Ivory roof, Red interior	**£500-750**
199	1961-71	**Austin 7 Countryman**	Blue body with Yellow interior, spun hubs	**£100-150**
			Electric Blue, Blue or Blue-Grey body with Red interior and 'wood' trim, spun hubs	**£90-110**
			Fluorescent Orange body, Box must have affixed a small oblong label stating: 'COLOUR OF MODEL MAY DIFFER FROM ILLUSTRATION'	**£150-200**
			Deep Grey body, Red interior, Brown 'woodwork', spun hubs	**£150-200**
		Promotional issue:	Luminous Pink body, Red roof, spun hubs	**£160-190**
200	1954-57	**Midget Racer**	Silver body, Red grille, Brown driver, solid Black rubber wheels. (Renumbered from 35b)	**£65-75**
200	1971-78	**Matra 630 Le Mans**	Blue body, racing number '5', '9' or '36', Speedwheels	**£25-30**
201	1979-80	**Plymouth Stock Car**	Blue body, racing number '34', wide plastic wheels	**£35-45**
202	1971-75	**Fiat Abarth 2000**	Fluorescent Red/White body, opening doors, Speedwheels	**£20-30**
202/2	1979-80	**Customised Land Rover**	Yellow body with white crash guard. White or Black rails/aerials (344 casting)	**£25-35**
203	1979-80	**Customised Range Rover**	Black body, Yellow/Red design, White plastic chassis/crash guard	**£20-25**
204	1971-74	**Ferrari 312 P**	Metallic Red body and opening doors, Speedwheels, RN '60'	**£25-30**
			Metallic Red body, White opening doors, Speedwheels, RN '60'	**£25-30**
205	1962-64	**Talbot Lago Racing Car**	Blue, Red or Yellow plastic hubs, RN '4', blister-packed ('230' on base – see also 23k and 230)	**£175-225**
205	1968-73	**Lotus Cortina Rally**	White body, Red bonnet and side stripe, 'Monte Carlo' logo, RN '7', 2 aerials/spotlamps, cast hubs	**£70-80**
206	1962-64	**Maserati Racing Car**	Red/White body, Red or Yellow plastic hubs, blister-packed, ('231' on base – see also 23n and 231)	**£175-225**
	1962-64	late issue:	As previous model but in lighter Yellow box, (see also 23n and 231)	**£120-140**
206	1978-80	**Customised Corvette**	Red/Yellow or White/Black, plastic chassis and wide wheels	**£20-30**
207	1962-64	**Alfa-Romeo Racing Car**	Red body, Red plastic hubs, blister-packed, ('232' on base – see also 23f and 232)	**£175-225**
	1962-64	late issue:	As previous model but in lighter Yellow box. (See also 23f and 232)	**£120-140**
207	1977-80	**Triumph TR7 Rally**	White/Red/Blue, RN '8', plastic chassis and wheels, 'Leyland'	**£25-35**
208	1962-64	**Cooper-Bristol Racing Car**	Dark Green, Red plastic wheel hubs, blister-packed, ('233' on base – see also 23g and 233)	**£175-225**
		variant:	As previous model but with Green metal hubs	**£150-200**
	1962-64	late issue:	Green body and plastic hubs, White flash and RN '6', lighter Yellow box, (see also 23f and 233)	**£100-120**
208	1971-75	**VW Porsche 914**	Yellow body, Black interior, cast detailed wheel hubs	**£25-30**
		promotional:	As above, but packed in a Yellow/Red promotional card box	**£70-80**
	1976-80		Metallic Blue/Black body, Speedwheels	**£25-30**
209	1962-64	**Ferrari Racing Car**	Blue, Yellow triangle, Yellow plastic hubs, blister-packed, ('234' on base – see also 23h and 234)	**£175-225**
	1962-64	late issue:	As previous model but in lighter Yellow box, (see also 23h and 234)	**£175-225**
210	1962-65	**Vanwall Racing Car**	Green, Yellow plastic hubs, blister-packed, ('239' on base – see also 239)	**£175-225**
210	1971-73	**Alfa-Romeo 33 Tipo**	Red body, Black doors, White interior, racing number '36', cast wheels, leaflet in box	**£30-35**
211	1975	**Triumph TR7 Sports Car**	Metallic Blue body, Union Jack badge	**£90-100**
			Yellow body, Black bumpers and interior	**£90-100**
			Yellow body, Grey bumpers and interior	**£90-100**
			Red body, Black bumpers and interior	**£50-60**
			Red body, Grey bumpers and interior	**£50-60**
212	1965-70	**Ford Cortina Rally**	White body, Black bonnet, 'EAST AFRICAN SAFARI' and 'CASTROL' logos, RN '8', spotlight, Red interior. picture box	**£100-120**

213	1970-73	Ford Capri Rally	Metallic Red body, Black bonnet, Yellow interior, racing number '20', rigid plastic case	£100-120
	1973-75		Bronze body, Black bonnet, spotlights, wing mirrors, Speedwheels, rigid plastic case	£100-120
214	1966-69	Hillman Imp Rally	Dark Blue body, Red interior, 'MONTE CARLO RALLY' logo, RN '35', spun hubs, picture box	£55-65
215	1965-66	Ford GT Racing Car	White body with racing number '7', spun hubs	£40-50
	1966-70		White body with racing number '7', Silver spoked wheels	£35-40
	1970-74		Metallic Green body, Orange/Black stripe, Yellow interior, RN '7', Silver spoked wheels	£60-70
			Metallic Green body, Dark Blue/White stripe, White interior..	£60-70
			Yellow or Metallic Blue, removable bonnet, Silver or Gold spoked wheels	£35-45
216	1967-69	Dino Ferrari...............................	Red body, Light Blue interior	£40-50
	1969-75		Metallic Blue/Black, Silver or brass spoked wheels or Speedwheels	£30-40
217	1968-70	Alfa Romeo Scarabeo OSI	Pink body, cast spoked wheels	£30-35
	1969-74		Red, Orange or Green body, Speedwheels	£25-30
218	1969-73	Lotus Europa	Yellow body, Blue panels/roof, chequered flags, Gold engine	£35-45
	1973-75		Yellow/Black body or Metallic Blue body, Silver engine, Speedwheels	£30-35
219	1977-79	Leyland Jaguar XJ-5.3	White body, 'Leyland' decal. (Made in Hong Kong)...	£35-45
219	1978-79	'Big Cat' Jaguar........................	White/Red, Black 'Big Cat' decal. (unboxed)...	£35-45
			Boxed version with 'The Big Cat' logo...	£50-75
220	1954-56	Small Open Racing Car	Silver (Red hubs), or Red (Silver hubs), RN '4'. (Renumbered from 23a)	£40-50
220	1970-73	Ferrari P5	Metallic Red body, Yellow interior, cast hubs	£25-30
	1973-75		Metallic Red body, Yellow interior, Speedwheels	£25-30
221	1954-56	'Speed Of The Wind'
Racing Car............................	Silver diecast body with plain baseplate. (Renumbered from 23e)...	£40-45
221	1969-76	Corvette Stingray	Metallic Gold body, Silver or Gold spoked wheels	£25-35
	1976-78		Red or White body, Black bonnet, opening doors, Speedwheels	£25-35
222	1954-56	Streamlined Racing Car	Silver body with Red, Blue or Green trim. (Renumbered from 22s)...	£60-70
222	1978-80	Hesketh 308 E	Dark Blue or Bronze, RN '2', cast-detailed or Speedwheels	£20-30
		promotional issue:	As previous model but in 'OLYMPUS CAMERAS' box, (Swiss)...	£50-75
223	1970-75	McLaren M8A Can-Am	White body, Metallic Blue engine cover, cast detailed wheels	£20-25
	1976-78		Metallic Green body, Black engine cover, White interior, Speedwheels	£20-25
224	1970-74	Mercedes-Benz C111	White or Metallic Dark Red, White interior, cast wheels...	£20-25
225	1971-76	Lotus F1 Racing Car	Metallic Red body with racing number '7', inner pictorial box and stand	£20-25
	1976-77		Lime-Green or Metallic Blue body with racing number '7'	£20-25
226	1972-75	Ferrari 312 B2	Red body with racing number '5'	£20-25
	1976-80		Bronze or Gold body, Black, White or Yellow rear wing, racing number '5'	£20-25
227	1975-77	Beach Buggy	White/Grey, Yellow/White, Green/Grey or Pink/Black body	£20-25
	NB		See also 'Factory samples' listing at the end of this section.	
228	1970-72	Super Sprinter	Blue/Silver or Blue/Orange body, suspension, Speedwheels	£20-25
230	1954-60	Talbot Lago Racing Car	Blue body, Yellow racing number '4', Blue diecast hubs, 103 mm	£100-120
	1960-62		Blue body, Yellow racing number '4', spun aluminium hubs	£100-120
231	1954-60	Maserati Racing Car	Red body, White flash and RN '9', Red diecast hubs. (See also 23n and 206)	£100-120
	1960-62		Red body, White flash and racing number '9', spun aluminium hubs. (See also 23n and 206)	£100-120
232	1954-60	Alfa-Romeo Racing Car	Red body, White racing number '8', Red diecast hubs, White racing driver. (See also 23f and 207)	£100-120
	1960-62		Red body, White racing number '8', spun aluminium hubs, White racing driver	£100-120
233	1954-60	Cooper-Bristol Racing Car	Green body, White flash and RN '6', Green diecast hubs. (See also 23f and 208)	£100-120
	1960-62		Green body, White flash and racing number '6', spun aluminium hubs. (See also 23f and 208)	£100-120
234	1954-60	Ferrari Racing Car	Blue body, Yellow nose, diecast hubs and RN '5'. (See also 23h and 209)	£100-120
	1960-62		Blue body, Yellow nose and racing number '5', spun aluminium hubs. (See also 23h and 209)...........	£100-120
	1962-62		Blue body, Yellow triangle on nose, RN '5', spun hubs, boxed...	£175-225
		South African issue:	Red body, RN '36', spun hubs (as UK issue but with dimpled rivets). South African box	£175-225
235	1954-60	H.W.M. Racing Car	Light Green body, Yellow RN '7', Green diecast hubs. (Renumbered from 23j)............................	£100-120
236	1956-59	Connaught Racing Car..............	Light Green body, Red seats, Mid-Green hubs, RN '32', White driver..	£75-85
237	1957-60	Mercedes-Benz Racing Car.......	Gloss White body, Red interior, Red hubs or spun hubs, Red RN '30', Blue driver......................	£75-85
	1960-62		Matt Cream body, Red hubs or spun hubs, RN '30', Blue driver...	£75-85
	1962-64		Matt Cream body, plastic hubs, RN '30', Tan driver..	£50-60
		late issue:	Matt White body, Red plastic hubs, RN '30', Blue driver, late issue Yellow window box............	£100-120
			As previous issue but with Yellow driver	£100-120
238	1957-60	Jaguar 'D' type	Turquoise body, Blue interior, White driver, RN '4', Blue diecast hubs	£80-100
	1960-62		Turquoise body, Blue interior, White driver, RN '4', spun aluminium hubs	£80-100
	1962-65		Turquoise body, Blue interior or Turquoise interior, White or Yellow driver, RN '4',
Blue or Yellow plastic hubs, in lighter Yellow box	£130-150
239	1958-60	Vanwall Racing Car	Green body, Green hubs, White or Yellow driver, racing number '25', '26' or '35', 'VANWALL' logo	£100-120
	1960-62		Green body, White driver, RN '35', spun aluminium hubs	£80-100
	1962-65		Green body, White or Tan driver, RN '35', Yellow plastic hubs. In lighter Yellow box................	£150-175
	1962-65		Green body, Yellow driver, RN '35', Yellow plastic hubs. In lighter Yellow box........................	£150-175
240	1963-70	Cooper Racing Car	Blue/White, RN '20', spun aluminium hubs, suspension..	£40-50
241	1963-70	Lotus Racing Car	Green body with racing number '36', suspension, spun hubs	£40-50
			Green body with racing number '24', spun hubs	£40-50
242	1963-71	Ferrari Racing Car	Red body, RN '36', suspension, opening engine cover, spun hubs	£40-50
243	1963-71	B.R.M. Racing Car	Green, Yellow opening engine cover, RN '7', suspension, spun hubs	£40-50
	1963-71		Metallic Green, Yellow opening engine cover, racing number '7'...	£40-50
	NB		Gold, US export issue 'see-through' window boxes. Model nos. 237 - 243 housed in
these boxes may attract a premium of 50%.	
254	1956-59	Austin Taxi (FX3) ....Two-tone:	Yellow upper body and hubs, Dark Green lower body, Black chassis ('254'), interior and driver	£90-120
		Spun hubs:	Black body, spun hubs, Grey chassis ('254'), interior and driver	£110-130
			Blue body, Light Blue hubs	£500-750

Cars

260	1971-72	VW 'Deutsche Bundespost'	Yellow body (129 casting, 100mm), German export model	£100-150
262	1959-60	Volkswagen 'PTT' Car	(181 casting, 90mm, fixed doors), Yellow/Black, 'PTT', Yellow cast hubs, Swiss Post export model	£500-750
	1960-62		As previous issue but with spun aluminium hubs, Swiss export	£500-750
	1962-66		As previous issue but with plastic hubs, Swiss export	£500-750
			NOTE 262 models listed above should be in the correct French / German box with 'Auto Suisse VW' and 'Schweizer Postauto VW' on the end flap.	
	1966-68	129 casting (100mm):	Yellow/Black, opening doors, spun aluminium hubs, hard plastic case	£150-200
	1968-72		Yellow/Black, opening doors, plastic hubs, Swiss export	£100-125
	1972-76		Yellow/Black, opening doors, Speedwheels, Swiss export	£100-125
340	1954-66	Land Rover	Mid-Green body, Light Brown interior and Green cast hubs, Tan cast driver, (renumbered from 27d)	£65-75
	1966-69		Orange body, Green interior, Red cast hubs, Tan cast driver	£75-85
			Orange body, Deep Blue interior, Red cast hubs	£75-85
	1969-71		Dark Red body, Red cast hubs, Yellow interior, Blue plastic driver	£100-125
	1971		Red body, Yellow interior, Blue plastic driver, Green or Yellow plastic hubs	£100-125
			Orange body, Dark Green interior, Blue plastic driver, Red plastic hubs	£100-125
341	1954-66	Land-Rover Trailer	Orange body (Red hubs), or Green body (Green hubs). (Renumbered from 27m)	£20-30
			Olive-Drab body	£150-200
342	1966-72	Austin Mini-Moke	Metallic Green, Grey canopy with 1 or 2 windows, bubble-packed or boxed	£35-45
	1972-75		Metallic Greenish-Blue, 1 canopy window, bubble-packed or boxed	£35-45
344	1954-61	Estate Car (Plymouth)	Fawn with Brown or Red panels, Cream diecast hubs with treaded tyres	£80-100
		(renumbered from 27f)	Fawn with Brown panels, spun hubs	£120-140
344	1970-72	Land Rover Pick-Up	Metallic Blue or Metallic Red body, bubble-packed	£15-20
	1973-78		Metallic Blue or Metallic Red body, bubble-packed	£15-20
370	1969-76	Dragster Set	Yellow/Red, driver, 'FIREBALL', 'INCH-PINCHER', starter unit	£40-50
405	1954-66	Universal Jeep	Red body and hubs or Green body and hubs. (Renumbered from 25y)	£80-90
	1966-67		Orange body, red plastic hubs, boxed in late lighter yellow box	£200-300
		South African issues:	Green body with Red hubs or Off-White body with Red hubs	£300-400
448	1963-68	Chevrolet El Camino Pick-Up with Trailers	Turquoise/Cream/Red Pick-up and 2 trailers, 'Acme Trailer Hire'	£200-250
449	1961-69	Chevrolet El Camino Pick-up	Turquoise body, White roof, Red interior, spun hubs	£80-90
			Turquoise body, White roof, Pale Turquoise interior, spun hubs	£150-200
			Turquoise body, White roof, Lemon interior, spun hubs	£150-200
			NB Various shades of Turquoise are known to exist.	
		South African issue:	All-Turquoise body, spun hubs	£500-750
		South African issue:	Cream over Chocolate Brown lower body, spun hubs	£500-750
		South African issue:	Turquoise over Cream lower body, spun hubs	£500-750
475	1964-66	Model 'T' Ford	Blue body, Yellow panels and wheels, driver/female passenger	£45-55
476	1967-69	Morris Oxford ('Bullnose')	Yellow body, Blue chassis, Fawn hood, driver	£45-55
516	1965-66	Mercedes-Benz 230 SL	Metallic Red, Cream roof, windows. (French issue)	£75-95
675	1954-?	Ford US Army Staff Car	Olive-Drab body, White star, export-only (to US) in 'plain' printed box. (See also 170m)	£175-250
2162	1973-76	Ford Capri	Metallic Blue, Black roof, Black or Blue interior, 175 mm (1:25 scale, vacuform packed on card base)	£70-90
2214	1974-76	Ford Capri Rally Car	Red, Black roof and bonnet, RN '12', Black or Blue interior, 175 mm (1:25 scale, vacuform packed)	£80-100
2253	1974-76	Ford Capri Police Car	White/Orange, 'POLICE', Blue light, suspension, windows, 175 mm (1:25 scale, vacuform packed)	£80-100

Dinky Toys cars made by Meccano, Paris, France and sold in Britain

24kz	1939-40	Peugeot Car	Red or Blue, tinplate front bumper, rubber tyres for UK	NGPP
516		Mercedes-Benz 230sl	Bronze body, Cream interior	£70-80
518	1962-65	Renault 4L	Brown or Grey body, suspension, steering, windows, 85 mm. (French issue)	£65-85
524	1965-67	Panhard 24c	Dark Metallic Grey body, (French issue)	£65-85
532		Lincoln Premiere	Metallic Light Green body, Dark Green roof	£70-80
530	1965-66	Citroën DS19	Light Green body, Light Grey roof. (French issue)	£65-85
535	1962-65	Citroën 2cv	Blue body, suspension, steering, windows, 88 mm. (French issue)	£65-85
550	1962-65	Chrysler Saratoga	Pink/White body, windows, suspension, steering, 129 mm. (French issue)	£65-75
551	1959-64	Rolls-Royce Silver Wraith	Same as UK issue 150 'Made in France'.	£75-85
553	1962-65	Peugeot 404	Green or White, suspension, steering, windows, 102 mm. (French issue)	£65-75
555	1962-65	Ford Thunderbird	White, driver, windscreen, suspension, steering, 121 mm. (French issue)	£65-75

Dinky Toys cars made in Hong Kong

Models **57-001 to 57-006** all have spun hubs, detailed end-flap picture boxes, and are in a scale of 1:42. Hong Kong made models were issued in tab-ended alternative pictorial card boxes or rare yellow 'see-through' cellophane window boxes.

57-001	1965-67	Buick Riviera	Light Blue body with Cream roof and Red interior, cast wheels	£80-100
57-002	1965-67	Chevrolet Corvair Monza	Red body, Black roof, White interior, cast wheels	£80-100
57-003	1965-67	Chevrolet Impala	Yellow body with White roof and Red interior, cast wheels	£80-100
		US / Canadian issue:	Yellow body with Yellow roof, cast wheels	£80-100
57-004	1965-67	Oldsmobile Dynamic '88'	White body, Blue roof, Red interior, cast wheels	£125-150
57-005	1965-67	Ford Thunderbird	Blue body with White roof, Red interior, cast wheels	£100-125
57-006	1965-67	Nash Rambler Classic	Light Green body with Silver roof trim, Cream interior, cast wheels	£125-150
180	1979-80	Rover 3500	White body with opening doors, plastic wheels	£20-25
219	1978-79	'Big Cat' Jaguar	White/Red, Black 'Big Cat' decal. (This model was bubble-packed or sold unboxed)	£35-45

Dinky Toys made in Italy by Polistil under licence to Dinky Tri-ang

122	1979-80	Volvo Estate Car	Orange body, Brown interior, plastic wheels, Brown card box	£20-30
			Cream body, Red interior, cast wheels	£20-30
243	1979-80	Volvo 'Police' Car	White body, Brown card box	£15-20

'Mini-Dinky' models

Models 10 – 61 inclusive were made in a scale of 1:65.
Models 94 – 99 inclusive were made in a scale of 1:130.

Mini-Dinky models were issued in 1968 and were made in Hong Kong and Holland. Each model was sold with a free red plastic garage. The cars are fitted with Flexomatic Independent Suspension. Racing cars 60 and 61 were made by Best Box of Holland (now EFSI). The models listed are illustrated in the 1968 US issued 3-page fold-out leaflet which advertised them as 'Swinging Value' at 59 cents and 69 cents. Models 94-99 Construction Vehicles are illustrated in a US issued 'Mini-Dinky' fold-out launch leaflet '1'. The Market Price Range is **£30-40** each.

10	**Ford Corsair** ....Yellow or Metallic Gold	
11	**Jaguar 'E' typ** ....Red or Metallic Maroon	
12	**Corvette Stingray**..Blue or Metallic Dark Blue	
13	**Ferrari 250 LM** ....Red or Metallic Maroon	
14	**Chevrolet Chevy II** .....Yellow or Met. Maroon	
15	**Rolls-Royce Silver Shadow**......................Blue	
16	**Ford Mustang**..White, Cream or Metallic Blue	
17	**Aston Martin DB6**...............................White	
18	**Mercedes Benz 230 SL** ....White/Black	
19	**MGB Roadster**....................................Blue	
20	**Cadillac Coupé de Ville** ....Silver or White	
21	**Fiat 2300 Station Wagon** ....Blue or Yellow/White	

22	**Oldsmobile Toronado** ....Metallic Pale Blue
23	**Rover 2000** ....Blue
24	**Ferrari Superfast**.................................... Red
25	**Ford Zephyr 6**.....................................Silver
26	**Mercedes 250 SE** ....White or Bronze
27	**Buick Riviera** ....Blue
28	**Ferrari F 1** ....Red, '7'
29	**Ford F 1**...White
30	**Volvo 1800s**...Blue
31	**Volkswagen 1600TC** ....Blue or Metallic Green
32	**Vauxhall Cresta** ....Silver or Dark Green
33	**Jaguar** ....Red

57	**Chevrolet Corvair Monza Club Coupé** ....Red/Black
60	**Cooper** ....Blue '10'
61	**Lotus Racing Car** ....Green, '4'
94	**International Bulldozer**......................Yellow
95	**International Skid Shovel** ....Yellow
96	**Payloader Shovel**..................................White
97	**Euclid R40**......................Yellow, 10 wheels
98	**Michigan Scraper** ....Yellow
99	**Caterpillar Grader** ....Orange
-	**'Mini-Dinky' 12-Car Collector Case**, with models **£400-600**

'Dinky Toys' issued by Airfix Products Ltd.

Issued by Airfix as 'DINKY TOYS'; made in France to 1:43 scale. Supplied in the last design of Red/Yellow/Blue 'Dinky Toys' window box with header card. They were all issued circa 1980 and all are in the Market Price Range of **£10-15**.

500	**Citroën 2cv** ......Red/Orange or Green body, 'duck' motif, open roof	
500	**Citroën 2cv** ......Red/Orange or Green body, 'duck' motif, closed roof...	
501	**Fiat Strada**......Blue or Metallic Green body, no decals	
502	**BMW 530** ......Purple body with 'flame' decal on doors	
502	**BMW 530** ....Metallic Green with Black 'cougar' decal	
503	**Alfetta GTV**....Red or Yellow body, Green 'clover leaf' on bonnet	

504	**Citroën Visa**....Red body, no decals	
505	**Peugeot 504** .....Blue body with 'flame' decal on doors	
505	**Peugeot 504** ....Greenish-Gold with Black 'cougar' decal on doors............	
506	**Alfa-Sud** ......Not seen ....NGPP	
507	**Renault 14** ....Not seen ....NGPP	
508	**Ford Fiesta** ......Not seen ....NGPP	

COUGAR Model Toys

Many of the 'Airfix Dinky Toys' appeared erratically in the early 1980s (in France, then in the UK), under the name 'Cougar Model Toys' with these common features: Plastic base marked 'Dinky Toys made in France' and the code '1/43 07 80'. Presented in a blister-pack on card with 'Metal Cougar' and 'Fabrique par Solido'. Numbers printed on card are 100 less than numbers moulded on base. Market Price Range is **£10-15**. (TW = tinted windows)

1301-1401	**Citroën 2cv6**	Orange-Red body with 'ducks' decal, Grey base/interior/open roof .... Green body with 'ducks' decal, Grey base, Orange interior, Tan open roof ....
1302-1402	**Citroën Visa**	Metallic Jade Green, no decal, White plastic base, Dark Cream interior............. Metallic Red body, no decal, Grey plastic base and interior ....
1303-1403	**Fiat Ritmo**	Metallic Orange body, no decal, Dark Cream plastic base and interior .... Metallic Blue body, no decal, Yellow plastic base and interior ....

1304-1404	**BMW 530**	Metallic Green, 'cougar' decal, Grey base, Black/Grey interior, Green TW .... Metallic Purple, 'flames' decal, Grey base, Black/Grey interior, Yellow TW ....
1305-1405	**Alfetta GTV**	Red body, 'cougar' decal, Tan base, Black and Tan interior, Yellow TW .... Yellow body, 'clover leaf' decal, Tan base, Black and Tan interior, Blue TW ....
1306-1406	**Peugeot 504**	Metallic Yellow, 'cougar' decal, Brown base and TW, Black/Brown interior .... Metallic Blue body, 'flames' decal, Blue base and interior, clear windows ....

AIRFIX – matchbox sized miniatures made in Hong Kong

Although announced in 1980, only a few seem to have appeared in the UK. Market Price Range **£10-15**.

101	**'56 Corvette** ....White body with Red flash, bubble-packed..............	
103	**Chevette** ....Yellow, 'Turbo' decal, Silver base, bubble-packed ...	
104	**Honda Accord** ....Lilac body, Orange flash, Silver base, bubble-pack ..	
105	**Toyota Celica** ....Red body, '3', Silver base, Orange bubble-pack	
106	**Datsun 280Z**...........Brown body, bubble-packed...............................	
107	**BMW Turbo** ....Orange body, Black/Yellow flash, bubble-packed.....	
108	**Alfa Romeo** ....Purple body with Yellow flash, bubble-packed	
110	**Stepside Pick-up**....Blue and Brown body, bubble-packed	
110	**Camper**...................Yellow and Two-tone Brown body	
113	**Pick-up** ....Red and Black body, '4 x 4' decal..........................	
114	**Firebird** ....Black body..	
115	**Camaro** ....Red body with racing-number 'Z28'	

116	**'63 Corvette** ....Metallic Blue body ....
117	**'71 Corvette** ....Yellow body with 'Vette' decal...........................
119	**Ford Van** ....Blue body with Orange flash ....
120	**Renegade Jeep** ....Yellow/Green body, Silver base, Green packaging....
121	**Chevy Blazer** ....Red body ....
122	**Sun Van** ....Orange body with 'Sun Van' decal, Blue packaging .
123	**Yamaha 250 MX**.......Blue body with 'Yamaha' decal........................
124	**Honda MT 250** ....Orange body with 'Honda' decal.........................
125	**Kawasaki Fll 250**....Red body with 'Kawasaki' decal.........................
126	**Suzuki TM 400** ....Yellow/Black body with 'CCI' and 'Suzuki' decals...
129	**T-Bird Convertible** Red and White body ....
130	**Chevy Convertible** . Metallic Blue and White body ....

'Matchbox Dinky' – 'The Collection' 1988 onwards

See under Matchbox Collectibles in the 'Modern Diecasts' section.

Collectors notes

Wooden prototypes, first castings and factory colour samples

These are unique items, produced as samples within the factory to aid the design and development process. Some were made for publicity and catalogue illustration purposes prior to actual volume production. Price guidance is usually not possible since they so rarely come to market in significant quantities. However, the sale in 2001 by Christie's of the Remy-Meeus Collection has enabled us to list the following:

Pre-war items

38a Frazer-Nash BMW, Blue with Grey interior, Turquoise hubs....**£500-800**
38a Frazer-Nash BMW, (first casting), Green with Dark Green
    seats, fabricated, painted tinplate baseplate.........................**£300-400**
38d Alvis, (first casting), Blue with Tan seats, 'ALVIS' in
    Indian ink on base **£250-350**
38e Armstrong-Siddeley Coupé, (colour sample), plain Brown
    dashboard, production baseplate painted Khaki................**£200-300**

38f Jaguar Sports Car, (wooden prototype),
    Dark Green body, 'JAGUAR' in Indian ink on base **£600-800**
38f Jaguar Sports Car, (first casting), Green body, Grey seats, etc ..**£300-400**

39a Packard Sedan, (wooden prototype),
    Dark Blue with Silver windows, 'PACKARD' on base ...**£600-1,000**
39b Oldsmobile Six Sedan, (wooden prototype), Dark Green with Silver
    windows, 'Oldsmobile Six Sedan' in Indian ink on base **£500-800**
39c Lincoln Zephyr, (wooden prototype of saloon version, not coupé),
    unpainted, with 'Lincoln Zephyr' in pencil on base............**£600-800**
39d Buick Viceroy, (wooden prototype), Maroon with Silver
    windows, 'BUICK' in pencil on base **£800-1,000**
39e Chrysler Royal Sedan, (wooden prototype), Red with Silver
    windows, 'CHRYSLER' in Indian ink on base **£800-1,000**
39f Studebaker State Commander Coupé, (wooden prototype),
    Yellow Ochre with Silver windows, 'STUDEBAKER' in
    Indian ink on base...**£700-900**

39 Series Hupmobile, (wooden prototype), Green with Silver
    windows, 'HUPMOBILE' in Indian ink on base.
    Not issued as a production model **£800-1,200**
39 Series Luxicab, (wooden prototype), Black and Pale Yellow
    with Silver windows, 'LUXICAB' in pencil on rear spare wheel
    cover and '1st sample not approved' in pencil on base.
    Not issued as a production model **£800-1,000**
39 Series Luxicab, (wooden prototype), Black and Canary Yellow
    with Silver windows, 'LUXICAB' in pencil on rear spare
    wheel cover. Not issued as a production model **£800-1,000**

Post-war paint colour samples

38b Sunbeam-Talbot, Red body, hubs and tonneau. Tie-on label stating:
    'Approved 22 Oct 1948', plus paint code details.................**£300-500**
38e Armstrong-Siddeley Coupé, Green body, Light Grey interior,
    Green hubs. Tie-on label stating:
    'Approved 22 Oct 1948', plus paint code details.................**£300-500**
39b Oldsmobile Sedan, Beige body, Fawn hubs. Tie-on label stating:
    '1 Oct 1948', plus paint code details..................................**£300-500**
39e Chrysler Royal Sedan, Cream body, Light Green hubs.
    Tie-on label stating: '1 Oct 1948', plus paint code details ..**£300-500**
40b Triumph 1800, Black body, Silver hubs, rear window pillars.
    Two tie-on labels stating: '30/9/48', + paint code details....**£500-800**
40d Austin Devon, Red body, Maroon hubs. Tie-on label stamped:
    '6 Jan 1950', plus paint code details..................................**£400-600**
40e Standard Vanguard, Fawn body, Fawn hubs, axle clip,
    open rear wheel arches. Tie-on label stating:
    '18 Oct 1948', plus paint code details................................**£400-600**

We are also aware of the following (these were not in Christie's sale, NPP)

107 Sunbeam Alpine in Maroon with Grey interior (unfinished casting) ....
107 Sunbeam Alpine in Light Blue with Cream interior (unfinished casting)..
110 Aston-Martin in Grey with Blue interior (unfinished casting) ....
111 Triumph TR2 in Pink with Blue interior..
122 Volvo 256DL Estate in White..
122 Volvo 256DL Estate in Red..
122 Volvo 256DL Estate in Green...
170 Ford Granada Ghia in Metallic Silver..
181 Volkswagen Saloon in Pale Blue (with baseplate, 1970s)........................
181 Volkswagen Saloon in Pale Blue (with spun hubs, 1970s) ....
181 Volkswagen Saloon in Metallic Blue ....
181 Volkswagen Saloon in Turquoise..
190 Monteverdi 375L in Metallic Gold (Copper), White interior, cast wheels.
190 Monteverdi 375L in Metallic Black, Red interior, cast wheels ....
211 Triumph TR7. Metallic Green body, Red, Grey or Green interior ....
227 Beach Buggy. Copper body, Grey hood, 'fire' design.............................
57-001 Buick Riviera with Slate Grey body (Hong Kong made model)..........

Dinky Toys wooden prototypes (pre-war):

(above) **39e Chrysler Royal Sedan**, Red with Silver
windows, 'CHRYSLER' in Indian ink on base

(above right) **38f Jaguar Sports Car**,
Dark Green body, 'JAGUAR' in Indian ink on base

(right) **39 Series Luxicab**, Black and Canary Yellow
with Silver windows, 'LUXICAB' in pencil on
rear spare wheel cover. Not issued as a production model

Identification of casting types

The 25 Series Lorries 1934 - 1950

Type 1: (**1934-36**), 'open' chassis (usually black), tinplate radiator, no headlamps,
no front bumper, 'smooth' cast hubs (various colours) with large white tyres. 105 mm.

Type 2: (**1936-46**), 'open' chassis (usually black), diecast radiator with headlamps but
no front bumper, 'smooth' cast hubs (various colours), with large white tyres. 105 mm.

Type 3: (**1947-48**), 'closed' chassis (only in black), diecast radiator with headlamps but
no front bumper, 'smooth' or 'ridged' wheel hubs (only in black) ,with black tyres. 105 mm.

Type 4: (**1948-50**), detailed moulded chassis (only in black), diecast radiator with headlamps and
with bumper, 'ridged' coloured wheel hubs with black tyres. 110 mm.

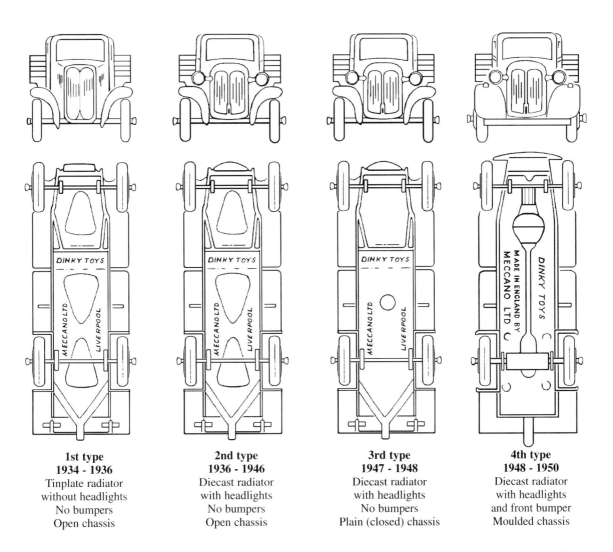

1st type	**2nd type**	**3rd type**	**4th type**
1934 - 1936	**1936 - 1946**	**1947 - 1948**	**1948 - 1950**
Tinplate radiator	Diecast radiator	Diecast radiator	Diecast radiator
without headlights	with headlights	with headlights	with headlights
No bumpers	No bumpers	No bumpers	and front bumper
Open chassis	Open chassis	Plain (closed) chassis	Moulded chassis

25 Series Trucks 1934-50 Wheel types The first pre-war issues have cast metal wheels followed by chrome (rare) or diecast hubs with large white tyres. The early post-war issues c.1946 have smooth hubs and large black tyres. **1947-48** issues have ridged black hubs with large black tyres. The last issues **c.1949-50** have coloured ridged hubs and attract a premium. Similarly early cast or chrome hubs also attract a premium.

Foden cab types

1947 - 1952
Foden 'DG'
(1st type) cab
Exposed radiator
Colour flashes on sides

1952 - 1964
Foden 'FG'
(2nd type) cab
Radiator behind grille
No colour flashes on sides

Guy cab types

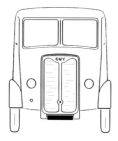

Guy 1st type cab 1947 - 1954
Exposed radiator
No gusset at either
side of number plate

Guy 2nd type cab 1954 - 1958
Exposed radiator
With gusset at each
side of number plate

Guy Warrior cab 1958 - 1964
Radiator behind grille
Restyled front with
sidelights in wings

28 and 280 Series Delivery Vans

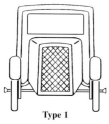

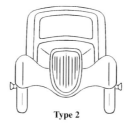

Type 1

Type 2

Type 3

Type 1: (**1933-35**), two-piece lead body with *'HORNBY SERIES'* (early issues) or *'DINKY TOYS'* cast-in under cab roof, tinplate radiator, no headlamps, thinly-painted coloured solid wheel/tyre castings (some silver plated), 84 mm. (Coloured wheels tend to attract a premium to the price of the model.)

Type 2: (**1935-39**), one-piece diecast body, cast-in shield-shaped radiator, rear wheel spats, cast smooth wheel hubs with rubber tyres (usually white), 81 mm. All carried advertising.

Type 3: (**1939-41**), one-piece diecast body with rear wheel spats, cast smooth wheel hubs (various colours) with black tyres, open rear windows, 83 mm. All carried advertising.

Type 3: (**1947-54**), one-piece diecast body with rear wheel spats, cast ridged wheel hubs (usually black) with black tyres, filled-in rear windows, cast boss under roof , 83 mm. No advertising.

Identification of Ford Transit Van castings (not illustrated)

Type 1: (**1966-74**), has sliding driver's door, opening hinged side door, and twin rear doors.

Type 2: (**1974-78**), non-sliding driver's door, one side-hinged door, one top-hinged rear door.

Type 3: (**1978-80**), as Type 2 but with a slightly longer bonnet (18 mm.)

Commercial Vehicles Box Types Introduction

A mint condition commercial vehicle without its correct box is worth a fraction of the value of its boxed equivalent. Furthermore, as model boxes made from card do not survive as well as their die-cast contents, pristine box examples are scarce and becoming scarcer. The condition of a box is of paramount importance and attention is drawn to the section in the main catalogue introduction, namely: 'Classifying the Condition of Models and Boxes'.

The following listing provides collectors with a working knowledge of the range of box types issued. In addition details are given of their dates of issue, their design and of the models which used them. See also the colour sections for examples of many types of boxes.

Whilst every care has been taken in preparing the listing other variations no doubt exist and information on these is welcomed.

Similarly with no 'dates of birth' available the dates of issue shown are approximate and again any further information is welcomed.

Commercial Vehicles Box Identification

Box Pictures
To assist identification, pictures of the various box types have been included in the colour section.

Model Colour Identification Marks
These are shown on the box lid and label and take the form of either a circular colour spot or a capital letter, e.g. 'R' for red. A colour spot may be a single colour or in the case of the later two-tone colours models a two-tone colour spot.

'Lead-free' labels 'LF'
In the 1950s the government introduced new regulations concerning the lead content of die-cast models. Consequently, to indicate that a model complied with the new regulations, a round white label with 'LF' in blue was added to box end labels for a short time. Alternatively, an 'LF' coloured ink stamp was used. (See example in the colour section.)

Model Reference Numbers
These are always shown on the box lid and label.

Dual numbered boxes c. 1953 – 1954
A new numbering system was introduced which resulted in models being issued displaying both the old and new reference numbers. The information was shown in one of two ways:
    (a) A black new number stamped alongside the old number
    (b) A small old model number shown in red on either side of a larger black new number, e.g. 511 911 511". (See examples in the colour section). Dual numbered boxes (issued for a relatively short period) may attract a premium.

Quality Control Box Markings. 1947 – 1957
    (a) Factory Checkers Marks
A quality control mark may be found on the base of the buff coloured boxes. This takes the form of a coloured ink stamp of a reference number within a circle, e.g. 'M42' or 'M19'. See the examples shown in the colour section. Stamped on the underside of the blue covered box lid may be found a similar ink stamp e.g. 'ZQ Z8'.
    (b) Date Stamps
Ink stamped on the base of boxes or box lids may be found a purple date stamp relating to the date of the model's issue. Recorded examples include: 'GR950' on a (25x) orange coloured box; '10 KR 55' on a (933) blue/white stripe box; 'H656' on a (902) blue/white stripe box; 'KB956' on a (433) yellow covered box lid; '01057' on a (689) military blue/white box.
The Editor would welcome any further information on this subject.

Pre-war issues 1933 – 1939
Apart from sets (see the Gift Sets listing) commercial vehicles were sold unboxed. They were usually packaged in half-dozen retailers trade packs such as Nos. 28/1, 28/2 and 28/3 Delivery Vans.

Post-war Issues 1947 – 1979
In 1947 the first individual boxes were introduced to house the exciting new range of 'Supertoys' models. However, the small commercial vehicles continued to be sold unboxed from trade packs until 1953/54.
The boxes have been catalogued into four types as follows:
    Type 1 1947-75 - Boxes with lift-off lids
    Type 2 1953-75 - All card boxes with tuck-in end flaps
    Type 3 1963-79 - Display boxes
    Type 4 1964-64 - Export only boxes

A 1947-50
Buff plain card box with separate labels on the box top and one box end. The half red and white box labels show 'DINKY SUPERTOYS' plus the model number. In addition the main label displays an illustration of the model and whilst the main design of the label remains constant, the position of the model does vary as follows:

i) Facing inwards on the right side of the label.
 Models recorded using this box: 501 (1st type), 521 and 563.

ii) Facing outwards on the left side of the label.
Models recorded using this box: 502, 503, 511, 512, 513 (all 1st types). The small separate label attached to the right side of the box lid is white with red model information text. Some labels include a line drawing of the model eg. 503 and 513.

iii) Buff plain card box with a single 'wrap round' red and white label which covers the box lid from end to end with 'DINKY SUPERTOYS' in red on the larger Foden type box, one end of the label contains information about the model in German, French and Spanish. In addition, the model number on the top and ends is now white on a circular black background. The model picture is facing inwards from the right and the models recorded in this box to date are: 504 Tanker 1st type and 531.

iv) As previous issue but the model picture is facing outwards from the left. Models recorded: 511, 512, 521 and 533.

B c.1950
Green covered box with red and white wrap-around label. Models recorded in this box: 501, 502, 503, 504 (1st and 2nd types), 504 'MOBILGAS', 511, 512, 513 and 521. Model picture facing inwards from the right. 'DINKY SUPERTOYS' in red letters.

C c.1950
(i) Pale or dark blue covered box with wrap-around red and white label. Model picture facing inwards from the right with 'DINKY SUPERTOYS' logo. Models recorded: 501, 502, 503, 504 (1st and 2nd types), 505, 511, 512, 513, 514 (all issues except 'Spratts'), 531/931, 532/932 and 533/933.

(ii) Pale or dark blue box with wrap-around orange and white label with 'DINKY SUPERTOYS'. Model picture facing inwards from the right front. Beneath the model picture is a black factory code, e.g. on the 522 Big Bedford lorry issue the code is '50522'. Models recorded: 504 (1st / 2nd), 511, 514 'LYONS' and 'SLUMBERLAND', 531 and 571.

(iii) Same as C(ii) but with model picture facing outwards from the left. Models recorded: 502(1st), 503 (2nd) and 512.

(iv) Same as C(ii) but with model picture facing inwards from the right front but with 'DINKY TOYS'. Models recorded: 501(1st type), 504 Tanker (1st and 2nd types), 504 'MOBILGAS', 514 'WEETABIX', 514 'SLUMBERLAND', 514'SPRATTS', 521, 522, 564, 591/991, and 917.

(v) Same as C (iv) but with model picture facing outwards from the left front. Models recorded: 502, 503 (1st types), 512, 513 (1st types).

(vi) Same as C (iv) but with model picture facing inwards from the left front. Models 505 (1st type), 532 and 581 US issue.

D (i) Blue and white striped box lid with dark blue bottom section. Box lid is white with dark blue parallel stripes. 'DINKY TOYS' logo is shown in red plus a colour picture of the model facing inwards from the right. The model number is on the left of the picture. Colour identification spots shown as appropriate on box ends. Models recorded:
409, 418, 582, 511, 511/911, 512, 512/912, 513, 513/913, 901/2/3(2nd type), 911/12/13. 917, 921, 923 ('ketchup bottle'), 923 ('baked beans can'), 930, 931, 932/33, 941/42, 963, 980, 982, 991.

NB The 417 Leyland Comet Lorry yellow/green issue was housed in a box with a blue/yellow picture.

(ii) As D (i), but with 'DINKY SUPERTOYS' logo and with the model picture facing inwards from the right. Models recorded:
901/2/3, 905, 913, 918/9, 923, 930, 934/5/6, 942/3, 948, 954, 958, 960, 963/4, 966/7/8/9, 973, 977, 982/3/4, 986, 991, 994.
On the box side is a note stating the colour of the model which may vary from

the one illustrated on the box front. This only happened when a model was issued for a short time and hence some of the rarest models were issued in this manner (e.g. 902 Foden Flat Truck in yellow/green livery was issued in box with red/green model picture; 913 Guy Flat Truck with tailboard in yellow/green livery was issued in box with all-green model picture; 934 Leyland Octopus Wagon in blue and yellow livery was issued on the standard box with a yellow/green model picture but displaying a dark blue colour spot).
The Editor would welcome any further examples.

(iii) As D (ii), but with model picture facing outwards from the left. 'DINKY SUPERTOYS' logo. Model recorded No.982.

(iv) As D (ii), but with model picture facing inwards from the left. 'DINKY SUPERTOYS' logo. Model recorded No. 979.

(v) Plain blue and white striped box with no model picture on lid. A white end label 'DINKY SUPERTOYS' and the model details in blue letters. Models recorded: 920 and 923.

E Yellow covered box lid with blue bottom section.
(i) c.1956 - 1959
On two of the box sides is a picture of the model set against a white shadow background. The top of the box lid has a 'DINKY TOYS' logo in red. Colour spots shown as appropriate. In addition white circular 'LF' (lead free) labels may be found. Models recorded: 408/9, 417, 419, 430/1/2/3.
NB. The rare 408 Big Bedford Lorry in pink and cream livery was issued in this box but with the standard maroon and fawn model box picture.

(ii) Yellow covered box lid but with red side panels with pictorial scene with 'DINKY TOYS' logo in red. The box lid shows the model picture facing inwards from the right with a pictorial scene in an end panel on the left. Models recorded: 401, 408, 417, 419, 425, 430, 434, 448, 450, 925, 960, 964, 972 and 978.

(iii) Same as previous issue but with 'DINKY SUPERTOYS' logo. Models recorded: 908, 934, 935, 944, 958/9, 962, 964, 972 and 978.
NB. No. 935 Leyland Octopus with chains in the rare dark blue and grey livery was issued in the standard box with the green and grey version illustrated but with a dark blue spot displayed.

(iv) All yellow covered lid with a pictorial scene in the middle of the box lid top. 'DINKY SUPERTOYS' in red. Models recorded: 959, 987/8/9.

F 'One off' box issues with lift-off lids.

(i) Plain dark blue covered box with no picture. White label on box lid end with dark blue text. Model recorded: 982 Pullman Car Transporter in rare mid-blue livery with brownish-grey decks.

(ii) Orange covered box (c.1950) with white/orange wrap-around lid label. Models recorded: 25x Breakdown Truck and 14c Coventry Climax Fork Lift Truck.

TYPE 2   1953 - 1975
ALL CARD BOXES WITH TUCK-IN END FLAPS

A 1953 - 1964
(i) Deep yellow box with 'DINKY TOYS' in red plus the model's name and type in black. A white reference number on a black or red oval background is on the box end flaps but no reference is shown on the box face. The model is pictured on the box sides with or without a white shadow background. Colour spots shown as applicable. Foreign language information is shown on one of the box end flaps. Box used for small and medium size models, e.g., 431/432. Box in general use during the model renumbering period. Consequently dual numbered boxes will be found.
Very few boxes were issued displaying just the old type of reference number. Recorded models to date: 25d, e, f, g and 30e. In addition, 29c Bus and 29e Coach have been identified. Please send details if you have any other examples. Later issues display 'WITH WINDOWS' captions.

(ii) Plain light yellow box with two red sides and no model picture. The 'DINKY TOYS' logo, the model type and its reference number are shown in yellow and white. Colour spots are shown as appropriate. Models recorded: 252, 413, 414 and 428 plus 070 and 071 Dublo Dinky.

(iii) 1963 - 1970
Yellow box with red end features panel around the front right side, with or without an upward pointing white arrow. Models recorded: 273, 274, 435.

(iv) 1966 - 1969
A detailed full colour picture box with 'DINKY TOYS' in red plus a pictorial scene on two sides. A yellow laurel leaf design on a black background incorporates the model number Models recorded: 280, 402, 407 'KENWOOD', 914, 923, 944/5, 959/60, 965, 970, 972 and 978.

(v) 1968 - 1974
White fronted box with a narrow yellow band across the face. The box front displays 'DINKY TOYS' in red plus the model number and type in black and white letters. A colour picture of the model is shown on two sides. Models recorded: 407, 438/9/40, 91, 917, 974, 978 and 980.

(vi) 1966 - 1970
Picture box used for large commercials with two full pictorial sides with 'DINKY TOYS' in red. The other sides are yellow and red. Models recorded: 434 'AUTO SERVICES', 914 and 945.

(vii) 1970 - 1975
Heavy card box used for heavy models e.g. 924 Centaur Dump Truck. Box has white face with a colour picture of model combined with a black band across the face and sides.

(viii) Promotional Box Types
(a) No. 274 'JOSEPH MASON PAINTS' Minivan. Dark red box with white letters plus an enclosed leaflet.
(b) No. 491 Plain yellow box with red letters. 'JOBS DAIRY'.
(c) No. 917 Mercedes-Benz LP1920 Truck with 'HENRY JOHNSON' logo. Plain white card box with no lettering
(d) No. 940 Mercedes-Benz, 'FISONS', plain white box

TYPE 3   1963 - 1979   DISPLAY BOXES

A 1970 - 1976 Vacuform packs
Models displayed on a black card base with a blue surface with 'DINKY TOYS' in red and white. The model is covered by a close-fitting see-through protective plastic cover. Known examples include: 407,416, 438/9, 915, 944, 945 'ESSO' and 'LUCAS' issues.

B 1976 - 1979 Window boxes
Cellophane fronted window boxes with a dark blue and red header card giving the model's name and 'DINKY DIECAST TOYS' in yellow and white letters. Known examples include: 275, 432, 440, 451, 940, 950 and 980.
C   1963 - 1966 Fold-back lid display box
224 Commer Convertible Truck and 975 Ruston Bucyrus Excavator which also had a coloured outer box display wrapper issued for a while.

TYPE 4   1964 - 1966   EXPORT ONLY BOXES

A 1964 - 1966
An all-yellow card and cellophane 'see-through' display box.
'DINKY' plus the model type and number is shown across the box front in red letters plus 'A MECCANO PRODUCT MADE IN ENGLAND'. Box issued with a card protection strip. Known models include: 275, 434, 492, 914. A version of this box was used for the 944 'SHELL BP' tanker - see picture in the colour section, Also used for the U.S. Export Series: 'MARVELS IN MINIATURE' which is shown on the sides of the box front in red capital letters, e.g. 275, 434, 437, 448 and 965. Later issues display the range on the base of the box.

B c.1965
Same as previous issue but all-gold box with two black and red diagonal stripes. A rare box type. Known issues include 434 and 989.

INNER BOX LININGS and MODEL SUPPORTS

To be complete a box should contain all its original model supports. The following issues all had supports or linings. In some instances top and bottom linings were included (2).
14c, 400, 561, 581, 908(2), 924, 930(3), 958, 964, 965, 967, 968, 969(2), 972, 974, 976, 977(2), 979(2), 980, 982, 983(2), 984(2), 985(2), 986, 989(2).

Dinky Toys Commercial Vehicles

Market Price Range (MPR) for pre-1954 unboxed commercial vehicle models: Prior to 1954, virtually all smaller, non-Supertoy commercial vehicle models were sold unboxed from retailer's trade boxes of either 6, 4 or 3 models. Consequently, all pre-1954 issues have been priced as being unboxed. Post-1954 models were all boxed and have been priced accordingly. As a consequence, models which have been renumbered will be found to have two differing prices – one for the pre-1954 unboxed version and another for its boxed and renumbered successor.

See also the Trade Box section for details of individual boxes and packs that were used to supply shops.

Ref	Year(s)	Model name	Colours, features, details	Market Price Range
14a	1948-54	B.E.V. Truck	Mid-Blue body with Blue hubs, Fawn driver, hook, (renumbered 400)	£30-35
			Grey body (with Blue, Grey or Red hubs), Fawn driver, hook	£30-35
14c	1949-54	Coventry Climax Fork Lift	Orange, Brown or Dark Red body, Green forks, Fawn driver, 1 packing piece, (renumbered 401)	£25-30
14z	1938-40	Three-wheel Delivery Van	'Triporteur' with Green, Red, Grey, Blue or Yellow body, Black hubs,	
			White tyres, driver is always a different colour from van, French model	NGPP

22 Series

Ref	Year(s)	Model name	Colours, features, details	Market Price Range
22c	1933-35	Motor Truck	Two-piece lead body with 'HORNBY SERIES' cast-in, tinplate radiator,	
			diecast coloured or plain wheels.	
			Blue cab, Red or Yellow or Cream truck body	£300-400
			Red cab, Green, Blue or Cream truck body	£300-400
			Yellow cab, Blue truck body	£300-400
22c	1935-40	Motor Truck	Orange-Red, Maroon, Green or Blue (diecast one-piece) body, open rear window,	
			coloured diecast hubs	£125-150
			Dark Blue body, chrome hubs	£125-150
			Off-white body, Mid-Blue hubs	£125-150
	1945-47		Red, Green or Brown body, open rear window, Black diecast hubs	£60-70
	1948-50		Red, Green or Brown body, closed rear window, Black diecast hubs	£60-70
22d	1933-34	Delivery Van	Lead body, tinplate radiator, 'HORNBY SERIES' cast-in.	
			Orange/Blue body or Blue/Yellow body, Red wheels, no advertising, Type 1	£500-750
	1934-34		As previous models but with 'DINKY TOYS' cast-in.	£400-500
	1934	Delivery Van 'MECCANO'	Orange cab and chassis, Blue van with Red/Black 'Meccano Engineering For Boys'	£2,000-2,500
22d	1934-35		Yellow body (lead), 'Meccano Engineering For Boys' in Red and Black,	
			Type 1, 84 mm. 22d till April 1935, (renumbered 28n)	£900-1,200

25 Series

Ref	Year(s)	Model name	Colours, features, details	Market Price Range
25a	1934-36	Wagon	Maroon, Green, Red or Blue body, Black chassis, Type 1	£300-400
	1936-40		Maroon, Green, Red or Blue body, Black or Red chassis, Type 2	£125-150
	1936-40		Blue body with Orange chassis, Type 2	£150-200
	1946		Grey, Green or Blue, Type 2, smooth hubs	£80-100
	1947-48		Grey, Green, Red, Orange or Blue body, Black chassis, Type 3	£70-80
	1948-50		Grey, Green, Light Blue or Orange body, Black chassis, Type 4	£70-80
			Cream or Red body, Black chassis, Type 4	£70-80
25b	1934-36	Covered Wagon	Blue body, Cream tilt, Black chassis, Type 1	£300-400
	1936-40		Green body, Green, Cream or Yellow tilt, Black chassis, Type 2	£140-180
			Cream/Yellow or Fawn/Cream, Black chassis, Type 2	£140-180
			Orange body, Cream tilt, Green chassis, Type 2	£150-200
	1936-40	Covered Wagon		
		'CARTER PATERSON'	Green body, Blue hubs, Green tilt, Black chassis, Type 2, 'Express Carriers London'	£300-350
		'CARTER PATERSON'	Green body, Blue hubs, Type 2, 'Special Service To The Seaside'	£400-500
		'MECCANO'	Green body, Cream tilt, Black chassis, Type 2, 'Engineering For Boys'	£300-400
			Variation with chrome hubs	£500-600
		'HORNBY TRAINS'	Fawn body, Cream tilt, Black chassis, Gold lettering, Type 2	£300-400
	1945-47	Covered Wagon	Green/Green, Grey/Light or Dark Grey, Blue/Grey, Black chassis, Type 3	£100-140
	1947-50		Green/Green, Grey/Grey, Cream/Red, Cream/Blue, Black chassis, Type 4	£100-140
			Yellow body, Blue tinplate tilt, Black ridged hubs	£300-400
25c	1934-36	Flat Truck	Dark Blue body, Black chassis, Type 1	£150-200
	1936-40		Green or Stone body, Black chassis, Type 2	£125-150
	1946		Fawn, Green or Grey body, smooth hubs, Type 2	£70-80
	1947-48		Green, Blue or Grey body, Black chassis, Type 3	£70-80
	1948-50		Green, Blue, Orange or Stone body, Type 4	£70-80
	NB		Some pre-war (1934-40) Truck issues will be found with a '20 mph' disc on the rear.	
25d	1934-35	Petrol Tank Wagon	Same chassis casting as other 25 series lorries but with hook removed.	
		(plain, unlettered)	Red body, no advertising, Black chassis, Type 1, open windows to back of cab	£500-700
		'SHELL BP'	Red body, Black chassis, Type 1	£400-500
		'SHELL'	Red body, Blue hubs, Type 1, 'SHELL LUBRICATING OIL' in Gold serif lettering	£400-500
		'ESSO'	Green body, Black chassis, Type 1	£400-500
		'POWER'	Green body, Black chassis, Type 1	£400-500
		'PRATTS'	Green body, Black chassis, Type 1	£400-500
		'CASTROL'	Green body, Black chassis, Blue hubs, Red logo, Type 1	£400-500
		'TEXACO'	Red body, Black chassis/hubs, White logo 'PETROLEUM & PRODUCTS', Type 1	£400-500
	1936-46	'PETROL'	Red body, Black chassis, Black or White lettering, Type 2	£150-200
		'SHELL BP'	Red body, Black chassis, Blue or chrome hubs, Type 2	£250-300
		'MOBILOIL'	Red body, Black chassis, Type 2	£250-300

25d Petrol Tank Wagon list continues overleaf:

25d Petrol Tank Wagon list continued from previous page:

		'TEXACO'	Red body, Black chassis, Type 2	£250-300
		'PETROL'	Green body, Black chassis, Type 2	£250-300
		'ESSO'	Green body, Black chassis, Black or Blue hubs, Gold lettering, Type 2	£250-300
		'POWER'	Green body, Black chassis, Type 2	£250-300
		'CASTROL'	Green body, Black chassis, Black or Blue hubs, Red lettering, Type 2	£250-300
		'REDLINE GLICO'	Blue body, Black chassis, Red panel, Gold lettering, Type 2	£250-300
	1945	'POOL' (Wartime)	Grey body, White chassis, Black hubs, Black lettering, Type 2	£400-500
	1945-46	'POOL' (Wartime)	Grey body, Black chassis, Type 2	£300-400
	1945-46	'PETROL' (Wartime)	Grey body, Type 2	£300-400
	1946-47	'PETROL'	Red or Green body, Black chassis, Type 3	£100-150
	1947-48	'PETROL'	Orange body, Type 4	£300-400
	1948-50	'PETROL'	Red, Light Green or Mid-Green body, Black chassis, Type 4	£70-100
	1948-?	'PETROL'	Yellow body, Black chassis, Type 4	£200-300
25e	1934-35	**Tipping Wagon**	Maroon/Yellow body, Black chassis, Type 1	£150-200
	1936-40		Maroon/Yellow, Brown/Turquoise or Fawn/Fawn body, Black chassis, Type 2	£100-125
			Fawn/Fawn body, Black chassis, Type 2	£100-125
	1946		Grey, Green or Fawn, Type 2	£70-80
	1947-48		Grey, Stone, Green or Yellow body, Black chassis, Type 3	£70-80
	1948-50		Grey, Stone or Brown body, Black chassis, Type 4	£70-80
	1948-50		Blue/Pink body, Black chassis, Type 4	£70-80
	NB		Some early post-war 25 series Trucks variations exist with smooth hubs.	
25f	1934-35	**Market Gardeners Lorry**	Green body, Black chassis or Yellow body, Green chassis, Type 1	£100-125
	1936-40		Green or Yellow body, Black chassis, Type 2	£70-80
			Green body, Yellow chassis, Type 2	£150-200
	1945-47		Green, Grey or Yellow body, Black chassis and hubs, Type 3	£70-80
	1947-50		Green, Grey, Yellow or Red body, Black chassis and hubs, Type 4	£70-80
			Orange body, Black chassis and hubs, Type 4	£140-160
			Green or Yellow body, Black chassis, Yellow hubs, Type 4	£70-80
25g	1935-40	**Trailer**	Dark Blue or Green body with cast-in hook, tinplate drawbar	£35-40
	1946-47		Green, Stone, Pale Blue or Orange body, cast-in hook, tinplate drawbar	£15-20
	1947-48		Green, Stone, Pale Blue or Orange body, cast-in hook, wire drawbar	£15-20
	1948-49		Green, Stone, Pale Blue or Orange body, tinplate hook, wire drawbar	£15-20
25g	1950-54		Green or Red body with tinplate hook and wire drawbar, (renumbered 429)	£15-20
25m	1948-52	**Bedford End Tipper**	Dark Green cab and truck body, Black hubs, crank-handle operates tipper	£90-120
	1948-54		Orange cab and truck body, Black hubs	£90-120
			Orange cab and truck body, Light Green hubs	£500-750
			Cream cab and truck body, Red hubs	£500-750
			Dark Green cab and truck body, Light Green hubs	£300-400
			Red cab, Cream back, Red cast hubs	£90-120
			Yellow cab, Mid-Blue back, Yellow cast hubs	£90-120
	NB		25m was renumbered 410 in 1954. All 25m models were sold from trade packs of six.	
25p	1948-54	**Aveling Barford Road Roller.**	Mid or Pale Green body with driver and hook, Red wheels, (renumbered 251)	£30-40
			All-Orange body, Tan driver	£150-200
25r	1948-54	**Forward Control Lorry**	Orange body, Black hubs	£60-70
		(renumbered 420)	Orange body, Green hubs	£75-85
			Cream body, Black hubs	£60-70
			Cream body, Blue hubs	£75-85
			Dark Brown body, Green hubs	£75-85
			Green body, Cream hubs	£75-85
25s	1937-40	**Six-wheeled Wagon**	Reddish-Brown body, Cream, Brown or Grey tilt, holes in seat (but no figures)	£100-125
			Royal Blue body	£200-250
	1945-48		Brown (various shades), Green or Dark Blue body, Grey or Light Blue tilt, with or without holes for figures (but no figures)	£100-125
			Brick Red body, Grey tinplate tilt, Black hubs	£125-150
25t	1945-47	**Flat Truck and Trailer**	(25c Flat Truck (Type 3), and matching 25g Trailer), Green, Blue, Orange or Stone	£140-160
	1947-50		(25c Flat Truck (Type 4), and matching 25g Trailer), Green or Orange	£120-140
25v	1948-54	**Bedford Refuse Wagon**	Fawn body, Green opening shutters and rear door, (renumbered 252). (Trade box contains 4)	£80-90
25w	1948-54	**Bedford Truck**	Light Green cab, truck body and hubs	£90-120
		(renumbered 411)	Dark Green cab, Light Green truck body, Light Green hubs	£300-400
			Light Green cab and truck body, Red hubs	£500-750

25x 1949-54 **Commer Breakdown Lorry**
'DINKY SERVICE' logo. First issues in Trade Boxes of 4, then individually in Orange card boxes.
(renumbered 430)

Originally sold from Trade (Set) Boxes of 6 models.
Note that colour-washed metal cast wheels on 1st type vans tend to attract a price premium.

		Tan cab and chassis (various shades), Light Green back, Red hubs, Black logo	£100-120
		Dark Grey cab, Violet Blue back, Red hubs, White logo	£130-150
		Dark Grey cab, Royal Blue back, Red hubs, White logo	£115-135

28 Series Delivery Vans

28a	1934	'HORNBY TRAINS'	Orange body, 'Hornby Trains' logo, 1st Type	£1,000-1,500
28a		'HORNBY TRAINS'	Yellow body, 'Hornby Trains British & Guaranteed' in Gold,	
	1934-35		Type 1, 84 mm.	£1,000-1,500
	1935-36		Type 2, 81 mm.	£250-350
28a		'GOLDEN SHRED'	Cream body, 'Golden Shred Marmalade' on right hand side, 'Silver Shred Marmalade' on left hand side,	
	1936-39		Type 2, 81 mm.	£1,000-1,500
	1939-41		Type 3, 83 mm.	£300-400
28b		'PICKFORDS'	Dark Blue, 'Pickfords Removals & Storage, Over 100 Branches' in Gold,	
	1934-35		Type 1, 84 mm.	£1,000-1,500
	1935	'PICKFORDS'	Dark Blue. Late version with diecast hubs, White tyres, Type 1	£1,000-1,500
	1935-35		Type 2, 81 mm.	£300-400
28b		'SECCOTINE'	Blue body, 'Seccotine Sticks Everything' in Gold,	
	1935-39		Type 2, 81 mm.	£300-400
	1939-41		Type 3, 83 mm.	£300-400
28c		'MANCHESTER GUARDIAN'	'The Manchester Guardian' in Gold,	
	1934-35		Black/Red body, Type 1	£1,000-1,500
	1935-39		Red body, Type 2.	£300-400
	1939-41		Red body, Type 3	£300-400
28d		'OXO'	Blue body, 'Beef In Brief' and 'Beef At Its Best' in Gold,	
	1934-35		Type 1	£1,000-1,500
	1935-39		Type 2	£300-400
	1939-41		Type 3	£500-700
28e		'ENSIGN LUKOS'	Orange body, 'Ensign Cameras' and 'Ensign Lukos Films' in Gold,	
	1934-35		Type 1	£1,000-1,500
28e		'FIRESTONE'	'Firestone Tyres' in Gold,	
	1934-35		White body, Type 1	£1,000-1,500
	1935-39		Blue or White body, Type 2	£300-400
	1939-41		Blue or White body, Type 3	£200-300
28f		'PALETHORPES'	Pale Grey-Blue body, Pink sausage decal, 'Palethorpes Royal Cambridge' on van sides, 'Palethorpes Model Factory' on rear,	
	1934-35		Type 1	£1,000-1,500
	1935-38		Type 2	£400-500
28f		'VIROL'	Yellow body, 'Give Your Child A Virol Constitution' in Black,	
	1938-39		Type 2	£300-400
	1939-41		Type 3	£300-400
28g		'KODAK'	Yellow body, 'Use Kodak Film To Be Sure' in Red,	
	1934-35		Type 1	£1,000-1,500
	1935-39		Type 2	£300-400
	1939-41		Type 3	£300-400
28h		'SHARPS TOFFEES'	'Sharps Toffee, Maidstone' in Gold,	
	1934-35		Black/Red body, Type 1	£1,000-1,500
	1935-35		Red body, Type 2.	£400-500
28h		'DUNLOP'	Red body, 'Dunlop Tyres' in Gold,	
	1935-39		Type 2	£300-400
	1939-41		Type 3	£300-400
28k		'MARSH & BAXTER'	Dark Green body, 'Marsh's Sausages' and pig logo in Gold,	
	1934-35		Type 1	£1,000-1,500
	1935-39		Type 2	£300-400
	1939-41		Type 3	£500-600
28L		'CRAWFORDS'	Red body, 'Crawfords Biscuits' in Gold,	
	1934-35		Type 1	£500-600
28m		'WAKEFIELD'S CASTROL'	Green body, 'Wakefield Castrol Motor Oil' in Red,	
	1934-35		Type 1	£1,000-1,500
	1935-39		Type 2	£300-400
	1939-41		Type 3	£1,500-2,000
28n		'MECCANO'	Yellow body, 'Meccano Engineering For Boys' in Red and Black,	
	1934-35		Type 1. Was 22d	£1,000-1,500
	1935-35		Type 2	£300-400
28n		'ATCO'	Green body, 'Atco Lawn Mowers Sales and Service' in Gold/Red,	
	1935-39		Type 2	£300-500
	1939-41		Type 3	£500-600
28p		'CRAWFORDS'	Red body, 'Crawfords Biscuits' in Gold,	
	1935-39		Type 2	£300-400
	1939-41		Type 3	£800-1,000
28r		'SWAN'	Black body, 'Swan Pens' and logo in Gold,	
	1936-39		Type 2	£300-500
	1939-41		Type 3	£200-300
28s		'FRYS'	Brown or Cream body, 'Frys Chocolate' in Gold,	
	1936-39		Type 2	£300-500
	1939-41		Type 3	£300-400
28t		'OVALTINE'	Red body, 'Drink Ovaltine For Health' in Gold/Black,	
	1936-39		Type 2	£300-400
	1939-41		Type 3	£300-400
28w		'OSRAM'	Yellow body, 'Osram Lamps - a G.E.C. Product' in Gold/Black,	
	1936-39		Type 2	£300-400
	1940-41		Type 3	£300-500
28x		'HOVIS'	White body, 'Hovis For Tea' in Gold/Black,	
	1936-39		Type 2	£400-600
	1939-41		Type 3	£300-400

28 series Delivery Vans list continues overleaf:

28 series Delivery Vans list continued from previous page:

28y		'EXIDE'	Red body, 'Exide Batteries' and 'Drydex Batteries' in Gold/Black,	
	1936-39		Type 2	£300-400
	1939-41		Type 3	£300-400
		NB	Further issues in this series were numbered 280a - 280f.	

30 Series

30e	1935-40	Breakdown Car (Crane Lorry) ..	Red, Yellow, Green, Brown or Grey body, Black wings, Black or Blue hubs,	
			rear window	£70-80
			Blue body, Dark Blue wings, Blue hubs, rear window	£100-120
	1946-46		Red or Grey body, Black wings, rear window	£60-70
	1947-48		Red, Grey or Green body and wings, no rear window	£40-50
30j	1950-54	Austin Wagon	Blue body with hook, Mid-Blue hubs	£100-120
		(renumbered 412)	Light, Medium or Dark Maroon body, Maroon or Red hubs	£100-150
			Brown body, Tan hubs	£400-500
			Dark Blue body, Mid-Blue hubs	NGPP
			Red body, Red hubs	NGPP
30m	1950-54	Rear Tipping Wagon	Maroon or Orange cab, Pale Green rear, 'Dodge' on baseplate	£60-70
		(renumbered 414)	Blue or Dark Blue cab, Grey rear	£60-70
30n	1950-54	Farm Produce Wagon	Green/Yellow, Yellow/Green or Blue/Red body, hook, (renumbered 343)	£60-70
30p	1950-54	Petrol Tanker	Based on a Studebaker vehicle.	
30p	1950-51	'PETROL'	Red or Green body, cast in aluminium	£80-90
	1951-52	'PETROL'	Red or Green body, cast in mazak	£80-90
30p	1952-54	'MOBILGAS'	Red body, Blue lettering on White background, (renumbered 440)	£80-90
30pa	1952-54	'CASTROL'	Green body and hubs, some cast in aluminium, most in mazak, (renumbered 441)	£80-90
30pb	1952-54	'ESSO'	Red body and hubs, 'MOTOR OIL - ESSO - PETROL', (renumbered 442)	£80-90
30r	1951-54	Fordson Thames Flat Truck	Red or Green body with hook	£60-70
		(renumbered 422)	Brown body, Brown hubs	£60-70
			Brown body, Maroon hubs	NGPP
30s	1950-54	Austin Covered Wagon	Maroon body, Cream cover, Cream hubs, sold unboxed	£100-150
		(renumbered 413)	Dark Blue body, Light Blue cover, Light Blue hubs, sold unboxed	£300-400
			Mid-Blue body, Light Blue cover, Light Blue hubs, sold unboxed	£100-150
30v	1949-54	Electric Dairy Van 'EXPRESS DAIRY'	Cream body, Red chassis, hubs and logo, (renumbered 490)	£75-90
			Grey body, Blue chassis, hubs and logo	£75-90
30v	1949-54	Electric Dairy Van 'N.C.B.'	Cream body, Red chassis, hubs and logo, (renumbered 491)	£75-90
			Grey body, Blue chassis, hubs and logo	£75-90
30w	1952-54	Hindle-Smart Helecs	Maroon body, 'British Railways', hook, trailer uncouples, (renumbered 421)	£60-70

31 Series

31	1935-35	Holland Coachcraft Van	Red, Green, Blue or Orange, 'Holland Coachcraft Registered Design', lead body	£1,000-2,000
	1935-36		Red, Blue or Orange, 'Holland Coachcraft Registered Design', diecast body	£1,000-2,000
	1935		Mid-Green body, Gold stripe, Silver advert., Chrome hubs	£1,000-2,000
	1935		Cream body with Red coachline	£1,000-2,000
		NB	A Red variant from 1935/6 was sold by Christie's in 2001 for £2,350.	
31a	1951-54	Trojan 15 cwt Van 'ESSO'	Red body and hubs, (renumbered 450)	£80-90
31b	1952-54	Trojan 15 cwt Van 'DUNLOP' ..	Red body and hubs, 'The Worlds Master Tyre', (renumbered 451)	£60-70
31c	1953-54	Trojan 15 cwt Van 'CHIVERS'.	Green body and hubs, 'CHIVERS JELLIES' and design, (renumbered 452)	£60-70
31d	1953-54	Trojan 15 cwt Van 'OXO'	Mid-Blue or Violet-Blue body, Mid-Blue hubs, 'BEEFY OXO', (renumbered 453)	£250-300

33 Series

33a	1935-36	Mechanical Horse	Red, Green, Blue or Yellow body, 2.5 mm. trailer step. **NB** 1st type have long slot and chrome hubs...	£150-175
	1936-40		As previous model but trailer step is 9.5 mm. long	£125-150
	1946-?		As previous model but also in Brown, Grey or Khaki	£125-150
33b	1935-40	Flat Truck Trailer	Red, Green, Blue or Yellow body, no sides	£45-55
33c	1935-40	Open Truck Trailer	Red, Green, Blue or Yellow body with sides	£45-55
33d	1935-40	Box Van Trailer	Green tinplate body on cast chassis, no advertising	£100-125
		'HORNBY TRAINS'	Dark Blue body, 'Hornby Trains British and Guaranteed' in Gold	£125-175
		'HORNBY TRAINS'	Green body, 'Hornby Trains British and Guaranteed' in Gold	£125-175
		'MECCANO'	Green body, 'Meccano Engineering For Boys' in Red and Black	£125-175
		NB	Models 33a and 33d combined and given Ref No 33r	£200-300
33e	1935-40	Dust Wagon Trailer	Blue or Yellow 33c (Open Trailer) with Blue tinplate top	£70-90
			Grey or Green 33c (Open Trailer) with Green or Blue tinplate top	£70-90
	1946-47		Grey or Red body with Blue tinplate top	£70-90
33f	1935-40	Petrol Tank Trailer	Green (33b) chassis/Red tank, or Red chassis/Green tank, no logo	£70-90
		'ESSO'	Green chassis/Red tank with 'ESSO' in Gold	£70-90
		'CASTROL'	Red chassis/Green tank, 'Wakefield Castrol'	£70-90
33r	1935-40	Railway Mechanical Horse and Trailer Van	33a Mechanical Horse and 33d Box Van Trailer in railway liveries. These were also available separately as 33ra and 33rd (see below).	
33r		'L.N.E.R.'	Blue and Black, 'L.N.E.R. Express Parcels Traffic'	£200-300
33r		'L.M.S.'	Maroon and Black, 'L.M.S. Express Parcels Traffic'	£200-300
33r		'G.W.R'	Brown and Cream, 'G.W.R. Express Cartage Services'	£200-300
33r		'S.R.'	Green (Cream cab roof) and Black, 'Southern Railway'	£200-300

33ra	1935-40	Mechanical Horse 'L.N.E.R.'	Blue and Black, 'L.N.E.R. 901'	£200-300
33ra		'L.M.S.'	Maroon and Black, 'L.M.S. 2246'	£200-300
33ra		'G.W.R.'	Brown and Cream, 'G.W.R. 2742'	£200-300
33ra		'S.R.'	Green (Cream roof) and Black, '3016 M'	£200-300
33rd		Railway Trailer 'L.N.E.R.'	Blue and Black, 'L.N.E.R. Express Parcels Traffic'	£200-300
33rd		'L.M.S.'	Maroon and Black, 'L.M.S. Express Parcels Traffic'	£200-300
33rd		'G.W.R.'	Brown and Cream, 'G.W.R. Express Cartage Services'	£200-300
33rd		'S.R.'	Green and Black, 'Southern Railway'	£200-300
33w	1947-54	Mechanical Horse and Open Wagon	Grey, Fawn, Dark or Mid-Green, Olive, Red, Brown, Blue or Yellow cab, with Maroon, Brown, Light or Mid-Green, Olive or Cream trailer, (renumbered 415)	£75-95

34 Series

34a	1935-40	'ROYAL AIR MAIL SERVICE'	Blue car body with Silver lettering and Gold crest	£200-250
34b	1938-47	'ROYAL MAIL' Van	Red body, Black bonnet/wings/roof/hubs, open rear windows	£100-150
	1948-51		Red body, Black bonnet/wings/roof, Black or Red hubs, filled-in rear windows	£80-100
	1952-52		Red body/roof/hubs, Black bonnet/front wings, filled-in rear windows	£100-125
34c	1948-54	Loudspeaker Van	Fawn, Green, Brown or Blue body (280 casting) Black loudspeakers, (renumbered 392)	£60-70
			Brown, Blue or Green body (280 casting) Silver loudspeakers	£60-70
60y	1938-40	Thompson Aircraft Tender	Red with 'Shell Aviation Services' in Gold; Black or White solid rubber wheels	£250-350
151b	1937-40	6-wheel Covered Wagon	Gloss Green body, tinplate canopy, seat holes, spare wheel, (renumbered 25s)	£125-150
151b	1947-54	6-wheel Covered Wagon	Matt-Green or Greenish-Brown body, (export only from 1950), (renumbered 620)	£60-70
251	1954-63	Aveling Barford Road Roller	Mid or Dark Green body, Red rollers, (renumbered from 25p)	£35-45
			Lime Green body, Red rollers	£50-60
252	1954-60	Bedford Refuse Wagon	Fawn body, Green tinplate shutters, Red hubs, window glazing in some, (renumbered from 25v)	£125-150
	1960-63		Lime Green body, Black tinplate shutters, Cream hubs, with or without window glazing	£125-150
	1963 only		Orange cab, Light Grey back, Green tinplate shutters and diecast hubs, window glazing, Black grille	£300-350
	1964		Orange cab, Light Grey back and diecast hubs, Green plastic shutters, window glazing	£250-350
	1964-65		Orange cab, Light Grey back, Green plastic shutters, Red plastic hubs, window glazing	£250-350
			As previous model but with matt-Black base	£250-350
260	1955-61	'ROYAL MAIL' Van	(Morris 'J') Red body, Black roof, Gold 'E II R' crest	£100-125
260	1971-72	Volkswagen 'DEUTSCHE BUNDESPOST'	Yellow body (129 casting, 100mm), made for German Market	£100-150
261	1955-61	Telephone Service Van	(Morris 'Z') Olive-Green/Black, 'POST OFFICE TELEPHONES', ladder	£100-125
273	1965-70	Mini Minor Van 'R.A.C.'	Blue body, White roof, Black base, Red interior, 'ROAD SERVICES'	£100-125
			As previous model but with Blue interior	£100-125
			With Red interior, Silver baseplate and redesigned rear doors	£100-125
	NB		Factory errors have resulted in some rear door logos reading 'ROAD ROAD' instead of 'ROAD SERVICES' as normal.	NGPP
274	1964-73	Mini Minor Van 'A.A.'	Yellow body, White roof, 'PATROL SERVICE', original 'entwined' logo	£100-125
			Same, but with Yellow roof, Blue interior	£100-125
			Yellow body, White roof, Red interior, 'AA SERVICE', modern 'simple' logo, Silver or Black base	£65-75
			As previous model but with Blue interior	£65-75
			With Yellow roof and Blue interior	£65-75
	Note:	'AA' logo designs	a) Embossed paint 'AA', b) Waterslide transfer in square recess, c) Waterslide transfer on raised panel	
	Rear door casting variations:		a) Rear door hinge pins extend directly into chassis holes, b) Rear door hinge pins located into slots	
	Central base colour variations:		a) Red, b) Blue, c) White	
274	1970-70	'JOSEPH MASON PAINTS'	(Mini Minor Van). Promotional in special Red box with advert card. 650 issued. Maroon body, Red seats and rear van body base, roof sign, 'PAINTS' labels, spun hubs.	£300-400
275	1964-66	Brinks Armoured Car	Grey/Blue, 'Brinks Security Since 1859', 2 figures, 2 crates, plastic hubs	£110-130
	1966-70		Same as previous model but no driver or crates, US packaging	£50-60
			Grey body White roof, Blue base, metal hubs, assembled in USA	NGPP
	Mexican issue:		Blue body with Grey doors and Red/White/Blue crests, plastic hubs	£750-1,000
279	1965-71	Aveling Barford Diesel Roller	Orange body, Grey engine covers, Blue rollers	£150-200
	1971-80		Yellow cab, Black roof, Silver rollers	£25-35
			Yellow cab, Black roof, Black rollers	£25-35
			Yellow cab, Blue roof, Yellow square engine covers, Silver rollers	£25-35
			Yellow cab, Black roof, Yellow square engine covers, Silver rollers	£25-35
			Yellow cab, Grey Roof, Yellow square engine covers, Silver rollers	£25-35
280	1945-47	Delivery Van	Red or Blue body, Type 3, open rear windows	£50-60
	1948-54		Red or Blue body, Type 3, filled-in rear windows, no advertising	£50-60
280	1966-68	Mobile 'MIDLAND BANK'	White/Silver, Blue stripe, Gold crest, opening doors, figure	£70-80

280 Series Delivery Vans

Delivery Vans numbered 280a - 280k are an extension of the 28 series.
They were supplied to shops in Trade Boxes and sold individually unboxed.

280a		'VIYELLA'	Blue body, 'Viyella for the Nursery' in White and Black,	
	1937-39		Type 2	£250-350
	1939-41		Type 3	£175-225
280b		'LYONS TEA'	Dark Blue body, 'Lyons Tea Always the Best' in Red and White,	
	1937-39		Only issued as Type 2	£350-450

280b		'HARTLEYS JAM'	Cream body, 'Hartleys is Real Jam' in Red/Green,	
	1939-39		Type 2	£800-1,000
	1939-40		Type 3	£300-400
280c		'SHREDDED WHEAT'	Cream body, Red stripe, 'Welwyn Garden City, Herts' in Black,	
	1937-39		Type 2	£250-350
	1939-40		Type 3	£175-225
280d	1937-40	'BISTO'	Yellow body, 'Ah! Bisto' with logo, Type 2	£300-500
280d	1940	'BISTO'	Yellow body, wording altered to 'Bisto' with logo,	
	1938-39		Type 2, with large Bisto Kids transfer	£300-400
			Type 2, small Bisto Kids transfer, with pie on table	£600-800
	1939-40		Type 3, small Bisto Kids transfer with pie on table	£300-400
280e	1937-39	'ECKO'	Dark Green body, 'ECKO Radio' in Gold, Type 2	£250-350
280e		'YORKSHIRE EVENING POST'	Cream body, 'Yorkshire Evening Post - The Original Buff'	
	1938-39		Type 2	£300-350
	1939-39		Type 3	£600-800
280f		'MACKINTOSHS'	Red body, 'Mackintosh's Toffee' in Gold,	
	1937-39		Type 2	£600-800
	1939-40		Type 3	£300-400
280g	1939 ?	'BENTALLS'	Green body, Yellow upper side panels, White roof, 'Bentalls Kingston on Thames' and 'Phone Kin: 1001' in Yellow, promotional, Type 2. Two examples known	£5,000-8,000
280h	1939 ?	'BONNETERIE'	Dark Red, 'Maison de Bonneterie, Leverancier', promotional, Type 2	£2,000-3,000
280i	1939 ?	'LIVERPOOL ECHO'	Promotional, Type 2, no other details available	£2,000-3,000
280j	1939	'FENWICK'	Budget-priced models, having the same generic cab but with different rear body types.	
	Apple Green body, White roof, 'Newcastle on Tyne', promotional, Type 2			
			Two examples known	£2,000-3,000
280k	1939	'H. G. LOOSE'	Dark Green body, 'H. G. LOOSE' on Cream panel, 'Looe' and 'Phone 123', promotional, Type 2. One example known	£2,000-3,000
343	1954-64	Dodge Farm Produce Wagon	Green cab with Yellow back and hubs, or Yellow cab with Green back and hubs	£70-80
		(renumbered from 30n)	Yellow cab with Green back and hubs	£70-80
			Red cab with Blue back and hubs	£100-125
			Late issues with plastic hubs and boxed in the late lighter Yellow box	£125-150

'Convoy' Series (380-387)

380	1977-79	Skip Truck	Yellow and Orange body	£10-20
381	1977-80	Farm Wagon	Yellow and Brown body	£10-20
382	1978-80	Dumper Truck	Red body/Grey back, Red body/Black back or Yellow body/Grey back	£10-20
383	1978-80	'N.C.L.' Truck	Yellow body, 'NATIONAL CARRIERS Ltd'	£10-20
384	1977-79	Fire Rescue Wagon	Red body, White fire escape	£10-20
385	1977-79	'ROYAL MAIL' Truck	Red body	£10-20
386	1979	'AVIS' Truck	Red body. Catalogued but not issued	NPP
387	1979	'PICKFORDS' Truck	Red and Blue body. Catalogued but not issued	NPP
?	1979	'HARRODS' Truck	Khaki body	NGPP
?	1979	'POST OFFICE TELEPHONES'	Khaki body	NGPP
?	1979	'A.A.' Truck	Yellow body	NGPP
?	1979	'AMERICAN FIRE BRIGADE'	No details	NGPP
		NB	See also 687 Convoy Army Truck in the Military Vehicles section.	
390	1978	Customised Transit Van	Metallic Blue body with 'VAMPIRE' and 'flame' design, Type 3	NGPP
400	1954-60	B.E.V. Truck	Dark Blue or Mid-Blue or Grey with Blue, Grey or Red hubs, 1 packing piece, (renumbered from 14a)	£30-35
401	1954-64	Coventry Climax Fork Lift	Orange body, Green forks, Tan driver, (renumbered from 14c)	£30-35
			Red body, Green forks	£300-400
402	1966-69	Bedford 'COCA-COLA' Truck	Red cab and back, White roof, 'COCA-COLA', six trays of crates	£90-110
404	1967-72	Climax Fork Lift	Red/Yellow body with 'CG4' rear logo	£25-35
			Red/Yellow front with all Red rear, plus stick-on 'CG4' label	£20-25
	1978		Yellow body with 'Climax' on fork guide and 'TC4' on engine cover	£20-25
406	1963-66	Commer Articulated Truck	Yellow/Grey, Blue plastic hubs, Supertoy, (424 without accessories)	£90-110
407		Ford Transit Vans	See 'Commercial Vehicles Identification' pages for an explanation of casting Types 1, 2 and 3.	
	1966-69	'KENWOOD'	Blue/White, 'KENWOOD', promotional. Type 1	£50-60
	1970-71	'TELEFUSION'	White body, 'Colour TV, Telefusion'. Intended promotional not issued	NPP
	1970-75	'HERTZ'	Yellow body, 'Hertz Truck Rentals', promotional. Type 1	£50-60
	1970-73	'AVIS'	Red body, 'Avis Truck Rentals'. Kit only but not issued	NPP
		'PELTZ BADKEREI'	Blue lower body, Yellow upper half, promotional	£50-60
408	1956-63	Big Bedford Lorry	Maroon cab, Fawn back, Fawn or Cream hubs, (with window glazing from 1961)	£110-120
		(renumbered from 522 / 922)	Blue cab, Yellow back, Yellow or Cream hubs	£200-250
			Pink cab, Cream back, Cream hubs	£1.500-2.000
409	1956-63	Bedford Articulated Lorry	Yellow cab and back, Black wings, Red hubs, Yellow box	£110-130
		(renumbered from 521 / 921)	As previous model but with window glazing. Lighter Yellow box	£150-200
410	1954-61	Bedford Tipper Truck	Red cab, chassis and diecast hubs, Cream back	£150-180
		(renumbered from 25m)	Yellow cab, chassis and diecast hubs, Mid-Blue back, window glazing	£150-180
	1962-63		Red cab, chassis and plastic hubs, Cream back, window glazing	£200-250
			Yellow cab, chassis and plastic hubs, Dark or Mid-Blue back, window glazing	£200-250

410		**Bedford CF Vans**		
	1972-72	**'SIMPSONS'**	Red/Black, 'Simpsons' and logos, Canadian promotional	£35-45
	1974	**'DANISH POST'**	Yellow body, 'Danish Post' emblem, Danish promotional	£35-45
	1974-75	**'JOHN MENZIES'**	Dark Blue body with 'John Menzies' logo, promotional	£25-30
	1974-74	**'BELACO'**	Brown/Black, 'Belaco Brake and Clutch Parts', promotional	£35-45
	1975-76	**'M.J. HIRE'**	White body, 'M.J. Hire Service', promotional	£25-30
	1975-77	**'MODELLERS WORLD'**	White body, 'Modellers World'. This is a Code 2 model	£25-30
	1975-75	**'MARLEY TILES'**	Red body with 'Marley Building' logo	£25-30
	1979	**'COLLECTORS GAZETTE'**	White body, 'Collectors Gazette' logo. A Code 2 model	£25-30
	1972-74	**'ROYAL MAIL'**	Red body with 'ROYAL MAIL' and 'E II R' crest	£15-20
	1974-80	**'ROYAL MAIL'**	As previous model but with raised rectangle on roof	£15-20
		NB	Many Code-2 issues exist (produced by John Gay) and include the following liveries: 'MOBIL', 'BN', 'HERTZ TRUCK RENTAL', 'JIMMY CARTER', 'MATRA', 'ELF', 'SILVER JUBILLEE 1952-1977', 'KLG', 'PORTAKABIN', 'WIMPEY'.	
411	1954-59	**Bedford Truck**	Mid-Green cab, chassis, back and hubs, (renumbered from 25w)	£120-140
	1954-56		Same, but with Black front mudguards	£120-140
	1959-60		Mid-Green cab and body, Pale Green hubs, gloss base, block-tread tyres	£125-150
412	1954-60	**Austin Wagon**	Powder Blue body, Lemon or Dark Blue hubs, (renumbered from 30j)	£350-450
			Maroon body, Pale Red hubs	£120-140
			Dark Blue body, Mid-Blue hubs	£140-160
			Lemon Yellow body, Mid-Green or Blue hubs	£350-450
412	1974-80	**Bedford CF Van 'AA'**	Yellow body, 'AA SERVICE', headboard, plastic hubs	£15-20
413	1954-60	**Austin Covered Wagon**	Maroon body, Cream tinplate tilt, Cream hubs, (renumbered from 30s)	£100-150
			Dark Blue body, Mid-Blue tinplate tilt, Light Blue hubs	£200-250
			Mid-Blue body, Mid-Blue tinplate tilt, Light Blue hubs	£100-150
			Red body, Light Grey tinplate tilt, Cream or Grey hubs	£300-400
			Red body, Beige tinplate tilt, Red hubs	£300-400
			Light or Mid-Blue body, Cream tinplate tilt, Lemon-Yellow hubs. Plain box	£275-325
			Red body, Grey or Beige tinplate tilt, Grey hubs	£275-325
			Maroon body, Beige tinplate tilt, Red hubs	£200-250
			Olive-drab body, (Royal Army Volunteer Reserve)	NGPP
414	1954-64	**Dodge Rear Tipping Wagon**	Red cab and hubs, Green back	£80-100
		(renumbered from 30s)	Orange cab and hubs, Green back	£80-100
			Greyish-Blue cab, Grey back, Mid-Blue hubs	£80-100
			Mid-Blue cab and hubs, Grey back	£80-100
			Violet-Blue cab, Grey back and hubs	£100-125
			Royal Blue cab, Grey back and hubs	£125-150
		NB	Early issues with or without bonnet louvres.	
415	1954-59	**Mechanical Horse and Wagon**	(Models 33a + 33d), Blue horse/Cream trailer or Red horse/Brown trailer, (renumbered from 33w)	£125-175
		Ford Transit Vans	See 'Commercial Vehicles Identification' pages for an explanation of casting Types 1, 2 and 3.	
416	1975-78	**Ford Transit Van, 'FORD'**	Orange-Yellow body, cast hubs, '1,000,000 TRANSITS', Type 2, promotional	NGPP
416	1975-78	**Ford Transit 'MOTORWAY'**	Yellow body, 'Motorway Services', special lights, Type 2	£25-35
417	1978-79	**Ford Transit 'MOTORWAY'**	As previous model but Type 3 casting	£20-30
417	1956-58	**Leyland Comet Lorry with Stake Body**	(Stake body secured by a rivet. Yellow box. Renumbered from 531 / 931).	
			Dark Blue cab and chassis, Dark Yellow back, Pale Blue hubs	£140-160
			Dark Blue cab and chassis, Brown back, Mid-Blue hubs	£300-350
	1958-59		Yellow cab and chassis, Light Green back, Mid-Green hubs	£400-500
418	1956-59	**Leyland Comet with Hinged Tailboard**	(Back of model secured by a rivet. Yellow box. Renumbered from 532 / 932).	
			Green cab and chassis, Orange back, Light Green hubs	£110-130
			Dark Blue cab and chassis, Mid-Blue back, Blue, Cream or Red hubs	£110-130
419	1956-59	**Leyland Comet Cement Lorry**	Yellow body, 'Portland Blue-Circle Cement', 1 packing piece, (renumbered from 533 / 933)	£110-130
420	1954-61	**Forward Control Lorry**	Cream body, Mid-Blue hubs	£80-100
		(renumbered from 25r)	Red body, Cream hubs	£80-100
			Red body, Mid-Green hubs	£80-100
			Mid-Green body, Cream hubs	£80-100
			Mid-Green body, Red hubs	£80-100
421	1955-59	**Electric Articulated Vehicle**	(Hindle-Smart), Maroon body, 'British Railways', hook, (renumbered from 30w)	£70-80
422	1954-60	**Fordson Thames Flat Truck**	Dark Green or Red body, window glazing, hook, (renumbered from 30r)	£70-80
			Bright Green body and hubs	£100-130
424	1963-66	**Commer Convertible Articulated Vehicle**	Yellow or Grey cab, 406 plus Blue trailer canopy and 'stake' body fittings	£130-150
425	1964-69	**Bedford TK Coal Wagon**	Red body, 'HALL & Co.', window glazing, 6 coal bags, scales	£100-125
428	1955-64	**Large Trailer**	Grey body, hook, Red hubs, Black front axle mount, Supertoy, (renumbered 951)	£20-25
	1967-71		Red body with hook, Silver hubs, Silver front axle mount	£20-25
			Yellow body, Red hubs	£20-25
429	1954-64	**Trailer**	Dark Green or Red, hook, axle pivot is part of main casting, (renumbered from 25g)	£20-25
430	1954-64	**Commer Breakdown Truck**	'DINKY SERVICE' logo, operable crane, late issues have window glazing, (renumbered from 25x).	
			Tan cab, Green back with Black logo, Red hubs. Yellow or Blue/White striped box	£100-120
			Cream cab, Pale Blue back with Black logo, Red hubs. Yellow box	£300-400
			Dark Stone cab, Blue back with Black logo, Red hubs. Yellow box	£300-400
			Red cab, Pale Grey back with Blue logo, Blue or Red metal hubs. Yellow box	£300-400
			Red cab with glazing, Pale Grey back with Blue logo, Blue plastic hubs. Yellow box	£300-400
			Red cab with glazing, Pale Grey back with Blue logo, Red plastic hubs. Yellow box	£500-750

430	1977-80	Johnson 2 ton Dumper	Orange/Red body with Blue driver, Black or Orange engine	£20-25
431	1956-58	Guy 4 ton Lorry (2nd type)	Red cab/chassis, Grey back, Red hubs, unpainted hook, (renumbered from 511 / 911)	£350-450
			Dark Blue cab/chassis, Light Blue back, Mid-Blue hubs	£350-450
431	1958-60	Guy Warrior 4 ton Lorry	Light Tan cab (no window glazing), Dark Green back, Mid-Green hubs	£350-450
			Light Tan cab (with window glazing), Dark Green back, Mid-Green hubs	£350-450
	1960-64		Red cab (with window glazing), Red chassis, Dark Green back, Red hubs	£350-450
432	1956-57	Guy Flat Truck (2nd type)	Mid-Blue cab/chassis/hook, Red flatbed, Mid-Blue hubs, (renumbered from 512 / 912)	£300-350
	1956-57		Red cab/chassis/hook, Mid-Blue flatbed and hubs	£300-350
432	1958-60	Guy Warrior Flat Truck	Green cab (no window glazing), Red flatbed, Red hubs	£300-350
	1960-64		Green cab (with window glazing), Red flatbed, Red hubs	£300-350
432	1976-79	Foden Tipping Lorry	White cab, Red chassis, Yellow rear body, (same casting as 668)	£35-45
433	1956-57	Guy Flat Truck with Tailboard (2nd type)	Dark Green cab/chassis/hook, Mid-Green flatbed and hubs, (renumbered from 513 / 913)	£200-300
			Violet Blue cab/chassis/hook, Orange body, Light Blue hubs	£200-300
433	--- ---	Guy Warrior Flat Truck with Tailboard	Listed in the 1958 catalogue but not issued	NPP
434	1964-66	Bedford TK Crash Truck	White body with Green flash, 'TOP RANK Motorway Services', Blue or Red interior	£60-70
	1966-70		Red or Metallic Red cab, Pale Grey back, 'AUTO SERVICES'	£60-70
435	1964-66	Bedford TK Tipper	Grey cab with Blue roof, Red back	£50-60
	1966-68		Yellow cab with Yellow or Black roof, Silver back	£50-60
	1968-71		White cab and roof, Silver back with Blue sides	£50-60
			Blue cab, Orange and Grey back	£75-100
			Red cab, Black roof, Silver back, Red sides	£50-60
436	1963-69	'ATLAS COPCO' Lorry	Yellow body, Pale Grey interior, matt baseplate	£50-60
			Yellow body, Dark Blue interior, gloss baseplate	£50-60
437	1962-70	Muir Hill 2WL Loader	Red body with hook, no grille detail	£20-25
			Yellow body with Red or Silver hubs	£20-25
	1970-78		Yellow with Red arms with hook, with or without grille detail	£20-25
			Orange body with Orange or Black arms	£30-40
438	1970-77	Ford D800 Tipper Truck (with opening doors)	Metallic Red cab, Yellow tipper, Yellow or Silver hubs	£35-40
			Metallic Red cab, Dark Metallic Blue tipper, Yellow hubs	£35-40
			Orange cab, Orange or Yellow tipper, Silver hubs	£35-40
			Bright Red cab, Orange tipper, Silver hubs	£35-40
			Bright Red cab, Bright Red tipper, Silver hubs	£35-40
	promotional issue:		White cab, Blue back, Silver chassis, with cardboard load 'POLCARB'.	
			Packed in plain White box with folded leaflet	£200-250
439	1970-76	Ford D800 Snow Plough	Dark Metallic Blue cab, Orange tipper, Yellow plough, White hubs	£40-50
	1976-78		Dark Metallic Blue cab, Pale Blue tipper, Yellow plough, Silver hubs	£40-50
			Light Metallic Blue cab, Orange tipper, Dark Yellow plough, Silver hubs	£40-50
			Medium Blue cab, Yellow plough, Powder Blue tipper, Silver hubs	£40-50
			Orange cab and tipper, Dark Yellow plough, Silver hubs	£40-50
			Orange cab, Dark Yellow tipper and plough, Silver hubs	£40-50
			All-Orange body, cast Silver hubs	£40-50
440	1977-78	Ford D800 Tipper Truck (non-opening doors)	Orange cab, Yellow tipper, Silver or Black chassis	£35-40
			Orange cab, Orange tipper, Black chassis	£35-40
			Orange cab, Light Blue tipper, Black chassis	£35-40
			Red cab, Red Tipper, Black chassis, Silver hubs	£35-40
			Red cab, Orange Tipper, Silver chassis, Silver hubs	£35-40
			Red cab, Light Blue Tipper, Black chassis, Silver hubs	£35-40
			Red cab with Black roof, Red Tipper, Red hubs	£35-40
440	1954-58	Petrol Tanker 'MOBILGAS'	Red body and hubs, 'MOBILGAS' in White letters with Blue borders, (renumbered from 30p)	£110-140
	1958-61		Red body and hubs, 'MOBILGAS' in Blue letters on White background	£110-140
441	1954-60	Petrol Tanker 'CASTROL'	Mid-Green body and hubs, (renumbered from 30pa)	£110-140
442	1954-60	Petrol Tanker 'ESSO'	Red body and hubs, 'ESSO MOTOR OIL - PETROL', (renumbered from 30pb)	£110-140
442	1973-79	Land Rover Breakdown Crane	White and Red body, 'Motorway Rescue', operable winch	£25-30
	1974-		White/Red or All-Red body, 'FALCK', export model for Denmark	£25-30
443	1957-58	Petrol Tanker 'NATIONAL'	Yellow body and hubs, 'NATIONAL BENZOLE MIXTURE'	£150-175
448	1963-68	Chevrolet El Camino Pick-Up with Trailers	Turquoise/Cream/Red Pick-up and 2 trailers, 'Acme Trailer Hire'	£200-250
449	1961-69	Chevrolet El Camino Pick-up	Turquoise body, White roof, Red interior, spun hubs	£80-90
			Turquoise body, White roof, Pale Turquoise interior, spun hubs	£150-200
			Turquoise body, White roof, Lemon interior, spun hubs	£150-200
	NB		Various shades of Turquoise are known to exist.	
	South African issue:		All-Turquoise body, spun hubs	£300-400
	South African issue:		Cream over Chocolate Brown lower body, spun hubs	£500-750
	South African issue:		Turquoise over Cream lower body, spun hubs	£500-750
449	1977-79	Johnston Road Sweeper	Yellow or Lime-Green body, (non-opening doors)	£30-35
			All Yellow body, promotional with 'JOHNSTON' stickers, normal box	£40-50
			All Yellow body, promotional with 'JOHNSTON' stickers, special box	£70-80
			Orange cab, Metallic Green rear	£40-50
450	1954-57	Trojan Van 'ESSO'	Red body, White stripe, Red or Maroon hubs, 'Esso' logo, (renumbered from 31a)	£110-140
			Maroon hub version issued in U.S.A. trade packs	NGPP

450	1965-70	**Bedford TK Van 'CASTROL'** ...	Green/White body, 'CASTROL - The Masterpiece In Oils' £100-125
451	1954-57	**Trojan Van 'DUNLOP'**	Red body and hubs, 'Dunlop The Worlds Master Tyre', (renumbered from 31b) £110-140
451	1971-77	**Johnston Road Sweeper**	Orange cab (449 with opening doors), Metallic Green tank £30-35
	1971-77	....	Metallic Green cab (449 with opening doors), Orange tank £30-35
452	1954-57	**Trojan Van 'CHIVERS'**	Green body, Mid-Green hubs, 'CHIVERS JELLIES' logo, (renumbered from 31c) £110-130
453	1954-54	**Trojan Van 'OXO'**	Mid-Blue or Violet-Blue body, Mid-Blue hubs, White 'BEEFY OXO', (not boxed), (was 31c) £250-300
454	1957-59	**Trojan Van 'CYDRAX'**	Light Green body and hubs, 'DRINK CYDRAX' logo £120-140
455	1957-60	**Trojan Van 'BROOKE BOND'** .	Dark Red body, Red hubs, 'BROOKE BOND TEA' logo £125-150
		promotional issue:	As previous issue with White label on roof. The Red logo states: 'Since 1924 more
			than 5,700 Trojan 'Little Red Vans' supplied. Replaced on a long life basis'.
			A similar label is attached to its (normal) box £400-600
465	1959-59	**Morris 10 cwt Van 'CAPSTAN'**	Light Blue and Dark Blue body, Mid-Blue hubs, 'Have A CAPSTAN'.................................£160-180
470	1954-56	**Austin A40 Van 'SHELL-BP'**	Red and Green body with 'SHELL' and 'BP' decals £115-135
470	1954	**Austin A40 Van 'OMNISPORT'**	Factory drawing exists but model not issued...NPP
471	1955-60	**Austin A40 Van 'NESTLES'**	Red body, Yellow wheel hubs, 'NESTLES' logo..£100-125
472	1956-60	**Austin A40 Van 'RALEIGH'**	Dark Green body with 'RALEIGH CYCLES' decals £120-150
480	1954-56	**Bedford CA Van 'KODAK'**	Yellow body, 'Kodak CAMERAS & FILMS' in Red and Black £95-115
481	1955-60	**Bedford CA Van 'OVALTINE'** ..	Blue body with 'Ovaltine' and 'Ovaltine Biscuits' logo on Cream panel and sides £100-130
482	1956-60	**Bedford Van 'DINKY TOYS'**	Cream and Light Orange body, 'Dinky Toys' logo in Red £100-125
490	1954-60	**Electric Dairy Van**	
		'EXPRESS DAIRY'	Cream body with Red chassis, hubs and logo, (renumbered from 30v) £80-100
			Grey body with Blue chassis, hubs and logo £80-100
491	1954-60	**Electric Dairy Van 'N.C.B.'**	Cream body with Red chassis, hubs and logo, export model, (renumbered from 30v).........£80-100
			Grey body, Blue chassis, hubs and logo, export model..£80-100
491	1960	**Electric Dairy Van**	
		'JOB'S DAIRY'	Cream/Red. 1176 made for promotional purposes (Code-2)..£120-140
492	1954-57	**Loudspeaker Van**	Blue or Green body, Silver loudspeakers, (280 casting, Type 3), (renumbered from 34c)...........£80-90
492	1954-?	**Loudspeaker Van**	Fawn, Blue or Green body (280 casting), Black loudspeakers, (renumbered from 34c)...........£80-90
492	1964-64	**Election Mini-Van**	White body (as 273), Orange loudspeakers, 'Vote for Somebody', figure, Yellow 'see-through' box £120-140
501	1947-48	**Foden Diesel 8-Wheel Wagon**	**1st type cab** with flash, spare wheel, hook on some, no tank slits in
			chassis, no chain-post bosses, Black 'herringbone' tyres, Supertoy.
			Pale Grey cab and back, Red flash and hubs, Black chassis, no hook...............................£600-800
			Dark Blue cab and back, Silver flash, Blue hubs, Black chassis, no hook £400-600
			Brown cab and back, Silver flash, Brown hubs, Black chassis, no hook............................£300-400
			Red cab and back, Silver flash, Red hubs, Black chassis, no hook, (US only issue) £3,000-4,000
			Dark Grey cab and back, Red flash, chassis and hubs, small unpainted hook on some £300-400
	1948-52	....	Hook and tank-slits in chassis (introduced 1948), Black 'radial' tyres.
			Dark Blue cab/chassis, Light Blue flash/hubs, small unpainted hook...............................£800-1,000
			Red cab/chassis/hubs, Silver flash, Fawn back, unpainted hook, slits on some £300-400
	1952-54	(renumbered 901)..........................	**2nd cab**, no flash, large painted hook, Supertoy hubs, (renumbered 901).
			Violet-Blue cab/chassis, Mid-Blue back and hubs, Grey tyres £400-500
			Red cab/chassis, Fawn back, Red hubs, Grey tyres...£250-350
502	1947-48	**Foden Flat Truck**	**1st type cab** with flash, spare wheel, hook on some, no tank slits in
			chassis, no chain-post bosses, Black 'herringbone' tyres, Supertoy.
			Green cab and back, Silver flash, Black chassis, Green hubs, no hook.............................£350-450
			Pale Blue cab and back, Dark Blue flash/chassis/hubs, no hook......................................£650-750
	1948-52	....	Hook and tank-slits in chassis introduced in 1948, Black 'radial' tyres.
			Dark Blue cab/wings/chassis, Red flash and back, Blue hubs, slits on some £1,000-1,250
			Brownish-Orange cab/chassis, Light Green flash and back, Green hubs, slits on some.
			In Dark Blue box showing 2nd cab model £550-650
	1952-52	....	**2nd cab**, no flash, large painted hook, Supertoy hubs.
			Dark Blue cab/chassis, Red back, Pale Blue hubs, chain-post bosses £2,000-2,500
	1952-54	(renumbered 902)..........................	Dull Orange cab/chassis, Green back and hubs, chain-post bosses..................................£350-450
			Red cab/chassis, Green back and hubs £350-450
			Yellow cab/chassis, Green back and hubs £1,000-1,250
503	1947-48	**Foden Flat Truck with Tailboard**	**1st type cab** with flash, spare wheel, hook on some, no tank slits in
			chassis, no chain-post bosses, Black 'herringbone' tyres, Supertoy.
			Red cab and flatbed, Black flash and chassis, Red hubs, no hook....................................£500-600
			Pale Grey cab and flatbed, Dark Blue flash and chassis, Blue hubs, no hook....................£500-600
			Mid-Grey cab and flatbed, Mid-Blue chassis and hubs..£500-600
	1948-52	....	Hook and tank-slits in chassis introduced in 1948, Black 'radial' tyres.
			Dark Green cab/chassis, Light Green flash/flatbed/hubs, small hook...............................£500-600
			Deep Blue cab/chassis, Dull Orange flatbed, Light Blue hubs, hook, slits £500-600
	1952-52	....	**2nd cab**, no flash, large painted hook, Supertoy hubs.
			Dark Green cab/chassis, Light Green flatbed and hubs, Grey tyres, bosses £1,500-2,000
	1952-56	(renumbered 903)........................	Dark Blue cab/chassis, Orange flatbed, Light Blue hubs, chain-post bosses £250-350
	1952-53		Dark Orange cab/chassis, Yellow flatbed and hubs, Grey tyres, bosses £1,700-2,000
	1953-54	(renumbered 903)........................	Dark Blue cab/chassis, Yellow flatbed, Light Blue hubs, chain-post bosses £500-600
504	1948-52	**Foden 14 ton Tanker**..................	**1st type cab** with flash, spare wheel, tinplate tank, hook,
			no advertising, Black 'fine radial tread' tyres, Supertoy.
			Dark Blue cab/chassis, Silver flash, Light Blue tank and hubs..£250-350
			Dark Blue cab/chassis, Light Blue flash, tank and hubs £250-350
	1948-52	....	Red cab/chassis, Silver flash, Fawn tank, Red hubs...£450-550
	1952-57	....	**2nd cab**, no flash, large painted hook, Supertoy hubs.
	1952-52	....	Dark Blue cab/chassis, Light Blue tank and hubs, Grey tyres.
			Model housed in 2nd type picture box £2,000-2,500
	1952-53	....	Red cab/chassis, Fawn tank, Red hubs, Grey tyres £450-550

504	1953-54	**Foden 14 ton Tanker**		
		'MOBILGAS' (renumbered 941)	Red cab/chassis/tank/hubs, 'MOBILGAS', Grey tyres.	
			With Red 'Pegasus' logo at cab end of tank facing the cab	**£350-450**
			Same, but with Red 'Pegasus' logo at rear of tank facing away from cab	**£1,500-2,000**

505	1952-52	**Foden Flat Truck with Chains...**	**1st type cab** with flash, spare wheel, hook, slits in chassis, 'dimpled' post bosses, Black 'fine radial tread' tyres, Supertoy. Blue covered box showing 1st type cab.	
			Green cab/chassis/flatbed, Mid-Green flash and hubs	**£1,500-2,000**
			Maroon cab/chassis, Silver flash, Maroon flatbed and hubs	**£2,000-2,500**
	1952-54		**2nd cab**, no flash, large painted hook, Supertoy hubs.	
			Green cab/chassis/flatbed, Light Green hubs, 'dimpled' chain-post bosses	**£250-350**
			Maroon cab/chassis/flatbed/hubs, 'dimpled' chain-post bosses	**£250-350**
	1954-56	(renumbered 905)	Green cab/chassis/body, Light Green hubs, 'rounded' chain-post bosses	**£250-350**
			Maroon cab/chassis/body/hubs, 'rounded' chain-post bosses	**£250-350**

511	1947-48	**Guy 4 ton Lorry**	**1st type cab** casting, Supertoy, spare wheel, small unpainted hook.	
			Green cab, back and hubs, Black chassis and wings	**£200-300**
			Brown cab, back and hubs, Black chassis and wings	**£250-350**
			Fawn cab and back, Red chassis, wings and hubs	**£250-350**
			Maroon cab and back, Black chassis and wings	**£200-300**
			Grey cab, back and hubs, Red chassis and wings	**£200-300**
	1948-52		**1st type cab** casting, Supertoy, large painted or unpainted hook.	
			Red cab/chassis/wings/ 'ridged' hubs, Fawn back	**£250-350**
			Dark Blue cab/chassis/wings, Light Blue back and 'ridged' hubs	**£200-300**
	1952-54	(renumbered 911, 431)	Red cab/chassis/wings/ 'grooved' hubs, Fawn back	**£250-350**
			Dark Blue cab/chassis/wings, Light Blue back and 'grooved' hubs	**£200-300**
	1954		**2nd type cab**, Violet-Blue cab and chassis, Mid-Blue back and hubs	**£300-400**

512	1947-48	**Guy Flat Truck**	**1st type cab** casting, Supertoy, spare wheel, small unpainted hook.	
			Maroon cab, flatbed and hubs, Black chassis and wings	**£250-350**
			Dark Brown cab, flatbed and hubs, Black chassis and wings	**£300-400**
			Yellow cab and flatbed, Black chassis and wings, Red hubs	**£700-800**
			Khaki cab and flatbed, Black chassis and wings, Green hubs	**£400-500**
			Grey cab and flatbed, Red chassis and wings, Red hubs	**£450-500**
			Grey cab and flatbed, Black chassis, Black hubs	**£400-500**
			Red cab and flatbed, Black chassis, Black hubs	**£500-600**
	1948-48		Brown cab/chassis/wings, Green flatbed, Green 'ridged' hubs	**£300-400**
	1948-54	(renumbered 912, 432)	**1st type cab** casting, Supertoy, small or large unpainted hook.	
			Blue cab/chassis/wings, Red flatbed, Light Blue 'ridged' hubs	**£250-350**
	1949-54		Orange cab/chassis/wings, Green flatbed, Green 'ridged' hubs	**£400-500**
	1952-54		Blue cab/chassis/wings, Red flatbed, Light Blue 'grooved' hubs	**£250-350**
	1954		**2nd type cab**, Red cab and chassis, Mid-Blue back and hubs	**£350-450**
			Mid-Blue cab, chassis and hubs, Red back	**£300-350**

513	1947-48	**Guy Flat Truck with Tailboard**	**1st type cab** casting, Supertoy, spare wheel, small unpainted hook.	
			Green cab and flatbed, Black chassis, wings and hubs	**£200-300**
			Dark Yellow cab and flatbed, Black chassis, wings and hubs	**£700-800**
			Dark Yellow cab and flatbed, Dark Blue chassis, wings and hubs	**£700-800**
			Grey cab and flatbed, Black chassis, wings and hubs	**£200-300**
			Grey cab and flatbed, Dark Blue chassis, wings and hubs	**£750-1,000**
	1948-52		**1st type cab**, 'ridged' hubs, Supertoy, small or large unpainted hook.	
			Dark Green cab/chassis/wings, Mid-Green back and hubs, small hook	**£250-350**
			Dark Blue cab/chassis/wings, Orange back, Light Blue hubs, large hook	**£250-350**
	1952-54	(renumbered 913, 433)	**1st type cab**, Supertoy, 'grooved' hubs, large unpainted hook.	
			Dark Green cab/chassis/wings, Green body and hubs	**£250-350**
			Deep Blue cab/chassis/wings, Orange body, Light Blue hubs	**£250-350**
			Yellow cab/chassis/wings, Green hubs	**£1,000-1,200**
	1954		2nd type cab, Blue cab and chassis, Orange back, Light Blue hubs	**£200-300**

514 Guy Vans

514	1950-52	**Guy Van 'SLUMBERLAND'**	Red **1st type cab**/chassis/body and 'ridged' hubs, 'Slumberland Spring Interior Mattresses', spare wheel, Supertoy	**£250-350**
514	1952-52	**Guy Van 'LYONS'**	Dark Blue **1st type cab**/body, Light Blue 'ridged' hubs, 'Lyons Swiss Rolls', spare wheel, Supertoy	**£700-900**
			Same model but rear axle in cast mounts	**£700-900**
514	1952-52	**Guy Van 'WEETABIX'**	Yellow **1st type cab**/body, Yellow 'ridged' hubs, 'More Than a Breakfast Food', spare wheel, Supertoy	**£1,500-2,000**
	1952-54		As previous model but with Yellow 'grooved' hubs	**£1,500-2,000**
514	1953-54	**Guy Van 'SPRATTS'**	Red/Cream **1st type cab**/body, Red 'grooved' hubs,	
		(renumbered 917)	'Bonio Ovals & Dog Cakes', spare wheel, Supertoy	**£300-400**

521	1948-48	**Bedford Articulated Lorry**	Red body, Black wings, Black or Red hubs, '20' transfer, 'Supertoys' on base, Brown box	**£200-250**
	1949-50		Yellow body, Black wings, Black hubs, '20' transfer, 'Supertoys' on base.	
			Brown box with Red/White label	**£200-250**
	1950-54	(renumbered 921, 409)	Yellow or Yellowish-Orange body, Black wings, Red hubs, '20' transfer, 'Supertoys' or 'Dinky Toys' on base. Blue box, Orange or White label	**£120-140**

522	1952-54	**Big Bedford Lorry**	Maroon cab, Fawn truck body, Fawn hubs, Supertoy	**£110-130**
		(renumbered 922, 408)	Blue cab, Yellow truck body, Yellow hubs, Supertoy	**£200-250**

531	1949-54	**Leyland Comet Lorry**		
		with Stake Body	Red cab and chassis, Yellow back and hubs, Blue box	**£240-280**
		(renumbered 931, 417)	Blue cab and chassis, Brown back, Red or Blue hubs, Blue box....................................	**£240-280**
			Violet-Blue cab and chassis, Orange-Yellow back, Red hubs, Blue box	**£240-280**
		NB Odd colours:	Be wary of colour combinations not listed. The screw fitting makes it easy to interchange the chassis and body components.	
532	1952-54	**Leyland Comet Lorry**		
		with Hinged Tailboard..............	Green cab and chassis, Orange back, Cream hubs, Blue box..	**£130-150**
		(renumbered 932, 418)	Green cab and chassis, Orange back, Green hubs, Blue box	**£130-150**
			Dark Blue cab and chassis, Mid-Blue back, Cream hubs, Blue box..............................	**£240-280**
			Dark Blue cab and chassis, Mid-Blue back, Red hubs, Blue/White box	**£130-150**
		NB Odd colours:	Be wary of colour combinations not listed. The screw fitting makes it easy to interchange the chassis and body components.	
533	1953-54	**Leyland Comet Cement Wagon**.	Yellow body, 'PORTLAND BLUE-CIRCLE CEMENT', Supertoy, (renumbered 933, 419)	**£110-130**
551	1948-54	**Trailer**...	Grey body, Black hubs, hook, Supertoy	**£20-30**
		(renumbered 951)	Yellow body, Black hubs, hook, Supertoy	**£100-125**
			Green body, Black hubs, hook, Supertoy	**£100-125**
	1969-73	...........................Gift Set issue:	Red body, Grey front chassis, protruding chromed hubs. Only in GS 339	GSP
561	1949-54	**Blaw Knox Bulldozer**.................	Red body, Green or Black rubber tracks, driver, lifting blade, Supertoy.	
		(renumbered 961)	Blue body with Orange/White label, or 'natural' card box with Red/White label, 1 packing piece	**£40-50**
561	1962-64	**Citroën Delivery Van**	Light Blue body, Red/Yellow 'CIBIE' logo, sliding door. French issue	**£60-70**
562	1948-54	**Muir Hill Dump Truck**	Yellow body, metal wheels/tyres, hook, (renumbered 962)..	**£15-20**
563	1948-54	**Blaw Knox Heavy Tractor**	Red, Orange or Blue 561 without the dozer blade.	
		(renumbered 963)	Brown cardboard box has Red/White label, 1 packing piece..	**£60-70**
			Dark Blue body, Mid-Blue rollers, Green rubber tracks, driver.	
			Brown box with Black/White picture label	**£175-200**
564	1952-54	**Elevator Loader**	Renumbered 964 – see that entry for details.	
571	1949-54	**Coles Mobile Crane**	Yellow and Black, operable crane, Supertoy, (renumbered 971)	**£30-40**
579	1961-63	**Simca Glaziers Lorry**	UK issue: Yellow and Green body, mirror/glass load, 'MIROITIER'	**£70-80**
		French issue:	Grey and Green body, mirror/glass load, 'SAINT GOBAIN'	**£80-90**
581	1953-54	**Horsebox**	Maroon body (cast in aluminium) 'British Railways', 2 packing pieces, (renumbered 981).....................	**£70-80**
581	1953-54	....US issue:	Maroon, 'Hire Service', 'Express Horse Van', 'Express'. Blue box has Orange/White labels with picture of US model, 2 packing pieces, (renumbered 980)	**£500-700**
581	1962-64	**Berliet Flat Truck**......................	Red and Grey body, 6 wheels plus spare, hook. French issue......................................	**£70-80**
		NB	The French issues listed above have been included because they were sold in the U.K.	
582	1953-54	**Pullmore Car Transporter**	Bedford cab/chassis, aluminium trailer with 'DINKY TOYS DELIVERY SERVICE' logo on sides.	
		(renumbered 982)	Same logo on rear ramp plus '20' sign. No window glazing, 'DINKY TOYS' on baseplate, Black grille/bumper, Silver trim.	
	1953 only		Light Blue cab, trailer and hubs, Fawn decks, six lower deck retaining rivets. Model only issued for very short period	**£700-900**
	1953-54	....	As previous model but decks may be Fawn or Grey. Four lower deck retaining rivets	**£120-150**
	1954 only	....	Dark Blue cab, trailer and hubs, Fawn decks, four lower deck retaining rivets.	
			Model supplied in 582/982 all Dark Blue box with White end label	**£500-750**
			Model supplied in 582/982 Blue/White striped box	**£300-400**
591	1952-54	**A.E.C. Tanker**..............................	Red/Yellow, 'SHELL CHEMICALS LIMITED', Supertoy, (renumbered 991)...................	**£140-175**
620	1950-54	**6-wheel Covered Wagon**.............	Matt-Green or Greenish-Brown body, 'Export only' (to USA), (renumbered from 151b)	**£60-70**
752	1953-54	**Goods Yard Crane**	Yellow operable crane on Blue (or Dark Blue) base (steps in some). Dark Blue box, (renumbered 973)..	**£30-40**
893	1962-64	**Unic Pipe Line Transporter**	Beige articulated body, spare wheel, 6 pipes. French issue	**£90-110**
894	1962-64	**Unic Boilot Car Transporter**......	Grey body, 'Dinky Toys Service Livraison'. French issue	**£100-120**
901	1954-57	**Foden 8-wheel Diesel Wagon**	**2nd type cab**, Supertoy, spare wheel, large hook.	
		(renumbered from 501)	Red cab and chassis, Fawn truck body, Red hubs	**£230-350**
902	1954-56	**Foden Flat Truck**	**2nd type cab**, Supertoy, spare wheel, large hook.	
		(renumbered from 502)	Yellow cab and chassis, Green flatbed body, Green hubs	**£1,000-1,250**
	1954-57	....	Orange cab and chassis, Green flatbed body, Green hubs	**£250-350**
	1957-59	....	Dark Red cab and chassis, Green flatbed, Green hubs	
			(NB Red similar to colour of 919 Guy 'GOLDEN SHRED' van)..................................	**£2,000-3,000**
			Cherry-Red cab, wings and chassis, Green flatbed body	**£600-700**
			Orange cab and chassis, Fawn flatbed body, Mid-Green hubs......................................	**£500-600**
903	1954-55	**Foden Flat Truck with Tailboard**	2nd type cab, Supertoy, spare wheel, large hook.	
		(renumbered from 503)	Dark Blue cab and chassis, Yellow flatbed, Light Blue hubs.......................................	**£500-600**
	1954-57	....	Dark Blue cab and chassis, Orange flatbed, Light Blue hubs	**£250-350**
	1957-60	....	Pale Blue cab and chassis, Fawn flatbed, Pale Blue hubs..	**£500-600**
905	1954-56	**Foden Flat Truck with Chains**...	**2nd type cab**, Supertoy, spare wheel, large hook.	
		(renumbered from 505)	Maroon cab, chassis and flatbed, Maroon hubs, 'rounded' chain-post bosses....................	**£250-350**
	1954-58	....	Green cab, chassis and flatbed, Light Green hubs, 'rounded' chain-post bosses..............	**£200-300**
	1956-57	....	Maroon cab, chassis and flatbed, Maroon hubs, 'rounded' chain-post bosses....................	**£250-350**
			As previous issue but with Red hubs..	**£300-350**
	1957-64	....	Red cab and chassis, Grey flatbed, Red metal hubs, 'rounded' chain-post bosses.............	**£250-350**
	19??-64	....	Red cab and chassis, Grey flatbed, Red plastic hubs..	**£450-550**

Commercial vehicles

908	1962-66	**Mighty Antar and Transformer**	Yellow cab, Red/Grey trailer, Supertoy, plastic transformer, 3 packing pieces	**£300-400**

911 1954-56 **Guy 4 ton Lorry** .... 2nd type cab casting, Supertoy, 'grooved' hubs, large hook.
(was 511, renumbered 431)
Red cab and chassis, Grey back, Red hubs..**£350-450**
Dark Blue cab and chassis, Light Blue back and hubs............................**£350-450**

912 1954-56 **Guy Flat Truck**.......................... 2nd type cab casting, Supertoy, 'grooved' hubs, large hook.
(was 512, renumbered 432)
Orange cab and chassis, Green flatbed body and hubs..........................**£350-450**
Mid-Blue cab and chassis, Red flatbed body, Mid-Blue hubs...............**£200-250**
Dark Green cab and chassis, Light Green flatbed body and hubs..........**£300-400**

913 1954-54 **Guy Flat Truck with Tailboard** . 2nd type cab casting, Supertoy, 'grooved' hubs, large hook.
(was 513, renumbered 433)
Yellow cab and chassis, Green body, Green hubs **£1,000-1,200**
1954-56 .... Dark Green cab and chassis, Green flatbed body and hubs...................**£200-300**
Deep Blue cab and chassis, Orange flatbed body, Light Blue hubs.
Usually in Blue/White striped box with picture of Green lorry **£200-300**
Deep Blue/Orange model in box with correct colours **£1,000-1,200**

914 1965-70 **A.E.C. Articulated Lorry** .... Red cab, Grey trailer, Green tilt 'British Road Services' **£110-130**
915 1973-74 **A.E.C. with Flat Trailer** .... Orange cab, White trailer, 'Truck Hire Co Liverpool' **£55-65**
Orange cab, White trailer, 'Thames Board Mills', bubble-packed. Truck carries load
of four Brown card tubes with 'UNILEVER' logos in Black ....**NGPP**

917 1954-56 **Guy Van 'SPRATTS'** .... Red **2nd type cab**, chassis and Supertoy hubs, Cream/Red van body with
(renumbered from 514)
'Bonio Ovals & Dog Cakes' design **£300-350**

917 1968-74 **Mercedes Truck and Trailer** ...... Blue cab/chassis (White roof), Yellow trailers, White tilts, pictorial stand and tray **£45-55**
Blue cab/chassis (White roof), Yellow trailers, Yellow tilts, pictorial stand and tray **£55-65**
Dark Blue cab/chassis, Yellow trailers, Dark Blue tilts, pictorial stand and tray **£65-75**
'MUNSTERLAND'.................... Dark Green cab and trailers, White tilts, Green logo, pictorial stand and tray, promotional..................**£250-350**
'HENRY JOHNSON' .... Dark Green body, White tilts, plain White box, promotional...........................**£200-250**

918 1955-58 **Guy Van 'EVER READY'** .... Blue **1st type cab** with small square sides to front number plate (never seen) ....**NGPP**
Blue **2nd type cab**/body, Red 'grooved' hubs, 'Ever Ready Batteries For Life', spare wheel, Supertoy ..**£300-350**
919 1957-58 **Guy Van 'GOLDEN SHRED'** ... All Red **2nd type cab** and body, Yellow Supertoy hubs,
'Robertsons Golden Shred' and 'golly' design, spare wheel **£600-750**
920 1960-60 **Guy Warrior Van 'HEINZ'** .... Red cab and chassis, window glazing, Yellow van body and Supertoy hubs,
spare wheel, 'HEINZ 57 VARIETIES' and 'Tomato Ketchup' bottle design....**£1,250-1,500**

921 1954-56 **Bedford Articulated Vehicle**....... Yellowish-Orange body, Black wings, Red hubs, Supertoy, (was 521, renumbered 409).............**£120-140**
922 1954-56 **Big Bedford Lorry** .... Maroon cab, Fawn back, Fawn hubs, Supertoy, (was 522, renumbered 408)....................**£110-130**
Blue cab, Yellow back, Yellow hubs...**£150-175**
923 1955-58 **Big Bedford Van 'HEINZ'** .... Red/Yellow, 'Heinz 57 Varieties' plus Baked Beans can, Supertoy...............**£300-400**
1958-59 .... As previous model but with 'Tomato Ketchup' bottle advertising **£1,000-1,250**
924 1972-76 **Aveling Barford 'CENTAUR'**.... Red/Yellow body, tipping dump truck **£30-40**
925 1965-69 **Leyland Dump Truck** .... 8-wheeled Supertoy with 'SAND BALLAST GRAVEL' on tailgate.
White (tilting) cab and chassis, Blue cab roof, Orange diecast tipper **£150-190**
As previous model but with tinplate tipper in Orange, Pale Grey or Red **£150-190**
930 1960-64 **Bedford Pallet-Jekta Van** .... Orange and Yellow body, 'Dinky Toys' and 'Meccano', 1 packing piece, Supertoy **£250-300**
931 1954-56 **Leyland Comet Lorry**
with Stake Body .... Violet-Blue cab and chassis, Orange-Yellow back, Red hubs, Supertoy, (was 531, renumbered 417)....**£240-280**
932 1954-56 **Leyland Comet**
with Hinged Tailboard.............. Green cab and chassis, Orange back, Cream hubs...............................**£110-130**
(was 532, renumbered 418)
Green cab and chassis, Red back, Cream hubs................................**£120-150**
Dark Blue cab and chassis, Mid-Blue back and hubs.........................**£110-130**
Dark Blue cab, chassis and back, Red hubs......................................**£110-130**
Dark Blue cab and chassis, Light (Powder) Blue back, Cream hubs.....**£300-400**
Red cab and chassis, Mid-Blue back and hubs..................................**£300-400**
NB Odd colours: Be wary of colour combinations not listed. The screw fitting makes it easy to
interchange the chassis and body components.

933 1954-56 **Leyland Comet Cement Wagon**. Yellow body, 'Portland Blue-Circle Cement', Supertoy, (was 533, renumbered 419)....................**£110-130**
934 1956-58 **Leyland Octopus Wagon** .... Yellow cab and chassis, Green truck body secured to chassis by a screw, Green band
around cab (but without Yellow band above radiator), Red diecast Supertoy hubs, 1 packing piece **£175-225**
1958-59 .... As previous model but with Green diecast hubs. Body secured by rivet.......................**£175-225**
1958-63 .... As previous model but with Yellow band immediately above radiator,
Red diecast hubs, body secured by rivet..**£300-350**
1963-64 .... Dark Blue cab/chassis, Yellow truck body, Red diecast hubs **£1,000-1,500**
1963-64 .... Dark Blue cab/chassis, Yellow truck body, Grey plastic hubs **£1,000-1,500**
1964-64 .... Dark Blue cab/chassis, Yellow truck body, Red plastic hubs **£1,000-1,500**
935 1964-66 **Leyland Octopus Flat Truck**
with Chains............................... 6 chain-posts, 8 wheels, flatbed held by rivet, Supertoy, 1 packing piece.
Green cab/chassis, Pale Grey flatbed body, Red plastic hubs...........**£1000-1200**
Green cab/chassis, Pale Grey flatbed body, Grey plastic hubs..........**£1200-1400**
Blue cab/chassis, Yellow cab flash, Pale Grey flatbed and hubs.......**£3000-4000**
936 1964-69 **Leyland 8-wheel Chassis** .... Red/Silver, 'Another Leyland on Test', three '5-ton' weights **£75-85**
940 1977-80 **Mercedes-Benz LP.1920 Truck** .. White cab, Pale Grey cover, Red chassis, hubs and interior **£35-45**
As above but with Black interior and White hubs....................................**£40-50**
'HALB UND HALB' .... 'MAMPE' & 'BOSCH' on Blue cab, Elephant design. Promotional **£100-150**
'FISON'S' .... White body, Red interior, chassis and hubs, Grey plastic cover,
'FISON'S THE GARDEN PEOPLE' labels, 2 peat samples. Promotional.....................**£200-250**

941	1956-56	**Foden 14 ton Tanker**		
		'MOBILGAS'	Red body and hubs, Black filler caps, Black or Grey tyres, Supertoy, (renumbered from 504)	£350-450
942	1955-57	**Foden 14 ton Tanker**		
		'REGENT'	Dark Blue cab/chassis, Red/White/Blue tank, Black tyres, Supertoy	£350-450
943	1958-64	**Leyland Octopus Tanker**		
		'ESSO'	Red body and diecast hubs, Red tinplate tank with waterslide transfers, 'ESSO PETROLEUM', diecast hubs, spare wheel, hook, Supertoy, 1 packing piece	£300-400
			As previous model but with plastic hubs	£300-400
			With plastic hubs, logos on self-adhesive labels	£350-450
944	1963-70	**Leyland Octopus Tanker**		
		'SHELL-BP'	White/Yellow cab and body, Grey chassis and plastic hubs	£250-350
			White/Yellow cab and body, Grey chassis, Black plastic hubs	£500-750
			White/Yellow cab and body, Grey chassis, Red plastic hubs	£500-750
			White/Yellow cab and body, White chassis, Grey or Black hubs	£250-300
	Export issue:		Yellow cab, White chassis, White plastic tank, Red plastic hubs. 'See-through' export box	NGPP
	NB		Each issue has 'SHELL' and 'BP' sticky labels on the front half of the plastic tank.	

944	1963-64	**Leyland Octopus Tanker**		
		'CORN PRODUCTS'	Only 500 of these promotionals issued White body and plastic tank, 'Sweeteners For Industry' in White on Black labels. In 944	**Notable Auction Result**: In 1999, Vectis Auctions sold a 944 Leyland Octopus 'Corn Products' Tanker for **£4,000**.
			'ESSO' box with 'CORN PRODUCTS' sticker, wrapped in Green/Grey striped gift paper	£2,000-3,000

945	1966-75	**A.E.C. Fuel Tanker 'ESSO'**	'ESSO PETROLUEUM' on White body, 'Tiger in Your Tank' logo on rear, 1 packing piece	£70-80
	1975-77		As previous model but without logo at rear, card boxed or bubble-packed	£60-70
	1977-77	**'LUCAS OIL' Tanker**	Green cab and tank, White design on labels, promotional, bubble-packed	£100-125
948	1961-67	**Tractor-Trailer 'McLEAN'**	Red cab, Light Grey trailer, Red plastic hubs, Supertoy, 2 packing pieces	£180-230
			As previous model but with Black plastic hubs	£175-225
	NB		The trailer moulding is light-sensitive and varies in shade from Pale Grey to Light Grey with a Greenish tinge, through to very Pale Brown. The 'McLean' logo can be Red or Light Orange.	

948	1964 ?	**Tractor-Trailer**		
		'BROWN SHOE Co.'	As 'McLean' model but with 'Brown Shoe Co.' adhesive labels. US Promotional (75 only made)	NGPP
950	1978-79	**Foden S20 Tanker 'BURMAH'**	Red cab, Red/White trailer, Black or Grey hatches, Red or Cream hubs	£40-50
950	1978	**Foden Tanker 'SHELL'**	Red cab, Red/White trailer, Cream hubs	£60-70
951	1954-56	**Trailer**	Grey body with hook, Red hubs, (was 551, renumbered 428)	£20-25
			Dark Grey body with hook, Lemon Yellow hubs	£50-70
958	1961-66	**Guy Warrior Snow Plough**	Yellow/Black body and plough blade, spare wheel, 1 packing piece, Supertoy	£150-175
			Yellow/Black body, Silver plough blade	£150-175
			Silver blade version in box with picture showing Silver blade	£250-300
959	1961-68	**Foden Dump Truck & Bulldozer**	Red body, Orange back, model number badge, driver, windows, Supertoy	£50-60
			Red body and hubs, Dark Grey chassis, Silver back	£150-175
			All-Red body	£150-175
960	1960-68	**Albion Lorry Concrete Mixer**	Orange body, Yellow/Blue rotating drum, spare wheel, Supertoy	£40-50
			Orange body, Grey rotating drum	£40-50
961	1954-62	**Blaw-Knox Bulldozer**	Red or Yellow body, rubber tracks, Tan driver, Supertoy, (renumbered from 561)	£40-50
	1962-64		Blue body, rubber tracks, Tan driver	£40-50
	1963-64		Red or Yellow body, rubber tracks, Blue driver	£40-50
	1964-64		Orange plastic body with Silver engine detail, Black diecast lifting gear, Green plastic blade and exhaust pipe, Blue driver, Light Green or Olive-Green roller wheels	£200-250

Guy 4-ton Lorries with their boxes.

Back row:
511 Red/Fawn on Green box with Red/White label
431 Red/Fawn on Yellow box
Front row:
511 Dark Blue/Light Blue on Brown box with Red/White label
911 Dark Blue/Light Blue on Blu/White striped box
431 Dark Blue/Light Blue on Yellow box

Photo: Swapmeet Publications

962	1954-66	**Muir Hill Dumper**	Yellow body, hook, Supertoy, 1 packing piece, (renumbered from 562)	**£15-20**
963	1954-58	**Blaw Knox Heavy Tractor**	Red or Orange body, Green or Black tracks. Blue/White striped box, 1 packing piece, (was 563)	**£40-50**
	1958-59		Yellow body, Green or Black tracks. Blue/White striped box, 1 packing piece	**£40-50**
963	1973-75	**Road Grader**	Yellow/Red articulated body, Silver blade, Red lower arm	**£20-30**
			White or Yellow lower arm	**£30-40**
964	1954-68	**Elevator Loader**	Yellow with Mid-Blue or Dark Blue chutes, Blue or Yellow hubs, 1 packing piece	**£45-55**
		(renumbered from 564) Boxes:	Early Blue boxes were replaced by Blue/White boxes, then by Yellow 'Supertoys' boxes.	
		Late issue:	Mid-Blue with Yellow chutes, as shown on late picture box design	**£100-150**
965	1955-61	**'EUCLID' Dump Truck**	Yellow, 'STONE - ORE - EARTH', no windows, operable tipper, 1 packing piece	**£55-65**
		NB	1955-56 Grey backed logo, 1959-61 Red backed logo.	
	1961-69		As previous model but with window glazing	**£60-70**
965	1969-70	**'TEREX' Rear Dump Truck**	Yellow body (as previous model but 'TEREX' cast under cab), 1 packing piece	**£110-130**
966	1960-64	**Marrel Multi-Bucket Unit**	(Albion) Pale Yellow body, Grey skip and tyres, Black hubs, Supertoy, 1 packing piece	**£100-125**
967	1959-64	**BBC TV Control Room**	Dark Green, 'BBC Television Service', Supertoy, 1 packing piece	**£130-160**
967	1973-78	**Muir-Hill Loader/Trencher**	Yellow/Red or Orange/Black body, with driver	**£25-35**
968	1959-64	**BBC TV Roving-Eye Vehicle**	Dark Green body, BBC crest, camera, Supertoy, 1 packing piece	**£130-160**
969	1959-64	**BBC TV Extending Mast**	Dark Green body, BBC crest, dish aerial, mast, Supertoy, 2 packing pieces	**£130-160**
970	1967-71	**Jones Fleetmaster Crane**	(Bedford TK) Red and Black body, White folding crane, 2 packing pieces	**£50-60**
	1971-77		Metallic Red and Black with White folding crane	**£60-70**
	1971-77		Yellow and Black with White folding crane	**£60-70**
971	1954-64	**Coles Mobile Crane**	Yellow/Black body; Yellow crane, diecast hubs and driver, Supertoy, 1 packing piece, (was 571)	**£30-40**
	1964-66		Yellow/Black body; Silver crane, plastic hubs and driver, Supertoy	**£30-40**
972	1955-62	**Coles 20 ton**		
		Lorry-Mounted Crane	Yellow/Orange (no 'Long Vehicle' signs), 2 drivers, Supertoy, 1packing piece	**£40-50**
	1962-69		Yellow/Orange (with 'Long Vehicle' signs), 2 drivers, Supertoy	**£40-50**
	1967-69		Yellow/Black, Blue metal driver in lorry cab only, Yellow plastic hubs, Black tyres,	
			Black/White diagonal stripes around jib, Yellow 'COLES CRANE' at rear	**£100-150**
973	1954-59	**Goods Yard Crane**	Yellow operable crane on Blue base. Blue/White striped box with 1 packing piece, (was 752)	**£30-40**
973	1971-75	**Eaton 'YALE' Tractor Shovel**	Red/Yellow body with Yellow or Silver bucket exterior	**£20-30**
			Yellow/Red body, Silver wheels, no engine covers	**£25-35**
			All Yellow body, Blue wheels, engine covers	**£25-35**
974	1968-75	**A.E.C. Hoynor Car Transporter**	Blue/Yellow/Orange body, 'Silcock & Colling Ltd', 3 packing pieces	**£80-95**
975	1963-67	**Ruston-Bucyrus Excavator**	Yellow/Red/Grey plastic body, rubber tracks, with instructions	**£175-250**
976	1968-76	**'MICHIGAN' Tractor Dozer**	Yellow/Red body, driver, engine covers, Red hubs, 1 packing piece	**£20-25**
		Promotional:	All Yellow with Blue hubs. (100 / 200 made for Michigan Co.)	NGPP
977	1960-64	**Servicing Platform Vehicle**	Red and Cream body, operable platform, spare wheel, 2 packing pieces	**£150-200**
		NB	Version seen using 667 Missile Servicing Platform Vehicle chassis in the Red/Cream 977 livery	NGPP
977	1973-78	**Shovel Dozer**	Yellow/Red/Silver, Black or Silver plastic tracks, bubble-packed..	**£20-25**
978	1964-72	**Bedford TK Refuse Wagon**	Diecast cab, plastic tipping body, 2 plastic bins.	
			Green cab, Grey tipping body, Red hubs, White (later Grey) plastic roof rack	**£40-45**
	1973-74		Dark Metallic Green cab, Grey tipping body, White (later Grey) plastic roof rack	**£50-60**
	1975-77		Lime-Green cab, Black or Brown chassis, plastic or cast roof rack	**£45-55**
	1978-80		Yellow cab with Brown chassis, cast roof rack	**£35-45**
		NB	Over its 16-year production run, 978 came in five different types of packaging:	
			lidded box, pictorial and non-pictorial end-flap boxes, bubble-pack, and window box.	
979	1961-64	**Racehorse Transport**	Grey/Yellow, 2 horses, 'Newmarket Racehorse Transport Service Ltd', Supertoy, 2 packing pieces	**£200-250**
980	1954-60	**Horsebox (US issue)**	Maroon body (cast in aluminium), 'Hire Service', 'Express Horse Van', 'Express'.	
		(renumbered from 581)	In Blue/White striped box with picture of model and 'Hudson Dobson', 2 packing pieces	**£350-450**
980	1972-79	**Coles Hydra Truck 150T**	Lemon-Yellow body, triple extension crane, handle at side and rear	**£30-40**
			Yellow or Orange body, 2 side handles, no rear handle	**£50-60**
		'SPARROWS'	Red body, 'SPARROWS CRANE HIRE', (promotional model)	**£200-300**
981	1954-60	**Horsebox**	Maroon body (cast in aluminium), 'British Railways', 2 packing pieces, (renumbered from 581)	**£90-110**
982	1955-63	**Pullmore Car Transporter**	Bedford 'O' series cab and chassis plus aluminium trailer with 'DINKY TOYS DELIVERY SERVICE'	
		(renumbered from 582)	on sides. Same logo on rear ramp but without '20' sign. Black grille/bumper, Silver trim, 1 packing piece.	
	1955-61		Dark Blue cab and hubs, Light Blue trailer and decks, no window glazing.	
			Blue/White striped box has picture of 994 Loading Ramp introduced in 1955	**£100-120**
	1961-63		As previous issue but cab has window glazing	**£120-130**
983	1958-63	**Car Carrier and Trailer**	Red/Grey, 'Dinky Auto Service', 5 packing pieces, (Supertoys 984 and 985)	**£180-220**
984	1958-63	**Car Carrier**	Red/Grey body, 'Dinky Auto Service', 2 packing pieces, Supertoy	**£100-150**
984	1974-79	**Atlas Digger**	Red/Yellow body, Yellow arm/cylinders, Silver or Yellow bucket	**£30-40**
			Red/Yellow body, Black plastic arm, Black or Yellow cylinders, Silver bucket.	**£30-40**
985	1958-63	**Trailer for Car Carrier**	Red/Grey body, 'Dinky Auto Service', 2 packing pieces, Supertoy	**£50-60**
986	1959-61	**Mighty Antar with Propeller**	Red cab (window glazing on some), Grey low-loader, Bronze propeller, 3 packing pieces	**£300-350**
987	1962-69	**'ABC TV' Control Room**	Blue/Grey/Red, 'ABC TELEVISION', camera/operator/cable.	**£140-160**
988	1962-69	**TV Transmitter Van 'ABC-TV'**	Blue/Grey body, Red stripe, revolving aerial dish, Supertoy	**£160-180**
989	1963-65	**Car Transporter**	'AUTO TRANSPORTERS', Yellow/Light Grey/Blue, Supertoy boxed in all-card	
			picture box or export-only Gold 'see through' window box, 2 packing pieces	**£2,000-2,500**
990		**Pullmore Car transporter**		
		with Four Cars	See Gift Sets section.	
991	1954-70	**Large Trailer**	Renumbered from 551 – see that entry for details.	
991	1954-55	**A.E.C. Tanker**	Red/Yellow 'SHELL CHEMICALS LIMITED', Supertoy, (renumbered from 591)	**£130-150**
	1955-58		Red/Yellow, 'SHELL CHEMICALS', Supertoy	**£130-150**

Ford Transit casting types:

Type 1: **(1966-74)**, has sliding driver's door, opening hinged side door, and twin rear doors.
Type 2: **(1974-78)**, non-sliding driver's door, one side-hinged door, one top-hinged rear door.
Type 3: **(1978-80)**, as Type 2 but with a slightly longer bonnet (18 mm.)

Ref	Year(s)	Model name	Colours, features, details	Market Price Range
24a	1934-38	Ambulance	Types 1 or 2 criss-cross chassis, types 1, 2 or 3 grille, plated chrome or Black hubs, open windows.	
			Cream body (Red chassis), Cream body (Grey chassis)	**£250-350**
			Grey body (Dark Grey chassis), Grey body (Maroon chassis)	**£200-250**
			Notable Auction Result: A pre-production (lead) example of 24a was sold by Christie's in 2001 for **£470**.	
	1938-40	Ambulance	Type 2 criss-cross chassis, open windows, type 3 grille. See 30f.	
			Cream body (Red chassis), Cream body (Grey chassis)	**£200-250**
			Grey body (Dark Grey chassis), Grey body (Maroon chassis)	**£250-300**
			Black body, Black chassis (thought to be for export only)	**£500-750**
25h	1936-37	Streamlined Fire Engine	Red body, no tinplate chassis, tinplate ladder and bell, White tyres	**£175-225**
	1937-40		Red body, tinplate baseplate, ladder and bell, Black or White tyres	**£125-150**
25h	1948-54	(renumbered 250)	Red body and ladder, tinplate baseplate, brass bell, Black tyres	**£80-100**
25k	1937-39	Streamline Fire Engine	Red body, tinplate base, 6 firemen, ladder, bell, White tyres	**£400-500**
30f	1935-38	Ambulance	Grey body, Red wings/criss-cross chassis, plain radiator, open windows	**£150-200**
	1938-40		Grey body, Black moulded chassis, radiator badge, open windows	**£90-110**
	1938-40	South-African issue:	Grey body, Red cross, 'Bentley type' radiator	**£750-950**
	1946-47		Grey body, Black moulded chassis, open windows	**£90-110**
	1947-48		Cream body, Black moulded chassis, filled-in or open windows	**£90-110**
30h	1950-54	Daimler Ambulance	Cream body, Red crosses and wheels, no window glazing, (renumbered 253)	**£80-90**
30hm	1950-54	Daimler Military Ambulance	Military-Green body, Red crosses on White backgrounds, (US issue), (renumbered 624)	**£200-300**
123-P	1977	Austin Princess 'POLICE' Car	All-White, Bronze/Blue or White/Blue. (Model has not yet been seen)	NPP
195	1971-78	Fire-Chief's Range Rover	Red or Metallic Red, 'Fire Service', Speedwheels, bubble-packed	**£35-40**
243	1979-81	Volvo 'POLICE' Car	White body, plastic chassis. (Some made in Italy by Polistil)	**£35-40**
244	1977-81	Plymouth Fury Police Car	Black/White, 'POLICE', warning lights, plastic chassis and wheels	**£25-30**
250	1954-62	Fire Engine	Red body and hubs, Silver tinplate ladder, bell and trim, (renumbered from 25h)	**£100-120**
250	1967-71	Police Mini Cooper 'S'	White body, Austin Cooper 'S' boot lid transfer, roof sign and aerial, 'POLICE' on doors	**£55-65**
	1971-73		As previous model but cast boot detail, no aerial	**£45-55**
	1973-75		As previous model but with Speedwheels	**£35-45**
	NB		Boot casting variations: (1) 'Morris Mini-Minor' cast-in, (2) 'Austin Mini-Cooper S' cast-in.	
251	1971-72	U.S.A. 'POLICE' Car	(Pontiac Parisienne), White/Black, beacon, siren, 2 aerials, driver	**£55-65**
252	1969-74	R.C.M.P. Police Car	(Pontiac Parisienne), Blue/White, driver, Blue light, Speedwheels	**£45-55**
253	1954-58	Daimler Ambulance	Cream body, Red crosses and cast hubs, no window glazing, (renumbered from 30h)	**£75-85**
	1958-60		White body, Red crosses and cast hubs, no window glazing	**£75-85**
	1960-62		White body, Red crosses and cast hubs, with window glazing	**£75-85**
	1962-64		White body, Red plastic hubs, with window glazing	**£75-85**
254	1971-81	Police Range Rover	White body, Red stripes, 'Police', opening doors, aerial on some, Speedwheels	**£35-45**
255	1955-61	Mersey Tunnel Police Van	(Land Rover), Red body, 'Mersey Tunnel' and 'Police', hook	**£60-70**
255	1967-71	Ford Zodiac 'POLICE' Car	White body, driver, 'POLICE' on doors and roof sign, aerial	**£55-65**
255	1977-79	Police Mini Clubman	Blue/White body, 'POLICE', opening doors and bonnet, plastic wheels	**£30-35**
256	1960-64	Humber Hawk 'POLICE' Car	Black body, Cream interior, White 'POLICE' sign on roof, 'PC 49' licence plates, driver and observer, spun hubs	**£80-100**
257	1960-69	Canadian 'FIRE CHIEF' Car	(Nash Rambler), flashing light, suspension, window glazing	**£55-65**
258		**U.S.A. POLICE CAR**		
	1960-61	DeSoto Fireflite	(192), Black body, White front doors, 'POLICE' on doors, roof and bonnet, roof-light	**£80-100**
	1961-62	Dodge Royal Sedan	(191), Black body, White front doors, 'POLICE' on doors, roof and bonnet, roof-light	**£80-100**
	1962-66	Ford Fairlane	(149), Black body, White front doors, 'POLICE' on doors, roof and bonnet, roof-light, open window	**£70-80**
			Same but Dark Blue/White, with closed windows	**£70-80**
	1966-68	Cadillac 62	(147), Black/White, suspension/steering	**£80-100**
259	1961-69	Fire Engine (Bedford Miles)	Red body and hubs, 'FIRE BRIGADE' and crest, tinplate ladder and bell, Yellow box	**£70-85**
			As previous model but with 'AIRPORT FIRE TENDER' (from 276)	**£70-85**
			Red body, Silver cast wheels	**£100-125**
261	1967-77	Ford Taunus 'POLIZEI'	White and Green body, (German issue), box has card packing ring and label: 'Special contract run for Meccano Agent in W. Germany'	**£200-250**
263	1962-68	Superior Criterion Ambulance	Cream, 'AMBULANCE' on windows, stretcher, no beacon	**£50-60**
263	1978-80	E.R.F. Fire Tender	Yellow body, 'Airport Rescue', flashing light	**£40-50**
264	1962-65	R.C.M.P. Ford Fairlane	Dark Blue body, White doors, aerial, red beacon, 2 Mounties	**£75-85**
264	1965-68	R.C.M.P. Cadillac	Dark Blue body, White front doors, aerial, red beacon, 2 Mounties	**£90-110**
264	1978-80	Rover 3500 Police Car	White body, Yellow stripe with 'POLICE' and crest	**£20-30**
266	1976-79	E.R.F. Fire Tender	Red body, 'Fire Service', White wheeled escape ladder	**£50-60**
	1979-80		As previous model but with Metallic Red body	**£50-60**
	1976-79	Danish issue:	Red body, 'FALCK'	**£70-85**
267	1967-71	Superior Cadillac Ambulance	Cream and Red body, 'AMBULANCE' on roof, flashing light, stretcher, patient	**£50-60**
267	1978-79	Paramedic Truck	Red, Yellow cylinders, 2 figures, lapel badge, (TV Series 'Emergency')	**£20-30**
268	1973-77	Range Rover Ambulance	White, 'AMBULANCE', stretcher, bubble-packed	**£20-30**
269	1962-66	Jaguar Motorway 'POLICE' Car	White or matt-White body, aerial, roof-light, 2 figures	**£80-100**
269	1978-79	Ford Transit 'POLICE' Van	White/Red/Blue, figures/lights/signs/cones, Type 3 casting	**£35-45**

270	1969-72	Ford 'POLICE' Panda Car	Turquoise body, White doors, Blue/White roof sign, cast hubs	£45-55
	1972-77		As previous model but fitted with Speedwheels..	£40-50
271	1975-76	Ford Transit 'FIRE'	Red body, hose/axe/bells/plastic ladder, bubble-packed, Type 2..	£55-65
	........................Danish issue:	As previous model but with 'FALCK' logo	£65-75
272	1975-78	'POLICE' Accident Unit............	White, radar gun/beacon/aerial/cones/signs, Type 2 casting	£35-45
274	1978-79	Ford Transit Ambulance...........	White, 'AMBULANCE', Red crosses, beacon, Type 3 casting	£35-45
276	1962-69	Airport Fire Tender	Red body, 'AIRPORT FIRE CONTROL', bell, packing ring in box	£50-65
			As previous model but 'FIRE BRIGADE' logo (from 259), no crest	£50-65
276	1976-78	Ford Transit Ambulance	White body, 'AMBULANCE', Type 2 casting, packing ring in box	£30-40
277	1962-68	Superior Criterion Ambulance..	Metallic Blue, White roof and tyres, flashing light, box has lift-off lid and 1 packing piece	£60-80
			As previous model but in Gold 'see-through' box	£80-90
277	1977-80	'POLICE' Land Rover	Blue body, White tilt, flashing light..	£20-30
278	1964-69	Vauxhall Victor Ambulance.......	White, 'AMBULANCE', stretcher and patient, roof-box and light	£60-75
282	1973-79	Land Rover Fire Appliance	Red, 'Fire Service', metal ladder, bubble-packed	£30-40
	1974-78	........................Danish issue:	As previous model but with 'FALCK' logo	£35-45
285	1969-79	Merryweather Marquis.............	Metallic Dark Red body, escape ladder, working pump, 'FIRE SERVICE'	£55-65
			As previous model but (non-Metallic), Red body	£55-65
		Danish issue:	As previous model but Red or Metallic Dark Red body, 'FALCK' logo................................	£85-95
286	1968-74	Ford Transit 'FIRE'	Red, 'Fire Service', hose Type 1 casting, bubble-packed..	£75-90
			As previous model but with Metallic Red body	£75-90
		Danish issue:	As previous model but with 'FALCK ZONEN' logo..	£85-95
287	1967-71	Police Accident Unit	Cream lower body, Orange upper body, roof sign, aerial, Type 1 casting	£50-65
	1971-74		White body with Red lower panels, radar gun, roof rack, Type 1 casting	£50-65
288	1971-79	Superior Cadillac	White body with Red lower panels, 'AMBULANCE', stretcher and patient, no flashing light	£40-45
		Danish issue:	Black body/White roof, Blue interior and roof bar, 'FALCK' on roof bar and tailgate	£100-125
555	1952-54	Fire Engine (Commer)..............	Red body with Silver trim and ladder, no windows, (renumbered 955)........................	£75-85
624	1954-?	Daimler Military Ambulance.....	Military-Green body, Red crosses on White backgrounds, (US issue), (renumbered from 30hm)	£200-300
954	1961-64	Fire Station	Red, Yellow and 'brick' plastic, base 252 mm. x 203 mm	£175-225
955	1954-64	Fire Engine (Commer)...............	Red body and diecast hubs, with or without window glazing, (renumbered from 555)................	£75-85
	1964-70		Red body, Red plastic hubs, window glazing, Black or Grey tyres, housed in	
			Yellow box with drawing or scene, card packing	£120-140
956	1958-60	Turntable Fire Escape Lorry	(Bedford cab). Red body and diecast hubs, no windows, Silver deck and ladder	£80-100
	1960-70		Red body, diecast then plastic hubs, window glazing, instructions, 'Tested' label, card packing...........	£80-100
	NB		A version of 956 has been discovered (in Norway) that has 3 ladders instead of 2.	
956	1970-74	Turntable Fire Escape Lorry	(Berliet cab). Metallic Red body and hubs, windows, 'ECHELLE INCENDIE', Silver platform........	£175-225
			As previous model but with Black platform..	£150-200
	1974-?	.... Danish issue:	Metallic Red body and hubs, windows, 'FALCK'	£175-225
2253	1974-76	Ford Capri Police Car...............	White/Orange, 'POLICE', Blue light, suspension. (1/25 scale)	£80-100

'Dublo Dinky' models

'Dublo Dinky' models were made in a scale of 1:76.
All their wheels are plastic: smooth wheels are fairly soft and treaded wheels are hard.

Ref	Year(s)	Model name	Colours, features, details	Market Price Range
061	1958-59	Ford Prefect................................	Fawn or Grey body, Silver trim, Grey smooth wheels	£50-60
			As previous but with treaded Grey wheels	£65-75
062	1958-60	Singer Roadster	Orange or Fawn body, Red interior, Grey smooth or treaded wheels	£65-75
			Yellow body, Grey treaded wheels..	£75-85
063	1958-60	Commer Van..............................	Blue body, Silver trim, Grey smooth or treaded wheels	£45-55
064	1957-62	Austin Lorry	Green body, Black treaded or Grey smooth or treaded wheels	£45-55
065	1957-60	Morris Pick-up	Red body, Silver trim, Grey treaded wheels	£45-55
066	1959-66	Bedford Flat Truck	Grey body, Silver trim, Grey smooth wheels, with hook	£45-55
			Grey body, Silver trim, Grey smooth or treaded wheels, without hook................	£45-55
067	1959-64	Austin 'TAXI'............................	Blue lower body, Cream upper body, Black or Grey treaded wheels................	£65-75
068	1959-64	'ROYAL MAIL' Morris Van	Red body, 'E II R' crest, Grey or Black treaded wheels	£60-75
069	1959-64	Massey Harris Tractor	Blue body, Silver trim, Grey treaded wheels, hole for driver..	£45-55
			With Grey treaded wheels on front and very Light Tan rear wheels................	£75-85
070	1959-64	A.E.C. Mercury Tanker	Green cab, Red tank, Black or Grey treaded wheels, 'SHELL-BP'........................	£85-95
071	1960-64	Volkswagen Delivery Van...........	Yellow body with Red 'HORNBY DUBLO' logo, Black or Grey treaded wheels................	£60-70
072	1959-64	Bedford Articulated Truck	Yellow cab, Red semi-trailer, Black or Grey smooth or treaded wheels................	£50-60
073	1960-64	Land Rover/Trailer/Horse..........	Green car (Grey or Black treaded wheels), Tan or White horse. Trailers:	
			with Bright Green trailer (Green ramp, smooth Grey wheels)................................	£80-100
			with Green trailer (Brown ramp, treaded Grey wheels)	£80-100
			with Bright Green trailer (Black ramp, treaded Black wheels)................................	£80-100
			with Orange trailer (Black or Grey plastic wheels and ramp)........................	£80-100
076	1960-64	Lansing Bagnall Tractor & Trailer	Maroon tractor/trailer, Blue driver/seat, Black smooth or treaded wheels................	£50-60
078	1960-64	Lansing Bagnall Trailer.............	Maroon body, Black smooth or treaded wheels, hook, wire drawbar	£30-35
-	circa 1959	Shop Display Stand	Pale Yellow with Red logo and wording 'NEW SERIES / DUBLO DINKY', etc.	
			Stand dimensions: 28cm x 19cm overall	£300-500

Ref	Year(s)	Model name	Colours, features, details	Market Price Range
22e	1933-40	Farm Tractor	'Modelled Miniature' with 'HORNBY SERIES' cast-in, no hook, Yellow/Dark Blue (lead) body, Red or Yellow (lead) wheels	£200-300
			'DINKY TOYS' cast-in, with hook, Red or Yellow wheels are lead, diecast or both, Green/Yellow, Yellow/Blue, Red/Blue, Red/Red	£200-300
			Cream/Blue, Cream/Red, Blue/Cream	£200-300

> **Notable Auction Result**: A pre-war half-dozen Trade Box of 22e Tractors was sold by Christie's in 2001 for **£1,645.**

Ref	Year(s)	Model name	Colours, features, details	Market Price Range
27a	1948-54	Massey-Harris Tractor	Red body, Yellow cast wheels, driver, steering wheel, hook, (renumbered 300)	£70-80
27ak	1952-54	Tractor and Hay Rake	27a Tractor and 27k Hay Rake, (renumbered 310)	£150-175
27b	1949-54	Halesowen Harvest Trailer	Brown body, Red racks, Yellow metal wheels, (renumbered 320)	£25-35
27d	1950-54	Land Rover	Green or Orange body, tinplate windscreen frame, driver, (renumbered 340)	£60-70
			As previous model but with Red body	£65-75
	1952-53	...............Gift Set model:	Dark Brown body. Only in Gift Set No.2, Commercial Vehicles Set	GSP
27c	1949-54	M.H. Manure Spreader	Red body with drawbar, hook, working shredders, (renumbered 321)	£30-40
27f	1950-53	Estate Car	Pale Brown body, Brown side panels and hubs (renumbered 344)	£70-80
			Grey body with Red side panels	£100-125
27g	1949-54	Moto-Cart	Brown and Green body, driver, 3 metal wheels/tyres, body tips, (renumbered 342)	£40-50
27h	1951-54	Disc Harrow	Red/Yellow body, Silver disc blades, tinplate hook, (renumbered 322)	£20-25
27j	1952-54	Triple Gang Mower	Red frame, Yellow tines, Green wheels, cast-in hook, (renumbered 323)	£20-25
27k	1953-54	Hay Rake	Red frame, Yellow wheels, wire tines, operating lever, (renumbered 324)	£20-25
27m	1952-54	Land Rover Trailer	Orange or Green body and diecast hubs, drawbar and hook, (renumbered 341)	£20-25
27n	1953-54	'FIELD MARSHALL' Tractor	Orange body, Silver metal wheels, Tan driver, hook, (renumbered 301)	£85-95
			As previous model but with Green metal wheels	£140-160
30n	1950-54	Farm Produce Wagon	Model has stake sides to rear body, Black metal base and hook, (renumbered 343)	
			Yellow cab and chassis, Green back and hubs	£80-90
			Green cab and chassis, Yellow back and hubs	£80-90
			Red cab and chassis, Blue back and hubs	£80-90
105a	1948-54	Garden Roller	Green handle and Red roller sides, (renumbered 381)	£15-25
105b	1948-54	Wheelbarrow	Brown or Tan and Red body, single metal wheel, (renumbered 382)	£15-25
105c	1948-54	4 wheeled Hand Truck	Green/Yellow or Blue/Yellow, (renumbered 383)	£10-15
105e	1948-54	Grass Cutter	Yellow handle, Green metal wheels, Red blades, (renumbered 384)	£25-30
			Yellow handle, Grey metal wheels, Green blades, (renumbered 384)	£25-30
107a	1948-54	Sack Truck	Blue or Pale Green body with two small Black metal wheels, (renumbered 385)	£10-15
192	1970-74	Range Rover	Bronze body, various interior colours, cast detailed or Speedwheels	£25-35
	1973-79		Black or Yellow body, Speedwheels	£25-35
300	1954-62	Massey-Harris Tractor	Red body, Yellow and Grey cast wheels, 'MASSEY-HARRIS', Tan cast driver (renumbered from 27a)	£70-80
	1962-64		Red body, Yellow wheels (cast rear, plastic front, rubber tyres), cast driver	£125-150
	1964-66		Red body, Yellow/Black plastic wheels, Yellow exhaust, Blue plastic driver, Yellow/White 'flap' box	£125-150
300	1966-71	Massey Ferguson Tractor	As previous model but name changed to 'MASSEY-FERGUSON'	£70-80
301	1954-61	'FIELD MARSHALL' Tractor	Orange body, Green or Silver metal wheels, Tan driver, hook, (renumbered from 27n)	£120-140
			Orange body, Yellow or unpainted wheels, Tan driver, hook	£150-180
	1962-66		Orange body, Green wheels (plastic front, cast rear, rubber tyres)	£150-180
			Orange body, Green plastic hubs (front and rear), Black plastic exhaust	£150-180
	1964-66		Red body, Green plastic hubs, rubber tyres	£80-90
305	1965-67	David Brown 900 Tractor	Red cowl, Grey engine, Yellow cab/wheels, 'David Brown 990', in detailed picture box	£150-200
	1967-74		White cowl/cab/wheels, Grey engine, 'David Brown Selectamatic 990'	£60-70
	1974-75		White cowl/cab, Red engine/wheels, '995 David Brown Case, bubble-packed	£60-70
308		Leyland 384 Tractor	Models display a Blue/White 'LEYLAND' label. Later issues have a Blue plastic driver, Silver trim and Black rubber tyres.	
	1971-72		Metallic Red body, Cream hubs, no driver, plastic dome box	£70-85
	1973-74		Metallic Red body, White hubs, driver, Yellow/Red box	£60-75
	1975-77		Blue body, White hubs, driver, Yellow/Red box	£60-75
	1978		Orange body, White hubs, driver, Red/Blue hanging box	£80-100
	1978-79		Metallic Red body, Cream or White hubs, Red/Blue hanging box	£60-75
310	1954-60	Tractor and Hay Rake	300 Tractor and 324 Hay Rake in Blue/White box, (renumbered from 27ak)	£150-175
			Same, but late Yellow box issue (1 PP)	£200-250
319	1961-71	Weeks Tipping Trailer	Red/Yellow body, cast or plastic wheels, plain or planked trailer bed	£25-30
320	1954-60	Halesowen Harvest Trailer	Red/Brown body, Red racks, drawbar, hook, cast or plastic wheels, (renumbered from 27b)	£25-35
			Red body, Yellow racks, drawbar, hook, cast or plastic wheels	£25-35
321	1954-62	M.H. Manure Spreader	Red body, Yellow cast wheels, 'MASSEY-HARRIS', shredders (renumbered from 27c)	£25-35
321	1962-73		Red body, Red or Yellow plastic hubs, no logo	£25-35
322	1954-67	Disc Harrow	Red/Yellow body, Silver disc blades, tinplate hook, (renumbered from 27h)	£25-35
322	1967-73		White/Red body, Silver disc blades, no hook	£25-35
			All White version	NGPP
323	1954-63	Triple Gang Mower	Red frame, Yellow tines, Green wheels, cast-in hook	£35-45
324	1954-64	Hayrake	Red frame, Yellow wheels, wire tines, Black or Silver operating lever (renumbered from 27k)	£25-35
325	1967-73	David Brown Tractor and Disc Harrow	305 and 322 in White and Red	£80-90
			305 and 322 in Yellow and Red	£120-140
340	1954-66	Land Rover	Green body, Pale Brown interior and cast driver, Green cast hubs, (renumbered from 27d)	£80-100
340	1966-69		Orange body, Dark Green interior, Red cast hubs, Tan driver	£80-100
340			Orange body, Dark Green interior, Red plastic hubs, Blue cast or plastic driver	£110-130
	1969-71		Red body, Red plastic hubs, Yellow interior, Blue plastic driver	£125-150
			Red body, Yellow plastic hubs and interior, Blue plastic driver	£125-150
	1971		Red body, Green plastic hubs, Yellow interior, Blue plastic driver	£125-150
	NB		The last three issues were supplied in the late Lighter Yellow boxes.	
341	1954-73	Land Rover Trailer	Orange, Green or Red, drawbar and hook, cast or plastic hubs, (renumbered from 27m)	£25-30

139

Farm and Garden models

342	1954-61	Moto-Cart	Light or Dark Green with Tan back and driver, Red hubs, (renumbered from 27g)	£65-75
343	1954-61	Farm Produce Wagon	Red cab and chassis, Blue back and cast hubs, (renumbered from 30n)	£80-90
			Green cab and chassis, Yellow back and cast hubs	£80-90
343	1961-64		As previous models but no bonnet louvres, cast or plastic hubs	£80-100
344	1950-53	Estate Car	Pale Brown body, Brown side panels and diecast hubs, (renumbered from 27f)	£70-80
			As previous model but with spun aluminium hubs	£100-125
344	1970-72	Land Rover Pick-Up	Metallic Blue or Red, cast wheels	£20-25
	1972-78		Metallic Blue or Red, Speedwheels	£20-25
381	1954-58	Garden Roller	Green and Red, (renumbered from 105a)	£15-25
381	1977-80	Convoy Farm Truck	Yellow cab, Brown plastic high-sided truck body	£15-20
382	1954-58	Wheelbarrow	Brown and Red body, single metal wheel, (renumbered from 105b)	£15-25
383	1954-58	4 wheeled Hand Truck	Green or Blue body, (renumbered from 105c)	£10-15
384	1954-58	Grass Cutter	Yellow body, Green metal wheels, Red or Green blades, (renumbered from 105e)	£15-20
385	1954-58	Sack Truck	Blue with two small metal wheels, (renumbered from 107a)	£10-15
386	1954-58	Lawn Mower	Green/Red, separate grassbox, 'Dinky Toys' cast-in, (renumbered from 751)	£80-90
399	1969-75	Tractor and Trailer	300 combined with 428	£200-250
561	1949-54	Blaw Knox Bulldozer	Red body, Green or Black rubber tracks, driver, lifting blade, Supertoy.	
		(renumbered 961)	Blue box with Orange/White label, or 'natural' card box with Red/White label, 1 PP	£40-50
563	1948-54	Blaw Knox Heavy Tractor	Red, Orange or Blue 561 without the dozer blade.	
		(renumbered 963)	Brown cardboard box has Red/White label, 1 PP	£60-70
			Dark Blue body, Mid-Blue rollers, Green rubber tracks, driver.	
			Brown box with Black/White picture label	£175-200
564	1952-54	Elevator Loader	Renumbered 964 – see that entry (below) for details.	
751	1949-54	Lawn Mower	Green/Red, separate grassbox, 'Dinky Supertoys' cast-in, (renumbered 386)	£80-90
961	1954-62	Blaw-Knox Bulldozer	Red or Yellow body, rubber tracks, Tan driver, Supertoy, (renumbered from 561)	£40-50
	1962-64		Blue body, rubber tracks, Tan driver	£40-50
	1963-64		Red or Yellow body, rubber tracks, Blue driver	£40-50
	1964-64		Orange plastic body with Silver engine detail, Black diecast lifting gear, Green plastic blade and exhaust pipe, Blue driver, Light Green or Olive-Green roller wheels	£200-250
963	1954-58	Blaw Knox Heavy Tractor	Red or Orange body, Green or Black tracks. Blue/White striped box, 1 PP, (renumbered from 563)	£40-50
	1958-59		Yellow body, Green or Black tracks. Blue/White striped box, 1 PP	£40-50
964	1954-68	Elevator Loader	Yellow with Mid-Blue or Dark Blue chutes, Blue or Yellow hubs, 1 PP	£45-55
		(renumbered from 564) Boxes:	Early Blue boxes were replaced by Blue/White boxes, then by Yellow 'Supertoys' boxes.	
		Late issue:	Mid-Blue with Yellow chutes, as shown on late picture box design	£100-150

Dinky Toys Motor Cycles

See also Accessories and Gift Sets sections.

SWRW = solid White rubber wheels, SBRW = solid Black rubber wheels (both are of a larger diameter than those used on the small cars).

Ref	Year(s)	Model name	Colours, features, details	Market Price Range
041	1952-54	Police Motor Cyclist	Post-war reissue for US market of 37a	NGPP
042	1952-54	Civilian Motor Cyclist	Post-war reissue for US market of 37b	NGPP
043	1952-54	Police Motorcycle Patrol	Post-war reissue for US market of 42b	NGPP
044	1952-54	R.A.C. Motorcycle Patrol	Post-war reissue for US market of 43b	NGPP
045	1952-54	A.A. Motorcycle Patrol	Post-war reissue for US market of 44b	NGPP
14z	1938-40	'Triporteur'	Three-wheel delivery van with Green, Red, Grey, Blue or Yellow body, Black hubs, White tyres, rider is always a different colour from van, French model	£200-300
37a	1937-40	Civilian Motor Cyclist	Black motor cycle with Silver engine/exhaust detail, Blue, Maroon, Green or Black rider, SWRW or thick SBRW	£40-50
	1946-49		Black motor cycle without Silver detail, Green or Grey rider, thin SBRW	£40-50
37a	1950-54		Black motor cycle without Silver detail, Green or Grey rider, thin SBRW, export only (renumbered 041)	£40-50
37b	1937-40	Police Motor Cyclist	Black motor cycle with Silver engine/exhaust detail, Dark Blue rider, SWRW or thick SBRW	£75-85
	1946-49		Black motor cycle without Silver engine/exhaust detail, Dark Blue rider, thick SBRW	£40-50
37b	1950-54		As previous model, export only (renumbered 042)	£40-50
37c	1937-39	Signals Despatch Rider	Green motor cycle, Silver engine/exhaust detail, Khaki rider, SWRW or thick SBRW	£125-175
42b	1935-40	Police Motorcycle Patrol	Dark Blue motor cycle, Silver engine/exhaust detail, Dark Green/Black sidecar, Black figures, SWRW or thick SBRW	£75-95
	1946-49		As previous model but without Silver detailing and with thin SBRW	£45-55
42b	1950-55		Blue/Green, Blue figures, little detailing, SBRW, export only (renumbered 043)	£40-50
43b	1935-40	R.A.C. Motorcycle Patrol	Blue/Black motor cycle/sidecar, Silver engine/exhaust detail, Blue/Black rider with Red sash, SWRW or thick SBRW	£75-95
	1946-49		As previous model but no Silver detailing, thin SBRW. NB - two shades of Blue used post-war	£45-55
44b	1935-40	A.A. Motorcycle Patrol	Black/Yellow, Brown rider, more detailing, 5mm 'AA' badge, SWRW	£100-125
	1946-50		Black/Yellow, Tan rider, little detailing, 7mm 'AA' badge, SBRW (renumbered 270)	£50-60
	1950-55		As previous model but made for export only (renumbered 045)	£50-60
270	1959-62		Black/Yellow, Tan rider, 'AA' sign, solid Grey plastic wheels, (renumbered from 44b)	£40-50
271	1959-62	T.S. Motorcycle Patrol	Yellow motorcycle combination, Belgian equivalent of the A.A.	£150-200
272	1959-62	A.N.W.B. Motorcycle Patrol	Yellow motorcycle combination, Dutch equivalent of the A.A.	£250-300

Dinky Toys Military models

See also Action Kits, Aircraft, Ships, Gift Sets

Identification
Models issued **1933 - 1940**:.....Gloss or Matt Green or Camouflage finish with smooth diecast wheel hubs on thin axles.
Models issued **circa 1946**:.......Matt Green finish with smooth hubs and early tyres (black smooth, or thick black ribbed, or thin white tyres).
Models issued **1947 - 1949**:.....Matt Green finish with ridged hubs.
Models issued **circa 1950**:.......Finished in a glossy Olive Drab with ridged diecast hubs and black thin ribbed tyres.

Ref	Year(s)	Model name	Colours, features, details	Market Price Range
1	1954-55	**Military Vehicles (1) Set**	See 'Gift Sets' section.	
22f	1933-34	**Army Tank**	'Modelled Miniature' with 'HORNBY SERIES' cast-in.	
			Green lead body, Orange revolving turret, Red rubber tracks	£250-350
			Green lead body, Orange revolving turret, Green rubber tracks	£250-350
	1935-40		Green/Orange lead body, 'DINKY TOYS' cast-in, Red or Green tracks	£250-350
			Khaki lead body, 'DINKY TOYS' cast-in, Green tracks	£200-300
			Grey drab lead body, 'DINKY TOYS' cast-in, Red or Green tracks	£200-300
22s	1939-41	**Searchlight Lorry**	Green body, (22c casting)	£200-300
25b	19??-??	**Army Covered Wagon**	Military-Green body and hubs. South-African issue	£1,200-1,500
25wm	1952-54	**Bedford Military Truck**	Olive-Drab body, (made for export to the USA only) (renumbered 640)	£200-250
27m	1952-54	**Land Rover Trailer**	Olive-Drab body, (to accompany 25wm) (renumbered 341)	£300-400
28	19??-??	**Army Delivery Van**	Military-Green body and hubs, Type 3. South-African issue	£750-1,000
30hm	1950-54	**Daimler Military Ambulance**	Olive-Drab body, Red crosses on White backgrounds, (US issue) (renumbered 624)	£200-250
30sm	1952-54	**Austin Covered Wagon**	Olive-Drab body, made for export to USA only), (renumbered 625)	£200-250
37c	1937-41	**Signal Dispatch Rider**	Green body, Khaki rider, White or Black rubber wheels	£150-175
139am	1950-54	**US Army Staff Car**	(170m) Ford Fordor in Olive drab with White stars on roof and doors	£200-250
150	1937-41	**Royal Tank Corps Set**	See Gift Sets section.	
	1952-55	**Royal Tank Corps Set**	See Gift Sets section.	
150a	1937-41	**Royal Tank Corps Officer**	Khaki uniformed figure with Black beret, and binoculars in hand (renumbered 600)	£25-30
	1952-54		Khaki uniform; in 150 Set or in box of 12 x 150a	£100-120
150b	1938-41	**Royal Tank Corps Private**	Khaki uniform, seated. Box of 12	£50-70
	1952-54		Khaki uniform; in 150 Set or in box of 12 x 150b, (renumbered 604)	£100-120
150c	1937-41	**Royal Tank Corps Private**	Die-cast figure in Khaki uniform, standing, (also in sets 151 and 152)	£25-30
150d	1937-41	**Royal Tank Corps Driver**	Die-cast figure in Khaki uniform, sitting, (also in sets 151 and 152)	£25-30
150e	1937-41	**Royal Tank Corps NCO**	Die-cast figure in Khaki uniform, walking, (also in set 150)	£10-15
151	1937-41	**Medium Tank Set**	See Gift Sets section.	
151a	1937-41	**Medium Tank**	Gloss or Matt-Green body/base, White markings, chain tracks, aerial	£125-150
			As previous model but with Black rubber wheels instead of tracks	NGPP
	1947-49		(Matt) Green body, Black base, no markings, made for export only	£150-200
151b	1937-41	**6-wheel Covered Wagon**	Gloss Olive-Green body, tinplate canopy, seat holes, spare wheel	£150-200
	1937-41	.................................Lead issue:	Gloss Olive-Green body, Black ribbed tyres	£150-200
	1940		Camouflage body	£150-200
	1946		Matt Olive-Green with smooth hubs and early tyres	£150-200
	1947-49		Matt Olive-Green with ridged hubs	£150-200
	1950-54		Gloss Olive-Green, no seat holes, smooth tyres	£150-200
	1950-54		Matt-Green or Greenish-Brown body, 'Export only' from 1950 (renumbered 620)	£200-250
151c	1937-48	**Cooker Trailer**	Gloss or Matt-Green trailer, wire stand, hole in seat but no figure	£50-70
	NB		Two styles of baseplate lettering are known for 151c.	
151d	1937-48	**Water Tank Trailer**	Gloss Green	£50-70
152	1937-41	**Light Tank Set**	See Gift Sets section.	
152a	1937-41	**Light Tank**	Gloss or Matt Olive-Green body/base, White markings, chain tracks, aerial	£100-125
			As previous model but with Black rubber wheels instead of tracks	£125-175
	1947-50		Matt Olive-Green body, Black base, no markings, chain tracks, aerial	£150-200
	1950-54		Gloss Olive-Green body, Black base, no markings, made for export only (renumbered 650)	£150-200
			Mid (Chocolate) Brown variation	NGPP
152b	1937-41	**Reconnaissance Car**	Gloss Olive-Green body/base, six wheels	£100-125
	1946		Matt Olive-Green with smooth hubs and early tyres	£150-200
	1947-49		Matt Olive-Green with ridged hubs	£125-175
	1950-54		Gloss Olive-Green body, Black base, made for export only (renumbered 671)	£125-175
152c	1937-41	**Austin Seven**	Matt Green body, wire windscreen frame, hole in seat	£125-150
	1937-41	.................Camouflage issue:	Matt Green body	£100-125
	1940-41	.........................Lead issue:	Matt Green body	£100-150
153a	1946-47	**Jeep**	Gloss Dark Green, US White star on flat bonnet and left rear side, smooth hubs, solid steering wheel, no round hole in base	£150-200
	1947		As previous model but with open spoked steering wheel	£60-75
			As previous model but with Brown body	£150-200
	1948-52		Matt or Gloss Green body, raised 'domed' bonnet, round hole in base	£60-75
	1952-54		Matt Olive-Green body, some have rounded axle ends, US export only (renumbered 672)	£150-200
160	1939-41	**Royal Artillery Personnel Set**	See Gift Sets section.	
160a	1939-41	**Royal Artillery NCO**	Khaki uniform; part of 160 Set	£10-15
160b	1939-54	**Royal Artillery Gunner**	Khaki uniform, seated, hands on knees; part of 160 Set, (renumbered 608)	£10-15
	1952-55	.........................US only issue:	Khaki uniform, seated, hands on knees, Green box of 12	£150-200
160c	1939-41	**Royal Artillery Gunlayer**	Khaki uniform, seated, hands held out; part of 160 Set	£10-15
	1952-55	.........................US only issue:	Khaki uniform, seated, hands held out, Green box of 12	£150-200

160d	1939-41	**Royal Artillery Gunner**	Khaki uniform, standing; part of 160 Set	£10-15
	1952-55	...............................US only issue:	Khaki uniform, standing, Green box of 12	£150-200
161	1939-41	**Mobile Anti-Aircraft Set**	See Gift Sets section.	
161a	1939-41	**Searchlight on Lorry**	Gloss Green body, 151b casting plus diecast or lead searchlight	£200-250
161b	1939-41	**Anti-Aircraft Gun on Trailer**	Gloss Green, gun elevates, figure holes, cast drawbar and hook	£40-50
	1946-50		Matt Green or Dark Brown	£80-100
	1950-54		Glossy Olive-Green, US export issue (renumbered 690)	£125-175
162	1939-54	**18-pounder Field Gun Set**	See Gift Sets section.	
162a	1939-41	**Light Dragon Tractor**	Gloss Green body, holes in seats, chain tracks	£100-125
			As previous model but Black rubber wheels instead of tracks	£200-250
	1946-55		Matt Green body (holes in some), chain tracks	£100-150
162b	1939-41	**Ammunition Trailer**	Gloss Green body and baseplate, drawbar and hook	£20-25
	1946-55		Matt Green body, Black baseplate	£20-25
162c	1939-41	**18 pounder Gun**	Gloss Green body, drawbar cast-in, tinplate shield	£20-25
	1946-55	**18 pounder Gun**	Matt Green body and shield	£20-25
170m	1954-54	**Ford US Army Staff Car**	(139am) Olive-Drab, US issue, (renumbered 675)	£200-250
281	1973-76	**Military Hovercraft**	Olive-Drab body, Gunner, aerial, 'Army'	£25-35
341	1960	**Land Rover Trailer**	Olive-Drab body with drawbar and hook, (renumbered from 27m)	£300-400
600	1952-55	**Royal Tank Corps Officer**	US only re-issue (renumbered from 150)	£8-12
601	1966-76	**Austin Paramoke**	Olive-Drab, Tan hood, spun hubs, parachute	£40-50
	1976-78		Olive-Drab, Tan hood, Speedwheels	£30-40
602	1976-77	**Armoured Command Car**	Green or Blue-Green body with US star	£35-45
603	1957-68	**Army Private (seated)**	Diecast figure in Khaki uniform, Black beret, seated, box of 12	£40-50
	1968-71		Plastic figure in Khaki uniform, Black beret, seated, box of 12	£40-50
603a	1957-68	**Army Personnel Set**	Six diecast figures (Khaki uniforms, Black berets, seated)	£20-30
	1968-71		Six plastic figures (Khaki uniforms, Black berets, seated)	£20-30
604	1954-60	**Royal Tank Corps Private**	Die-cast, Khaki uniform, sitting, export only (to USA), box of 12 (renumbered from 150b)	£50-70
604	1960-72	**Army Personnel**	Six army driver figures (Khaki uniforms)	£20-30
604	1976-77	**Land Rover Bomb Disposal**	Olive-Drab/Orange, 'Explosive Disposal', robot de-fuser	£55-65
608	1954-55	**Royal Artillery Gunner**	Khaki uniform, seated, hands on knees. (US export issue) (renumbered from 160b)	£10-15
609	1974-77	**105 mm. Howitzer and Crew**	Olive-Drab body, three soldiers, bubble-packed	£30-40
612	1973-80	**Commando Jeep**	Army-Green or Camouflage, driver, two guns, jerricans, aerial	£25-35
615	1968-77	**US Jeep and 105 mm. Gun**	Olive-Drab body with US Army markings, driver	£35-45
616	1968-77	**AEC with Chieftain Tank**	AEC articulated Transporter 'ARMY' with 683 Tank	£55-65
617	1967-77	**VW KDF and 50 mm. Gun**	Grey, German markings, operable anti-tank gun	£55-65
618	1976-80	**AEC with Helicopter**	AEC articulated Transporter 'RESCUE', 724 Helicopter and net	£55-65
619	1976-77	**Bren Gun Carrier and AT Gun**	Khaki, plastic tracks, figures, gun/shells, White '57' on red shield	£35-40
	NB		Two variations exist: (i) '2035703 4', (ii) 'T2272616' plus star.	
620	1954-55	**6-wheel Covered Wagon**	Matt-Green or Greenish-Brown body, blued axles, export only (to USA) (renumbered from 151b) ...	£200-250
620	1971-73	**Berliet Missile Launcher**	Military-Green launcher body with White/Red 'NORD R20' missile	£100-120
621	1954-60	**3 ton Army Wagon**	(Bedford 'S') tin tilt, no windows, driver in some	£60-70
	1960-63	.....................................late issue:	(Bedford 'S') tin tilt, with window glazing, driver in some	£60-70
622	1954-64	**10 ton Army Truck**	(Foden) Olive-Drab, driver, tin tilt, Supertoys box	£70-80
	1954-64		(Foden) Olive-Drab, driver, tin tilt, Dinky Toys striped box	£70-80
	late issue:		As previous model but in a Yellow lidded picture box	£200-300
622	1975-78	**Bren Gun Carrier**	Green body, White star, driver, passenger, plastic tracks	£20-30
623	1954-63	**Army Covered Wagon**	(Bedford 'QL') Military-Green body with or without driver	£35-45
624	1954-?	**Daimler Military Ambulance**	Olive-Drab body, Red crosses on White backgrounds, (US issue) (renumbered from 30hm) ...	£250-350
625	1952-54	**Austin Covered Wagon**	Olive-Drab body, made for export only (to USA) (renumbered from 30sm)	£250-350
625	1975-77	**Six-pounder Gun**	Green anti-tank gun	£15-20
626	1956-61	**Military Ambulance (Ford)**	Olive-Drab body, Red crosses cast-in, driver on some, no windows	£40-50
	1961-62		Olive-Drab body, Red crosses cast-in, driver on some, with window glazing	£60-70
630	1973-78	**Ferret Armoured Car**	Olive-Drab body, plastic wheels, spare wheel	£15-20
640	1954-?	**Bedford Military Truck**	Olive-Drab body, made for export only (to the USA) (renumbered from 25wm) ...	£250-350
641	1954-61	**Army 1 ton Cargo Truck**	Olive-Drab, tin tilt, with or without driver, no windows	£35-40
	1961-62		As previous model but with window glazing, with or without driver	£40-50
642	1957-62	**R.A.F. Pressure Refueller**	RAF Blue, French roundel, with or without driver, Supertoys box	£80-90
	1957-62		RAF Blue, French roundel, with or without driver, Dinky Toys box	£90-110
643	1958-61	**Army Water Tanker**	Olive-Drab body, no windows, with or without driver	£30-35
	1961-64		Olive-Drab body with window glazing, with or without driver	£30-35
650	1954-55	**Light Tank**	Matt Green body, Black base, no markings, export only (to USA) (renumbered from 152a)	£100-125
651	1954-70	**Centurion Tank**	Matt or Gloss Olive-Drab body, metal rollers, rubber tracks, Supertoy. Blue/White box ...	£60-75
	Export issue:		Version housed in U.S. Gold 'see through' box	£100-120
	late issue:		Matt Green, plastic rollers, Yellow picture box with end flap	£150-200
654	1973-79	**155 mm. Mobile Gun**	Olive-Drab body with star, operable gun, plastic shells	£15-20
656	1975-79	**88 mm. Gun**	German Grey, fires plastic shells	£15-20
660	1956-61	**Tank Transporter**	Thornycroft Mighty Antar, Olive Green, no windows, driver in some	£70-80
	1961-64		With window glazing, Yellow box with 2 PP	£100-120
660a	1978-80	**Anti-Aircraft Gun with Crew** ...	Olive-Drab, 3 soldiers. (Bubble-packed model)	£15-20
661	1957-65	**Recovery Tractor**	Army Green, six diecast wheels, driver, operable crane, Supertoy, 1 PP	£80-100
			As previous model but with plastic wheels, in Yellow 'picture' box	£150-200
662	1975-77	**88 mm. Gun with Crew**	German Grey gun (656 without wheels), 3 crew, shells, bubble-packed	£15-20
665	1964-75	**Honest John Missile Erector** ...	Olive-Drab, Black/White missile, 10 wheels plus spare, Yellow box	£100-125
			Boxed on tray with plastic cover	£80-100
666	1959-64	**Missile Erector Vehicle and**		
		Corporal Missile Launcher	Olive-Drab body, metal erector gears, White missile with Black fins, 1 PP	£200-250
			Olive-Drab body, Black plastic erector gears, all-White missile, 1 PP	£125-150

667	1960-64	**Missile Servicing Platform**	Olive-Drab, windows, spare wheel, platform lifts, Supertoy, 1 PP...	£125-150
667	1976-78	**Armoured Patrol Car**	Olive-Drab body, aerial, spare wheel..	£15-20
668	1976-79	**Foden Army Truck**	Olive-Drab body, windows, plastic tilt and wheels	£25-35
669	1955-57	**U.S.A. Army Jeep**.....................	Olive-Drab body with White star, (US issue in 'plain' box)..	£200-300
670	1954-64	**Armoured Car**........................	Olive-Drab body, turret rotates, diecast wheels..	£20-25
	1964-70		Olive-Drab body, turret rotates, plastic hubs...	£20-25
671	1954-55	**Reconnaissance Car**	(Matt) Green body, Black base, made for export only (renumbered from 152b).......................................	£125-175
672	1954-55	**US Army Jeep**	Matt Olive-Green body, some have rounded axle-ends, US export only (renumbered from 153a)	£150-200
673	1953-61	**Scout Car**	Olive-Drab body, squadron markings, holes for personnel	£15-20
674	1966	**Austin Champ**	Olive-Drab body, driver, green extinguishers on bonnet, diecast hubs	£35-45
	1966-71		Military-Green body, driver, tinplate windscreen frame, plastic hubs	£20-25
674	1958-70	**'U.N.' Austin Champ**	White body, driver, tinplate windscreen frame. Made for export only	£250-300
675	1954-59	**Ford US Army Staff Car**	Olive-Drab body, US star on roof, small star on front doors, export only (to US),	
			'plain' printed box (renumbered from 170m)...	£200-250
676	1955-62	**Armoured Personnel Carrier** ...	Olive-Drab, squadron markings, 6 wheels, revolving turret...	£25-30
676a	1973-76	**Daimler Armoured Car**.............	Army-Green body, Speedwheels, 73 mm. (new version of 670)	£15-20
	1973-74	...................French made version:	With camouflage net ('Made in England' on base)	NGPP
677	1957-62	**Armoured Command Vehicle**	Olive-Drab body, 6 wheels, (based on an A.E.C. vehicle)...	£60-70
680	1972-78	**Ferret Armoured Car**	Sand or Army-Green, Speedwheels, spare wheel, bubble-packed	£10-15
681	1972-78	**DUKW Amphibious Vehicle**	RAF Blue or Army-Green body, Speedwheels, bubble-packed	£10-15
682	1972-78	**Stalwart Load Carrier**..............	Olive-Drab body, 6 Speedwheels, bubble-packed	£10-15
683	1972-80	**Chieftain Tank**	Olive-Drab body, plastic tracks, fires shells, bubble-packed..	£25-35
686	1957-71	**25-pounder Field Gun**	Olive-Drab, cast drawbar, (cast hubs, plastic from 1968)	£10-15
687	1957-67	**25-pounder Trailer**.................	Olive-Drab, cast drawbar, (cast hubs, plastic from 1968)	£10-15
687	1978-79	**Convoy Army Truck**	Green/Black body...	£10-15
688	1957-61	**Field Artillery Tractor**	Olive-Drab, driver in some, no windows, cast hubs...	£30-40
	1961-70		Olive-Drab, driver in some, windows, (plastic hubs from 1968)	£30-40
689	1957-65	**Medium Artillery Tractor**	Olive-Drab, driver in some, holes, 6 wheels, tin tilt, Supertoy	£80-100
			In Yellow picture box, with plastic driver and windows	£150-200
690	1954-55	**Anti-Aircraft Gun on Trailer**.....	Matt Green, made for export only (renumbered from 161b)..	£80-100
690	1974-80	**Scorpion Tank**	Olive-Drab, camouflage net, working gun, bubble-packed	£15-20
691	1974-80	**Striker Anti-Tank**....................	Olive-Drab, plastic tracks, aerials, 5 firing rockets	£15-20
692	1955-62	**5.5 Medium Gun**	Olive-Drab body, twin cast drawbar, elevating barrel	£15-20
692	1974-80	**Leopard Tank**	Grey with German markings, plastic tracks, bubble-packed...	£40-50
693	1958-67	**7.2 inch Howitzer Gun**.............	Olive-Drab body, cast drawbar, elevating barrel	£30-40
694	1974-80	**Hanomag Tank Destroyer**	Grey, German markings, plastic tracks/wheels, bubble-packed	£40-50
696	1975-80	**Leopard Anti-Aircraft Tank**	Grey-Green, German markings, plastic tracks, bubble-packed	£40-50
698	1957-64	**Tank Transporter Set**	Mighty Antar plus Centurion Tank	GSP
699	1955-58	**Military Vehicles (1) Set**	See Gift Sets section.	
699	1975-77	**Leopard Recovery Tank**	Grey-Green, German markings, dozer blade/jib, aerial, bubble-packed	£40-50
815	1962-64	**Panhard Armoured Tank**	Military-Green with French flag, (French issue)	£75-100
816	1969-71	**Berliet Missile Launcher**	Military-Green body, (French issue)...	£150-200
817	1962-64	**AMX 13-ton Tank**	Green body with French flag, (French issue)	£75-100
822	1962-64	**Half-Track M3**........................	Green body, rubber tracks, (French issue)	£75-100
884	1962-64	**Brockway Bridge Truck**	Military-Green, 10 wheels, bridge parts, inflatables. French issue	£200-250

**620 Berliet Missile Launcher
with 'Nord R20' Missile**

This model was made between 1971 and 1973. Its pictorial end-flap box is representative of many from that period.

Photo:
Swapmeet Publications

See also Gift Sets section.

Ref	Year(s)	Model name	Colours, features, details	Market Price Range
60a	1934-36	Imperial Airways Liner	(Armstrong-Whitworth Atalanta) cast body, tinplate wings, 4 x 2 PB, Plain or 'Sunray' effect, Silver/Blue, Gold/Blue, Yellow/Blue, Red/Cream, White/Blue/Green, White/Blue, Blue/Yellow, Cream/Green, Cream/Red with no markings	£200-300
	1936-39		Blue, Cream, Gold, Red, Silver or White. Black 'G-ABTI' marking	£200-300
	1939-41		Gold, Green or Silver, 'G-ABTI', 'Imperial Airways Liner' under wing, (reissued as 66a)	£200-300
60b	1934-36	De Havilland 'Leopard Moth'	Cast fuselage, tinplate wings, single 2-blade propeller. Green with Yellow tail and wingtips or Dark Blue/Orange, Silver/Green, Blue/Yellow, Blue/Red, Gold/Red, no markings, open windows	£100-150
	1936-39		All-over Green, Gold or Silver, 'Beige, Mid or Pale Blue, Red, 'G-ACPT', open windows	£100-150
60b	1939-41		As previous but blank side windows, 'DH Leopard Moth' under wing, (reissued as 66b)	£200-300
60c	1934-36	Percival 'Gull' Monoplane	Cast fuselage, tinplate wings, large 2-blade propeller. Reissued as 60k. Blue with Red tail and wingtips, Buff/White, Buff/Blue, Buff/Red, Gold/Green, Red/White, Silver/Green, White/Green, open windows with no markings	£100-150
	1936-39		White, Red, Yellow or Light Blue, 'G-ADZO' in Black, open windows, (renumbered 60k)	£100-150
60c	1936	'Lewis's' 'Amy Mollinson' Souvenir Issue	Mid-Blue with Silver wings and a Blue 'G-ADZO' marking. Sold at Lewis's of Liverpool department store in yellow box	NGPP
	1939-41		Same but blank or open side windows, 'Percival Gull' under wing, (reissued as 66c)	£200-300
60d	1934-36	Low Wing Monoplane	(Vickers Jockey) Cast body, tinplate wings, 2-blade propeller. Red with Cream tail and wingtips, Orange/Cream, Blue/Yellow, Silver/Red or Gold/Blue, no markings, no pilot	£100-150
	1936-41		Red, Orange, Blue, Gold or Silver, Black 'G-AVYP', pilot's head cast-in, (reissued as 66d)	£100-150
			Red with cream tail and wingtips, no pilot, with 'G-AVPY' marking	NGPP
			As previous but with pilot	NGPP
60e	1934-36	General 'Monospar'	Two-piece diecasting, 2 x 2-blade propellers. Blue with White tail and wingtips, Cream/Red, Gold/Red, Red/Cream, Salmon/Blue or Silver/Blue, no markings	£100-150
	1936-41		Silver, Lilac or Gold, 'G-ABVP' in Black, (reissued as 66e)	£100-150
			Same but with 'General Monospar', Cream, Gold, Lilac, Silver or Blue	£100-150
60f	1934-36	Cierva 'Autogiro'	Gold body with Blue rotors and trim, no pilot	£200-300
	1936-41		Gold body with Blue trim, unpainted rotors, pilot cast-in, (reissued as 66f)	£150-200
	1936-41		Red body with Cream trim, Cream or Silver rotors, pilot cast-in	£150-200
60g	1935-36	De Havilland 'Comet'	Cast fuselage and wings, enclosed wheels, 2 x 2-blade propellers. Red with Gold trim, Gold/Red or Silver/Blue, no markings	£100-125
			Silver body with black 'G-ACSR' with no 'DH Comet' shown	NGPP
	1936-41		Red, Silver or Gold, 'G-ACSR', 'DH Comet' under wing	£100-125
60g	1945-49	Light Racer (DH 'Comet')	Yellow, Red or Silver, 'G-RACE', 'Light Racer' under wing, 2 x 3 PB	£175-225
60h	1936-36	'Singapore' Flying Boat	Cast fuselage (126 mm.), tinplate wings, 4 x 2-blade propellers (early hulls lead). Silver with stencilled RAF roundels, no roller or 'gliding' hole	£250-350
	1936-39		As previous model but with plastic or wooden roller and 'gliding' hole, (renumbered 60m)	£250-350
	1939-41		Silver or Grey with accurate RAF roundel (waterslide transfers)	£250-350
	1940-41		As previous with gun seat, cutaway bow, no hole, name under wing	£250-350
60k	1936-41	Percival 'Gull' (Amy Mollison)	Blue/Silver version of 60c, 'G-ADZO' in Blue, special box	£150-200
60k	1936-41	Percival 'Gull' (H. L. Brook)	Blue/Silver version of 60c, 'G-ADZO' in Black, special box	£150-200
60k	1945-48	Light Tourer (Percival 'Gull')	Red, Silver or Dark or Light Green, 'Light Tourer' or 'Percival Tourer' under wing, no markings, small or large 2-blade propeller, (renumbered 60c)	£150-200
60m	1936-41	Four Engined Flying Boat	Red, Light Blue, Light Green, Dark Green, Gold, Cream or Silver, 'civilian' version of 60h with 'G-EUTG', 'G-EVCU', 'G-EXGF', 'G-EYCE' or 'G-EYTV'	£175-225
	NB		With or without bow hollow, wood or plastic roller or gliding hole.	
60n	1937-40	Fairey 'Battle' Bomber	Silver or Grey, RAF roundels, 1 x 3 PB, undercarriage	£90-120
	1938-41		Silver or Grey, RAF roundels, 1 x 3 PB, without undercarriage, (reissued as 60s)	£120-150
	NB		Early issues did not have name of plane cast in.	
60p	1936-39	Gloster 'Gladiator'	Silver, stencilled roundels, Red 1 x 2 PB, no name under wing	£100-140
	1939-41		Silver or Grey, transfer roundels, 'Gloster Gladiator' under wing	£100-140
60r	1937-40	Empire Flying Boat	Silver, 4 x 3 PB, Red plastic roller, hole, own box. Liveries: 'CALEDONIA' ('G-ADHM'), 'CANOPUS' ('G-ADHL'), 'CORSAIR' ('G-ADVB'), 'CHALLENGER' ('G-ADVI'), 'CLIO' ('G-AETY'), 'CALYPSO' ('G-AEUA'), 'CENTURION' ('G-ADVE'), 'CAPELLA' ('G-ADUY'), 'CERES' ('G-AETX'), 'CALPURNIA' ('G-AETW'), 'CAMILLA' ('G-AEUB'), 'CORINNA' ('G-AEUC'), 'CAMBRIA' ('G-ADUV'), 'CHEVIOT' ('G-AEUG'), 'CORDELIA' ('G-AEUD')	£250-350
	1940-49		As previous models but plastic, wood or brass roller, no hole. 'CALEDONIA', ('G-ADHM'), or 'CAMBRIA', ('G-ADUV'), (reissued as 60x)	£200-250
	NB		Camouflage issues: Early issues have Red/White/Blue roundels with a Yellow outer ring. The later (rarer) issues have a darker camouflage with just Blue/Red roundels.	
60s	1938-40	Medium Bomber	Camouflaged 60n with undercarriage, single roundel has Yellow ring, (reissue of 60n)	£100-150
60s	1940-41	Fairy 'Battle' Bomber	Camouflaged body, two Blue/Red roundels, no undercarriage, 1 x 3 PB	£150-200
	NB		Early issues did not have name of plane cast in.	
60t	1938-41	Douglas DC3 Air Liner	Silver, 'PH-ALI' 2 x 3 PB, hole, tail wheel on some, own box	£150-200
60v	1937-41	Armstrong Whitworth Bomber	Silver body, 'gliding' hole in some, RAF roundels, 2 x 3 Red PB, (reissued as 62t)	£150-200
60w	1938-41	Flying Boat 'Clipper III'	Silver body, 'USA NC16736', 4 x 3 PB/SBX, plastic roller, 'gliding' hole. (Sikorsky S32)	£140-160
	US issue:		Silver body, 'NC 16736' markings, 'gliding' hole, Red plastic roller, leaflet	£150-200
60w	1945-48	Flying Boat	Silver, Blue or Green, no markings, 4 x 3 PB, brass roller	£100-130
60x	1937-41	Atlantic Flying Boat (reissue of 60r)	Blue/Cream, 'DAUNTLESS' ('G-AZBP'), 4 x 3 PB, name under wing	£175-225
			Green/Cream, 'WHIRLWIND' ('G-AZBT')	£175-225
			Black/White, 'DREADNOUGHT' ('G-AZBV')	£175-225
			Orange/Cream 'SWIFTSURE' ('G-AZBU') and Blue/Cream 'ENTERPRISE' ('G-AZBR') and Black/Cream 'ENDEAVOUR' ('G-AZBQ'), Red/Cream 'VALORIUS' ('G-AZBS')	£175-225

62a	1939-41	Vickers-Supermarine 'Spitfire' .	Silver body (short nose), RAF roundels, 1 x 3 PB	£100-130
	1940-41	'Meccano Spitfire Fund'	Model 62a in special souvenir box (at 2/6 each). Brass ring through fin allows use as badge	
			or pendant. Proceeds went to Spitfire Fund.	
			Blue, Green, Grey, Magenta, Red, Yellow, or Camouflage	£500-750
			Chromium plated version (originally 10/6)	£1,000-1,200
62a	1945-49	'Spitfire'	Silver, (long nose, bubble cockpit) RAF roundels, 1 x 3 PB	£100-150
62b	1939-41	Bristol 'Blenheim' Bomber	Silver body, RAF roundels, Red 2 x 3 PB, name under wing	£100-150
62b	1945-49	Medium Bomber	Silver body, RAF roundels, Red 2 x 3 PB, name under wing	£60-80
62d	1940-41	Bristol 'Blenheim' Bomber	62b in Camouflage/Black/White, RAF roundels, 2 x 3 PB	£100-150
62e	1940-41	Vickers-Supermarine 'Spitfire' .	62a in Camouflage/Black/White, RAF roundels, 1 x 3 PB	£100-150
62f	1939 ?	D.H. Flamingo Airliner	Not issued	NPP
62g	1939-41	Boeing 'Flying Fortress'	Silver, 4 x 3 PB, 'gliding' hole, name under wing, with 'U.S.A.A.C.' markings/stars, own box	£140-160
			Pale Grey version	NGPP
62g	1945-48	Long Range Bomber	Silver body, Red 4 x 3 PB, no hole, not boxed	£90-120
62h	1938-41	Hawker Hurricane Fighter	Camouflaged body, RAF roundels, 1 x 2 PB, undercarriage on some	£100-130
62k	1938-41	The King's Aeroplane	Airspeed 'Envoy', Silver/Red/Blue, 'G-AEXX', 2 x 2 PB, own box	£150-175
62m	1938-41	Airspeed 'Envoy' Monoplane .	Red ('G-ACVJ'), Silver ('G-ADCB'), Blue ('G-ADAZ'), Green ('G-AENA'), or Yellow ('G-ACVJ')	£120-150
62m	1945-48	Light Transport Plane	Red, Yellow, Silver or Blue body, 'G-ATMH', 2 x 2 PB, name under wing	£100-125
62n	1938-41	Junkers 'Ju90' Air Liner	Silver body, ('D-AALU', 'D-AIVI', 'D-AURE', or 'D-ADLH'), 4 x 3 PB, own box	£200-300
62p	1938-41	'Ensign' Air Liner	Silver body, Red 4 x 3 PB, gliding hole in some, own box. Liveries:	
			'ENSIGN' ('G-ADSR'), 'ELSINORE' ('G-ADST'), 'EXPLORER' ('G-ADSV'),	
			'ECHO' ('G-ADTB'), 'ETTRICK' ('G-ADSX'), 'ELYSIAN' ('G-ADSZ')	£150-200
62p	1945-49	Armstrong Whitworth Air Liner	As previous casting but no hole, name under wing, 4 x 3 PB, no box,	
			Silver, Blue, Green, with Silver or Grey/Green trim, 'EXPLORER' or 'ECHO' markings	£100-125
62r	1939-41	D.H. 'Albatross' Mail Liner	Silver, 'G-AEVV', Red 4 x 3 PB, hole, name under wing, own box	£150-175
62r	1945-49	Four Engined Liner	Grey, Light Blue or Silver, no markings, no hole, not boxed, 145 mm	£100-130
			Grey, Fawn, Light Blue or Silver, 'G-ATPV', Red 4 x 3 PB, 145 mm	£100-130
62s	1939-41	Hawker 'Hurricane' Fighter	Silver body, RAF roundels, with or without undercarriage, 1 x 2 or 3 PB	£90-120
	1945-49		Silver body, RAF roundels, no undercarriage, 1 x 3 PB	£60-70
62t	1939-41	Armstrong Whitley Bomber	Light Green/Brown camouflage, Yellow ring roundels, 2 x 3 PB, box	£125-160
	(reissue of 60v)		Dark camouflage version, Yellow roundels	£200-300
			Dark camouflage, Red and Blue roundels	£150-200
62w	1939-41	'Frobisher' Class Air Liner	Silver body (casting as 62r), 4 x 3 PB, hole, own box, 3 liveries:	
			'FROBISHER' ('G-AFDI'), 'FALCON' ('G-AFDJ'), 'FORTUNA' ('G-AFDK'), (renumbered 68b)	£150-200
62x	1939-41	British 40 Seat Airliner	Grey/Green, Red/Maroon, TT-Green, Yellow/Maroon, Two-tone Blue,	
			'G-AZCA', not boxed, with or without gliding hole, (renumbered 68a)	£125-175
62y	1939-40	Giant High Speed Monoplane ...	Blue/Brown, Blue/Silver, Olive/Green, Blue/Cream, Yellow/Maroon,	
			Red/Maroon, TT-Blue or TT-Green, 'D-AZBK', not boxed	£100-125
	1945-49		Light/Dark Green, Grey/Green or Silver, no hole or box, 'G-ZBK'	£100-125
63	1939-41	Mayo Composite Aircraft	Models 63a and 63b together in special box (see below)	£200-300
63a	1939-41	Flying Boat 'MAIA'	Silver body, 'G-ADHK', 'Mayo Composite' under wing, no hole	£100-150
63b	1939-41	Seaplane 'MERCURY'	Silver, 'G-ADHJ', 'Mercury Seaplane' under wing, 'hole' in some	£75-100
63b	1945-49	Seaplane	Silver body, 'G-AVKW', no 'gliding' hole, 'Seaplane' under wing	£90-120
	1952-57		Reissue of 63b Seaplane, same as previous model, (renumbered 700)	£90-120
66a	1940-41	Heavy Bomber	Camouflaged body, RAF roundels, 4 x 2 PB, no name under wing, (reissue of 60a)	£250-300
66b	1940-41	Dive Bomber Fighter	Camouflaged body, RAF roundels, 1 x 2 PB, (reissue of 60b)	£150-200
66c	1940-41	Two Seater Fighter	Camouflaged body, RAF roundels, 1 x 2 PB, (reissue of 60c)	£150-200
66d	1940-41	Torpedo Dive Bomber	Camouflaged body, RAF roundels, 1 x 2 PB, (reissue of 60d)	£150-200
66e	1940-41	Medium Bomber	Camouflaged body, RAF roundels, 2 x 2 PB, 'General Monospar' under, (reissue of 60e)	£150-200
66f	1940-41	Army Co-operation Autogiro .	Silver body and blades, Red/White/Blue roundels, (reissue of 60f)	£150-200
67a	1940-41	Junkers Ju89 Heavy Bomber	Black/Pale Blue body, German markings, no hole, own box	£250-300
68a	1940-41	'Ensign' Air Liner	Camouflaged body, RAF roundels, no 'gliding' hole, 4 x 3 PB	£150-200
68b	1940-41	'Frobisher' Class Air Liner	Light or Dark Camouflage, RAF roundels, 4 x 3 PB, 'hole' in some, (renumbered from 62w)	£150-200
70a	1946-49	Avro 'York' Airliner	Silver body, 'G-AGJC', Red 4 x 3 PB. Early version has Silver propeller pins,	
			tinplate base and blued cockpit, (renumbered 704)	£80-100
70b	1946-49	Tempest II Fighter	Silver with blued canopy, Yellow band on fuselage roundels, pointed spinner, (renumbered 730)	£35-45
70c	1947-49	Viking Air Liner	Silver or Grey body, 'G-AGOL', Red 2 x 4 PB, large pointed spinners, (reissued as 705)	£55-65
70d	1946-49	Twin-Engined Fighter	Silver body with blued canopy, (reissued as 731)	£35-45
	variation:		As previous model but 'N' in 'MECCANO' is reversed	NGPP
70e	1946-49	Gloster 'Meteor'	Silver body with blued canopy, Black engine intakes, large roundels, (renumbered 732)	£35-45
70f	1947-49	Lockheed 'Shooting Star'	Silver body with blued canopy, Black air intakes, USAF star on port wing, (renumbered 733)	£35-45
700	1954-57	Seaplane	Silver body with 'G-AVKW' marking, (renumbered from 63b)	£75-100
			Silver body, 'G-AVKW', no 'gliding' hole, 'Seaplane' under wing	£75-100
700	1979	Spitfire Mark II ('Jubilee')	Plated model on plinth, 1 x 3 PB, 'Diamond Jubilee of the RAF', special Blue card display box	£100-125
701	1947-49	Short 'Shetland' Flying Boat .	Silver, 'G-AGVD', Black 4 x 4 PB, first Supertoys aircraft, own box	£300-400
702	1954-55	DH 'Comet' Jet Airliner 'BOAC'	White/Blue body, Silver wings and tail, 'G-ALYV', Gold wheels, (renumbered 999)	£110-130
704	1954-59	Avro 'York' Airliner	Silver body, 'G-AGJC', Red 4 x 3 PB, 160 mm. ('704' beneath wing), (renumbered from 70a)	£70-90
705	1952-62	'Viking' Air Liner	Silver body with 'G-AGOL' marking, flat head spinners, (renumbered 70c)	£60-75
			Silver or Grey body, 'G-AGOL', Red 2 x 4 PB	£60-75
706	1956-57	Vickers 'Viscount' Airliner	Silver/Blue/White, 'AIR FRANCE', 'F-BGNL', Red 4 x 4 PB	£100-125
708	1957-65	Vickers 'Viscount' Airliner	Silver/White or Metallic Grey/White, 'B.E.A.', 'G-AOJA'	£100-125
710	1965-76	Beechcraft S35 'Bonanza'	Red/White, Bronze/Yellow, or Red/Blue/White body, 1 x 2 PB	£40-50
	German Promotional:		Green/White, 'GLUCK MIT WICKULER' on towing pennant and box	£400-500
712	1972-77	US Army T.42A	Military Green (715), Beechcraft plus wing-tip tanks, 2 x 2 PB	£60-75
715	1956-62	Bristol 173 Helicopter	Turquoise body with Red rotors and stripes, 'G-AUXR'	£40-50
715	1968-76	Beechcraft C55 'Baron'	White/Yellow or Red/Yellow body, Yellow 2 x 2 PB	£40-50
716	1957-62	Westland Sikorsky S-51	Red and Cream helicopter body, 2 x 3-blade rotors	£40-50
717	1970-75	Boeing '737'	White/Blue body, White or Blue engine pods, 'LUFTHANSA'	£55-65
718	1972-75	Hawker 'Hurricane' Mk.IIc	Camouflaged body, RAF roundels, Black 1 x 3 PB, guns	£65-75
719	1969-77	Spitfire Mk.II	Camouflaged, RAF roundels, Black 1 x 3 PB (battery-operated), (renumbered 741)	£55-70
			Early issues in 'Battle of Britain' pictorial card box	£50-60

721	1969-80	**Junkers Ju87b Stuka**	Camouflage/Yellow, German markings, 1 x 3 PB, cap-firing bomb	£55-70
			Early issues in 'Battle of Britain' pictorial card box	£50-60
722	1970-80	**Hawker 'Harrier'**	Metallic Blue/Olive Camouflage, RAF markings, pilot, aerial	£65-80
723	1970-73	**Hawker Siddeley HS 125**	Yellow/White/Blue or Metallic Blue/White, drop-down door/steps	£35-45
724	1971-79	**'Sea King' Helicopter**	Metallic Blue/White, 5-blade rotors, with 'Apollo' space capsule	£50-60
			Early issues in card picture box with pictorial inner stand	£40-50
725	1972-77	**Royal Navy 'Phantom II'**	Dark Blue body, Black nose, roundels, decals in bubble-pack	£80-90
726	1972-74	**Messerschmitt Bf-109E**	Desert camouflage, 1 x 3 PB, decals in bubble-pack	£100-125
	1974-76		Grey/Green camouflage, Yellow wing-tips/nose, decals in bubble-pack	£100-150
727	1976-77	**U.S.A.F. Phantom F4 Mark II**	Brown/Olive camouflage, 2 missiles, 2 figures, (no transfers issued), US market	£500-750
728	1972-75	**R.A.F. 'Dominie'**	Metallic Blue and camouflage, roundels, retractable wheels, bubble-pack	£40-50
729	1974-76	**Multi-Role Combat Aircraft**	Grey/Camouflage, swing-wings, decals in bubble-pack	£40-50
730	1952-55	**Tempest II Fighter**	Same as 70b but without blued canopy and with flat spinners, (renumbered from 70b)	£30-40
730	1972-76	**US Navy 'Phantom II'**	Grey/Red, 'NAVY', 'USS Saratoga', fires missiles, retractable wheels	£80-90
731	1952-55	**Twin-Engined Fighter**	Silver body, no blued canopy, (reissue of 70d)	£25-35
731	1973-76	**S.E.P.E.C.A.T. 'Jaguar'**	Metallic Blue and camouflage body, Orange pilot, opening cockpit	£40-50
732	1952-62	**Gloster 'Meteor'**	Silver body without blued canopy, small roundels, (reissue of 70e)	£25-35
			Shiny Silver body finish with large roundels	NGPP
732	1974-80	**Bell 'POLICE' Helicopter**	Orange/Blue/White or Red body, sign boards and cones	£35-45
732	1979	**'M.A.S.H.' Helicopter**	Green body with 'M.A.S.H.' stickers	NGPP
733	1952-62	**Lockheed 'Shooting Star'**	Silver body with blued canopy, (reissue of 70f)	£25-35
			Variant with 'in' of 'Made in England by Meccano Ltd' missing	NGPP
733	1973-76	**German 'Phantom II'**	Grey/Green camouflage body, 'Bundesluftwaffe', two white missiles, instructions and transfers, (German/Austrian market)	£200-300
733	1976-77	**US F-4K 'Phantom II'**	Brown camouflage, retractable wheels, fires missiles, (US market only)	£80-90
734	1955-62	**Supermarine 'Swift'**	Grey/Green camouflaged body, RAF markings	£30-40
734	1975-78	**P47 'Thunderbolt'**	Metallic Silver/Black, Red 1 x 4 PB, retractable wheels, 'U.S.A.A.F.'	£125-150
735	1956-66	**Gloster 'Javelin'**	Camouflaged 'delta-wing' body, RAF markings, smooth then treaded wheels	£35-45
736	1955-63	**Hawker 'Hunter'**	Camouflaged body, RAF markings	£30-40
736	1973-78	**Bundesmarine 'Sea King'**	Grey/Orange helicopter, German markings, decals in bubble-pack	£25-35
737	1959-68	**P.1B 'Lightning' Fighter**	Silver (metal wheels) or Metallic Grey (Black plastic wheels)	£60-80
738	1960-65	**DH 110 'Sea Vixen' Fighter**	Grey/White body, Black nose, RAF roundels, 'ROYAL NAVY'	£60-80
739	1975-78	**A6M5 'Zero Sen'**	Metallic Green/Black, Japanese markings, decals in bubble-pack	£60-80
741	1978-80	**Spitfire Mk.II**	Camouflaged body, (non-motorised version of 719)	£60-80
749 (992)	1955-56	**RAF Avro 'Vulcan' Bomber**	Silver body (aluminium), only 500 models were made (for Canadian market). 992 is the catalogue (and box) number, '749' is cast into the model, (renumbered 992) Two castings exist; one has pointed wingtips, the other more rounded	£1,500-2,000
997	1962-65	**Caravelle SE 210 Airliner**	Silver/White/Blue, 'AIR FRANCE', metal or plastic wheels, Yellow lidded picture box with card support	£100-150
998	1959-64	**Bristol 'Britannia'**	Silver/White body, Red or Blue lines, 'CANADIAN PACIFIC', 'CF-CZA', striped picture box with card support	£175-200
	1964-65		Metallic Grey/White body, Red lines, 'CANADIAN PACIFIC', 'CF-CZA', Yellow lidded picture box with card support	£200-250
999	1955-65	**DH 'Comet' Jet Airliner**	White/Blue body, White tailfin, 'G-ALYV' or 'G-ALYX' registration, (renumbered from 702)	£100-125
			White/Blue body, Blue tailfin, 'G-ALYX' registration	£100-125
			As previous model but with Silver/Grey wings	£100-125

BOX TYPES: Many 1970-79 issues were 'vacuform' packed and these include model nos: 710,712, 715, 717, 718, 721 to 734 inclusive, plus 736 and 739.
Recommended reading:
'**Dinky Toys Aeroplanes - A Collectors Guide and Checklist**'. Contact D.C. Barratt, 230 Earlham Road, Norwich, Norfolk, NR2 3RH. (Tel: 01603-453650).

701 Shetland Flying Boat

Meccano introduced a new range of models in 1947 and called them 'Dinky Supertoys'. The first two issues were the Foden Diesel 8-wheeled Wagon and the Shetland Flying Boat shown here. The box is plain brown with a red and white label.

Photo:
Swapmeet Publications

Buses, Taxis, Trams and Trains

Ref	Year(s)	Model name	Colours, features, details	Market Price Range
16	1936-37	Silver Jubilee Set	Locomotive and two interlocking coaches, 'LNER' and '2590' cast-in, open windows, smooth hubs with White tyres, special box.	
			Silver loco and coaches, Grey, Mid-Blue, Dark Blue, Red or Orange trim	£200-250
			Silver loco and coaches with Dark Blue trim	£200-250
			Cream loco and coaches with Red trim	£250-275
			Blue loco and coaches with Dark Blue trim	£250-275
			Green loco and coaches with Dark Green trim	£250-275
16	1937-40	Streamlined Train Set	As previous models but with a change of name and box	£200-250
	1946-52		Blue/Black loco, 'LNER', Brown/Grey coaches, closed windows, Black tyres. Individually boxed in buff box with divisions and yellow label on end of lid.	£125-150
	1952-54	(renumbered 798)	As previous model but with 'BR' crest on tender	£100-125
16z	1935-40	Articulated Train	Two-tone Blue, or Gold/Red, or Cream with Red, Blue or Orange. French issue sold in UK	£200-250
17	1935-40	Passenger Train Set	Black/Maroon loco 17a, Maroon tender 17b, Maroon/Cream coaches 20a/20b	£200-300
			Black/Green loco 17a, Green tender 17b, 2 Green/Cream coaches 20a/20b	£200-300
			Lead and mazak set in 2nd type box with correct colour spot	£400-500
17a	1934-40	Locomotive	Black/Maroon or Black/Green, diecast cab/boiler, lead chassis	£100-125
17b	1934-40	Tender	Maroon or Green diecast body	£40-50
18	1935-40	Tank Goods Train Set	Green/Black loco (21a), and 3 Green/Black open wagons (21b)	£200-300
19	1935-40	Mixed Goods Train	Maroon/Black loco (21a), Green/Red open wagon (21b), Red/Blue 'SHELL' tanker wagon (21d), Yellow/Red/Green lumber wagon (21e)	£400-500
	rare box version:		Set in 3rd type pictorial landscape box	£800-1,000
20	1935-40	Tank Passenger Set	Green/Black loco (21a), 2 Brown/Green coaches (20a), Guard's van (20b)	£300-400
20a	1935-40	Coach	Brown/Cream or Green/White roof, diecast body, lead chassis	£40-60
20b	1935-40	Guard's Van	Brown/Cream or Green/White roof, diecast body, lead chassis	£40-60
21	1932-33	Hornby Train Set	Blue/Red loco (21a), Green open wagon (21b), Green/Blue crane wagon (21c), Red/Blue 'SHELL' tank wagon (21d), Yellow/Red/Green lumber wagon (21e), 'HORNBY SERIES' cast into lead body. Red card box	£500-600
	1934-35	Modelled Miniatures Train Set	Contents as previous set, in Red card box	£400-500
21a	1932-34	Tank Locomotive	Red/Blue 0-6-0 tank loco, 'HORNBY SERIES' cast into lead body	£50-75
	1934-41		Maroon/Black or Green/Black, 'DINKY TOYS' cast into lead body	£50-75
21b	1932-34	Open Wagon	Green/Red, Green/Blue, Green/Black, Maroon/Black, 'HORNBY SERIES' cast into lead body	£40-50
	1934-41		Colours as previous model, 'DINKY TOYS' cast into lead body	£40-50
21c	1932-34	Crane Wagon	Green body, Blue chassis, 'HORNBY SERIES' cast into lead	NGPP
21d	1932-34	Tanker Wagon	Red tank, Blue or Black chassis, 'HORNBY SERIES' cast-in, lead	£35-45
	1934-41		Red tank, Blue or Black chassis, 'DINKY TOYS' cast-in, lead	£35-45
21e	1932-34	Lumber Wagon	Brown/Blue, Yellow/Red or Yellow/Black, 'HORNBY SERIES' in lead	£35-45
	1934-41		Brown/Blue, Yellow/Red or Yellow/Black, 'DINKY TOYS', lead	£35-45
26	1934-40	G.W.R. Rail Car	Early issues are lead, later issues are mazak, plastic rollers.	
			Cream roof, Brown, Green, Yellow or Red body	£100-125
			Green body with Red roof	£125-150
26z	1937-40	Diesel Road Car	Cream roof, Red, Green, Orange, Yellow or Blue body. (French)	£100-125
27	1934-38	Tram Car	Plastic or metal wheels, Red 'OVALTINE' or 'LIPTONS TEA' or no logo.	
			Red, Orange, Green, Yellow or Light or Dark Blue body, Cream upper windows and roof	£200-250
			Light Blue or Dark Blue body, Cream lower/upper windows and roof	£200-250
29	1934-38	Motor Bus	Plastic or metal wheels, no logo, or Silver or Red 'MARMITE'.	
		(renumbered 29a)	Blue, Green, Maroon, Yellow or Red body, Cream or Silver roof	£200-250
29b	1936-46	Streamlined Bus	Green, Orange or Red coach body, all with Cream wheel covers, Black or White tyres, smooth hubs	£100-125
			Two-tone Blue, Yellow/Orange, Red/Maroon, Two-tone Green, or Turquoise/Red, smooth Black hubs, open rear window	£100-125
	1946-47		Cream and Dark Blue, smooth hubs, open windows	£100-125
	1947-50		Grass Green/Light Green, Light Green/Dark Green, Grey/Blue or Two-tone Blue body, Black tyres on ridged hubs, filled-in rear window	£100-125
29c		Double Decker Bus	The different casting types are shown in the diagrams above.	
	1938-40	'DUNLOP TYRES'	1st Type AEC/STL, cutaway wings, stairs cast-in, smooth hubs, White tyres, crimped axle ends. Advert in Black on Yellow rectangle.	
	regular issues:		Cream upper deck and roof with Red, Light Blue, Maroon, Green or Orange lower deck	£300-400
	1938	early Grey roof issues:	As previous but with Grey roof	£300-400
	late issue:		Dark Blue lower deck, Cream upper deck and roof	£300-400
	1938-40	without advertisements:	As above but without advertisements	£200-300
	Baseplates:		1st issue 'Made in England', 29 mm x 2 mm	
			2nd issue 'Made in England', 28 mm x 1.5 mm	
	1946	without advertisements:	1st type AEC/STL grille, cutaway wings, no staircase, six vertical inside body ribs, smooth Black hubs.	
	colours:		Green lower deck with Cream or Grey upper-deck	£100-150
			Red lower deck with Cream or Grey upper deck	£100-150
	1947-48	without advertisements:	As previous model but with post-war Black ridged hubs	£85-95
			As previous model but with Two-tone Green body	£130-160
	1948-49	without advertisements:	3rd type, Leyland or AEC grille, straight-across wings, Black ridged hubs. Early issues had 6 vertical inside body ribs, later issues had 5 (3 on n/s, 2 on o/s)	
	colours:		Red or Green lower deck, Cream upper deck	£90-110

	1949-53	...............without advertisements:	2nd type, AEC/Regent grille, straight-across wings, lengthwise chassis strengthener with hole in chassis centre, or (1952) eight vertical inside body ribs, ridged hubs, plus in (1953) '29c' cast in chassis.	
		colours:	Red or Green lower deck, Cream or White upper deck, hubs match the lower deck colour	£90-110
29c	54-54	**'DUNLOP'** .... (renumbered 290)	3rd type Leyland Titan grille and straight across wings, early issues have recessed stop lights, late issues (1959) protrude. Logo 'DUNLOP -The World's Master Tyre' in Black and Red. Sloping and upright designs exist.	
		colours:	Red or Green lower deck, Cream upper deck, hubs match lower deck colour	£80-100
29dz	39-40	**Autobus**	Green or White body, metal wheels, (French issue sold in UK)	£80-90
29e	48-52	**Single Deck Bus**	Mid-Blue body, Dark Blue flashes, Black hubs	£80-90
			Mid-Blue body and hubs, Dark Blue flashes	£90-110
			Cream body and hubs, Red flashes	£60-80
			Cream body, Blue flashes, Black hubs	£60-80
			Light Green body, Dark Green flashes, Black hubs	£80-90
			Light Green body and hubs, Dark Green flashes	£140-160
29f	50-54	**Observation Coach** .... (renumbered 280)	Grey body and hubs, Red flashes and hubs	£70-80
			Cream body and hubs, Red flashes and hubs	£80-90
29g	51-54	**Luxury Coach** .... (renumbered 281)	Maroon, Cream flashes and hubs	£65-75
			Orange body with Cream flashes and hubs	£80-100
			Fawn body with Orange flashes, Green hubs	£80-100
			Fawn body with Cream flashes and hubs	£100-130
			Blue body with Cream flashes, Yellow hubs	£130-160
			Cream body with Blue flashes and hubs	£80-100
			Cream body with Red flashes and hubs	£100-130
			Cream body, Orange flashes, Green hubs	£100-130
		NB	Market Price Ranges for models 29f, g and h are based on their being unboxed as compared to prices for the boxed renumbered issues 280, 281 and 282.	
29h	52-54	**Duple Roadmaster Coach** .... (renumbered 282)	Dark Blue body, Light Blue hubs, Silver coachlines	£80-100
			Red body and hubs, Silver coachlines	£80-100
			Green lower body, Cream upper body and hubs	£150-200
		NB	Early issue had a flat roof underside. Later issues have a rib front to back.	
36g		**Taxi with Driver**	'TAXI' cast into Black roof, driver cast into chassis.	
	36-46	....	Grey, Dark Blue or Red body, Black roof, open rear window	£150-200
			Green body, Black roof	£80-90
			Yellow body, Black roof, open rear window	£400-500
	47-50	....	Dark Blue, Green, Light Green, Red, Maroon or Brown body, Black roof on all, some open rear windows (usually filled-in)	£80-100
40h	1952-54	**Austin Taxi** (FX3)..........Chassis: (Renumbered 254)	Diecast chassis with cast-in driver and model number.	
			Yellow body and hubs, Black chassis ('40H'), interior and driver	£90-110
			Dark Blue body, Light Blue hubs, Black chassis ('40H'), interior and driver	£90-110
			Yellow body and hubs, Brown chassis ('40H'), interior and driver	£90-110
			Mid-Blue body and hubs, Black chassis ('40H'), interior and driver	£200-250
067	59-64	**Austin Taxi** (FX3)......................	See ref. 067 in the 'Dublo Dinky' section.	

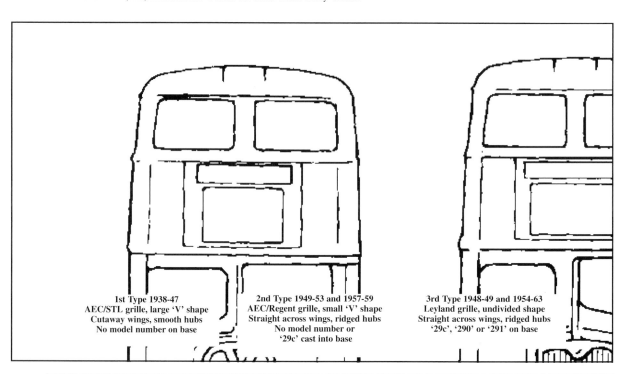

1st Type 1938-47	2nd Type 1949-53 and 1957-59	3rd Type 1948-49 and 1954-63
AEC/STL grille, large 'V' shape	AEC/Regent grille, small 'V' shape	Leyland grille, undivided shape
Cutaway wings, smooth hubs	Straight across wings, ridged hubs	Straight across wings, ridged hubs
No model number on base	No model number or	'29c', '290' or '291' on base
	'29c' cast into base	

115	79-79	**United Biscuits Taxi**	Yellow/Blue/Black, casting as 120, promotional...**£45-55**
120	79-80	**Happy Cab**...............................	White/Yellow/Blue, solid wheels, 'flower-power' stickers..**£45-55**
241	77-77	**'SILVER JUBILEE TAXI'**	Silver body and hubs, Union Jack on bootlid, 284 casting **£30-35**

254	1956-59	**Austin Taxi** (FX3) ....Two-tone:	Yellow upper body and hubs, Dark Green lower body, Black chassis ('254'), interior and driver **£90-110**
		Spun hubs:	Black body, spun hubs, Grey chassis ('254'), interior and driver **£110-130**
265	60-64	**Plymouth U.S.A. Taxi**.............	Yellow/Red, '25c First 1/5 Mile, 5c Additional', windows..**£80-90**
266	60-66	**Plymouth Canadian Taxi**...........	Yellow/Red body with 'Taxi' and '450 Metro Cab'..**£100-125**
268	62-67	**Renault Dauphine Mini Cab**.....	Red body with 'Meccano', 'Kenwood', and other adverts..**£90-110**
278	78-80	**Plymouth Yellow Cab**	Yellow body, 'Yellow Cab Co', plastic chassis and wheels **£20-30**
280	54-60	**Observation Coach**	Grey body, Red flashes and hubs...**£100-120**
		(renumbered from 29f)	Cream body and hubs, Red flashes...**£100-120**
			Cream body, Red flashes and hubs...**£130-160**
281	54-59	**Luxury Coach**............................	Cream body, Blue flashes and hubs..**£125-150**
		(renumbered from 29g)	Cream body, Red flashes and hubs...**£175-225**
			Cream body, Orange flashes, Green hubs..**£175-225**
			Cream body, Orange flashes, Cream hubs...**£125-150**
			Maroon body, Cream flashes and hubs...**£90-120**
			Mid-Blue body, Cream flashes, Yellow hubs...**£200-250**
			Fawn body, Orange flashes, Green hubs..**£125-150**
			Fawn body, Cream flashes and hubs...**£125-150**
		NB	Prices shown assume that models are in boxes with correct colour spot.
282	54-60	**Duple Roadmaster Coach**	Dark Blue body, Light Blue hubs, Silver coachlines..**£80-100**
		(renumbered from 29h)	Red body and hubs, Silver coachlines...**£80-100**
			Light Blue body and hubs, Silver coachlines...**£80-100**
			Yellow body, Red coachlines and hubs..**£125-150**
		US issue:	Dark Green lower body, Cream upper body and hubs...**£150-200**
		US issue:	As previous model but with Red hubs...**£150-200**

282	1967-69	**Austin 1800 Taxi**........................	Blue/White body, Red/White 'TAXI' labels on doors and roof..**£65-75**
283	1956-63	**B.O.A.C. Coach**	Dark Blue/White, *'British Overseas Airways Corporation'*, White tyres after 1960 ....**£80-90**
		NB	Model based on Commer Harrington Contender Coach.
283	1971-77	**Single Deck Bus**........................	Red body with White band, operable doors and bell, 'RED ARROW'.....................................**£40-50**
			As previous model but Metallic Red finish..**£50-60**
284	1972-79	**London Taxi** (FX4)....................	Black (or very Dark Blue) body, detailed boot on some, Speedwheels, driver, 'TAXI'...................**£30-40**
289		**Routemaster Bus**	'London Transport', Route '221', 'KINGS CROSS', driver/conductor,
			cast hubs, spun hubs or Speedwheels
	1964-65	'TERN SHIRTS'	Red body, 'FOR 8am CRISPNESS' transfers **£80-100**
	1966-69	'SSSCHWEPPES'	Red body, Blue-Green logo on White transfers, spun hubs...**£80-100**
	1969-80	'ESSO'	Red body, White label, 'ESSO SAFETY-GRIP TYRES'...**£50-60**
			Same as previous issue but with transfers...**£100-150**
	'ESSO' variant:		Deep Purple body, 'London Transport' and 'ESSO SAFETY-GRIP TYRES'
			logos, Blue driver and clippie **£300-400**
	1968-68	'LONDON STORES'	Red body, Black/Gold logo 'Festival of London Stores', promotional......................................**£100-150**
	1970	'INGERSOLL RAND'	Red body, promotional...**£100-125**
	1974-74	'MECCANO'	Gold body, 'MECCANO - DINKY TOYS'. (Very few issued to Press only) ....**NGPP**
	1977-79	'MADAME TUSSAUDS'	Red body, driver/conductor, White lower deck seating, Blue on White advert., cast wheels...............**£80-100**
			Red body, driver/conductor, Dark Blue lower deck seating, White on Blue ad., plastic wheels............**£80-100**
			Red body, with figures, packed in 'SCHWEPPES' picture box **£100-120**
	1977-77	'WOOLWORTHS'	Silver body, (Silver Jubilee limited issue) figures in some **£25-30**
	1977-77	'EVER READY'	Silver body, (New Zealand Silver Jubilee issue) no figures ....**NGPP**
	1979	'THOLLENBEEK'	Gold body, 'Thollenbeek 1929-79', Belgian promotional **£90-110**
		'FORDATH'	Red body, Light Blue upper deck seating, Deep Blue lower deck seating. Issued in plain White box
			with 'WITH THE COMPLIMENTS OF FORDATH LIMITED' labels to box ends. Promotional.........**£175-225**
	1979	'GREENLINE JUBILEE'...........	All-Green body, 'GREENLINE GOLDEN JUBILEE' promotional..**£70-80**
		'VISIT BLACKPOOL ZOO'	Cream body, plastic wheels, 'BLACKPOOL TRANSPORT' promotional **£90-110**

290		**Double Decker Bus**	Type 2 (AEC grille), 'DUNLOP - The World's Master Tyre' advert may be
		(renumbered from 29c)	upright or sloping, '290' cast on base, diecast hubs match lower deck.
	1954-59	'DUNLOP'...............................	Green lower deck, Cream upper deck..**£80-100**
			Red lower deck, Cream upper deck..**£80-100**
	1959-61	'DUNLOP'	Type 3 (Leyland grille), diecast hubs match lower deck colour, roof route
			box added, Mid Green or Dark Green lower deck, Cream upper deck.....................................**£80-100**
			Red lower deck, Cream upper deck..**£80-100**
	1961-63	....	Same colours as previous with sloping lettering but with spun hubs.......................................**£100-120**
	1963		Same body colours but with Green or Red plastic hubs...**£125-150**
	1963	'EXIDE BATTERIES'.................	Red or Green lower deck, Cream upper deck with '290' cast into base....................................**NGPP**

291		**Double Decker Bus**	Type 3 (Leyland grille) with route '73' on roof route box.
	1961-62	'EXIDE BATTERIES'.................	Red body with Red diecast hubs, logo in Black and Yellow..**£100-120**
	1962-63	....	Same body colours as previous model but with spun aluminium hubs......................................**£125-150**
	1963	....	Same body colours as previous but with Red plastic hubs..**£125-175**

291 - 293		**Atlantean City Bus**....................	A Leyland double-decker bus available in several versions:
291	1974-77	'KENNINGS'	Orange body, White engine cover and interior, 'VAN & TRUCK HIRE' **£40-45**
			As previous model but with Pale Blue engine cover and interior...**£40-45**
			As previous model but seen with 'Yellow Pages' stickers...**NGPP**
	1977	'LONDON & MANCHESTER	
		ASSURANCE'	White model on plinth. 'Your Best Man For Life'. (500 issued to agents)................................**£400-500**

292	1962-65	'RIBBLE'	Red and White body with or without 'REGENT' advertisement	£80-100
			Red and Cream body with 'CORPORATION TRANSPORT' fleetname	£80-100
			As previous model but no fleetname or logo	£80-100
292	1977	'LONDON COUNTRY'	Green body, shown in 1977 catalogue, but never issued.	
293	1963-65	'BP'	Green/Cream body, Yellow logo and smooth roof, 'BP IS THE KEY'	£80-100
			As previous model but with ribbed roof	£100-120
293	1973-78	Swiss Postal Bus 'PTT'	Yellow body with Cream roof, clear or tinted windows, (296 casting)	£25-35
295	1963-69	Atlas Kenebrake Bus	Light Blue/Grey body, suspension, windows	£50-70
			As previous model but all Blue body, Red interior	£70-90
295	1973-74	Atlantean Bus 'YELLOW PAGES'	Yellow body, 'Let Your Fingers Do The Walking'	£40-50
295	1974-76		As previous model but deeper shade of Yellow	£40-50
			As previous model but finished in Silver, no front or rear destination blinds	NGPP
296	1972-75	Duple Viceroy 37 Coach	Metallic Blue body, clear or tinted windows, bubble-packed	£25-35
			As previous model but Yellow and Cream body (see also 293)	£30-40
297	1977-77	Silver Jubilee Bus	Leyland Atlantean (291) Silver/Black body, 'National'	£30-35
		'WOOLWORTHS'	Silver Jubilee Bus (Leyland Atlantean) Silver body, promotional	£30-35
949	1961-66	Wayne 'SCHOOL BUS'	Deep Yellow body, Red body lines and interior, windows, Supertoy	£160-190
			As previous model but with Black lines on sides	£160-190
952	1964-71	Vega Major Luxury Coach	Pale Grey with Maroon flash, with electric lights, Supertoy. Pictorial box	£90-110
			As previous model but Cream body with Maroon flash	£90-110
			Late issues with Red interior, clear indicators, cast hubs	£70-90
953	1963-65	Continental Touring Coach	Pale Blue body, White roof, 'Dinky Continental Tours', Supertoy	£225-275
954	1972-77	Vega Major Luxury Coach	As 952 but without electric lights	£70-80
961	1973-77	Vega Major Coach 'PTT'	Orange/Cream body, 'P.T.T.' and emblem, Swiss model (in normal box)	£125-150
		box variant:	961 in Swiss box (Red/White/Yellow, 'Autocar Postal', 'Postauto', etc),	
			plus label 'Special contract run 1973 Swiss Post Office Bus - also	
			specially boxed for Swiss Meccano Agent for sale under their name'	£200-250
784	1972-74	Dinky Goods Train Set	Blue loco 'GER', one Red Truck, one Yellow Truck	£30-40
798	1954-59	Express Passenger Train Set	Green/Black loco, BR crest, Cream/Maroon coaches (Grey roofs), Black hubs/tyres	£125-150
		(renumbered from 16)	Green/Black loco, BR crest, Cream/Maroon coaches/roofs/hubs, Black tyres	£125-150
			Green/Black loco, BR crest, Cream/Maroon coaches/roofs, Red hubs, White tyres	£125-150

Dinky Toys Ships, Boats and Hovercraft

Ref	Year(s)	Model name	Colours, features, details	Market Price Range
50a	1934-41	Battle Cruiser 'HMS Hood'	Battleship Grey, (without name cast underneath 1939-41) 146 mm	£30-35
50b	1934-41	Battleship 'Nelson' Class	Battleship Grey, 'HMS Nelson' underneath (no name 1939-41) 117 mm	£30-35
50b	1934-41	Battleship 'Nelson' Class	Battleship Grey, 'HMS Rodney' underneath (no name 1939-41) 117 mm	£30-35
50c	1934-41	Cruiser 'HMS Effingham'	Battleship Grey, (without name cast underneath 1939-41) 100 mm	£30-35
50d	1934-41	Cruiser 'HMS York'	Battleship Grey, (without name cast underneath 1939-41) 98 mm	£30-35
50e	1934-41	Cruiser 'HMS Delhi'	Battleship Grey, (without name cast underneath 1939-41) 81 mm	£30-35
50f	1934-41	Destroyer 'Broke' Class	Battleship Grey, no wording underneath, 57 mm	£15-20
50g	1935-41	Submarine 'K' Class	Battleship Grey, wire mast, no wording underneath, 57 mm	£15-20
50h	1935-41	Destroyer 'Amazon' Class	Battleship Grey, no wording underneath, 52 mm	£15-20
50k	1935-41	Submarine 'X' Class	Battleship Grey, wire mast, no wording underneath, 61 mm	£15-20
51b	1934-40	Norddeutscher-Lloyd 'Europa'	Black hull, White superstructure, Brown funnels, name under, 165 mm	£35-45
51c	1934-40	Italia Line 'Rex'	Black hull, White decks, Red/White/Green funnels, name under, 152 mm	£35-45
51d	1934-40	CPR 'Empress of Britain'	Canadian Pacific Railway colours – White hull, Cream funnels, 130 mm	£30-35
51e	1935-40	P & O 'Strathaird'	White hull, Cream funnels, name underneath, 114 mm	£30-35
51f	1934-40	'Queen of Bermuda'	Furness-Withy Line, Grey/White hull, Red/Black funnels, 99 mm	£30-35
51g	1934-40	Cunard 'Britannic'	'White-Star' Liner, Black/White/Brown hull, Black/Tan funnels, 121 mm	£30-35
52	1934-35	Cunard White-Star Liner 'No. 534'	Black/White/Red, '534' cast underneath, boxed, no rollers, 175 mm	£70-80
			Same model but '534 Queen Mary' cast underneath	£60-75
52	1935-35	(renumbered 52b)	As previous model with 'Queen Mary' cast underneath, but without '534'	£60-75
52a	1935-41	Cunard White-Star Liner 'Queen Mary'	Black/White/Red, boxed, with plastic rollers, 175 mm	£60-75
	1946-49		Black/White/Red, boxed, with brass rollers	£60-75
52b	1935-36	Cunard 'Queen Mary'	Black/White/Red, boxed, without rollers, (renumbered from 52)	£60-75
52c	1935-40	'La Normandie'	Black/White, Red/Black funnels, boxed, made in France, pictorial insert	£60-75
52c	1939	Cunard 'Queen Elizabeth'	Announced in 1939 catalogue but never produced	NPP
52m	1936-40	Cunard 'Queen Mary'	Renumbered from 52b, without rollers, supplied unboxed	£20-30
53az	1938-39	Battleship 'Dunkerque'	Battleship Grey, with or without plastic rollers, boxed French issue	£40-60
281	1973-76	Military Hovercraft	Olive Drab body, Gunner, aerial, 'ARMY'	£25-30
290	1970-76	SRN-6 Hovercraft	Red or Metallic Red body, Blue or Black skirt	£20-25
671	1976-78	Mk.1 Corvette	White/Grey/Brown/Black plastic body, fires missiles	£20-25
672	1976-77	OSA-2 Missile Boat	Grey/Whit/Black, fires missiles	£20-25
673	1977-78	Submarine Chaser	Grey/White/Black, fires depth charges	£20-25
674	1977-78	Coastguard Missile Launch	White/Blue/Red/Yellow, 'Coastguard', fires missiles	£20-25
675	1973-77	Motor Patrol Boat	Grey hull with Cream/Black/Red	£20-25
678	1974-77	Air-Sea Rescue Launch	Grey/Black/Yellow, Orange dinghy, pilot/launch	£20-25
796	1960-62	Healey Sports Boat on Trailer	Cream hull with Green, Red or Yellow deck (plastic), Orange cast trailer	£25-30
797	1966	Healey Sports Boat	Sold without trailer from trade box of 6	£15-20

150

Ref	Year(s)	Model name	Colours, features, details	Market Price Range
100	1967-75	Lady Penelope's 'FAB 1'	Pink body, clear or tinted sliding roof (Pink stripes on early issues), rockets/harpoons, Lady Penelope and Parker figures (TV series 'Thunderbirds').	
			Card picture box with pictorial inner stand	£150-200
			As previous model but with Luminous Pink body	£200-250
101	1967-73	Thunderbirds II and IV	Gloss Green body with Yellow legs, plastic Thunderbird IV inside	
			Card picture box with pictorial inner stand	£150-200
	1973-73		Metallic Dark Green, Yellow legs, Thunderbird IV inside. Bubble-packed	£150-200
			Turquoise body	NGPP
102	1969-75	Joe's Car	Metallic Green, driver, battery powered, 139 mm. (TV series 'Joe 90')	
			Card picture box with pictorial inner stand	£100-125
103	1968-75	Spectrum Patrol Car	TV series 'Captain Scarlet', shaped hubs, 'screaming motor', Red body with Yellow base, Yellow or Cream plastic interior. Card picture box with pictorial inner stand	£100-125
			Metallic Red body with White base, Yellow or Cream plastic interior	£75-100
			Metallic Gold body, Blue tinted windows, Yellow or Cream interior	£75-100
		Pre-production prototype:	Yellow body, Lemon interior, aerial, cast wheels, (resin body)	£400-500
104	1968-72	Spectrum Pursuit Vehicle	Metallic Blue, 'SPV', separate seat/figure, 160 mm. ('Captain Scarlet')	£100-125
	1973-75		As previous model but seat and figure attached to door	£75-100
105	1968-75	Maximum Security Vehicle	White body, Red or Blue interior, 'RADIOACTIVE' crate, ('Cpt. Scarlet')	£75-100
			Late issue without Red body stripe	£75-100
106	1967-70	'The Prisoner' Mini-Moke	White body, Red/White canopy, 'bicycle' decal on bonnet, 73 mm	£150-175
			With axles penetrating spun hubs	£300-350
			With cast hubs and painted or unpainted side sills	£280-320
			NB Windscreen: Silver or Black metal, add	£30-40
106	1974-77	Thunderbirds II and IV	Metallic Blue body, Black metal base, Yellow legs, 153 mm. Vacuum-packed	£80-100
			Metallic Blue body, White plastic base, Yellow legs, 153 mm	£80-100
	1977-79		Metallic Blue body, Black plastic base, Red legs, 153 mm	£80-100
107	1967-68	'Stripey the Magic Mini'	White/Red/Yellow/Blue stripes, with Candy, Andy and the Bearandas.	
			Card picture box with pictorial inner stand	£175-225
108	1969-71	Sam's Car ('Joe 90')	Card box with tray, pictorial backing, 'WIN' badge, instructions.	
			Silver body, Lemon interior	£80-100
			Gold body, Lemon interior	£100-120
	1971-75		Pale (Powder) Blue body, Lemon interior, Red engine cover	£120-140
			Metallic Red body, Red or Silver trim, Lemon interior	£120-140
			Wine Red body, Lemon interior	£150-175
109	1969-71	Gabriel's Model 'T' Ford	Yellow/Black, (TV series 'The Secret Service'). Card picture box with pictorial inner stand	£75-85
111	1976-78	Cinderella's Coach	Pink/Gold, plastic figures and horses. ('The Slipper & The Rose')	£20-25
112	1978-80	Purdey's TR7	Yellow body, Black 'P' logo, Speedwheels. ('The New Avengers')	£45-55
			As previous model but with Yellow 'P' in Black logo on bonnet	£100-125
			As previous model but with Silver 'P' logo on bonnet	£35-45
113		John Steed's Jaguar XJC	Metallic Dark Blue, Gold pinstripes, rubbery 'Steed' inside. Officially not issued	NGPP
115	1979-79	United Biscuits Taxi	Yellow/Blue/Black, casting as 120, promotional, 86 mm	£50-60
120	1979-80	Happy Cab	White/Yellow/Blue, solid wheels, 'flower-power' stickers, 86 mm	£40-45
281	1968-70	'PATHE NEWS' Camera Car	Black body, Camera and operator, opening doors, (Fiat 2300), 108 mm	£100-120
350	1970-71	Tiny's Mini Moke	Red body, White/Yellow striped top, 73 mm. ('The Enchanted House')	£120-150
351	1971-79	U.F.O. Interceptor	From Gerry Anderson's TV series 'U.F.O.', 'S.H.A.D.O.' labels on Light Metallic Green body. Initially packed in card box with pictorial inner mount (prices 20% higher), later bubble-packed.	
			with Black nose, White missile, clear canopy, Red or Orange skids	£120-140
			with Black nose, White missile, Blue canopy, Red or Orange skids	£90-120
			with Red nose, Yellow missile, clear canopy, Red or Orange skids	£80-100
			with Red nose, Yellow missile, Blue canopy, Red or Orange skids	£80-100
	NB		The Red nose issues are housed in bubble packs.	
352	1971-75	Ed Straker's Car	Gold plated body, Blue interior, keyless motor, (TV series 'U.F.O.')	£80-100
			Yellow body, Blue or White interior, Silver trim	£80-100
			Red body, Silver trim	£70-80
353	1971-79	'SHADO 2 Mobile'	Green body, uneven roof, operable rocket, 145 mm. (TV series 'U.F.O.')	£70-80
			Green body, Brown rollers, Red interior, flat smooth roof, inner carded packing	£150-200
			Metallic Blue body	£120-150
354	1972-77	Pink Panther	Pink car and Panther, flywheel drive, card endflap box, 175 mm	£35-45
	1977-79	Pink Panther	Similar to previous model but without flywheel, bubble-packed	£35-45
			N.B. A single experimental Green diecast version exists (Christie's sale 4/95).	
355	1972-75	Lunar Roving Vehicle	Metallic Blue, White astronauts, front/rear steering, 114 mm	£35-45
357	1977-80	Klingon Battle Cruiser	Metallic Blue, fires 'photon torpedoes', 220 mm. (from 'Star Trek')	£35-45
358	1976-80	'USS Enterprise' ('NCC 1701')	White body, Yellow or White 'photon torpedoes', shuttlecraft, 234 mm	£50-60
359	1975-79	Eagle Transporter	White/Green body, Red cones/landing gear, unapplied decals, (from 'Space 1999')	£55-65
360	1975-79	Eagle Freighter	White, Red cargo pod, 'RADIOACTIVE' drums, (from 'Space 1999')	£55-65
			As previous model but with White cargo pod	£55-65
361	1978-80	Zygon War Chariot	Mid-Green body, two Red spacemen and rocket motor	£25-35
361	1978-80	Galactic War Chariot	Metallic Green body, two White/Yellow spacemen, Silver rocket motor	£25-35
361	1978-80	Missile-firing War Chariot	Metallic Blue body, two Red spacemen/rocket motor, blister card	£25-35
362	1978-79	Trident Star Fighter	Black/Orange, fires rockets, drop-down stairway, 170 mm	£30-35
			Metallic Gold body. 500 only issued to guests at a special Meccano Dinner in 1979	£100-150
363	1979-79	Cosmic Interceptor	Metallic Silver/Blue, 2 pilots, Marks & Spencer model ('St.Michael' box)	£35-45
363	1979-80	Zygon Patroller	Metallic Silver/Blue, 2 pilots, ('368' in some catalogues, '363' on box)	£30-35
			Yellow/Red/Blue version in 'U.S.S. Enterprise' box	NGPP
364	1979	NASA Space Shuttle	White booster and shuttle, decals, instructions, plastic Orange satellite. Pictorial window box	£80-100
366	1979	Space Shuttle	unboxed version of 364 without booster, with plastic or cardboard load	£20-30
367	1979-80	Space Battle Cruiser	White/Red body, pilot, plastic weapons, 187 mm	£35-45

Novelty, Space, Film and TV-related

368	1979-79	**Cosmic Cruiser**............................	Blue body, Marks & Spencer model (in 'St.Michael' box)..	£35-45
368	1979-80	**Zygon Marauder**........................	Red/White, 4 spacemen, ('363' in some catalogues, '368' on box)................................	£30-35
371	1980	**Pocket-size 'USS Enterprise'**.....	Small version of 358, bubble-packed, released after factory closure, (renumbered 801)........	£45-55
372	1980	**Pocket-size Klingon Cruiser**......	Small version of 357, bubble-packed, released after factory closure, (renumbered 802)........	£45-55
477	1970-72	**Parsley's Car**.............................	Green/Black/Yellow, head swivels, ('The Adventures of Parsley').	
			Card picture box with pictorial inner stand	£80-90
485	1964-67	**Santa Special Model 'T' Ford**....	Red/White body, Santa Claus, Xmas tree/toys/decals, 79 mm.......................................	£75-95
486	1965-69	**'Dinky Beats' Morris Oxford**	Pink/Green, 'Da gear', 3 beat-group figures, 92 mm...	£75-95
602	1976-77	**Armoured Command Car**..........	Green or later Blue-Green body, White star, driver, scanner, fires sparks, (TV series 'The Investigator')..	£35-45
801	1980	**Pocket-size 'USS Enterprise'**.....	Small version of 358, bubble-packed, released after factory closure, (renumbered from 371)....	£35-45
802	1980	**Pocket-size Klingon Cruiser**......	Small version of 357, bubble-packed, released after factory closure, (renumbered from 372)....	£35-45

Dinky Toys 'Action Kits'

These Action Kits were issued in the 1970s. Screws were usually included to attach their bases (which have no model numbers).
Paint supplied with the kit is not always the same colour or shade as on the relative model when supplied built and finished.

Ref	Year(s)	Model name	Colours, features, details	Market Price Range
1001	1971-77	**Rolls-Royce Phantom V**..................	Various colours (usually Blue), casting as 152	£20-30
1002	1971-75	**Volvo 1800s Coupé**........................	Yellow paint, 116 casting...	£20-30
1003	1971-75	**Volkswagen 1300**............................	Red and White paint supplied, casting as 129..	£20-30
1004	1971-77	**Ford Escort Police Car**..................	Blue and White paint, 'POLICE' transfers, casting as 270...	£20-30
1006	1973-77	**Ford Escort Mexico**........................	Red paint and 'MEXICO' transfers, casting as model 168..	£20-30
1007	1971-75	**Jensen FF**......................................	Various colours of paint (usually Blue), casting as 188..	£20-30
1008	1973-77	**Mercedes-Benz 600**........................	Red, Yellow or Green paint supplied, casting as model 128...	£20-30
1009	1971-75	**Lotus F1 Racing Car**.......................	Green paint and 'gold leaf' transfers, casting as 225..	£20-30
1012	1973-75	**Ferrari 312-B2**..............................	Red paint and 'SHELL' transfers supplied, casting as 226..	£20-30
1013		**Matra Sports M530**........................	Not issued	NPP
1014	1975-77	**Beach Buggy**..................................	Blue paint, casting as 227..	£20-30
1017	1971-77	**Routemaster Bus**............................	Red paint and 'ESSO Safety-Grip Tyres' transfers, 289 casting.....................................	£20-30
1018	1974-77	**Leyland Atlantean Bus**..................	Various (mostly White), usually 'NATIONAL' transfers, as 295	£30-40
?		**Leyland Atlantean Bus**..................	'YELLOW PAGES'. There are three variations of this:	
			1) With Mid-Blue interior, reversed front 'Yellow Pages'...	NGPP
			2) White interior, reversed front 'Yellow Pages' sign..	NGPP
			3) White interior, correct reading front 'Yellow Pages'..	NGPP
1023	1972-77	**A.E.C. Single Decker Bus**..............	Green paint and 'GREEN LINE' transfers, casting as 283...	£30-40
1025	1971-75	**Ford Transit Van**..........................	Red paint and 'Avis Truck Rental' transfers supplied, casting as 407.............................	£20-30
1027	1972-75	**Lunar Roving Vehicle**....................	Blue/White paint, casting as model 355...	£20-30
1029	1971-77	**Ford D800 Tipper Truck**................	Green or Yellow paint supplied, casting as model 438...	£20-30
1030	1974-77	**Land Rover Breakdown Truck**........	Red or White paint in kit, casting as 442...	£20-30
1032	1975-77	**Army Land Rover**...........................	Military-Green paint and various 'ARMY' transfers in kit, casting as 344..........................	£20-30
1033	1971-77	**U.S.A. Army Jeep**..........................	Military-Green paint and military transfers supplied, casting as 615...............................	£20-30
1034	1975-77	**Mobile Gun**...................................	Military-Green paint, 654 casting..	£20-30
1035	1975-77	**Striker Anti-Tank Vehicle**..............	Military-Green paint and transfer supplied, casting as 691	£20-30
1036	1975-77	**Leopard Tank**................................	Military-Green paint and transfers supplied, casting as 692..	£20-30
1037	1974-77	**Chieftain Tank**..............................	Military-Green paint and transfers, casting as 683..	£20-30
1038	1975-77	**Scorpion Tank**...............................	Military-Green paint and transfers, casting as 690..	£20-30
1039		**Leopard Recovery Tank**.................	Not issued	NPP
1040	1971-77	**Sea King Helicopter**.......................	White with Blue or Orange paint plus 'USAF' transfers, casting as 724.............................	£20-30
1041	1973-76	**Hawker Hurricane Mk.IIc**..............	Camouflage paints and RAF roundels in kit, casting as 718...	£30-35
1042	1971-77	**Spitfire Mk.II**...............................	Camouflage paints and RAF roundels in kit, casting as 719...	£25-35
1043	1974-76	**S.E.P.E.C.A.T. Plane**......................	Blue and Green paints and transfers supplied, casting as 731......................................	£20-30
1044	1972-75	**Messerschmitt BF-109e**...................	Brown paint and Luftwaffe transfers in kit, casting as 726...	£20-30
1045	1975-76	**Multi-Role Combat Aircraft**	Camouflage paints and transfers supplied, casting as 729..	£20-30
1050	1975-77	**Motor Patrol Boat**.........................	Black/Blue/White paints and stickers, casting as model 675..	£20-30

Collectors notes

Auction Results – Dinky Toys Military Vehicles

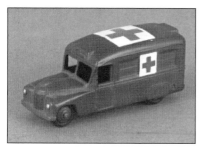

624 US issue
Daimler Military Ambulance
Mint – £320

625 US issue
Austin Covered Wagon
Near Mint – £230

640 US issue
Bedford Military Truck
Mint – £250

Pre-war 161 Mobile Anti-Aircraft Unit
plus 603 12 Army Personnel (seated)
Fair condition – £160

667 Missile Servicing Platform
'E' condition model and box – £120

620 Berliet Missile Launcher
Mint, in Good picture box – £150

689 Medium Artillery Tractor and
651 Centurion Tank. Both 'E', in Good
'pictorial' boxes – £120

674 'UN' Austin Champ
Near Mint model and box– £360

660 Tank Transporter
'E' condition, including
yellow box – £230

675 US issue
Army Staff Car
Near Mint, in 'plain' box – £180

669 US issue
Army Jeep (unboxed)
Good+ condition – £170

699 Military Vehicles Gift Set No.1
Contents and box both in
Good+ condition – £160

Models sold by Vectis Auctions Ltd., Fleck Way, Thornaby, Stockton-on-Tees, TS17 9JZ. Pictures reproduced by their kind permission.

Dinky Toys 124 'Holidays' Gift Set
This set was available between 1964 and 1966. It contains 952 Vega Luxury Coach, 137 Plymouth, 142 Jaguar and 796 Healey Sports Boat.
A stepped insert holds the models securely in the closed box and helps to display them when open.

Dinky Toys 399 Farm Tractor and Trailer
Set consists of a red 300 Massey-Harris Tractor and 428 Large Trailer in red and silver. It was produced between 1969 and 1973.
Photos: Swapmeet Publications

BOX TYPES

Sets 001-006: Housed in Green card boxes with plain Yellow inserts.
Sets 1, 2, 3, 4, 5, 6: Oblong boxes with Yellow insert card and train picture on lid.
c 1932   Purple marbled 'Modelled Miniatures' box.
c 1936   Blue patterned 'MECCANO DINKY TOYS' box, pictorial insert card
c 1939   Green box with plain insert, 'DINKY TOYS' label
1952-56   Green box with Yellow insert, stripe lid label
Train sets 17, 18, 19 and 20 box sequence:
    'Modelled Miniatures' : 'Meccano Dinky Toys' : 'Dinky Toys'.

Sets 24, 25 and 30 series:
c 1934   Purple marbled 'Modelled Miniatures' box.
c 1935   Purple marbled 'MECCANO DINKY TOYS' box with
    Yellow/Red label picturing eight assorted cars and lorries.
    Purple insert with Gold script on two central lines
    'MECCANO DINKY TOYS No '24', '25' or '30'.
NB The 24 Series and 30 series sets also contained a purple packing
    card stating 'PLEASE REMOVE THIS PACKING CARD

TO DISPLAY CONTENTS'.
c 1936   Blue patterned box lid with Yellow/Red label picturing eight
    assorted cars and lorries. Purple insert with no Gold Script on
    25 series (no details available on 24 and 30 series).

Sets 12, 42, 43, 44 and 49 (Pre-war issue):
    Blue landscape boxes with inner Blue/Green pictorial inserts.
Sets 151, 152, 156, 161, 162:
    Grey/Blue or Blue (152) display boxes with inner pictorial
    scenic backdrop and packing boards.

Early Post-war USA Special Sets: Sets for the US market were distributed by
H. Hudson Dobson of New York. They are housed in flat boxes with a mottled
greenish-blue lid. The picture label on the lid depicts a boy's face plus line
drawings of various models. The lid often still retains a red 'H. Hudson Dobson'
label. The Set number and type are shown on the main label, e.g. 'No. 6
Commercial Vehicles'. Sets 1, 2, 3 and 6 are listed – the Editor would welcome
any new information on the contents of these, and of Sets 4 and 5.

Ref	Year(s)	Set name	Contents	Market Price Range
			Pre-war sets without 'fatigue' and with pristine boxes attract a premium, as do early Accessory Sets in 'Modelled Miniatures' boxes.	
001	1954-56	**Station Staff ('0' gauge)** (renumbered from 1)	(35mm). 1b Guard (flag in right hand), 1c Ticket Collector (right arm extended), 1d Driver, 1e Porter (with oblong bags), 1f Porter (standing)	**£90-120**
002	1954-56	**Farmyard Animals (6)**	2 x 2a horses, 2 x 2b cows, 1 x 2c pig, 1 x 2d sheep, simplified painting, (renumbered 2)	**£200-300**
003	1954-56	**Passengers ('0' gauge)** (renumbered from 3)	(35mm). 3a Woman (with child on left), 3b Businessman (Brown suit and case), 3c Male hiker (no stick), 3d Female hiker (Blue shirt), 3e Newsboy (Grey tray), 3f Woman (Light Red coat, round case)	**£90-120**
004	1954-56	**Engineering Staff ('0' gauge)** (renumbered 4)	(35mm). 2 x 4b Fitter (all-Blue and all-Brown), 4c Storekeeper (all-Brown), 4d Greaser, 4e Engine-Room attendant	**£80-100**
005	1954-56	**Train and Hotel Staff ('0' gauge)**	(35mm). 5a Conductor, 2 x 5b waiters, 2 x 5c Porter (both Brown or Blue), (renumbered from 5)	**£90-120**
006	1954-56	**Shepherd Set**	6a Shepherd (Green hat), 6b sheepdog (all-Black), 4 x 2b sheep, (renumbered from 6)	**£200-300**
007	1960-67	**Petrol Pump Attendants**	1 male (White overalls), 1 female (White coat), plastic, 35 mm. tall	**£30-40**
008	1961-67	**Fire Station Personnel**	Set of 6 fire-fighters in Blue uniforms plus hose, plastic, 35 mm. tall	**£30-40**
009	1962-66	**Service Station Personnel**	Set of 8 plastic figures in various colours and stances, 35 mm. tall	**£30-40**
010	1962-66	**Road Maintenance Personnel**	Set of 6 workmen using pick, barrow, shovels, drill etc, plus hut, brazier, barrier, and 4 lamps. Plastic, figures are 35 mm. tall	**£60-70**
050	1961-68	**Railway Staff ('00' gauge)**	12 Blue plastic figures in a clear plastic box. Early issues contained a Policeman, later ones a Shunter	**£40-50**
051	1954-59	**Station Staff ('00' gauge)**	6 plastic figures in a green card box (re-issue of pre-war Hornby-Dublo Set D1), (renumbered 1001)	**£35-45**
052	1961-69	**Railway Passengers ('00')**	11 plastic figures plus a seat, in a clear plastic box	**£35-45**
053	1954-59	**Passengers ('00' gauge)**	6 Blue plastic figures (re-issue of pre-war Hornby-Dublo Set D2), (renumbered 1003)	**£35-45**
054	1962-70	**Railway Station Personnel**	4 plastic figures plus 8 pieces of furniture in a clear plastic box, ('OO' gauge)	**£35-45**
1	1931-39	**Station Staff (6) (large)**	(40mm). 1a Station Master, 1b Guard (flag in left hand), 1c Ticket Collector (with open arms), 1d Porter (round/oblong bags), 1f Porter (walking). 'HORNBY SERIES' (early issues), 'DINKY TOYS' (later)	**£225-275**
1	1939-41	**Station Staff (6) (small)**	(35mm). As previous set but smaller figures	**£100-125**
1	1939-41	**Station Staff (6)**	(35mm). 1a and 1d as above, 1b Guard (flag in right hand), 1c Ticket Collector (right arm extended), 1e Porter (oblong bags), 1f Porter (standing)	**£150-200**
1	1946-54	**Station Staff (5)** (renumbered 001)	(35mm). 1b Guard (flag in right hand), 1c Ticket Collector (right arm extended), 1d Driver, 1e Porter (with oblong bags), 1f Porter (standing)	**£90-120**
1	1954-55	**Military Vehicles (1) Set** (renumbered 699)	621 3-ton Wagon, 641 1-ton Truck, 674 Austin Champ, 676 Armoured Car. Blue/White box with Blue cut-out base packing piece on top	**£300-400**
No.1	1934-39	**Railway Accessories Set**	'Miniature Luggage and Truck'. A Porter's truck and 4 pieces of luggage (tinplate and cast), items not available separately	**£100-125**
No.1	1946-48	**Commercial Vehicles Set**	29c Bus, 25b Wagon, 25d Tanker, 25e Tipper and 25f Market Gardeners Lorry. In mottled Green, Blue and Fawn box with inner Green card cut-out base. Box lid has Light Green and Blue silhouette label	**£2,500-3,000**
No.1	1952-54	**Farm Gear Gift Set** (renumbered 398)	27a Massey-Harris Tractor, 27b Harvest Trailer, 27c Manure Spreader, 27h Disc Harrow, 27k Hay Rake. In Blue/White box with inner cut-out base plus packing piece on top	**£1,000-1,500**
2	1934-35	**Farmyard Animals**	2 x 2a horses, 2 x 2b cows, 1 x 2c pig, 1 x 2d sheep, in 'Modelled Miniatures' box	**£750-1,000**
2	1935-40	**Farmyard Animals**	Six items as previous set but displayed in 'Dinky Toys' box	**£500-600**
2	1946-54	**Farmyard Animals**	Six items as previous set but simplified (less detailed) painting, (renumbered 002)	**£200-300**
No.2	1934-?	**Railway Accessories Set**	'Milk Cans and Truck'. A 4-wheel barrow and 6 milk churns, not available separately	NGPP
No.2	1946-48	**Private Automobiles Set**	39a Packard, 39b Oldsmobile, 39c Lincoln, 39d Buick, 39e Chrysler. Inner Green card base in Green, Blue and Orange mottled box, Green and Blue silhouette lid label (export only issue)	**£2,500-3,000**
No.2	1952-53	**Commercials Vehicles Set**	25m Bedford End Tipper, 27d Land Rover (Dark Brown), 30n Farm Produce Wagon, 30p 'Mobilgas' Tanker, 30s Austin Covered Wagon. In Blue/White box with inner cut-out base plus packing piece on top	**£2,500-3,000**
3	1932-39	**Passengers (large)**	(40mm). 3a Woman (with child on right), 3b Businessman (left hand on chest), 3c Male hiker (with stick), 3d Female hiker (White shirt), 3e Newsboy (running), 3f Woman (Red jacket, oblong case). 'HORNBY SERIES' (early issues), 'DINKY TOYS' (later)	**£225-275**
3	1932-39	**Passengers (small)**	(35mm). As previous set but smaller figures. Oblong Green box with scenic background	**£150-175**
3	1939-41	**Passengers**	3a Woman (with child on left), 3b Businessman (case in left hand), 3c Male hiker (no stick), 3d Female hiker (White shirt), 3e Newsboy (standing), 3f Woman (Red coat, round case)	**£125-175**

3	1946-54	**Passengers**..................................	3a Woman (with child on left), 3b Businessman (Brown suit and case),
		(renumbered 003).........................	3c Male hiker (no stick), 3d Female hiker (with Blue shirt),
			3e Newsboy (Grey tray), 3f Woman (Light Red coat, round case)....................£90-120
No.3	1934-?	**Railway Accessories Set**	'Platform Machines Etc'. A posting box, ticket machine, label machine
			and two benches, not available separately....................NGPP
No.3	1947-52	**Private Automobiles Set** .... (i)	30d Vauxhall, 36a Armstrong, 36b Bentley, 38a Frazer-Nash, 39b Oldsmobile. Inner Green card
	(export only issue)		cut-out base in Green, Blue and Orange mottled box, Green and Blue silhouette lid label £1,250-1,500
No.3	1947-52	**Private Automobiles Set** ....(ii)	30d Vauxhall, 36b Bentley, 36d Rover, 38a Fraser Nash, 38c Lagonda. Inner Green card
	(export only issue)		cut-out base in Green, Blue and Orange mottled box, Green and Blue silhouette lid label £2,500-3,000
No.3	1952-54	**Passenger Cars Set**.....................	27f Estate Car, 30h Daimler Ambulance, 40e Standard Vanguard, 40g Morris Oxford,
			40h Austin Taxi, 140b Rover 75. Blue/White box with cut-out tray plus packing piece on top......£3,000-4,000
4	1932-41	**Engineering Staff (6) (large)**	(40mm). 4a Electrician, 2 x 4b Fitter (Blue/White and Brown/White),
			4c Storekeeper (Brown/Black), 4d Greaser, 4e Engine-Room attendant
			'HORNBY SERIES' (early issues), 'DINKY TOYS' (later)....................£200-250
4	1932-41	**Engineering Staff (6) (small)**.....	As previous set but smaller figures....................£150-175
4	1946-54	**Engineering Staff (5)**.................	2 x 4b Fitter (all-Blue and all-Brown), 4c Storekeeper (all-Brown),
		(renumbered 004)..........................	4d Greaser, 4e Engine-Room attendant....................£125-175
No.4	1934-?	**Railway Accessories Set**	A combination of No.1 ('Miniature Luggage & Truck'), No.2 ('Milk Cans & Truck'),
			and No.3 ('Platform Machines Etc'). Individual items were not available separately....................NGPP
No.4	1953-54	**Racing Cars Set**.........................	23f Alfa-Romeo, 23g Cooper-Bristol, 23h Ferrari, 23j HWM and
		(renumbered 249)	23n Maserati. Blue/White striped box with one packing piece....................£750-1,000
No.4	1948 only	**Commercial Vehicles Set**	Contains 25d, 25f, 25w, 29c and 30e. Brown/Green box with silhouette lid label. (US export)........£2,000-2,500
5	1932-39	**Train and Hotel Staff (large)**	(40mm). 5a Conductor, 2 x 5b waiters, 2 x 5c Porter (1 Red, 1 Green),
			'HORNBY SERIES' (early issues), 'DINKY TOYS' (later)....................£300-350
	NB		Also sold in USA – boxes often display 'H. Hudson Dobson' label.
5	1932-39	**Train and Hotel Staff (small)**.....	As previous set but smaller figures....................£150-175
5	1939-41	**Train and Hotel Staff**.................	5a Conductor, 2 x 5b waiters, 2 x 5c Porter (both Brown or Blue)....................£125-175
5	1946-54	**Train and Hotel Staff**.................	5a Conductor, 2 x 5b Waiter, 2 x 5c Porter (Brown or Blue), (renumbered 005)....................£90-120
5	c1950	**Military Vehicles Set**.................	153a (672) US Army Jeep, 161b (690) Mobile AA Gun, 151a Medium Tank, 151b (620) Transport
			Wagon, and 152b (671) Reconnaissance Car. Green box, inner Green card base and card cut-out
			packing piece,. Blue, Light Green and Red mottled lid has Purple and Yellow label £2,000-2,500
6	1934-36	**Shepherd Set**.............................	6a Shepherd (Dark Brown smock, hat and leggings, Black boots, lamb
			under arm), 6b Collie dog (Black/White), 4 x 2b sheep (Beige,
			'Hornby Series' cast-in, set presented in 'Modelled Miniatures' box £500-750
6	1936-40	**Shepherd Set**.............................	As previous set but in 'Dinky Toys' box....................£250-350
6	1946-54	**Shepherd Set**.............................	6a Shepherd (all Brown below neck, Green hat), 6b Collie dog (all Black),
		(renumbered 006)..........................	4 x 2b sheep (without 'Hornby Series')....................£150-200
No.6	1946-48	**Commercial Vehicles Set**	29c Bus, 29b Streamline Bus, 25h Fire Engine, 30e Breakdown Car and 30f Ambulance.
	(US export issue)		Mottled Purple-Blue box with inner Purple cut-out card base, Yellow/Maroon silhouette lid label ..£2,000-2,500
12	1937-41	**Postal Set**....................................	12a GPO Pillar Box, 12b Air Mail Pillar Box, 12c Telephone Call Box,
			12d Telegraph Messenger, 12e Postman, 34b Royal Mail Van. Blue box with Yellow insert.................£500-600
15	1937-41	**Railway Signals Set**	1 x 15a 'Home' and 1 x 15a 'Distant' (single-arm signals), 2 x 15b 'Home/Distant'
			(double-arm signals), 1 x 15c 'Home' and 1 x 15c 'Distant' (double-arm signals).
			Yellow box with Purple insert, 'DINKY TOYS' on lid £150-175
16	1936-37	**Silver Jubilee Train Set**	Locomotive and two interlocking coaches, 'LNER' and '2590' cast-in,
			open windows, smooth hubs with White tyres, special box, 300 mm.
		1:	Silver loco / coaches, Grey, Mid-Blue, Dark Blue, Red or Orange trim....................£200-250
		2:	Silver loco and coaches with Dark Blue trim £200-250
		3:	Cream loco and coaches with Red trim....................£250-275
		4:	Blue loco and coaches with Dark Blue trim....................£250-275
		5:	Green loco and coaches with Dark Green trim....................£250-275
16	1937-40	**Streamlined Train Set**.................	As previous models but with a change of name and box £200-250
16	1946-52	**Streamlined Train Set**.................	Blue/Black loco, 'LNER', Brown/Grey coaches, solid windows, Black tyres....................£125-150
16	1952-54	**Streamlined Train Set**.................	As previous model but with 'BR' crest on tender, (renumbered 798).
			Long portrait 'ladder' box with train picture....................£125-145
17	1934-40	**Passenger Train Set**	Black/Maroon loco 17a, Maroon tender 17b, Maroon/Cream coaches 20a/20b.
			Long portrait 'ladder' box with train picture....................£300-400
			Black/Green loco 17a, Green tender 17b, two Green/Cream coaches 20a/20b
			Long portrait 'ladder' box with train picture....................£300-400
			Lead and Mazak set in 2nd type box with correct colour spot....................£400-500
18	1934-40	**Tank Goods Train Set**.................	Green/Black loco (21a), and 3 Green/Black open wagons (21b).
			Long portrait 'ladder' box with train picture....................£300-400
19	1935-40	**Mixed Goods Train**	Maroon/Black loco (21a), Green/Red open wagon (21b), Red/Blue 'SHELL' tanker wagon (21d),
			Yellow/Red/Green lumber wagon (21e). Long portrait 'ladder' box with train picture £400-500
		rare box version:	Set in 3rd type pictorial landscape box....................£800-1,000
20	1934-40	**Tank Passenger Set**	Green/Black loco (21a), 2 Brown/Green coaches (20a), Guard's van (20b)....................£300-400
21	1932-33	**Hornby Train Set**	Blue/Red loco (21a), Green open wagon (21b), Green/Blue crane wagon (21c),
			Red/Blue 'SHELL' tank wagon (21d), Blue/Red/Black lumber wagon (21e).
			Contained in plain Red 'Hornby Series' box....................£500-600
21	1934-35	**Modelled Miniatures Train Set**..	As previous set, but in 'Modelled Miniatures' Red card box....................£400-500
22	1933-35	**Motor Vehicles Set**	22a and 22b Cars, 22c Motor Truck, 22d Delivery Van, 22e Tractor, 22f Tank, with
			'Hornby Series' or 'Dinky Toys' cast-in.
			'Modelled Miniatures' box, Purple lid, full-size full-colour label with pictures of models £2,000-2,500

23	1936-40	**Racing Cars Set**........................	Three models: 23c Mercedes-Benz, 23d Auto-Union, 23e 'Speed of the Wind'. Blue or Yellow box **£400-600**
24	1934-40	**Motor Cars Set** ....1st issue:	24a Ambulance, 24b Limousine, 24c Town Sedan, 24d Vogue Saloon,
			24e Super Streamlined Saloon, 24f Sportsman's Coupé, 24g Sports Tourer (2 seater),
			24h Sports Tourer (4 seater). Purple and Gold marbled box,
			lid has colour top label and Yellow/Red end label with code 'DT24' **£6,000-8,000**
		later issue:	Blue box lid (with colour label), Purple inner (A2205) **£5,000-6,000**
25	1934-37	**Commercial Motor Vehicles**......	25a Wagon, 25b Covered Wagon, 25c Flat Truck, 25d Tank Wagon, 25e Tipper,
			25f Market Gardener's Lorry. Mauve 'grained' box lid (colour label) (A1052) **£2,000-2,500**
		revised set:	Contains 25b, d, e, f, g and h **£1,700-1,900**
28/1	1934-40	**Delivery Vans Set in Trade Box**.	(1st type) 28a Hornby, 28b Pickfords, 28c Manchester Guardian,
			28d Oxo, 28e Ensign Lukos, 28f Palethorpes Sausages (A1008) **£6,000-8,000**
		revised set:	28a Hornby, 28b Pickfords, 28c Manchester Guardian,
			28e Firestone, 28f Palethorpes, 28n Atco Mowers **£6,000-8,000**
28/2	1934-40	**Delivery Vans Set in Trade Box**.	(1st type) 28g Kodak, 28h Sharps Toffees, 28k Marsh's,
			28L Crawfords Biscuits, 28m Wakefield Castrol, 28n Meccano (A1008)........................**£6,000-8,000**
		revised set:	28d Oxo, 28g Kodak, 28h Dunlop Tyres, 28k Marsh's,
			28m Wakefield Castrol, 28h Crawfords **£6,000-8,000**
28/3	1936-40	**Delivery Vans Set in Trade Box**.	(2nd type) 28r Swan Pens, 28s Frys Chocolate, 28t Ovaltine,
			28w Osram Lamps, 28x Hovis, 28y Exide Batteries **£2,500-3,000**
30	1935-37	**Motor Vehicles**...........................	30a Chrysler 'Airflow', 30b Rolls-Royce, 30c Daimler, 30d Vauxhall,
			30e Breakdown Car (22c 2nd casting), 30f Ambulance **£3,000-4,000**
	1937-41	....	As previous set but 30g Caravan replaces 30f Ambulance **£2,500-3,500**
33/1	1935-37	**Mechanical Horse and Five** **Assorted Trailers**.......................	33a Mechanical Horse, 33b Flat Truck, 33c Open Wagon, 33d Box Van, 33e Dust Wagon, 33f Petrol Tank with 'WAKEFIELD CASTROL' logo. Blue 'grained' box lid, large colour label.........**£600-800**
33/2	1935-37	**Mechanical Horse and Four** **Assorted Trailers**.......................	33a Mechanical Horse, 33b Flat Truck, 33c Open Wagon and 33e Dust Wagon. In Green display box (code A2036) with Yellow inner tray **£600-800**
35	1935-41	**Small Cars Set**	35a Saloon Car, 35b Racer and 35c MG Sports Car. In display type box (A2222) with tuck in flap and scenic backdrop.......................................**£600-800**
36	1936-41	**Motor Cars with Drivers,** **Passengers and Footmen**	36a Armstrong-Siddeley, 36b Bentley, 36c Humber, 36d Rover, 36e British Salmson 2-seater, 36f British Salmson 4-seater, all with figures. Set housed in Blue landscape box with Yellow tray with Purple inner and Brown board top packing piece. Box code A2205, dated 6-38..**£5,000-7,500**
37a	1937-41	**Motor Cycles Set**	Six of 37a civilian Motor Cyclists in various colours, hand-painted detail, solid White rubber tyres. Blue box with Green and White pictorial inner......................................**£400-600**
37	1938-40	**Motor Cycles Set**	Contains 37a (civilian), 37b (Police), 37c (Signals Despatch) **£400-600**
39	1939-41	**USA Saloon Cars Set**	39a Packard, 39b Oldsmobile, 39c Lincoln, 39d Buick, 39e Chrysler, 39f Studebaker. Mauve box with full colour label on lid..**£1,250-1,750**
42	1935-40	**Police Set**....................................	42a Police Box, 42b Motor Cycle Patrol, 42c Point-Duty Policeman (White coat), 42d Point-Duty Policeman (Blue uniform), in Blue box with pictorial inner (A2114) **£300-400**
43	1935-41	**'R.A.C.' Set**	43a RAC Box, 43b RAC Motor Cycle Patrol, 43c RAC Guide directing traffic, 43d RAC Guide saluting. Blue box, pictorial inner part, (A2064).............................**£400-600**
44	1935-41	**'A.A.' Set**	44a AA Box, 44b AA Motor Cycle Patrol, 44c AA Guide directing traffic, 44d AA Guide saluting. Blue box, pictorial inner part, (A2065) **£400-600**
46	1937-41	**Pavement Set**	Dark Grey 'stone' effect (cardboard) pavement pieces in a box......................................**£100-150**
47	1935-41	**Road Signs Set**............................	12 road signs, 47e to 47t, (White under base, triangles usually filled-in) Yellow box and inner, box code A2073...**£175-225**
47	1948-54	....................................US issue:	12 road signs, 47e to 47t, (Black under base, open triangles), (renumbered 770). Plain card box with Yellow label on end of lift up lid..**£100-125**
	US issue:	White under bases, filled-in triangles, in a plain box marked 'Made in England'. Made for sale by H. Hudson Dobson, 200 5th Avenue, New York...NGPP	
49	1935-41	**Petrol Pumps Set** ....'Pratts':	49a, 49b, 49c, 49d, 49e. White rubber hoses, Blue box **£150-200**
49	1946-50	**Petrol Pumps Set**................plain:	49a, 49b, 49c, 49d, 49e. Yellow plastic hoses, Yellow box **£90-110**
	(renumbered 780)	'Pratts':	49, 49b, 49c, 49d, 49e. White rubber hoses, Yellow box **£150-200**
		plain:	49, 49b, 49c, 49d, 49e. White plastic hoses, Yellow box **£100-140**
50	1934-42	**Ships of the British Navy**	50a 'Hood', 50b 'Nelson', 50b 'Rodney', 50c 'Effingham', 50d 'York', 50e 'Delhi', 3 x 50f 'Broke', 50g 'X'-class Submarine, 3 x 50h 'Amazon', 50k 'K'-class Submarine. Blue box with Green/Blue label on lid...........................**£200-300**
51	1934-40	**Great Liners Set**	51b 'Europa', 51c 'Rex', 51d 'Empress of Britain', 51e 'Strathaird', 51f 'Queen of Bermuda', 51g 'Britannic' **£200-250**
60	1934-35	**Aeroplanes Set**............................ (1st issue)	60a Imperial Airways, 60b Leopard Moth, 60c Percival Gull, 60d Low-Wing Monoplane, 60e General Monospar, 60f Autogiro, no registration letters. Dark Blue box with Green, Blue and White 'Atlanta' airliner on lid label, Yellow/Green side label dated '5-34'......**£1,200-1,500**
60	1936-41	**British Aeroplanes Set** .... (2nd issue)	60a Imperial Airways, 60b Leopard Moth, 60c Percival Gull, 60d Low-Wing Monoplane, 60e General Monospar, 60f Autogiro. All the planes in this set (except 60f) have 'GA-' markings **£1,000-1,250**
	Box Type i)	Blue box with multicoloured label plus '150 varieties' slogan	
	Box Types ii) and iii)	Same as previous but with '200' or '300 varieties' slogans (code A1040).	
60p	1938-41	**Gloster Gladiator Set**.................	Six planes in Silver livery with RAF roundels **£400-600**
60s	1938-41	**'Medium Bomber' Set**	Two renumbered 62n Fairey 'Battle' Bombers in Stone-colour box **£150-200**

60z	1937-41	'Avions' Set	French Aeroplanes Set with 60az 'Arc-en-Ciel', Potez 58, Hanriot 180t, 61az DeWetoine 500, Breguet Corsair, 60f Cierva Autogiro. Blue box	£900-1,200
61	1937-41	R.A.F. Aeroplanes Set	60h 'Singapore' Flying Boat, 2 x 60n Fairey 'Battle' Bombers, 2 x 60p Gloster 'Gladiator' Biplanes. Contained in Blue box with full colour label on lid	£500-700
61z	1937-40	'Avions' Set	French Aeroplanes Set with DeWoitine D338, Potez 56, Potez 58, 61az DeWetoine 500d, Farman F360, 60f Cierva Autogiro. Blue box	£900-1,200
62h	1939	Hawker Hurricane Set	Six planes, camouflaged tops, Black undersides, mounted on card base with 'DINKY TOYS No.62h HAWKER HURRICANE SINGLE SEATER FIGHTER'. Green box dated 7-39	£400-600
62d	1939	Bristol Blenheim Bomber Set	Six planes, camouflaged, mounted on card base with 'BRISTOL BLENHEIM BOMBER MARK IV - DINKY TOYS 62d'. Green box.	£400-600
62s	1939-41	Hurricane Fighters Set	Six Fighters, Silver fuselages, RAF roundels, undercarriages, Blue box	£300-400
64	1939-41	Aeroplane Set	60g Light Racer, 62h 'Hurricane' (Camouflaged), 62k 'Kings Aeroplane', 62m Light Transport, 62s 'Hurricane' (Silver), 63b Seaplane 'Mercury'. (In 1940 either 62a 'Spitfire' or 62s were substituted for 62h and 62s)	£750-1,000
64z	193?-4?	'Avions' Set	French Aeroplanes Set with 61az Dewoitine 'F-ADBF', 64a Amiot 370, 64b Bloch 220 'F-AOHJ', 64c Potez 63, 64d Potez 662 'F-ARAY'. Blue box, Yellow inner.	£2,000-2,500
65	1939-41	Aeroplane Set	60r Flying Boat, 60t 'DC3', 60v 'Whitely' Bomber, 60w 'Clipper III', 62n Junkers, 62p 'Ensign', 62r 'Albatross', 62w 'Frobisher'. Blue box, illustrated leaflet enclosed	£1,750-2,000
66	1940-41	Camouflaged Aeroplanes Set	66a Heavy Bomber, 66b Dive Bomber Fighter, 66c Fighter, 66d Torpedo, 66e Medium Bomber, 66f Army Autogiro (Silver). Yellow-Brown box	£2,000-3,000
68	1940-41	Camouflaged Aeroplanes Set	2 x 60s 'Battle' Bombers, 2 x 62d 'Blenheim', 3 x 62h 'Hurricane' (Camouflage), 3 x 62s 'Hurricane' (Silver), 62t 'Whitely', 68a 'Ensign', 68b 'Frobisher'. Blue or Yellow box, light or dark camouflage. Models display two roundels: Red inside Blue on the wings, and White/Blue/Red on the fuselage sides	£2,500-3,500
	1940-41	US issue:	Camouflaged version of 60s, 62d, 62e, 62h, 62t, 68a and 68b. Box picture shows civilian aircraft. Red label states 'Sold by Meccano Company of America Inc., 200 5th Avenue, New York'	£2,500-3,500
101	1936-40	Dining-Room Furniture	101a Table, 101b Sideboard, 2 x 101c Carver Chair, 4 x 101d Chair	£250-350
102	1936-40	Bedroom Furniture	102a Bed, 102b Wardrobe, 102c Dressing Table, 102d Dressing Chest, 102e Dressing Table Stool, 102f Chair. Brown or Pink. Green box	£250-350
103	1936-40	Kitchen Furniture	103a Refrigerator, 103b Kitchen Cabinet, 103c Electric Cooker, 103d Table, 103e Chair. Light Blue/White or Light Green/Cream	£250-350
104	1936-40	Bathroom Furniture	104a Bath, 104b Bath Mat, 104c Pedestal Basin, 104d Stool, 104e Linen Basket, 104f Toilet. Brown or Pink. Green box	£250-350
118	1965-69	Towaway Glider Set	135 Triumph 2000 (Cream/Blue), Cream/Red trailer, Yellow glider	£150-200
121	1963-66	Goodwood Racing Set	112 Austin-Healey Sprite, 113 MGB, 120 Jaguar, 182 Porsche, 9 Service Station (009) plastic figures plus seated and standing drivers. In Buff/Red display box with stepped insert	£1,000-1,250
122	1963-65	Touring Gift Set	188 Caravan, 193 Station Wagon, 195 Jaguar, 270 'AA' Patrol, 295 Atlas Kenebrake, 796 Healey Sports Boat on Trailer. In Buff/Red display box with stepped insert	£750-1,000
123	1963-65	Mayfair Gift Set	142 Jaguar, 150 Rolls-Royce, 186 Mercedes-Benz, 194 Bentley, 198 Rolls-Royce, 199 Austin Mini Countryman, plastic figures (3 male, 1 female). Buff/Red display box with stepped insert	£1,250-1,500
124	1964-66	Holidays Gift Set	952 Vega Luxury Coach, 137 Plymouth, 142 Jaguar, 796 Healey Sports Boat. In Buff/Red display box with stepped insert	£600-800
125	1964-66	Fun Ahoy! Set	130 Ford Corsair with driver, 796 Healey Sports Boat with pilot. Window box	£200-250
126	1967-68	Motor Show Set	127 Rolls-Royce, 133 Cortina, 151 Vauxhall Victor, 171 Austin 1800. In Buff/Red display box with stepped insert	£1,000-1,250
126	1968-69	Motor Show Set	127 Rolls-Royce, 159 Cortina, 151 Vauxhall Victor, 171 Austin 1800. In Buff/Red display box with stepped insert	£1,000-1,250
149	1958-61	Sports Cars Set	107 Sunbeam Alpine, 108 MG Midget, 109 Austin-Healey, 110 Aston-Martin, 111 Triumph TR2, all in 'competition finish'. Blue/White striped box	£1,000-1,200
150	1937-41	Royal Tank Corps Personnel	150a Officer, 2 x 150b Private, 2 x 150c Private, 150e N.C.O. Attached by cord to Yellow card in Yellow box or Grey/Blue box with Yellow inner, code A2187	£200-300
	1946-50	US export only Set:	Post-war issue of pre-war figures in original Green box with 'H. Hudson Dobson' label	£200-300
	1952-55	reissue, US only:	Contains 1 x 150a, 2 x 150b, 2 x 150c, 1 x 150e. Green box with one packing piece	£200-300
151	1937-41	Medium Tank Set	151a Tank, 151b 6-wheel Wagon, 151c Cooker Trailer, 151d Water Tank Trailer, 50d Royal Tank Corps Driver. Drop-front Blue box with pictorial inner, one packing piece with cut-outs	£250-350
152	1937-41	Light Tank Set	152a Tank, 152b Reconnaissance Car, 152c Austin 7 Car with 150d Royal Tank Corps Driver. Drop-front Blue box with pictorial inner, one packing piece with cut-outs	£250-350
156	1939-41	Mechanised Army Set	151a Tank, 151b 6-wheel Wagon, 151c Cooker Trailer, 151d Water Tank Trailer, 152a Tank, 152b Reconnaissance Car, 152c Austin 7 Car with 150d Royal Tank Corps Driver, 161a Lorry with Searchlight, 161b AA Gun on Trailer, 162a Light Dragon Tractor, 162b Ammunition Trailer, and 162c 18-pounder Gun. Drop-front Grey-Blue box (codes: '11-39', 'A2308') with contents shown on lid, four packing pieces.	£2,000-3,000
160	1939-41	Royal Artillery Personnel (reissued as 606 in 1954)	160a N.C.O., 2 x 160b Gunner, 160c Gunlayer, 2 x 160d Gunner (standing). Grey-Blue box (code: A2308) dated 11-39, Yellow box (code: A2303) and inner box dated 12-39. Production of this set continued post-war but only for export (to USA)	£200-300
	1952-55	reissue, US only:	Contains 1 x 160a, 3 x 160b, 2 x 160d, 1 x 150e. Green box with inner card stand	£200-300
161	1939-41	Mobile Anti-Aircraft Unit	161a Lorry with Searchlight and 161b A.A. Gun on Trailer. Blue or Green box ('A2257' on some), 1 packing piece with cut-outs	£400-500
162	1939-54	18-pounder Field Gun Unit	162a Light Dragon Tractor, 162b Trailer, 162c Gun. Blue box, 1 packing piece with cut-outs	£150-200
201	1965-68	Racing Cars Set	240 Cooper, 241 Lotus, 242 Ferrari, 243 B.R.M.	£300-400
237	1978-79	Dinky Way Set	Contains: 178 Mini Clubman, 211 Triumph TR7, 382 Convoy Truck, 412 Bedford 'AA' Van. **N.B.** Export only version of Set 240.	£80-100
240	1978-80	Dinky Way Set	211 Triumph TR7, 255 Police Mini, 382 Dump Truck, 412 Bedford Van, 20ft of 'roadway', 20 road signs, decal sheet	£60-80

245	1969-73	**Superfast Gift Set**	131 Jaguar 'E'-type, 153 Aston-Martin DB6, 188 Jensen FF	£100-125
246	1969-73	**International Gift Set**	187 De Tomaso Mangusta, 215 Ford GT, 216 Ferrari Dino	£100-125
249	1962-63	**World Famous Racing Cars**	230 Talbot-Lago, 231 Maserati, 232 Alfa-Romeo, 233 Cooper-Bristol, 234 Ferrari, 239 Vanwall. Bubble-packed onto large display card	£1,000-1,500
249	1955-58	**Racing Cars Set**	Contains 231, 232, 233, 234, 235, (renumbered from 4)	£700-900
294	1973-77	**Police Vehicles Gift Set**	250 Mini-Cooper, 254 Range-Rover, 287 Accident Unit. (Replaces Set 297)	£130-160
297	1963-73	**Police Vehicles Gift Set**	250 Mini-Cooper, 255 Ford Zodiac, 287 Accident Unit. (Replaced by Set 294)	£150-175
298	1963-66	**Emergency Services Set**	258 Ford Fairlane, 263 Ambulance, 276 Fire Tender, 277 Ambulance, with Ambulance-man, Ambulance-woman and Policeman	£600-800
299	1957-59	**Post Office Services**	260 'Royal Mail' Morris Van, 261 'GPO Telephones' Van, 750 Call Box, 011 Messenger, 012 Postman (but no Pillar Box!). Blue and White striped box	£350-450
299	1963-66	**Motorway Services Set**	434 Bedford Crash Truck, 269 Motorway Police Car, 257 Fire Chief's Car, 276 Airport Fire Tender, 263 (later 277) Criterion Ambulance	£800-1,100
299	1978-79	**'Crash Squad' Action Set**	244 Plymouth Police Car and 732 Bell Helicopter	£45-55
300	1973-77	**London Scene Set**	Contains 289 Routemaster Bus 'ESSO' and 284 London Taxi	£65-75
302	1979-?	**Emergency Squad Gift Pack**	Paramedic Truck and Plymouth Fire Chief Car plus figures of Gage and DeSoto. Not issued	NPP
303	1978-80	**Commando Squad Gift Set**	687 Convoy Army Truck, 667 Armoured Car, 732 Army helicopter	£75-100
304	1978-79	**Fire Rescue Gift Set**	195 Fire Chief Range Rover, 282 Land Rover, 384 Convoy Fire Truck	£70-90
306	1979-?	**'Space' Gift Pack**	358 'USS Enterprise', 357 Klingon Battle Cruiser, plus Galactic War Chariot. Not issued	NPP
307	1979-?	**'New Avengers' Gift Pack**	Purdey's TR7, John Steed's Special Leyland Jaguar, plus a 'fly-off' assailant!. Not issued	NPP
309	1978-80	**Star Trek Gift Set**	357 Klingon Battle Cruiser and 358 'USS Enterprise'.	£80-100
398	1964-65	**Farm Equipment Gift Set** (reissue of Set No.1)	300 Massey-Harris Tractor, 320 Harvest Trailer, 321 Manure Spreader, 322 Disc Harrow, 324 Hay Rake. Grey box with hinged lid	£1,000-1,250
399	1969-73	**Farm Tractor and Trailer**	300 Massey-Harris Tractor and 428 Large Trailer (Red/Silver). Yellow window box	£200-250
399	1977-79	**'Convoy' Gift Set**	380 Skip Truck, 381 Farm Truck, 382 Dumper Truck. 'Window' box	£35-45
606	1954-55	**Royal Artillery Personnel**	1 x 160a, 2 x 160b, 1 x 160c, 2 x 160d. Export only (to USA), (reissue of 160)	£150-200
616	1976-78	**AEC Transporter and Tank**	Militarised version of 974 with 683 Chieftain Tank and camouflage net	£65-80
618	1976-79	**Transporter and Helicopter**	Militarised versions of 974 and 724 with camouflage netting	£70-80
619	1976-78	**Bren-Gun Carrier Set**	622 Bren-Gun Carrier and 625 6-pounder Anti-Tank Gun	£35-45
677	1972-75	**Task Force Set**	680 Ferret Armoured Car, 681 D.U.K.W., 682 Stalwart Load Carrier	£35-45
695	1962-66	**Howitzer and Tractor**	689 Medium Artillery Tractor and 693 7.2in. Howitzer.	£250-350
697	1957-71	**Field Gun Set**	688 Field Artillery Tractor, 687 Trailer, 686 25-pounder Field Gun	£80-100
698	1957-65	**Tank Transporter Set**	660 Mighty Antar Tank Transporter and 651 Centurion Tank. One packing piece in box	£160-190
699	1955-58	**Military Vehicles (1) Set** (renumbered from No.1)	621 3-ton Wagon, 641 1-ton Truck, 674 Austin Champ, 676 Armoured Car. Blue/White Striped box with inner lining and stand	£250-350
754	1958-62	**Pavement Set**	Twenty various Grey cardboard pieces representing paving	£30-40
766	1959-64	**British Road Signs**	Country Set 'A'. Six signs of the times, mostly 55 mm high. Yellow box	£55-65
767	1959-64	**British Road Signs**	Country Set 'B'. Six signs of the times, mostly 55 mm high. Yellow box	£55-65
768	1959-64	**British Road Signs**	Town Set 'A'. Six signs of the times, mostly 55 mm high. Yellow box	£55-65
769	1959-64	**British Road Signs**	Town Set 'B'. Six signs of the times, mostly 55 mm high. Yellow box	£55-65
770	1950-54	**Road Signs Set**	12 road signs, 47e to 47t, (Black under base, open triangles) US export only, (renumbered 47)	£125-175
771	1953-65	**International Road Signs**	Set of 12 various road signs with Silver posts and bases, in Yellow box	£100-125
772	1959-63	**British Road Signs**	(Sets 766, 767, 768 and 769). 24 various road signs in a Red/Yellow box	£150-200
780	1950-54	**Petrol Pumps Set** (renumbered 49)	49a, 49b, 49c, 49d, 49e (plain). Yellow plastic hoses, export only	£90-110
			Version issued in picture box	£100-150
784	1972-74	**Dinky Goods Train Set**	Blue loco 'GER', one Red Truck, one Yellow Truck	£30-40
798	1954-59	**Express Passenger Train Set** (renumbered from 16)	Green/Black loco, 'BR' crest, Cream coaches (Grey roofs), Black tyres	£100-125
			Green/Black loco, 'BR' crest, Cream coaches/roofs/hubs, Black tyres	£100-125
			Green/Black loco, 'BR', Cream coaches/roofs, Red hubs, White tyres	£100-125
851	1961-	**Sets of vehicle 'Loads'**	2 each of 846 Oil Drums, 847 Barrels, 849 Packing Cases and 850 Crates	£30-40
900	1964-70	**'Site Building' Gift Set**	437 Muir-Hill Loader, 960 Albion Concrete Mixer, 961 Blaw-Knox Bulldozer, 962 Muir-Hill Dumper, 965 Euclid Rear Dump Truck. Grey/Red/Yellow box	£700-900
950	1969-70	**Car Transporter Set**	974 AEC Car Transporter with 136 Vauxhall Viva, 138 Hillman Imp, 162 Triumph 1300, 168 Ford Escort, 342 Austin Mini-Moke. Not issued	NPP
957	1959-65	**Fire Services Gift Set**	257 Fire Chief's Car, 955 Fire Engine, 956 Turntable Fire Escape	£350-450
990	1956-58	**Car Transporter Set**	Contains 982 Pullmore Car Transporter, one packing piece, and these cars: 154 Hillman Minx (Light Green/Cream), 156 Rover 75 (Cream/Blue), 161 Austin Somerset (Red/Yellow), 162 Ford Zephyr (Green/White)	£750-950
1001	1952-54	**Station Staff ('00' gauge)**	Set of 6 Blue figures (re-issue of pre-war Hornby-Dublo Set D1), (renumbered 051). Green card box	£45-55
1003	1952-54	**Passengers ('00' gauge)**	Set of 6 Blue figures (re-issue of pre-war Hornby-Dublo Set D2), (renumbered 053). Green card box	£45-55
49N2269	1965	**Road Racers Set**	Contains: 113 MGB, 114 Triumph Spitfire, 120 Jaguar E-type, 237 Mercedes-Benz, 238 Jaguar D-type, 242 Ferrari Racing Car, 243 BRM Racing Car. Special set for US mail-order company Sears-Roebuck	NGPP

Collectors notes

A page from the December 1935 'Meccano Magazine'.

Christie's Auction – The Remy-Meeùs Collection

22a Sports Car
'Hornby Series' on underside
VG-E – £305

22c Motor Truck
'Hornby Series' on underside
VG-E – £998

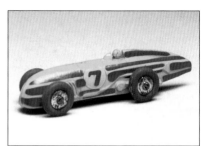

23a Racing Car, 'Humbug' pattern
Silvered Tootsie Toy hubs, blue tyres
VG – £1,292

24c Town Sedan, 2nd type chassis and
Grille, plated Tootsie Toys hubs
F – £305

24d Vogue Saloon
2nd type chassis, 1st type grille
VG – £493

24g Sports Tourer Four Seater
2nd type chassis and body type
With spare wheel cover G – £???

36e British Salmson
2 seater with driver
G-VG – £822

36f British Salmson
4 seater with driver
VG – £763

36g Pre-War Taxi
Rare yellow/black livery
F – £1,292

39cu U.S. Issue Lincoln Zephyr Coupe
Two tone red and maroon livery
Blued rear steel axle, VG – £2,820

39cu U.S. Issue Chrysler Royal Sedan
Two tone yellow and red livery
E – £2,820

36a Post-War Armstrong Siddeley
With blue hubs
E – £188

Models sold by Christie's of South Kensington, London. Pictures reproduced by their kind permission.

Christie's Auction – The Remy-Meeùs Collection

Half-Dozen Trade Box, code A1002, (April 1934)
With three 23 series Racing Cars without racing number or driver,
two stub exhaust manifold without pipe, G-VG, box G – £763

Half-Dozen Trade Box, code A2032 (1934/5)
With six no 32 airflow saloons
G-E, box VG – £3,055

Pre-War 23 Series Racing Cars Set
With blue box code A2144
Models and box G – £705

Pre-War 36 Series Motor Cars, (with drivers, passengers
and footmen), with models 36a 36 a,b,c,d,e &f all VG
Box code A2205, circa 1937 condition VG – £4,112

Two 28 Series 1st type Vans, G-VG 'Oxo' – £881, 'Meccano' – £3,525

39e Red pre-war Chrysler Royal Sedan wooden prototype VG – £1,645

22b pre-war red and blue Sports Coupe, VG-E – £1,057

39 series black and canary yellow Luxicab pre-war wooden prototype, VG - never issued as a production model – £1,527

38f Jaguar, pre-war 1st casting prototype with plain baseplate G-VG – £1,527

Models sold by Christie's of South Kensington, London. Pictures reproduced by their kind permission.

Auction Results – Dinky Toys

Gift Set 299
Post Office Services
VG models, box VG – £411

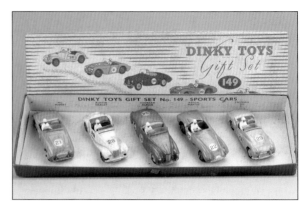

Gift Set 149
Sports Cars
G-VG models, box G – £881

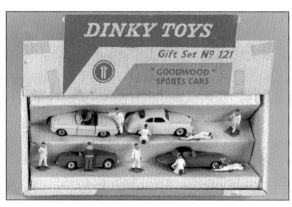

Gift Set 121
"Goodwood" Sports Cars
Models VG-E, box G-VG – £1,292

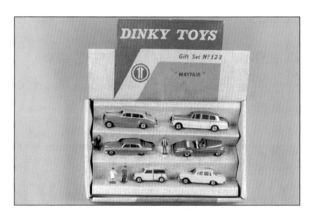

Gift Set 123
"Mairfair"
Models excellent, box VG – £1,175

Pre-War Red No 31
Holland Coachcraft Van, some fatigue, some chipping
Otherwise VG – £2,350

Pre-War Set No 60
2nd type aeroplanes set
Models F-G, box G (code A1040) – £822

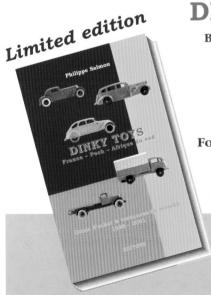

Auction Results – Dinky Toys

23b Hotchkiss Racing Cars
Excellent – £185

30b Rolls-Royce
Excellent – £180

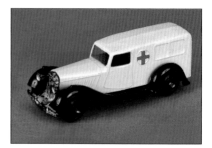

30f Ambulance
Near Mint – £110

36e British Salmson
Near Mint – £100

38b Sunbeam-Talbot
Near Mint – £210

38f Jaguar SS100
Good+ – £110

39eu Chrysler Royale
US issue
Mint – £1,600

39eu Chrysler Royale
US issue. Excellent, apart from
bonnet marks – £850

103 Austin-Healey Sports
Excellent – £230

108 MG Midget Sports
Mint, in Excellent box – £205

110 Aston-Martin DB3 Sports
Mint, in Excellent box – £130

110 Aston-Martin DB3 Sports
Unusual Light Green
Near Mint, in Excellent box – £310

Models sold by Vectis Auctions Ltd., Fleck Way, Thornaby, Stockton-on-Tees, TS17 9JZ. Pictures reproduced by their kind permission.

Auction Results – Dinky Toys

153 Standard Vanguard
Name inside roof, closed wheel arches,
large lettering. Near Mint, boxed – £180

154 Hillman Minx
Mint, in Good+
dual-numbered box – £180

156 Rover 75 Saloon
Near Mint, boxed – £160

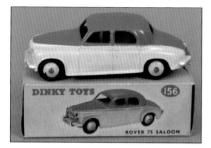

156 Rover 75 Saloon
Excellent, in Good+ box – £260

170 Ford Fordor Sedan
'Lowline'
Mint, in Excellent box– £200

170 Ford Fordor Sedan
'Highline'
Near Mint, including box– £270

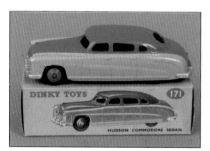

171 Hudson Commodore Sedan
'Highline'
Mint, in Excellent box – £320

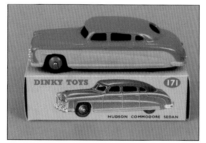

171 Hudson Commodore Sedan
'Lowline'
Mint, boxed – £410

171 Hudson Commodore Sedan
'Highline'
Mint, boxed – £250

171 Hudson Commodore Sedan
'Lowline'. Mint (apart from two
small scratches), boxed – £220

172 Studebaker Land Cruiser
Mint, boxed – £180

178 Plymouth Plaza
Mint, in plain Yellow/Red box – £230

Models sold by Vectis Auctions Ltd., Fleck Way, Thornaby, Stockton-on-Tees, TS17 9JZ. Pictures reproduced by their kind permission.

Auction Results – Dinky Toys

154 Hillman Minx
Mint, in Excellent box – £240

154 Hillman Minx
Mint, in Near Mint box – £220

157 Jaguar XK120
Mint, in Excellent box– £190

157 Jaguar XK120
Mint, boxed – £320

157 Jaguar XK120
Mint, in Excellent box – £160

159 Morris Oxford
Mint, in Near Mint box – £160

161 Austin A40 Somerset
Mint, in Near Mint box – £360

161 Austin A40 Somerset
Mint, boxed – £215

165 Humber Hawk
All Green upper body variation
Near Mint, boxed – £200

Gift Set No.4 – Racing Cars
All Near Mint, in Excellent box
£1,300

234 Ferrari Racing Car
Yellow triangle on nose
Mint, in Lighter Yellow late box – £250

114 Triumph Spitfire Sports Car
Metallic Purple, Gold interior
Mint, in Excellent box – £140

Models sold by Vectis Auctions Ltd., Fleck Way, Thornaby, Stockton-on-Tees, TS17 9JZ. Pictures reproduced by their kind permission.

Auction Results – Dinky Toys

501 Foden Diesel 8-wheel Wagon
1st type cab
Near Mint, in Good+ 'Buff' box – £370

501 Foden Diesel 8-wheel Wagon
1st type cab.
Good+, in Excellent 'Green' box – £270

501 Foden Diesel 8-wheel Wagon
2nd type cab
Excellent, in Good 'Blue' box – £360

502 Foden Flat Truck
1st type cab
Near Mint, in Good+ 'Buff' box – £550

503 Foden Flat Truck with Tailboard
1st type cab
Good+, in Excellent 'Buff' box – £320

503 Foden Flat Truck with Tailboard
1st type cab
Near Mint, in Good 'Buff' box – £470

504 Foden 14-ton Tanker
1st type cab
Excellent model and 'Green' box – £160

505 Foden Flat Truck with Chains
1st type cab. Excellent, in Good
'Blue' box. (Estimate £1,500 - £2,000)

511 Guy 4-ton Lorry
1st type cab
Near Mint model and box – £290

511 Guy 4-ton Lorry
2nd type cab
Mint, in Excellent box – £280

512 Guy Flat Truck
1st type cab
Excellent model and 'Buff' box – £440

512 Guy Flat Truck
2nd type cab
Mint, in Good+ box – £580

Models sold by Vectis Auctions Ltd., Fleck Way, Thornaby, Stockton-on-Tees, TS17 9JZ. Pictures reproduced by their kind permission.

Auction Results – Dinky Toys

25b Covered Wagon
Type 4
Near Mint – £580

412 Austin Wagon
Mint, in Excellent box – £420

430 Commer Breakdown Lorry
Scarce colours
Mint, in Excellent box– £640

430 Commer Breakdown Lorry
Near Mint, in Excellent
Yellow box– £340

417 Leyland Comet Lorry
Mint, in Good box – £680

418 Leyland Comet Wagon
with Hinged Tailboard
Mint, in Near Mint box – £520

431 Guy Warrior 4-ton Lorry
Near Mint, in Good box – £300

432 Guy Warrior Flat Truck
Mint, in Good+ box – £320

450 Trojan Van
Near Mint, in Good
dual-numbered box – £140

455 Trojan Van
Mint, in Excellent box – £165

465 Morris Van
Near Mint, in Excellent box – £180

482 Beford Van
Near Mint, including box – £110

Auction Results – Dinky Toys

934 Leyland Octopus Wagon
Mint, in near mint box – £200

941 Foden Tanker
Near mint model and box – £300

980 US issue Horsebox
Near mint in 'E' box complete
with internal packaging

981 Horsebox
Near Mint, in 'E' box – £100

254/40 H Austin Taxi
Mint in good dual
numbered box – £170

254 Austin Taxi
Mint in near mint box – £190

254 Austin Taxi
Near mint model and box – £160

254 Austin Taxi
Mint in 'E' box
Rare violet shade – £520

299 Post Office Services
Gift set contents 'E' in
Near mint box – £360

106 'Prisoner' Mini Moke
Near mint in 'E' box – £180

No 270 'A.A'
Trade box for six
All near mint in mint box – £520

410 Bedford Van, pre-production,
never issued, 'Fire Brigade Control
Unit', mint boxed – £300

Models sold by Vectis Auctions Ltd., Fleck Way, Thornaby, Stockton-on-Tees, TS17 9JZ. Pictures reproduced by their kind permission.

Auction Results – Dinky Toys

512 Guy Flat Truck
1st type cab
'E' in good+ box – £300

512 Guy Flat Truck
Near mint in 'E' 'buff' box – £560

919 Guy Van
Near mint in 'E' box – £600

920 Guy Warrior Van
Excellent in 'plain' box – £900

979 Racehorse Transporter
'E' model and box – £200

29E Single Deck Bus
Excellent – £200

281 Luxury Coach
Mint in good box – £200

953 Continental Touring Coach
Excellent model and box – £260

Pre-War 290 Double Decker Bus
No sign of fatigue
Near mint – £1,300

Pre-War 37 Tram Car
Minor fatigue only
Excellent – £400

Pre-War 28K Type 1 Delivery Van
Excellent condition – £2,000

Pre-War 28g Type 1 Delivery Van
Good condition – £1,100

Models sold by Vectis Auctions Ltd., Fleck Way, Thornaby, Stockton-on-Tees, TS17 9JZ. Pictures reproduced by their kind permission.

Dinky Toys Accessories (Pre-War)

See also: Public Transport Models, Ships, Motor Cycles and Gift Sets sections.
Approximate size of figures: large 40mm (scale 1:42); small 35mm (scale 1:48).
Pre-war box sequence: 'Modelled Miniatures'; 'Meccano Dinky Toys'; 'Dinky Toys'.

Ref	Year(s)	Model name	Colours, features, details	Market Price Range
1	1939-41	Station Staff (large)	see Gift Sets section.	
1	1939-41	Station Staff (small)	see Gift Sets section.	
1a	1932-41	Station Master (large)	Dark Blue uniform with Gold or Silver buttons on long coat	£30-35
1a	1932-41	Station Master (small)	As previous version but smaller	£20-25
1b	1932-39	Guard (large)	Dark Blue coat (Gold or Silver buttons), blowing whistle, flag in left hand	£30-35
1b	1932-39	Guard (small)	As previous version but smaller	£20-25
1b	1939-41	Guard (large)	Dark Blue coat (Gold or Silver buttons), blowing whistle, flag in right hand	£30-35
1b	1939-41	Guard (small)	As previous version but smaller	£20-25
1c	1932-41	Ticket Collector (large)	Dark Blue uniform (Gold or Silver buttons), slightly open arms	£30-35
1c	1932-41	Ticket Collector (large)	As previous model but with only right arm extended	£30-35
1c	1932-41	Ticket Collector (small)	As previous version but smaller	£20-25
1d	1932-39	Driver (large)	Mid-Blue uniform (Gold or Silver buttons) holding oil-can	£30-35
1d	1939-41	Driver (small)	As previous version but smaller	£20-25
1e	1932-39	Porter with Bags (large)	Dark Blue uniform, oblong case in right hand, round hat-box in left	£30-35
1e	1939-41	Porter with Bags (small)	Dark Blue, oblong case in each hand. (Smaller than previous model)	£20-25
1f	1932-39	Porter (large)	Dark Blue uniform, walking, no luggage	£30-35
1f	1939-41	Porter (small)	Dark Blue, standing, no luggage. (Smaller than previous model)	£20-25
2a	1932-41	Horses	One Light Brown or Dark Brown horse, one White horse	£20-30
2b	1932-41	Cow	3 versions were available; Light Brown, Dark Brown, or Black and White	£20-25
2c	1932-41	Pig	A Pink porker	£15-20
2d	1932-41	Sheep	White sheep with Black hand-painted detail	£15-20
3a	1932-39	Woman and Child (large)	Woman in Green coat, child (in Red) is on woman's right	£30-35
3a	1939-41	Woman and Child (small)	Woman in Green suit with Grey scarf and Red hat, child on woman's left	£20-25
3b	1932-39	Business Man (large)	Dark Blue suit/hat, walking stick in right hand, left hand holds lapels	£30-35
3b	1939-41	Business Man (small)	Grey suit, left hand holds attach case	£20-25
3c	1932-39	Male Hiker (large)	Brown clothing, Khaki rucksack, walking stick in right hand	£30-35
3c	1939-41	Male Hiker (small)	Brown clothing, Khaki rucksack, no walking stick	£20-25
3d	1932-41	Female Hiker (large)	Blue skirt, White blouse, walking stick in right hand	£30-35
3d	1932-41	Female Hiker (small)	All Blue clothing, or Dark Blue skirt, White blouse	£20-25
3e	1932-41	Newsboy (large)	Brown or Blue clothing, running, papers in right hand and under left arm	£30-35
3e	1939-41	Newsboy (small)	Dark Blue clothing, standing, papers in Cream tray	£20-25
3f	1932-39	Woman	Red jacket, White skirt, coat over left arm, oblong case in right hand	£25-30
3f	1939-41	Woman	Dark Red coat, Black collar, coat over left arm, round case in right hand	£25-30
4	1932-39	Engineering Staff	See the Gift Sets section.	
4a	1932-41	Electrician (large)	Blue overalls, White sleeves, carrying equipment	£30-35
4a	1932-41	Electrician (small)	Blue overalls, White sleeves, carrying equipment	£20-25
4b	1932-41	Fitter (large)	All-Blue overalls, or Brown overalls /White sleeves, carrying equipment	£30-35
4b	1932-41	Fitter (small)	As previous model but smaller	£20-25
4c	1932-41	Storekeeper (large)	Brown coat, Black trousers, holding forms in right hand, casting as 1a	£30-35
4c	1932-41	Storekeeper (small)	Brown coat, Black trousers, holding forms in right hand, casting as 1a	£20-25
4d	1932-41	Greaser (large)	Brown overalls, holding oil-can in right hand, casting based on 1d	£30-35
4d	1932-41	Greaser (small)	Brown overalls, holding oil-can in right hand, casting based on 1d	£20-25
4e	1932-41	Engine-Room Attendant (large)	Blue overalls, with or without White sleeves	£30-35
4e	1932-41	Engine-Room Attendant (small)	Blue overalls, with or without White sleeves	£20-25
5	1932-39	Train and Hotel Staff	See the Gift Sets section.	
5a	1932-41	Pullman Car Conductor (large)	White jacket, Blue trousers, slightly open arms, casting as 1c	£30-35
5a	1932-41	Pullman Car Conductor (small)	White jacket, Blue trousers, slightly open arms, casting as 1c	£20-25
5b	1932-41	Pullman Car Waiter (large)	White jacket, Blue trousers, two slightly different poses were available	£30-35
5b	1932-41	Pullman Car Waiter (small)	White jacket, Blue trousers, two slightly different poses were available	£20-25
5c	1932-41	Hotel Porter (large)	Red jacket/Brown trousers, or Green jacket/Blue trousers, casting as 1e	£30-35
5c	1932-41	Hotel Porter (small)	Red jacket/Brown trousers, or Green jacket/Blue trousers, casting as 1e	£20-25
6	1933-40	Shepherd Set	See the Gift Sets section.	
6a	1932-41	Shepherd	Brown with Dark Brown hat	£50-75
6b	1932-41	Sheep-dog	Black and White sheep-dog	£20-30
12	1937-41	Postal Set	See the Gift Sets section.	
12a	1935-40	GPO Pillar Box 'GR'	Red, with or without Red/Yellow 'Post Office' sign on top, White panel	£25-30
12b	1935-40	Air Mail Pillar Box	Blue body, 'Air Mail', White panel, casting as 12a	£35-40
12c	1936-40	Telephone Box	Cream with Silver windows	£20-30
12d	1938-40	Telegraph Messenger	Dark Blue body, picked out detail in darker Blue, Brown pouch, 35 mm	£20-25
12e	1938-40	Postman	Dark Blue body, darker Blue detail, Brown post bag and badge, 35 mm	£20-25
13	1931-40	'HALLS DISTEMPER'	Figures (lead) usually White, Cream (cardboard) panel, Red lettering	£250-300
15	1937-41	Railway Signals Set	See the Gift Sets section.	
15a	1937-41	Single Arm Signal	One Red 'Home' signal, or Yellow 'Distant' signal	£30-40
15b	1937-41	Double Arm Signal	One Red 'Home' signal and one Yellow 'Distant' signal on single pole	£40-50
15c	1937-41	Junction Signal	Two Red 'Home' signals, OR two Yellow 'Distant' signals on single pole	£65-75
30g	1936-39	Caravan Trailer	2 wheels, drawbar, body length 81 mm. open roof windows,	
			Blue/Cream, Red/Cream, Green/Cream, Orange/Cream, Two tone-Green,	£90-120
			Chocolate and Beige, Blue hubs	£150-175
	1939-40		As previous models but with filled-in roof windows	£80-110

42	1935-41	**Police Set**	See the Gift Sets section.	
42a	1936-40	**Police Box**	Dark Blue box, 'POLICE' in Silver	£25-35
42c	1936-40	**Point Duty Policeman**	(cast in lead), White coat, Black helmet, 42 mm tall	£25-35
42d	1936-40	**Point Duty Policeman**	(cast in lead), Dark Blue uniform, White gauntlets, 40 mm tall	£25-35
43	1935-41	**'RAC' Set**	See the Gift Sets section.	
43a	1935-40	**'RAC' Box**	Blue and White (tinplate) call-box with 'RAC' emblem	£100-125
43c	1935-40	**'RAC' Guide**	(cast in lead), Blue uniform, Red sash, directing traffic, 37 mm tall	£25-35
43d	1935-40	**'RAC' Guide** (saluting)	(cast in lead), Blue uniform with Red sash, 36 mm tall	£25-35
44	1935-41	**'AA' Set**	See the Gift Sets section.	
44a	1935-40	**'AA' Box**	Black/Yellow tinplate box with 'AA' badge and 3 signs	£100-125
44c	1935-40	**'AA' Guide**	(cast in lead), Tan uniform, Blue sash, directing traffic, 37 mm tall	£20-25
44d	1935-40	**'AA' Guide** (saluting)	(cast in lead), Tan uniform, Blue sash, 36 mm tall	£20-25
45	1935-40	**Garage**	Cream/Orange (tinplate), Green opening doors, boxed, 127 x 90 mm	£250-350
46	1937-40	**Pavement Set**	Dark Grey 'stone' effect (cardboard) pavement pieces in a box	£100-150
47	1935-41	**Road Signs Set**	See the Gift Sets section.	
47a	1935-41	**4-face Traffic Lights**	Black on White post, Yellow beacon, White base, 62 mm high	£15-20
47b	1935-41	**3-face Traffic Lights**	Black on White post, Yellow beacon, White base, 62 mm high	£15-20
47c	1935-41	**2-face Traffic Lights**	Back-to-back lights, Black on White post, Yellow beacon, White base	£15-20
47c	1935-41	**2-face Traffic Lights**	Lights at 90 degrees, Black on White post, Yellow beacon, White base	£15-20
47d	1935-41	**Belisha Beacon**	Black on White post, Orange globe, White base, 51 mm high	£15-20
47e	1935-41	**'30 MPH' Limit Sign**	Black on White post, Red top '30', 52 mm high	£15-20
47f	1935-41	**De-restriction Sign**	Black on White post, diagonal Black bar on White circle, 52 mm high	£15-20
47g	1935-41	**'School' Sign**	Black on White post, Red top, Black 'beacon' design, 51 mm high	£15-20
47h	1935-41	**'Steep Hill' Sign**	Black on White post, Red top, Black 'incline' design, 51 mm high	£15-20
47k	1935-41	**'S-Bend' Sign**	Black on White post, Red top, Black 'S-Bend' design, 51 mm high	£15-20
47m	1935-41	**'Left-Hand Bend' Sign**	Black on White post, Red top, Black 'curve' design, 51 mm high	£15-20
47n	1935-41	**'Right-Hand Bend' Sign**	Black on White post, Red top, Black 'curve' design, 51 mm high	£15-20
47p	1935-41	**'T-Junction' Sign**	Black on White post, Red top, Black 'T' design, 51 mm high	£15-20
47q	1935-41	**'No Entry' Sign**	Black on White post, Red 'bar' design, 48 mm high	£15-20
47r	1935-41	**'Major Road Ahead' Sign**	Black on White post, Red top, Black lettering, 54 mm high	£15-20
47s	1935-41	**'Crossing No Gates' Sign**	Black on White post, Red top, Black 'loco' design, 51 mm high	£15-20
47t	1935-41	**'Roundabout' Sign**	Black on White post, Red top, Black 'arrows' design, 51 mm high	£15-20
		NB	Pre-war issues have filled in triangles.	
48	1935-41	**Filling/Service Station**	Yellow with Blue, Orange or Green base, Green, Brown or Yellow roof, tinplate. Orange box	£300-400
49	1935-41	**Petrol Pumps Set**	See the Gift Sets section.	
49a	1935-53	**Bowser Petrol Pump**	Green pump body, White rubber hose, (Yellow plastic post-war), 46 mm	£25-35
49b	1935-53	**Wayne Petrol Pump**	Pale Blue pump, White rubber hose, (Yellow plastic post-war), 39 mm	£25-35
49c	1935-53	**Theo Petrol Pump**	Blue or Red pump, White rubber hose, (Yellow plastic post-war), 58 mm	£25-35
49d	1935-53	**'SHELL' Petrol Pump**	Red pump body, White rubber hose, (Yellow plastic post-war), 53 mm	£25-35
49e	1935-40	**'Pratts' Oil Bin**	Yellow bin body and opening tinplate lid, 'Pratts Motor Oil', 32 mm	£40-50
			49e was only available post-war in Set 49 and without 'Pratts' logo	£25-35
101	1935-40	**Dining Room Set**	See the Gift Sets section.	
101a	1935-40	**Dining Table**	'Wood' effect dining-room table, 64 mm	£30-35
101b	1935-40	**Sideboard**	'Wood' effect sideboard with opening doors, tinplate back, 63 mm	£30-35
101c	1935-40	**Carver Chair**	'Wood' effect chair with armrests, 33 mm high	£15-20
101d	1935-40	**Dining Chair**	'Wood' effect chair without armrests, raised 'leather' cushion	£10-15
102	1935-40	**Bedroom Set**	See the Gift Sets section.	
102a	1935-40	**Bed**	Brown or Pink double bed	£30-35
102b	1935-40	**Wardrobe**	Brown or Pink wardrobe with opening door, tinplate back, 63 mm	£30-35
102c	1935-40	**Dressing Table**	Brown or Pink, opening drawers, tinplate mirror, 51 mm	£30-35
102d	1935-40	**Dressing Chest**	Brown or Pink, opening drawer, tinplate back, 40 mm high	£30-35
102e	1935-40	**Dressing Table Stool**	Brown or Pink stool, 13 mm high	£15-20
102f	1935-40	**Chair**	Brown or Pink	£10-15
103	1935-40	**Kitchen Set**	See the Gift Sets section.	
103a	1935-40	**Refrigerator**	Light Blue/White or Light Green/Cream, door, tinplate back and food tray	£35-45
103b	1935-40	**Kitchen Cabinet**	Light Blue/White or Light Green/Cream, opening doors/drawer, tin back	£35-45
103c	1935-40	**Electric Cooker**	Light Blue/White or Light Green/Cream, opening door, tinplate back	£35-45
103d	1935-40	**Kitchen Table**	Light Blue/White or Light Green/Cream, 34 mm high	£30-35
103e	1935-40	**Kitchen Chair**	Light Blue/White or Light Green/Cream, casting as 102f	£10-15
104	1935-40	**Bathroom Set**	See the Gift Sets section.	
104a	1935-40	**Bath**	Pink/White or Light Green/White, Gold taps, 69 mm	£35-45
104b	1935-40	**Bath Mat**	Mottled Green (rubber) mat, 50 x 37 mm	£10-15
104c	1935-40	**Pedestal Hand Basin**	Pink/White or Light Green/White, Gold taps, tinplate mirror, 63 mm	£30-35
104d	1935-40	**Bathroom Stool**	Pink/White or Light Green/White, 15 mm high	£15-20
104e	1935-40	**Linen Basket**	Pink/White or Light Green/White, hinged lid, 22 mm high	£15-20
104f	1935-40	**Toilet**	Pink/White or Light Green/White, hinged lid, 34 mm high	£35-45
	1935-40	**'Dolly Varden' Dolls House**	Not given a reference number, made of 'leather board' (heavy reinforced cardboard), and supplied packed flat. Cream/Brown upper storey, Red brick ground floor, Red roof, 476 x 260 mm base, 476 mm high	£500-750
		NB	It is not really possible to give individual prices for single 'Dolly Varden' items as they are very rarely available in collectable condition. Boxed sets sell for £200-300, for example. See Gift Sets section for more price information.	

Dinky Toys Accessories (Post-War)

See also: Public Transport Models, Ships, Motor Cycles and Gift Sets sections.

Ref	Year(s)	Model name	Colours, features, details	Market Price Range
001	1954-56	**Station Staff ('0' gauge)**	1b Guard (flag in right hand), 1c Ticket Collector (right arm extended), 1d Driver, 1e Porter (with oblong bags), 1f Porter (standing), (renumbered from 1)	**£90-120**
001	1979-80	**'Space War Station'**	Dinky Builda card (54001)	**£15-20**
002	1954-56	**Farmyard Animals (6)**	2 x 2a horses, 2 x 2b cows, 1 x 2c pig, 1 x 2d sheep, simplified painting, (renumbered from 2)	**£200-300**
002	1979-80	**'Blazing Inferno'**	Dinky Builda card (54002)	**£15-20**
003	1954-56	**Passengers ('0' gauge)**	3a Woman (with child on left), 3b Businessman (Brown suit and case), 3c Male hiker (no stick), 3d Female hiker (Blue blouse), 3e Newsboy (Grey tray), 3f Woman (Light Red coat, round case), (renumbered from 3)	**£90-120**
004	1946-54	**Engineering Staff ('0' gauge)**	2 x 4b Fitter (all-Blue and all-Brown), 4c Storekeeper (all-Brown), 4d Greaser, 4e Engine-Room attendant, (renumbered from 4)	**£90-120**
005	1954-56	**Train and Hotel Staff**	('0' gauge), 5a Conductor, 2 x 5b waiters, 2 x 5c Porter (Brown or Blue), (renumbered from 5)	**£90-120**
006	1954-56	**Shepherd Set**	6a Shepherd (Green hat), 6b sheepdog (all-Black), 4 x 2b sheep, (renumbered from 6)	**£150-200**
007	1960-67	**Petrol Pump Attendants**	1 male (White overalls), 1 female (White coat), plastic	**£15-20**
008	1961-67	**Fire Station Personnel**	Set of 6 plastic fire-fighters in Blue uniforms plus hose, supplied in a bag. (Also present in GS 298)	**£65-75**
009	1962-66	**Service Station Personnel**	Set of 8 plastic figures in various colours and stances. Supplied in a bag or a Yellow box	**£65-75**
010	1962-66	**Road Maintenance Personnel**	Set of 6 workmen using pick, barrow, shovels, drill etc, plus hut, brazier, barrier, and 4 lamps Plastic, figures are 35 mm tall. Supplied in a bag or a Yellow box	**£65-75**
011	1954-56	**Telegraph Messenger**	Mid-Blue uniform, detailing in darker Blue, Brown pouch, 35 mm, (renumbered from 12d)	**£10-15**
012	1954-56	**Postman**	Mid-Blue body, darker Blue detail, Brown post bag and badge, 35 mm, (renumbered from 12e)	**£15-20**
013	1954-56	**Cook's Man**	(Agent for the Thomas Cook travel company), Dark Blue coat, 40 mm high, (renumbered from 13a)	**£20-30**
050	1961-68	**Railway Staff ('00' gauge)**	12 Blue plastic figures in a clear plastic box. Early issues contained a Policeman, later ones a Shunter	**£40-50**
051	1954-56	**Station Staff ('00' gauge)**	6 plastic figures in a clear plastic box (re-issue of pre-war Hornby-Dublo Set D1), (renumbered 1001)..	**£35-45**
052	1961-69	**Railway Passengers ('00')**	11 plastic figures plus a seat, in a clear plastic box	**£35-45**
053	1954-59	**Passengers ('00' gauge)**	6 Blue plastic figures (re-issue of pre-war Hornby-Dublo Set D2), (renumbered 1003)	**£35-45**
054	1962-70	**Railway Station Personnel**	4 plastic figures plus 8 pieces of furniture in a clear plastic box, ('OO' gauge)	**£35-45**
1	1946-54	**Station Staff**	See the Gift Sets section.	
1a	1946-54	**Station Master**	Dark Blue uniform (cap, long coat), (in Set 001 till 1956)	**£20-25**
1b	1946-54	**Guard**	Dark Blue uniform, blowing whistle, flag in right hand (see Set 001)	**£15-20**
1c	1946-54	**Ticket Collector**	Blue uniform, only right arm is extended (in Set 001 till 1956)	**£15-20**
1e	1946-54	**Porter with Bags**	Blue uniform, oblong case in each hand (in Set 001 till 1956)	**£15-20**
1f	1946-54	**Porter**	Dark Blue uniform, standing, no luggage (in Set 001 till 1956)	**£15-20**
2	1946-54	**Farmyard Animals**	See the Gift Sets section.	
2a	1946-54	**Horses**	3 versions; Dark Brown horse (Black tail and mane), Light Brown horse (Light Brown tail and mane), White horse (2 in Set 002 till 1956)	**£20-25**
2b	1946-54	**Cows**	Light Brown, Dark Brown, or Black/White (2 in Set 002 till 1956)	**£20-25**
2c	1946-54	**Pig**	Cream body (in Set 002 till 1956)	**£15-20**
2d	1946-54	**Sheep**	White body with Black hand-painted detail (in Set 002 till 1956)	**£15-20**
3	1946-54	**Passengers**	See the Gift Sets section.	
3a	1946-54	**Woman and Child**	Woman in Green suit and hat (Brown scarf), child on left (see Set 003)	**£20-25**
3b	1946-54	**Business Man**	Brown suit, left hand holds attache case (in Set 003 till 1956)	**£20-25**
3c	1946-54	**Male Hiker**	Brown clothing, Khaki rucksack, no stick (in Set 003 till 1956)	**£20-25**
3d	1946-54	**Female Hiker**	Blue or Dark Blue skirt and shirt, stick in right hand (see Set 003)	**£20-25**
3e	1946-54	**Newsboy**	Dark Blue clothing, standing, papers in Grey tray (in Set 003 till 1956)	**£20-25**
3f	1946-54	**Woman**	Light Red coat, round case in right hand (in Set 003 till 1956)	**£20-25**
4	1946-54	**Engineering Staff**	See the Gift Sets section.	
4a	1946-54	**Electrician**	Blue overalls, White sleeves, carrying equipment (in Set 004 till 1956)	**£15-20**
4b	1946-56	**Fitters**	2 versions; one in Blue, the other Brown, carrying equipment (Set 004)	**£15-20**
4c	1946-54	**Storekeeper**	Brown coat, Black trousers, holding forms in right hand	**£15-20**
4d	1946-54	**Greaser**	Brown overalls, holding oil-can in right hand	**£15-20**
4e	1946-56	**Engine-Room Attendant**	Blue overalls, Blue sleeves	**£10-15**
5	1946-56	**Train and Hotel Staff**	See the Gift Sets section.	
5a	1946-56	**Pullman Car Conductor**	White jacket, Blue trousers, slightly open arms, casting as 1c	**£20-25**
5b	1946-56	**Pullman Car Waiter**	White jacket, Blue trousers, two slightly different poses are known	**£20-25**
5c	1946-56	**Hotel Porter**	Red jacket/Brown trousers, or Green jacket/Blue trousers, casting as 1e	**£20-25**
6	1946-54	**Shepherd Set**	See the Gift Sets section.	
6a	1946-54	**Shepherd**	Brown with Green hat	**£40-50**
6b	1946-56	**Sheep-dog**	All-Black sheep-dog..	**£20-30**
12c	1946-54	**Telephone Box**	Red call-box with Black window frames, 58 mm high, (renumbered 750)	**£20-30**
12d	1946-54	**Telegraph Messenger**	Dark Blue body, picked out detail in darker Blue, Brown pouch, 35 mm, (renumbered 011)	**£15-20**
12e	1946-54	**Postman**	Mid-Blue body, darker Blue detail, Brown post bag and badge, 35 mm, (renumbered 012)	**£15-20**
13a	1952-63	**Cook's Man**	(An Agent for the Thomas Cook travel company), Blue coat, 40 mm high, (renumbered 013) ...	**£20-30**
30g	1948-50	**Caravan**	Orange/Cream body, 'Caravan Club', drawbar	**£45-55**
42a	1954-60	**Police Hut**	Dark Blue hut, 'POLICE' in Silver, 66 mm high, (renumbered 751)	**£20-30**
47	1946-50	**Road Signs Set**	See the Gift Sets section.	
49	1946-50	**Petrol Pumps Set**	See the Gift Sets section.	
49e	194?-?	**Oil Bin**	As pre-war 'Pratt's' Oil Bin but only available post-war in Set 49 and without 'Pratts' logo	**£25-35**
117	1963-69	**Four Berth Caravan**	Blue/Cream, clear roof, suspension, detailed interior	**£25-35**
			Yellow/Cream, clear roof, suspension, detailed interior	**£25-35**
188	1961-63	**Four Berth Caravan**	Green/Cream or Blue/Cream, windows, detailed interior	**£25-35**
	1963-63		As previous model but larger windows, (this model replaced by 117)	**£25-35**
190	1956-62	**Caravan**	Orange/Cream, or Blue/Cream, drawbar, metal jockey wheel	**£25-35**
	1962-64		Orange/Cream, or Blue/Cream, drawbar, plastic jockey wheel..............................	**£25-35**

163

502	1961-63	**Garage**	Blue/Grey plastic garage, opening door, 272 mm (French issue)	£90-110
750	1954-62	**Telephone Box**	Red call-box with Black window frames, 58 mm high, (renumbered from 12c)	£25-35
751	1954-60	**Police Hut**	Dark Blue hut, 'POLICE' in Silver, 66 mm high, (renumbered from 42a)	£25-35
752	1953-54	**Goods Yard Crane**	Yellow with Blue or Dark Blue, mazak or cast-iron base, (renumbered 973)	£40-50
753	1962-67	**Police Crossing**	Black/White box on traffic island with policeman directing traffic	£80-100
754	1958-62	**Pavement Set**	Grey cardboard paving slabs (20 items in box)	£50-60
755	1960-64	**Lamp Standard (Single)**	Grey/Fawn/Orange, plastic single-arm lamp on metal base	£20-30
756	1960-64	**Lamp Standard (Double)**	Grey/Fawn/Orange, plastic double-arm lamp on metal base	£30-40
760	1954-60	**Pillar Box**	Red and Black pillar box with 'E II R' cast-in	£25-35
763	1959-64	**Posters for Hoarding**	Six different coloured poster advertisements (on paper)	£25-35
764	1959-64	**Posters for Hoarding**	Six different coloured poster advertisements (on paper)	£25-35
765	1959-64	**Road Hoardings (6 Posters)**	Green plastic hoarding, 'David Allen and Sons Ltd'	£50-60
766-772		**Road Sign Sets**	See the Gift Sets section.	
773	1958-63	**4 face Traffic Lights**	Black/White, Black base, similar to 47a but without beacon, 62 mm	£15-20
777	1958-63	**Belisha Beacon**	Black/White post on Black base, Orange globe, casting as 47d, 51 mm	£10-15
778	1962-66	**Road Repair Boards**	Green and Red plastic warning signs, 6 different	£30-40
780	1950-54	**Petrol Pumps Set**	See the Gift Sets section.	
781	1955-62	**'ESSO' Petrol Station**	'ESSO' sign, no kiosk, 2 pumps ('ESSO' and 'ESSO EXTRA')	£60-75
782	1960-70	**'SHELL' Petrol Station**	'SHELL' sign, Green/Cream kiosk, 4 Red/Yellow 'SHELL' pumps	£60-75
783	1960-70	**'BP' Petrol Station**	'BP' sign, Green/Cream kiosk, 4 Green/White 'BP' pumps	£60-75
785	1960-64	**'SERVICE STATION'**	Fawn and Red plastic, with 'BP' sign, 335 x 185 mm (unbuilt kit, boxed)	£175-225
786	1960-66	**Tyre Rack with tyres**	Green tyre rack with 21 assorted tyres and 'DUNLOP' on board	£35-45
787	1960-64	**Lighting Kit**	Bulb and wire lighting kit for model buildings	£20-25
788	1960-68	**Spare Bucket for 966**	Grey bucket for use with 966 Marrel Multi-Bucket Unit	£10-15
790	1960-64	**Granite Chippings**	Plastic bag of imitation granite chippings (50790)	£15-20
791	1960-64	**Imitation Coal**	in a plastic bag.	£15-20
792	1960-64	**Packing Cases (3)**	White/Cream plastic packing cases, 'Hornby Dublo', 38 x 28 x 19 mm	£15-20
793	1960-64	**Pallets**	Orange pallets for 930 Bedford Pallet-Jekta Van and 404 Conveyancer	£15-20
794	1954-64	**Loading Ramp**	Blue loading ramp for use with 582/982 Carrimore Transporter, (renumbered from 994)	£15-20
846	1961-	**Oil Drums**	Pack of 6 oil drums. French issue	£15-20
847	1961-	**Barrels**	Pack of 6 barrels. French issue	£15-20
849	1961-	**Packing Cases**	Pack of 6 packing cases. French issue	£15-20
850	1961-	**Crates of Bottles**	Pack of 6 crates. French issue	£15-20
851	1961-	**Sets of vehicle 'Loads'**	Two each of 846 Oil Drums, 847 Barrels, 849 Packing Cases and 850 Crates	£50-60
954		**Fire Station Plastic Kit**	Red doors, Cream roof, Grey floor, clear roof, 'FIRE STATION'. 'DINKY TOYS' in Red	£200-250
994	1954-55	**Loading Ramp**	Renumbered from 794 to 994 then back to 794 after only a year!	£15-20
973	1954-59	**Goods Yard Crane**	Yellow with Blue or Dark Blue mazak or cast-iron base, steps in early issues, (renumbered from 752)	£40-50
1001	1952-54	**Station Staff**	See the Gift Sets section.	
1003	1952-54	**Station Staff**	See the Gift Sets section.	

Spare tyres, batteries, bulbs, etc.

020	1968-75	**Spare tyre**... Black tyre, 16 mm (5/8") in diameter. Yellow box of 12	£15-20	083 (as 099)	**Spare tyre**... Grey tyre, 20 mm in diameter	NGPP
021	1970-75	**Spare tyre**... Black tyre, 20 mm (3/16") in diameter. Yellow box of 12	£15-20	084	**Spare tyre**... Black 'recessed' tyre, 18 mm dia.	NGPP
022	1971-76	**Spare tyre**... Black tyre, 16 mm (5/8") in diameter. Yellow box of 12	£15-20	085 (as 092)	**Spare tyre**... White tyre, 15 mm in diameter	NGPP
023	1971-76	**Spare tyre**... Black tyre, 16 mm (5/8") in diameter. Yellow box of 12	£15-20	086	**Spare tyre**... Black fine tread tyre, 16 mm dia.	NGPP
024	1971-76	**Spare tyre**... Black tyre, 23 mm (59/64") in diameter. Yellow box of 12	£15-20	087 (as 60687)	**Spare tyre**... Black big 'tractor' tyre, 35 mm dia.	NGPP
				089 (as 60689)	**Spare tyre**... Black 'tractor front tyre', 19 mm dia.	NGPP
025	1976 only	**Spare tyre**... Black tyre, 17 mm in diameter. Yellow box of 12	£15-20	090 (as 60790)	**Spare tyre**... Black fine tread tyre, 14 mm dia.	NGPP
026	1976 only	**Spare tyre**... Black tyre, 21 mm in diameter. Yellow box of 12	£15-20	090 (as 60791)	**Spare tyre**... White fine tread tyre, 14 mm dia.	NGPP
027	1976 only	**Spare tyre**... Black tyre, 27 mm (1-1/16") in diameter. Yellow box of 12	£15-20	091 (as 60036)	**Spare tyre**... Black block tread tyre, 13 mm dia.	NGPP
				092 (as 14094)	**Spare tyre**... Black block tread tyre, 15 mm dia.	NGPP
028		**Spare tyre**... Not issued	NPP	092 (as 14095)	**Spare tyre**... White block tread tyre, 15 mm dia.	NGPP
029	1976 only	**Track** ... Black Track. Box of 6	£15-20	093 (as 13978)	**Spare tyre**... Black medium tractor tyre, 27 mm dia.	NGPP
030	1968-76	**Track** ... Black Track. Box of 6	£15-20	094 (as 6676)	**Spare tyre**... Black smooth tyre, 18 mm diameter	NGPP
031	1976-78	**Track** ... Black Track. Box of 6	£15-20	095 (as 6677)	**Spare tyre**... Black block tread tyre, 18 mm dia.	NGPP
032	1973-76	**Track** ... Black Track. Box of 6	£15-20	096 (as 7067)	**Spare tyre**... Tyre, 19/32, (15 mm) in diameter	NGPP
033	1973-76	**Track** ... Black Track. Box of 6	£15-20	097 (as 7383)	**Spare wheel** Solid rubber wheel, 12 mm dia.	NGPP
				098 (as 10118)	**Spare wheel** Solid rubber wheel, 12 mm dia.	NGPP
034	1971-72	**Battery**... 1.5 volt battery	£10-15	099 (as 10253)	**Spare tyre**... Black block tread tyre, 20 mm dia.	NGPP
035	1970-76	**Battery**... 1.5 volt battery	£10-15	099 (as 10253)	**Spare tyre**... Grey block tread tyre, 20 mm dia.	NGPP
034	1964-76	**Battery**... 1.5 volt battery	£10-15			
036		**Battery**... 1.5 volt battery for use with 276 Fire Tender and 277 Ambulance	NGPP	6676 (as 094)	**Spare tyre**... Black smooth tyre, 18 mm diameter	NGPP
				6677 (as 095)	**Spare tyre**... Black block tread tyre, 18 mm dia.	NGPP
				7067 (as 096)	**Spare tyre**... Tyre, 19/32, (15 mm) in diameter	NGPP
037		**Lamp** ... Red light-bulb for use with 277	NGPP	7383 (as 097)	**Spare wheel** Solid rubber wheel, 12 mm dia.	NGPP
038		**Lamp** ... Blue (or Orange) light-bulb for use with model 276 Airport Fire Tender	NGPP	10118 (as 098)	**Spare wheel** Solid rubber wheel, 12 mm dia.	NGPP
				10253 (as 099)	**Spare tyre**... Black block tread tyre, 20 mm dia.	NGPP
039		**Lamp** ... Clear light-bulb for 952 Vega Coach	NGPP	13978 (as 093)	**Spare tyre**... Black medium tractor tyre, 27 mm dia.	NGPP
				14094 (as 092)	**Spare tyre**... Black block tread tyre, 15 mm dia.	NGPP
081		**Spare tyre**... White fine tread tyre, 14 mm dia.	NGPP	14095 (as 092)	**Spare tyre**... White block tread tyre, 15 mm dia.	NGPP
082		**Spare tyre**... Black narrow tread tyre, 20 mm dia.	NGPP	60036 (as 091)	**Spare tyre**... Black block tread tyre, 13 mm dia.	NGPP
				606087 (as 087)	**Spare tyre**... Black big 'tractor' tyre, 35 mm dia.	NGPP
				606089 (as 089)	**Spare tyre**... Black 'tractor front tyre', 19 mm dia.	NGPP
				607090 (as 090)	**Spare tyre**... Black fine tread tyre, 14 mm dia.	NGPP
				607091 (as 090)	**Spare tyre**... White fine tread tyre, 14 mm dia.	NGPP

Dinky Toys Catalogues (UK issues)

Pre-war Catalogues, leaflets and listings

Hornby 'Modelled Miniatures' were introduced in 1931 as model railway accessories. The first catalogue listings appeared in Hornby Train catalogues, Meccano catalogues and in the 'Meccano Magazine'.

Ref	Year(s)	Publication	Cover features, details	Price
-	1932-33	Hornby 'Book of Trains'	First 'Modelled Miniatures' listed as 'Railway Accessories'	£40-50
-	1932	Meccano trade catalogue	First 'Modelled Miniatures' listed as 'Railway Accessories'	£40-50
-	1933	'Meccano Magazine'	42 Hornby 'Modelled Miniatures' listed in December issue	£20-25
-	1933-34	Hornby 'Book of Trains'	Accessories are depicted in full colour	£40-50
-	1934	Meccano trade catalogue	'Modelled Miniatures' briefly renamed 'Meccano Miniatures'	NGPP
-	1934	'Meccano Magazine'	February issue contained the last published 'Modelled Miniatures' listing	£30-40
-	1934	'Meccano Magazine'	April issue contained the first 'Meccano Dinky Toys' listing	£30-40
-	1934	'Meccano Magazine'	The May, June, July, August, September and November issues each reflected the increasing number of varieties of 'Dinky Toys'	£15-20
-	1934	'Meccano Magazine'	'150 varieties of Dinky Toys' on double pages in October and December issues	£15-20
-	1934-35	Hornby 'Book of Trains'	Catalogue shows 150 'Dinky Toys' in full colour on a double page	£50-75
13/834/900	1934-35	Meccano Catalogue	Boat plane and model plus boy on cover, 3 pages of Dinky Toys	NGPP
16/934/100	1934-35	'Hornby Trains/Meccano Catalogue	Blue cover, full colour design of 'The World', lists 150 models of Dinky Toys	£70-90
-	1934-35	Meccano Book	Cover depicts viaduct over river, complete Dinky Toys range is listed	NGPP
-	1935	'Meccano Magazine'	January to November issues have various Dinky Toys listings	£15-20
-	1935	'Meccano Magazine'	December issue shows 200 varieties of Dinky Toys in Black and White	£15-20
7/835/65	1935-36	Hornby 'Book of Trains'	Catalogue features 200 varieties of Dinky Toys in full colour	£40-50
-	1935-36	Hornby/Meccano	Catalogue with the same cover as the 1934-35 issue	£70-90
-	1936	'Meccano Magazine'	The February and August issues featured a road layout and a competition; the May issue introduced the 'Queen Mary' model	£15-20
-	1936-37	Hornby 'Book of Trains'	The catalogue features full colour pictures of the Dinky Toys range	£40-50
-	1937	Hornby/Meccano	Catalogue with 1934-35 'World' cover again. Seven pages of listings	£50-70
-	1937	'Meccano Magazines'	Details given in the monthly listings of the superb new 'Army' range	£15-20
13/637/25	1937	8-page Leaflet	8 page fold-out buff leaflet. Front page depicts the 1937 Army models	£35-45
13/638/1150	1938	Hornby/Meccano	74 page Catalogue, full Dinky Toys listings. Numerous b/w pictures	£30-40
13/638/1150/UK	1938	'Wonder Book of Toys'	Two boys with Meccano models plus 11 pages with Dinky Toys	NGPP
8/1238/25	1938	'DINKY TOYS' Catalogue	(Booklet). Cover shows boy and 6 models including 29c Bus, 151a Tank, and 63 Mayo Composite Aircraft. Brown print on pale-yellow paper	£75-100
-	1938	'Meccano Magazine'	Details of the full range (with pictures) are published each month	£15-20
1/439/10	1939	'DINKY TOYS' leaflet	'New Products' leaflet detailing items such as the Presentation Aeroplane Sets Nos 64 and 65. Black printing on pinkish paper	£20-30
-	1939	'MECCANO' booklets	with complete Dinky Toys listings, various	NGPP
13/639/1	1939	Hornby/Meccano	74 page Catalogue, full Dinky Toys listings and Black/White pictures	£30-40
13/639/11500 UK	1939	'A Wonder Book of Toys'	Green and Yellow cover depicts two boys with their Meccano models. The booklet includes 13 pages of Dinky Toys information	£30-40
2/739/10 (1P)	1939	'DINKY TOYS' Catalogue	Famous Red/Yellow cover picture of schoolboy with outstretched arm and 17 models. Contains 14 black and white pages	£200-250
-		'Toys Of Quality'	Maroon Express train features on cover plus 'The Hornby Railway Co' logo. 13 pages of Dinky Toys listings are included	£30-40
-	1939	Trade catalogue	Cover depicts boy with Dinky Toys and Hornby pictures with 'MECCANO TOYS OF QUALITY' logo	£30-40
2/1139/20(3P) UK	1939	'DINKY TOYS' Catalogue	Superb Red and Yellow cover picture of schoolboy with outstretched arm and 17 models. Contains 10 Black/White pages of listings and pictures	£100-150
-	1939	'Meccano Magazine'	Each month contained Dinky Toys listings	£15-20
16/1040 /100	1940	'Meccano' Price List	All products listed but no pictures	NGPP
16/1040 /200	1940	'DINKY TOYS' leaflet	Listing of models with pictures	£15-20
-	1940	'Meccano Magazine'	Wartime Dinky aircraft and the Meccano 'Spitfire Fund' are featured	£15-20
16/541/25 UK	1941	'DINKY TOYS' leaflet	Wartime camouflaged aircraft feature in this leaflet	£15-20
16/641/20 UK	1941	'DINKY TOYS' leaflet	Similar to previous leaflet, military models listed	£15-20
16/1141 /20 UK	1941	'DINKY TOYS' leaflet	Listing of models and retail prices	£15-20

Full Dinky Toys listings also appeared in the toy catalogues of major retailers such as Gamages and Bentalls. These catalogues are difficult to find. Each: £30-40

Post-War Catalogues, leaflets and listings
Early Post-War period, 1945 – 1954

There were at least two editions per annum so the following listings are not complete. The 'leaflet' approach reflects the shortage of paper in early post-war years.

Ref	Year	Publication	Cover features, details	Price
16/1145/75 UK	1945	Meccano leaflet	leaflet lists the models to be reintroduced after the War and features pictures of 23e, 29c, 39a, 62s, 62p. Sepia print on cream paper	£10-15
16/546/30 UK	1946	Meccano leaflet	Sepia printed listing on cream paper featuring pictures of models 70a, 38c, 29c, 23e	£10-15
16/1146 /65 UK	1946	Meccano leaflet	Blue/Black print on cream paper, featuring models 70a, 38c, 70b, 38e	£10-15
16/347/50 UK	1947	Meccano leaflet	Brown print on light cream paper. Models depicted are 70a, 70b, 70c, 70e, 38c, 38e, 38f, and 153a Jeep	£10-15
16/448/30	1948	Meccano General Products	booklet with green printing on light cream paper	£10-15
16/948/200	1948		Same as previous issue but with mauve print on light cream paper	£10-15
16/1248 /5	1948	'Dinky Toys Tyre Sizes'	Simple Leaflet giving information on Dinky Toys spare tyres	£10-15
16/449/100	1949	Meccano General Products	booklet with brown printing on light cream paper	£10-15
	1949	Independent shop listings	Full Dinky Toys listings and pictures featured in the catalogues published by the larger toy shops such as Bentalls, Gamages, etc	£15-20
16/450/150	1950	Meccano General Products	booklet with pale Blue/Black printing on light cream paper	£10-15
-	1950	Independent shop listings	Full Dinky Toys listings and pictures featured in the catalogues of larger toy shops such as Gamages, Bentalls, etc	£15-20

16/251/33 1951	**Meccano General Products**.....booklet with brown printing on light cream paper	£10-15
- 1951	**Independent shop listings**........Full Dinky Toys listings and pictures featured in the catalogues of larger toy shops such as Bentalls, Gamages, etc	£15-20
13/952/250 1952	**Price List**...................................Beige leaflet with pictures and prices	£10-15
13/953/678 1953	**Meccano Catalogue**.................Includes Dinky Toys, Meccano and Hornby Dublo	£15-20
16/453/500 1953	**4-page Leaflet**..........................Buff leaflet; front page shows date '15th April 1953' and boy shouting 'DINKY TOYS' £15-25
16/853/25 1953	**Price List**...................................Beige leaflet with pictures and prices	£15-20
16/854/25 1954	**Price List**...................................Beige leaflet with pictures and prices	£10-15

Meccano Magazines, 1942 - 1952

During the latter part of the war and especially during the early post-war years when Dinky Toys catalogues were not issued, the Meccano Magazine was the main source of new information for collectors. It advised on the reintroduction of models after the war and of the forthcoming new releases. Consequently the Magazines of this period are highly collectable in their own right.

1942 - September 1943. No Dinky Toys adverts or listings appeared.

September 1943 - December 1944. Back page adverts for Meccano incorporated listing and pictures of De Havilland Flamingo Aircraft and Buick 'Viceroy' Saloon.

January - November 1945. Back page adverts said 'Sorry, not available but will be ready after the war'.

December 1945. Advert on back page announced 'Ready during December'.

1946. Virtually every month a new model was added to the listing printed on the inside front cover. A picture of each model was shown.

January - September 1947. New models added regularly each month.

October 1947. First advert appears of Dinky Supertoys with pictures of 501 Foden Diesel Wagon, 502 Foden Flat Truck, 503 Foden Flat Truck with Tailboard, 511 Guy 4 ton Lorry, 512 Guy Flat Truck, 513 Guy Flat Truck with Tailboard, and 701 Short 'Shetland' Flying Boat.

1948. Single page advert every month, new models continually introduced.

1949, 1950, 1951. Double page advert each month listing new models.

1952. Double page adverts each month. The December issue shows Gift Sets No1 Farm Gear and No2 Commercial Vehicles.

Prices for Meccano Magazines of this period range between **£10-15** each.

UK Catalogue editions, 1952 – 1965

The series included fourteen editions although not all issues were given an edition number. More than one catalogue was issued in some issues. It was common for catalogues to be overprinted with the name and address of the toy retailer. In addition to issuing Dinky Toys catalogues, Meccano Ltd continued to issue 'Meccano Toys Of Quality' leaflets which provided a full listing of Dinky Toys with their retail prices plus details of their 'Hornby', 'Hornby-Dublo' and 'Meccano' products. As many as five printings per annum were produced using green, pink, blue or buff paper. When in perfect condition these leaflets sell for **£5-8** each.

16/152/50 1952	**(February) 16 pages**................Cover features unknown 'C6321'	£40-50
15/852/165 1952	**(September) 16 pages** ....Cover shows hands holding 27f Estate Car, 'Dinky Toys' logo....................................	£40-50
1953	**24 page catalogue** ....Cover shows boy wearing green sweater, 'Dinky Toys' and 'Price 3d'...........................	£40-50
7/953/150 1953	**24 page catalogue** ....As next item: 7/953/360.	
7/953/360 1953	**(1st October) 24 pages** ....(1) Cover features 555 Fire Engine, 522 Big Bedford Lorry and 25x Breakdown Lorry, price '2d'	£40-50
13/953/678 1953	**(1st October)**............................(2) Cover shows 'Meccano Magic Carpet', two boys plus globe with flag............................	£40-50
7/754/600 1954	**(1st September) 24 pages** ....Cover features 157 Jaguar, 480 'Kodak' Van, 641 Army Truck, 'Dinky Toys' logo, price '2d'	£30-40
7/455/250 1955	**(May) 8 page leaflet** ....251, 641, 170 and 401 on cover, 'Dinky Toys' and 'Dinky Supertoys'..........................	£15-20
7/755/945 1955	**24 page catalogue** ....'Dinky Toys','Supertoys', 481 'Ovaltine' Van on cover, ('2d').....................................	£30-40
7/456/800 1956	**(June) 32 pages** ....Cover has 942 'REGENT' Tanker, 255 Mersey Tunnel 'Police' Land Rover, 157 Jaguar XK120, 'Dinky Toys' & 'Dinky Supertoys', '2d'	£30-40
7/657/820 1957	**(August) 28 pages** ....Cover shows 290 'DUNLOP' Double Decker Bus etc, 'Dinky Toys', and 'Dinky Supertoys', price '2d UK'	£30-40
7/458/856 1958	**28 page catalogue** ....Houses of Parliament shown on front cover with 'Dinky Toys' and 'Dinky Supertoys', price '2d UK'	£30-40
7/559/900 1959	**28 page catalogue** ....Red Jaguar XK120 Coupe (157) on front cover with 'Dinky Toys' and 'UK Seventh Edition', price '3d'	£20-25
7/3/800 1960	**32 page catalogue** ....Motorway bridge on cover, 'Dinky Toys' and 'UK Eighth Edition'..............................	£20-25
7/561/700 1961	**32 page catalogue** ....Black/Yellow cover with 6 models, 'Dinky Toys', 'UK 9th Edition'	£20-25
72537/02 1962	**32 page catalogue** ....Cover features 120 Jaguar 'E' type, 'Dinky Toys', price '2d'	£15-20
7/263/400 1963	**?**..No details available for this reference number	NGPP
13/163/200 1963	**32 page catalogue** ....Motor Show stands featured on cover, '11th Edition', 'UK', '2d'	£15-20
13/763/400 1963	**32 page catalogue** ....11th Edition, 2nd impression	NGPP
7/164/450 1964	**8 page catalogue** ....'Widest Range & Best Value In The World' and 'Dinky Toys' logos Price '3d'	£15-20
7/64/45 1964	**8 page catalogue** ....(2nd printing). As 7/164/450 except that page 8 shows Bedford TK instead of accessories......£15-20
7/265/200 1965	**16 page catalogue** ....Rolls-Royce (127) on cover with 'Dinky Toys by Meccano' Price '3d'.........................	£15-20
72557/02 1965	**16 page catalogue** ....Cover features cars 127, 128, 133, 151 and 178..	£15-20

UK Catalogue editions, 1966 – 1978

72561/2 1966	**106 page catalogue** ....'1st Edition', '6d', 'Always Something New From Dinky' on the cover. Accompanied by separate (pink) price list..................................	£25-30
72561/2 1966	**(after 21st July)**.......................2nd edition, same cover as 1st, 104 pages plus (buff) price list.................................	£20-25
72571 1967	**104 page catalogue** ....'No.3', '6d' 12 models on cover, same logo as 72561/2. Price list (green paper) included £20-25
72580 1968	**104 page catalogue** ....'No.4', '6d', Spectrum Pursuit Vehicle (104) on cover. Logo as 72561/2. Buff price list..........£20-25
72585 1969	**(1st Sept) 24 pages** ....'No.5', '3d', (2nd printing). Cover features 102 'Joe's Car', has same logo as 72561/2 ....£15-20
165000 1970	**24 page catalogue** ....'No.6', '3d', many models on cover. Same logo as 72561/2	£15-20
100103 1971	**24 page catalogue** ....'No.7', '2p', '1971 Meccano Tri-ang Ltd' on rear cover. Same logo as on 72561/2. (Note the change to Decimal Currency in 1971)	£10-15
100107 1972	**(1st November) 28 pages**..........'No.8', '2p', 2nd printing, shows 683 Chieftain Tank, 'Dinky Toys'	£10-15
100108 1972	**28 pages** ....'No.8', '2p', 725 Phantom, 784 Goods Train etc. on cover	£10-15
100109 1973	**(October) 40 pages** ....'No.9', '3p', 2nd printing, shows 924 'Centaur', 'Dinky Toys'	£10-15
100113 1974	**(May) 48 pages** ....'No.10', '4p', cover shows 731 S.E.P.E.C.A.T. and 'Dinky Toys'	£10-15
100115 UK....................1975	**(June) 48 pages** ....'No.11', '5p', 'Dinky Toys' and 675 Motor Patrol Boat on cover................................	£10-15
100118 UK....................1976	**48 page catalogue** ....'No.12', '5p', 'Dinky Toys' and 358 'USS Enterprise' on cover..................................	£10-15
100122 (UK)..................1977	**44 page catalogue** ....'No.13' and '5p'. Cover features 357 Klingon Battle Cruiser	£5-10
100100 1978	**44 page catalogue** ....'No.14', '5p', 'AIRFIX GROUP' and 180 Rover 3500 on cover.................................	£5-10

Leaflets and Price Lists, 1954 – 1978

Further information. It is known that other leaflets, literature and price lists were published. The Editor would welcome more information to add to these listings.

no ref.	1957	**Booklet**	Yellow cover, 'A NEW SERIES' and 'DUBLO DINKY TOYS' in red	**£20-30**
DT/CF/3 16/257/250 (1P)	1957	**Leaflet and Price List**	Yellow front leaflet '1st January 1957', pictures of 716, 162, 626, and 250 Fire Engine, 'Dinky Toys' and 'Dinky Supertoys' in Red	**£25-35**
DT/CL/20 16/1157/100uk	1957	**Two-sided Leaflet**	Headed 'Dublo Dinky Toys' in Red on Yellow. Pictures of first 3 issues: 064, 065, 066	**£10-15**
DT/CF/5 16/159/100	1959	**Illustrated price list**	Colour cover showing 983 Transporter and cars, etc.	**£10-15**
DT/CF/6 16/759/1002ndP	1959	**Price List with colour pictures**	Leaflet cover shows nos. 998, 967, 968 and 986. Dated '1959/UK' on front	**£10-15**
DT/CF/7 16/160/100 (3P)	1960	**Illustrated price list**	Colour cover with 666 Missile Vehicle and 785 Service Station, etc.	**£10-15**
DT/CF/8 16/160/100 (4P)	1960	**Illustrated price list**	Colour cover with 930 Pallet-Jekta plus GS 951 Fire Service, etc.	**£10-15**
DT/CF/11 8/561/100	1961	**Illustrated price list**	(72535/02) Colour cover with 4 cars and 'Purchase Tax Surcharges 26th July 1961'	**£10-15**
72557/02	1965	**Leaflet**	Cover with 133, 127, 128, 151 and 171, with price list.	**£10-15**
72579	1967	**Leaflet**	Trade Fair leaflet, 'THUNDERBIRDS'	**£10-15**
72569	1968	**Leaflet**	Features 103-105 'Captain Scarlet' vehicles.	**£10-15**
100217	1971	**Leaflet**	Four page 'Action Kits' leaflet.	**£10-15**
100261	1971	**Single sheet**	Full-colour flyer featuring 'All Action Fighting Vehicles'	**£10-15**
no ref.	72-75	**Dinky Driver's Diary**	6 models pictured on the cover, plus descriptions and diagrams of 1970s models inside	NGPP
no ref.	1979	**Trade Catalogue 1979**	'Fifty New Models', 11½ x 8¼ inches.	**£20-30**

Meccano Trade Catalogues listing Dinky Toys

These were issued for many years but little information has been recorded (please send any information that you may have). For example:
Ref. 100126 – **1978 Trade Catalogue** with 'Todays World', 'Todays Meccano', Todays Dinky Toys' on the cover plus colour design of late 1970s models on Motorway with 'Meccano' buildings in background.
Ref. 100102 – **1979 Trade Catalogue** 'Today's Meccano & Dinky'.

Overseas Catalogues

Catalogues were often adapted so that they could be switched for use in most countries in the world irrespective of the language or the currency used. An example of this is the 1965 catalogue:

72257/02UK	1965	**UK catalogue**	16 pages. Cover depicts 5 cars namely Nos.127, 128, 133 and 171 plus a description of various model features	**£15-20**
72557	1965	**Overseas edition**	16 pages. The cover is the same but replacing the features listing is a panel with 'Precision Diecast Scale Models' printed in English, German, French, Spanish, Italian and Swedish. The catalogue pages contain only the basic English model name and number - all the English text having been removed. The models are the same as 72257/02	**£20-25**
72559	1965	**Overseas edition**	24 pages. Whilst the cover is the same as 72557, the listings are entirely different for they feature both English and French Dinky Toys, including the French issues sold in the UK.	**£40-50**

Price lists. Prior to the overseas editions being despatched, price lists in the correct language and currency would be inserted.
The Editor would like to express his thanks to the many collectors around the world who have contributed to this listing. New information would be welcomed.

Dinky Toys Overseas Catalogue editions recorded to date

Africa

KENYA	1961	**Illustrated List**	**£50-75**
RHODESIA	1953	**Illustrated Price List**	**£75-100**
	1954	**Illustrated Price List**	**£75-100**
SOUTH AFRICA			
7/655/20	1955	**Catalogue** Ovaltine Van + 7 others, prices in shillings/pence, 24 pages	**£50-75**
TANGANYIKA & UGANDA		**Combined Catalogue**	**£75-100**

Australia

Agents (in 1952): E. G. Page & Co. (Sales) Pty., Ltd., Danks Building, 324 Pitt Street, Sydney, Australia.

13/852/12	1952	**Catalogue** Cover shows boy with green sweater. An example sold at auction in 1998 for **£250**	
7/757/30	1957	**Catalogue** Piccadilly Circus, colour, vertical, no prices, 28 pages	**£75-100**
100100	1978	**44 page Catalogue** ('No.14') ...'20c' on cover. 'Liberty Trading Pty Ltd, Surrey Hills, Marshall St. NSW' on checklist	NGPP

Belgium and Luxembourg (French printing)

Agents: P FREMINEUR et Fils, Rue des Bogards 1, Bruxelles 1

13/736/265	1936	**Meccano Catalogue**	**£75-100**
16/1053 /10	1954	**Catalogue** Same cover as 1953 UK issue	**£30-40**
16/1054 /2	1954	**Catalogue** Same cover as 1954 UK issue	**£30-40**
16/656/156	1956	**Catalogue** (DT/CL/5) Same cover as 1956 UK issue	**£30-40**
16/1258/12.5 Belgium	1958	**Leaflet** (printed in England)......(DT/CL/32 on cover) 168 Singer and 178 Plymouth on cover. Text in French and Flemish	**£30-40**
7/539/-	1959	**Catalogue** with Red Jaguar XK140 on cover	**£30-40**
no ref.	1960	**48 page Catalogue** English and French models in one catalogue. Printed and issued only in Belgium and/Luxembourg. Cover depicts Land Rover plus two French Dinky Toys cars. 'Frs 3-'.	**£75-100**

Belgium (Flemish printing)

16/1054 /2 1954	**Illustrated price list**		£40-50
72551 1966	**1st Edition price list** ....in French and Flemish, 164 pages		£40-50

Canada

Agents: Meccano Limited, 675 King Street West, Toronto and 187 - 189 Church Street, Toronto.

Pre-War Editions

10/34 1934	**Leaflet** ....Yellow leaflet with 'LOCKE BROS. OF MONTREAL' stamp		£50-60
7/38 1938	**Leaflet** ....Ten page fold-out leaflet showing the full range		£50-60
13/840/5 1940	**Leaflet** ....Twelve pages in black and white, size 8.75 x 5.875 inches. Cover shows boy with outstretched arms plus 62h, 151a, 36g, 43a, and 33r. 'The Fascinating Collecting Hobby'		£50-60
6/41 1941	**Leaflet** ....Twelve page fold-out leaflet showing the full range		£50-60

Post-War Editions

16/351/25 1951	**Catalogue** ....Boy with 3 models, pictures in blue, 16 pages		£50-60
7/953/150 1953	**Catalogue** ....555 Fire Engine, 522 Big Bedford, 25x Breakdown Truck, 28 pages		£40-50
16/355/90 1955	**Illustrated price list** ......Printed on Off-White leaflet		£30-35
7/655/90 1955	**Catalogue** ....Illustration of Bedford 'Ovaltine' Van plus seven other models		£40-50
7/556/90 1956	**Catalogue** ....Regent Tanker/Tunnel, 1st June 1956 in colour, 32 pages		£40-50
16/656/18c 1956	**Illustrated price leaflet** ....(DT/CL/4) in colour, featuring 131 Cadillac and 660 Tank Transporter		£15-20
16/756/18 1956	**Illustrated price leaflet** ......in colour, featuring 706 Vickers 'Air France' Airliner		£15-20
7/757/90 1957	**Catalogue** ....Piccadilly Circus, vertical, in colour, with prices, 28 pages		£40-50
7/559/90 1959	**Catalogue** ....Red Jaguar + 6 models on cover, in colour, 28 pages		£40-50
3/41/25 7252 3/42 1961	**Catalogue** ....Black with 7 models and '9th' on cover, Canada/English, 32 pages		£30-40
13/163/100 7254 2/42 ..1963	**Catalogue** ....Motor Show 11th, Canada/English, 32 pages		£30-40
13/1063 /50 7254 8/42..1963	**Catalogue** ....Flyer 8in x 10¼in. 10 models on cover, Canada 1963, 8 pages		£10-15
7/364/150 1964	**Trade Catalogue** ......8 page catalogue plus 4 page trade price list (half catalogue width, in centre)		NGPP
7/464/150 72550/42 1964	**Catalogue** ....'12th', 8in x 11in, Canada/English, 8 pages		£10-15
None 1964	**Catalogue** ....Flyer, 5½ x 3½, shows 6 Hong Kong models, 12 pages		£10-15
None 1965	**Catalogue** ....1st Edn 8½ x 5½, 5 models on cover, 16 pages		£20-25
72561 1966	**Catalogue** ....1st Edition, 108 pages		£30-40
72561 1966	**Catalogue** ....2nd Edition, 106 pages		£30-40
72571 1967	**Catalogue** ....3rd edition, 106 pages		£30-40
72580 1968	**Catalogue** ....4th Edition, 106 pages		£30-40
72585 1969	**Catalogue** ....5th Edition, 24 pages		£20-30

Cyprus

(Distributor unknown)

No Ref........1969	**Catalogue** ....Same as UK issue		£20-25

Egypt

(Distributor unknown)

5/652/2 1952	**Catalogue** ....Different page nine from UK issue with pictures of US 39 Series cars and British cars		£20-25

Eire and Channel Islands

Agents: S.J. Gearey, 1 St Stephens Green, Dublin. (Ceased trading 1968).
Agents from 1969: Kilroy Bros Ltd, Shanowen Road, Whitehall, Dublin 9.

7/755/20 1955	**Catalogue** ....'Eire' and 'C.I.' on cover		£20-25
7/659/75 1959	**Catalogue** ....'Eire' on cover		£20-25
7/364/7 1964	**Catalogue** ....'Eire' on cover		£20-25
No.5 1969	**Catalogue** ....'Irish' on cover Distributed by Kilroy Bros Ltd.		£20-25

Hong Kong

Representatives: W.R.Loxley & Co. Ltd., Jardine House, 11th Floor, 20 Pedder Street, Hong Kong.

DT/CF/5 1959	**Illustrated price list** ......Same cover as 1959 UK issue DT/CF/5		£20-25

Italy

Agents: Alfredo Parodi, Piazza 8, Marcellino 6, Genova

Post-War Editions

16/657/5 1957	**Leaflet** ....with 101-105		£10-15
16/3/57/5 1957	**Leaflet** ....677 and 472 'Raleigh'		£10-15
16/357/5 1957	**Leaflet** ....642 and 455 Brooke Bond Tea		£10-15
16/857/5 1957	**Leaflet** ....237 Mercedes front, 136, 236, 238 back		£10-15
16/457/5 1957	**Leaflet** ....697 Military Set		£10-15
16/457/5 1957	**Leaflet** ....661 and 919 'Golden Shred'		£10-15
no ref 1957	**Leaflet** ....with 163, 236 and 238 on racing circuit		£20-25
no ref 1957	**Leaflet** ....with 237, 661, and 919 'Golden Shred'		£20-25
16/357/5 1957	**Illustrated price list** ......with 'Italy' printed after the reference number.		£20-25
12/757/50 1957	**Leaflet** ....(DT/CL/15) 642 and 455 'Brooke Bond' shown		£20-25
7/857/50 1957	**Catalogue** ....Same cover as UK issue 7/657/820		£30-40
DT/CL/12 1957	**Leaflet** ....with 677 and 472 on cover		£20-25
7/758/50 1958	**Catalogue** ....Same cover as UK issue 7/458/856		£30-40
7/364/40 7225 0/37 1964	**Catalogue** ....12th 8in x 11in, includes 4 pages of French Dinky, 12 pages		£20-30

Malaya and Singapore

Agents: King & Co, Singapore.

16/557/25 (IP)...............1957   **Catalogue (8 pages)**.................Cover depicts 170, 626, 716, 955, includes other pictures and price list in $ (DT/CF/3)...........**£40-50**
7/958/10 1958   **Catalogue** ....Same cover as UK, 4 pages with prices in $ **£40-50**

Netherlands/Holland

Agents: Hausemann & Hotte NV, Kromboomsloot 57-61, Amsterdam

Pre-War Editions
1/736/5 1936   ....Yellow paper with Black ink **£75-100**
13/637/75 1937   ....Yellow paper with Black ink **£75-100**
13/738/22 1938   ....Yellow paper with Black ink **£75-100**

Post-War Editions - Some black/white, later coloured as per UK issues
16/954/108 1954   **Illustrated price list** ....Printed in French **£15-20**
8/1255/50 (DT/L/7) 1955   ....no details..**£30-35**
16/256/30n (DT/CL/2)..1956   ....no details..**£20-25**
16/256/30n (DT/L/9) 1956   ....no details..**£20-25**
16/1158 /20 1958   ....'Nederland Frs 3-'. Cover same as 1958 UK issue **£30-35**
16/256/30 (72538/29) ...1962   ....no details..**£20-25**
72571 1967   **Catalogue** ....3rd Edition, price list in Dutch, florins, 162 pages...**£40-50**
no ref...........................1970   **Catalogue** ....6th Edition includes 8 pages of French Dinky, 32 pages..................................**£20-30**

Portugal

-                   1956   **Illustrated Catalogue** ....no details...**£40-50**
DT/CF/4 1957   **Illustrated Leaflet** ....Produced for Portugal, illustrating English Dinky Toys...**£50-70**
7/858/5 1958   **Illustrated Catalogue** ....Houses of Parliament on cover, produced for the Portuguese market...................**£30-40**
-                   1959   **Illustrated Catalogue** ....no details...**£40-50**
5/261/25 1961   **Illustrated Catalogue** ....9th edition catalogue, produced for the Portuguese market...........................**£30-40**
-                   1963   **Illustrated Catalogue** ....no details...**£30-40**
7255049 ....1960s   **Illustrated Catalogue** ....Produced for the Portuguese market, cover shows a group of 1960s cars **£30-40**
72585 1969   **'No.5' Catalogue** ....Produced for the Portuguese market, cover features 'Joe 90's Car'.....................**£30-40**

Spain

DT/CL15 SP 16/457/5 ..1957   **Illustrated Leaflet** ....Similar to Italian leaflet with 697 on colour front of single sheet, unpriced list on reverse.......**£10-15**

Sweden

Agents: Ludvig Wigart & Cos, AB Helsingborg.

7/654/14 1954   **4 pages**........................3 pages colour pictures plus price list in Kroner with Swedish text **£30-40**
16/357/15 1957   **Leaflet** ....Leaflet depicts 455 'Brooke Bond' Trojan plus 642 RAF Tanker and
price list in Kroner with Swedish text...**£15-20**
14/561/60 1961   **Catalogue** ....Same as 1961 UK issue, text in Swedish..**£20-30**
72580 1968   **162 page Catalogue**.................Same as UK 1968 edition, but in Swedish...**£20-30**

Switzerland

Agents: Riva & Kunzmann SA Basel 2, Switzerland. From 1965 address changed to Prattela, Switzerland.

7/356/20 1956   **Catalogue** ....Ovaltine Van + 7 others, prices in francs, 24 pages....................................**£40-50**
72537/25 1962   **Catalogue** ....10th Edition, 48 pages, same as UK issue 72537/02 plus French Dinky **£40-50**
13/163/175 1963   **Catalogue** ....11th Edition, 48 pages, same as UK issue 13/163/20 plus French Dinky **£40-50**
72559 1965   **Catalogue** ....24 pages, same cover as UK issue 72557 plus French Dinky **£40-50**

United States of America

Agents: H. Hudson Dobson, PO Box 254, 26th St and Jefferson Avenue, Kenilworth, NJ.
In 1952 the address was: PO Box 254, 906 Westfield Avenue, Elizabeth, NJ.
From 1957 the address changed to 627 Boulevard, Kenilworth. New York showroom: 200, Fifth Avenue, PO Box 255.
Models sold by this distributor will often be found with an 'H.Hudson Dobson' label
From 1963: Lines Bros Inc, 1107 Broadway, New York. From ?: AVA International, Box 7611, Waco, Texas 76710.

War-Time Issue
no ref...........................1941   **Large leaflet**.........................No details available ....NGPP

Post-War Editions
no ref...........................1951   **Catalogue** ....Boy's side face, 5 models, black and white, green printing, 16 pages **£50-75**
no ref...........................1952   **Catalogue** ....Hands holding 27f (139b and 25x in picture). Unlike the UK edition,
39b, 39c and 39e are shown in two-tone colours...**£50-75**
7/753/150 1953   **Catalogue** ....Same cover as 1953 UK issue 7/953/360 ....**£50-75**
7/954/150 1954   **Catalogue** ....Same cover as 1954 UK issue 7/754/600 ....**£50-75**
7/753/150 1954   **Catalogue** ....157 Jaguar, 480 Kodak, 641 Army, Separate price list, 28 pages **£50-75**

no ref...........................1955   **Catalogue** ....20 models on cover, 5 French, black and white, prices in $, 32 pages **£50-75**
no ref...........................1956   **Catalogue** ....'Ever-Ready' + 11 others, Feb 57, black/white, prices in $, 32 pages **£50-75**
no ref...........................1957   **Catalogue** ....Yellow/Red cover shows model 697 plus Red lined sections displaying
English and French models. Red panel with US address of H.Hudson Dobson.
36 black/white pages of English and French models...**£75-100**

Catalogues

West Germany

Agents: Biengngraeber of Hamburg.

Meccano Catalogues 1954 - 1958

with colour 'Dinky Toys' and 'Hornby-Dublo' listing. Details known to the compiler relate solely to issues in the mid-1950's period. 'MECCANO TOYS OF QUALITY' logo on each cover.

Meccano Magazines 1952 - 1975

With the introduction of yearly Dinky Toys catalogues from 1952 the Meccano Magazine lost its somewhat unique role as a combined magazine/catalogue. However, with the help of 'The Toyman' and his monthly articles plus superb colour advertising of new models, the Magazine continued to provide a valuable service for collectors. Meccano Magazines of this period are in the price range of **£5-10**.

Dinky Toys Club Licences and Newsletter

Factory drawings

UNISSUED MODELS

A number of models were planned but not actually produced by Meccano. This is list of known factory drawings and plans for such models. **Austin A40 Van** 'OMNISPORT' drawing dated 31-8-57. **Guy Warrior Van** 'GOLDEN SHRED' drawing dated 26-3-57, Job No. 14794. **Leyland Fuel Tanker** drawing dated 30-9-65, Job No. 62520. **Single-Deck Bus** drawing dated 14-5-34, Job No. 6763. **Jowett Javelin Saloon** drawing dated 10-10-47, Job No. 12886. **Renault Fregate** drawing dated 4-7-57, Job No. 20106. **Triumph Dolomite** (intended 38e) drawing dated 1939. **Vampire Jet** drawing dated 27-11-45, Job No. 12157. **Firebrand Aircraft** drawing dated 18-12-45, Job No. 12159.

PRODUCTION MODELS

In October 2000, Christie's South Kensington sold part of the Mike and Sue Richardson collection of Meccano General Assembly Drawings for the Dinky Toys range. The following is a small selection of items from that sale. The reference numbers are 'Job Numbers'.

Drawings – English Saloon Cars. 13866/7 Jaguar XK120 and Base, 20335 Base XK150, 20329 Spring XK150, 13381/3 **Austin Atlantic Body and**

Base, 20121/2 and 20118/9 **Rolls-Royce Silver Wraith** (various parts), 62035/6/7 Chauffuer and Passengers, 13360/1/2 Rover 75, 14844/5 **Spring and Base for Humber Hawk**, 14982/4 **Singer Gazelle Body and Base**, 14088/9 **Austin A30 Body and Base**, 14721/3 **Sunbeam Rapier Body and Base**, 14721/3 **Sunbeam Rapier Body and Base**, 14745/7 **Hillman Minx Body and Base**, 7889 Ford Zephyr Body, 14097/8 **Vauxhall Cresta Body and Base**, 14937/8 **Fiat 600 Body and Base**, 14847/8 **Austin A105 Body and Base**. (All 1950s). In all, 33 items sold in one lot for ... £750

Drawings – Buses. 10897/8 **Double Deck Omnibus Body and Base** (both with dyeline copies), Memo 15954 about 17693 **'Dunlop' Transfers**, 13480/2 **Luxury Coach and Base**, 13750/2 **Duple Roadmaster Coach and Base**, 13424/6 **Observation Coach and Base**. 12 items in one lot sold for ... £420

Drawings – Fodens. 12163/6 and 12822 **Cab and Chassis, Body and Tanker Body**, 12164/5/9 **Bogie, Clip and Washer for Spare Wheel** + 7 drawings for **Chains, Stanchions, Tank parts**, etc. 13 items sold for ... £550

Drawings – Leyland Octopus. 7874 **Cab and Chassis**, 7875 **Front Bogie**, and Memo 20649 **Label for 'ESSO'**. 3 items sold as one lot for ... £120

Dinky Toys Trade Boxes

Virtually all Dinky Toys models were supplied in their own individual boxes from around 1954. Before then, most small models were supplied to shopkeepers in 'Trade Boxes' containing 3, 4, 6 or 12 identical models separated by strips of card. (Some aircraft and ship models were an exception to this general rule). A single item would be sold without further packaging except perhaps for a paper bag.

These Trade Boxes have become collectors items in their own right whether full or empty (the latter selling for between £20 and £50 depending on its rarity and that of its original contents. Most of these boxes that come to auction are full and the listing below derives mostly from the survey of such items undertaken for the 8th Edition. We are grateful to David Cooke for updating and enhancing the listing for this Edition. It is known that other trade packaging of this type exists and the Editor would welcome any additional information on the subject.

Pre-war boxes. Plain card boxes with a covering of coloured paper:
YP = Yellow paper, **GP** = Grey paper, **OP** = Orange paper, **BP** = Blue paper

Post-war boxes. Often plain Brown card boxes (various shades) were used with a Yellow contents label affixed to one end (occasionally both ends). Where coloured, the outer covering is part of the structure of the box rather than being simply pasted on as with the pre-war boxes. Later boxes are better referred-to as 'packs' where they contain individually boxed models. The packs were flimsy plain grey or greyish-brown with no label, just printing applied directly to the outer surface.

YC = Yellow card box, **BY** = Brown card box with a yellow label
OC = Orange card box, **GC** = Green card box, **BC** = Blue card box
GB = Grey box (printed, no label), **GBP** = Grey-brown pack

Ref	Models, number in box, box type	Market Price Range
069	**Massey-Harris Tractor**, 6, GB	£150-200
078	**Lansing Bagnall Trailers**, 6	£140-170
12c	**Telephone Box**, 6, YP	£150-200
12d	**Telegraph Messenger**, 6, GP	£60-70
12d	**Telegraph Messenger**, 6, GC, '50175'	£50-60
12e	**Postman**, 6, GP	£80-90
12e	**Postman**, 6, GC, '50176'	£70-80
13a	**Cook's Man**, 6, GC '50174'	£50-60
14a	**B.E.V. Truck**, 6, BY or YC	£90-110
22g	**Streamline Tourer**, 6, YP, 'A2018'	£1,500-1,750
23	**Racing Car**, 6, YP, 'A1002'	£1,500-2,000
23a	**Racing Car**, 6, BY	£1,000-1,250
23a	**Racing Car**, 6, YC	£1,000-1,250
23b	**Small Closed Racing Car**, 6, YC	£200-300
23c	**Large Open Racing Car**, 6, YC	£200-300
23e	**'Speed of the Wind' Racing Car**, 6, YC	£200-300
23f	**Alfa Romeo Racing Car**, 6, YC, '50189'	£250-300
23s	**Streamlined Racing Car**, 4, YC, '50012'	£200-225
24g	**Sports Tourer**, 6, YP, 'A1017'	£1,500-2,000
25b	**Covered Wagon**, (common colours), 6, BY	£200-300
25d	**Petrol Wagon**, 6, YP, 'A1022'	NGPP
25d	**Petrol Wagon**, (common colours), 6, BY	£200-300
25e	**Tipping Wagon**, 6, YP, 'A1023'	NGPP
25e	**Tipping Wagon**, 6, BY	£250-350
25f	**Market Gardeners Lorry**, 6, YP, 'A1024'	NGPP
25f	**Market Gardeners Lorry**, 6, BY, '(VK29)'	£250-350
25f	**Market Gardeners Lorry**, 6, BY, '(AS39)'	£250-350
25h	**Fire Engine**, 6, BY	£300-400
25h	**Fire Engine**, 6, YC, '50019'	£300-400
25j	**Jeep**, 6, BY, '(M26)'	£250-350
25m	**Bedford Truck** (common colours), 4, YC	£150-200
25m	**Bedford Truck**, 4, YC, '50021'	£150-200
25p	**Aveling Barford**, 4, BY, '(M___)'	£150-200
25p	**Aveling Barford**, 4, YC, '50022'	£150-200
25r	**Forward Control Lorry**, 6, BY, '(M23)'	£200-250
25t	**Flat Truck and Trailer**, 3, YC	£300-325
25v	**Refuse Truck** (common colours), 4, BY	£200-300
25v	**Refuse Truck** (common colours), 4, YC	£200-300
25w	**Bedford Truck** (common colours), 4, YC	£200-300
25y	**Universal Jeep**, 4, YC, '50159' on some	£150-225
26	**GWR Rail Car**, 6, YP, 'A1001'	£900-1,200
27	**Tram Car**, 6, YP	£900-1,200
27a	**Massey-Harris Tractor**, 3, BY	£150-200
27a	**Massey-Harris Tractor**, 3, YC	£150-200
27b	**Harvest Trailer**, 3, YC	£75-85
27c	**MH Manure Spreader**, 3, YC	£85-100
27d	**Land Rover**, 4, YC	£150-200
27d	**Land Rover**, 6, GBP	£225-275
27f	**Estate Car**, 4, YC	£150-200
27g	**Motocart**, 3, YC	£100-150
27h	**Disc Harrow**, 4, YC, with or without '50035'	£60-80
27j	**Triple-Gang Mower**, 3, YC, '50156'	£150-200
27m	**Land Rover Trailer**, 4, YC, '50161'	£75-100
28/1	**Delivery Vans**, 1st Type, 6, YP, 'A1008'	£5,000-7,500

Ref	Models, number in box, box type	Market Price Range
29a	**'Q' type Bus**, 6, YP	£1,000-1,200
29b	**Streamlined Bus**, 6, BY, '(M24)'	NGPP
29c	**AEC Bus**, 6, YP, 'A2226'	NGPP
29c	**AEC Bus**, 6, BY, models flat in box	£200-300
29c	**AEC Bus**, 6, BY, models vertical in box	£200-300
29e	**Single Deck Bus**, 6, BY, '(M23)'	NGPP
29f	**Observation Coach**, 6, YC	£300-400
29g	**Luxury Coach**, 6, YC, '50042'	£400-500
29h	**Duple Roadmaster Coach**, 6, YC, '50163'	£300-400
30b	**Rolls Royce**, 6, BY	£300-400
30d	**Vauxhall**, 6, BY	£300-400
30e	**Breakdown Lorry**, 6, YP, 'A2060'	£150-200
30f	**Ambulance**, 6, BY, '(M28)'	£300-400
30f	**Ambulance**, 6, BY, '(M35)'	£300-400
30g	**Caravan**, 6, YP, 'A2106'	£100-150
30h	**Daimler Ambulance**, 4, YC, '5004-9' on some	£200-300
30j	**Austin Wagon**, 6, YC	£250-300
30m	**Rear Tipping Wagon**, 6, YC, '50052' on some	£150-200
30p	**'Mobilgas' Tankers**, 6, YC, '50051'	£500-600
30pa	**'Castrol' Tanker**, 6, YC, '50146'	£500-700
30pb	**'Esso' Tanker**, 6, YC, '50147'	£500-700
30r	**Thames Flat Truck**, 6, YC	£130-160
30s	**Austin Covered Wagon**, 6, YC	£150-200
30v	**Electric Milk Float**, 6, YC	£250-300
30v	**NCB Milk Float**, 6, YC	£250-300
30w	**Electric Articulated Vehicle**, 6, YC, 50059	£300-400
31a	**Trojan 'Esso' Van**, 6, YC, 50149	£500-600
31b	**Trojan 'Dunlop' Van**, 6, YC	£500-600
31c	**Trojan 'Chivers' Van**, 6, YC, '50151'	£600-800
32	**Chrysler Airflow**, 6, OC, 'A2032'	£2,000-3,000
33a	**Mechanical Horse**, 6, OP, 'A2037'	NGPP
33w	**Horse and Wagon**, 3, BY	£110-150
34b	**Royal Mail Van**, 6, BY	£300-400
34c	**Loudspeaker Van**, 6, BY, '(VK49)'	£150-180
34c	**Loudspeaker Van**, 6, YC, '50062'	£150-180
35a	**Saloon Car**, 6, YC, '50063'	£290-330
35b	**Racer** (Silver/Red), 6, YC, '(CZ35)'	£280-330
35c	**MG Sports Car**, 6, YC	£250-300
36a	**Armstrong-Siddeley**, 6, BY	£400-500
36a	**Armstrong-Siddeley**, 6, YC	£400-500
37b	**Police Motor Cyclist**, 6, YC	£150-200
37c	**Signals Despatch Rider**, 6, GP, 'A2237'	£150-200
38b	**Sunbeam-Talbot**, 6, YC	£400-500
38c	**Lagonda Sports Coupé**, 6, BY	NGPP
38e	**Armstrong-Siddeley**, 6, YC	£450-550
39a	**Packard Super 8**, 6, BY	£400-500
39d	**Buick Viceroy**, 6, BY, '(M24)'	£400-500
39e	**Chrysler Sedan**, 6, YC, 'A2290'	£1,000-1,500
40a	**Riley**, 6, BY, '(M___)'	£350-450
40b	**Triumph 1800**, 6, BY	£350-450
40b	**Triumph 1800**, 6, YC	£350-450
40e	**Standard Vanguard**, 6, BY	£350-450
40e	**Standard Vanguard**, 6, BY, '(M50)'	£350-450
40d	**Austin Devon**, 6, YC	£350-450

40f	**Hillman Minx**, 6, YC, '50049' on some	**£250-350**
40g	**Morris Oxford**, 6, YC, '50049' on some	**£350-450**
40h	**Austin Taxi**, 6, YC, '50097'	**£350-450**
40j	**Austin Somerset**, 6, YC	**£350-450**
42a	**Police Box**, 6, YC	**£140-170**
43b	**'RAC' Motorcycle Patrol**, CB x 6	**£200-300**
44b	**'AA' Motorcycle Patrol**, CB x 6	**£200-300**
47c	**Two-face Traffic Lights**, 12, YC	**£40-70**
47d	**Belisha Beacon**, 12, OC, 'A2058', (pre-war)	NGPP
50a	**Battle Cruiser HMS 'Hood'**, 6, YP, 'A1030'	NGPP
50f/50h	**Destroyers 'Broke' and 'Amazon' Class**, 12, YP, 'A1035'	NGPP
50g/50k	**Submarines 'K' and 'X' Class**, 12, YP, 'A1036'	NGPP
62s	**Hurricane Fighters**, 6, BP	**£300-400**
70d	**Twin Engined Fighter**, 6, YC	**£110-130**
70e	**Gloster Meteor**, 6, YC	**£40-60**
70f	**Shooting Star**, 6, YC	**£100-150**
105a	**Garden Roller**, 6, BY	**£80-90**
105a	**Garden Roller**, 6, YC	**£80-90**
105b	**Wheelbarrow**, 6, YC	**£80-90**
105c	**4-wheeled Hand Truck**, 6, YC	**£40-60**
105e	**Grass Cutter**, 6, YC, '50132' on some	**£90-110**
106	**Austin A90 Atlantic**, 6, YC	NGPP
107a	**Sack Truck**, 6, YC	**£90-110**
139a	**Ford Fordor**, 6, YC	**£350-450**
139b	**Hudson Commodore**, 6, YC	**£500-700**
140a	**Austin Atlantic**, 6, YC, '50136' on some	**£500-700**
140b	**Rover 75**, 6, YC, '50137'	**£350-450**
152b	**Reconnaissance Car**, 6, BY or YC	**£400-500**
152c	**RTC Austin 7**, 6, YP, 'A2196'	**£400-500**
160b	**Royal Artillery Gunners**, 12, YP	**£200-250**
161b	**Mobile AA Gun**, 6, BY or YC	**£300-400**
188	**Jensen FF**, 6, GB	**£150-200**
253	**Daimler Ambulance**, 4, YC	**£150-200**
260	**VW 'Deutsche Bundespost'**, 6, GB	**£150-200**
270	**'AA' Motor Cycle**, 6, YC	**£200-300**
272	**'ANWB' Motor Cycle**, 6, YC	**£250-350**
432	**Foden Tipping Lorry**, factory shrink-wrapped trade pack of 6	**£80-100**
551	**Trailer** (Grey/Red), BY or YC, '(M44)'	**£45-65**
551	**Trailer** (various colours), 3, BC, '50551'	**£65-85**
551	**Trailer** (various colours), 3, GB, '(M49)'	**£65-85**

551	**Trailer** (various colours), 3, GB, '(IH89)'	**£65-85**
603a	**Army Personnel** (metal), 12, YC, early boxes long, later issues square.	**£80-110**
603a	**Army Personnel** (plastic), 12, YC	**£40-50**
673	**Scout Car**, 6, YC	**£65-85**
675	**Ford US Army Staff Car**, 6, GB	NGPP
677	**Armoured Command Vehicle**, 6, GB	**£150-200**
687	**Field Gun Trailer**, 6, YC	**£65-85**
705	**Viking Airliner**, 6, YC	**£200-300**
750	**Telephone Call Box**, 6, YC	**£200-300**
751	**Police Hut**, 6, YC	**£150-180**
755	**Lamp Standard, single-arm**, 6, YC	**£30-40**
756	**Lamp Standard, double-arm**, 6, YC	**£30-40**
760	**Pillar Box**, 6, YC or GC	**£150-200**
768	**Racks with Tyres**, 6, YC	**£75-100**
773	**Traffic Lights**, 12, YC	**£150-175**
777	**Belisha Beacon**, 12, YC	**£65-90**
786	**Tyre Rack**, 6, YC	**£120-160**
788	**Spare Bucket** for 966, 6, YC	**£175-225**
797	**Healey Raceboats**, 6, YC	**£150-200**
994	**Loading Ramp**, 3, GB	**£55-80**
10253	**Tyres**, 12, YC	**£10-15**
14095	**Tyres**, 12, YC	**£10-15**

Dual numbered boxes

221/23e	**'Speed of the Wind' Racing Car**, 6, YC	**£100-140**
222/23s	**Streamlined Racing Car**, 4, YC	**£75-100**
156/140b	**Rover 75**, 6, YC	**£200-250**
158/40b	**Triumph 1800 Renown**, 6, YC	**£200-250**
161/40j	**Austin A40 Somerset**, 6, YC	**£200-250**
200/35b	**Midget Racer**, 6, YC, '(CZ35)'	NGPP
220/23a	**Racing Car**, 6, YC	**£200-300**
281/29g	**Luxury Coach**, 6, YC	**£150-200**
300/27a	**Massey-Harris Tractor**, 3, YC	**£65-95**
342/27g	**Motocart**, 3, YC	**£80-120**
340/27d	**Land Rover**, 4, YC	**£150-200**
381/105a	**Garden Roller**, 6, YC	**£80-120**
382/105b	**Wheelbarrow**, 6, YC	**£60-80**
383/105c	**4-wheeled Hand Truck**, 6, YC	**£80-120**
384/105e	**Grass Cutter**, 6, YC	**£80-120**
385/107a	**Sack Truck**, 6, YC	**£50-70**
405/25y	**Universal Jeep**, 4, YC	**£80-120**
411/25w	**Bedford Truck**, 4, YC	**£80-120**
413/30s	**Austin Covered Wagon**, 6, YC	**£160-200**
420/25r	**Forward Control Lorry**, 6, YC	**£200-250**
421/30w	**Electric Articulated Vehicle**, 6, YC	**£60-90**
422/30r	**Fordson Thames Flat Truck**, 6, YC	**£70-100**
429/25g	**Trailer**, 6, YC	**£80-120**
451/31b	**Trojan Van 'Dunlop'**, 6, YC	**£160-200**
452/31c	**Trojan Van 'Chivers'**, 6, YC	**£160-200**
490/30v	**Electric Dairy Van 'Express Dairy'**, 6, YC	**£120-160**
491/30v	**Electric Dairy Van 'N.C.B.'**, 6, YC	**£120-160**
751/42a	**Police Hut**, 6, YC	**£50-80**

Trade Packs of BOXED models

106	**'The Prisoner' Mini-Moke**, 6	**£600-800**
159	**Morris Oxford**, 3 Green, 3 Tan	**£250-350**
161	**(40j) Austin Somerset**, 6	**£600-800**
190	**Caravan**, later type, 6	**£175-200**
195	**Jaguar 3.4 Saloon**, 6	**£400-500**
292	**Leyland Atlantean Bus**, 6	**£350-450**
471	**Austin Van 'NESTLE'**, 6	**£300-400**
491	**Electric Dairy Van 'N.C.B.'** 6	**£300-400**

NB Expect Trade Boxes containing rare colour variations to attract a corresponding premium.

NB See also Gift Sets for 62h and 62d pre-war Aeroplane Trade Box items.

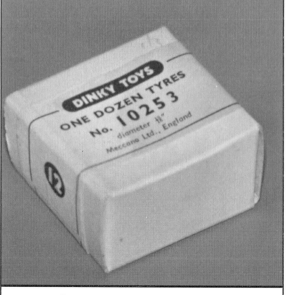

A yellow pack of twelve **Tyres**, reference 10253

220 Racing Car on dual-numbered ('220' and '23a') yellow box with 23a Racing Car on '23a' yellow box.

Four 25y Jeeps with their yellow box.

Trojan Van 'Dunlop' on yellow box with dual-numbering '451' and '31b'.

Two 270 'AA' Motor Cycle Patrol models on their yellow box.

An example of a Trade Pack for 292 Leyland Atlantean Buses. The six models within would all have been individually boxed.

Dinky Toys Trade Accessories

Trade Display Unit packed in plain cardboard box. Black wooden case with 'Property of Meccano Ltd Liverpool' in black on gold; three shelves in light blue/white/yellow; four gold supports with two yellow and two red supports; four red tin flags 'DINKY TOYS'; three tin flags 'ASK FOR BOOKLET', 'OVER 200 MODELS', and 'ALWAYS SOMETHING NEW'; plus two red and two yellow balls..**£400-500**

Glass Display Case. Oak frame with three glass shelves. Size approximately 32" (80 cm.) wide, 24" (60 cm.) high, 9" (22 cm.) deep. With 'DINKY TOYS' in green lettering on glass front..**£300-400**

Trade Display Stand Large yellow folding cardboard stand which non-erected measures approximately 28" (70 cm.) x 14" (35 cm.); three display levels with 'DINKY TOYS' logo in green plus 'MECCANO PRODUCT' in red on top header board. Outer corrugated cardboard packing has green printed instruction leaflet. **£200-300**

Trade Display Stand Small yellow and red folding cardboard stand which non-erected measures approximately 12" (31 cm.) x 7" (15 cm.); with one 'DINKY TOYS' and two 'DINKY SUPERTOYS' logos in red plus yellow 'MASTERPIECES IN MINIATURE' logo on red background. **£75-100**

Display Stand (circa 1950 - 1960) Large metal stand which measures approximately 36" x 21" x 22" (91.5 x 53 x 56 cm.); with nine display shelves covered in black plastic track. Metal advertisement affixed to top states in yellow/red/black 'A MOTOR SHOW FOR GIRLS AND BOYS', 'PRECISION DIE-CAST MODELS BY MECCANO', 'BEST RANGE', 'BEST VALUE IN THE WORLD'. Lower large transfer also in yellow/red/black repeats the message..**£400-500**

Window Sign (plastic), Top half is dark blue with white 'MECCANO' logo, bottom half is yellow with red 'Dinky Toys' logo. Approximately 18" x 6". **£70-80**

Counter Display (cardboard), Small display stand suitable for a single new model, 'ALWAYS NEW MODELS' logo in white on red background, header states 'DINKY TOYS' in red on yellow.............................**£70-80**

Counter Display (cardboard) 'BATTLE OF BRITAIN' Blue/yellow displaying 719 Spitfire MkII and 721 Junkens JU 87b Stuka.............**£100-150**

Shop Display Carousel with tripod base supporting four stacks of clear plastic. **£200-300**

Illuminated Shop Display Sign with 'DINKY TOYS' in large wooden letters above a glass panel lettered either 'Made by Meccano Ltd' or 'British and Guaranteed'...**£300-400**

Shelf Display Card in 'landscape' format, featuring the Hesketh 308E Racing Car with 'OLYMPUS' advertising ....NGPP

Illuminated Counter or Window display unit 13" x 9"" with perspex front 'DINKY TOYS' and 'NEW MODELS EVERY MONTH' logo. **£100-1500**

Counter Carousel Unit with 'Always Something New from Dinky' around its edge. Red/Yellow 'DINKY TOYS BY MECCANO' sign on top, 26" high overall. **£200-250**

Metal Counter Display Sign, triangular in shape with red 'DINKY TOYS' on yellow background, approximately 8" x 1" x 1".....................................**£30-40**

Electric Revolving 'Meccano' Wooden Display Stand 'DINKY TOYS - LOOK FOR THE NAME ON THE BASE' logo, (28" square and 10" high) ... **£250-350**

Pre-War 'Meccano Dinky Toys' Advertising Sign. An example of this double-sided hanging sign was sold by Christie's', South Kensington for £632. It shows pictures and details of 22, 24, 25 and 28 series models available in 'Season 1934'. Date code: '16/734/1'. Size: 11in x 9in (28cm x 23cm). **£500-600**

- c.1959 'Dublo Dinky' Shop Display Stand. Pale Yellow with Red logo and wording 'NEW SERIES / DUBLO DINKY', etc. Stand dimensions: 28cm x 19cm overall..**£300-500**

Dinky Toys Price Tickets. Aluminium tags to place on toys plus sheet of 200 self-adhesive labels showing model number and price.......................**£200-250**

Note: This section is far from complete and the Editor would welcome details of other trade stands, posters, display cards, promotional material and advertising signs.

Shop window posters

100362	1972	**Self-adhesive poster**	Double-sided poster featuring 'All Action Fighting Vehicles' and '10 Great Fighting Vehicles'	**£20-25**
100367	1973	**Self-adhesive poster**	Double-sided poster featuring 'Highway Action Models'	**£20-25**
100482	1971	**Self-adhesive poster**	Single-sided poster advertising 'No 451 Road Sweeper'	**£15-20**
100537	?	**Self-adhesive poster**	Single-sided poster advertising 'No 654 155mm Mobile Gun'	**£15-20**
100595	?	**Self-adhesive poster**	Single-sided poster advertising 'No 694 Hanomag Tank Destroyer'	**£15-20**
100741	?	**Self-adhesive poster**	Single-sided poster advertising 'No 432 Foden Tipper Truck'	**£15-20**
100604	?	**Self-adhesive poster**	Single-sided poster advertising 'No 656 88mm Gun'	**£15-20**
100742	?	**Self-adhesive poster**	Single-sided poster advertising 'No 430 Johnson 2-ton Dumper'	**£15-20**
100602	?	**Self-adhesive poster**	Single-sided poster advertising 'No 293 Swiss PTT Bus'	**£15-20**
100524	?	**Self-adhesive poster**	Single-sided poster advertising 'No 410 Bedford Van'	**£15-20**
100734	?	**Self-adhesive poster**	Single-sided poster advertising 'No 668 Foden Army Truck'	**£15-20**
100523	?	**Self-adhesive poster**	Single-sided poster advertising 'No 682 Stalwart Load Carrier'	**£15-20**
100531	?	**Self-adhesive poster**	Single-sided poster advertising 'No 683 Chieftain Tank'	**£15-20**
100496	?	**Self-adhesive poster**	Single-sided poster advertising 'No 725 F-4K Phantom II'	**£15-20**

Dinky Toys Numerical Index

Lone Star

Robert Newson has provided the following information on Lone Star models.

'Lone Star' was the trade name of Die Casting Machine Tools Ltd (DCMT) who started in 1939 as manufacturers of diecasting machines. They were based at Palmers Green in North London. After the war they started making diecast toys which were distributed by The Crescent Toy Co Ltd. In the Crescent Toys section of this catalogue, the items listed as 'early post-war models' were all made by DCMT with the exception of the Locomotive and the Racing Car. From 1950 DCMT arranged their own distribution direct to wholesalers. Over the next four decades DCMT Lone Star made several ranges of diecast vehicles including

'Slikka Toys' (early 1950s), 'Modern Army Series' (mainly 1960s), 'Roadmaster Majors' (1960s and 1970s), 'Farmer's Boy' (1980s) and the well known 'Lone Star Locos' miniature railway system (later called 'Treble-O-Lectric' or 'Treble-O-Trains'). The four ranges of most interest to collectors are listed here - the original DCMT 'Roadmasters' of 1956, the 1:50 scale 'Roadmasters' (1960s), the 'Impy' and 'Flyers' series made in various forms from 1966 to the mid 1980s, and the miniature 'Tuf-Tots' (1970s).

NB See the 'Miscellaneous Models' colour section for Lone Star pictures.

DCMT Lone Star Roadmasters

This was a short-lived series introduced in 1956, consisting of three sports cars and four veteran cars, all around 1:35 to 1:40 scale. The models had diecast bodies but all other components were plastic. Plastic drivers and passengers were included with the models.

-	-	**1904 Darracq 'Genevieve'** ....Black or Red body, Yellow plastic chassis; Metallic Blue or Silver body, Black plastic chassis............**£200-300**
-	-	**1904 Daimler 'Windsor' Phaeton** ....Red body, Yellow plastic chassis **£60-70**
-	-	**1912 Ford Model 'T'** ....Silver body, Black plastic chassis **£60-70**
-	-	**1912 Morris Oxford 'Bullnose'** ....Metallic Blue body, Black plastic chassis **£80-100**
-	-	**Daimler Conquest Roadster** ....Red, Metallic Light Blue, Pale Yellow, Pale Green or Pale Blue...**£80-100**
-	-	**Ford Thunderbird** ....Red, Metallic Light Blue, Pale Yellow, Pale Green or Pale Blue...**£80-100**
-	-	**MG Midget TF**..Metallic Light Blue or Red **£80-100**

Lone Star Roadmasters - 1:50 scale

In 1960 Lone Star produced four American cars on behalf of the US firm of Tootsietoy. These were the first four models listed below and they had 'Tootsietoy Classic Series' cast underneath. This arrangement only lasted for a couple of years, as by 1962 there were eight models available, all now marked 'Lone Star Roadmasters'. The models featured plated grilles, bumpers and wheels, and had windows but no interior detail. Around 1964 the plated parts were replaced by less attractive painted or self-coloured plastic, and vacuum-formed interiors were fitted. Five further numbers were added to the range before they were withdrawn around 1966.

1258	-	**Farm King Tractor and Trailer** ..Red tractor, 'Farm King' paper label, Blue trailer, 'Farm Estates Co.' paper label. (Roadmaster Major)...**£60-70**
1470	-	**Chevrolet Corvair** ....Red or Orange-Red **£60-70**
1471	-	**Rambler Rebel Station Wagon**....Sea-Green, Metallic Blue-Green or Green with Cream roof, Metallic Brown with White roof or all Green **£60-70**
1472	-	**Cadillac 62**................................Pale Blue, Blue with Cream roof or all Blue **£60-70**
1473	-	**Ford Sunliner Convertible**..........White or Light Blue; Red interior **£60-70**
1474	-	**Chevrolet El Camino Pick-Up**.....Yellow or Orange **£60-70**
1475	-	**Dodge Dart Phoenix** ....Metallic Dark Blue or Mid Blue **£60-70**
1476	-	**Rolls-Royce Silver Cloud II** ....Grey with Black upper half or Metallic Blue **£70-80**
1477	-	**Dodge Dart Police Car** ....Black, 'POLICE PATROL' or 'POLIZEI' **£70-80**
1478	-	**Rambler Ambulance** ....White, Red Cross transfer on bonnet **£70-80**
1479	-	**Chevrolet Corvair**......................Red body, 'FIRE CHIEF', 'FEUERWEHR' or 'BRANDWEER' **£70-80**
1480	-	**Chevrolet Corvair**......................Army Staff Car (continued after 1966 as no.1273 in ``Modern Army'' series), Olive Green **£60-70**
1481	-	**Rambler Military Ambulance** .....(continued after 1966 as no.1274 in 'Modern Army' series), Olive Green **£70-80**
1482	-	**Citroën DS19** ....Turquoise **£60-70**
-	-	**Rambler Police Car** ....White body, 'POLIZEI' on bonnet **£70-80**

Lone Star 'Tuf-Tots'

The first thirteen Tuf-Tots were introduced in 1969, and the next five followed in 1970. The remainder had appeared by 1972. They were available boxed or bubble-packed, and when bubble-packed there was an additional '2' in front of the model number to give a four-digit reference. Later, models were sold in open counter-top trays.

The trucks were based on a common US Ford chassis. Most models exist in numerous colour variations. The series was discontinued after 1980. Market Price Range is **£5** to **£10**.

601	**Ford Petrol Tanker**......'ESSO' labels ....
	.......................'ESSO' cast into sides............................
602	**Citroën DS Convertible with Driver** ....
603	**Chevrolet Corvette Stingray Convertible with Driver**......................
604	**Dodge Dart Convertible with Driver** ....
605	**Mercedes-Benz 280SL Convertible with Driver** ....
606	**Ford 'TT' Tow Truck** ....
607	**Ford 'Big L' Dumper Lorry** ....
608	**Jeep and Trailer**...........'Herts. Farm', scale 85:1................
609	**Ford 'Autos' Flat Truck** with metal petrol pump island ....
	.......................with plastic petrol pump island..........
610	**Ford Tipper Lorry** ....'LS Construction Co.' labels..........................
	.......................with ribs cast onto body instead of labels........
611	**Ford Luton Van** ....with 'Express Freight' labels ....
	.......................with ribs cast onto body instead of labels........
612	**Ford Articulated Low-Loader** 'Apache' ....
613	**Chris Craft Capri Speedboat** (plastic) **on Trailer**, scale 86:1............
614	**Ford Refuse Lorry**........with 'City Refuse' labels..........................
	.......................with 'City Refuse' cast lettering ....

615	**Ford Cement Mixer** ....
616	**Ford Milk Float** ....'Milk, Milk, Milk' cast on each side ....
617	**Ford Cattle Transporter**...
618	**Ford Skip Lorry** ....
619	**Citroën DS Coupé** ....
620	**Chevrolet Corvette Stingray Coupé** ....
621	**Dodge Dart Coupé** ....
622	**Mercedes-Benz 280SL Coupé**, scale 86:1.........................
623	**Routemaster Bus** ....with 'London Bus' advertisements ....
624	**ERF Fire Engine**...........with ladder, 'Fire Brigade' labels...................
625	**Caravan**..
626	**Ford Circus Cage Lorry** with plastic lion, 'Circus' cast-in......
627	**Tractor Shovel**..

Gift Sets

2570	**Building Site Playset** ....4 models plus sand hopper...............
2571	**Garage Playset**.............4 models plus car ramp.....................
2572	**Highway Playset**..........4 models plus street and traffic lights..........
2573	**Travel Playset**...............4 models plus 'Stop' barrier...............
2574	**Dutch Farm Playset**.....4 models plus windmill.....................
2575	**Bridge Playset** ....4 models plus girder bridge................

579	**Commercial Vehicle Set** 6 models...............................
580	**Car and Trailer Set** ....6 models ....
581	**12 Vehicle Set** ....12 models ....
582	**Highway Set** 3 models plus sand hopper, car ramp, street and traffic lights...............
583	**Travel Set** 3 models plus girder bridge, windmill and 'Stop' barrier.......................

In the following listing the year shown is the date of introduction. Most models remained in production until 1976. **IW** = Impy wheels, **FW** = Flyers wheels, **HSW** = Hi-Speed wheels, **BPW** = black plastic wheels.

7	1971	**Vauxhall Firenza**, IW / FW, RHD and LHD	£15-25
8	-	**Ford Capri**, not issued	NPP
9	1970	**Maserati Mistral**, IW or FW	£10-20
10	1966	**Jaguar Mk.X**, IW or FW	£10-20
11	1966	**Chevrolet Corvette Stingray GT**, IW or FW	£10-20
12	1966	**Chrysler Imperial**, IW or FW	£10-20
13	-	**Ford Thunderbird**, not issued	NPP
13	1971	**Toyota 2000 GT**, Flyers wheels	£10-20
14	1966	**Ford Zodiac Mk.III Estate**, IW or FW	£10-20
15	1966	**Volkswagen Microbus**, IW or FW	£10-20
16	1966	**Ford Zodiac Mk.III Estate 'POLICE' Car**, IW or FW	£10-20
16	-	**Chrysler Imperia 'POLICE' Car**, IW or FW	£10-20
16m	-	**Mercedes-Benz 220 SE 'POLIZEI' Car**, Impy wheels	£10-20
17	1966	**Mercedes-Benz 220 SE**, IW or FW	£10-20
18	1966	**Ford Corsair**, IW or FW	£10-20
19	1967	**Volvo 1800 S**, IW or FW	£10-20
20	1967	**Volkswagen Ambulance**, IW or FW	£10-20
21	1967	**Fiat 2300 S Coupé**, IW or FW	£10-20
22	1967	**Rolls-Royce Silver Cloud III Convertible**, IW or FW	£10-20
23	1967	**Alfa Romeo Giulia 1600 Spider**, IW or FW	£10-20
24	1967	**Foden Tilt-cab 8w Tipper**, black plastic or HSW	£10-20
25	1967	**International Harvester Tractor Shovel**	£10-20
26	1967	**Foden Tilt-cab Petrol Tanker**, 'MOBIL', BPW or HSW	£10-20
27	1967	**Ford Taunus 12M**, IW or FW	£10-20
28	1967	**Peugeot 404 Saloon**, IW or FW	£10-20
29	-	**Cement Mixer Lorry**, not issued	NPP
29	1971	**Foden Tilt-cab Box Van**, 'LUCAS', BPW or HSW	£15-20
29	1972	**Foden Tilt-cab Box Van**, 'EXPRESS FREIGHT' labels, black plastic wheels	£15-25
30	1967	**AEC Merryweather Fire Engine**, black plastic or HSW	£10-20
31	1967	**Ford Transit Breakdown Lorry**, 'ESSO', BPW or HSW	£10-20
32	1968	**'FIRE CHIEF' Car**, Ford Corsair, red, IW or FW	£10-20
32		**'FEUERWEHR' Car**, Ford Corsair, red, Impy wheels	£10-20
33	1968	**Austin-Western Mobile Crane**, elevating jib	£10-20
34	1968	**Euclid Crawler Tractor**, rubber tracks	£10-20
35	-	**Articulated Flat Truck**, not issued	NPP
36	1969	**Lotus Europa**, Flyers wheels	£10-20
37		**Ford GT**, not issued	NPP
38	1971	**Chevrolet Corvette Stingray**, Flyers wheels	£15-25
39	1971	**Ford Mustang**, Flyers wheels	£15-25
40	1973	**Cadillac Eldorado**, Flyers wheels	£10-20
41	1972	**Leyland Builders Supply Lorry**, 4 girders, 8 HSW	£10-20
41	1973	**Leyland Builders Supply Lorry**, 4 girders, 6 HSW	£10-20
41	1973	**Foden Half-cab Builders Supply Lorry**, 4 girders,6 HSW	£10-20
42	1972	**Foden Half-cab Tipper**, 'TILCON' labels, 8 HSW	£15-25
43	1973	**Leyland Flat Lorry with Pipes**, 6 HSW	£10-20
43	1973	**Foden Half-cab Flat Lorry with Pipes**, 6 HSW	£10-20
44	1972	**Leyland Marine Transport Lorry**, Speedboat, 8 HSW	£10-20
44	1973	**Leyland Marine Transport Lorry**, Speedboat, 6 HSW	£10-20
44	1973	**Foden Half-cab Marine Transport Lorry**, Speedboat, 6 HSW	£10-20
46	1973	**Leyland Dropside Lorry**, 6 Hi-Speed wheels	£10-20
47	1973	**Leyland High-Side Lorry**, 6 Hi-Speed wheels	£10-20
47	1973	**Foden High-Side Lorry**, Half-cab, 6 HSW	£10-20
48	1973	**Leyland Hopper Lorry**, 6 HSW	£10-20
48	1973	**Foden Half-cab Hopper Lorry**, 6 HSW	£10-20
49	1973	**Foden Half-cab Tipper**, 6 HSW	£10-20

IMPY GIFT SETS All are scarce, hence NGPP

301	1967	**Six-piece Gift Set**	NGPP
302	1967	**Six-piece Gift Set**	NGPP
303	1968	**'MOBIL' Gift Set**	NGPP
304	1968	**Five-piece Commercial Vehicle Gift Set**	NGPP
309	1968	**Twelve-piece Gift Set**	NGPP

IMPY ACCESSORIES

401	1967	**Car Lifting Ramp**	£5-10
402	1967	**Lock-Up Garage** (plastic)	£5-10
403	-	**Service Station** (not issued)	NPP
404	1968	**'MOBIL' Petrol Pump Island**, Canopy, Forecourt Sign	£5-10
406	-	**Fire House** (not issued)	NPP

IMPY TWO-PACKS

422	**VW Ambulance** (20) and **Mercedes-Benz 'Polizei'** (16M)	£20-30
423	**Fiat 2300S** (21) and **Breakdown Lorry** (31)	£20-30
424	**Foden Tanker** (26) and **Ford Taunus** (27)	£20-30
425	**Ford Zodiac** (14) and **Tractor** (25)	£20-30
427	**Alfa Romeo** (23) and **'MOBIL' Petrol Pumps** (404)	£20-30
431	**Chevrolet Corvette** (11) and **Fiat 2300S** (21)	£20-30
432	**Fire Engine** (30) and **Ford Corsair 'FEUERWEHR'** (32)	£20-30

IMPY series, post-1976

The Market Price Range is shown as £5 - £10 but as yet there is little collectors' interest in these recent models.

50	**Six-wheel Tipper**	£5-10
51	**Six-wheel High Side Lorry**	£5-10
52	**Six-wheel Flat Lorry with Crane**	£5-10
53	**Six-wheel Flat Lorry with Speedboat**	£5-10
54	**Six-wheel Cement Mixer**	£5-10
55	**Six-wheel Luton Van**	£5-10
56	**Six-wheel Dropside Lorry**	£5-10
57	**Six-wheel Flat Lorry with Water Tank**	£5-10
58	**Six-wheel Hopper Lorry**	£5-10
59	**Six-wheel Flat Lorry with Pipes**	£5-10
60	**Six-wheel Flat Lorry with Planks**	£5-10
61	**Six-wheel Petrol Tanker**	£5-10
71	**Range Rover**	£5-10
72	**Cadillac Eldorado**	£5-10
73	**Chevrolet Corvette Stingray**	£5-10
74	**Toyota 2000 GT**	£5-10
75	**Range Rover Police Car**	£5-10
76	**Chevrolet Corvette Stingray 'GT Rally'**	£5-10
77	**Jaguar Mk.X**	£5-10
78	**Maserati Mistral**	£5-10
79	**Ford Mustang**	£5-10
80	**Lotus Europa**	£5-10
81	**Volvo Coupé**	£5-10
82	**Mercedes-Benz**	£5-10
181	**Articulated Flat Lorry with Crane**	£5-10
182	**Articulated Petrol Tanker**	£5-10
183	**Articulated Low Loader with Tuf-Tots car**	£5-10
184	**Articulated Flat Lorry with Pipes and water tank**	£5-10
185	**Cadillac Eldorado with Tuf-Tots Speedboat on trailer**	£5-10
185	**Range Rover with Tuf-Tots Speedboat on trailer**	£5-10
185	**Range Rover 'RNLI' with boat on trailer**	£5-10
185	**Jaguar Mk.X with Cabin Cruiser on trailer**	£5-10
186	**Crane Lorry** (no.52) with Impy car	£5-10
187	**Luton Van** (no.55) with Trailer	£5-10
188	**Articulated Low Loader with Cabin Cruiser**	£5-10
189	**Articulated Flat Lorry with Planks**	£5-10
190	**Petrol Tanker** (no.61) with Trailer	£5-10
191	**High Side Lorry** (no.51) with Trailer	£5-10
192	**Cement Mixer** (no.54) with Flat Trailer	£5-10
1251	**Articulated Car Transporter**	£5-10
1252	**AEC Merryweather HTTL Fire Engine** (re-packed no.30)	£5-10
1256	**Car Transporter** (no.1251) with four Impy cars	£30-40

Lone Star Sets

'International Peace Force Vehicles' Set (made 1974) contains:
1271 Small Tank, 1272 Searchlight on Trailer, 1273 Mortar Launcher, 1274 Radar Detector Unit, 1275 Ack-Ack Gun, 1276 Silver Small Canon, 1277 All Blue Military Jeep ....NGPP

'GULLIVER COUNTY' Series. Boxed set of three Coaches. White card box with scene depicting a coach, fire engine, articulated lorry and two cars.
i) Mid-Green Coach, Grey wheels, 'SCHOOL BUS' logo on sides
ii) Cream Coach, Grey wheels, 'SCHOOL BUS' logo on sides
iii) Mid-Green Coach, Grey wheels, 'GREENLINE' logo on sides
Price for set...£100-150

'War in the Desert' Set includes 3 German and 3 US military vehicles ...NGPP

Miscellaneous items

Routemaster Bus. Made 1972-89 from two castings which include seats and stair details. Red body, Silver trim, paper adverts on sides 'SEE LONDON BY BUS' and 'BUY LONE STAR'. Route is '29 VICTORIA', Black plastic tyres. Cast into base: 'LONE STAR' and 'MADE IN ENGLAND', No. 1259 ....£5-10
RAC Land Rover and Caravan ....no details...NGPP

'Aircraft of the World' Series (1:250 scale)

'Scandinavian Airlines' Caravelle £40-50
'Pan American' Boeing 707 ....£50-60

NB The Editor would welcome any new information on Lone Star products.

★★ ★★★

The greatest *IMPY* yet!

No 24

FODEN Tilt-Cab TRUCK

Here's a really great model for you—with *all* the authentic details ! 3¾″ long, this die-cast metal model has all these features :–

★ Tilting Cab
★ Windows, seats and steering wheel
★ Die-cast chassis
★ Die-cast engine
★ Non-scratch tyres
★ Tipping back with hinged loading flap

LONE ★ STAR
Roadmaster **IMPY**
Super Cars
have everything

Remember, IMPYs are the die-cast models with ALL the Real-Car features ! Additions to the series are coming along all the time !

Next on the list are:

★ **Ford Taunus**
★ **Tractor**
★ **Rolls Royce**
  Silver Cloud III
★ **Merryweather**
  Fire Engine

An advertisement for **Lone Star Impy** models as it appeared in the 'Eagle and Boy's World' comic of 24 June 1967.

When replying to advertisements, please mention 'John Ramsay's Catalogue'.

Matchbox Toys

Introduction

The company was founded in 1947 by the unrelated Leslie and Rodney Smith who combined their names to form 'Lesney' Products Ltd. They were soon joined by Jack Odell – a recognised die-casting expert.

The most famous of the various early products was the 'Coronation Coach'. During the 1950s the company developed the highly successful Matchbox '1-75' and 'Models of Yesteryear' ranges.

Following a difficult trading period Lesney Products Ltd was bought in 1982 by the Universal Toy Co. of Hong Kong.

In May 1992 it was announced in the 'New York Times' that 'Tyco Toys Inc.' had acquired by merger the Universal Matchbox Group. Matchbox then became known as 'Tyco-Matchbox' although the products were still marketed under the famous Matchbox brand name. Late in 1992 Tyco Toys announced the formation of a new division called Matchbox Collectibles which became responsible for the sales and marketing of Matchbox 'Models of Yesteryear'.

In 1996 Mattel Inc., the world's largest toymakers agreed to merge with Tyco Toys Inc. and planned to use its powers to boost overseas sales. The quality of products issued by Matchbox Collectibles in recent years has been quite superb with demand often outstripping supply. The emphasis now, however, has become more focussed on US buyers for whom the names 'Yesteryear', 'Dinky', 'Superfast', etc. have less impact. With the new millennium has come a new market strategy that is reflected in the 'Thematic' and 'Platinum' listings that follow.

The Models of Yesteryear section has been completely replaced by a unique new listing specially prepared for the Catalogue by Horace Dunkley, the leading authority on Yesteryears. The Editor is indebted to Hardy Ristau of Berlin who has revised the 'Regular Wheels' issues and to Nigel Cooper of Chineham, Basingstoke for additional information. Please note that the Superfast issues have been given their own new comprehensive section which follows the 'Regular Wheels' issues.

'Moko' Products

'Moko' Products was a toy distribution firm founded by Moses Kohnstam who came to Britain from Nuremburg, Germany at the turn of the century.

Moko provided the distribution and storage facilities and, irrespective of the supplier, all toys were marketed as Moko products. The early issues after the Second World War were housed in plain cardboard boxes with 'tuck in' ends. These usually had only single colour printing that did not include a picture of the model. During the early 1950s the packaging became much more attractive with brightly coloured boxes displaying a picture of the model inside. Moko will best be remembered for their distribution of the early Matchbox '1-75' toys under the name of 'MoKo-Lesney'. Moses Kohnstam was succeeded by Richard Kohnstam in 1953.

The following listing of Moko items constitutes all the information available to publish at present. Additional information would be welcomed by the Editor.

Year(s)	Details	MPR
c1948-53	**Mechanical Tractor** Probably early Lesney. Orange body, Green rubber tracks, Black wheels, Green/Black driver, (early issue in plain box)	**£125-150**
1950-55	**Mechanical Tractor** As previous model but with Orange wheels, (later issue in picture box)	**£125-150**
1947-50	**Excavator (with open cab)** Orange body and jib, Black digger and chassis, Green rubber tracks, Orange crank handle. Early card box has 'Moko TOYS OF DISTINCTION' logo	**£100-125**
1950-55	**'RUSTON BUCYRUS' Excavator** Yellow over Red body with Black '10 RB' logo. Black or Dark Green chassis, jib, digger, crank wheel and rubber tracks. Later box with full colour picture	**£125-150**
1950-55	**Builders Crane** All Blue crane base and jib with unpainted metal hook. Later card box with full colour picture	**£125-150**
1947-50	**Crawler Bulldozer** Red body and dozer blade (possibly early Lesney). Early plain card box	**£125-150**

Year(s)	Details	MPR
1950-55	**Model Motor Scooter** Dark Red scooter with Black seat. Female figure has blonde hair, blue sweater, red trousers. Later box with full colour picture	**£250-350**
1950-55	**Drummer Boy (Mechanical)** Red body, Gold trim, Black busby. Cream/Yellow drum, Gold drumsticks	**£500-750**
1947-50	**Hayrick** Yellow/Green body	**£160-200**
1947-50	**Fairground Carousel** Blue/Red base and centre column, Maroon/Blue roof, 2 Red and 2 Blue seated figures. Plain card box	**£500-750**
1947-50	**Mechanical Mouse** Grey body with Red eyes plus curling tail. Early plain card box	**£100-150**
c1950	**Peregrine Puppet**	NGPP
c1950	**'Jumbo, the Walking Elephant'**. Mechanical / tinplate. With diagonal printing	**£150-200**
	With horizontal printing	**£200-300**

Moko 'Farmette' Series

Miniature size models packed in end-flap type boxes with colour picture of the model. The die-cast horses have dark brown bodies and white feet.

No.1	1950-53	**Timber Trailer with two Horses**	Green body, four Red wheels, timber load	**£150-200**
No.2	1950-53	**Farm Cart with two Horses**	Mid or Dark Blue cart body, Red raves, four Red 12-spoke wheels	**£150-200**
No.3	1950-53	**Bull Wagon with two Horses**	Green wagon body, two horses in tandem, Brown metal bull, four Red 12-spoke wheels	**£150-200**

'Treasure Chest' Series

Packed in Brown 'Chests' with Yellow 'Strapping'.

No.10	1950-53	**Hay Cart**	Orange body, two Green raves, two Green wheels, one horse	**£50-75**
No.11	1950-53	**Millers Cart**	Blue body, two Red wheels, three White sacks, one horse	**£50-75**
No.12	1950-53	**Water Cart**	Green/Red cart, two Red wheels, one horse	**£50-75**

The early 'Lesney' toys

Lesney Products issued their first diecast toys in 1948. Whilst production ceased during the Korean war period (1950-52), the models produced formed the basis from which the 1-75 series was launched in 1953. They were sold in boxes under the name of 'MoKo' who were ultimately to also market all the early 1-75 series models. **NB Models were sold boxed.**

Road Roller ....All Green (shades) body and flywheel,
  unpainted wheels..**£250-300**
  As previous model but with Red roller
  wheels and Yellow flywheel **£250-300**
  With a driver but without a flywheel.............**£175-200**
  Without a driver and without flywheel.........**£150-175**

Cement Mixer..............All Green or All-Blue body, Red wheels......**£150-175**
  Pale Green body, Red or Yellow drum
  and wheels..**£200-250**
  Dark Green body, Red or Yellow drum
  and wheels..**£200-250**
  Red body, Green drum and wheels..............**£200-250**
  Orange engine cover, Black drum,
  Yellow wheels...**£200-250**

Caterpillar Tractor .....Orange or Yellow body, Red roller wheels,
  Black rubber tracks, driver **£125-150**

Caterpillar Bulldozer..Green, Orange or Red body, driver,
  Black rubber tracks **£125-150**
  Yellow body, Red dozer blade and wheels **£125-150**

Prime Mover...............Orange tractor (Green engine on some),
  Blue trailer, Red/Yellow dozer,
  'BRITISH ROAD SERVICES' **£800-1,000**
  As previous model but with Beige trailer......**£500-600**

**'MASSEY-HARRIS'
  Tractor** ....Red body, Cream hubs, Black rubber tyres ...**£200-300**

Milk Cart ....Orange body, White driver and six crates,
  Black or Brown horse, Black or Grey wheels,
  'PASTEURISED MILK' cast into cart..........**£400-500**
  As previous model but with Blue body **£600-700**

Soap-Box Racer..........Brown box, Grey spoked wheels (16 and 9),
  Dark Blue boy with Pink face...........................NGPP

Quarry Truck ....Yellow body, Black tyres, 'LAING'.
  Only one example known to exist ....NPP

**Covered Wagon
  with Barrels**..............Green body, White cover, two Red barrels,
  six Mid-Brown horses (with White tails),
  with postilion rider and wagon driver **£200-250**

**Covered Wagon
  without Barrels** ....As previous model but with Chocolate Brown
  horses and no barrels **£200-250**

**'RAG & BONE
  MERCHANTS' Cart**.Yellow body, Red wheels, Black horse,
  Brown driver, with seven pieces of 'junk':
  mangle-wheel, bike frame, bedhead, bath,
  bucket, box, cistern..**£750-1,000**
  Same but Green body, Red wheels ....NGPP

**Coronation Coach
  (large)**.......................Gold coach with King and Queen, eight White
  horses, Gold/Red trappings, four Red riders.
  200 issued...**£500-750**

**Coronation Coach
  (large)**.......................Gold, Silver or Gilt coach with just the
  Queen inside. Horses and riders as for
  previous model...**£150-200**

**Coronation Coach
  (small)** ....Silver or Gold coach, eight White horses,
  Red/Gold trappings, four Red riders,
  'A MOKO TOY BY LESNEY' cast into
  horsebar (1,000,000 sold) **£85-100**

'Muffin The Mule' .....White body, Red/Gold harness, Black trim ...**£250-300**
Excavator ....Digger and chassis are Dark Brown **£100-125**
Motor Scooter.............Blue Scooter ....NGPP

Breadbait Press ....1st type: Red body, unpainted
  'butterfly' press...**£40-50**
  2nd type: As 1st type but with Green press....**£50-60**
  3rd type: As 2nd type but with 'MILBRO'
  cast onto Red body...**£60-70**

An early Lesney catalogue cover

Matchbox Model Identification

Model Number is always cast into the base, chassis or body. Obvious exceptions are the early models which were not numbered. 'Lesney' is cast into the base, chassis or body of all issues between 1953 and 1982.

'Matchbox' or **'Matchbox Series'** is shown on the base or chassis of all issues after 1965. All issues after 1957 had the model name on the base or chassis. Exceptions include those without a base (e.g., No.24 Excavator).

Suspension and **windows**. All car models were fitted with window glazing after 1961 and with suspension after 1965.

Baseplates are metal castings until the late 1970s when plastic bases introduced. From 1983 they are marked 'Made in Macau' and from 1986 'Made in China'.

Wheels were metal castings on early models and were gradually changed to grey, silver or black plastic. **Superfast wheels** introduced in late 1960s and issues from 1968-69 may be found with either type. Novelties such as **'Laser Wheels'** introduced in the late 1980s. **'Rolamatics'** were introduced in the 1970s having working parts that were operated by pushing. See the Superfast section for models with these features.

Model descriptions. This Catalogue tries to give original makers description of model names and colours but early Matchbox listings are known to be inaccurate graphically. Maker's catalogue photographs are often taken of mock-ups months before production starts while model designs become changed before release. Because of space limitations, it has been necessary to include a number of descriptive abbreviations (refer to list at the foot of this page).

Dimensions refer to the greatest overall measurement (usually the length).

Ref.	Intro.	Details	MPR

MB 1

| 1a | 53 | **Diesel Road Roller** (Aveling Barford) | |

Red metal roller wheels, Tan driver cast-in, no number, crimped axles, 49mm. **Type 1**: curved lower canopy ends and thin braces above canopy supports, **Type 2**: straight ends and thick braces above supports, brace extension.
Dark Green body, Type 1 ....**£100-125**
Dark Green body, Type 2 ....**£50-70**
Light Green body, Type 2 ....**£100-120**

| 1b | 56 | **Diesel Road Roller** (Aveling Barford) | |

Light Green body, Red metal roller wheels, Lt or Dk Tan driver, high peaked canopy, no number, hook, 57 mm.............**£35-45**

| 1c | 58 | **Diesel Road Roller** (Aveling Barford) | |

Light Green body and driver, Red metal roller wheels, number cast-in, high peaked canopy, hook, 62 mm **£60-80**
Dark Green body **£30-40**

| 1d | 62 | **Diesel Road Roller** (Aveling Barford) | |

Green body and driver, Red plastic rollers, 67 mm **£15-20**

| 1e | 67 | **Mercedes Truck** | |

Turquoise body, Orange canopy, Black plastic wheels, 75 mm ..**£8-12**
See Superfast section for subsequent issues.

MB 2

| 2a | 53 | **Muir Hill Site Dumper**. Dark Green body, Red dumper, | |

Green painted MW, 42 mm.....................................**£80-100**
Same but with unpainted MW....................................**£30-40**

| 2b | 57 | **Muir Hill Site Dumper**. Same but: | |

Tan driver, metal wheels, 46 mm **£30-40**
Same but GPW, crimped axles.....................................**£40-50**
Same but GPW, rounded axles.....................................**£30-40**

| 2c | 62 | **Muir Hill Dumper Truck** | |

Red body, Green dumper, '*LAING*',
Black plastic wheels, 54 mm **£15-25**
Same but '*MUIR HILL*' logo and
picture-box (72 only known)..**£60-80**

| 2d | 67 | **Mercedes Trailer**. Turquoise body, Orange top, BPW.............**£8-10** |

See Superfast section for subsequent issues.

MB 3

| 3a | 53 | **Cement Mixer** | |

Orange MW, Blue main body **£25-35**
GPW, crimped axles..**£80-90**
GPW, rounded axles..**£80-90**

| 3b | 61 | **Bedford Tipper Truck**. (All have Grey body and chassis) | |

Maroon back, GPW, 24 treads **£150-200**
Maroon back, GPW, 45 treads **£200-250**
Maroon back, BPW **£20-30**
Red dump, GPW **£80-100**
Red dump, BPW..**£25-35**

| 3c | 67 | **Mercedes Ambulance**. Cream or Off-White body ....**£10-15** |

See Superfast section for subsequent issues.

MB 4

| 4a | 54 | **Massey Harris Tractor**. (with mudguards over rear wheels), | |

Red body, Gold or Yellow rear hubs, Tan driver.................**£40-50**

| 4b | 57 | **Massey Harris Tractor**. (without mudguards over rear wheels), | |

metal wheels, Gold or Yellow rear hubs......................**£30-35**
Grey plastic wheels...**£70-80**

| 4c | 60 | **Triumph T110 Motor Cycle** | |

Steel Blue bike/sidecar, Silver spoked wheels, BPT **£90-120**
Same but with Copper body..**£1,500-2,000**

| 4d | 66 | **Stake Truck** Blue stake body | **£50-60** |

Green stake body **£8-12**
See Superfast section for subsequent issues.

MB 5

| 5a | 54 | **London Bus** (52 mm). | |

'Buy Matchbox Series' on paper label **£45-55**

| 5b | 57 | **1957 London Bus** (57 mm). | |

'Buy Matchbox Series' decal, metal wheels............................**£40-50**
'Buy Matchbox Series' decal, Grey plastic wheels **£60-70**
'Players Please' decal, GPW **£90-110**
'BP Visco-Static' decal, GPW **£200-220**

| 5c | 60 | **Routemaster** (66 mm). | |

'Players Please' decal, GPW **£75-90**
'News of the World', GPW. (Reported but not seen) ....NGPP
'Peardrax', GPW or BPW.......................................**£500-750**
'BP Visco-Static' decal, Grey or Black plastic wheels **£25-35**
'Baron of Beef' decal, Grey or Black plastic wheels..........**£350-400**

| 5d | 65 | **Routemaster** (70 mm). | |

'BP Longlife' decal ....**£15-20**.
'BP Visco-Static' decal or label **£12-16**
'Baron of Beef' decal...**£250-300**
'Pegram' label **£300-350**
See Superfast section for subsequent issues.

MB 6

| 6a | 54 | **Quarry Truck** 55mm. | |

Orange body, Grey tipper with six ribs, metal wheels..............**£25-30**
Same but with Grey plastic wheels, domed/crimped axles ...**£450-750**

| 6b | 59 | **Euclid Quarry Truck** | |

Yellow body, four ribs, decals, six BPW, '*Euclid*' **£20-30**
Knobbly GPW, domed axles...**£1,200-1,600**

| 6c | 63 | **Euclid Dump Truck** | |

Six Black wheels (rear double wheels are one piece) **£15-18**
Ten Black wheels (rear wheels are normal double wheels)......**£12-15**

| 6d | 68 | **Ford Pick Up** Red body, White canopy, chrome grille ....**£8-12** |

Same but White grille **£12-15**
See Superfast section for subsequent issues.

MB 7

| 7a | 54 | **Horse Drawn Milk Float** | |

Dark Orange body, White driver,
crates and logo, metal wheels **£45-60**
As previous but with GPW **£75-95**
Pale Orange body, metal wheels **£50-65**
Pale Orange body, White hat and
crates only, Grey plastic wheels...............................**£70-85**

Abbreviations used in this listing:
BPT = Black plastic tyres
BPW = Black plastic wheels
GPW = Grey plastic wheels

MPR = Market Price Range
MW = metal wheels
RN = racing or rally number
SPW = Silver plastic wheels

Pale Orange body, Silver driver
and crates, Grey plastic wheels.....................................**£400-600**
7b 61 **Ford Anglia** Light Blue, Green windows, GPW, 67 mm **£60-70**
With Silver plastic wheels..**£40-50**
With Black plastic wheels...**£25-35**
7c 67 **Refuse Truck.** Orange-Red body, Grey and Silver dumper **£8-12**
See Superfast section for subsequent issues.

MB 8

8a 55 **Caterpillar Tractor** (42 mm).
Yellow body and rollers, Red driver, Green tracks.................**£200-250**
Same but with unpainted rollers **£40-45**
Orange body and driver, Gold or Silver grille, Green tracks **£55-65**
Yellow body/driver, Silver or Yellow grille,
Green or Grey tracks...**£30-35**
8b 58 **Caterpillar Tractor** (42 mm).
Yellow body and driver, no.'8' cast-in, Green rubber tracks.....**£60-70**
8c 61 **Caterpillar Tractor** (48 mm).
Yellow body, metal rollers, Green tracks..................................**£20-30**
Same but with Silver rollers **£55-70**
Same but with Black rollers **£25-35**
8d 64 **Caterpillar Tractor** (51 mm).
Yellow body, no driver, Green rubber tracks, Black rollers **£12-15**
8e 66 **Ford Mustang**
White body, Black wheels with Silver hubcaps.........................**£15-20**
White body, Silver wheels with Black tyres..............................**£12-15**
Orange body, Silver wheels **£250-350**
See Superfast section for subsequent issues.

MB 9

9a 55 **Dennis Fire Escape** (57mm).
Red body, no front bumper, metal wheels, crimped axles.........**£45-55**
9b 58 **Dennis Fire Escape** (58mm).
Red body, with front bumper, MW, number cast underneath....**£40-50**
Same but with GPW...**£300-400**
9c 59 **Merryweather Marquis Series III Fire Engine**
Red body with Tan ladder, GPW, crimped axles, 64 mm.........**£45-55**
Same but with rounded axles **£30-40**
Same but with Gold ladder **£35-45**
With Gold ladder and BPW **£20-25**
With Silver ladder, BPW...**£60-70**
With Tan ladder, BPW **£50-60**
9d 66 **Boat and Trailer** (76mm, 77mm).
Blue/White boat, Blue trailer, Black plastic wheels **£10-15**
See Superfast section for subsequent issues.

MB 10

10a 57 **Scammell Mechanical Horse**
Red cab, Gold trim, Grey trailer, crimped axles, MW, 56mm ..**£60-70**
10b 57 **Scammell Mechanical Horse**
Red Cab, Brown trailer, crimped axles, metal wheels, 75 mm .**£50-60**
Red cab, Gold trim, Light Brown trailer, Grey plastic wheels..**£80-90**
Red cab, Silver trim, Light Brown trailer, Grey plastic wheels **£55-70**
10c 60 **Foden 8-wheel Sugar Container**
Dark Blue body, with crown on rear decal, Grey wheels........**£80-100**
Without crown, Grey wheels...**£80-100**
Without crown, Silver wheels...**£100-120**
Without crown, Black wheels..**£45-55**
10d 66 **Leyland Pipe Truck**
Red body, 6 or 7 Grey pipes, Silver base and grille **£10-15**
Same but White base and grille **£40-50**
See Superfast section for subsequent issues.

MB 11

11a 55 **E.R.F. Road Tanker**. All models with metal wheels.
Green body, Gold trim...**£1500-1750**
Dark Yellow body, Silver trim ....**£120-140**.
Light Yellow body, Silver trim...**£75-100**
Red body, Gold trim, small 'ESSO' decal on rear of tank **£90-110**
Same but large 'ESSO' decal..**£55-65**
Same but two small 'ESSO' decals on tank sides **£250-350**
Same but two large 'ESSO' decals on sides.........................**£175-200**
11b 58 **'ESSO' Petrol Tanker (E.R.F.)**.
All models with red body and 'ESSO' decal at rear.
Metal wheels, Gold trim...**£250-300**
Metal wheels, Silver trim ....**£40-50**.
Grey plastic wheels **£40-50**

Silver plastic wheels..**£600-700**
Black plastic wheels..**£60-70**
11c 65 **Jumbo Crane**
Yellow body and weight box **£12-15**
Yellow body, Red weight box **£8-12**
11d 69 **Mercedes Scaffolding Truck**
Silver body, Yellow plastic scaffolds, BPW **£8-12**
See Superfast section for subsequent issues.

MB 12

12a 55 **Land Rover**
Green body, Silver trim on some, Tan driver, MW, 43 mm **£25-35**
12b 59 **Land Rover Series II**
Green body, Black plastic wheels, crimped axles.....................**£50-60**
BPW, rounded axles **£25-35**
Grey plastic wheels **£230-270**
12c 65 **Land Rover Safari**
Green body, Brown luggage, BPW **£12-15**
Blue body, Brown or Red-Brown luggage, BPW.....................**£10-14**
Metallic Gold body, Red-Brown luggage, BPW **£500-700**
See Superfast section for subsequent issues.

MB 13

13a 55 **Wreck Truck** (51mm).
Tan body, Red crane and hook, MW on crimped axles.............**£30-40**
13b 58 **Wreck Truck** (54mm).
Light Brown body, Red crane and hook, '13' cast-in, MW **£35-45**
Same but with GPW...**£60-80**
13c 60 **Thames Trader Wreck Truck**
All models with Red body and crane.
Yellow side decals, knobbly Grey MW (24 treads), Red hook .**£40-50**
Fine tread Grey wheels (45 treads), Grey hook........................**£65-80**
BPW, Silver or Grey hook **£30-40**
13d 65 **Dodge Wreck Truck**
Green cab, Yellow body, Grey hook, 'BP' decal............**£1,000-1,500**
note: Fakes from 1970 have red hooks, 'BP' labels,
crimped axles and the thick crane casting. Only the original
Green cab version has a thin crane. But these fakes (only 24
were produced) are now sought after by many collectors
and are also very valuable (**£400-500**)!
Yellow cab, Green body, Grey hook **£15-20**
Same but with Red hook...**£10-15**
See Superfast section for subsequent issues.

MB 14

14a 55 **Ambulance (Daimler)** (49mm). Cream body, Silver trim,
Red cross on roof, MW on crimped or domed/crimped axles,
no number, 'Ambulance' cast on sides **£30-35**
14b 58 **Daimler Ambulance** (59 mm). All have a 'Red Cross' on roof.
Cream body, metal wheels **£35-45**
Cream body, Grey plastic wheels ....**£50-60**.
Off-White body, metal wheels ....**£100-125**.
Off-White body, GPW..**£35-45**
Off-White body, SPW...**£150-200**
14c 62 **Bedford Lomas Ambulance**
All models with 'Red Cross' and 'LCC Ambulance' on sides.
White body, Black wheels..**£80-120**
White body, Silver wheels...**£200-250**
Off-White body, Silver wheels **£75-85**
Off-White body, locating marks for Red Cross cast into
roof, Silver grille, Silver wheels..**£300-400**
Off-White body, Grey wheels..**£150-180**
Off-White body, Black wheels...**£25-30**
14d 68 **Iso Grifo**
Metallic Blue body, Blue interior...**£25-30**
Dark Metallic Blue, Blue interior **£8-12**
See Superfast section for subsequent issues.

MB 15

15a 55 **Diamond T Prime Mover**
Yellow body, six MW, hook, no number, 55 mm **£1200-1600**
Orange body, six metal wheels **£25-30**
Same but with ten MW...**£300-400**
15b 59 **Super Atlantic Tractor**
Orange body, Black base, hook, BPW, 67 mm.........................**£20-30**
Orange body, knobbly GPW **£500-750**

15c 63 **Tippax Refuse Collector**. All models with Blue body,
Grey container and Black wheels.
With knobbly tread wheels (24 treads), decal............................**£60-70**
With fine tread wheels, *'Cleansing Service'* decal or label.......**£12-16**
15d 68 **Volkswagen 1500 Saloon**
Off-White or Cream body, '137' decals on doors **£25-35**
Same but '137' labels on doors.....................................**£15-20**
See Superfast section for subsequent issues.

MB 16

16a 55 **Transporter Trailer**. Tan body, 6 MW (crimped axles or
domed and crimped axles) **£25-30**
16b 60 **Super Atlantic Trailer**
Tan body, Grey plastic wheels **£60-75**
Orange body, GPW **£500-750**
Orange, BPW, Black drawbar **£25-30**
Orange, BPW, Orange drawbar...................................**£30-40**
16c 63 **Scammell Snow Plough**. Grey body, Orange tipper,
Red/White or Orange/White decal, GPW **£80-100**
With Black plastic wheels **£12-16**
16d 69 **Case Bulldozer Tractor**
Red/Yellow body, Green rubber tracks, hook, 64 mm................**£8-10**
See Superfast section for subsequent issues.

MB 17

17a 55 **Bedford Removals Van**. All models with
'MATCHBOX REMOVALS SERVICE' decals and MW.
Light Blue body, Silver trim **£200-250**
Maroon body, Silver trim **£250-300**
Maroon body, Gold trim...**£200-250**
Green body, Silver trim...**£40-50**
17b 58 **Bedford Removals Van**
Green body, MW, decal with or without Black outline **£35-45**
Green body, Grey plastic wheels, decal with outline................**£60-75**
Dark Green body, GPW, decal with outline **£150-200**
17c 60 **Austin FX3 Taxi**
Maroon body, Mid-Grey interior, Tan driver, GPW **£45-55**
Same but with SPW, Mid-Grey interior...........................**£100-125**
US issue: With Pale Grey interior and Silver plastic wheels **£60-80**
17d 64 **Foden Tipper**
Red chassis, Orange tipper, *'HOVERINGHAM'*, Black base....**£15-20**
Same but with Red base...**£10-15**
See Superfast section for subsequent issues.

MB 18

18a 55 **Caterpillar Bulldozer** (46 mm).
Yellow body, Red blade, Green tracks....................................**£30-35**
18b 58 **Caterpillar Bulldozer** (50 mm).
Yellow body and blade, Green tracks................................**£50-60**
Same but with Grey tracks..**£80-100**
18c 61 **Caterpillar Bulldozer** (58 mm).
Yellow body and blade, Green tracks, metal rollers................**£15-20**
Same but Silver plastic rollers....................................**£125-150**
Same but Black plastic rollers.....................................**£15-20**
18d 64 **Caterpillar Bulldozer** (62 mm). Yellow body and blade,
no driver, Green tracks, Silver plastic rollers **£100-125**
Black plastic rollers..**£10-15**
18e 69 **Field Car**. Yellow body, Red-Brown roof, Red hubs.........**£10-15**
Same but unpainted base...**£7-10**
Same but with Green hubs.......................................**£220-250**
See Superfast section for subsequent issues.

MB 19

19a 56 **MG Midget TD**
Cream body, Brown driver, Red
seats, MW, no number, 51 mm **£65-75**
Off-White body, metal wheels **£90-130**
19b 58 **MG 'MGA' Sports Car**. All models with Off-White body,
Red seats and Tan driver.
Metal wheels, Gold trim...**£200-250**
Metal wheels, Silver trim **£80-100**
Grey plastic wheels, Silver trim...................................**£80-100**
Silver plastic wheels...**£200-300**
19c 62 **Aston Martin DBR5**. All models with Metallic Green body,
Yellow wheels, White driver.
Number '19' **£25-35**
Number '41' or '52'...**£90-100**
Number '3' or '5'...**£55-70**

19d 65 **Lotus Racing Car**. Dark Green body, Yellow wheels,
White driver, racing number '3' as decal or label **£9-12**
Orange body, RN '3'...**£30-40**
See Superfast section for subsequent issues.

MB 20

20a 56 **E.R.F. Stake Truck**
Light Green body, Silver trim, metal wheels..................**£1,500-1,750**
Maroon body, Gold trim, MW **£220-260**
Maroon body, Silver trim, MW **£25-35**
Maroon body, Silver trim, Grey plastic wheels **£250-300**
Dark Red body, metal wheels **£40-50**
Dark Red body, GPW...**£250-300**
20b 59 **E.R.F. 68G Truck**. All models with Dark Blue body and
'EVER READY' decals on sides.
Early decals are with Orange outline, later with Red outline.
GPW, crimped axles **£65-75**
GPW, rounded axles **£45-65**
Silver plastic wheels..**£100-150**
Black plastic wheels..**£55-75**
20c 65 **Chevrolet Impala Taxi**
Orange-Yellow body, Cream interior, GPW, Taxi decal..**£1,000-1,500**
Orange-Yellow body, Cream interior, BPW, Silver base, Taxi decal .**£30-40**
Same but with unpainted base....................................**£10-12**
Same but with red interior..**£12-18**
Yellow body, Cream interior, Taxi label **£80-100**
Same but with Red interior..**£18-22**
See Superfast section for subsequent issues.

MB 21

21a 56 **Bedford Coach** (57 mm).
Green body and base, *'LONDON-GLASGOW'*, MW...............**£60-70**
21b 58 **Bedford Coach** (68 mm).
All models with Black base and *'LONDON TO GLASGOW'* decals.
Green body, metal wheels **£60-70**
Green body, Grey plastic wheels **£70-80**
Dark Green body, GPW..**£80-100**
21c 61 **Commer Bottle Float**
All models with Pale Green or Blue body and Black base.
On early models the bottles are Cream, later are White.
Bottle on door, SPW, clear windows **£100-130**
Bottle on door, SPW, Green windows **£60-70**
Cow on door, SPW..**£50-60**
Cow on door, GPW..**£100-130**
Cow on door, BPW...**£20-25**
21d 68 **Foden Concrete Truck**
Yellow body, Red chassis, Black wheels **£8-12**
See Superfast section for subsequent issues.

MB 22

22a 56 **Vauxhall Cresta**. Body colours and shades from Dark
Red to Maroon, roof from White to Cream **£35-40**
22b 58 **Vauxhall Cresta**
Pale Pink or Cream body, without windows, metal wheels....**£400-500**
Same but Grey plastic wheels **£65-85**
Same but with windows **£100-130**
Pale Pink body, Blue-Green side panels, GPW **£1,500-2,000**
Light Metallic Brown body, Blue-Green side panels, GPW .**£100-130**
Light Grey body, Lilac side panels, Grey or SPW..................**£80-110**
Light Gold body, Grey or SPW...................................**£90-120**
Dark Gold body, Silver wheels....................................**£90-120**
Metallic Copper body, Grey, Silver or Black wheels **£120-140**
22c 65 **Pontiac GP Sports Coupé**
Red body, Pale Grey interior, BPW, pattern no. on base..........**£15-20**
Red body, Pale Grey interior, BPW, no pattern no. on base......**£15-20**
See Superfast section for subsequent issues.

MB 23

23a 56 **Berkeley Cavalier Caravan**
Pale Blue, *'On Tow MBS 23'*, metal wheels, 65 mm................**£30-40**
23b 57 **Berkeley Cavalier Caravan**. All have *'ON TOW'* rear decal.
Pale Blue, metal wheels **£25-35**
Lime-Green, metal wheels **£75-90**
Lime-Green, GPW...**£55-70**
Metallic Lime-Green, GPW **£1000-1250**
23c 60 **Bluebird Dauphine Caravan**
All models without windows and with *'ON TOW'* rear decal.
Metallic Lime-Green body, Grey plastic wheels **£500-600**

Metallic Mauve body, Maroon base.......................................**£500-600**
Metallic Mauve body and base, Grey plastic wheels **£35-45**
Metallic Mauve body and base, Silver wheels **£30-40**
Metallic Mauve body and base, Black wheels.........................**£300-400**
NB A few issues of 23c are known to exist fitted with
plastic windows **£800-1,000**
23d 65 **Trailer Caravan**
Yellow body, knobbly-tread wheels **£10-15**
Yellow body, fine-tread wheels..**£30-40**
Pink body, knobbly-tread wheels...**£30-40**
Yellow body, fine-tread wheels..**£8-12**
See Superfast section for subsequent issues.

MB 24

24a 56 **'Hydraulic' Excavator**
Orange-Yellow body, metal wheels, 'WEATHERILL', 58 mm..**£25-35**
Same but Yellow body, metal wheels, 'WEATHERILL' **£35-50**
24b 59 **'Hydraulic' Excavator**
Yellow body, Grey plastic wheels, crimped axles **£35-40**
Yellow body, Grey plastic wheels, rounded axles **£25-30**
Yellow body, Black plastic wheels...**£15-20**
24c 67 **Rolls-Royce Silver Shadow**
All models with Metallic Red body and Black base.
Black wheels with Silver hubcaps **£12-18**
Silver wheels with Black tyres...**£10-15**
See Superfast section for subsequent issues.

MB 25

25a 56 **Bedford 12 cwt Van**
Dark Blue body, Black base, 'DUNLOP' decals, MW..............**£25-35**
Grey plastic wheels **£30-40**
Black plastic wheels...**£750-1,000**
25b 60 **Volkswagen 1200**
Metallic Steel-Blue body, GPW, clear windows, 62 mm **£40-50**
As previous model but with Green tinted windows **£60-70**
Same but with SPW **£35-45**
25c 64 **Bedford Petrol Tanker**
Yellow cab, Green chassis, White tank, 'BP', BPW **£12-18**
Same but Grey plastic wheels **£350-450**
64 German issue: Dark Blue cab and chassis,
White tank, 'ARAL', Black plastic wheels..........................**£175-200**
25d 68 **Ford Cortina Mk.II**
Metallic Light Brown body, Black plastic wheels....................**£10-15**
Gift Set issue: Same but with Yellow roof rack **£35-50**
See Superfast section for subsequent issues.

MB 26

26a 56 **E.R.F. Cement Mixer**
Orange body, Gold trim, MW, crimped axles, 45 mm **£220-250**
Same but with Silver trim **£30-35**
With GPW, Silver trim **£70-80**
With SPW, Silver trim **£300-400**
26b 61 **Foden Cement Mixer** (66mm)
Orange body, Lt or Dk Grey barrel, small knobbly GPW.....**£500-600**
Orange body, Orange barrel, Grey or Black plastic wheels **£18-25**
Orange body, Orange barrel, Silver plastic wheels..............**£400-500**
26c 68 **G.M.C. Tipper Truck**
Red cab, Green chassis, Silver tipper, BPW, 67 mm..................**£6-10**
See Superfast section for subsequent issues.

MB 27

27a 56 **Bedford Low Loader** (78mm)
Pale Blue cab, Dark Blue trailer, six MW, crimped axles **£500-600**
Pale Green cab, Tan trailer...**£60-75**
27b 58 **Bedford Low Loader** (95mm)
Pale Green cab, Tan trailer, metal wheels................................**£80-90**
Same but with GPW **£95-110**
Dark Green cab, Light Brown trailer, Grey plastic wheels ...**£100-130**
27c 60 **Cadillac Sixty Special**
Metallic Pale Green/White, Crimson base, SPW **£275-300**
Silver-Grey body, Off-White roof, SPW **£100-125**
Metallic Lilac body, Pink roof, Crimson base, GPW or SPW ..**£70-80**
Same model but with Black base **£70-80**
Same but Black base and BPW...**£90-110**
27d 66 **Mercedes 230 SL**
White body, Red interior...**£10-15**
See Superfast section for subsequent issues.

MB 28

28a 56 **Bedford Compressor**
Orange/Yellow body, Silver trim, metal wheels, 47 mm...........**£20-30**
Yellow body, Silver trim, MW, domed/crimped axles..............**£40-50**
28b 59 **Ford Thames Compressor Truck**
Yellow body, Black wheels, crimped axles...............................**£40-50**
Yellow body, Black wheels, rounded axles...............................**£20-25**
Yellow body, Grey wheels **£300-400**
28c 64 **Jaguar Mk.10**
Pale Metallic Brown, Cream seats, BPW, 74 mm **£20-25**
With 'Matchbox' lapel badge...**£50-60**
With GPW and without 'Matchbox Series' on base.............**£400-500**

Matchbox Motor Cycles and Sidecars
66b Harley-Davidson   36b Lambretta Motor Scooter   4c Triumph T110

28d 68 **Mack Dump Truck**
Orange body, Red wheels...**£10-12**
Orange body, Yellow wheels......................................**£12-15**
See Superfast section for subsequent issues.

MB 29

29a 56 **Bedford Milk Delivery Van**
Light Brown body, White bottle load, metal wheels, 57 mm....**£25-30**
Same but GPW, White or Cream bottles **£30-35**
29b 61 **Austin A55 Cambridge**
Two-tone Green body, Green tinted windows, GPW **£30-35**
Same but SPW, clear or tinted windows......................**£20-25**
Same but with BPW..**£20-25**
29c 66 **Fire Pumper Truck**
Red body, with or without *'Denver'* decal **£8-12**
See Superfast section for subsequent issues.

MB 30

30a 56 **Ford Prefect**
Grey-Brown body, Red and Silver trim, MW, 58 mm...............**£25-35**
Same but with GPW..**£30-40**
Same but Light Blue body, Grey plastic wheels, 58 mm **£150-180**
30b 61 **Magirus-Deutz Crane Lorry**
Light Brown body, Red or Orange crane, GPW **£1,750-2,000**
Silver body, Orange jib and hook, Grey or Silver wheels........**£45-55**
Silver body, Orange jib, Grey or Silver hook, Grey or BPW...**£25-30**
30c 65 **8 Wheel Crane Truck**
Green body, Orange jib **£10-12**
Turquoise body, Orange jib......................................**£300-400**
See Superfast section for subsequent issues.

MB 31

31a 57 **Ford Station Wagon**
Yellow body, metal wheels, hook, 66 mm **£30-35**
Yellow body, Grey plastic wheels..............................**£40-50**
31b 60 **Ford Station Wagon**
Yellow body, Black base, Grey wheels........................**£220-250**
Yellow body, Black base, Silver wheels......................**£200-230**
Yellow body, Crimson base, clear or Green windows..........**£180-210**
Metallic Green body, Pink roof, Crimson base, GPW or SPW.**£25-35**
Same but with Black base, SPW..................................**£60-70**
Same but with Black base, GPW..................................**£60-70**
Same but with Black base, BPW..................................**£70-90**
31c 64 **Lincoln Continental**
Metallic Blue body, BPW...**£12-15**
Sea Green body **£10-12**
Metallic Lime Green body **£1,200-1,500**

MB 32

32a 57 **Jaguar XK-140**
Off-White body, Black base, metal wheels, 60 mm **£25-35**
Same but with GPW..**£40-50**
Bright Orange-Red body, GPW **£130-160**
Dark Red, Black base, GPW **£130-160**
32b 62 **Jaguar 'E'-type**
Metallic Red body, Green windows, Grey tyres, 66 mm **£120-140**
Metallic Red body, clear windows, grey tyres.................**£34-45**
Metallic Red body, clear windows, Black tyres...............**£30-35**
32c 68 **Leyland Tanker**
Green chassis, White tank, Silver base and grille, 'BP' decal..**£30-40**
Green chassis, White tank, Silver base and grille, 'BP' label.....**£8-12**
Green chassis, White tank, White base and grille, 'BP' label.**£40-50**
Blue chassis, White tank, Silver base and grille,
'ARAL' label...**£100-125**
See Superfast section for subsequent issues.

MB 33

33a 57 **Ford Zodiac**. Dark Green body, hook,
no windows, MW, 68 mm.......................................**£30-40**
58 Dark Blue body, hook, no windows, metal wheels..............**£400-500**
58 Sea-Green body, hook, no windows, metal wheels **£80-90**
Same but with GPW..**£60-75**
59 Metallic Mauve body, Orange panels, no windows, GPW......**£80-100**
60 Same but with Green tinted windows, GPW or SPW **£60-80**
33b 63 **Ford Zephyr 6**. Sea-Green body, GPW, 67 mm.....................**£30-35**

same but with SPW..**£20-30**
same but with BPW..**£15-20**
33c 68 **Lamborghini Miura**
Yellow body, White interior, 71 mm. Black plastic wheels.......**£12-15**
Yellow body, White interior, Chrome hubs **£250-300**
Metallic Gold body, White interior, Chrome hubs **£250-300**
See Superfast section for subsequent issues.

MB 34

34a 57 **Volkswagen 15cwt Van**
All models with Blue body and 'MATCHBOX' side decals.
Metal wheels **£30-35**
Grey plastic wheels..**£30-40**
Silver plastic wheels...**£200-300**
34b 62 **Volkswagen Caravette**
All models with Pale Green body and Green interior.
Silver wheels **£180-220**
Knobbly-tread Grey wheels (24 treads).....................**£25-35**
Fine-tread Grey wheels (45 treads).........................**£50-60**
Black wheels **£20-30**
34c 67 **Volkswagen Camper**
Silver body, with high roof (7 windows) **£20-25**
same but lower roof (1 window).................................**£15-20**
See Superfast section for subsequent issues.

MB 35

35a 57 **E.R.F. Marshall Horse Box**
Red cab, Light Brown box, metal wheels, 52 mm **£25-35**
Same but with GPW..**£30-40**
With Silver plastic wheels...**£125-150**
With Black plastic wheels...**£75-90**
35b 64 **Snow-Trac**. Red body, Silver base, White tracks,
'Snow Trac' cast on sides.....................................**£20-25**
same but with *'Snow Trac'* decals on sides **£15-20**
same but without *'Snow Trac'* **£12-15**
See Superfast section for subsequent issues.

MB 36

36a 57 **Austin A50 Cambridge**
Blue-Green body, Black base, metal wheels, 60 mm **£20-25**
Same but with GPW..**£25-35**
Pale Blue body, GPW...**£30-40**
36b 61 **Lambretta and Sidecar**
Pale Metallic Green Scooter and side-car, BPW, 49 mm **£60-80**
36c 66 **Opel Diplomat**
Metallic Gold body, Silver engine **£10-15**
Metallic Gold body, Grey engine..............................**£35-45**
See Superfast section for subsequent issues.

MB 37

37a 57 **Karrier Bantam Lorry**
All models with *'COCA-COLA'* side and rear decals.
Orange-Yellow body, uneven load, metal wheels.................**£140-160**
Yellow body, uneven load, metal wheels.......................**£140-160**
Orange-Yellow body, even load, metal wheels.................**£45-55**
Orange-Yellow body, even load, grey plastic wheels..........**£180-220**
Yellow body, even load, metal wheels.........................**£40-50**
Yellow body, even load, Grey plastic wheels **£200-230**
37b 60 **Karrier Bantam Lorry**
All models with *'COCA-COLA'* side and rear decals.
GPW, crimped axles..**£75-85**
GPW, rounded axles..**£35-45**
Silver plastic wheels...**£400-500**
Black plastic wheels...**£75-85**
37c 66 **(Dodge) Cattle Truck**. Yellow body, Grey cattle box,
2 White bulls, Silver plastic base................................**£15-20**
Unpainted metal base **£8-12**
See Superfast section for subsequent issues.

MB 38

38a 57 **Karrier Refuse Collector**
All models with *'Cleansing Department'* side decals.
Grey-Brown body, MW **£280-320**
Grey body, metal wheels..**£25-30**
Grey body, GPW, crimped axles................................**£35-50**
Grey body, GPW, rounded axles................................**£25-35**

Silver body, GPW..**£40-50**
Silver body, SPW..**£300-350**

38b 63 **Vauxhall Victor Estate**
Yellow body, Red interior, Grey wheels **£150-200**
same but with Silver wheels **£18-25**
same but with Black wheels **£15-20**
Yellow body, Green interior, GPW **£40-50**
same but with Silver wheels **£20-30**
same but with Black wheels **£15-20**

38c **Honda Motorcycle and Trailer**
Metallic Green bike, Orange trailer without decals.................**£30-40**
Same, but Orange trailer with 'Honda' decals....................**£80-120**
Same, but Yellow trailer with 'Honda' decals or labels **£8-12**
See Superfast section for subsequent issues.

MB 39

39a 57 **Zodiac Convertible**
Pale Peach body, Light Brown base/interior/driver, MW......**£250-300**
Same but with Light Green base and interior, metal wheels.....**£30-40**
Same but with Light Green base, Grey plastic wheels.............**£35-45**
Dark Peach body, Blue-Green base and interior, GPW............**£35-45**
Same but with SPW **£75-90**
Dark Peach body with Sea-Green base, Grey plastic wheels.....**£50-60**

39b 62 **Pontiac Convertible**. Metallic Purple body, Crimson base,
Red steering wheel, SPW..**£100-125**
same but with Grey wheels **£250-300**
Lemon body, Crimson base, Red steering wheel,
SPW or GPW...**£50-75**
Same but Cream steering wheel.................................**£25-35**
Lemon body, Black base, SPW..................................**£50-75**
Same but with Grey wheels **£35-45**
Same but with Black wheels **£15-20**

39c 67 **Ford Tractor**
Blue body, Yellow engine cover, Black plastic tyres, 55 mm.....**£8-12**
Blue body and engine cover.......................................**£12-15**
All-Orange body, Yellow hubs...................................**£40-50**
See Superfast section for subsequent issues.

MB 40

40a 57 **Bedford 7 Ton Tipper**
Red body, Brown tipper, metal wheels, 53 mm...................**£35-45**
Same but with Grey plastic wheels, domed crimped axles **£30-35**
Same but with Grey plastic wheels on rivetted axles..............**£30-35**

40b 61 **Leyland Tiger Coach**
Steel Blue body, GPW **£75-85**
Silver plastic wheels..**£25-35**
Black plastic wheels..**£20-25**

40c 67 **Hay Trailer**. Blue body, Yellow plastic hay racks
and wheels, Black plastic tyres **£6-10**

NB No. 40c deleted in 1972 but appeared in Two-Packs between 1976-1981.

MB 41

41a 57 **Jaguar 'D'-Type** (55 mm)
Green body, MW, No '41'..**£30-40**
Green body, MW, No '52'..**£250-300**
Green body, GPW, No '41' **£90-120**

41b 60 **Jaguar 'D'-Type** (62 mm)
All models with Green body and Black base.
GPW, crimped axles, No '41' **£50-60**
same but with rounded axles **£40-50**
Wire hubs with Black tyres, No '41' **£35-40**
same but with No '5' or '6' **£75-90**
Red hubs with Black tyres **£250-300**

41c 65 **Ford GT Racer**. All models with racing number '6'.
White body, Red hubs, BPT..**£200-250**
White body, Yellow hubs, Black tyres.........................**£10-15**
Yellow body, Yellow hubs, black tyres (US set)..............**£150-200**
See Superfast section for subsequent issues.

MB 42

42a 57 **Evening News Van**
Yellow body, *'EVENING NEWS'* decals, MW, 57 mm............**£35-40**
GPW with 24 treads **£45-55**
GPW with 45 treads **£120-150**
BPW with 24 treads **£100-125**
BPW with 45 treads **£120-150**

42b 65 **Studebaker Lark Wagonaire** (with hunter and dog figures),

Blue body, sliding rear roof painted as body **£65-75**
same but rear roof painted Light Blue **£12-15**

42c 69 **Iron Fairy Crane**. Red body, Yellow boom, BPW **£10-15**
See Superfast section for subsequent issues.

MB 43

43a 58 **Hillman Minx**
Light Green body, Silver/Red trim, metal wheels, hook **£300-350**
Blue/Grey body, Pale Grey roof, metal wheels **£30-35**
Same but with GPW..**£60-70**
Turquoise body, Cream roof, Grey plastic wheels....................**£60-70**

43b 62 **A.B. Tractor Shovel**
Yellow body, driver and shovel....................................**£90-110**
Yellow body and shovel, Red driver and base........................**£15-20**
Yellow body, driver and base, Red shovel.........................**£20-30**
Yellow body, Red driver, base and shovel **£200-250**

43c 68 **Pony Trailer**
Yellow body, Grey ramp, Light Brown base, BPW..................**£12-18**
same but with Dark Green base **£8-12**
See Superfast section for subsequent issues.

MB 44

44a 58 **Rolls-Royce Silver Cloud**
Metallic Silver-Blue body, Red trim, metal wheels, 67 mm **£25-35**
44 60 As previous but with GPW **£30-40**
Same but with SPW **£50-60**

44b 64 **Rolls-Royce Phantom V**
Metallic Mauve body, Black wheels............................**£20-25**
Same but with Grey wheels **£60-80**
Same but with Silver wheels......................................**£90-120**
Metallic Silver-Grey body, BPW.................................**£90-110**
Same but with Black wheels **£300-350**

44c 67 **GMC Refrigerator Truck**
Red body, Sea-Green container, Black wheels, 76 mm..............**£8-12**
See Superfast section for subsequent issues.

MB 45

45a 58 **Vauxhall Victor**
Red body, MW, 61 mm...**£2,000-3,000**
Yellow or Lemon body, MW **£35-45**
Yellow body, metal wheels, no dashboard casting bar **£250-300**
Yellow or Lemon body, GPW, no window glazing **£35-45**
same but with clear windows **£70-80**
same but with Green windows **£70-80**
Lemon, Green windows, SPW **£70-80**
Yellow body, SPW **£80-100**
Yellow body, BPW **£80-100**

45b 65 **Ford Corsair with Boat**
Cream body, Red interior, Black wheels, Silver painted base...**£25-30**
Same but with unpainted base.....................................**£10-15**
Same but with Grey wheels **£50-60**
Models with white interior are pre-productions **£600-800**
See Superfast section for subsequent issues.

MB 46

46a 58 **Morris Minor 1000**
Pale Brown body, no windows, metal wheels, 53 mm....**£2,000-3,000**
Dark Green body, Black base, MW, domed crimped axles.......**£60-70**
Dark Blue/Green body, MW **£70-80**
Same but with GPW..**£100-125**
Blue body, GPW...**£125-150**

46b 60 **'PICKFORDS' Removals Van**
Dark Blue body, Grey wheels, three line decal **£90-120**
Dark Blue body, Silver wheels, three line decal....................**£90-120**
Dark Blue body, Grey wheels, two line decal **£100-130**
Dark Blue body, Silver wheels, two line decal......................**£180-220**
Green body, Grey wheels..**£65-75**
Green body, Silver wheels..**£80-100**
Green body, Black wheels...**£60-70**
'BEALES BEALESONS' Van. Light Brown body,
'Beales Bealesons' decal, BPW, without box.....................**£500-700**
Same but in special White box with 'sun' and
'It's A Pleasure' decal **£800-1,000**

46c 68 **Mercedes-Benz 300 SE**. Green body..............................**£12-15**
69 Metallic Blue body..**£9-12**
See Superfast section for subsequent issues.

MB 47

47a 58 Trojan Van
Red body, *'BROOKE BOND TEA'* decals, MW, 58 mm **£30-40**
Same but with GPW..**£35-45**

47b 63 Commer Ice Cream Van *'LYONS MAID'*,
Metallic Blue body, BPW **£75-100**
Same but with Blue body..**£25-35**
Blue body, Grey wheels **£200-300**
Blue body, Black wheels, White side decals **£35-45**
Cream body, *'LYONS MAID'*..................................**£180-220**
Cream body, White side decals......................................**£50-60**
'LORD NIELSENS ICE CREAM',
Cream body, Red/White labels...................................**£50-60**
Blue body, Black plastic wheels **£125-150**

47c 68 DAF Container Truck
Sea Green body, Grey roof, Yellow container, BPW................**£55-65**
Silver body, Grey or Silver roof, Yellow container, BPW..........**£8-12**
See Superfast section for subsequent issues.

MB 48

48a 58 Meteor Sports Boat and Trailer
Black trailer, Light Brown boat, Blue hull, metal wheels **£25-30**
With Grey plastic wheels......................................**£30-35**
With Silver plastic wheels....................................**£130-160**

48b 61 Sports Boat and Trailer
Boat with Cream or White deck and Red hull or
with Red deck and Cream or white hull,
Dark Blue trailer, Black wheels **£15-20**
Dark Blue trailer, Grey wheels **£75-100**
Light Blue trailer, Black wheels.................................**£20-30**

48c 66 (Dodge) Dumper Truck
Red body, Silver trim, wide or narrow BPW, 76 mm.................**£8-12**
See Superfast section for subsequent issues.

MB 49

49a 58 M3 Personnel Carrier
Military Green, White *'Star'* bonnet decal, MW and rollers **£20-30**
Grey plastic wheels, metal rollers **£20-30**
Grey plastic wheels and rollers **£350-400**
Grey plastic wheels, Silver rollers............................**£60-80**
BPW and rollers, Grey tracks **£25-35**
BPW and rollers, Green tracks................................**£35-45**

49b 67 (Mercedes) Unimog
Light Brown body, Sea-Green base, 61 mm.....................**£12-15**
Light Brown body, Red base **£700-800**
Light Blue body, Red base **£8-12**
See Superfast section for subsequent issues.

MB 50

50a 58 Commer Pick-Up
Pale Brown body, MW, 64 mm...............................**£25-35**
Pale or Light Brown body, GPW **£35-45**
Light Brown body, SPW **£100-130**
Red and White body, SPW...................................**£400-500**
Red and Grey body, SPW **£120-150**
Red and Grey body, GPW...................................**£80-100**
Red and Grey body, BPW....................................**£80-100**

50b 64 John Deere Lanz Tractor
Green body, Yellow hubs, Grey tyres, 50 mm.................**£15-20**
Same but Black tyres.......................................**£10-15**
With Green hubs, Black tyres **£500-600**

50c 69 Ford Kennel Truck
Metallic Green body, White grille, smooth kennel floor **£15-20**
Same but textured kennel floor **£8-12**
Same but with Silver grill **£12-15**
See Superfast section for subsequent issues.

MB 51

51a 58 Albion Chieftain
All models with Yellow body, Tan or Light Beige load,
'PORTLAND CEMENT' decals, metal wheels.......................**£40-50**
'BLUE CIRCLE PORTLAND CEMENT' decals, MW..............**£30-40**
Same but with GPW **£35-45**
Same but with SPW **£100-130**
Same but with knobbly BPW.................................**£200-250**

51b 64 Tipping Trailer
Green body, three Yellow barrels, Yellow hubs, Grey tyres......**£10-15**

With Yellow hubs, Black tyres...............................**£6-10**
With Green hubs, black tyres................................**£250-300**

51c 69 AEC Mammoth Major 8 Wheel Tipper
Orange body, Silver tipper, *'DOUGLAS'*, White base grille.....**£50-60**
Same but chrome base......................................**£20-25**
Yellow body, Silver tipper, *'DOUGLAS'*......................**£40-50**
Yellow body, Silver tipper, *'POINTER'*.......................**£12-18**
See Superfast section for subsequent issues.

MB 52

52a 58 1948 Maserati 4 CLT
Red body, Cream driver, no decal, BPW, 61 mm....................**£30-40**
Same with racing number '52'................................**£35-45**
Red body, racing number '52', wire wheels, BPT.............**£200-250**
Lemon body, wire wheels, '52'...............................**£35-45**
Same but number '3' or '5'.................................**£70-100**

52b 65 B.R.M. Racing Car
Blue body, Yellow hubs, BPT, '5'...........................**£8-12**
Same but with racing number '3' **£60-75**
Dark Blue (Ultramarine) body, racing number '5'...............**£60-80**
Gift Set model: Red body, Yellow hubs with Black tyres **£60-80**
Dark Cherry Red body, Yellow hubs, racing number '5' **£100-120**
See Superfast section for subsequent issues.

MB 53

53a 58 Aston Martin DB2-4 Mk.I
Metallic Green body, MW, 65 mm...........................**£30-40**
Same but with GPW **£35-45**
Metallic Red, knobbly GPW **£150-220**
Metallic Red, knobbly BPW..................................**£150-200**

53b 63 Mercedes-Benz 220SE
Maroon body, Silver wheels **£15-25**
Maroon body, Grey wheels **£30-40**
Maroon body, Black wheels **£60-75**
Dark Red body, Grey wheels **£35-45**
Dark Red body, Black wheels................................**£12-18**

53c 68 Ford Zodiac Mk.IV
Light Metallic Blue body, BPW..............................**£8-12**
Light Metallic Green body, Black plastic wheels.................**£500-750**
See Superfast section for subsequent issues.

MB 54

54a 58 Saracen Personnel Carrier
Olive Green body, six BPW, crimped axles, 57 mm **£25-35**
Same but with rounded axles **£20-25**

54b 65 Cadillac Ambulance
White, Red cross label or decal and roof lights, BPW **£8-12**
See Superfast section for subsequent issues.

MB 55

55a 58 DUKW Amphibian
Olive Green body, MW, 71 mm..............................**£15-20**
Same but GPW or BPW.....................................**£20-30**
In box with Green model picture (normally Red picture) **£100-150**

55b 63 Ford Fairlane 'POLICE' Car
Non-metallic Dark Blue, BPW................................**£250-300**
Metallic Blue, knobbly BPW.................................**£80-100**
Metallic Blue, BPW..**£35-45**
Metallic Blue, GPW..**£900-1,200**
Metallic Blue, SPW..**£200-300**

55c 66 Ford Galaxy 'POLICE' Car
White body, *'Police & Shield'* decal, Blue roof light.............**£80-100**
same but with Red roof light................................**£12-15**

55d 68 Mercury 'POLICE' Car
White body, *'Police & Shield'* labels, Red roof light...........**£250-300**
Same but with Blue roof light...............................**£12-15**
See Superfast section for subsequent issues.

MB 56

56a 58 London Trolley Bus. All models with Red body,
'DRINK PEARDRAX' and destination decals.
Black poles, metal wheels **£130-150**
Black poles, GPW **£250-300**
Red poles, metal wheels **£40-50**
Red poles, GPW or BPW **£35-45**
Red poles, SPW **£140-160**

56b 65 Fiat 1500 (all have BPW)
Sea-Green body, Brown luggage **£12-18**
Same but with Red-Brown luggage **£8-12**
Gift Set version: Red body, Red-Brown luggage **£60-80**
See Superfast section for subsequent issues.

MB 57

57a 58 Wolseley 1500
Pale Green body, GPW, Gold trim, 55 mm **£180-200**
Same but with Silver trim **£30-40**
57b 61 Chevrolet Impala
All models with Metallic Blue body and pale Blue roof.
Clear windows, Black base, SPW...**£80-100**
Clear windows, Dark Blue base, SPW **£60-70**
Green windows, Dark Blue base, SPW **£20-25**
Same but with GPW...**£30-40**
Green windows, Pale or Light Blue base, SPW **£100-125**
Black base, GPW..**£70-80**
Black base, SPW...**£70-80**
Black base, BPW...**£40-50**
57c 66 Land Rover Fire Truck
Red body, *'KENT FIRE BRIGADE'*, BPW, 64 mm **£12-16**
Same but with GPW...**£400-600**
See Superfast section for subsequent issues.

MB 58

58a 58 AEC 'BEA' Coach
Dark Blue body, White letters, Grey wheels, 65 mm **£40-50**
Dark Blue body, Black letters on White ground, Grey wheels .**£35-45**
Same but with Silver wheels...**£100-130**
Same but with Black wheels...**£120-150**
58b 62 Drott Excavator
Red body, Silver base, Black rollers, Green tracks...................**£12-18**
Same but with Silver rollers...**£70-90**
Orange body, Silver base, Black rollers....................................**£20-25**
Orange body and base, Black rollers **£15-20**
58c 68 DAF Girder Truck
White body, Red base and 12 girders, 6 BPW, 75 mm **£8-12**
See Superfast section for subsequent issues.

MB 59

59a 58 Ford Thames Van 'SINGER'
Pale Green body, Red seats, GPW **£40-50**
Same but SPW, rivetted axles **£175-225**
Dark Green body and Grey plastic wheels, rivetted axles....**£140-160**
Dark Green body, Silver plastic wheels, rivetted axles **£150-200**
59b 63 Ford Fairlane Fire Chief
All models with Red body and *'FIRE CHIEF'* decals on
doors and bonnet, Black wheels..**£40-50**
With Grey wheels **£100-125**
With Silver wheels **£500-600**
With *'SHIELD'* decals on doors **£200-250**
59c 66 Ford Galaxie Fire Chief
Red body, Blue dome light, *'FIRE CHIEF & SHIELD'*, BPW **£10-15**
Same but with Red dome light...**£250-350**
See Superfast section for subsequent issues.

MB 60

60a 58 Morris J2 Pick Up
All with Light Blue body and *'BUILDERS SUPPLY COMPANY'*
decals. 'Supply Company' in Black, Grey plastic wheels.........**£50-60**
'SUPPLY COMPANY' in White, with rear window,
GPW or BPW...**£25-35**
Same but with SPW **£40-50**
Without rear window, GPW...**£90-120**
Without rear window, BPW **£35-45**
60b 66 Site Hut Truck
Blue body, Yellow and Green plastic building, Black wheels.....**£8-12**
See Superfast section for subsequent issues.

MB 61

61a 59 Ferret Scout Car
Olive Green body, Tan driver, Black plastic wheels, 57 mm **£20-25**
61b 66 Alvis Stalwart 'BP'
White body, Green wheels with BPT, smooth carrier bed........**£25-30**
Same but with ribbed carrier bed **£10-15**
White body, Yellow wheels with Black tyres **£35-45**

Two-Pack version: Military Olive Green body, Black wheels .**£15-25**
See Superfast section for subsequent issues.

MB 62

62a 59 AEC General Service Lorry
Olive Green body, tow hook, six BPT, 68 mm.........................**£25-30**
62b 63 Commer TV Service Van
All models with Cream body and Red plastic ladder, aerial and
three TVs. *'RENTASET'*, knobbly Grey wheels (24 treads).**£120-150**
'RENTASET', Black wheels...**£40-50**
'RENTASET', fine-tread Grey wheels (45 treads) **£220-250**
'RADIO RENTALS', BPW **£50-60**
'RADIO RENTALS', fine-tread Grey wheels **£350-400**
62c 68 Mercury Cougar
Cream body, White interior, Chrome hubs **£1500-1750**
Metallic Lime Green body, Red interior....................................**£10-15**
See Superfast section for subsequent issues.

MB 63

63a 59 Service Ambulance (Ford)
Olive Green body, Red crosses, BPW, crimped axles **£30-35**
Same but with rounded axles **£25-30**
63b 63 Alvis Foamite Crash Tender
Red body, Silver hose nozzle, six BPW, 63 mm **£60-70**
With Gold hose nozzle...**£20-30**
63c 68 Dodge Crane Truck
Yellow body, Red hook, 76 mm **£8-12**
Yellow body, Yellow hook **£10-15**
See Superfast section for subsequent issues.

MB 64

64a 59 Scammell Breakdown Truck
Olive Green body, metal or plastic hook, BPW, 64 mm **£25-35**
64b 66 MG 1100
Green body, White seats, driver, dog, BPT, 67 mm **£8-12**
See Superfast section for subsequent issues.

MB 65

65a 59 Jaguar 3.4 litre
Dark Blue body, Silver rear number-plate, GPW, 62 mm **£45-55**
As previous but with Blue rear number plate **£35-45**
Metallic Blue body and number plate, Grey plastic wheels ..**£100-130**
65b 62 Jaguar 3.8 Sedan
Metallic Red body, Silver base, Silver plastic wheels, 68 mm..**£80-90**
Red body, Silver plastic wheels **£150-200**
Red body, Grey plastic wheels **£35-45**
Red body, Black plastic wheels **£20-25**
65c 67 Claas Combine Harvester
Red body, Yellow blades and front hubs, no hole in base **£80-100**
As previous but with hole in base..**£6-10**
See Superfast section for subsequent issues.

MB 66

66a 59 Citroën DS 19
Yellow body, Silver trim, GPW **£35-45**
Same but with SPW...**£100-120**
66b 62 Harley-Davidson Motor Cycle
Metallic Bronze bike and sidecar, spoked wheels, BPT...........**£70-80**
66c 66 'GREYHOUND' Coach
Silver-Grey body, clear windows, Black plastic wheels............**£60-70**
Silver-Grey body, Amber windows, Black plastic wheels **£10-12**
See Superfast section for subsequent issues.

MB 67

67a 59 Saladin Armoured Car
Olive Green body, six BPW, crimped axles, 61 mm **£25-35**
Same but with rounded axles **£25-30**
67b 67 Volkswagen 1600 TL
Red body, Black wheels with Silver hubcaps **£15-20**
Red body, Silver wheels with black tyres **£10-15**
Gift Set version: Red body with Maroon plastic roof rack **£50-60**
Metallic Purple body, Chrome hubs with Black tyres **£250-300**
See Superfast section for subsequent issues.

MB 68

68a 59 **Austin Radio Truck Mk.II**
Olive Green body and base, BPW, crimped axles **£30-35**
Same but with rounded axles **£25-30**

68b 65 **Mercedes Coach** (all have BPW)
Turquoise/White body, US issue **£200-250**
Orange/White body, BPW **£8-12**
See Superfast section for subsequent issues.

MB 69

69a 59 **Commer Van 'NESTLES'**
Maroon body, driver, Yellow logo, GPW, 56 mm **£35-45**
Red body, GPW with 20 treads **£55-70**
Red body, GPW with 36 treads...**£75-85**

69b 65 **Hatra Tractor Shovel**
Orange body, Orange wheels, Grey tyres, 78 mm **£60-75**
With Red hubs, Grey tyres **£25-35**
With Red hubs, Black tyres...**£15-20**
With Yellow hubs, Black tyres..**£10-15**
Yellow body, Yellow hubs...**£10-15**
Yellow body, Red hubs..**£70-90**
Orange body, Yellow shovel **£250-300**
See Superfast section for subsequent issues.

MB 70

70a 59 **Ford Thames Estate Car**
Turquoise and Yellow body, Grey wheels, no windows...........**£30-35**
Grey wheels, clear windows **£35-40**
Grey wheels, Green windows ....**£25-30.**
Silver wheels, clear windows **£35-40**
Silver or Black wheels, Green windows **£25-30**

70b 66 **Ford Grit Spreader**
Red body, Pale Lemon container, BPW, 68 mm........................**£8-12**
Red body, Dark Yellow container, Black or Grey slide, BPW ..**£25-35**
See Superfast section for subsequent issues.

MB 71

71a 59 **200 gallon Water Truck**
Olive Green body, BPW..**£25-30**
Same model with first *'Matchbox Collectors'* badge **£55-65**

71b 64 **Jeep Gladiator Pick-Up**
Red body, Green interior, Black plastic wheels, 66 mm **£50-60**
Red body, White interior..**£10-15**

71c 69 **Ford Heavy Wreck Truck** (all BPW)
Red and White body, Amber windows, smooth loadbed.......**£200-250**
Same but with ribbed loadbed..**£200-250**
Same but with Green windows **£8-12**
Military Green body **£8-12**
See Superfast section for subsequent issues.

MB 72

72a 59 **Fordson Major Tractor**. All models with Blue body.
Grey front wheels, Orange rear hubs with Grey tyres, 50 mm .**£35-40**
Black front wheels, Orange rear hubs with Black tyres **£35-40**
Orange hubs front and rear, Grey tyres....................................**£35-40**

Orange hubs front and rear, BPT **£30-35**
Yellow hubs front and rear, Grey or Black tyres **£800-1,000**

72b 66 **Jeep CJ5**
Orange-Yellow body, Yellow hubs, White interior..............**£600-700**
Yellow body, Yellow hubs, Red interior **£8-12**
See Superfast section for subsequent issues.

MB 73

73a 59 **Leyland R.A.F. 10 ton Refueller**
Airforce-Blue body, roundel, six GPW, 66 mm.......................**£35-45**
Same but with BPW **£800-1,100**

73b 62 **Ferrari F1 Racing Car**. Red body, Grey or White driver,
RN '73', 'spoked' metal hubs, Black plastic tyres **£20-25**

73c 68 **Mercury Commuter Station Wagon**
Metallic Lime Green body, Silver hubs, Black plastic tyres **£8-12**
See Superfast section for subsequent issues.

MB 74

74a 59 **Mobile 'REFRESHMENTS' Bar**
White body, Pale Blue base, Blue interior, GPW **£100-130**
Cream body, Light Blue base, Grey plastic wheels **£110-140**
Pink body, Light Blue base, Grey plastic wheels **£300-400**
Silver body, Light Blue base, Grey plastic wheels **£30-40**
Silver body, Light Blue base, Silver plastic wheels **£35-45**
Silver body, Light Blue base, Black plastic wheels.............**£600-800**
Silver body, Sea Green or Dark Blue base **£60-75**

74b 66 **Daimler Fleetline Bus**
Cream body, 'ESSO' decals **£12-18**
Cream body, 'ESSO' labels **£25-35**
Green body, 'ESSO' labels **£15-20**
Red body, 'ESSO' labels **£25-35**
See Superfast section for subsequent issues.

MB 75

75a 60 **Ford Thunderbird**
All models have Cream body and Peach side panels.
Blue base, Silver wheels **£30-35**
Blue-Green base, Silver wheels **£150-200**
Black base, Silver wheels...**£70-80**
Black base, Grey wheels **£55-75**
Black base, Black wheels..**£250-300**

75b 65 **Ferrari Berlinetta**
Metallic Green body, wire wheels, Silver painted base...........**£50-60**
Metallic Green body, wire wheels, unpainted base **£10-15**
Metallic Green body, Silver wheels with Black tyres..............**£12-18**
Red body, Chrome hubs with Black tyres **£250-300**
Red body, wire wheels **£400-500**
See Superfast section for subsequent issues.

A1a	1957	**'ESSO' Petrol Pump Set** ....Red pumps, White figure..	£25-35
A1b	1963	**'BP' Petrol Pump Set** ....White pumps, Yellow/White decal	£25-35

A2 1957 **Car Transporter**............................Box type 1: Dark Blue/Yellow front and back 'MOKO - LESNEY' line-drawing box.
  Box type 2: Yellow front/back, Blue end tabs, 'LESNEY MATCHBOX SERIES' logo.
  1: Pale blue body, Dark Blue logo 'MATCHBOX CAR TRANSPORTER', metal wheels on tractor and trailer, 1st type box............................**£50-60**
  2: Pale Blue body, Red 'CAR COLLECTION Ltd CAR TRANSPORTER', GPW (tractor), BPW (trailer), 1st box....................**£150-200**
  3: Pale Blue body, Red 'CAR COLLECTION Ltd CAR TRANSPORTER', Black plastic wheels on tractor and trailer, 1st type box **£35-45**
  4: Pale Blue body, Red 'CAR COLLECTION Ltd CAR TRANSPORTER', Grey plastic wheels on tractor and trailer, 1st type box **£35-45**
  5: Red cab and lower deck, Grey upper deck and sides, BPW, Red logo: 'CAR COLLECTION Ltd' on Pale Yellow background, 2nd box...**£150-200**

A3	1957	**Garage** ....Yellow/Green/Red, opening doors, all metal..............................	£25-35
A4	1960	**Road Signs Set**..............................Eight Red/White/Black signs 'Lesney' on base............................	£25-35
A5	1960	**'HOME STORES' Shop**.....................Food shop with window display and opening door..................	£25-35
?	c1958	**Service Station and Showroom**.......'MATCHBOX GARAGE', Red plastic building with Yellow base and roof sign.....	£50-75
		Same but Yellow plastic building with Red base and roof sign...................................	£50-75
MG1	1960-63	**Service Station and Showroom**.......'MATCHBOX', Yellow plastic building and ramp, Red sign 'MATCHBOX'	£150-200
		Same but White plastic building with Green base and Yellow sign 'BP'	£150-200
MG1	c1968	**Service Station**..............................Green and Yellow plastic building and card forecourt 'BP'	£75-100
MF1	1963-67	**Fire Station** ....White building with Green roof, 'MATCHBOX FIRE STATION' on a Brown or Red background	£175-225

'Matchbox' Series Painting Books

Four different types of cover and contents numbered 1 to 4.
Mint unused set of books..**£2,000-3,000**

Major Packs Series

Ref.	Details	MPR	Ref..	Details	MPR
M1 58	**Caterpillar Earthmover** Yellow body, MW, crimped or rounded axles, 99mm **£35-45**		**M6** 60	**Scammell Transporter 'PICKFORDS'** Dark Blue tractor, Maroon low-loader, BPW, 279mm **£60-75**	
M1 63	**'BP' Petrol Tanker** Green/Yellow/White body, knobbly or fine tread BPW........**£25-35**			Blue tractor, Bright Red low-loader, Black plastic wheels **£120-140**	
M2 58	**Bedford Articulated Truck 'WALLS ICE CREAM'** All versions have a Light Blue tractor cab, 101mm.		**M6** 66	**Racing Car Transporter 'BP'** Green body, Silver ramp/rear door, Red hubs with BPT,	
	Cream trailer, metal wheels.................................**£50-60**			'Monza/Le Mans/Sebring/Nurburgring' on sides...............**£220-250**	
59	Cream trailer, Grey plastic wheels....................**£45-55**			With 'Le Mans/Sebring/Silverstone/Nurburgring' on sides ...**£40-50**	
59-61	White trailer, Grey plastic wheels....................**£60-80**		**M7** 60	**Thames Trader Cattle Truck 'JENNINGS'**, Dark Red cab,	
M2 61	**Bedford Tractor and York Trailer 'DAVIES TYRES'**			Light Tan box trailer, knobbly GPW **£60-70**	
	Orange cab, Silver trailer, clear windows, knobbly BPW....**£60-75**			With Dark Tan trailer, Red rear lamp, knobbly GPW **£60-70**	
	With Green tinted windows, knobbly BPW **£45-60**			As previous model but with knobbly BPW **£60-70**	
	With Grey knobbly tread wheels **£75-90**			Same but with Grey fine-tread wheels (45 treads)..............**£80-100**	
	With Black fine tread wheels (45 treads) **£60-80**			Same but with Black fine-tread wheels (45 treads)............**£70-80**	
	With Grey fine tread wheels (45 treads) **£120-140**			Light Blue cab, base and rear ramp, Metallic Copper back,	
	Silver cab, Dark Red trailer, Black base **£180-220**			Grey plastic wheels..**£2,000-3,000**	
M2 64	**Bedford Tractor and York Trailer 'LEP INTERNATIONAL'**		**M8** 61	**'MOBILGAS' Petrol Tanker**	
	Silver cab, Dark Red trailer, Dark Red base **£100-120**			Red body, White 'MOBILGAS' logo, knobbly GPW **£60-80**	
	Silver cab, Dark Red trailer, Black base **£55-70**			With Black knobbly-tread wheels (24 treads) **£125-150**	
M3 59	**Mighty Antar Tank Transporter and Centurion Tank**			With Black fine-tread wheels (45 treads) **£150-180**	
	Both models in Military Olive Green, Transporter always		**M8** 64	**Guy Warrior Car Transporter** Blue-Green cab, Orange trailer,	
	has Black wheels. Tank with metal rollers **£30-40**			Orange wheels with Grey tyres, 209 mm.	
	Tank with Grey plastic rollers.........................**£220-250**			'FARNBOROUGH-MEASHAM' in Black, White outline .**£80-100**	
	Tank with Black plastic rollers........................**£30-40**			'FARNBOROUGH-MEASHAM' in White, Black outline ...**£35-50**	
M4 59	**Ruston Bucyrus Excavator**		**M9** 62	**Inter-State Double Freighter 'COOPER-JARRETT'**.	
	Maroon cab, Yellow shovel arms, Black base, Green tracks .**£50-70**			All versions have a Dark Blue cab.	
M4 65	**'FREUHOF' Hopper Train**			Silver trailers, one-piece double wheels, Yellow lettering **£75-90**	
	Maroon tractor, two Silver trailers, Red wheels, BPT..........**£35-45**			Same but double wheels are two separate wheels **£60-80**	
M5 59	**'MASSEY FERGUSON 780' Combine Harvester**			Same but Orange lettering **£120-140**	
	Red body, Yellow blades, Silver front wheels, Black rear **£35-45**			Grey trailers, Yellow lettering **£100-120**	
	Orange front wheels, Black rear wheels **£55-65**		**M10** 62	**Whitlock Dinkum Dumper**	
	Yellow front wheels, Black rear wheels **£70-80**			Yellow body, 'DD-70', unpainted metal wheels, 108 mm **£45-65**	
	Orange front and rear wheels with Black tyres **£60-70**			Same but Red plastic hubs with Black tyres **£50-70**	
	Yellow front and rear wheels with Black tyres........**£75-90**				

Lincoln Industries 'Matchbox Series'

Collectors should be aware that a range of models exists which were made in New Zealand and which at first sight appear to be Matchbox Miniatures. The packaging in particular is strikingly similar to early Lesney Matchbox boxes, even to the extent of having 'MATCHBOX SERIES' printed in a banner as on the Lesney boxes.

It seems that the makers, Lincoln Industries, were so taken with the Lesney idea of 'a model in a matchbox' that they were tempted to capitalise on it by adopting it themselves. 'Lincoln Industries Ltd' and 'Made in New Zealand' are also clearly marked on the boxes so confusion should be avoidable. The

models are a little cruder than genuine Matchbox products and all seem to have metal wheels. They are nevertheless collectable and include: a Utility Truck, Breakdown Truck, Large Parcels Van, Ambulance, and a sports car resembling a Jaguar XK120.

These auction results were achieved by Vectis Auctions Ltd. in July 2000:
4506 Coach......................Green body..**£170**
4509 Ambulance ....Red cross on roof **£140**
4510 Jaguar XK120 ....Cream, with driver **£560**
The Editor would welcome more details of these products.

Matchbox Presentation and Gift Sets

Presentation Sets

The first presentation set was sold in the USA in 1957 and consisted of an enlarged normal 'Matchbox' containing eight of the sixty-four models that Lesney manufactured at that time. The first sets were not sold in the UK until 1959.

Ref	Year(s)	Set name	Contents, features, details	Market Price Range
PS 1	1957	**Matchbox Presentation Set**	Contains models 1 - 8 (only available in USA)	**£1500-2500**
PS 2	1957	**Matchbox Presentation Set**	Contains models 9 - 16 (only available in USA)	**£1500-2500**
PS 3	1957	**Matchbox Presentation Set**	Contains models 17 - 24 (only available in USA)	**£1500-2500**
PS 4	1957	**Matchbox Presentation Set**	Contains models 25 - 32 (only available in USA)	**£1500-2500**
PS 5	1957	**Matchbox Presentation Set**	Contains models 33 - 40 (only available in USA)	**£1500-2500**
PS 6	1957	**Matchbox Presentation Set**	Contains models 41 - 48 (only available in USA)	**£1500-2500**
PS 7	1957	**Matchbox Presentation Set**	Contains models 49 - 56 (only available in USA)	**£1500-2500**
PS 8	1957	**Matchbox Presentation Set**	Contains models 57 - 64 (only available in USA)	**£1500-2500**
PS 1	1959	**Private Owner Set**	Contains 19 MGA, 43 Hillman Minx, 45 Vauxhall Victor, A-3 Garage	**£150-175**
PS 2	1959	**Transporter and 4 Cars Set**	Contains 30 Ford, 31 Ford Station Wagon, 33 Ford Zodiac, 36 Austin A50, and an A-2 Transporter	**£150-175**
PS 3	1959	**Transporter and 6 Cars Set**	Contains 22 Vauxhall Cresta, 32 Jaguar XK, 33 Ford Zodiac, 43 Hillman Minx, 44 Rolls-Royce Silver Cloud, 45 Vauxhall Victor and an A-2 Transporter	**£250-350**
PS 4	1959	**Commercial Vehicle Set**	Contains No.5 Bus, 11 Petrol Tanker, 21 Long Distance Coach, 25 'Dunlop' Van, 35 Horse Box, 40 Bedford Tipper, 47 'Brooke Bond' Van and 60 Morris Pickup	**£400-450**
PS 5	1959	**Army Personnel Carrier Set**	Contains M3 Personnel Carrier, 54 Saracen, 55 DUKW, 61 Ferret, 62 General Service Lorry, 63 Ambulance, M-3 Tank Transporter	**£200-250**

Gift Sets

The packaging for the first UK issued sets consisted of a frail blue box with a yellow lid panel on which were displayed (in red) the models making up the set. Sets in similar packaging were issued for the German market. Note however that contents may vary within the same type of box (the G4 Farm set listed below is an example). Please advise us of any other different model combinations you may have.

Ref	Year(s)	Set name	Contents, features, details	Market Price Range
	c1960	**Garage Set 'C'**	'MATCHBOX' Sales and Service Station (Red/Yellow), Roadway Layout, Accessories Pack No.1 (Esso petrol pumps), Accessory Pack No.2 (Car Transporter, Blue/Red lettering), Major Pack No.6 ('Pickfords' Transporter), 1-75 series models (5c, 29b, 31b, 42a, 45a, 46b, 57b, 74a). All models are individually boxed and housed in larger display box printed with 'MATCHBOX SERIES' and pictures of the garage and models, etc.	**£750-1000**
G 1	1960-61	**Commercial Motor Set**	Contains: 5b 'Players Please', 20a, 37a (even load), 47a, 51a, 59a, 60a and 69a. (All models in G 1 had Grey plastic wheels).	**£300-400**
G 1	1962-63	**Commercial Vehicle Set**	Contains 5c 'Visco-Static', 10c, 12b, 13c, 14c, 21c, 46b, 74a.	**£300-400**
G 1	1965	**Motorway Set**	Contains 6, 10, 13, 33, 34, 38, 48, 55, 71 and R-1 layout	**£200-250**
G 1	1967	**Service Station Set**	A1 Service Station, 31c or 32c, 13d and 64b in pictorial display case.	**£125-150**
G 2	1960-61	**Car Transporter Set**	A-2 Transporter (metal wheels) and cars 22b, 25b, 33b, 39a, 57b and 75a	**£500-700**
G 2	1960-61	2nd issue:	A-2 Transporter (with Grey plastic wheels to tractor and Black plastic wheels to trailer), plus cars 7b, 22b, 25c, 27c, 57b and 75a	**£500-600**
G 2	1962-63	**Car Transporter Set**	Contains models 25b, 30b, 31b, 39b, 48b, 65b and Accessory Pack No.2.	**£700-900**
G 2	1965	**Car Transporter Set**	Contains 22c, 28c, 36c, 75b and Major Pack 8b.	**£400-500**
G 2	1967	**Transporter Set**	Contains M86 Transporter, 14d, 24c, 31c and 53c.	**£100-125**
G 3	1960-61	**Building Constructors Set**	Contains 2, 6, 15, 16, 18, 24, 28 and M-1	**£150-175**
G 3	1962-63	**Constructional Plant Set**	Contains 2, 6, 15, 16, 18, 24, 28 and M-1	**£200-250**
G 3	1963-64	**Farm and Agricultural Set**	Contains K3, K11, M5 and M7	**£100-140**
G 3	1965	**Vacation Set**	Contains 12c, 23c, 27d, 42b, 45b, 56b, 68b, and Sports Boat on Trailer	**£200-300**
G 3	1968	**Farm Set**	Contains 12c, 37d, 40c, 43c, 65c, 72b, 47c and 39c	**£75-95**
G 4	1960-61	**Farm Set** (1st issue)	M-7 Cattle Truck (GPW), 12b Land Rover (BPW), 23b Berkeley Caravan (Lime Green, BPW), 31b Ford (Met.Green/Pink/Maroon, SPW), 35a Horse Box (MW), 50a Commer (Lt.Brown, SPW), 72a Fordson (Orange rear hubs, GPW)	**£200-250**
		(2nd issue)	M-7 Cattle Truck (GPW), 12b Land Rover (BPW), 23c Bluebird Dauphine Caravan (Metallic Mauve, SPW), 31b Ford (Yellow, Maroon base, clear windows, SPW), 35a Horse Box (SPW), 50a Commer (SPW), 72a Fordson (Orange rear hubs, GPW)	**£175-225**
G 4	1963	**Agricultural Implements Set**	Contains 12, 23, 31, 35, 50, 72 and M-7	**£175-225**
G 4	1963	**Grand Prix Set**	Contains 13c, 14b, 19c, 41b, 47b, 52a, 32b, 73b and Major Pack No.1, R-4 Racetrack, instructions	**£400-500**
G 4	1965	**Racetrack Set**	13d, 19d Green, 19d Orange, 41c White, 41c Yellow, 52b Blue, 52b Red, 54b, Major Pack M-6 29c	**£200-250**
G 4	1968	**Race 'n' Rally Set**	19d Orange, 19d Green, 52b Blue, 52b Red, 29d, 3c, 41c, 67b, 25d, 8e	**£125-150**
G 5	1960-61	**Military Vehicles**	Contains 54, 62, 63, 64, 67, 68 and M-3	**£150-200**
G 5	1963	**Army Gift Set**	Contains 54a, 62a, 63a, 67a, 68a, 64a and Major Pack No.3	**£150-200**
G 5	1965	**Army Gift Set**	Contains 12, 49, 54, 61, 64, 67 and M-3 (picture box)	**£140-160**
G 5	1965	**Fire Station Set**	Contains Fire Station, 29c, 54b and 59c.	**£150-200**
G 6	1965	**Commercial Trucks Set**	Contains 6, 15, 16, 17, 26, 30, 58 and 62	**£100-150**
G 6	1966	**Truck Set**	Contains 16c, 17d, 25c, 26b, 30c, 69b, 70b, 71b	**£100-150**
G 9	1963	**Major Series Set**	Contains Major Packs 1, 2, 4 and 6	**£250-350**
G 9	1965	**Service Station Set**	Contains 13, 33, 71, A-1, MG-1	**£100-125**
G 10	1963	**Service Station Set**	Contains Service Station, 13c, 25b, 31b, and Accessory Pack No.1	**£100-125**
G 10	1965	**Fire Station Set**	Contains MF-1, 14, 59, 2 of No.9	**£100-125**
?	?	**Matchbox Traffic Game**	Contains two cars (No.45 Ford Corsair and No.56 Fiat 1500) plus game board, etc.	**£150-175**
?	?	**'GAF' Racing Car Game**	Belgian game set contains four 24d 'TEAM MATCHBOX' racing cars including the rare Metallic Blue and Yellow variants. Set issued by 'GAF', not by Matchbox.	**£300-400**

Following successful sales of Major Models, Lesney Products decided to further develop the range by introducing a larger scale toy. The name chosen was 'King-Size'. In 1966 the popular Major Models were discontinued in name but were themselves built into the King-Size range.

K1-1	60	**Hydraulic Shovel**	
		All Yellow body, Grey plastic wheels, 'WEATHERILL' ...**£25-30**	
K1-2	63	**Tipper Truck**	
		Red cab and chassis, Orange tipper, 'HOVERINGHAM' ..**£30-35**	
	NB	'HOVERINGHAM GRAVELS LTD' issued models in their own outer box to their customers.	
K1-3	70	**'O & K' Excavator**	
		Red body, Silver shovel, tinted windows, BPT..................**£20-25**	
K2-1	60	**Dumper Truck**	
		Red body, 'MUIR HILL 14B', Black or Green MW........**£25-30**	
K2-2	64	**Dumper Truck**	
		Yellow body, 'KW DART' logo, 6 Red wheels, BPT........**£25-30**	
K2-3	68	**Scammell Wreck Truck**	
		White body, Red jib and wheels, Grey hook, 'ESSO' **£30-35**	
		Gold body version...**£30-35**	
K3-1	60	**Caterpillar Bulldozer**	
		Yellow body, Red engine, Grey metal rollers....................**£25-30**	
		As previous model but with Red metal rollers..................**£25-30**	
		As previous model but with Yellow metal rollers.............**£25-30**	
K3-2	65	**'HATRA' Tractor Shovel** Orange body, Red wheels......**£25-30**	
K3-3	70	**'MASSEY FERGUSON' Tractor and Trailer**	
		Red body, Yellow trim **£25-30**	
K4-1	60	**'McCORMICK INTERNATIONAL' Tractor**	
		Red body, Green wheels **£30-35**	
		As previous model with Orange or Red wheel hubs..........**£25-30**	
K4-2	67	**GMC Tractor and Hoppers**	
		Dark Red cab, 2 Silver hoppers, 'FREUHOF' logo............**£50-55**	
K4-3	69	**Leyland Tipper**	
		Dark Red cab and chassis, Silver tipper 'W. WATES'........**£25-30**	
		As previous model but with Yellow/Green body colours**£500-600**	
		With Red cab and chassis, Green tipper............................**£25-30**	
		With Blue cab and chassis, Silver tipper 'Miner' label **£25-30**	
		With Silver tipper and 'LE TRANSPORT' logo.................**£30-35**	
K5-1	61	**Tipper Truck**	
		Yellow body and tipper, Red wheels, 'FODEN' logo........**£25-30**	
K5-2	67	**Racing Car Transporter**	
		Green body, Silver drop down rear door, Red wheels.......**£35-40**	
K5-3	70	**Tractor and Trailer**	
		Yellow body, Red chassis, 'MUIR HILL' **£25-30**	
K6-1	61	**Earth Scraper**	
		Orange body, Red engine, 'ALLIS CHALMERS'..............**£30-35**	
K6-2	67	**Mercedes Ambulance**	
		White body, Red badge, ambulance-man, stretcher **£25-30**	
K7-1	61	**Rear Dumper**	
		Yellow body, Red engine, 'CURTISS-WRIGHT'..............**£25-30**	
K7-2	67	**Refuse Truck**	
		Red body and wheels 'CLEANSING DEPARTMENT' **£25-30**	
		Blue body version..**£25-30**	

K8-1	62	**Prime Mover and Transporter with Crawler Tractor**	
		Orange bodies, Yellow tractor, 'LAING', unpainted or Red plastic wheels, Green tracks....................................**£75-80**	
K8-2	67	**Guy Warrior Transporter** 'FARNBOROUGH - MEASHAM'	
		Blue cab, Yellow car transporter **£50-60**	
		Orange cab, Orange or Yellow transporter **£50-60**	
K8-3	70	**'CATERPILLAR TRAXCAVATOR'**	
		Yellow body and shovel, Blue or White driver.................**£30-35**	
K9-1		**'AVELING BARFORD' Diesel Road Roller**	
		Green body, Red wheels and driver **£25-30**	
K9-2	67	**'CLAAS' Combine Harvester**	
		Red body, Yellow blades and wheels, ...**£25-30**	
		Green body, Red blades and wheels.................................**£25-30**	
K10-1	63	**'AVELING BARFORD' Tractor Shovel**	
		Blue-Green body, Red seat and wheels **£30-35**	
K10-2	66	**Pipe Truck**. Yellow body, Red wheels, 6 Grey pipes........**£30-35**	
		('Super-Kings' issue) Purple body, Grey or Yellow pipes..**£25-30**	
K11-1	63	**'FORDSON SUPER MAJOR' Tractor and Trailer**	
		Blue tractor, Grey/Blue trailer **£35-45**	
K11-2	69	**DAF Car Transporter** Yellow body, Yellow/Red decks..**£25-30**	
		Metallic Blue body, Gold trailer decks.............................**£25-30**	
K12-1	63	**Breakdown Truck** 'MATCHBOX SERVICE STATION',	
		Green body, Yellow jib...**£50-60**	
K12-2	69	**Scammell Crane Truck**	
		Yellow body and chassis, 'LAING' on crane.....................**£30-35**	
K13-1	63	**Concrete Truck**	
		Orange body and barrel, 'READYMIX' logo.....................**£35-45**	
		As previous model but with 'RMC' logo.........................**£35-45**	
K14-1	64	**Jumbo Crane**	
		Yellow body and crane, 'TAYLOR JUMBO CRANE'.......**£30-35**	
K15-1	64	**Merryweather Fire Engine**	
		Red body, Silver ladder, 'KENT FIRE BRIGADE'..........**£40-45**	
K16-1	66	**Tractor and Twin Tippers**	
		Green cab, Yellow tippers, 'DODGE TRUCKS' in Red....**£45-55**	
		Yellow cab, Blue tippers same logo ....NGPP	
K17-1	67	**Low Loader and Bulldozer**	
		Green cab and loader, Red/Yellow Bulldozer **£35-45**	
K18-1	66	**Articulated Horse Box** 'ASCOT STABLES',	
		Red cab, Brown box, 4 White horses.................................**£35-45**	
K19-1	67	**Scammell Tipper** Red body, Yellow tipper, Silver trim ...**£25-30**	
K20-1	68	**Tractor Transporter (Ford)**	
		Red body, Yellow rack, 3 Blue/Yellow tractors (MB39c)...**£40-50**	
		As previous model but with Orange tractors.................**£100-150**	
K21-1	69	**Mercury Cougar** Gold body, Cream or Red seats...........**£25-30**	
K22-1	69	**Dodge Charger** Blue body, Yellow or Pale Blue seats **£25-30**	
K23-1	69	**Mercury 'POLICE' Car**	
		White body with 'HIGHWAY PATROL' logo **£25-30**	
K24-1	69	**Lamborghini Miura** Red body, Cream seats....................**£25-30**	

'Battle-Kings' issued 1974

Models packed in 'window' boxes. Each has a 'military' theme and includes three plastic soldiers. Expect to pay **less than £15** for any of these items.

K101	**Sherman Tank**	K111	**Missile Launcher**
K102	**M48 AS Tank**	K112	**DAF Ambulance**
K103	**Chieftain Tank** ...	K113	**Crane Truck** ......
K104	**King Tiger Tank**.	K114	**Army Aircraft**
K105	**Hover Raider**......		**Transporter** ....
K106	**Tank Transporter**	K115	**Petrol Tanker** ....
K107	**155mm Gun**........	K116	**Troop Carrier**
K108	**Half Track**..........		**and Howitzer** .....
K109	**Sheridan Tank**....	K117	**Rocket Launcher**
K110	**Recovery Vehicle**	K118	**Army Helicopter**

'Sea-Kings' issued 1976

These models were packed in 'window' boxes. Expect a Market Price of **less than £12** for any of these 'Sea-Kings'.

K301	**Frigate 'F109'**	
K302	**Corvette 'C70'**	
K303	**Battleship '110'**	
K304	**Aircraft Carrier with 4 aircraft '36'**	
K305	**Submarine Chaser 'C17'**	
K306	**Convoy Escort 'F101'**	
K307	**Helicopter Carrier with 2 Helicopters** .	
K308	**Guided Missile Destroyer**	
K309	**Submarine '117'**	
K310	**Anti Aircraft Carrier**	

'Big MX' models 1972 - 1974

Special packaging contained models and accessories powered by an 'Activator Gun' which plugged into them and operated the mechanisms.

MX1	**Incinerator Site** + K7 Refuse Truck	**£40-50**
BM2	**Mechanised Tractor Plant** and Winch Transporter (K20-1 Ford),	
	with Blue/Yellow MB39c Tractors ..	**£40-50**
	with Orange MB39c Tractors	**£100-150**
BM3	**Mechanised** (K12 Scammell) **Crane Truck** and Building Site	**£50-70**
BM4	**Mechanised Coal Delivery Hopper** and (K4 Leyland) Tipper	**£30-40**
BM5	**Mechanised Quarry Site** and (K8, silver/red) Traxcavator.............	**£30-40**
BM6	**Fire Rescue Scene** with mechanised (K15 Merryweather) Fire Engine plus 4 figures and scenery	**£75-100**

'King-Size' Gift Sets

---	1963	**King-Size Set** ....Contains K1-1, K2-1, K3-1, K5-1, K6-1..		**£60-65**
---	1965	**Construction Set** ....Contains K16-1, K7-1, K10-1, K13-1, K14-1..		**£75-80**
---	1966	**King-Size Set** ....Contains K16-1, K11-1, K12-1, K15-1..		**£40-45**

After 1970 the 'King Size' range developed into the larger 'Super-Kings' Series. They were fitted with extra wide speed slick tyres to give them extra power, extra speed.

During the period 1971-79 certain issues were sold as 'SPEED KINGS' and retailed in different coloured packaging. These have been identified in the listings by the abbreviation (**SPK**). Individual model variations have been identified by the listing of either its colour, advertisement or logo.

Market Price Range. In general 'Super-Kings' are not very collectable and most models may be purchased for under £25. We regret we are unable to provide more specific information on the individual model prices.

The Super-Kings listings represent the best if somewhat limited information that we have available. Further information on the rare issues and price levels would be welcomed.

K2	77	'24 HOUR' Car Recovery Vehicle.........
K?	9?	Mod Tractor and Trailer........................
K3	80	Grain Transporter 'KELLOGGS' ....
K4	74	Big Tipper ....
K5	72	Muir Hill Tractor and Trailer ....
K6	71	Cement Mixer.......................................
K6	74	Motor Cycle Transporter 'HONDA' ......
K7	73	'TEAM MATCHBOX' Transporter.........
K8	81	Animal Transporter 'ANITRAN' ....
K9	73	Fire Tender 'DENVER' ....
K10	76	'AUTO TRANSPORT' Transporter ....
K10	82	Bedford 'COURIER' Transporter ....
K11	76	'SHELL RECOVERY' Truck ....

K11 81 Dodge Van
'MICHELIN' ....
'SUCHARD EXPRESS' ....
'FRANKFURTER ALLGEMAINE' ....
'FRANCESOIR' ....

K12	75	Hercules 'LAING' Crane.......................
K13	71	DAF Building Transporter ....
K13	76	Aircraft Transporter.............................
K14	71	Scammell Freight Liner 'LEP' ....
K14	77	'SHELL' Breakdown Truck...................
K15	71	Merryweather 'KENT' Fire Engine........

K15 73 Londoner Bus issues. Main advert:
'HARRODS - ENTER A DIFFERENT
WORLD' ....
'CARNABY STREET' ....
'SILVER JUBILEE', ...
'HARRODS - MORE THAN MONEY'...
'LONDON DUNGEON' ....
'HAMLEYS - FINEST TOY SHOP' ....
'ROYAL WEDDING 1981' ....
'LONDON WIDE TOUR' ....
'ARABIC SCRIPT' (not issued)
'TELEGRAPH & ARGUS' ....
'MACLEANS TOOTHPASTE'................
'HERITAGE OF ENGLAND' ....
'BUTTERKIST' ....
'TOURIST LONDON' ....
'FIRESTONE' ....
'CHESTERFIELD 1984' ....
'LONDON PLANETARIUM' ....
'PETTICOAT LANE'................................
'NESTLES MILKY BAR' ....

K15 German issues:
 i) 'BERLIN IST EINE REISE WERT' -
  'BERLIN IS WORTH A TRIP' ....
 ii) '1237 BESUCHEN SIE BERLIN
  HAMPSTADT DER DDR 1987' -
  'BERLIN CAPITAL OF
  THE GDR - 750 YEARS (1987)'...........

K16 74 Ford LTS Tanker,
'TEXACO' ....
'CHEMCO' ....
'BP' ....
'LEP' ....
'ARAL' ....
'SHELL' ....
'EXXON' ....
'TOTAL' ....
'U.S. MATCHBOX CLUB' (NGPP).......
'QUAKER STATE' ....
'Battle Kings' issue ....
NB Some of these issues are scarce.

K17		**Container Trucks**
		'DBP' ....
		'PENGUIN' ....
		'7 UP' ....
		'GENTRANSCO' ....
K18	74	**Tipper Truck**
		'TARMAC' ....
		'US STEEL' ....
		'HOCH & TIEF' ....
K19	79	**Security Truck**
		'GROUP 4' ....
		'FORT KNOX' ....
K20	73	Cargo Hauler ....
	79	Peterbilt 'HEAVY DUTY' Wrecker ....
K21	71	Cougar Dragster (SPK) ....
	74	Tractor Transporter................................
	79	**Ford Transcontinental Truck**
		'CONTINENTAL' ....
		'POLARA' ....
		'SUNKIST' ....
K22	71	Dodge Dragster (SPK) ....
	74	**Hovercraft**
		'SEASPEED' ....
		'HOVERLLOYD' ....
K23	71	Mercury 'POLICE' Car (SPK) ....
	74	Low Loader 'HOCH & TIEF' ....
K24	71	Lamborghini Muira,
		Red or Blue/Yellow ....
	77	**Scammel Truck**
		'LONDON TO GENEVA' ....
		'MICHELIN' ....
		'GENTRANSCO' ....
		'BAUKNECHT' ....
K25	77	Powerboat and Trailer ....
		'SEABURST' ....
		'CHRYSLER' ....
	78	Digger and Plough, 'MUIRHILL'..........
K26	71	Mercedes Ambulance (SPK).................
K26	78	**Bedford Cement Truck**
		'McALPINE' ....
		'HOCH & TIEF' ....
K27	71	Camping Cruiser ....
	78	**Powerboat Transporter**
		'EMBASSY' ....
		'MISS SOLO' ....
K28	71	Drag Pack (SPK)....................................
	78	**Bedford Skip Truck**
		'HOCH & TIEF' ....
		'HALES' ....
K29	71	Muira 'SEABURST' Set (SPK) ....
	77	**Ford Delivery Van**
		'U-HAUL' ....
		'AVIS' ....
		'MR SOFTY' ....
		'BASSETTS' ....
		'TAA'...

K30	72	Mercedes C111, Gold, Lime or Blue .....
	78	Unimog/Compressor............................
K31	72	Bertone Runabout (SPK) ....
K31	78	**Peterbilt Refrigeration Truck**
		'CHRISTIAN SALVESON' ....
		'PEPSI'..
		'IGLOO' ....
		'GERVAIS GLACE' ....
		'DR KOCH'S TRINK' ....
		'DURA PENTA' (South African) ....
		'BURGER KING' ....
K32		No details of models issued ....
K33	78	Cargo Hauler ....
K34	72	Thunderclap (SPK) ....
	79	Pallet Truck ....
K35	72	Lightning (SPK) ....
	79	Massey Ferguson Tractor and Trailer .....
K36	72	Bandolero (SPK) ....
	78	'LAING' Transporter ....
K37	73	Sandcat, Orange or Gold (SPK) ....
	79	Leyland Tipper 'LAING' ....
K38	74	Gus's Gulpher (SPK) ....
	80	Dodge 'AMBULANCE' ....
K39	73	'MILLIGANS MILL' ....
	80	ERF Fire Engine (County) ....
K40	73	Blaze Trailer 'FIRE CHIEF' (SPK).......
	80	Ford Drinks Truck 'PEPSI' ....
K41	73	Fuzz Buggy 'POLICE' (SPK)................
	78	Brabham F1 (SPK).................................
	81	JCB Excavator.......................................
K42	73	Nissan 270X (SPK) ....
	79	Traxcavator Road Ripper ....
K43	73	'CAMBUSTER' (SPK) ....
	80/3	Mercedes Log Transporter ....
K44	73	'BAZOOKA' ....
	78	Surtees F1 ....
	81/3	Bridge Transporter ....
K45	73/8	Marauder (SPK) ....
K46	74	Racing Car pack with K34 and K35 ......
K47	73	Easy Rider Tricycle (SPK).....................
K48	74/8	Mercedes 350 SLC,
		Bronze or White (SPK) ....
K49	73	Ambulance (SPK) ....
	74	'MALTESER' Truck ....
K50	74	Street Rod (SPK) ....
K51	73	Barracuda, Blue or White (SPK) ....
K52	73/8	Datsun Rally Car (SPK).........................
		Yellow, Silver or Green 'CIBIE' ....
K53	76	Hot Fire Engine (SPK) ....
K54	76	AMX Javelin (SPK) ....
K55	76/8	Corvette 'CAPER CART' (SPK)
		Blue or Red ....
K56	76	Maserati Bora, Silver or Blue (SPK) .....
K57	76	Javelin Drag Racing Set,
		K38 & K39 (SPK).................................
K58	76/8	Corvette Power Boat Set,
		Blue or Red, K45 etc. (SPK) ....
K59	76	Ford Capri MkII,
		White or Beige (SPK) ....
K60	76/8	Ford Mustang,
		Metallic Turquoise or White (SPK)......
K61	76	Mercedes 'POLICE' Car (SPK).............
	78	Mercedes 'POLIZEI' Car (SPK) ....
K62	77	Doctors Car (SPK) ....
K63	77	Mercedes 'Binz'
		'AMBULANCE' (SPK)...........................

K64	78	*'FIRE CONTROL'* Range Rover (SPK)	K95	82	**Audi Quattro**	K130	87	*'PLANT HIRE'* Transporter ....
K65	78	Plymouth Mountain Rescue			*'H. MIKKOLA'*	K131	87	*'TEXACO'* Petrol Tanker ....
		i) *'EMERGENCY RESUCE'*			*'PACE'*	K132	87	*'FIRE'* Engine ....
		ii) *'BERGRETTUNG WACHT'*			*'PIRELLI'*	K133	87/89	*'REFUSE CITY'* Track, Red or White .
K66	79	Jaguar XJ12 *'POLICE'* Set	K96	83	Volvo *'AMBULANCE'*	K134	87	*'FIRE'* Spotters Plane Transporter.........
K67	78	Dodge Monaco (SPK)	K97	83	*'POLICE'* Range Rover	K135	87	Garage Transporter *'TEXACO'* ....
		i) *'FIRE CHIEF'*	K98	83	*'PORSCHE 944'*	K136	87	*'FERRARI'* Racing Car Transporter ......
		ii) *'HACKENSACK'*	K99	79/83	*'POLIZEI'* Range Rover	K139	87	*'WIMPEY'* Tipper Truck ....
K68	78	Dodge Monaco and Trailer (SPK)	K100	83	Ford Sierra 4i			
K69	78	Jaguar XJ12 and Caravan (SPK),				K140	87	Car *'RECOVERY'* Vehicle ....
		Blue and Cream, or Red and White	K101–K115		**Battle Kings** – see separate listing.	K141	87	Skip Truck *'ECD'* ....
	80	Dodge Monaco and Caravan (SPK).......				K142	87	BMW *'POLIZEI'* Car ....
			K101	83	Racing Porsche...................................		90	BMW *'POLICE'* Car ....
K70	79	Porsche Turbo, Green or Black.............	K102	83	Race Support Set.................................		90	BMW *'PACE'* Car ....
K71	79	Porsche *'POLIZEI'* Set	K103	83	Peterbilt Tanker Truck *'COMET'*	K143	87	*'EMERGENCY'* Van ....
K72	79	Brabham F1, Red or Green	K104	83	*Rancho Rescue Set 'COASTGUARD'* ..	K144	87/90	Land Rover,
K73	79	Surtees F1, White or Tan	K105	83/5	Peterbilt Tipper			*'FRANKFURT'*...................................
K74	79	Volvo Estate......................................			*'TAYLOR WOODROW'*,			*'ROAD MAINTENANCE'* ....
					White or Yellow	K145	88	*'IVECO'* Tipper/Tractor ....
K75	79	**Airport *'FIRE'* Rescue**	K106	83	Aircraft Transporter *'ACES'*...............	K146	88	Jaguar XJ6 ....
		'AIRPORT FIRE TENDER'	K107	83	*'SPEARHEADS'* Launch Transporter	K147	88	BMW 750iL ....
		'FLUGHAFEN-FEURWEHR'	K108	83	Digger/Plough Transporter...................	K148	88	Crane Truck *'PEX'* ....
		'SECURITE AEROPORT'	K109	83	*'SHELL'* Petrol Tanker........................	K149	88	Ferrari Testarossa ....
K76	79	Volvo Rally Set *'CIBIE'*						
K77	79	**Rescue Vehicle**	K110	84	Fire Engine	K150	89	Leyland Truck ....
		'STRASSEN SERVICE'	K111	85	Peterbilt Refuse Truck	K151	88	Skip Truck ....
		'SECOURS ROUTIER'	K112	85	Peterbilt *'FIRE'* Spotter	K152	88	Audi Quattro Saloon ....
		'HIGHWAY RESCUE'...........................	K113	85	Garage Transporter	K153	88	Jaguar XJ6 *'POLICE'* ....
			K114	85	Mobile Crane.....................................	K154	88	BMW 750iL *'POLIZEI'* ....
K78	79/83	**US Police Car**	K115	85	Mercedes-Benz 190E 2.3/16V	K155	88	*'FERRARI'* Testarossa Rally Car...........
		'POLICE', *'POLIZEI'* or		89	Mercedes-Benz Rally *'FUJI'*	K156	88	Porsche 911 Rally...............................
		'CITY POLICE'...................................	K116	85	Racing Car Transporter	K157	88	Porsche 944 Rally ....
K79	79	US Taxi, *'75c FIRST ¼ MILE'*	K117	85	Bulldozer Transport,	K158	88	Sierra XR4i Pace Car ....
K80	80	Dodge Custom Van			*'TAYLOR WOODROW'*.........................	K159	88	*'PORSCHE'* Racing Car Transporter ....
K81	81	*'SUZUKI'* Motor Cycle.......................	K118	85	Road Set K30 and K21			
K82	81	*'BMW'* Motor Cycle...........................	K119	85	*'FIRE'* Set with K110	K160	88	*'MATCHBOX'* Racing Car Transporter
K83	81	*'HARLEY DAVIDSON'*				K161	92	Rolls Royce Silver Spirit ....
		'POLICE' Motor Cycle.......................	K120	86	Bedford Car Transporter	K162	92	**Ford Sierra Cosworth,**
K84	81	Peugeot 305 *'EXPO'* or *'ELF'* logos.....	K121	86	Peterbilt Rescue Truck			*'TEXACO'* ....
K85	88	Audi Quattro Rally..............................	K122	87	DAF Road Train *'EUROTRANS'*...........			*'GEMINI'* ....
K86	82	VW Gold *'SHELL'*	K123	87	Leyland Cement Truck.........................	K163	90	*'SCHMIDT'* Snow Plough ....
K87	82	*'MF595'* Tractor and Rake...................	K124	87	Mercedes *'7 UP'* Truck	K164	91	*'SAFARI'* Range Rover ....
K88	81	**Security Van** (Money Box)	K126	87	DAF Helicopter *'RN'* Transporter.........	K165	90	*'POLICE'* Range Rover ....
		'VOLKSBANK'				K166	92	Mercedes 190E *'TAXI'* ....
		'SAVE YOUR MONEY'	K127	87	**Peterbilt Tanker,**	K167	91	Ford Transit *'SURF 'N' SUN'* ....
K89	81	Forestry Set *'KIELDER'*			*'TOTAL'*...	K168	92	Porsche 911 *'CARRERA 4'* ....
K90	82	Matro Rancho *'TRANSGLOBE'*			*'GETTY'* (US)	K171	91	Toyota 'Hi Lux' Pick Up ....
K91	82	Motor Cycle Racing Set	K128	87	DAF Aircraft Transporter.....................	K172	92	Mercedes-Benz 560SL ....
K92	82	Ford Helicopter Transporter.................	K129	87	**Powerlaunch Transporter,**	K173	92	Lamborghini *'DIABLO'* ....
K93	82	Road Lamp Maintenance Set			*'SPEARHEAD'*....................................	K175	92	*'SUZUKI'* Santana.............................
					'COASTGUARD'			

The 'Convoy' model range was launched in 1982 and early issues were made in England before manufacture was transferred to Macau. Many variations exist particularly in the USA where they have been used as promotionals linked to NASCAR truck racing. For a listing of the many variations available contact:
Carr Collectables, Central House, High Street, Ongar, Essex, CM5 9AA. Tel: (01277-366144).

Convoy models issued up to 1988:

CY1	Kenworth Boat Transporter	CY13	Peterbilt Fire Engine............................	CY28	Mack Container Truck...........................
CY2	Kenworth Rocket Transporter	CY14	Kenworth Boat Transporter	CY29	Mack Aircraft Transporter.....................
CY3	Peterbilt Container Truck		(MB 45e)	CY35	Mack Tanker.......................................
CY4	Kenworth Boat Transporter	CY15	Peterbilt Tracking Vehicle	CY36	Kenworth Box Car................................
	(MB 41f)	CY16	Scania Box Truck	CY104	Kenworth Aerodyne Cab and
CY5	Peterbilt Covered Truck.......................	CY17	Scania Petrol Tanker		Box Car Trailer ....
CY6	Kenworth Horse Box	CY18	Scania Container Truck	CY105	Kenworth Aerodyne Tanker ....
CY7	Peterbilt Petrol Tanker	CY19	Peterbilt Box Car	CY106	Peterbilt Tipper Truck..........................
CY8	Kenworth Box Truck (MB 45e)	CY20a	Scania Tipper	CY107	Mack CH-600 Box Car..........................
CY9	Kenworth Box Truck (MB 41f).............	CY20b	Kenworth Tipper	CY109	Ford Aeromax Box Car ....
CY10	Kenworth Racing Transporter	CY21	DAF Aircraft Transporter......................	CY110	Kenworth Box Car................................
	(MB 66f)	CY22	DAF Power Boat Transporter.................	CY201	Fire Rescue Set ....
CY11	Kenworth Helicopter Transporter	CY23	Scania Covered Truck	CY202	Police Set ....
	(MB 75e)	CY24	DAF Box Car	CY203	Construction Set ....
CY12	Kenworth Aircraft Transporter.............	CY25	DAF Box Truck	CY204	NASA Set ....
		CY26	DAF Container Truck		
		CY27	Mack Box Truck		

Matchbox Catalogues

1957 **Folded Leaflet** ...... Yellow cover has Blue edging and depicts No.1 Diesel Roller. Colour pictures of nos. 1 - 42 of '1-75'series........................**£50-75**

1957 **Folded Leaflet** ...... Blue/Yellow cover featuring MOY No.1 Allchin 7hp Traction Engine 1st series box. Contents list first nine Yesteryears...........**£75-100**

1958 **16-page catalogue** .Cover shows Rolls-Royce (44), emerging from box. Models 1 - 60 in colour inside, early 'Major Packs' and Accessory Packs ..**£50-75**

Reprints ....Catalogue reprinted for DTE in 1982 ....**£15-20**

1959 **Leaflet** ....'Everyone buys MATCHBOX TOYS by LESNEY'. Blue with line drawings. Gives details of Presentation and Gift Sets **£200-300**

1959 **Folded Leaflet** ...... Features first 14 Yesteryears in colour......**£75-100**

1959 **16-page catalogue** .Same cover as 1958 catalogue with '1959 Edition'. Lists 1-75's, Major Packs and accessories. Colour pictures **£50-75**

1959 **24-page catalogue** .'UK' and '2d' on cover with MOY No.9, 1-75 series, No.'43', and Accessory No.'2'. Colour contents show MB 1 - 72 and MOY 1 - 14 plus Accessories and Major Packs. ..**£50-75**

1960 **32-page catalogue** .'UK' and '3d' on cover featuring logo *'ALL THE MATCHBOX POCKET TOYS BY LESNEY'* plus semi-circle picture of MOY and 1-75's. Contents illustrate all ranges **£50-75**

1961 **32-page catalogue** .'International Pocket Catalogue' on cover with picture of 1-75 model No.5 Bus. New style smaller catalogue listing all issues in colour plus International price list..............**£50-75**

1962 **20-page catalogue** .'2d', 'International Pocket Catalogue' and '1962 Edition' on cover. All issues listed, European price list included **£35-45**

1963 **20-page catalogue** .No.53 Mercedes-Benz printed on cover with '2d' and '1963 Edition'. Contents include good Gift Set pictures and listings.**£10-14**

1964 **32-page catalogue** .'3d' on cover depicting Blue Mk.10 Jaguar (No.28). '1964 Matchbox Prices' on back cover. Contents include superb Gift Set pictures and listings **£8-11**

1965 **32-page catalogue** .Cover features Motor Racing Cars. '1965 Matchbox Prices' on back cover. Excellent full colour Gift Set pictures. (Price 3d)........**£8-11**

1966 **40-page catalogue** .London scene and 'Price 3d' on cover. Excellent pictures of mid-sixties Gift Sets plus history of Matchbox...........................**£8-11**

1967 **40-page catalogue** .Cover shows flags and 1-75 issues, 'Price 3d'. Contents list and depict Veteran Car Gifts. ...**£8-11**

1968 **40-page catalogue** .1968 car picture and 'Price 3d' on cover. Includes details of manufacturing processes.**£8-11**

1969 **48-page catalogue** .Cover features Motorway scene. Contents include detailed history of the real cars making up the MOY range **£8-11**

2nd edition: ....The 2nd edition of the 1969 catalogue includes first reference to 'Superfast' issues.**£8-11**

1970 **64-page catalogue** .Only drawings of models (no photographs) throughout. Superfast track featured. '6d', 'MATCHBOX SUPERFAST' and a collage of models on cover......................**£5-8**

1971 **64-page catalogue** .'24p' on Blue/Red cover with scorpion design. 'Speed Kings' listed plus pictures of first Superfast Gift Sets...............................**£5-8**

1972 **72-page catalogue** .Yellow 'MATCHBOX' and '3p' on cover. Contents feature launch of 'Scream'n Demon' bikes and excellent Gift Set pictures...............**£5-8**

1973 **80-page catalogue** .'5p' and '1973' on cover of the largest Matchbox catalogue produced. Contents include good 'Super Kings' and Aircraft Kit listing ...**£5-8**

1974 **64-page catalogue** .'2p' and '1974' on cover. Includes first 'SKYBUSTERS' listing...............................**£5-8**

1975 **64-page catalogue** .'2p' and '1975' on cover. Contents feature 'Rolamatics' and 'Battle Kings'......................**£5-8**

1976 **64-page catalogue** .'1976' on cover. Contents feature 'Sea Kings' plus 'Baby Dolls' and 'Disco Girl Dolls' **£5-8**

1977 **80-page catalogue** .'1977' on cover. Contents list the 'Two Pack' (TP) range of 1-75's. Good Gift Set pictures and listings of 1-75's **£5-8**

1978 **64-page catalogue** .'1978' on cover. Includes good 'SKYBUSTERS' and 1-75 Gift Set pictures ..**£5-8**

79-80 **80-page catalogue** .'5p' and '1979-80' on cover. The contents feature good pictures of Gift Sets G1 - G8. '900' TP series introduced **£4-6**

80-81 **80-page catalogue** .'5p' on cover. All ranges listed including 'Walt Disney' and 'Power Track' equipment .**£3-4**

81-82 **64-page catalogue** .'5p' and '1981-82' on cover. 'Adventure 2000' space models pictured. 'Playtrack', 'Popeye' and 'Streak Sets' listed...................................**£2-3**

82-83 **64-page catalogue** .'1982-83' on cover. 'Convoy' series introduced, good MOY pictures...................**£2-3**

1984 **64-page catalogue** .'1984' on cover. 'MATCHBOX SPECIALS' introduced, good Gift Set pictures, 'Burnin' Key Cars', 'Rough Riders' and 'Lock Ups' ...**£2-3**

1985 **48-page catalogue** .'1985' and 'chequered flag' design on cover. All ranges listed plus introduction of 'Trickshifters', 'Power Blasters', 'Matchmates' and 'Carry Cases'. (Printed in Italy)............**£1-2**

1986 **48-page catalogue** .'1986' on cover. 'High Riders', 'Twin-Pack', 'Action Packs' listed inside. 'Motor City'.......**£1-2**

1987 **72-page catalogue** .'1987' on cover. Listing includes 'Superfast Lasers', 'Pocket Rockets', 'Speed Riders', 'Streak Racing', 'Hot Rod Racers', 'Turbo 2', 'Turbo Specials' and 'Demolition Cars'.........**£1-2**

1988 **88-page catalogue** .'1988' on cover. Listing includes Miniatures Gift Sets pictures, 'Lasers', 'Super GT Sport' and 'Super Miniatures', 'Team Convoy', 'Road Blasters', 'Motor City' and 'Action Matchbox'. Also includes 'MICA' and 'Junior Matchbox Club' membership details **£1-2**

1989 **80-page catalogue** .'1989' on cover. Listings include 'Miniatures', 'Twin-Pack', 'Motor City' Gift Sets, 'Dinky Collection', 'World Class', 'Conn-Nect-Ables', 'Flashbacks', 'Super ColourChangers' and 'Skybusters ColourChangers'..........................**50p**

1990 **48-page catalogue** .'1990' on cover. Contents include 'Superfast Minis' listing plus normal range of products....**50p**

1991 **56-page catalogue** .'1991' on cover. Includes 'Graffic Traffic', 'Action Series', 'Lightning Series', 'Matchbox 2000' range and Matchbox 'Railways' **£1-3**

1991 **A4 leaflet** ....Full-colour sheet with MOY on one side and the 'Dinky Collection' on the other **50p**

Overseas Catalogue Editions

During the 1960s there were normally six editions of each catalogue: British, International, U.S.A., German, French and French-Canadian. The catalogues were usually of the same format as the UK editions but with the appropriate language and currency. 'INTERNATIONAL CATALOGUE' was shown on the front cover together with the edition, e.g. 'EDITION FRANCAISE', 'INTERNATIONAL' or 'U.S.A. EDITION'. The 1960 'International Pocket Catalogue' listed the national prices for every product in Australia, Austria, Belgium, Spain, Denmark, Eire, France, Germany, Great Britain, Holland, Hong Kong, Italy, Kenya and East Africa, Singapore and Malaysia, South Africa, Sweden and Switzerland. From 1972 the country-specific editions only listed the model range available in that country.

Market Price Range Prices are equivalent to those asked for UK editions.

Other Matchbox literature

'Mike and The Modelman' (1st edition 1970), was a childrens' book issued by Lesney telling the Matchbox story. A copy in perfect condition should cost between £10 - £15.

Trade Catalogues have been published for many years and occasionally become available for sale. Those before 1970 are scarce and no price information is possible at present. Those from the 1970-80 period tend to be in the region of £10-15 while post-1980 editions sell for £2-5 depending on content and condition.

The Matchbox Collectors Passport (introduced in 1987), also served as a catalogue providing a full colour listing of the MOY range available in the years in which it was current. In 1991 the Dinky Collection then available was also pictured with the Special Editions and the Passport scheme model offer.

Matchbox King Size models as advertised in the 1963 Matchbox Pocket Catalogue

An illustration from 'Matchbox News', Lesney's Press Office advertising literature, showing a 'Superfast' No.34 Formula 1 Racing Car.

Matchbox Superfast 1969 - 1983

This listing refers to Superfast models produced between 1969 and 1983. In this period, most models in the range were presented in picture boxes with some variations being sold in Twin Packs and carded 'bubble packs'. The 'cut-off point' for many collectors of these Matchbox Miniatures is 1983 when picture boxes ceased. 'See-through' window boxes sealed at both ends were then introduced.

All the models listed have 'Made in England' bases. Those with 'Macau', 'China', 'Thailand' or elsewhere are too numerous to mention and are outside the scope of this listing. There are also many wheel variations for the models listed, such as 5-spoke, 4-spoke, 'dot-dash' etc., but again, only specific wheel variations such as hub colour are noted.

Due to limitations of space, it has been necessary to introduce the use of the following abbreviations into the listing. These have been mainly restricted to indicate colour of bases and window glazing.

Windows	Base colour
AG = amber glass	BB = black base
BG = blue glass	GB = grey base
CG = clear glass	SB = silver base
GG = green glass	UB = unpainted base
OG = orange glass	WB = white base
PG = purple glass	YB = yellow base

Wheels	General
	BE = black engine
BW = black wheels	CE = chrome engine
NW = narrow wheels	LE = limited edition
UW = unpainted	SE = silver engine
WW = wide wheels	TP = Twin Pack

MB 1e   Mercedes Truck

70-70 Metallic gold body, yellow or orange canopy, green glass, narrow wheels...**£8-12**
76 Military olive drab green body, tan canopy, purple glass, WW, '4TS702K' decals (TP) **£20-25**
76-80 Same but military olive green **£6-9**
76-80 Red body, yellow or orange canopy, purple glass, wide wheels, 'Transcontinental' (TP).......................**£5-8**
80-82 Light blue body, light orange canopy, purple glass, WW, 'IMS' (TP)...........**£8-10**

MB 1f   Mod Rod

71 Yellow body, OG, SE, red wheels, UB or SB, 'spotted cat's head' label **£20-30**
71-75 Same but with black wheels..............**£7-12**
  Black wheels and silver base **£12-15**
71-75 Same but with 'Wildcat' label **£7-12**
73 Same but with 'Flower' label **£18-25**
74 Same but with 'Scorpion' label **£20-30**
78 Striped silver body, black wheels, glass and engine, UB. (U.S.A. 'Roman Numeral' LE) **£10-15**

MB 1g   Dodge Challenger

76-79 Red body, white roof, silver interior **£4-6**
76-79 Same but with white interior..............**£8-10**
76-79 Same but with red interior **£10-12**
80-82 Blue body, white roof, red interior.......**£4-6**
82-83 Orange body, blue roof, black interior, UB or SB, 'Revin Rebel' **£4-6**
82 Same but with white roof..................**£7-10**

MB 2d   Mercedes Trailer

70 Metallic gold body, yellow or orange canopy, green glass, narrow wheels...**£8-12**
76 Military olive drab green body, tan canopy, WW, '4TS702K' (TP)' **£20-25**
76-80 Same but military olive green **£6-9**
76-80 Red body, WW, yellow or orange canopy, 'Transcontinental' (TP)...........**£5-8**
80-82 Light blue body, light orange canopy, WW 'IMS' (TP)...................**£8-10**

MB 2e   Jeep Hot Rod

71-75 Pink body, white or cream seats, light or dark green base....................**£10-15**
  Same but white base........................**£40-50**
75-76 Red body, white or cream seats, white base.....................................**£10-15**
  Same but green base.......................**£40-50**

MB 2f   Rescue Hovercraft

76-78 Light or dark lime green body, fawn or light brown skirt, red or silver air intakes, amber or red windows, 'Rescue' **£4-7**
76-79 Same but metallic light or dark green body.................................**£4-6**
  Same but with red windows................**£6-8**
78 Same but black skirt....................**£6-9**
  Same but red or purple windows **£7-10**
78-80 Pale green body, black skirt, purple or AG, '2000' or 'Rescue' **£10-15**

MB 2g   S-2 Jet

81-82 Black/yellow, yellow or red glass **£3-6**
82-83 Metallic light blue and white or grey, clear glass, 'Viper' on some.................**£3-6**

MB 3c Mercedes 'Binz' Ambulance

70-73 Cream or off-white body, light blue glass, red cross on doors and bonnet, NW, opening rear door....................**£15-18**
  Same but with dark blue glass **£15-18**
77-80 Cream body, dark blue glass, red cross on doors, rear door cast shut (TP).....**£8-12**
78-80 Military olive-green body, WW with silver hubs, rear door cast shut (TP)**£15-25**
  Same but with black hubs **£10-15**

MB 3d   Montiverdi Hai

73-78 Orange body, pale yellow interior, black or UB, '3' on bonnet **£5-8**
  Same but with '6' on bonnet.............**£12-15**
  Orange body, pale yellow interior, black base, '3' or '6' on bonnet......**£12-15**

MB 3e   Porsche Turbo

78-79 Metallic brown body, cream interior, clear glass, black base .**£5-8**
79-80 Metallic brown body, UB................**£7-10**
  Silver body, CG, cream or red interior, black or dark grey base **£3-6**
  Tan interior, black base **£10-15**
  Tan interior, dark grey base............**£10-15**
  Tan interior, brown base..................**£15-20**
  Red interior, brown base..................**£7-10**
80-82 Metallic green body, cream interior, clear glass, black or dark grey base **£4-6**
  With light or dark yellow interior.......**£3-5**
  Same but with unpainted base..........**£6-9**
  Red interior, dark GB or BB............**£10-15**
  Red body, tan interior, opaque glass, black base, 'Porsche Turbo 90'.....**£9-12**
82-83 Red body, tan or white interior, CG, black or dark grey base, 'Porsche Turbo 90' on some..**£3-6**

MB 4d   Stake Truck

70-72 Orange-yellow cab, green stake body, green glass...........................**£12-15**
  Same but bright yellow cab **£50-60**

MB 4e   Gruesome Twosome

71-75 Gold body, SB or UB, cream interior, purple glass..............................**£6-10**

With white or yellow interior...........**£10-15**
  Gold body, SB, cream interior, AG..**£60-75**
75 Red body, SB or UB, yellow interior, purple glass....................................**£10-12**
  Same but with cream interior..........**£12-15**
  Orange-red body, SB or UB, cream interior, purple glass.......................**£20-25**

MB 4f   Pontiac Firebird

75-77 Metallic light blue body, UB, AG........**£5-8**
78-80 Same but metallic dark blue............**£12-15**

MB 4g   '57 Chevy

80-81 Purple body, silver interior, UB, CG....**£4-6**
82-83 Red body, silver interior, SB or UB, CG, 'Cherry bomb' **£6-8**
  Same but with black base................**£15-25**

MB 5e   Lotus Europa

69-70 Dark metallic blue body, ivory interior, UB, NW **£12-15**
  As previous model but without 'Superfast' cast on base **£120-150**
  Dark metallic blue body, ivory interior, UB, NW, '20' and stripe labels from G5 racing set **£15-18**
70-75 Pink body, ivory interior, silver base, NW or WW **£20-30**
  Same but with unpainted base **£10-12**
  Same but UB, NW, '20' and stripe decals from G5 set **£15-18**
77-78 Black body, ivory interior, UB, NW, 'JPS' (Japanese issue).............**£20-25**
  Same but without 'JPS' (TP) **£12-15**

MB 5f   Seafire Boat

75-79 White deck, blue hull, orange-yellow, blue or lemon man, black or red exhausts **£3-5**
79-82 Red deck, white hull, orange-yellow or lemon man, red exhausts, black trailer (TP)...**£7-10**
81 Red deck, blue hull, lemon man, red exhausts, black trailer (TP)........**£55-65**
81 White deck, brown hull, orange -yellow man, red exhausts...............**£65-80**
  White deck, brown hull, lemon man, red exhausts **£65-80**
82 Black deck, yellow hull, red man, red exhausts, black trailer (TP) **£25-35**
83 Red deck, yellow hull, red man, red exhausts, black trailer (TP).......**£35-45**

MB 5g   US Mail Truck

78-82 Dark or light blue body, matt or gloss white roof (small or large windows), white base, black wheels, black or silver hubs, 'US Mail' and red stripe on some....**£5-7**
  Same but with black base...................**£6-8**
78 Pale blue body, white roof, 'sleet and snow' base, 'US Mail' and red stripe, U.S.A. Ltd edition **£9-12**

MB 5h   4x4 Jeep Off-Road

82-83 Metallic light or dark bronze body, black base, 'Golden eagle' **£3-5**

MB 6d   Ford Pick-up

70-71 Red body, white roof, white or chrome grille, NW or WW, black base........**£10-15**
  Metallic green or UB **£25-35**
  Green or Grey base **£10-15**

MB 6e   Mercedes 350sl

74-75 Orange body, black roof, UB, ivory or pale yellow interior, amber or CG **£7-10**
75-79 Yellow body, black roof, UB, pale yellow interior, amber or CG **£6-9**

77 Silver body, black roof, UB, pale
yellow interior, CG, 'Rennservice'
(German issue) **£35-45**
Same but without 'Rennservice' **£25-35**

79 Metallic bronze body, black roof, UB,
pale yellow interior, amber glass ...**£10-15**

79-81 Metallic bronze, white roof, AG,
UB, pale yellow or cream interior **£5-8**

81-82 Metallic red body, white roof, UB,
pale yellow interior, AG or CG **£4-7**

MB 6f   Mercedes Convertible

82-83 Metallic blue body, white interior, UB
or SB, silver side stripe on some **£4-6**

83-84 Maroon body, white interior, black base,
SB or UB..**£5-8**

MB 7c   Ford Refuse Truck

70-72 Orange or orange-red cab, grey tipper,
narrow or wide wheels.....................**£10-15**

MB 7d   Hairy Hustler

71-74 Metallic bronze body, AG, yellow
side stripe '5' , bonnet square '5',
grey or black base **£8-10**
Same but purple glass **£30-40**
Metallic bronze body, AG, blue side
stripe '5' , bonnet square '5',
unpainted or black base.....................**£8-10**
Same but green base **£12-15**
Same but green base, plain sides **£12-15**
Same but black base, plain sides......**£10-12**
Metallic bronze body, AG, round '3'
side labels, bonnet square '5', BB **£20-25**
Metallic bronze body, AG, round '3' or
square '137 side labels, bonnet 'Scorpion'
label, green or black base **£35-45**

75-77 White body, AG, red stripes with
black/white check pattern, grey base,
('Streakers' version)...........................**£7-10**
Same but white/black base...................**£7-10**

78 White body, AG, grey base **£20-25**

78-79 Yellow body, AG, 'flames', BB,
US 'Roman Numeral' Ltd Edition...**£10-15**

MB 7e   Volkswagen Golf

76-77 Metallic lime green body, yellow interior,
AG, BB, roof-rack, black surfboards...**£6-8**

77-81 Same but metallic light green body **£6-8**

77-81 Metallic dark green body, yellow or
lemon interior, AG, black or grey base,
roof rack and black surfboards............**£6-8**
Same but with orange glass **£6-8**
Red interior, grey base **£20-25**

77 Yellow body and interior, matt black
base, 'ADAC' , (German issue).......**£20-25**

79-80 Red body, yellow interior, CG or AG,
BB, roof rack, surfboards, (TP) **£12-15**
Red body, red interior, CG, BB, roof
rack and black surfboards (TP).......**£30-40**

81-82 Yellow body, red interior, CG, BB or
GB, roof rack and black surfboards.....**£4-6**

82-83 Silver body, red interior, CG, BB,
Green stripes and 'Golf' **£3-5**
Same but with tan interior...............**£15-20**
Same but red interior, grey base **£3-5**

MB 8e   Ford Mustang

70 White body, red interior, BB, CG **£70-80**

70-71 Red body, red interior, BB, CG....**£200-250**
Same but with ivory interior **£80-120**
Orange-red body, red interior........**£60-70**
Same but with ivory interior **£40-50**

MB 8f   Wildcat Dragster

71 Pink body, yellow interior, black
and orange 'Wild cat' labels, BB.....**£12-15**

71-75 Orange body, yellow interior, BB,
black/orange 'Wild cat' labels **£10-12**
Same but with UB or orange base ...**£20-25**
With dark or bright yellow base **£20-25**

Same but with grey base **£10-12**
Orange body, yellow interior, BB,
yellow/orange 'Wild cat' labels **£10-12**
Same but without labels..................**£12-15**
Same but grey base **£10-12**
Same but with UB or green base **£20-25**
Orange, yellow interior, black base,
'Rat Rod' labels **£30-40**
Same but with 'Sailboat' labels **£40-50**

MB 8g   De Tomaso Pantera

75-81 White body, red interior, blue base,
'8' and 'Pantera' bonnet and side
labels on some...................................**£9-12**
Same but orange interior.....................**£4-6**
With UB **£6-8**
White body, orange interior, yellow
'Sun' in black or green circle bonnet
label, no side labels, blue base.............**£7-9**
White body, orange interior, blue base,
'9' bonnet label, no side labels **£12-15**

81-82 Blue body, black interior, '8' and
'Pantera' bonnet and side labels on
some, black base, US issue **£4-6**

NB MB8g can be found with the larger rear
wheels swapped with the smaller front.

MB 8h   Rover 3500

81 Yellow body, red interior, sunroof,
black base, (G1 Gift set) **£225-250**
Metallic bronze body, white interior,
sunroof, black base..........................**£10-12**
Same but dark or light tan interior.....**£5-8**

MB 9d   Boat and Trailer

70-72 White hull, light turquoise deck,
dark blue trailer **£10-12**

76-83 White hull, light blue deck,
light blue trailer (TP) **£10-12**

82 White hull, black deck,
light or dark blue trailer (TP)..........**£40-50**
Same but with black trailer **£20-25**

MB 9e   AMX Javelin

72-78 Metallic lime green body with opening
doors, yellow interior, AG,
black air intake, UB or SB...................**£6-8**
Same but with silver air intake **£20-25**
Metallic lime green body, orange interior,
AG, black air intake, UB or SB **£8-10**
Same but white interior, UB **£25-30**
Same but with blue interior.............**£35-40**

76-78 Metallic light blue body, yellow or
orange-yellow interior, AG,
black air intake, UB or SB **£4-6**

78-81 Metallic dark blue body with cast-in
doors, orange-yellow interior, AG, UB
or SB, black air intake   (TP)...............**£4-6**

80-81 Blue body with cast-in doors, UB or
SB, orange-yellow interior, AG, black
air intake, white '1', (US Ltd.Ed.).....**£8-10**

81-83 Metallic dark green body, cast-in
doors, orange-yellow interior, AG,
UB or SB, black air intake, (TP) **£4-6**

82 Red body, cast-in doors, UB or SB,
orangey-yellow interior, AG, black air
intake, (TP).....................................**£20-25**

MB 9f   Ford Escort RS2000

78-82 White body, tan interior, BB, CG, '9',
'Ford', 'Shell', and 'Dunlop' decals..**£8-10**
Same but with grey base **£10-12**
Same but red interior, black base **£70-80**
White body, tan interior, BB, CG,
'Phantom' decals, (TP) **£18-20**

80-82 Blue body, tan interior, BB, CG,
'Phantom' decals, (TP) **£8-10**
Same but with black base **£10-12**
Same but with blue-grey base.........**£15-18**

82-84 Green body, tan interior, BB, CG,
'Phantom' decals (TP) **£8-10**

Same but with grey base **£10-12**
Green body, white interior, BB, CG,
'Phantom' decals, (TP) **£20-25**
Same but with red interior **£70-80**

MB 10d   Pipe Truck

70 Red body, silver base and grille,
6 grey pipes on sprue **£40-50**

70-73 Same but orange-red body **£18-20**
Orange body, silver base and grille,
6 Grey or yellow pipes on sprue......**£12-15**
Same but grey base and grille.........**£20-25**

MB 10e   Piston Popper

73-80 Metallic blue body, yellow interior,
AG, 'Superfast' on UB **£80-100**
Metallic blue body, yellow interior,
AG, 'Rola-Matic' on UB **£6-8**
Same but with silver base **£12-15**
Metallic blue body, yellow interior,
CG, 'Rola-Matic' on UB or SB **£12-15**

80 White body, yellow interior, AG,
'Rola-Matic' on UB (German
multi-pack issue) **£200-225**

80-81 Yellow body (with red flames), AG,
yellow interior, 'Rola-Matic' on
UB, US Ltd. Ed..................................**£8-10**

MB 10f   Plymouth Gran Fury Police Car

79-81 White body, black panels, blue or pale
or dark yellow glass, UB, 'Police'......**£4-6**

82-83 Same but with 'Metro Police Traffic
Control', shield and '012', UB or SB..**£4-6**
Same but 'Mercury' base from no 55..**£6-8**

MB 11d   Scaffolding Truck

70-72 Silver body, red base and grille, green
glass, yellow scaffolding, NW,
'Builders Supply Company'.............**£12-15**

MB 11e   Flying Bug

72-77 Red body, SB, grey glass, yellow
exhausts, silver helmet, square cut or
heart-shape bonnet decal...................**£8-10**
Same but UB, square cut decal........**£12-15**
Same but heart shape bonnet decal....**£8-10**
Heart-shape decal, UB, black glass ...**£20-30**

78 Orange body, UB, black glass and
exhausts, flying beetle bonnet decal,
US Ltd. Ed.......................................**£12-15**

MB 11f   Car Transporter

NB MB11f usually comes with 3 cars: 1 red,
1 blue and 1 yellow. Other combinations
are common (e.g., 1 blue and 2 yellow)
but this does not affect the price.

77-80 Orange cab, white or beige back, BB
or UB, blue, purple or green glass **£5-8**

80-83 Red cab, beige or grey back, BB, SB
or UB, blue or purple glass **£5-8**

83 Dark orange cab, beige or grey back,
black base, blue glass **£5-8**

MB 12c   Safari Land-Rover

70 Metallic blue body, white interior,
UB, NW, brown luggage..........**£800-1,000**

70-71 Metallic gold body, white interior,
UB, NW, brown luggage..................**£12-15**

MB 12c   Setra Coach

71 Metallic gold body, grey roof, unpainted
base, clear glass................................**£20-25**
Same but with white roof...............**£18-20**

72-73 Yellow body, white roof, UB, CG....**£15-18**
Same but with green glass **£150-200**

73-74 Metallic crimson body, white roof,
unpainted base, clear glass..............**£10-12**
Same but with green glass **£12-15**

74-75 Metallic purple body, white roof,
unpainted base, clear glass..............**£10-12**
Same but with green glass **£12-15**

MB 12e   Big Bull

75-79   Orange body, green shovel,
black tracks and rollers £30-40
Same but with yellow rollers £12-15
Same but with orange rollers £5-7

MB 12f   Citroën CX

79-82   Light or dark metallic blue body, pale
yellow or cream or ivory interior, SB or
GB or BB or UB, clear or blue glass...£5-8
Light metallic blue, tan interior £8-10
Dark metallic blue, red interior........£80-90

82-83   Yellow body, red interior, black base,
dark blue glass, (TP).........................£8-10
With clear glass, BB, GB or SB, (TP).£5-7
Yellow, red interior, BB, CG, 'Team
Matchbox' in black or blue, (TP) £8-10

83   White body, red interior, BB or UB,
blue glass/lights, 'Ambulance', (TP) ...£5-7
Same but 'Police', 'Marine Division'
and '8' prints, blue stripes, (TP) £5-7

MB 13d   Dodge Wreck Truck

70-71   Yellow (or lighter yellow) cab, green
back, yellow crane, red hook 'B.P.' .£18-20

MB 13e   Baja Buggy

71-78   Metallic light green body, orange interior,
UB, SE, black or red exhausts, red or
orange bonnet flower label.................£6-8
With red exhausts, no bonnet label...£8-10
With red exhausts, 'Police' bonnet
label from 55d £15-18
Same but with red interior £18-20
Metallic light green body, orange interior
from 47c, UB, SE, red exhausts,
orange bonnet flower label.........£150-200

78   Metallic dark green body, orange interior,
UB, SE, red exhausts, orange flower
bonnet label, ...£6-8
Same but 'Sun' label from 47c ...£10-12

MB 13f   Simon Snorkel

78-80   Light red body, SB or UB, blue glass,
blue lights, yellow crane and man £3-5
Same but amber glass and lights......£20-30

80-82   Dark red body, SB or UB, blue glass,
blue lights, Yellow crane and man.......£3-5

82   Same but white crane and man £8-10

MB 14d   Iso Grifo

69-71   Metallic dark blue body, pale or dark
blue interior, UB, NW.....................£18-20
Same but with white interior........£200-225

71-75   Lighter metallic blue body, white
interior, UB or SB, NW £12-15
Sky blue, white interior, UB, NW ...£15-18

77-78   Lighter powder blue, white interior,
UB, WW, (Japanese issue)..............£18-20

MB 14e   Mini Ha Ha

75-82   Red body, dark blue glass, UB, 'flesh'
coloured man, brown helmet,
4 circle side labels...........................£15-20
Same but with purple man £20-25
'Flesh' man, light blue glass...............£6-8
Purple man, light blue glass.............£12-15
Pink man, light blue glass................£8-10
Red body, light blue glass, 'flesh' or
pink man, 2 circle side labels..........£10-12

MB 14f   Leyland Petrol Tanker

82-83   Red cab, white tank, 'ELF' with red/blue
stripes or orange/turquoise stripes £4-6

MB 15d   Volkswagen 1500

69-70   Off white or cream body, cream interior,
'137', 'Monte Carlo' £20-25

70-72   Metallic red body, cream interior,
'137', 'Monte Carlo' on some £15-18

77-78   Off white body, cream interior, '137',
no bumper decal (Japanese issue)....£18-20

MB 15e   Forklift Truck

72-77   Red body, yellow hoist, grey forks, UB,
black steering wheel, 'horse' and
'Lansing Bagnall' labels £4-6
Same but with green or black base £6-8

77-82   Red body, unpainted hoist, yellow forks,
UB, black steering wheel, 'horse' and
'Lansing Bagnall' labels £4-6
Same but with green or black base £6-8
Same but no steering wheel £4-6
Same but with black or grey forks.....£4-6
Red body, unpainted hoist, red forks,
UB, no steering wheel, 'horse' and
'Lansing Bagnall' labels £8-10

82-83   Orange body, unpainted hoist, black
forks and roof, UB or SB or BB, no
steering wheel, 'Hi-Lift' labels...........£6-8

NB   Models can be found with 'horse' label
facing forwards or backwards and
before or after 'Lansing Bagnall'.

MB 16d   Case Bulldozer

69-74   Red body, yellow cab, shovel, engine and
base, green rubber tracks.....................£6-8
Same but with black tracks £10-12

77   Military olive drab green body, black
shovel, BB, black tracks (TP) £35-40
Same but olive green body (TP)......£15-18

MB 16e   Badger

74-80   Metallic bronze body, SB, silver radar,
green glass (Rola-Matic).................£10-12
Same but BB, cream radar £6-8
Same but with light or dark grey base .£6-8
Dark grey or black base, black radar ...£6-8
Same but with purple glass £10-12
Black base, white radar, green glass ...£6-8
Same but with dark grey base £6-8

76   Military olive drab green body, light grey
base, cream radar, green glass(TP) .£25-30

76-78   Same but olive green body (TP)......£12-15

MB 16f   Pontiac Firebird

80-81   Metallic light brown body, red interior,
UB, 'Eagle' bonnet label on most......£4-6

81-82   Same but metallic light gold body £3-5
Same but metallic dark gold body £3-5

82-83   White body, red interior, UB or SB,
'Eagle' bonnet label with stripe and
'Firebird' labels on most....................£2-4

MB 17e   Horse box

70   Red cab, dark green box, grey door,
chrome base and grille, two white
horses on sprue...............................£35-40

70-71   Same but orange-red cab.................£20-25
Orange-red cab, light grey-white box,
mustard door £18-20
Same but orange cab £15-18
Yellow-mustard cab, dark green
box, grey door £15-18

MB 17f   'Londoner' Buses

Unless otherwise stated all buses have red bodies
and white interiors. Most have metal bases in gloss
or matt black, grey, brown or unpainted. Before
changing to the Titan bus some were fitted with
plastic bases. Factory issued models are listed first,
then Lesney issued promotional models.

72-74   'Swinging London' 'Carnaby Street'...£4-6
73   Silver plated Gift Ware version........£70-80
73   Gold plated Gift Ware version £70-80
73-80   'Berger Paints'. (Brushes may be at
front or rear of label)..........................£4-6
73   Same but silver body.......................£70-80
73   Same but gold body £70-80
73   Same but orange body.....................£45-50
73   Same but cream body, brown roof ...£60-65

75   'Esso Extra Petrol' £65-70

77   'Silver Jubilee 1952-77'. Silver body
with red interior, special issue box ..£12-15
Same but red body, white interior £65-70

78   'Matchbox 1953-78'...........................£4-6
Same but orange body......................£65-70
Same but blue body £35-40

72   'Preston Guild Merchant'................£75-80

73   'Impel 73' Trade Fair......................£35-40
'London and Kensington Hilton' £75-80
'The Baron of Beef'........................£80-85
'Sellotape Selbstklebebander' £200-250
'Sellotape Packaging Systems' £125-150
'Sellotape Electrical Tapes' £125-150
'Barclays Bank'................................£55-60
'Chambourcy Yogurt'......................£65-70
'Interchemicals and Plastics' £200-250

74   'Typhoo puts the 'T' in Britain'......£65-70

76   'Impel 76' Trade Fair. Cream body
with brown roof, white interior.......£25-30
'British Airways Busch Gardens' £55-60
'Ilford HP5 Film' £90-100
'A.I.M. Building Fund 1976' £35-40
'Selfridges'.......................................£8-10
'Santa Claus, Aviemore Centre' £35-40
'Amcel takes you places' £65-70
'Eduscho Kaffee' £100-125

77   'New! The Museum of London' £15-20
'Army and Navy' £15-20
'Jacob's the Biscuit Makers'
Red body with white interior £25-30
Orange body with white interior......£12-15

78   'Aral-Deutschlands Autopartner'
Blue body with white interior £45-50
Same but red body £85-90

79   'Impel 79' Trade Fair......................£25-30

80   'You can't kid a Bisto kid'...............£8-10
'Borregaard Paper'...........................£70-90

MB 17g   Leyland Titan Bus

82   'Berger Paints' £2-4
'Laker Skytrain' £2-4

82   'Chesterfield Transport Centenary'.....£3-5
'Matchbox No.1, Montepna'
Pale blue/white (Greek issue) £10-12
Same but red body £15-18
'I.C.P. Interchemicals'....................£50-60

MB 18e   Field Car

70-75   Light yellow body, light brown roof,
white interior, SB, NW or WW £15-18
Same but WW, UB £12-15
Black roof, UB, WW £25-30

76   Military olive drab green body, tan roof,
black interior, BB, 'A' square door
labels, black wide wheels (TP) £25-30

76-80   Same but olive green body (TP) £12-15
Same but 'RA391' bonnet label......£10-12
With circled star bonnet label (TP)..£20-25

77-78   White body, black roof, black interior,
BB, Black/white checked bonnet label,
black wide wheels (TP)..................£200-225
Same but silver wheel hubs (TP).£200-225
Orange body, black roof, black interior,
BB, black/white checked bonnet label,
black wide wheels (TP)...................£12-15
Same but silver wheel hubs (TP) £12-15
Orange body, black roof, black interior,
SB, black/white checked bonnet label,
black wide wheels (TP)...................£20-25

78-80   Metallic ruby-red body, tan roof, black
interior, SB or BB, '44', 'Champion' and
'Goodyear' bonnet label (TP).............£6-8

80   Dark orange body, black roof, black
interior, BB or SB, 'AC Filters' and '179
Scout Racing' labels, US Ltd. Ed.....£20-25
Same but no labels, US Ltd. Ed......£20-25

82-83   Dark yellow body, black or tan roof,
black interior, SB, black/white
checked bonnet label, (TP) £25-30
Orange, black roof and interior, BB,
black/white checked bonnet, (TP)....£18-20

Orange body, black or tan roof, white
interior, BB, '44', 'Champion' and
'Goodyear' bonnet label, (TP).........**£18-20**

MB 18f   Hondarora

74-75   Red body, chrome forks etc., SE, black
seat, 'Honda' tank labels, WW **£12-15**

75-80   Same but no labels **£8-10**

Same but black wheels............................**£8-10**

Red body, black forks etc., SE, white
seat, 'Honda' tank labels, WW **£65-70**

Same but with black seat **£10-12**

76   Orange body, black forks etc., SE,
black seat, WW, 'Honda' labels,
(King Size set 6)...............................**£18-20**

76   Military olive drab green body, black
forks etc., BE, black seat, no labels,
WW (TP)..**£25-30**

76-78   Same but military olive green (TP) **£12-15**

81-82   Metallic green body, black forks etc.,
BE or SE, black seat, no labels,
black wheels...**£6-8**

82-83   Yellow body, black forks etc., SE, black
seat, no tank labels, black wheels **£4-6**

Same but with brown or tan rider **£4-6**

MB 19d   Lotus Racing Car

70   Metallic purple body, UB, SE, white
driver, round No.'3' side labels **£20-25**

MB 19e   Road Dragster

70-75   Light red body, UB or SB, off-white
interior, '8' labels normal or sideways **£6-8**

Same but with 'Scorpion' labels.....**£35-40**

72   Metallic pink body, UB, off-white
interior, large 'Wynns' labels,
(Promotional issue) **£45-50**

Same but small 'Wynns' labels.......**£55-60**

75   Metallic purple body, UB, off-white
interior, 'Scorpion' labels................**£40-45**

Same but with '8' labels or no labels **£8-10**

Metallic red body, UB, off-white
interior, '8' labels as normal **£200-250**

MB 19f   Cement Truck

76-81   Red body, yellow barrel with red stripes,
unpainted base, green glass................**£3-5**

Same but black stripes or no stripes **£3-5**

79   Red body, grey barrel with red stripes
unpainted base, green glass................**£5-7**

Same but with purple glass...............**£8-10**

81-82   Red body, lemon barrel with red stripes
unpainted base, green glass................**£3-5**

Same but black stripes or no stripes ...**£3-5**

Same but with purple glass.................**£6-8**

MB 19g   Peterbilt Cement Truck

82-83   Metallic green body, orange barrel,
yellow or white 'Big Pete'...................**£2-5**

MB 20d   Lamborghini Marzal

69   Metallic red body, white interior,
unpainted base...................................**£15-18**

70   Same but with 'Avon' and '2' labels
from G3 Racing Specials set.............**£18-20**

71   Bright pink body, white interior,
unpainted base...................................**£10-12**

Bright pink, silver base **£20-30**

Same but with 'Avon' and '2' labels
from G3 Racing Specials set...........**£12-15**

71-75   Orange or orange-pink body, white
interior, unpainted base **£10-12**

72   Yellow body, white interior, UB,
('Brroom Stick' blister pack issue)..**£30-35**

MB 20e   Police Patrol

75-80   White body, UB, orange 'Police' stripe,
orange light and interior (Rola-Matic)..**£4-6**

Same but with red 'Police' stripe.........**£6-8**

White body, UB or SB, orange 'Police'
stripe, blue or yellow light & interior..**£5-8**

Same but with black base...................**£8-10**

White body, UB, 'Ambulance' and Red
Cross, orange light and interior........**£12-15**

76-78   White body, UB, orange 'Site Engineer'
stripes, orange light and interior,
(G3 Consruction Set) **£30-35**

Same but with orange body **£25-30**

Orange body, UB, orange 'Police'
stripe, orange light and interior,
(G3 Construction Set) **£25-30**

76   Military olive drab green body, UB,
yellow and red 'Police' arrow, orange
light and interior (TP) **£30-35**

Same but 'Ambulance' labels **£30-35**

76-77   Military olive green body, UB, yellow
and red 'Police' arrow, orange light
and interior (TP)...............................**£15-20**

Same but with 'Ambulance' labels..**£15-20**

80   Blue body, UB, yellow 'Paris-Dakar 81'
stripe, orange or yellow light and interior,
(French issue blister pack)................**£25-30**

81   White body, UB, blue 'County Sheriff'
labels, blue light and interior **£8-10**

Same but with '017', 'Sheriff'
and blue roof **£12-15**

81-83   White body, UB, yellow 'Police' and
'shield' stripe above chequered stripe .**£4-6**

Same but with black base....................**£6-8**

White body, UB, black 'Police' on
sides, yellow light and interior.........**£12-15**

83   Light brown or beige body, UB, yellow
'Securite-Rallye Paris-Dakar 83'......**£8-10**

MB 21d   Foden Concrete Truck

70-73   Dark yellow cab, yellow barrel, red
body and shute, green base **£12-15**

Same but bright yellow cab,
green or dark green base **£15-20**

MB 21e   Rod Roller

73-78   Yellow body, black wheels with
metallic red hubs, GB, 'flame'
label from 40d on bonnet **£18-20**

Same but with matt red hubs **£15-18**

Yellow or darker yellow body, black
wheels, GB or BB, 'flame' or no label**£6-9**

MB 21f   Renault 5TL

78-79   Metallic blue body, red interior,
black or silver base.........................**£12-15**

Metallic blue body, tan interior,
black, dark grey or silver base **£4-7**

Yellow body, red interior, BB or SB,
'Le Car' and stripe prints.................**£12-15**

Yellow body, tan interior, BB or SB
or dark grey base, 'Le Car' prints........**£4-7**

79-81   Silver body, red interior, BB or SB,
'A5' and stripe prints **£12-15**

Same but no tampo prints **£4-6**

Silver body, tan interior, SB **£15-20**

81-82   Silver body, red interior, dark grey or
BB or SB, 'Le Car' and stripe prints ...**£4-7**

82-83   White body, tan interior, BB, 'Renault'
and '4' on green prints.......................**£4-6**

Same but 'Renault' roof prints............**£4-6**

White body, white interior, BB, 'Renault'
and '4' on green prints **£6-8**

White body, tan interior, BB, 'Roloil'
and '21' on yellow prints...................**£4-6**

Same but with orange base **£15-20**

White body, white interior, BB, 'Roloil'
and '21' on yellow prints...................**£6-8**

MB 22c   Pontiac GP Sports Coupé

70   Red body, grey interior, BB **£500-600**

Light purple, grey interior, BB **£25-30**

Dark purple, grey interior, BB **£25-30**

MB 22d   Freeman Intercity

70-71   Metallic purple body, off-white interior,
UB, yellow arrow labels on some........**£8-10**

71-72   Metallic gold body, off-white interior,
UB, yellow arrow labels **£12-15**

72-75   Metallic red body, off-white interior,
UB or SB, arrow labels on some **£6-8**

MB 22e   Blaze Buster

75-80   Red body, silver interior, UB, yellow
ladder, 'Fire' labels **£2-4**

Same but with black ladder...............**£20-25**

Same but with white ladder **£125-150**

Red body, silver or white interior,
BB, yellow ladder, 'Fire' labels...........**£2-4**

Same but dark grey base **£3-5**

80-82   Dark red body, white interior, grey or
BB, yellow ladder, 'Fire' labels...........**£2-4**

83   Light red body, white interior, BB, dark
yellow ladder, 'Fire' labels **£2-4**

Same but 'No.32' on yellow labels....**£8-10**

MB 23e   Volkswagen Camper

70-72   Blue body, orange interior and hinged
roof, UB, CG, rear sailboat side labels
on some, petrol filler cap, NW.........**£30-40**

Same but no filler cap **£15-18**

72-75   Orange body, orange interior and hinged
roof, UB, CG, sailboat labels, NW..**£80-90**

Light or dark orange body, white interior,
orange hinged roof, UB, CG, sailboat
labels on some, NW **£12-15**

77-80   Military olive green body, no interior,
cast roof, BB, dark blue glass, Red
Cross, wide wheels (TP)..................**£15-18**

80   White body, no interior, cast roof, BB,
light or dark green glass, 'PizzaVan',
wide wheels (USA Ltd edition) **£20-25**

MB 23f   Atlas Truck

75-81   Metallic blue body, orange tipper with
yellow and red arrow labels, chrome
interior, AG, UB................................**£10-12**

Same but without tipper labels............**£6-8**

Metallic blue body, orange tipper, grey
interior, CG, SB...................................**£4-6**

Same but with AG **£6-8**

Metallic blue body, orange tipper,
grey interior, CG, UB...........................**£4-6**

Same but with AG **£6-8**

With CG and SB **£8-10**

81   Metallic blue body, silver tipper, grey
interior, CG, SB...................................**£8-10**

81-82   Same but red body, black interior **£10-12**

MB 24c   Rolls-Royce Silver Shadow

70-73   Light metallic red body, cream
interior, black base **£12-15**

Dark metallic red body, cream
interior, black base **£10-12**

Same but with pink base **£18-20**

Same but SB or grey base **£15-18**

Same but with metallic green base ..**£20-30**

77-78   Light metallic gold body, cream
interior, UB, (Japanese issue) **£80-120**

Same but BB (Japanese issue) **£18-20**

MB 24d   Team Matchbox

73   Bright yellow body, white man,
'4' (or '8') and 'Team Matchbox'
bonnet label **£180-200**

Metallic blue body, white man,
'1' and 'Team Matchbox' label ...**£225-250**

Same but '5' and 'Team Matchbox'
bonnet label **£200-225**

Metallic green body, white man,
'5' (or '8') and 'Team Matchbox'
label, (G4 'Team Matchbox' set).....**£25-30**

73-78   Metallic red body, white man,
'8' and 'Team Matchbox' label **£3-5**

78-80   Metallic ruby-red body, white man,
'44', 'Champion', 'Goodyear',
black trailer (TP) **£6-8**

82-83   Same but orange body, yellow man .**£40-50**

MB 24e   Diesel Shunter

78 Metallic dark green body, light brown
control panel, red base 'Railfreight' **£6-8**
Same but with 'D1496-RF' labels **£4-6**

78-83 Light or dark yellow body, light brown
control panel (or none), red base,
'D1496-RF' **£3-5**

MB 25d   Ford Cortina GT

70 Metallic light brown body, off white
interior, unpainted base **£50-60**

70-72 Same but metallic light blue body ...**£15-18**
Same but metallic dark blue body ...**£18-20**

MB 25e   Mod Tractor

72-78 Metallic purple body, BB, yellow seat,
headlights cast on rear mudguards...**£25-30**
Without lights on rear mudguards........**£6-8**
Metallic purple body, BB, red seat ..**£80-90**
Metallic purple, UB, yellow seat **£8-10**

76-79 Red body, BB, yellow seat (TP) **£8-10**

MB 25f   Flat Car Container

78-80 Light beige container red roof, black flat
car, 'United States Lines' labels **£8-10**
Same but with 'N.Y.K.' labels **£2-4**
Same but with 'Sealand' labels **£4-6**
Dark beige container, red roof, black
flat car, 'N.Y.K.' or 'Sealand' labels ...**£2-4**
Same but with 'OCL' labels **£10-12**
Dark brown container, red roof, black
flat car, 'N.Y.K.' labels **£12-15**

MB 25g   Audi Quattro

82-83 White and black, 'Audi' and '20' **£3-5**

MB 26c   GMC Tipper Truck

70-72 Red tipping cab, silver tipper, green
chassis, green glass, wide wheels **£10-12**

MB 26d   Big Banger

72-76 Red body, UB, 'Big Banger',
dark blue glass..................................**£6-8**
Same but with amber glass **£8-10**

78 Dark brown, 'Brown Sugar', WB,
amber, black or blue glass (USA)....**£12-15**

81-83 White body, BB, 'Cosmic Blues'
clear or blue glass, (US issue)........**£10-12**

MB 26e   Site Dumper

76-78 Yellow body, yellow dumper,
black seats, black base **£4-6**

78-81 Same but with red dumper **£2-4**
Same but dark grey base **£8-10**
Same but brown base **£12-15**

81-82 Orange-red body, silver dumper, white
seats, black base **£2-4**
Same but wheels have yellow hubs **£6-8**
Orange-red body, silver dumper, white
seats, dark grey base **£2-4**
Same but wheels have yellow hubs **£6-8**

MB 26f   Cable Truck

82-83 Orange-yellow body, red base, blue
glass, two light grey cable drums **£10-15**
Same but dark grey or BB **£3-5**

83 Bright yellow body, BB, blue glass,
two dark grey cable drums..............**£40-50**
Same but dark red body **£10-12**

MB 27d   Mercedes 230sl

70-71 White body, red interior, clear glass,
unpainted base, narrow wheels **£25-30**

71 Same but yellow body....................**£20-25**

71-73 Yellow body, black interior,
CG, UB, NW or WW **£12-15**

MB 27e   Lamborghini Countach

73-75 Yellow body, BB, red glass, '3' **£4-6**
Same but with amber glass **£6-8**
Same but with purple glass **£8-10**

Yellow body, UB, red glass, '3' **£6-8**
Same but with purple glass **£8-10**

75 Orange body, UB, red glass, '3' **£20-30**
Same but with amber glass **£20-30**

75-81 **Lamborghini 'Streakers'.** All have
green/black 'Streaker' prints and a red
'8' on the bonnet.
Orange body, chrome interior, BB **£6-8**
Same but with amber or green glass ..**£8-10**
Orange body, grey interior, BB, GG....**£6-8**
Same but with purple glass **£8-10**
Orange body, grey interior, UB, green
glass, red '8' on bonnet.....................**£6-8**
Same but with brown base **£8-10**
Orange body, yellow interior, BB or
dark grey base, green glass **£6-8**
Orange, chrome interior, UB, green
or amber glass, red '8' on bonnet **£8-10**
Orange body, grey interior, dark grey
base, green glass................................**£6-8**
Same but with purple glass **£8-10**
Orange body, beige interior,
dark grey base, green glass **£6-8**
Same but with purple glass **£8-10**
Orange body, beige interior, BB, GG ..**£6-8**

MB 27f   Swing Wing

81-83 Red/white, red glass **£2-4**
Red/white, dark yellow-orange glass...**£3-5**
Red/white, red or black 'Jet Set'.........**£3-6**

MB 28d   Mack Dump Truck

70-73 Metallic lime green body and dumper,
UB, cab steps cast closed................**£12-15**
Same but with steps cast open **£15-18**

77-79 Military olive drab green body/dumper,
BB, cab steps cast closed (TP)........**£35-40**
Military olive green (TP) **£15-18**

MB 28e   Stoat

73-76 Metallic gold body, UB or BB, dark
brown man, (Rola-Matic issue)..........**£3-6**

77 Military olive drab green body, BB,
dark brown man, (TP) **£35-40**

77-79 Military olive green body, BB, dark
brown man, (TP) **£15-18**

MB 28f   Lincoln Continental

79 Light red body, white roof,
beige interior, clear glass, UB **£4-6**

79-81 Dark red body, beige, dark brown
or grey interior, clear glass, UB **£4-6**

MB 28g   Formula Racing Car

81-83 Metallic brown-grey body, BB or UB,
white driver, 'Exxon' and '8' prints **£3-5**

MB 29c   Fire Pumper Truck

70 Red body, white back and ladders,
UB, blue glass, narrow wheels........**£35-40**

81 Same but 'P1' and 'Los Angeles Fire
Dept.', wide wheels ('Code Red') ...**£12-15**

MB 29d   Racing Mini

70-72 Metallic bronze body, SB or UB,
off-white interior, '29' on yellow
labels (orange edges)......................**£15-18**

72-76 Orange body, SB or UB, cream or
off-white interior, '29' on yellow
labels (orange edges)......................**£12-15**
Same but with green label edges **£10-12**

76-81 Red body, SB or UB, off-white or
cream interior, '29' on yellow
labels (green edges) (TP) **£8-10**
Red body, SB, cream interior, '3' on
white circle door labels (TP)...........**£35-40**
Same but with no labels **£10-12**

MB 29e   Tractor Shovel

76-78 Light yellow body, red shovel, silver
engine and seat, yellow base.............**£4-6**

77 Lime green body, yellow shovel, silver
engine and seat, yellow base
(German PS1000 set issue)..............**£60-70**

78-81 Yellow body, red shovel, silver or
black engine and seat, yellow base **£2-4**
Same but with cream base **£8-10**
Same but with black base **£6-8**
Yellow body, red shovel, black engine
and seat, yellow base, yellow hubs......**£6-8**
Yellow body, black shovel, black engine
and seat, yellow base........................**£2-4**
Same but with cream base **£8-10**
Same but with black base **£6-8**

79 Yellow body, black engine
and seat, BB, black stripes, ('C' prints
on some), (G5 Construction Set) **£6-8**

81 Orange-red body, red shovel, dark grey
engine and seat, black base, ...**£20-25**

82-83 Same but with black shovel **£10-12**

MB 30c   8-wheel Crane

70 Red body, dark orange crane arm with
yellow hook, UB **£225-250**
Same but with gold crane arm **£18-20**

MB 30d   Beach Buggy

70-76 Light metallic purple body, yellow
spots, UB, white interior **£15-18**
Same but with yellow interior.............**£6-8**
Same but dark metallic purple body **£6-8**

NB The yellow spots on this model can
vary from only a few spots to almost
an entire body covering.

MB 30e   Swamp Rat

76-81 Military green deck, light brown hull,
'Swamp Rat' labels on some **£6-8**

MB 30f   Articulated Truck

81-83 Metallic steel-blue cab, WB,
red glass, silver trailer **£4-6**
Blue cab, WB or YB, silver trailer **£2-4**

83 Blue cab, pale yellow or WB, blue
trailer with 'Pauls' white labels,
(Ltd. blister-pack issue of 900)........**£25-30**
Blue cab, WB or YB, yellow
trailer, 'International' labels...............**£8-10**
Red cab, YB, yellow trailer with
'International' labels **£8-10**
Red cab, YB, silver trailer **£10-12**

MB 31e   Lincoln Continental

70 Sea-green body, white interior,
unpainted base, CG, NW ....**£1,000+**
Metallic lime-green body, white
interior, UB, CG, NW **£10-12**
Same but with wide wheels **£20-25**

MB 31d   Volksdragon

71-77 Red body, purple glass, UB or SB,
yellow or cream interior,
'eyes' label on some........................**£8-10**
Red body, purple glass, UB or SB,
yellow interior, 'flower' label **£15-18**

78 Black body, purple glass, UB, yellow
interior, 'bug'/ 'flames' (US issue)..**£12-15**

MB 31e   Caravan

77-83 White body, off-white or light brown
interior, UB, AG, orange or yellow door,
orange stripe with white bird labels.....**£4-6**
White body, light yellow interior, light
blue, orange or yellow door, orange
stripe with white bird labels on some ..**£2-4**
Same but dark blue door, blue stripe
with white bird labels on some **£4-6**

MB 32c   Leyland Petrol Tanker

70-73 Dark green cab and body, white tank,
SB, blue glass, 'B.P.' labels in centre
or front of tank, NW **£12-15**

Dark green cab and body, white tank,
GB, 'B.P.' labels in centre of tank ...**£30-40**
Blue cab and body, white tanker, SB,
'Aral' labels in centre of tank, (German
issue in Aral Tankwagen box) **£80-100**
Metallic purple cab and body,
silver tank, SB, no labels **£100-125**
Same but with 'N.A.M.C.' labels **£150-175**
Red cab and body, white tank,
SB, 'N.A.M.C.' labels.................**£300-400**

MB 32d   Maserati Bora

73-78 Metallic crimson body, lime green base,
yellow interior, stripe and '8' label......**£5-7**
Same but with dark green or UB **£6-9**
Same but dark green base, '3' label.**£12-15**
Same but with no label.............................**£6-8**
79 Metallic gold, SB, yellow interior,
no bonnet label, tow hook, (TP) **£35-40**

MB 32e   Field Gun

77-81 Military green body, light or dark brown
base, 2 soldiers and 4 shells on sprue,
black wide wheels...............................**£3-5**
Same but black wheels, silver hubs.**£30-40**
78 Military olive green body, no base,
soldiers or shells, black wheels (TP) ...**£3-5**

MB 32f   Excavator

81-82 Orange-red body, dark grey or black
swivel base, silver-grey tracks **£6-8**
82-83 Yellow body, black swivel base, black
tracks, black stripes & 'CAT' prints ..**£8-10**
Same but with no 'CAT' print **£6-8**

MB 33c Lamborghini Miura P400

69 Yellow body, red interior, UB, NW .**£80-90**
70 Light metallic bronze body,
red interior, UB, NW.......................**£20-30**
Dark metallic bronze body,
red interior, UB, NW...................**£75-100**
70 -73 Light metallic gold body, off-white
interior, UB, NW **£12-15**
Same but dark metallic gold body ...**£12-15**
Dark metallic gold body, red interior,
UB, NW **£20-30**
Light metallic gold body, off-white
interior, red or pink-red base, NW..**£18-20**
77-78 Light gold body, off-white interior,
UB or BB, WW (Japanese issue)....**£18-20**

MB 33d   Datsun 126X

73-75 Yellow body, orange base, AG............**£4-6**
Same but with unpainted base **£30-40**
75-77 Yellow body, orange base, AG,
red/orange or red/black flame prints,
('Streakers' issue)..........................**£7-10**
78 Yellow body, BB, AG, red/black flame
prints, (US Roman Numeral issue)..**£18-20**
Gold plated body, BB, black glass,
green prints, (US Roman Numeral).**£12-15**

MB 33e   Police Motorcycle

77-79 White frame, chrome or black engine,
white bars, UW, blue man, white or
black seat and panniers, 'Police'.........**£4-6**
79 White frame, chrome engine, white bars,
UW, green man, seat and panniers,
'Polizei' (German) **£12-15**
79 Same but cream frame, man has white
helmet and gloves (King Size 71
German Polizei Patrol set) **£15-18**
79 All black bike and wheels, dark blue
man, white helmet, 3 stripes and shield,
white seat and panniers, 'Police',
gold star tank labels (KS 66 set)......**£18-20**
79 White frame, black engine and wheels,
white bars, blue man, white helmet
and gloves, white seat and panniers,
'Police' labels...................................**£8-10**

79-81 White frame, black engine, white bars,
black wheels, green man, seat and
panniers, 'Polizei' labels (German) **£6-8**
79 Same but white helmet and gloves **£8-10**
79-81 Same but white helmet and gloves,
UW, (KS 66 Police Patrol set) **£15-18**
81 White frame, black engine white bars,
black wheels, green man, white
seat and panniers, 'LAPD' labels ...**£15-18**
81 White frame, chrome engine, black
bars, black wheels, no man, white
seat and panniers, 'Police' labels.....**£10-12**
81-82 Black frame, chrome engine, white
bars, black wheels, blue man, white
seat/panniers, 'LAPD' (Code Red)..**£12-15**

MB 34d   Formula I Racing Car

71-72 Metallic purple body, UB, CG, yellow
or blue stripe, '16' label, 4 NW......**£12-15**
71 Same but yellow stripe, 'Wynns'
labels (Promotional issue)............**£45-50**
72-75 Yellow body, UB, CG, blue bonnet
stripe, '16' label, 4 NW or WW **£6-8**
Same but front NW, rear WW **£8-10**
Yellow body, UB, CG, yellow stripe,
'16' label, 4 NW **£8-10**
Yellow body, UB, AG, blue or yellow
stripe, '16' label, 4 WW...................**£12-15**
73-75 Metallic blue body, UB, CG, yellow
or blue stripe, '15' label, 4 WW (or
front NW, rear WW) (G4 set) **£25-30**
Orange body, UB, CG, blue or
yellow stripe, '16', 4 WW (or front
NW, rear WW) (G4 set) **£20-25**
Orange-yellow body, UB, CG, blue
stripe, '16' label, 2 NW, 2 WW **£15-18**

MB 34e   Vantastic

75-78 Orange body, WB, GG, white interior,
rear stripes labels.................................**£6-8**
Same but motif instead of stripes.......**£8-10**
Same but with stripes and UB **£100-150**
78 Orange body, WB, GG, white interior,
'Jaffa Mobile', (Promotional) **£200-250**
78 Orange body, WB, GG or CG, white
interior, bonnet 'Sun' label **£20-30**
78-81 Orange body, WB, GG, white interior,
'34', rear stripes labels on some **£4-6**

MB 34f   Chevy Pro-Stocker

81-83 White body, UB, blue '34' prints.........**£2-4**
Same but with no tampo prints **£4-6**
White body, red base, blue '34' **£8-10**

MB 35c Merryweather Fire Engine

69-71 Metallic red body, GB, white ladder,
'London Fire Service', NW **£18-20**
71-75 Red body, GB, white ladder, 'London
Fire Service', NW or WW **£12-15**
Red, GB, 'Flame-Proof Wool' **£50-80**
Same but in promotional box **£100-150**
Red body, BB, ladder, 'London
Fire Service', wide wheels...............**£20-25**
Same but with tan base **£25-30**
Red body, GB, different style ladder,
'London Fire Service', WW, (TP) ..**£12-15**
81 Red body, GB, white ladder and man
from 13f, 'Los Angeles City Fire
Dept.' prints, WW, (Code Red) **£12-15**

MB 35d   Fandango

75-77 White body, red interior, red base,
red or silver rear disc, arrow and '35'
bonnet label (Rola-Matic)...................**£4-6**
White body, red interior, UB, red rear
disc, arrow and '35' bonnet label **£20-30**
White body, red interior and base,
silver rear disc, stripe and '6' bonnet
label from 41c **£15-18**
77-82 Red body, red interior, red base,
blue arrow and '35' bonnet label,
blue or silver rear disc...................**£80-100**

Red body, off-white interior, WB,
blue arrow and '35' label, blue, silver
or red rear disc **£4-6**
Red body, off-white or white interior,
UB, blue rear disc, arrow and '35' **£6-8**
Red body, white interior, UB, blue rear
disc, 'Sun' bonnet label from 47d....**£12-15**

MB 35e   Zoo Truck

82 Red body, blue cage, light brown lions,
blue glass, black base.........................**£2-4**
Same but with red base **£20-25**
Same but with grey base **£8-10**
83 Red body, silver cage, light or dark
brown lions, blue glass, black base......**£2-4**

MB 36c   Opel Diplomat

70 Metallic light or dark gold body,
silver grille, white interior, BB **£15-20**
Same but without silver grille.........**£12-15**

MB 36d   Hot Rod Draguar

70-73 Metallic dark red body, off-white or
light yellow interior, silver 'Draguar'
label..**£10-12**
Same but with orange interior.........**£12-15**
Same but lemon or white interior **£6-8**
73-75 Metallic pink body, light yellow
interior, silver 'Draguar' label **£12-15**
Metallic pink body, cream interior,
no boot label....................................**£8-10**
Metallic pink body, light or dark
yellow interior, no boot label **£6-8**
Same but with amber glass **£8-10**

MB 36e   Formula 5000

75-77 Orange body, blue or yellow man,
'Formula 5000' and orange or yellow
'3', '5000' on rear spoiler...................**£3-5**
77 Same but red body, yellow man...........**£6-8**
77-78 Red body, yellow man, 'Texaco 11' on
bonnet, no spoiler label or 'Marlboro'.**£5-8**
78-80 Same but 'Champion' on rear spoiler..**£6-8**

MB 36f   Refuse Truck

80-82 Metallic red cab, all-yellow container,
red load, no labels **£3-5**
Same but without 'Collectomatic'
on container...................................**£50-75**
82-83 Blue cab, all-yellow or all-orange
container, black or red load,
'Metro DPW66' on side labels **£2-4**
Same but orange container with
yellow opening back, red load **£4-6**

MB 37c   Cattle Truck

70-71 Orange-yellow cab and body, grey
back and 2 white cattle.....................**£8-10**
71 Same but orange cab and body **£20-25**
Orange cab and body, silver back **£80-90**
72 Bright-yellow cab/body, grey back ..**£60-70**

MB 37d   Soopa Coopa

72-75 Metallic light blue body, yellow interior,
AG, unpainted or silver base...............**£4-6**
75-76 Metallic light purple body, yellow
interior, AG, UB, 'flower' label **£8-10**
Same but with red base **£150-200**
77 Orange body, yellow interior, AG,
SB, 'Jaffa Mobile' (Promotional) ..**£90-100**

MB 37e   Skip Truck

76-81 Red cab/body, yellow skip, chrome
interior, AG, BB **£6-8**
Same but grey interior, clear glass.......**£3-5**
Same but with brown base **£5-8**
Red cab/body, yellow skip,
orange interior, CG, BB **£6-8**

	Red cab/body, blue skip, grey interior, CG, BB	**£90-100**
77	Orange cab/body, yellow skip, grey interior, CG, BB (German issue)	**£60-70**
	Red skip (German PS1000 set)	**£60-70**
81-82	Metallic blue cab/body, yellow skip, grey interior, CG, gloss or matt BB	**£6-8**
	Same but with silver base	**£8-10**

MB 37f   Matra Rancho

82	Blue body, blue base, black interior	**£2-4**
83	Yellow body, yellow base, black interior, red side stripe prints	**£8-10**

MB 38c Honda Motorcycle and Trailer

70-71	Metallic blue-green bike, yellow trailer, 'Honda' labels	**£15-18**
71	Same but metallic pink bike	**£25-30**
72-73	Same but metallic purple bike	**£25-30**
77	Metallic green bike, orange trailer with 'Honda' labels on some (TP)	**£12-15**
82	Same but yellow trailer (TP)	**£10-12**

MB 38d   Stingeroo

73-76	Metallic purple body, purple forks white horse's head	**£8-10**
	Same but with pale blue forks	**£35-40**
	Same but with chrome forks	**£250-300**

MB 38e   Jeep

76-80	Military green body, gun, BB/seats, '21*11' or 'star' label	**£4-6**
77	Military olive drab green body, no gun, BB/seats, 'star' label, (TP)	**£45-50**
	Same but military olive green body	**£25-30**
	Same but with '21*11' label (TP)	**£18-20**
	Yellow body, BB/seats, 'Gliding Club', (TP with yellow glider trailer)	**£8-10**
	Same but with white base, (TP with yellow glider trailer)	**£30-40**
	Red body, BB/seats, 'Gliding Club', (TP with red glider trailer)	**£500+**

MB 38f   Ford Camper

80-82	Orange-red body, green glass, cream back with AG, UB with no.'35'	**£50-70**
	Same but camper back with no glass	**£2-4**

MB 38g   Ford Model 'A' Van

82	'CHAMPION SPARK PLUGS'	**£2-4**
84	'KELLOGGS'	**£2-4**
84	'TOY FAIR 84' (US), roof label	**£80-100**
	Same but without roof label	**£50-70**
84	'PEPSI COLA', 'Come Alive'	**£7-10**
	Same but without 'COME ALIVE'	**£10-15**
	'PEPSI COLA', 'Matchmates'	**£8-12**
84	'BEN FRANKLIN'	**£300-400**
84	'MATCHBOX USA'	**£20-25**
84	'ARNOTTS'	**£6-8**
84	'LARK LANE'	**£2-4**
84	'TITTENSOR FIRST SCHOOL'	**£2-4**
85	'BASS MUSEUM'	**£2-4**
85	'COLLECTORS GUIDE'	**£2-4**
85	'The AUSTRALIAN'	**£2-4**
86	'BBC 1925'	**£7-9**
86	'WEET-BIX'/'SANITARIUM'	**£6-9**
86	'H.H. BRAIN'	**£7-10**
86	'MATCHBOX SPEED SHOP'	**£2-4**
86	'ISLE of MAN TT 86'	**£2-4**
86	'SMITHS POTATO CRISPS'	**£2-4**
87	'W.H.SMITH & SON Ltd', Red	**£8-12**
87	'MICA' 2nd CONVENTION	**£125-175**
87	'JUNIOR MATCHBOX CLUB'	**£2-4**
87	'ISLE of MAN TT 87'	**£2-4**
87	'SILVO 1912-1987'	**£10-12**
87	'CHESTY BONDS'	**£2-4**
87	'DEWHURST'	**£2-4**
87	'ISLE of MAN POST OFFICE'	**£2-4**
87	'JOHN WEST SALMON'	**£2-4**
87	'This Van Delivers', with phone no.	**£10-12**
	without phone no.	**£300-400**
87	'RICE KRISPIES', Mid-Blue (UK)	**£2-4**

87	'RICE KRISPIES', Dark Blue, (US)	**£9-11**
88	'MICA 3rd CONVENTION'	**£8-10**
88	'MICA 1st N.A. CONVENTION'	**£6-9**
88	'JAMES NEALE & Sons'	**£2-4**
88	'ISLE of MAN TT 88'	**£2-4**
88	'ISLE of MAN POST OFFICE'	**£2-4**
88	'ROYAL MAIL'	**£2-4**
88	'MANX CATTERY'	**£2-4**
88	'MERVYN WYNN', gold 'island'	**£2-4**
	with black 'island'	**£20-25**
88	'P.M.G. 252' (Australia)	**£2-4**
88	'ALEX MUNRO'	**£2-4**
88	'CHESTER HERALDRY CENTRE'	**£2-4**
88	'W.H. SMITH & SON Ltd', Yellow	**£8-12**
88	'TOY MUSEUM, CHESTER'	**£2-4**
88	'COBB of KNIGHTSBRIDGE'	**£2-4**
88	'ROWNTREES JELLY'	**£2-4**
88	'SHERBERT FOUNTAIN'	**£2-4**
88	'GUERNSEY POST OFFICE'	**£2-4**
88	'RAYNERS CRUSHA'	**£2-4**
88	'HISTORICAL COLLECTION'	**£2-4**
88	'BIG SISTER' (Australia)	**£2-4**
88	'UNIROYAL' (Canada)	**£10-12**
88	'NATWEST BANK'	**£2-4**
88	'GREENS SPONGE MIXTURE'	**£2-4**
89	'MATCHBOX SERIES'	**£2-4**
89	'MICA 4th CONVENTION'	**£7-9**
89	'MICA 2nd N.A. CONVENTION'	**£7-9**
89	'SOUVENIR of CHESTER'	**£2-4**
89	'CHEESES'	**£2-4**
89	'ISLE of MAN TT 89'	**£2-4**
89	'JORDANS'	**£2-4**
89	'JUNIOR MATCHBOX CLUB'	**£2-4**
89	'RIBENA'	**£2-4**
89	'SHERBET FOUNTAIN',	
	Black base, normal box	**£2-4**
	Red base, Woolworths box	**£6-9**
89	'MOORLAND CENTRE'	**£2-4**
89	'LIGHTWATER VALLEY'	**£2-4**
89	'TANDY ELECTRONICS'	**£2-4**
89	'YORK FAIR' (US)	**£2-4**
89	'BALTIMORE ORIOLES' (US)	**£2-4**
89	'ASDA BAKED BEANS'	**£2-4**
89	'LION WHOLESALERS'	**£2-4**
89	'MB US COLLECTORS CLUB'	**£20-25**
89	'JACKY MAEDER' (Swiss)	**£6-9**
89	'JOHNSONS SEEDS'	**£2-4**
89	'SWARFEGA'	**£10-12**
89	'CAMPERDOWN' (Australia)	**NGPP**
90	'PAVA RUSTPROOFING' (Danish)	**£2-4**
90	'MATCHBOX 40th' (US)	**£10-15**
90	'CARMELLE' (Saudi-Arabia)	**£10-12**
90	'FRESH DAIRY CREAM'	**£2-4**
90	'LYCEUM THEATRE'	**£2-4**
90	'RICE KRISPIES', Dark Blue (US)	**£7-10**
90	'COCA-COLA'	**£2-4**
90	'ISLE of MAN TT 90'	**£2-4**
90	'MB USA 9th CONVENTION'	**£8-10**
90	'CANADA DRY'	**£12-15**
90	'YORK FAIR 1990'	**£2-4**
90	'PENN STATE' (US)	**£6-9**
90	'COLLECTORS CLUB 90' (US)	**£35-45**
90	'JOHNNY WALKER'	**£18-22**
90	'TYNE BRAND'	**£8-12**
90	'LYONS TEA'	**£7-10**
90	'PG TIPS'	**£10-12**
90	'MITRE 10'	**£2-4**
90	'WILLIAM LUSTY'	**£2-4**
90	'RUTTER Bros.' (US)	**£6-8**
90	'USA BASEBALL TEAMS', each	**£2-4**
	Set of 26	**£100-130**
91	'DAIRYLEA CHEESE'	**£7-10**
91	'COLLECTORS CLUB 91' (US)	**£45-55**
91	NAT. F'BALL LEAGUE (US) each	**£2-4**
	Set of 28	**£100-130**
	'MATCHBOX USA CLUB 15th'	**£45-55**
	'MB Collectors Club', silver	**£75-100**
	Green/orange	**£35-45**
92	'COLLECTORS CLUB 92 (US)	**£25-30**
92	'Nat Hockey League' set of 6 pairs	**£50-60**
92	'Nat Hockey League 92' set of 6	**£25-30**
92	'Flavours of Australia' set of 6	**£20-25**

93	'Wines of Australia' set of 6	**£25-30**
93	'USA COLLECTORS CLUB '93'	**£30-40**
94	'Pills, Potions and Powders' (6)	**NGPP**
95	'The Circus Comes to Town (6)	**NGPP**
95	'International Postal Trucks' (6), ea.	**£8-11**
	MICA European Conventions 1993, 1994, or 1995	**NGPP**

MB 39d   Clipper

73-79	Metallic crimson body, yellow interior, AG, unpainted base, chrome or white exhausts, (Rola-Matic)	**£10-15**
	With green base and amber glass	**£6-8**
	With green base and clear glass	**£8-10**

MB 39e Rolls-Royce Silver Shadow

79-81	Silver body, Red interior, SB or UB	**£4-6**
81-82	Metallic red body, off-white or yellow interior, silver or unpainted base	**£3-5**
82-83	Metallic gold-brown body, white interior, silver or unpainted base	**£4-6**
83	Ruby red body, white interior, matt black or matt silver base	**£3-5**

MB 40c   Hay Trailer

67-70	Dark blue body, yellow sides, BPT with yellow hubs	**£6-8**
79-79	Lt. yellow body, yellow sides, BPT (TP)	**£4-6**
	Same but with black fixed sides (TP)	**£4-6**
	Orange-yellow body, black fixed sides, black wheels (TP)	**£6-8**
79	Same but with light blue body, (TP)	**£7-9**
80	Same but with red body, (TP)	**£8-10**
81	Same but with beige body, (TP)	**£45-50**

MB 40d   Vauxhall Guildsman

71-74	Pink body, GG, cream interior, UB, blue circle flame bonnet label	**£6-8**
	Same but with silver base	**£15-20**
	With UB, black circle flame label	**£8-10**
	Same but with silver base	**£15-20**
75	Pink body, GG, cream interior, UB, blue '40' print (Streakers issue)	**£80-120**
75-76	Red body, AG or GG, cream interior, UB or SB, blue '40' (Streakers)	**£8-12**
76	Red body, GG or AG, cream interior, unpainted base, Blue circle flame bonnet label, (TP)	**£10-15**
	Red body, AG, UB, cream interior, no bonnet label, (TP)	**£10-12**

MB 40e   Horse Box

77-80	Orange cab, cream box, light or dark brown door, BB, SB, GB or UB	**£7-10**
80-83	Light metallic green cab, cream box, dark brown door, unpainted base	**£4-6**
	Same but with white door	**£6-8**
	Dark metallic green cab, cream box, dark brown door, UB, SB or BB	**£4-6**
	Same but lime green door, SB or BB	**£8-10**
83	Dark metallic green cab, dark brown box, white door, unpainted base	**£12-15**
	Yellow cab, dark brown box, lime green door, black base	**£15-18**
	Same but with white door	**£12-15**
	Orange cab, dark brown box, lime green door, BB, SB or UB	**£8-10**
	Same but white door	**£4-6**

MB 41c   Ford GT

69-70	White body, light or dark green or BB, red interior, '6' on bonnet, NW	**£15-18**
71-72	Metallic bronze body, dark green or BB, red interior, '6', NW or WW	**£10-15**
	Same but WW, cream base	**£20-25**
	Same but WW, grey base	**£12-15**
	WW, light or dark yellow base	**£20-25**
	Blue body, Yellow interior	**£20-25**
77	White body, red interior, 'Wildcat' or '6' label, BB, (Japanese issue)	**£18-20**
79	Yellow body, red interior, BB, no bonnet label, MP1 Italian issue	**£1,000+**

MB 41d   Siva Spyder

72-75   Metallic red body, cream interior, black
        band, unpainted base, clear glass **£6-8**
        Same but with chrome band...........**£15-18**
        Metallic red body, white interior, black
        band, unpainted base, clear glass **£6-8**
75-78   Metallic dark blue body, white or cream
        interior, black band, UB, CG, stars &
        stripes, '8', (Streakers issue)..............**£8-10**
77   Light blue body, off-white interior, black
        band, UB, black glass or CG, 'Spider'
        print, (US Roman Numeral issue)....**£12-15**

MB 41e   Ambulance

78-81   White body, grey interior, side stripe
        with 'Ambulance', red cross labels......**£3-5**
        Same but with yellow interior.............**£6-8**
        White body, grey interior, side stripe
        with 'Emergency Medical Services' **£4-6**
        Same but with yellow interior.............**£6-8**
        White body, grey interior, no stripe -
        only 'Ambulance' in grey letters **£12-15**
80   Silver body, grey interior, 'Paris-Dakar
        81' (French blistercard issue)........**£25-30**
        Same but with white rear doors ......**£30 -35**
81   Red body, grey interior, 'Notarzt' and
        red cross prints, (German issue).....**£18-20**
        White body, grey interior, side stripe
        with 'Ambulance', Blue Cross labels ..**£3-5**
        Same but with 'Pacific Ambulance,
        Emergency, 101' prints (Code Red).**£15-20**

MB 42c   Iron Fairy Crane

70   Red body, yellow boom/hook/base ..**£80-90**
        Light or dark orange-red body, lime
        boom, yellow hook, yellow base **£20-25**

MB 42d   Tyre Fryer

72-77   Metallic light blue body,
        yellow interior, unpainted base **£20-25**
        Same but with black base....................**£4-6**
        Metallic dark blue body,
        orange-yellow interior, black base ...**£10-15**
77   Orange body, yellow interior, BB,
        'Jaffa Mobile' (Promotional) **£90-100**

MB 42e Mercedes Container Truck

77   All-yellow body, BG, BB, 'Deutsche
        Bundespost' labels (German issue)..**£20-25**
77-80   Red cab/body, cream container with
        red doors and roof, BG, UB,
        'Sealand' or 'NYK' labels **£4-6**
        Same but with black base....................**£6-8**
        Same but with UB, 'OCL' labels **£8-10**
81   Same but with 'Confern Mobeltransport-
        betriebe' labels, PG (German issue) **£18-20**
        Dark blue cab and body, blue container
        BG, UB, 'Karstadt'(German issue)..**£20-25**
81-82   Red/white, 'Matchbox', BG or PG **£4-6**
        Metallic green/yellow, BG or PG,
        'Mayflower' and ship labels **£4-6**
        Same but with red glass **£8-10**
        Same but red/white body, BG or PG ...**£4-6**

MB 42   '57 Thunderbird

82-83   Red body, white interior, UB or SB.....**£2-4**

MB 43c   Pony Trailer

70-71   Yellow body, grey door, light green
        base, 2 white horses, NW................**£20-25**
        Same but with dark green base **£15-18**
76-79   Orange body, brown door, BB or GB,
        2 horses, 'horse head' labels (TP)....**£10-15**
79-83   Same but light brown body **£10-15**
83   Light brown body, brown door, BB,
        2 horses, 'Silver Shoes' or
        no labels (TP)................................**£10-12**

MB 43d   Dragon Wheels

72-77   Dark green, BB, 'Dragon Wheels'.....**£8-10**
        Same but with unpainted base **£15-20**

Light green, BB, 'Dragon Wheels' ..**£12-15**

MB 43e   Steam Locomotive

78-82   Red cab/sides, black engine, '4345' **£2-4**
        Same but with 'NP' labels **£5-7**
81   Green cab/sides, black engine, '4345' **£8-10**
81-83   Same but with side 'NP' labels (TP) ...**£6-8**

MB 44c   Refrigerator Truck

70   Red cab and body, green back, grey
        rear door, green glass, UB, NW.....**£90-100**
70-71   Yellow cab and body, red back, grey
        rear door, green glass, UB, WW **£10-12**

MB 44d   Boss Mustang

72   Yellow body, black bonnet, UB, WW..**£5-7**
        Same but with silver base **£20-30**
80   Green, UB, 'Cobra', (US Ltd. Ed.)..**£10-12**
82-83   Dark or light orange body, off-white
        interior, UB, 'The Boss' and '5' **£6-8**

MB 44e Passenger Coach / Caboose

78-83   Red/black, off-white roof, green glass,
        red '431 432' side labels....................**£6-8**
        Same but with clear glass.................**£8-10**
        Same but with no glass **£4-6**
        Red/black, off-white roof, no glass,
        red '5810 6102' side labels.................**£4-6**
        Same but with cream or tan roof **£6-8**
        Red/black, off-white roof, no glass,
        green '5810 6102' side labels **£6-8**
        Red/black, off-white or cream roof,
        no glass, green 'GWR' side labels.....**£8-10**
81-83   Green/black, off-white raised roof, no
        glass, green '5810 6102' labels (TP)....**£6-8**
        Red/black, off-white raised roof, no
        glass, red '431 432' labels (TP)...........**£4-6**
        Same but red '5810 6102' labels (TP).**£4-6**

MB 45c   Ford Group 6

70   Non-metallic green body, white interior
        CE, CG, UB, '7' label, NW **£250-300**
70-71   Dark metallic green body, CE,
        CG, UB or BB, '7' label, NW **£25-30**
        Same but 'Burmah' labels (G3 set) .**£20-25**
        Dark metallic green body, CE,
        CG, BB or GB, '45' label, NW **£12-15**
        Same but with pink base **£18-20**
71-73   Metallic lime green body, CE,
        AG, BB, '45' label, WW **£10-12**
        Same + 'Burmah' labels, (G3 set) ..**£12-15**
        Metallic lime green body,
        grey engine, AG, BB, '45', NW **£10-12**
        Same but grey or CE, GB, WW.......**£10-12**
73-76   Metallic dark or light purple body,
        grey or CE, AG, BB, '45', WW **£8-10**
        Metallic dark purple body, CE, AG,
        BB, 'eyes' label from 31d, WW **£25-30**

MB 45d   BMW 3.0 CSL

76-81   Light or dark orange body, cream
        interior, GG, 'BMW' label on some **£6-8**
        Same but with clear glass................**£10-12**
77   White body, cream interior, GG,
        'BMW' and 'Manhalter' signature
        label, (Austrian 50,000 issue) **£25-30**
        White body, GG, 'Polizei 123', blue
        or yellow light, (German issue) **£45-50**
        Same but no light or 'Polizei 123'...**£45-50**
82   Red body, GG, 'BMW' (G15) **£70-80**

MB 45e   Kenworth Cabover

82-83   White body, AG, blue/brown stripes ...**£2-4**

MB 46c   Mercedes 300se Coupé

70   Metallic blue body, white interior, UB,
        opening doors and boot, NW **£80-90**
70-71   Metallic light or dark gold body,
        opening doors and boot, NW **£45-50**
        Metallic light gold body, opening boot

but doors cast shut, NW..................**£20-25**
77   Military olive green body, boot and
        doors cast shut, NW **£12-15**
81   Silver body, WW, (Multi Pack)....**£125-150**

MB 46d   Stretcha Fetcha

72-77   All-white body, red base, BG,
        'Ambulance', large Red Cross labels..**£6-8**
        Same but no 'Amulance', small RC **£15-18**
        All-white body, red base, UB, 'Ambulance'
        and large Red Cross labels **£8-10**
        All-white body, 'Ambulance',
        large Red Cross labels, AG.............**£15-18**
        Same but no 'Amulance', small RC **£18-20**
77   All-red body, red base, BG, 'Unfall
        Rettung' labels (German issue)........**£30-35**
80   Lime green/white, WB or BB, AG,
        'Viper Van' prints (US Ltd. Ed.)......**£12-15**

MB 46e   Ford Tractor and Harrow

78-81   Blue body, yellow interior, UB, black
        wheels, yellow plastic harrow.............**£2-4**
        Same but black wheels, yellow hubs...**£4-6**
        Blue body, white interior, UB, black
        wheels, yellow hubs, yellow harrow....**£4-6**
79   Blue body, yellow interior, UB, black
        wheels, no harrow (TP).....................**£2-4**
81   Metallic lime green, yellow interior,
        BW, yellow hubs, no harrow (TP).....**£4-6**
81-83   Metallic green body, yellow interior,
        BW, yellow hubs, yellow harrow.........**£2-4**
83   Blue body, white interior, GB, BW
        with gold hubs, no harrow (TP)..........**£6-8**

MB 47c   DAF Container Truck

70-72   Silver cab/body, yellow tipper **£12-15**

MB 47d   Beach Hopper

73-78   Blue body with paint spots, light or
        dark pink base, orange interior, light
        brown man, clear or no windscreen,
        'Sun' label, wide WW (Rola-Matic)....**£5-8**
        Same but UB, no windscreen...........**£15-18**
        With light pink base, yellow interior,
        no windscreen, dark brown man......**£20-25**

MB 47e   Pannier Locomotive

79-82   Dark green and black, BB, 'G.W.R.' ...**£3-5**
        Same but with unpainted base **£6-8**
        Same but with brown or grey base ..**£10-12**

MB 47f   Jaguar SS100

82-83   Red body, light brown interior, BB.....**£2-4**
        Same but with grey base **£3-5**

MB 48c   Dodge Dumper Truck

69-71   Blue cab and body, yellow tipper,
        chrome base, NW or WW **£12-15**

MB 48d   Pie-Eyed Piper

72-77   Metallic blue body, silver engine and
        exhausts, BG, UB, '8' and stars...........**£6-8**
        Same but with amber glass **£10-12**
        Red body, 'Big Banger', CE and
        exhausts, BG, UB........................**£150-200**
78   White body, silver/black engine, black
        exhausts, glass and base, orange
        prints, (US Roman Numeral issue)..**£12-15**
81-83   Red body, SE, black exhausts, AG,
        BB, 'Red Rider' prints (USA) **£10-12**

MB 48e   Sambron Jack Lift

77-81   Yellow body, BB, red 'Sambron'...**£80-120**
        Same but with no tampo prints.........**£2-4**
        Yellow body, BB, yellow hubs...........**£4-6**
        Same but with grey or brown base **£7-10**
81-83   Yellow body, black forks, BB or GB ...**£3-6**

MB 49b   Unimog

70   Blue body, red base, green glass,
        silver or plain grille........................**£20-30**
70-71   Same but metallic steel-blue body ...**£20-25**

Auction Results – Matchbox Toys

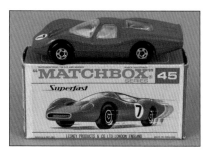

45 Ford Group 6
Non metallic green body
Near mint, boxed – £320

46 Mercedes 300 SE Coupe
Metallic blue
Mint, boxed – £120

28 Jaguar MK X
Pale metallic brown, (GPW Matchbox
Series on base) 'E' in mint box – £1,950

59 Ford Fairlane 'Fire Chief' Car
Bonnet and door decals
SPW white roof light – £820

25 Bedford Van "Dunlop"
Dark blue body, black base BPW
Mint in 'E' box – £1,900

74 Mobile Refreshment Bar
Silver body, light blue base
Mint in good+ box – £1,300

Models sold by Vectis Auctions Ltd., Fleck Way, Thornaby, Stockton-on-Tees, TS17 9JZ. Pictures reproduced by their kind permission.

Auction Results – Matchbox Toys

5 Routemaster Bus
"Drink Peardrax" BPW
Excellent in mint box – £550

5 Routemaster Bus
"Pegram" BPW
Near mint, boxed – £350

23 Berkeley Cavalier Caravan
Metallic lime green GPW
Good+ in near mint box – £900

8 Ford Mustang
Orange, red interior, chrome hubs
Mint, in near mint box – £380

9 Dennis Fire Engine (58mm)
Red body, gold trim with front bumper GPW,
near mint in mint box – £420

11 ERF Road Tanker
Green, gold trim, metal wheels
Good including box – £420

20 Chevrolet Impala "Taxi", orange
yellow, cream interior, rare GPW
Near mint, boxed – £2,000

22 Vauxhall Cresta
Pale pink/blue green GPW
Excellent in mint box – £2,100

26 Foden Cement Mixer
Orange, grey barrel and plastic wheels
£580

45 Ford Consait with boat
white interior BPW
Near mint in mint box – £820

31 Lincoln Continental, metallic lime green,
black plastic wheels
Excellent including box – £1,900

30 Magirus Deutz Crane Lorry
Light brown, red jib and hook GPW
Mint in excellent box – £6,500
(World Record for 1-75 model)

46 Morris Minor 1000
Pale brown, metal wheels
Mint, boxed – £3,500

46 Removals Van
"Beales Bealesons"
Near mint in white card box – £800

75 Ford Thunderbird, cream-peach side
panels, black base and wheels
Mint in 'E' box – £340

Auction Results – Spot-On Models

216 Volvo 122s
Lime green, white interior
Mint boxed – £180

229 Lambretta
Grey and red
Near mint, boxed – £260

Presentation set 4a
All models excellent to mint
In good+ box – £500

110/3 AEC Lorry
"British Road Services"
Near mint in excellent box – £400

116 Caterpillar
D9 Bulldozer
Excellent model & box – £800

158a/2 Bedford 2000 gal' Tanker
"Shell-BP"
Excellent, boxed – £600

Auction Results – Miscellaneous

Budgie "Supercar"
Excellent in good box – £270

Budgie 256 "Pluto" Aircraft Tanker
Excellent in good box – £130

Timpo Toys "Pickfords"
Good+ model and box – £130

"Chad Valley" Van
Near mint in good box – £390

Benbros Low Loader
Near mint in good box – £55

Crescent No 1276 Scammell Scarab
Excellent model and box – £150

Models sold by Vectis Auctions Ltd., Fleck Way, Thornaby, Stockton-on-Tees, TS17 9JZ. Pictures reproduced by their kind permission.

Auction Results – Miscellaneous

Zebra Toys No 16
Excellent in near mint box – £90

Zebra Toys No 30 Routemaster Bus
"Fina Petrol", mint in 'E' box – £160

Sundaw Products H131 Motorbus (Green) "Transport
Sevices" Excellent in good+ box – £650

Sundaw Products Motorbus (Red) "Transport
Services" Excellent in good box – £380

Benbros "United Dairies"
Good+ in excellent box – £160

Lone Star "Gulliver County Services" 3 single
deck bus, all good+ in 'E' box – £150

Morestones No 2 Foden 8 wheel lorry
Mint boxed with leaflet – £240

Lone Star Roadmaster cars
Trade box of 6
All near mint in excellent box – £210

Morestones AA Land Rover (large)
Near mint boxed – £180

No 4 Morestone's Series
Foden 14 ton Express Delivery
Diesel Wagon. Estimate – £150-200

Crescent Toys
1293 Vanwall Racing Car
Excellent including box – £285

Chad Valley Humber Super Stripe
Near mint in 'E' box – £180

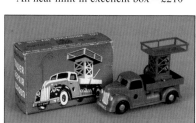

Chad Valley Tower Repair Wagon
Mint in 'E' box – £340

Chad Valley Fire Engine
Near mint in 'E' box – £200

Models sold by Vectis Auctions Ltd., Fleck Way, Thornaby, Stockton-on-Tees, TS17 9JZ. Pictures reproduced by their kind permission.

iv

71-72 Same but sky blue body, plain grille**£15-18**
78 Military olive green body, BB, GG, tan load, 'A' label in square (TP).....**£18-20**
Same but 'star' circle label, tan load on some, (TP)....................**£35-40**

MB 49c   Chop Suey

73-76 Metallic red-purple frame, chrome forks, CE, 'bull's head' **£250-300**
Same but with red forks **£8-10**
With black or orange forks **£35-40**

MB 49d   Crane Truck

76-79 Yellow body and crane arm, red hook, black base, green glass.........................**£4-6**
77 Red body, yellow crane arm, red hook, BB, CG (German PS1000 set) **£70-80**
Same but GG (German PS1000 set) **£60-70**
80-82 Yellow body, black crane arm, red hook, black base, purple or red glass..**£8-10**
Same but green glass...........................**£4-6**
82-83 Same but 'A1 Crane Service' on arm + 'Safety First', 'C', 'Cat' on some...**£8-10**

MB 50c   Kennel Truck

70-71 Dark or light metallic green body, BB, silver grille, 4 white dogs, NW.......**£12-15**
Dark Metallic Green body, Grey base, silver grille, 4 white dogs, NW.......**£15-18**
Same but with yellow base **£20-25**
72-73 Lime Green body, BB or GB, silver grille, 4 white dogs, WW.......**£10-15**
Same but white grille, BB or GB.....**£25-30**
Same but with unpainted base **£35-40**

MB 50d   Articulated Truck

73-79 Yellow cab/body, BB, light blue trailer with yellow chevron side labels, yellow or orange trailer body, red or PG **£7-10**
Same but no labels **£4-6**
80 Red cab/body, BB, light blue trailer, no labels, red trailer body, PG................**£35-40**
Yellow cab/ body, light blue trailer, no labels, yellow trailer body, white tow hook, purple glass (TP)...................**£4-6**
Red cab/body, silver trailer (red body), white hook on some, PG (TP).........**£35-40**
80 **Articulated Trailer** Light blue trailer (yellow body) (TP) **£4-6**
Silver trailer, red trailer body (TP) ..**£35-40**

MB 50e   Harley-Davidson

80-82 Light gold frame, black handlebars **£6-8**
82-83 Dark bronze frame, black bars........**£10-12**

MB 51c   8-wheel Tipper

70-71 Yellow cab and body, silver tipper, BG, SB, 'POINTER' labels on some **£20-25**
Same but with grey base **£50-60**

MB 51d   Citroën SM

72-74 Metallic bronze body, cream interior, unpainted base, NW **£12-15**
Same but with orange interior..........**£55-60**
Same but with yellow interior...........**£15-18**
With cream interior, silver base **£12-15**
75 Metallic blue body, yellow interior, unpainted base, NW **£25-30**
75-78 Same plus '8', UB (Streakers issue)..**£8-10**
With '8', UB and off-white or orange interior (Streakers issue) **£10-15**
79 Metallic blue body, orange interior, UB, roof rack, 'Yamaha Shell STP' (TP)**£15-18**

MB 51e   Combine Harvester

78-81 Red body, yellow blades/arm, BB, black 'regular wheels' **£6-8**
Same but with black Superfast wheels **£4-6**
Same but with yellow hubs...............**£8-10**
Red body, yellow blades/arm, no base, black Superfast wheels **£6-8**

Same but with yellow hubs..............**£10-12**
Yellow body, red blades/arm, no base, '2' print, Superfast wheels (Gift Set).**£8-10**

MB 51f   Pontiac Firebird SE

82-83 Red body, tan interior, silver base........**£2-4**

MB 51i   Motorcycle Trailer

79-82 Metallic blue body, 3 orange-yellow or yellow bikes (TP)...............................**£6-8**
Same but with 3 red bikes (TP) **£10-12**
82-83 Red body, 3 yellow bikes (TP) **£12-15**

MB 52c   Dodge Charger Mk.III

70-71 Metallic light or dark red body, black interior **£8-10**
Same but with '5' labels (G3 set) **£20-25**
71 Metallic purple body, black interior....**£8-10**
71-75 Metallic lime green, black interior.....**£8-10**
Same but with '5' labels (G3 set) **£20-25**
Same but with UB (G3 set).............**£20-30**

MB 52d   Police Launch

76-80 White deck, light blue hull, dark BG, orange stripes, 'Police', 2 light blue men, 2 horns **£8-10**
81 Same but with no roof horns...............**£2-4**
Same but light blue glass, no horns **£2-4**
Same but frosted BG, no horns...........**£6-8**
White deck, red hull, roof and rear, BG, 'Los Angeles Fire Department', 2 light blue men (Code Red issue)...**£25-30**
Same but 2 yellow men (Code Red)**£12-15**

MB 52e   BMW M1

81-83 Silver body, red interior, BB, CG, black stripes and '52' tampo prints **£2-4**
Same but blue-grey body **£8-10**
With BB, amber glass **£25-30**
With BB, CG, no tampo prints **£4-6**

MB 53c   Ford Zodiac Mk.IV

70 Metallic light blue body, NW **£300-400**
70-71 Metallic light green body, NW **£15-18**
Metallic dark green body, NW **£15-18**
Metallic emerald green body **£20-25**
72 Lime green body, wide wheels **£35-40**

MB 53d   Tanzara

72-74 Orange body, SE, silver interior, UB, AG **£5-7**
Same but with green glass **£10-12**
75-76 White body, SE, silver interior, UB, AG, blue/orange stripes/stars, '53' print, (Streakers).....................**£12-15**
Same but with no tampo prints **£18-20**
With blue/red stripes/stars, '53' **£10-12**
Same but with green glass **£12-15**
White body, red engine, red interior, UB, AG, blue/red stripes/stars, '53' tampo print, (Streakers)...................**£80-90**

MB 53e   CJ6 Jeep

77-80 Red body, yellow interior, light brown roof, UB, WW.................................**£3-5**
Same but with black interior................**£6-8**
With yellow interior, silver base **£4-6**
81-82 Metallic green body, yellow interior, light brown roof, UB, WW...............**£3-5**
Same but with black interior................**£6-8**
With yellow interior, silver base **£4-6**
Pale yellow body, dark brown roof, interior, BB or GB, 'CJ6' print.........**£8-10**

MB 53f   Flareside Pick-up

82-83 Blue body, '326' and 'Baja Bouncer' ..**£2-4**
Same but with some or prints or none .**£3-5**

MB 54b   Cadillac Ambulance

70 White body, silver grille, red roof lights, BB, small Red Cross door labels **£20-25**

Off-white body, plain grille, red roof lights, BlB, large Red Cross labels ..**£18-20**

MB 54c   Ford Capri

71 Pink or orange body, black bonnet, UB, wide wheels **£12-15**
72-75 Metallic crimson body UB or SB **£8-10**
76 Orange body, UB, (TP)....................**£12-15**

MB 54d   Personnel Carrier

76-79 Military green body, black base, green glass, light brown soldiers on some.....**£4-7**

MB 54e   Mobile Home

80-82 Cream or white body, brown door, side stripes on some, BB....................**£2-4**
Same but with grey or brown base **£3-6**

MB 54f   NASA Tracking Vehicle

82-83 White/red/black, BB, 'US Space Shuttle Command Centre', 'NASA' **£5-8**
Same but with grey base **£8-10**

MB 55d   Mercury Police Car

70 White body, 2 men, blue roof light, shields and 'Police' label **£30-35**
Same but with red roof light **£25-30**

MB 55e Mercury Estate Police Car

71-74 White body, off-white interior, no men, UB, 2 red roof lights, bonnet shield and 'Police' label and side shield labels.**£20-25**
Same but UB or SB, bonnet and side 'Police' arrow labels **£12-15**
Same but UB or SB, bonnet 'Police' arrow label, plain sides **£15-18**

MB 55f   Hellraiser

75-76 White body, red interior, UB, 'Stars and Stripes' bonnet label **£4-6**
77-78 Metallic blue body, red interior, SB, 'Stars and Stripes' bonnet label **£10-12**
Metallic blue body, off-white interior, UB or SB, 'Stars and Stripes' **£3-6**
Metallic blue body, off-white interior, SB, bonnet stripe and '3' label **£20-25**
Same but with no label.......................**£3-5**

MB 55g   Ford Cortina

79-80 Metallic green body, red interior, UB, clear glass, opening doors **£6-8**
Same but with light yellow interior ...**£8-10**
81 Metallic red body, light yellow interior, UB, opening doors **£6-8**
82-83 Metallic light brown body, white interior, UB or SB, opening doors, black stripe **£6-8**
Light red body, white interior, UB or SB, doors cast shut....................**£6-8**
Same but with gloss black base **£18-20**
Bright red body, white interior, UB or SB, opaque glass, doors cast shut (Gift Set issue) **£15-18**
83 Light red body, light brown interior, UB or SB, doors cast shut, black side stripe prints (TP) **£15-18**
Same but white interior (TP) **£6-8**

MB 56c   BMC 1800 Pinifarina

69-70 Metallic gold body, UB, NW **£12-15**
Same, with '17', 'Gulf' (G3 set) **£20-25**
71-73 Peach body, UB, NW **£25-30**
Orange body, UB, NW or WW **£8-12**
With '17' and 'Gulf' (G3 set).........**£18-20**

MB 56d   Hi-Tailer

74-78 White body, orange/blue stripes, UB, 'MB5 Team Matchbox', yellow man....**£4-6**
Same but with silver or red base.........**£6-8**
Same but with blue man **£4-6**
79 Red base, 'Martini 7' (Gift Set) **£10-12**

MB 56e   Mercedes 450 SEL

79-80	Metallic blue body, red interior	**£8-10**
	Same but with light brown interior	**£5-7**
81-83	Light brown body, light or dark brown interior, red 'Taxi' sign, UB or SB	**£4-6**

MB 57c   Land-Rover Fire Truck

70	Red body, white ladder, 'Kent Fire Brigade' labels	**£50-60**
	Same but with 'Kent Fire Brigade' labels cut around words	**£60-70**

MB 57d   Eccles Trailer Caravan

70-71	Cream body, orange roof, green interior, maroon side stripe labels	**£12-15**
	Same but brown side stripe labels	**£15-18**
	With brown stripe and flower labels	**£12-15**
72	Pale Yellow body, orange roof, green interior, brown stripe, flower labels	**£15-18**
76-78	Yellow body, red-orange roof, white interior, black stripe, flowers (TP)	**£10-12**
	Same but with side red dots label from K-27 Camping Cruiser set (TP)	**£25-30**
79-81	Light brown, red-orange roof, white interior, black stripe, flowers (TP)	**£8-10**
	Same but 'white bird' label (TP)	**£20-25**
82	White body, red-orange roof, white interior, 'Sunset', palm tree (TP)	**£15-18**

MB 57e   Wildlife Truck

73-80	Yellow body, clear back, red glass, orange or light brown lion, 'Ranger' (Rola-Matic version)	**£6-8**
	Same but with amber back	**£10-12**
81	White body, clear back, red glass, light brown lion, black/white camouflage prints, (Rola-Matic version)	**£8-10**
	Same but with amber glass	**£10-12**
	Same but with purple glass	**£12-15**
	Same but tinted detachable back	**£12-15**

MB 57f   Carmichael Rescue Vehicle

82	White body, 'Police Rescue'	**£8-10**
83	Red body, 'Fire'	**£10-15**

MB 58c   DAF Girder Truck

70	Cream or off-white cab and body, red base (with 'Pat App' on some)	**£80-100**
70-71	Metallic lime green cab and body	**£15-18**

MB 58d   Woosh 'n' Push

72-75	Yellow body, red interior, '2' label	**£4-6**
	Same but pale yellow interior	**£25-30**
	With red interior, 'flower' label	**£12-15**
76	Metallic red body, pale yellow interior, '2' label on roof	**£6-8**
	Same but '8' and stars label	**£12-15**

MB 58e   Faun Dump Truck

76-81	Yellow body, yellow tipper	**£2-4**
79	Yellow body, red tipper (G5 set)	**£25-30**
82-83	Yellow body, yellow tipper, 'CAT'	**£6-8**

MB 59e   Ford Galaxie Fire Chief

70	Red body, white interior, 'Fire Chief' and side shield labels	**£25-30**

MB 59d   Mercury Fire Chief

71-74	Red body, '59' or '73', 2 men, yellow 'Fire Chief' on bonnet, 'shield' labels on sides	**£15-18**
	Same but 'helmet & axes' on sides	**£12-15**
	Same but yellow bonnet 'helmet and axes' labels, plain sides	**£10-12**
	Same but yellow 'helmet and axes' labels on bonnet and sides	**£10-12**
	Same but with only '59' on base	**£10-12**
78	Same but with no men (TP)	**£8-10**
	Red body, CG, 'Fire', shield (TP)	**£8-10**
	Same but with purple glass (TP)	**£12-15**
79	White, CG, 'Police', shield (TP)	**£18-20**
81	Red body, 'Los Angeles Fire Dept'	

tampo prints (Code Red) **£12-15**
White body, CG or BG, 'Los Angeles Police' tampo prints, (Code Red) ... **£12-15**

82	White body, CG, PG or BG, 'Police' and shield, black wing panel prints	**£10-15**
	White body, CG or BG, 'Metro Police', black wing tampo prints as 10f	**£8-10**
	Same but with white wing panels	**£10-12**

MB 59e   Planet Scout

75-77	Metallic green and lime green	**£3-5**
78-80	Metallic red and light brown	**£8-10**
77	Avocado/black, PG or AG (Adventure 2000 K2005 Command Force set)	**£20-30**
80	Metallic blue/black, PG, (Adventure 2000 set)	**£50-60**

MB 59f   Porsche 928

80-81	Light metallic brown body, brown interior, black base, clear glass	**£4-6**
	Same but cream or off-white interior	**£6-8**
	With brown interior, amber glass	**£8-10**
	Dark metallic brown body, brown interior, black base	**£4-6**
	Same but with amber glass	**£8-10**
	Same but with brown glass	**£10-12**
	With clear glass, brown or grey base	**£8-10**
	With AG, brown or grey base	**£10-12**
81-82	Metallic blue body, brown interior, clear glass, black base	**£4-6**
	Same but with grey or silver base	**£6-8**
82-83	Black body, brown interior, 'Porsche'	**£4-6**
	Same but with red interior	**£6-8**

MB 60b   Truck with Site Office

70	Blue truck, yellow/green office	**£18-20**

MB 60c   Lotus Super 7

71-75	Orange body, black interior and boot, bonnet 'flame' label	**£8-10**
	Same but with Yellow body	**£12-15**
75-76	Same but blue stripe and check design + bonnet '60' prints, (Streakers)	**£12-15**

MB 60d   Holden Pick-up

77	Metallic ruby red body, yellow interior, AG, yellow bikes, '500' label	**£10-12**
77-80	Bright red body, yellow interior, AG, yellow bikes, '500' label	**£4-6**
	Same but with orange glass	**£6-8**
	Bright red body, red interior, orange or AG, olive green bikes, '500' label	**£8-10**
	Bright red body, red interior, orange or AG, olive green bikes, 'Sun' label	**£15-18**
	Bright red body, yellow interior, AG, yellow bikes, 'striped' bonnet label	**£15-18**
80	Metallic blue body, yellow interior, orange or amber glass, yellow bikes, 'Paris-Dakar 81' (French issue)	**£12-15**
81-83	Cream body, red interior, orange or AG, red bikes, stripes and Superbike'	**£5-7**
	Same but with yellow bikes	**£8-10**
	Cream body, red interior, AG, red bikes, 'Honda' labels	**£18-20**

MB 61b   Alvis Stalwart

66-71	White body, yellow detachable top, clear glass, 'BP Exploration' labels, regular black wheels, yellow hubs	**£30-40**
78	Metallic olive green body, fixed top, GG, black wide wheels (TP)	**£20-25**

MB 61c   Blue Shark

71-77	Metallic blue, UB or SB, CG, '86'	**£4-6**
	Same but with '69' label from 69d	**£8-10**
	Metallic blue body, SB, CG or AG, 'Scorpion' label on bonnet	**£25-30**
	Metallic blue body, UB or SB, AG, bonnet arrows '86' label	**£8-10**
	Same but '69' label from 69d	**£10-12**

MB 61d   Wreck Truck

78-80	Red body, white arms, red hooks, BB or GB, AG and 2 roof lights	**£3-6**
	With red or white arms, black hooks	**£3-5**
	Red body, red arms, red hooks	**£8-10**
	Red body, white arms, red hooks, BB, blue glass and 2 roof lights	**£25-30**
81	Red body, off-white arms, red hooks, BB, AG, 'Radio Despatches 24 Hour Towing' tampo prints (TP)	**£8-10**
81-82	Light yellow body, red arms, black hooks, AG, black or grey base	**£3-5**
	Same but with brown base	**£6-8**
	Same but with silver base	**£8-10**
	With red arms & hooks, BB or GB	**£3-5**
	Light yellow body, white arms, red hooks, BB or GB, AG and lights	**£20-25**
	Light yellow body, green arms, red or black hooks, BB or GB, AG lights	**£6-8**
	Dark yellow body, red arms, black hooks, BB, AG	**£3-5**
	Same but with brown base	**£6-8**
	Dark yellow body, red arms, red hooks, BB or GB, AG and lights	**£3-5**
	Dark yellow body, white arms, red hooks, BB, AG and lights	**£20-25**
	Dark yellow body, green arms, red or black hooks, BB, AG and lights	**£12-15**
	Same but with grey base	**£15-20**

MB 61e   Peterbilt Wreck Truck

82-83	Red-orange, white 'Eddies Wrecker'	**£2-4**
	Same but with black tampo prints	**£6-8**
	Blue body, no tampo print, from 'Highway Express' Gift Set)	**£20-25**

MB 62c   Mercury Cougar

70	Light metallic gold or gold-green body red interior	**£20-25**

MB 62d   Mercury Cougar Dragster

70	Light green body, red interior, UB, 'Rat Rod' labels	**£15-18**
70-73	Same but lime green body	**£10-12**
	Same but with silver base	**£25-35**
	Same but UB, 'Wild Cat' labels	**£25-30**

MB 62e   Renault 17TL

74-78	Red body, white interior, '9' label	**£6-8**
	Red-orange body, white interior, '9'	**£6-8**
	Same but label reversed to read '6'	**£8-10**
76	Red body, white interior, 'Fire' labels, (from G12 Rescue set)	**£15-18**

MB 62f   Chevrolet Corvette

79-81	Metallic ruby red body, grey interior, UB, CG, white bonnet prints	**£4-6**
	Same but with black interior	**£6-8**
	Same but white interior	**£12-15**
	Same but with black interior	**£6-8**
	Same but with grey interior	**£4-6**
81-83	Black body, grey interior, UB, CG, orange/yellow bonnet stripes	**£3-5**
	Same but with silver base	**£5-7**
83	Same but UB, opaque glass, (from Streak Racing set)	**£10-12**

MB 63c   Dodge Crane Truck

70-72	Yellow body, yellow crane, arm and hook (orange hook on some)	**£12-15**

MB 63d   Freeway Gas Tanker

73	Red/black/white, 'Castrol' labels	**£60-70**
73-77	Red/black/white, 'Burmah' labels	**£4-6**
	Same but with tow hook hole in rear	**£6-8**
76	Military olive drab green and black, 'Canadian' flag labels (TP)	**£300-400**
	Same but with 'French' flag (TP)	**£70-80**
76-77	Military olive green cab black base, '95 High Octane' labels (TP)	**£18-20**
77	Light blue/black/white, 'Aral' labels (German issue)	**£20-25**

78-79 Red/black/white, 'Chevron' labels,
tow hook hole in rear of tanker............**£6-8**
Same but with white tow hook (TP)..**£8-10**
Red/black/white, 'Burmah' labels,
cream tow hook (TP) **£8-10**

79-80 White/yellow, 'Shell' labels, PG...........**£6-8**
Same but with red glass **£10-12**
Yellow/black/white, 'Shell', PG **£15-18**

80-81 White/yellow, 'Exxon' labels...........**£15-18**
White/black, 'Exxon' labels............**£15-18**
White/yellow, 'Shell' labels,
cream tow hook (TP) **£6-8**
White/yellow, 'Exxon' labels,
cream tow hook (TP) **£15-18**

81-82 White/black/green, 'BP Super' **£8-10**
White/yellow, 'BP Super' (TP).......**£20-25**

MB 63dx Freeway Gas Trailer

78-79 White/red, 'Chevron' labels (TP) **£8-10**
Same but with 'Burmah' labels (TP).**£8-10**

80-81 White/yellow, 'Shell' labels (TP)......**£6-8**
White/yellow, 'Exxon' labels (TP)..**£15-18**

81-82 White/yellow, 'BP Super' (TP)......**£20-25**

MB 63e 4x4 Open Back Truck

82-83 Orange or light orange body, '24' and
'FWD' or '4x4' prints..........................**£4-6**

MB 64b MG 1100

70 Green body, white interior with man and
dog, unpainted base, clear glass..**£200-225**

70-71 Same but metallic light blue body ...**£18-20**
Same but metallic dark blue body ...**£20-30**

MB 64c Slingshot Dragster

71-72 Metallic pink body, BB, black exhausts,
bonnet flame and '9' labels..............**£10-12**

73 Orange body, BB, black exhausts,
bonnet flame and '9' label **£90-100**
Same but red exhausts.................**£150-200**

73-75 Metallic blue-green body, UB, red
exhausts, bonnet flame, '9' label ...**£15-18**
Same but BB, front NW or WW.........**£6-8**
Same but with '3'............................**£18-20**

MB 64d Fire Chief Car

76-79 Red body, 'Fire', some yellow shield
labels have black edging **£4-6**
Same but with orange body **£6-8**

MB 64e Caterpillar D-9 Tractor

79-81 Yellow body, brown roof, yellow shovel,
black tracks, orange or yellow rollers..**£4-6**

82 Yellow body, black roof, yellow shovel,
'C' on cab, black tracks, yellow rollers **£6-8**

82-83 Same but black shovel, black or silver
tow hook, 'C' on cab..........................**£4-6**
Same plus 'CAT' print, (black hook)...**£6-8**

MB 65c Claas Combine Harvester

67-72 Red body, yellow cutters, black base,
black wheels with yellow hubs **£8-10**

MB 65d Saab Sonnet III

73-76 Metallic blue body, yellow interior,
UB, AG, grey rear door **£6-8**

79 White body, yellow interior, UB, AG,
grey rear door, (Multi Pack)........**£200-225**

MB 65e Airport Coach

NB All Airport Coach models have white roofs

77-81 Metallic blue body, off-white or
pale yellow interior, AG or CG, UB,
'British Airways' **£6-9**
Same but with labels reversed **£10-12**
Metallic blue body, off-white interior,
UB, AG, 'American Airlines' labels .**£8-10**
Same but with clear glass.................**£10-12**
Same but pale yellow interior, AG **£8-10**
Same but with clear glass.................**£10-12**
Metallic blue, off-white or pale yellow
interior, AG, 'Lufthansa' (German) ...**£8-10**

Same but with clear glass.................**£10-12**

81 Orange body, pale yellow interior, UB,
AG, 'Schulbus' (German issue).......**£20-25**

81-83 Red body, 'TWA' **£6-8**
Red body, 'Qantas' **£6-8**

82 Red body, 'Fly Braniff' **£18-20**
White body, 'Stork SB'(Australian) **£12-15**
Metallic Blue body, 'Girobank'
(Promotional issue) **£10-12**

83 Metallic Blue body, UB or SB, AG,
'British' labels....................................**£6-8**
Metallic Blue body, UB or SB, AG,
'Australian' labels...............................**£8-10**
White body, UB or SB, 'Alitalia' **£10-12**
White body, UB or SB, 'Lufthansa' **£18-20**

MB 66c Greyhound Coach

70 Silver body, yellow interior, AG, matt
or gloss BB, 'Greyhound' **£15-18**
Same but with yellow or pink base..**£25-30**

MB 66d Mazda RX500

71-74 Orange body, SE, white base, PG **£6-8**
Same but with unpainted base **£15-20**
Orange body, SE, white base, AG **£10-12**

75-76 Red body, SE, WB, AG, white/green
'77' and stripes(Streakers version) **£6-8**
Same but with PG (Streakers).........**£10-12**
Same but UB, AG (Streakers).........**£10-12**
Red body, light brown engine, WB,
AG, '77' and stripes (Streakers).....**£12-15**
Same but with PG (Streakers)........**£15-18**

MB 66e Ford Transit

77-80 Orange body, green glass, UB,
brown load, green interior...............**£15-20**
Same but light brown interior **£12-15**
Same but light yellow interior **£4-6**
Orange body, amber glass, UB,
beige load, green interior **£15-20**
Light brown or light yellow interior **£12-15**

81-82 Yellow-orange body, off-white or green
interior, UB, brown load, green glass ..**£6-8**
Same but with beige load....................**£4-6**
Yellow-orange body, green interior, GB,
brown or beige load, green glass **£6-8**
Same but with black base.................**£15-20**

MB 66f Tyrone Malone Superboss

82-83 White body, blue/red stripes on some,
'Tyrone Malone' on white aerofoil.....**£4-6**
With plain white or cream aerofoil **£2-4**

MB 67b Volkswagen 1600TL

70 Dark or light red body,
white interior, UB, CG, NW **£60-70**

70-71 Metallic purple body (may be dark,
mid or light), white interior, UB, CG,
narrow or wide wheels **£18-20**

71-72 Metallic pink body, white interior,
UB, CG, NW or WW **£15-18**

MB 67c Hot Rocker

73-74 Metallic green-gold body, white interior,
UB, CG (Rola-Matic version).........**£10-12**
Same but with silver base **£20-30**
Same but metallic green body, UB **£8-10**
Same but with silver base **£20-30**

75-77 Red body, UB, (Rola-Matic version) ...**£6-8**
Same but with silver base **£20-30**

MB 67d Datsun 260Z 2+2

78-80 Metallic crimson body, white interior,
clear glass, black base **£6-8**
Same but with grey base **£8-10**

79 Metallic blue body, pale yellow
interior, matt black base (TP)...........**£15-20**
Same but with red interior (TP).......**£30-40**
Metallic blue body, red interior,
brown base (TP)................................**£40-50**

80 Metallic red body, pale yellow
interior, black base **£8-10**

81-83 Silver body, red interior, black base....**£4-6**
Same but grey or blue-grey base **£6-8**
Same but with brown base **£8-10**
Silver body, white interior, GB or BB,
red stripes, black 'Datsun 2+2' (TP)....**£6-8**
Silver body, black interior, BB, blue
stripes, black 'Datsun 2+2' (TP)........**£8-10**

83 Black body and interior, BB (TP)....**£20-30**

MB 68c Porsche 910

70-74 Metallic red body, pale yellow interior,
UB, AG, '68' label on bonnet, NW ...**£8-10**
Same + '68' side labels (G3 set)......**£20-25**
Metallic red body, pale yellow interior,
UB, AG, bonnet '68' label, WW **£8-10**
Same but with '45' label from 45c.**£25-30**
Silver body, White interior, UB ...**£100-125**

72 White body, pale yellow interior, UB,
AG, WW ('Brroom Stick' issue) **£30-35**

MB 68d Cosmobile

75-78 Metallic light blue body, yellow under,
white or silver interior, AG **£4-6**

77 Avocado body, white under, white
interior, AG, (Adventure 2000 set)..**£18-20**
Same but with purple glass (set)......**£15-18**
Same but with silver interior (set) ...**£20-30**

78-79 Metallic red body, beige under,
white or silver interior, AG **£8-10**

80 Metallic dark blue, black under, silver
interior, PG (Adventure 2000 set)....**£50-80**

MB 68e Chevy Van

79-80 Orange body, UB, BG, blue/red or
blue/white stripes **£4-6**
Same but CG, blue/red stripes **£10-12**
Same but BG, red/black stripes..........**£4-6**
Same but with green or red glass........**£6-8**

80-81 Orange body, 'Matchbox Collectors
Club' labels, BG (Ltd. Edition) **£15-18**

81-82 White body, 'Adidas' (German) **£18-20**
White body, 'USA-1' (US issue) **£10-12**
Green body, 'Chevy' with brown or
yellow segmented stripes **£4-6**

82-83 Yellow body, 'Collect Exciting
Matchbox' (Australian issue)..........**£18-20**
Silver body, blue glass, 'Vanpire' **£4-6**

MB 69c Rolls-Royce Silver Shadow

69-70 Metallic blue body, brown interior,
tan folded top, BB, AG, NW **£12-15**
Same but dark or light yellow base ..**£20-25**

71-72 Metallic light gold body, brown interior,
tan folded top, BB, AG, WW **£10-12**
Same but dark or light yellow base ..**£20-25**
Same but with silver base **£12-15**
With black folded top, BB **£10-12**
Same but with light yellow base **£20-25**
Same but with silver or grey base **£12-15**
With off-white interior, black folded
top, black base, AG, WW **£10-12**
Same but with grey base **£12-15**
Metallic dark gold, AG, off-white
interior, black folded top, BB, WW .**£10-12**
Same but with grey or silver base **£12-15**
Metallic dark gold body, brown interior,
black folded top, BB, AG, WW.......**£10-12**
Same but with grey or silver base....**£12-15**

72-73 Metallic lime gold body, off-white or
brown interior, black folded top,
BB, AG, WW **£10-12**
Same but with grey or silver base....**£12-15**

MB 69d Turbo Fury

73-77 Metallic red body, CG, '69' and
arrows label, (Rola-Matic version) ...**£8-10**
Same but AG (Rola-Matic version) .**£10-12**
Metallic red body, '86' and arrows
label, (Rola-Matic version) **£12-15**
Same but 'Scorpion' (Rola-Matic)...**£35-40**

MB 69e   Security Truck

78-83   Dark red body, cream roof, UB or SB,
BG, '732 2031', 'Wells Fargo' **£8-10**
Light red body, white roof, SB, CG,
'732 2031' and 'Wells Fargo' **£12-15**
Same but BG, UB or SB **£4-6**
Light red body, white roof, SB, BG,
'QZ 2031' and 'Wells Fargo' **£8-10**

81   Metallic dark green body, SB, BG,
'Dresdner Bank' (German promo)...**£15-18**

MB 70b   Grit Spreading Truck

70   Red cab and body, dark or pale yellow
grit spreader, UB, GG, NW **£10-12**

MB 70c   Dodge Dragster

71-75   Dark pink body, BB, 'snake' labels...**£8-10**
With purple, cream, light green, light
yellow, dark yellow or grey base ...**£25-30**
With brown or unpainted base **£35-40**
Dark pink body, BB, 'Wild Cat' **£40-50**
Dark pink body, 'Rat Rod' labels **£40-50**
Light pink body, BB, 'snake' labels **£15-18**
Bright pink body,BB, 'snake' labels **£15-18**

78   Yellow body, red glass, GB or BB,
side prints, (US Roman Numeral)....**£12-15**

MB 70d   S.P. Gun

76-80   Military green body, black or brown
tracks, (Rola-Matic version) **£3-6**

MB 70e   Ferrari 308 GTB

81-83   Red body and base, black stripe, CG ...**£4-6**
Red body and base, CG, 'Ferrari' **£3-5**
Same but with AG..............................**£6-8**

83   Red body, silver base, no 'Ferrari'...**£8-10**

MB 71c   Ford Heavy Wreck Truck

70-72   Red cab, white body, red crane and
hook, BB, GG, 'Esso' **£15-18**
Same but with yellow hook **£18-20**

79   Military olive green, black hook,
BB, GG, '3LGS64' labels (TP) **£18-20**

81   Dark blue, blue crane, black hook,
BB, GG, no labels (Multi Pack)......**£80-90**

MB 71d   Jumbo Jet

73-75   Metallic blue frame, red elephant head,
dark blue handlebars, black wheels **£6-8**
Same but light blue handlebars........**£20-25**

MB 71e   Cattle Truck

76-81   Metallic orange-red cab, dark yellow
back, BB, GG, or BG, 2 black cattle...**£8-10**
With GG or BB, SB **£6-8**
With AG, PG or orange glass, SB **£8-10**

79-83   Dark red cab, off-white back,
SB, BG, 2 black cattle (TP) **£6-8**
Same but with red or PG (TP) **£8-10**
Dark red cab, dark or light yellow back,
SB, PG, 2 black cattle (TP).................**£8-10**

81-83   Metallic light green cab, off-white back,
SB, OG, 2 brown cattle.......................**£6-8**
Metallic light or dark green cab, yellow
back, SB, red or OG, 2 brown cattle....**£4-6**
Metallic dark green cab, dark brown
back, SB, red or AG, 2 brown cattle....**£4-6**

83   Yellow cab, dark brown back, BB or SB,
red or AG, 2 light brown cattle..........**£4-6**
With dark or light brown back, UB **£4-6**

With light brown back, BB, red or AG,
2 light brown cattle **£4-6**
Yellow cab, dark brown back, BB, UB
or SB, red or AG, black tow hook,
2 light brown cattle (TP).....................**£4-6**

MB 71ex   Cattle Truck Trailer

79-83   Dark red body, off-white or light or dark
yellow back, SB, 2 black cattle (TP) ...**£4-6**

83   Yellow body, dark yellow back, SB,
2 light brown cattle (TP).....................**£4-6**

MB 72b   Standard Jeep

70-71   Dull yellow body, red interior, UB ..**£12-15**
Bright yellow body, red interior.......**£50-60**
Orange body **£15-20**

MB 72c   SRN Hovercraft

72-78   White body, BB, BG, 'R.N.L.I.' **£6-8**

MB 72d   Bomag Road Roller

79-82   Yellow/red, black roller, 2 wheels........**£4-6**
Same but 2 wheels have yellow hubs ..**£6-8**

MB 72e   Dodge Delivery Truck

82-83   Red cab, white back, 'Pepsi'................**£2-4**
Red cab, white back, 'Kelloggs'...........**£2-4**
Either of the above with gold hubs......**£4-6**
Red cab, white back, 'Smiths Crisps'
(Promotional offer)............................**£2-4**
Same but with gold hubs (Promo) **£4-6**

MB 73c   Mercury Commuter

70-71   Metallic lime green body, UB with '59',
'55' or '73', NW or WW **£25-30**

71-73   Red body, UB, 'Bull head' label on
bonnet of some, wide wheels...........**£10-12**

MB 73d   Weasel

74-76   Metallic green body, metallic green and
green base, (Rola-Matic).....................**£6-8**

76   Military olive drab green body,
metallic green and green base,
(Rola-Matic) (TP)............................**£35-40**

76-79   Same but with military olive green
body (Rola-Matic) (TP) **£12-15**
Military olive green body, olive green
and green base, (Rola-Matic) (TP) ..**£12-15**
Same but olive green and black base,
(Rola-Matic) (TP)............................**£12-15**

MB 73e   Ford Model 'A' Car

79-80   Cream body, dark green wings, GG...**£8-10**
Same but no spare wheel or glass........**£6-8**

80   White body, dark green wings, GG ...**£8-10**

80-82   Metallic green body, dark green wings,
GG or no glass **£3-5**

82-83   Light brown body, dark brown wings,
amber glass **£4-6**
Same but with clear glass....................**£6-8**

MB 74b   Daimler Bus

70-72   Red body, white interior, 'Esso'.......**£12-15**
Same but 'dayglo' pink body...........**£18-20**

72   Red body, 'Inn on the Park' labels ..**£70-80**
Red body, 'The Baron of Beef' **£80-90**
Red body, 'Big T Scotch Whiskey'
labels (Promotional).....................**£100-120**
Red body, 'NAMC', 'The Miniature
Vehicle' labels (Promotional).........**£90-100**
Red body, 'Swinging London' **£70-90**

Red body, 'Beefeater Gin' **£70-90**
Red body, 'Fly Cyprus Airways' **£70-90**
Red body, 'Barclays Bank' **£70-90**
Red body, 'Kensington Hilton' **£70-90**
Red body, 'I.C.P. Interchemicals' **£70-90**

MB 74e   Tow Joe

72-77   Metallic green-gold body, UB, AG and
roof light, green arms, Red hooks....**£10-12**
Same but with BB or SB...................**£10-12**
With UB and black hooks.................**£12-15**
Metallic green body, BB, AG and
roof light, green arms, red hooks........**£6-8**

76-81   Yellow body, BB, SB or UB, AG, red
arms, black hooks (TP) **£8-10**
With matt base, red or black hooks**£75-100**
Metallic green body, BB, AG,
red arms, black hooks (TP)..............**£25-30**
Same, BB or SB, white arms (TP).**£90-100**
Red body, BB, AG, red or green arms,
red or black hooks (TP) **£150-175**

82   Yellow body, UB, AG, red arms, black
hooks, 'Hitch Hiker' labels (TP) .**£100-125**

MB 74d   Cougar Villager

78-81   Metallic light or dark green body,
yellow interior, UB, AG...................**£6-8**

81-82   Metallic blue body, yellow or orange-
yellow interior, UB, AG.................**£15-20**

MB 74e   Fiat Arbath

82-83   White body, red interior, 'Matchbox' ..**£4-6**
Same but with black interior...........**£40-60**

MB 75b   Ferrari Berlinetta

70   Metallic green body, off-white interior,
unpainted base, clear glass...........**£100-125**

70-71   Red body, off-white interior, UB,
CG, silver grille on some **£40-50**

MB 75c   Alfa Carabo

71-75   Metallic Purple body, YB, NW..........**£8-10**
Same but with unpainted base **£10-12**

75   Metallic light pink body, YB, WW..**£15-18**

75-76   Metallic light pink or red body,
yellow/black/green prints, WW,
(Streakers version) **£10-12**

MB 75d   Seasprite Helicopter

77-81   White body, Red underside, BG or GG,
black rotors, blue 'Rescue' labels......**£8-10**
Same but with red glass...................**£12-15**
Same but with purple glass.............**£15-18**

MB 75e   Helicopter

82-83   White/orange, black interior, black skids,
AG, 'MBTV News' tampo prints **£6-8**
White/black, black or grey interior, black
skids, AG or CG, 'Police' and '36' **£4-6**
White/black, black or grey interior,
black or grey skids, AG, 'Rescue' **£6-8**

Matchbox Superfast and Miscellaneous Sets

G 1	1970	**Service Station Set**
		Contains 13e, 32d, 15e and 'BP' Service Station......**£100-125**
G 1	1981	**Transporter Set**
		Contains Transporter and 5 Superfast Cars **£30-35**
G 1	1984	**Transporter Set** Contains K10 plus 4 cars.................**£30-35**
G 2	1970	**Transporter Set**
		Contains Transporter and 5 Superfast models **£75-95**
G 2	1973	**Transporter Set**
		Contains Transporter and 5 Superfast models **£75-95**
G 2	1981	**Railway Set** Contains 43e, 2 x 44e, 25f......................**£10-15**
G 2	1987	**Car Transporter Set**
		Contains K120 Transporter plus MB25 Audi Quattro,
		MB33 Renault 11, MB55 Ford Sierra 4x4, MB74 Toyota,
		MB75 Ferrari Testarossa ....NGPP
G 3	1970	**Racing Specials Set**
		Contains 5e, 20d, 45c, 56c, 52c and 68c **£75-95**
G 3	1973	**'WILD ONES' Set** ....Contains 5 Superfast Cars....**£55-65**
G 3	1981	**Racing Car Set** Transporter and 4 Racing Cars.........**£10-15**
G 3	1987	**JCB Gift Set** No details **£25-30**
G 4	1970	**Truck SuperSet**
		Contains 47c, 63c, 58c, 49b, 16d, 21d, 11d and 51c **£55-65**
G 4	1973	**Team Matchbox Set**
		Contains Racing Car Transporter and 4 Racing Cars....**£55-65**
G 4	1981	**Military Assault** Landing Craft + 6 military models.....**£35-40**
G 5	1981	**Construction Set** Contains 5 construction models.....**£25-30**
G 6	1970	**Truck Set**
		Contains 1e, 10d, 21d, 26c, 30c, 60b, 70b and 49b.....**£75-85**
G 6	1973	**Drag Race Set** Contains 6 Superfast Cars...................**£40-50**
G 6	1981	**Farm Set** Contains 6 farming models........................**£30-35**
G 7	1973	**Ferry Boat** With Plastic Boat and 4 Superfast Cars....**£30-35**
G 7	1978	**Car Ferry Set** Contains 3 Cars and Sports Boat **£30-35**
G 7	1981	**Emergency Set** Contains 5 Rescue models **£30-35**
G 7	1984	**Emergency Set** With models 8, 12, 22, 57 and 75 ......**£30-35**
G 8	1984	**Turbo Charged Set**
		Contains Turbo Charger plus 7, 9, 52, 60 and 68..........**£20-25**
G 10	1986	**'PAN-AM' Set**
		Contains 10, 54, 64, 65 and 'Sky-Buster' Boeing.........**£25-30**
G 11	1978	**Strike Force Set** Contains 6 Army Vehicles **£45-50**
G 11	1986	**'LUFTHANSA' Set**
		Contains 30, 54, 59, 65 and 'Sky-Buster' Airbus **£30-40**

G 12	1978	**Rescue Set** Contains 6 Rescue Vehicles **£30-40**
G 13	1978	**Construction Set** Contains 6 Construction Vehicles..**£30-40**
G 14	1978	**Grand Prix Set** Transporter and 4 Racing Cars.........**£25-35**
G 15	1978	**Transporter Set** Transporter and 5 Superfast Cars **£25-35**
G 40	1988	**40 years Set**
		Aveling Barford Road Roller, London Bus, Horse Drawn
		Milk Float Massey Harris Tractor, Dennis Fire Engine.
		(Models may be distinguished from the original issues
		as they have 'Made in China' cast underneath).............**£20-25**
C 6		**Emergency Gift Set** All Japanese Set **£15-20**
C 11		**Airport Gift Set**
		Japanese Foam Pump, Ikarus Coach and Aircraft.........**£20-25**
		Cars Gift Set Japanese set:
		JPS Lotus, VW, Gold Rolls-Royce and Mercedes **£30-35**
		Las Vegas Dodge Set Car and Van **£120-140**
MG 9		**Gear Shift Garage**
		Gear lever operates car lift and four other functions......NGPP
MP804	1990	**Porsche Set**
		Contains MB3 (911), MB7 (959), MB59 (944).............NGPP
---	1971	**Matchbox Crash Game**
		With 4 assorted cars, racetrack, dice and instructions ....NGPP
SS 100		**Smash 'n' Crash** Action Playset with two vehicles....NGPP
		Multi-Pack Gift Set Contains 5 Superfast models......**£20-25**
		'Days Of Thunder'
		Film-related sets issued in the US only:
		i) Modified MB10 Buick Le Sabre in 5 liveries.............NGPP
		ii) Modified MB54f Chevrolet Lumina in 5 liveries ......NGPP
A1	70-73	**Service Ramp** 'CASTROL' **£25-35**
A2	1970	**'Superfast Auto Sales'**
		Plastic kit includes 'MATCHBOX SALES OFFICE',
		'STAR VALUE' stand, 3 'M' flagpoles and 4 lamp
		posts, plus pink card base, signs and advert. stickers.
		25 items in total..**£75-100**
A2	71-73	**'Matchbox' Sales Park**
		Pink card sales park with four lamp posts ....NGPP
A3	c1971	**'Brroooom Stick'**
		Blister-packed car with steering control. Contains
		No.20 Lamborghini Marzal in Yellow and
		No.68 Porsche in White ....NGPP

MICA – The Matchbox International Collectors Association

MICA was founded in 1985 and provides its Members with a bi-monthly magazine which is full of useful information about past, present and future issues across the whole Matchbox and 'Dinky Collection' range of products. All aspects of collecting are included and cover such topics as new releases, variations and past issues and it has a members' advertisement section. Every year, social conventions are held providing talks and exhibitions on Matchbox and where special Matchbox-only auctions take place. A special 'members only' model is issued to commemorate the event.

HOW TO CONTACT MICA
In the UK: Kevin McGimpsey, MICA, PO Box 120, Deeside, CH5 3HE, UK
Tel: 01244 539414, Fax: 01244 303335, E-mail: kevin@matchboxclub.com

In the US and CANADA:
Rita Schneider (Membership Secretary), MICA North America,
PO Box 28072, Waterloo, Ontario, Canada, N2L 6JB
Tel: 519 885-0529, Fax: 519 885-1902.

In AUSTRALIA, NEW ZEALAND and SOUTH PACIFIC:
Elaine Winkworth (Membership Secretary), MICA,
PO Box 26, Winston Hills, NSW 2153, Australia.
Telephone: (02) 9686-6685   Fax: (02) 9686-6970

RECOMMENDED READING
'The Yesteryear Book 1956 - 2000'. Kevin McGimpsey (Editor of the MICA Magazine) and Stewart Orr, assisted by several Club members have produced the ultimate book for MOY collectors. Its 250 pages are packed with details of every variation issued plus diagrams and superb colour photos. Contact MICA for details.

'Collecting Matchbox Diecast Toys – the First Forty Years'
This important book was published in 1989 and contains chapters on every aspect of Matchbox production since 1947. MICA members provided much of the technical input to this well-illustrated book which is now out of print.

Collectors notes

This listing has been researched and compiled by specialist collector Tony Martin of Farnham. Only individual known production models are listed.

Casting variations. The main differences between castings came about when dies were altered for use in other countries and when Matchbox International took over from Lesney. Where 'Made in Macau' or 'Made in Thailand' have been substituted for 'Made in England' for instance, this information appears on raised blocks usually cast on the underside of the model. Some are marked 'SP' instead of 'SB' in the casting. Different factory reference numbers can be found cast on the inside of otherwise identical components. These minor differences help to make collecting more interesting but they are not to be considered as variations which warrant a different price level.

Wheel mountings and retainers vary in thickness or extent depending on the country or year of manufacture. Some models were fitted with a wire undercarriage; this is shown in the listing where appropriate. SB 1 models made in England have wheel retainers 4mm wide and 1mm deep. Those made in Macau have wheel retainers 2mm wide and 1mm deep. SB 1 models from Thailand have wheel retainers 2mm wide and 2mm deep.

Printed detail. Some models have logos, printed detail or artwork applied as self-adhesive labels, most is applied by tampo-printing. There is much variation to be found here. Labels in particular are liable to be inaccurately cut, crooked, variable in size, shape or printing, wrongly applied or missing altogether.

Tampo-printing can also vary enormously in depth of colour or shade. But remember that these are toys made in the tens of thousands and odd items like these are bound to slip through the net. They have no greater significance than that and consequently no greater value.

Colours. Variations of shade and depth will inevitably be found particularly where metallic colours are used. Models described as being 'silver plated' or 'gold plated' (which also can vary in shade) are just 'vacuum-metallized'. Military models have a camouflage finish which, by its very nature, is likely to vary considerably.

Plastic parts originally specified as white can be found translucent, pure white, cream or ivory. Canopies are usually clear plastic but a variety of colours exists. It is quite possible that alternative colours will be found on models not normally thought to have them - please let us know if you discover any.

Country of manufacture:
E = England, M = Macau, C = China, T = Thailand

Price information:
MPR = Market Price Range
NGPP = no guide price is available at present

Country	Details	Market Price Range

SB 1 Lear Jet

Country	Details	MPR
E	Lemon/white, 'D-ILDE', wire undercarriage	£8-10
E	Lemon/white, 'D-ILDE'	£9-12
E	Yellow/white, 'D-ILDE', wire undercarriage	£8-10
E, M	Yellow/white, 'D-ILDE', 'Gates Lear Jet' on tanks	£8-10
M	Lemon/white, 'Gates Lear Jet' on tanks	£6-8
M	Red, 'Datapost', yellow lettering	£5-8
M	Purple/white, 'Federal Express' orange/white lettering	£5-8
M, T, C	White/orange, 'QXpress', pale orange stripes/band	£5-8
M, T	White, 'USAF'	£8-11
M	Color-Changer, 'USAF'	£8-11
M	White, 'JCB', 'G-JCB' markings (issued in set only)	£12-15
T, C	White, 'DHL' in red	£5-8

SB 2 Corsair A7D

Country	Details	MPR
E	Green/white, 'Stars and Stripes' on wings, 'LA282' on fin, wire undercarriage	£10-12
E	Green/white, 'Stars and Stripes' on wings, 'LA282' on fin	£10-12
E	Metallic light blue/white, 'Stars and Bars' on wings, 'LA282' on fin	£10-12
E	Metallic light blue/white, red/white/blue/yellow roundels on wings	£40-50
E, M	Metallic blue/white, 'Stars and Bars' on wings, 'LA282' on fin	£8-10
M, T	Camouflage, 'Stars and Bars' on wings, 'LA282' on fin	£5-7
M	Color-Changer, 'Stars and Bars' on wings, 'LA282' on fin	£8-11

SB 3-A A300B Airbus

This model was later renumbered SB28.

Country	Details	MPR
E	White/silver, `Air France' labels or tampo print, wire undercarriage	£5-8
E	White/silver, `Air France'	£5-8
E	White/silver, `Lufthansa', `D-AXJI'	£5-8
E	White/silver, `Delta', `N601DA'	NGPP

SB 3-B Space Shuttle

Country	Details	MPR
E	White/grey, `NASA UNITED STATES' label	£5-8
M	White/silver, `NASA UNITED STATES' labels	£5-8
T, C	White/black, `NASA UNITED STATES' labels	£5-8
T	White, no markings. (From 'Graffic Traffic' set)	£6-8

SB 4 Mirage F-1

Earlier issues have a slimmer nose section and are without a hole in the fuselage under the canopy.

Country	Details	MPR
E	Metallic red, yellow/blue/white/red roundels, wire undercarriage	£5-7
E	Metallic red, yellow/blue/white/red roundels	£6-9
E	Red, clear canopy, yellow/blue/white/red roundels	£10-12
M	Metallic maroon, yellow/blue/white/red roundels	£8-10
M, T, C	Yellow/red/blue, `VAQ132'	£6-8
M	Color-Changer, `VAQ132'	£6-8
M, T	White/blue, `Marines ZE-146'	£6-8
T	Red/blue/white, Patrouille de France colours	£6-8
C	Olive/cream camouflage, French roundels on wings	£6-8

SB 5 Starfighter F105

Country	Details	MPR
E	White/silver, `RCAF', blue canopy	£6-8
E	White/silver, `RCAF', blue canopy, wire undercarriage	£10-12
E	Red/silver, `RCAF', blue or clear canopy	£12-15

SB 6 MIG-21

Country	Details	MPR
E	Turquoise/white, round star-shaped labels	£5-8
E	Turquoise/white, star-shaped labels, wire undercarriage	£10-12
E	Blue/white, star-shaped labels, wire undercarriage	£25-30
M, T	Metallic silver, `23', red stars	£6-8
M, T	Black/yellow, `23 988'	£6-8
M	Color-Changer, `25 988'	£6-8
C	Camouflaged, red stars on wings	£6-8

SB 7 Junkers JU87-E Stuka

Country	Details	MPR
E	Black/silver, swastika on fin, wire undercarriage	£40-50
E	Green, swastika on fin, wire undercarriage	£10-12
E	Green, cross or no label on fin	£8-10
E	Gold-plated souvenir issue	£60-70
E	Black/beige/brown, plain fin	£9-12
E	Black/cream, plain fin	£20-25
M	Black/beige/brown, cross on fin	£9-12

SB 8 Spitfire

Country	Details	MPR
E	Dark brown/bronze, fin stripes, wire undercarriage	£30-40
E	Green/gold, fin stripes, wire undercarriage	£8-10
E	Green/gold, plain fin	£7-8
E	Plum/khaki camouflage, plain fin	£12-15
M	Tan/khaki camouflage, plain fin	£5-8

T	Gold/green/camouflage. Intended Kellogg's promotional, not issued	NPP

SB 9   Cessna 402

E	Metallic green/white, brown/orange labels, wire undercarriage	£8-10
E	Metallic light green/white, 'N7873Q'	£5-8
M	Light brown/light beige, 'N402CW'	£6-8
M, T, C	Blue/yellow, 'S7-402'	£6-8
M, T	White/red, 'DHL' in light brown	£6-8
C	Black, yellow 'S7-402' on wings, yellow shield on nose	£25-35
C	Olive, white stars on wings, flaming torch on nose	£25-35
C	White, 'Delivery Service' in red on wings	£6-8

SB 10   Boeing 747

E	'B.O.A.C.', wire undercarriage	£20-25
E	White/gold-plate, 'B.O.A.C.', mounted on pen-stand	£20-30
E	'British Airways', wire undercarriage	£8-10
E	'British Airways' tampo-printed	£8-10
E	White/gold-plate, 'British Airways', mounted on ash-tray	£15-20
E	'MEA' (Middle East Airlines)	£50-60
E	White/dark blue, 'Qantas' in red	£20-25
E	White/silver, 'Qantas' in red	£15-20
E	White/silver, 'United States of America'. 'Airforce One'	£30-40
E	White/blue, 'United States of America'. 'Airforce One'	£60-70
E, M	White with metallic blue or dark blue, 'British'	£25-30
M	'British Caledonian'	£9-12
M, T	'Pan Am'	£5-8
M	'All Nippon Airways', (in set only)	£70-80
M	'Cathay Pacific'	£6-8
M, T	'Lufthansa'	£6-8
M, T	'Virgin'	£6-8
M, T	'Aer Lingus'	£6-8
M, T	'KLM'	£6-8
M	'Japan Airlines'	£70-80
M	'Air France'	£70-80
T	'El Al'	£15-20
T	'South African Airlines'	£15-20
T	'Olympic'	£6-8
T	'Saudi Arabian Airlines'	£6-8
T	'Swissair'	£70-80

SB 11   Alpha Jet

E	Orange-red/white, 'Luftwaffe', wire undercarriage	£12-15
E	Red/white, 'Luftwaffe'	£8-10
E	Blue/red, no markings	£15-20
E, M	White/red, RAF markings, 'AT39'	£10-15
M	Blue/red, red/white/blue stripes on wings, Patrouille de France livery	£5-8
M, T	Blue, '162' on wings	£6-8
C	Black with green/black/yellow roundels, 'AT39'	£25-35
C	Olive, star and 'T30' in white on wings, flaming torch behind canopy	£25-35

SB 12   Mission Helicopter

Issued as a Skybuster in the USA, 'MB57' but no SB number on model £6-8

SB 12-A   Skyhawk

E	Metallic blue/white, 'Navy' on fin, wire undercarriage	£10-12
E	Metallic blue/white, 'Navy' on fin	£15-20
E	Metallic blue/white, 'US Marines'	£8-10

SB 12-B   Pitts Special

SB 12/b can be found with different propeller bosses.

E	Maroon/white, check pattern on wings	£12-15
E	Maroon/white, red/white flares on wings	£15-20
E	Maroon/white, red/white check pattern on top wing, red/white flares on bottom wing	£20-25
E, M	Green/white, red/white flares on wings	£12-15
M	Blue/white, 'Matchbox'	£7-10

M	Red, 'Red Rebels Aerobatics'	NGPP
M, T	Red, 'Virgin', '0293-38222'	£6-8
T	White, red pilot. From 'Graffic Traffic' set	£6-8

SB 13   DC10

E	Red/white, 'Swissair' label, wire undercarriage	£6-8
E	Red/white, 'Swissair' label	£6-8
E	White/silver, 'Swissair'	£6-8
M	White/grey, 'Swissair'	£6-8
E, M	White/silver, 'United'	£6-8
M	White, 'Japan Air Lines'	£70-80
M	White, 'UTA' in blue	£30-35
M, T	'Aeromexico' in red	£6-8
M, T	'Thai', pink/purple/gold stripe	£6-8
M, T	Silver, 'American' in red	£6-8
T	White, 'Scandinavian' in mauve, 'SAS' on fin	£12-15
T, C	White/blue/silver, 'KLM' in blue	£6-8
T	White/silver, 'SABENA' in turquoise	£6-8

SB 14   Cessna 210G

E	Orange/white, black/orange wing stripes, wire undercarriage	£10-12
E	Orange/white, black/orange wing stripes	£7-9
E	Orange/white, 'N94209' on wing	£7-9
E	Red/white, float plane (became SB 26, black floats)	£6-8

SB 15   Phantom F-4E

E	Metallic red/white, RAF markings, large or small fin labels	£8-10
E	Red/white, RAF markings	£15-20
M, T	Grey/orange, 'MARINES', 'AJ135' on fin	£6-8
C	White, '5000 Navy' in black	£6-8

SB 16   Corsair F4U-5N

E	Blue, 'NAVY' on one wing, star on other wing	£10-15
E	Dark orange, 'NAVY' and star	£15-20
M	Orange, 'NAVY' and star	£6-8

SB 17   Ramrod

E	Red/white, lightning labels on wings	£8-10

SB 18   Wild Wind

E	Lime green/white, yellow/orange labels, '7' on fin	£6-8
E	Lime green/white, yellow/orange labels, blue star on fin	£25-30
E	Green/white, orange labels, '7' on fin	£20-25
M	Green/white, orange labels, '7' on fin	NRP

SB 19   Commanche

E	Red/yellow, 'N246P' yellow labels on wings	£6-8
M	Red/yellow, 'N246P' tampo-printed	£6-8
M	White, 'XP' in black, yellow and green stripes on wings	£5-7
M, T, C	Tan/dark blue, 'Piper' on fuselage, 'Comanche' on wings	£6-8

SB 20   Helicopter

Either 'SB 20' or 'SB 25' may be found on the tail rotor of this issue. Some of those with 'SB 20' have been issued in 'SB 25' boxes.

E	Olive, 'Army', white or cream seats	£8-10
E, M	White/red, 'Police', white or cream seats	£8-10
E	White/light blue, 'Coast Guard'	£8-10
E	Yellow/white, no markings	£18-22
M	Metallic dark blue, 'Gendarmerie', 'JAB'	£25-30

SB 21   Lightning

E	Olive/grey or dark olive/grey, 'RAF' markings	£10-12
E	Silver/grey, 'RAF' markings	£10-12
E	Silver, 'RAF' markings	£12-15
E	Silver, 'USAF' markings	£40-50
M	Silver/grey, 'RAF' markings	£12-15

SB 22 Tornado

E, M	Grey/light grey/white, Luftwaffe markings	£6-8
M	Red/white, 'RAF 06' on fin	£5-7
T	Grey/white, 'RAF 06' on fin	£10-12
M, T, C	Grey/white, 'RAF J' on fin	NRP
M	ColorChanger, 'RAF J' on fin	£6-8
C	Grey and olive camouflage, RAF roundels on wings and tailplanes	£6-8

SB 23 Supersonic Airliner

E	White, 'Air France F-BVFA', 'Concorde' on fuselage	£100-150
E, M	White, 'Air France L-EJDA', no 'Concorde' markings	£6-8
T, C	White, 'Air France F-BVFA', no 'Concorde' markings	£6-8
E	White, 'Singapore Airlines'	£75-100
M, T	White, 'Supersonic Airlines', 'G-BSAA'	£6-8
T, C	White, 'British Airways', grey lining on wings	£6-8
T	White, 'British Airways', no lining on wings	£15-20
T	White, no markings (Graffic Traffic)	£6-8
T	White, 'Heinz' logo in red on wings, '57' in red on tail fin	£75-100

SB 24 F16A Fighter

E, M	White/red, 'USAF' markings	£6-8
E, M	White/red, no markings	£10-15
M, T	Red/white, 'USAF', United States Airforce	£8-10
M	White/black, 'Thunderbird' markings	£8-10
M, T, C	Camouflage, 'USAF', '13316' on fin	£6-8
M	Color-Changer, 'USAF', '13316' on fin	£6-8
T	White, no markings, red canopy, (Graffic Traffic)	£6-8
C	Camouflage, Israeli Airforce markings	£6-8

SB 25 Helicopter

SB 20 casting with 'SB 20' removed. Most have two rotor blades and skids. Sometimes issued in SB 20 boxes.

E	Yellow, 'Rescue'	£12-15
E	White/red, 'LA Fire Dept'	£20-25
M	White/red, '007' in black, only issued in a set	£15-18
M	Blue, 'RAF Rescue', yellow rotors	£6-8
C	Blue, 'RAF Rescue', black rotors	£5-8
C	Bluish grey, 'RAF Rescue', black rotors	£6-8
M	Dark blue, 'Air Aid', four wheels	£5-7
M, T	White, 'Shell'	£6-8

SB 26 Cessna Float Plane

E, M	Red/white, 'N246H', (numbered SB14 or SB 26)	£6-8
M	Black/white, 'C210F'	£6-8
M	White, '007 James Bond' in black, only issued in a set	£15-18
M, T	Red, 'Fire', '36' on nose and tail fin	£6-8
C	White, 'National Park Service' in green on wing, green prop.	£6-8
C	White, 'Forest Service' in green on wing, 'FS' on fin, green prop.	£6-8

SB 27 Harrier

E	White/red/blue, 'US Marines'	£8-10
M	White/red/blue, 'US Marines'	£5-8
E	White/red, no markings	£10-12
M	Blue/white or metallic blue/white, 'Royal Navy 100'	£5-8
T	Blue/white, 'Royal Navy'	£6-8
M, T	Light grey/white, 'RAF XZ131'	£6-8
M, T	Camouflage/white, 'US Marines'	£6-8
M	Color-Changer, 'US Marines'	£6-8

SB 28 A300B Airbus

Casting as SB 3.

M	White/silver, 'Lufthansa'	£6-8
M, T	White, 'Alitalia'	£6-8
M, T	Blue/silver, 'Korean Air'	£6-8
M	White/silver, 'Swissair'	£6-8
M	White, 'Iberia'	£6-8
M	White, 'Air Inter'	£25-30
M	Silver, 'Eastern'	£70-80
M, T	'Air France'	£6-8

T	White, 'Air Malta'	£10-12
T	White/silver, 'Delta'	NGPP

SB 29 SR71 Blackbird

M, T	Matt black, 'USAF'	£6-8
C	Silver/black, 'USAF'	£6-8

SB 30 Grumman Tomcat

M, T, C	Grey/white, 'Navy', '610'	£6-8
C	White, star and bars with '15' on wing	£6-8

SB 31 Boeing 747-400

There is no 'SB' on this model.

M, T	White/grey, 'Cathay Pacific' in red	£8-10
T	White/silver, 'Lufthansa'	£6-8
T, C	Grey/dark blue, 'British Airways'	£6-8
T	White/silver, 'Singapore Airlines'	£5-8

SB 32 A10 Thunderbolt

M, T	Camouflage	£5-8
C	Brown/sand, 'Desert Storm' livery	£6-8
C	Cream, orange and green 'blobs' over top of aircraft	£6-8

SB 33 Bell Jet Ranger

M, T	White/blue/orange	£6-8

SB 34 Hercules

M, T	White, 'USCG', orange wing tips	£6-8

SB 35 MIL HIND MI-24 Helicopter

T	Brown/beige, 'USSR', military markings	£6-8
C	Camouflage/grey, '0709' on side	£6-8

SB 36 Stealth Fighter

M, T, C	Dark grey, 'USAF' markings	£6-8
M	White, no markings, (Graffic Traffic)	£12-15
C	Black, 'USAF' markings	£6-8

SB 37 BAe Hawk T Mk.I

There is no 'SB' number marked on this model.

T	Red, 'Red Arrow' livery, white arrow on underside	£6-8
T	Red, 'Red Arrow' livery, no white arrow	£6-8

SB 38 BAe 146

T	White/grey, 'Dan Air'	£5-8
T	White/grey, 'Dan Air-London'	£25-30
C	White, 'Continental', blue/red cheat line	£6-8
C	White, 'Continental', blue/gold cheat line	£5-8

SB 39 Stearman PT17

T, C	Yellow, 'Crunchie'	£6-8
T	Silver, 'Australian National Airways', 'Royal Mail in black	£10-15
T	White, 'Circus Circus', issued in set only	£12-15
C	Blue or yellow, or blue/yellow, or yellow/blue, 'Ditec'	£30-35

SB 40 Boeing 737

T	White/blue/silver, 'Britannia'	£6-8
T	Blue/silver, 'KLM'	£6-8
T	White, 'Lufthansa'	£15-20

SB 41 Boeing 777

C	White, in prototype aircraft colours, in double pack only	**pack: £30-35**
C	Unpainted, in double pack only	**pack: £30-35**

Matchbox Models of Yesteryear

Many variants of Yesteryears have resulted from long production runs which often required renewal or modification of worn dies. Considerable numbers of model variations have thus been issued over the years, some of them quite minor. The objective of this listing is to identify for the Yesteryear collector all those price-significant variations which really do matter. Collectors requiring details of the all the variations issued should contact:

The Matchbox International Collectors Association (M.I.C.A.)
13a, Lower Bridge Street
Chester
Cheshire CH1 1RS England
Telephone: (01244) 346297

This new listing has been extensively updated by Yesteryear authorities Horace Dunkley and John Clark. It therefore provides a more meaningful and realistic guide to the somewhat buoyant nature of Yesteryear prices in recent times.

Identification

Common features. Many models have common identifying features and these are shown below to avoid unnecessary repetition in the Features column.
Model name and number. Both **'Models of Yesteryear'** and **'Made in England by Lesney'** are cast underneath all models issued up to the end of 1982. With the change of ownership this was replaced by **'Matchbox Intl Ltd.'** From 1987 **'Made in Macau'** appears on the base. All models have their 'Y' number shown underneath.

Wheels. All the wheels prior to 1970 were of metal construction. From 1972 (approximately), plastic wheels were used on all models. Nevertheless the models issued at this changeover period are to be found with either metal or plastic wheels. The varieties of wheels are:
  Metal Spoked Wheels
  Metal or Plastic Spoked Wheels
  Plastic Bolt Head Wheels
  Plastic Spoked Wheels
  Solid Spoked Wheels

Scale of models ranges from 1:34 to 1:130. The scale of each model is usually shown on its box.

Logos and designs. The early models had waterslide transfers. Labels have also been used and currently models are tampo printed. The abbreviation 'RN' means 'racing (or rally) number'.
Catalogue listings. Do not place too much reliance on the model colours shown in catalogues. Very often the pictures shown are from mock-ups in colours never actually issued. For example, the 1969 catalogue showed a picture of a blue Y-5 Peugeot that was issued in yellow. Similarly the 1973 catalogue showed a silver Hispano Suiza which was then issued in red.
Bumpers, dashboards, headlights, radiator shells and windscreens. All assumed to be of metal construction prior to 1974 (approx.), after which plastic was increasingly used.
Base plate and chassis are usually of metal construction. Exceptions include the Y30 Mack Truck.
Tyres are of treaded black plastic unless otherwise indicated.
Seats are all made of plastic unless otherwise indicated.

Boxes

1956-57	All card box with just a plain black number shown on box ends. Line drawing of model on the front of box.
1957-60	All card box with line drawing of model used for first 15 models issued, blue number shown on white circle on endflap.
1960-61	As first box but with a red number. All card box with coloured picture of the model (3 varieties of this box exist). All card box with model pictures on the box endflaps.
1968-69	Pink and yellow box with clear window.
1968-70	As previous box with hanging display card (developed in the US market and led to blister-pack design).
1969-70	Mauve and yellow box with window.
1974-78	'Woodgrain' window box in various colours.
1979-83	'Straw' (light cream), window box.
1984-90	'Red' (maroon), window box.
1990	'New-style red'. Bigger, folded clear plastic
1993-94	New style direct mail high quality card boxes with full colour box model picture designs.
From 1995	Matchbox 'direct-mail' boxes have become more pictorial and specialised.

Market Price Range
NGPP = no price grading possible at present.
GSP = Gift Set price

Intro	Ref, details	MPR

Y1-1 Allchin Traction Engine

Scale 1:80. Early issues have rear wheel treads with a straight-across pattern, second type are diagonal; third type has a smooth tread.

1956	Green body, full gold trim, straight across treads on rear wheels. Copper boiler door	**£150-200**
	Green body, full gold trim, straight across treads on rear wheels. Green boiler door	**£200-300**
	Green body, full gold trim, angled treads on rear wheels. Copper boiler door	
	Green body, full gold trim. Red angled treads on rear wheels. Copper boiler door	**£100-125**
	Green body, full gold trim, angled treads on rear wheels. Gold boiler door	**£70-90**
	Green body, full gold trim. Red angled treads on rear wheels. Gold boiler door	**£100-125**
1960	Green body, full gold trim, angled treads on rear wheels. Green boiler door	**£175-250**
	Green body, partial gold trim, angled treads on rear wheels. Green boiler door	**£175-250**
	Green body, partial gold trim, angled treads on rear wheels. Gold boiler door	**£70-90**
1963	Green body, partial gold trim. Red angled treads on rear wheels. Gold boiler door	**£100-125**
	Green body, partial gold trim, angled treads on rear wheels. Silver boiler door	**£90-110**
	Green body, partial gold trim. Red angled treads on rear wheels. Silver boiler door	**£100-125**
1965	Green body, partial gold trim. Smooth rear wheels. Gold boiler door	**£750-1,000**
	Green body, partial gold trim. Smooth rear wheels. Silver boiler door	**£750-1,000**

Intro	Ref, details	MPR

Y1-3 1911 Ford Model 'T'

Scale 1:42. All Y1-3 models have 'brass effect' finish wheels.

1964	Red body and chassis, 2 holes in base, Black smooth roof, twin brake lever	**£90-120**
	Red body and chassis, 2 holes in base, Black smooth roof, single brake lever	**£10-20**
	Red body and chassis, no holes in base, Black smooth roof, single brake lever	**£10-20**
	Red body and chassis, no holes in base, Black smooth roof, small wheels, single brake lever	**£35-45**
	Red body and chassis, no holes in base, Black textured roof, single brake lever	**£80-100**
1964	All models produced from this date had no base holes, only single brake levers and chrome effect finish wheels. Milky White body, Red chassis, Black textured roof, Bright Red seats, 12-spoke wheels	**£80-100**
	Milky White body, Red chassis, Black textured roof, Dark Red or Black seats, 12-spoke wheels	**£80-100**
	Milky White body, Red chassis, Dark Red textured roof, Dark Red or Black seats, 12-spoke wheels	**£5-10**
	Milky White body, Red chassis, Dark Red textured roof, Dark Red or Black seats, 24-spoke wheels	**£5-10**
	Milky White body, Red chassis, Dark Red textured roof, Bright Red seats, 12-spoke wheels	**£15-25**
1975	Cream body, Red chassis, Dark Red textured roof, Dark Red or Black seats, 12-spoke wheels	**£10-15**
	Cream body, Red chassis, Dark Red textured roof, Dark Red or Black seats, 24-spoke wheels	**£10-15**
	Cream body, Red chassis, Dark Red textured roof, Bright Red seats, 12-spoke wheels	**£15-25**
1984	Black body and chassis, Black textured roof, Fawn seats, Brass 12-spoke wheels (in 'Connoisseur Collection')	GSP

Two fine collections of Models of Yesteryear showing various stages in the
early development of their box design.

Y1-3 1936 Jaguar SS100

Scale 1:38. All have Black seats and Chrome wheels with 12 or 24 spokes.

1977 Off-White body, small side lights, 24-spoke wheels **£165-175**
     Light Cream body, large side lights, 24-spoke wheels **£5-10**
1978 Steel Grey body, large side lights, 24-spoke wheels **£150-175**
1979 Steel Blue body, large side lights, 12 or 24-spoke or solid wheels..**£5-10**
1981 Dark Green body, large side lights, 24-spoke wheels......................**£5-8**
1986 Pale Yellow body, large side lights, 24-spoke wheels **£50-60**
     Yellow over sprayed Dark Green body, large side lights,
     24-spoke wheels..**£20-40**
NB The above have 'Lesney' bases.
The following models all have large side lights and 24-spoke wheels.
1987 Dark Yellow body, 'Made in Macau' base **£8-12**
1991 Bright Red body, 'Made in China' base **£10-15**
1992 Model made entirely in pewter, mounted on wooden plinth.........**£20-25**
1994 Bright Red body, Tan steering wheel, 'Made in China' base........**£15-20**

Y2-1 1911 'B'-type London Bus

Scale 1:100. The diecast driver may be found in any shade of mid or dark blue, sometimes black.

1956 Red body, Grey wheels, 4 over 4 windows **£100-150**
The following models all have 8 over 4 windows.
1956 Red body, Grey wheels, bare metal ceiling **£55-80**
1958 Red body, Grey wheels, Tan ceiling **£55-80**
1959 Red body, Grey wheels, Tan ceiling, riveted axles......................**£55-80**
1961 Red body, Black wheels, Tan ceiling, riveted axles **£75-95**

Y2-2 1911 Renault Two-Seater

Scale 1:40. Note that the red pigment used in the plastic seats is prone to fading in bright light.

1963 Green body, 4-prong spare tyre carrier, gap at sides
     between bonnet and radiator **£50-80**
1964 Green body, 4-prong spare tyre carrier, no bonnet/radiator gap....**£20-30**
     Green body, 3-prong spare tyre carrier, no bonnet/radiator gap....**£15-25**
1968 Green body, Black plastic steering wheel....................................**£10-20**

Y2-3 1914 'Prince Henry' Vauxhall

Scale 1:47. The model usually has 24-spoke wheels.

1970 Red body and chassis, Brass petrol tank.....................................**£5-15**
     Red body and chassis, Copper petrol tank...............................**£250-300**
1975 Blue body and chassis, Copper petrol tank, Bright Red seats....**£650-850**
     Blue body and chassis, Brass petrol tank, Cream seats...................**£5-10**
     Blue body and chassis, Copper petrol tank, Cream seats..............**£10-20**
1978 Blue body and chassis, 12-spoke Chrome wheels, Cream seats **£25-30**
     Orange body, Black chassis **£100-125**
1979 Bright Red body, Black chassis **£5-10**

Y2-4 1930 4½ litre Bentley

Scale 1:40.
1985 Dark Green body and chassis, 'Made in England' base....................**£5-7**
1988 Dark Green body and chassis, 'Made in Macau' base **£15-20**
1989 Dark Blue body and chassis, 'Made in Macau', plain White box..**£30-35**
1990 Dark Blue body and chassis, 'Made in Macau', window box.........**£8-12**
1991 Dark Blue body and chassis, 'Made in China' base.....................**£10-20**
1991 Burgundy body and chassis, 'Made in China' base......................**£10-15**

Y3-1 1907 'E'-class Tramcar

Scale 1:130. All versions have a bright Red body with Yellow 'LONDON TRANSPORT' fleetname and 'NEWS OF THE WORLD' decals.

1956 Cream roof, Silver lights, metal wheels, thin 'cowcatcher'
     guards, gap under stairs, hole to top deck, Black base..............**£125-175**
     Same but with Grey base **£150-250**
1957 Cream roof, Silver lights, metal wheels, thick 'cowcatcher'
     guards, gap under stairs, hole to top deck, Black base................**£80-100**
     Cream roof, Gold lights, metal wheels, thick guards,
     gap under stairs, hole to top deck, Grey base **£150-250**
1958 Cream or White roof, Silver or Gold lights, metal wheels,
     thick guards, partial gap or no gap under stairs, hole to
     top deck, Black base **£50-65**
1962 White or Cream roof, Gold lights, Black plastic wheels.............**£50-70**
1965 White roof, Gold lights, Black plastic wheels,White guards **£90-170**

Y3-2 1910 Benz Limousine

Scale 1:54. The model usually has Dark Green or Dark Red seats and radiator grille (exceptions noted).

1965 Cream body and chassis, Dark Green roof,
     open rear mudguard struts...**£15-25**
     Cream body and chassis, Dark Green roof,
     closed rear mudguard struts...**£10-20**
1969 Cream body and chassis, Light Yellow roof...........................**£140-225**
     Light Green body, Dark Green roof...**£150-225**
     Light Green body, Light Yellow roof, open rear struts **£200-275**
     Light Green body, Light Yellow roof, closed rear struts...............**£10-20**
     Light Green body, Light Yellow roof, Black plastic
     steering wheel...**£10-20**
1970 Light Green body, Black roof, Light Green metal or
     Black plastic steering wheel..**£90-125**
     Dark Green body, Light Yellow roof, 2 holes in base **£250-300**
     Dark Green body, Light Yellow roof, no holes in base **£350-400**
     Dark Green body, Black roof, 2 holes in base or no holes...........**£15-25**
1984 Black body and chassis, Matt Black roof, Tan seats, Brown grille.
     In Connoisseur Set ....GSP

Y3-3 1934 Riley MPH

Scale 1:35. Except where noted, models have Chrome 12 or 24-spoke wheels.

1974 Purple body and chassis, Black seats and grille **£175-225**
     Purple body and chassis, Off-White seats and grille.....................**£30-50**
1975 Ruby Red body and chassis, Black seats and grille,
     Chrome 24-spoke wheels **£175-225**
     Ruby Red body and chassis, Off-White seats.................................**£10-15**
1976 Same but Bright Red body and chassis **£10-15**
1977 Light Red body and chassis, Off-White seats, Chrome 12 or
     24-spoke or Red 12-spoke wheels...**£5-20**
1979 Blue body and chassis, RN '6', Chrome 12 or 24-spoke or
     Red 12-spoke wheels **£5-20**
     Blue body and chassis, RN '3', Chrome 24-spoke wheels **£30-35**

Y3-4 1912 Ford Model 'T' Tanker

Scale 1:35. **Except where noted**, wheels have 12 spokes; chassis and seats are Black.

'BP'
1981 Green body, Red tank, 'No. Y12' cast on base,
     'B.P.' with shadow effect...**£90-120**
     Same but without 'No. Y12' cast on base **£5-10**
     Green body, Red tank, 'B.P.' without shadow effect.......................**£5-10**
     Green body, Red tank, Black tank filler caps...............................**£50-75**
     Green body, Red tank, Gold or Chrome wheels............................**£15-25**

'ZEROLENE'
1981 Green body and tank, Gold or Red wheels.................................**£30-60**

'EXPRESS DAIRY'
1983 Blue body and tank, Gold, Red or Chrome wheels........................**£5-20**
     Blue body and tank, Tan seat, Gold wheels..................................**£20-25**

'CARNATION'
1984 Cream body, Plum Red tank and chassis, Bright Red
     12 or 24-spoke or Gold 12-spoke wheels, 'Lesney' base................**£5-10**
     Cream body, Plum Red tank and chassis, Pinkish Tan seat,
     Bright Red 12-spoke wheels, 'Lesney' base.................................**£20-30**
     Cream body, Plum Red tank and chassis, Bright Red
     or Plum Red 12 spoke wheels, 'Matchbox Int'l' base **£5-15**

'MOBILOIL'
1985 Bright Red cab, Dark Blue tank, Black seats, Red wheels........**£10-20**
     Bright Red cab, Dark Blue tank, Pinkish Tan seat,
     Red or Gold 12-spoke wheels...**£5-15**

'CASTROL'
1986 Dark Green body and tank, Dark Tan, Pinkish Tan or
     Black seat, Maroon wheels, 'Lesney' base..................................**£10-20**
     Dark Green body and tank, Pinkish Tan seats,
     Gold wheels, 'Lesney' base **£10-15**
     Dark Green body and tank, Dull Red, Maroon,
     Gold or Chrome wheels, 'Matchbox Int'l' base **£5-15**

Matchbox 'Models of Yesteryear'

'RED CROWN'
1986 Bright Red body and tank, 'Lesney' base......................................£15-20
Bright Red body and tank, Matchbox 'Limited Edition' base £10-15
Bright Red body and tank, 'Matchbox © 1985' base....................£20-30
Same but 'Matchbox ©1986' base £10-15

'SHELL'
1989 Yellow body and tank, Black chassis, 'Matchbox Macau' base £5-10

Y4-1 1928 Sentinel Steam Wagon

Scale 1:100. **'SAND & GRAVEL SUPPLIES'**. All have Black chassis.

1956 Blue cab and body, Grey metal wheels, crimped axles £50-70
Blue cab and body, Grey metal wheels, riveted axles £80-110
Blue cab and body, Black plastic wheels, riveted axles £100-130

Y4-2 1905 Shand-Mason Fire Engine

Scale 1:63. All have Red metal body, two horses, three plastic firemen, and metal wheels (13 spokes front, 15 rear).

1960 'Kent' Fire Brigade, Grey Horses, Dark Grey or
White manes and tails £450-600
'Kent' Fire Brigade, White horses..£125-150
1963 'London' Fire Brigade, White horses, hose locker horizontal ...£175-225
'London' Fire Brigade, White horses, no hose locker ribs £100-125
1965 'London' Fire Brigade, Bronze horses..............................£250-300
'London' Fire Brigade, Black horses...£100-150

Y4-3 1909 Opel Coupé

Scale 1:38.

1967 White body and chassis, roof to body pins,
Maroon grille and seats £100-125
Same but with Red grille, Maroon seats.....................................£20-30
1968 White body and chassis, roof to body pins, Red grille and seats ...£10-15
1970 White body and chassis, roof to seat pins, Red grille and seats.....£10-15
Same but with Maroon seats...£10-20
1971 White body and chassis, Tan textured roof with rear window,
Red seats £250-300
Same but with Maroon seats £275-325
1975 Orange body, gloss Black chassis, Black textured roof,
Maroon seats £25-30
Same but with matt Black chassis £5-10
1984 Bright Red body, Dark Red chassis, Tan textured roof,
Ruby Red seats, in Connoisseur Set ....GSP

Y4-4 1930 Duesenberg 'J' Town Car

Scale 1:43. **Except where noted,** hood colour is the same as the seat colour.

1976 White body, Orange-Red or Red chassis, Yellow seats.........£1750-2000
White body, Orange-Red or Red chassis, Black seats...........£1750-2000
1976 Dark Red body and chassis, Black seats, hollow air horns £15-20
Dark Red body and chassis, Black seats, solid air horns £10-15
Dark Red body and chassis, Black seats,
Chrome 12-spoke wheels...£20-25
Dark Red body and chassis, Maroon seats £200-250
Dark Red body and chassis, Dark Green seats £90-120
1979 Light Green body and chassis, Lime Green side and rear panels,
Dark Green seats, solid or 24-spoke Chrome wheels....................£60-75
Light Green body and chassis, Lime Green rear panel only,
Dark Green hood seats, solid or 24-spoke Chrome wheels.............£5-10
Light Green body and chassis, Lime Green side panels,
Black seats, Chrome solid wheels...£15-20
1983 Brown body and chassis, Dark Cream side panels, Light Cream,
Beige or Rust Brown seats, Chrome 24-spoke or
solid wheels, 'Lesney' or 'Matchbox Int'l' base £5-10
1986 Silver body, Blue chassis and side panels, Black seats,
Blue 24-spoke wheels, 'Matchbox Int'l England' base...................£5-10
Same but with 'Matchbox Int'l Macau' base £25-30
Same but with 'Matchbox Int'l China' base................................£15-20
1989 Powder Blue body, Dark Blue chassis, Off White hood, Tan seats,
Chrome 24-spoke wheels, 'Matchbox Int'l Macau' base.................£5-10
Same but with 'Matchbox Int'l China' base................................£10-15
1997 Maroon body, Dark Tan chassis and seats, Black hood,
'Matchbox Int'l China' base £20-25

Y5-1 1929 Le Mans Bentley

Scale 1:55. All are finished in British Racing Green

1958 British Racing Green body, Grey folded hood, Silver radiator ..£120-130
Same but with Gold radiator...£130-150
1959 British Racing Green body and folded hood, Gold radiator..........£50-75
Same but with Green radiator..£70-80
1960 British Racing Green body and folded hood,
Gold radiator, riveted axles £50-75
1961 Same but steering wheel is also in British Racing Green £80-125

Y5-2 1929 4½ litre Bentley

Scale 1:52. Model has Union Jacks and racing numbers on its sides, folded windscreen and silver 24-spoke wheels, (spare on nearside).

1962 Apple Green body, Black RN '5', Green or
Dark Red seats and tonneau £250-300
1963 British Racing Green body, Black RN '5', Green seats £35-45
Same but with Dark Red seats..£50-60
Same but with Bright Red seats..£20-25
1968 British Racing Green body, Bright Red seats, Black RN '3' £30-40
Same but with Red RN '6'..£75-100

Y5-3 1907 Peugeot

Scale 1:43. Except where noted, the model has 12-spoke wheels.

1969 Yellow body and chassis, Black roof, no rib on rear edge of
front seat side panels..£75-100
Yellow body and chassis, Black roof, cast rib on rear edge of
front seat side panels, Dark Orange windows £10-20
Same but with Pale Amber windows..£10-20
Same but with Clear windows..£130-150
1975 Yellow body and chassis, Gold roof, Pale Amber windows £130-150
Orange-Gold body, Matt Black roof, Pale Amber windows £75-100
Orange-Gold body and roof, Pale Amber windows £10-15
Orange-Gold body and roof, Dark Orange windows £10-15
1976 Light Gold body, matt Black roof, Pale Amber windows £75-100
Same but with Light Gold roof..£10-15
1977 Light Gold body and roof, Clear windows,
Chrome 12 or 24-spoke wheels £130-160

Y5-4 1927 Talbot Van

Scale 1:47.

'LIPTONS TEA' (with royal crest)
1978 Dark Green body, matt Black chassis and roof,
shadow effect to Light Yellow 'Liptons Tea' £40-50
Dark Green body, gloss Black chassis, matt Black roof,
shadow effect to Light Yellow 'Liptons Tea' £7-12
Same but without shadow effect to 'Liptons Tea' £35-40
Dark Green body, gloss Black chassis, matt Black roof, shadow
effect to 'Liptons Tea', Chrome 12 or 24-spoke wheels £20-25

'LIPTONS TEA' (with City Road address)
1978 Dark Green body, matt Black roof, 'Liptons Tea' with
shadow effect, Dark Green or Olive Green 12-spoke wheels £50-60
Dark Green body, matt Black roof, no shadow effect to
'Liptons Tea, Dark Green 12-spoke wheels £5-10
Same but with Olive Green 12-spoke wheels.............................£10-15
Same but with Chrome 12-spoke wheels....................................£15-25
Same but with Chrome 24-spoke wheels....................................£15-25
Dark Green body, gloss Black roof,
Olive Green 12-spoke wheels..£30-35
Dark Green body, Olive Green 12-spoke wheels,
Lime Green tampo printing, gloss or matt Black roof £40-50

'CHOCOLAT MENIER'
1978-79 Royal Blue body, gloss Black chassis, Off-White
tampo printing, Chrome 12-spoke wheels £15-20
Royal Blue body, gloss Black chassis, Light Yellow
tampo printing, Chrome 12-spoke wheels £5-8
Same but with Chrome 24-spoke wheels....................................£15-20
Same but with Red 12-spoke wheels...£15-25
Same but with solid Red wheels..£20-30
Same but with Dark Green 12-spoke wheels...............................£20-30

'TAYSTEE BREAD'
1980 Bright Yellow body and chassis, Bright Red or
Dark Red 12-spoke wheels **£5-8**
Same but with Black chassis...**£5-10**
Same but with solid Red wheels **£15-20**

'NESTLES'
1981 Blue body and Black chassis, matt Black roof **£230-250**
Same but with gloss Black roof.......................................**£230-250**
Same but with Dark Grey roof...**£5-10**
Same but with Light Grey roof...**£20-30**

'CHIVERS'
1982 Cream body, Dark Green chassis, Black seat, Brass trim,
Dark Red or Bright Red 12-spoke wheels **£5-8**
Same but with Tan seat, Bright Red 12-spoke wheels **£10-15**
With Black seat, Chrome trim, Bright Red 12-spoke wheels........**£10-15**

'WRIGHTS'
1982 Dark Brown body and roof, Beige chassis, Gold trim and
12-spoke wheels..**£150-200**
Same but with Beige roof and chassis **£5-8**
Same but with Chrome trim and 12-spoke wheels.....................**£15-20**
Same but with or Chrome trim and Gold 12-spoke wheels **£15-20**

'EVER READY'
1983 Dark Blue body, Gloss Black chassis, Tan or Black seats **£5-8**
Same but with Pinkish Tan seats **£10-15**

'DUNLOP'
1984 Black body and chassis, Dark Yellow 12-spoke wheels,
Tan or Black seats **£5-15**
Same but with Light Yellow 12-spoke wheels **£35-45**

'ROSES'
1985 Light Cream body, Bright Green chassis and roof,
Black or Tan seats **£5-25**
1986 Light Cream body, Dark Green chassis, Bright Green roof,
Black or Tan seats **£5-25**
1987 Light Cream body, Bright Green chassis and roof,
Red 12-spoke wheels **£10-25**
1988 Light Green body, Bright Green chassis and roof,
'Matchbox Int'l Macau' base **£25-30**

'LYLES'
Bright Green body, Black chassis, Gold 12-spoke wheels.............**£5-10**
Same but with Black 12-spoke wheels **£20-25**

Y5-5 1929 Leyland Titan Bus

Scale 1:76.

'SOUTHDOWN'
1989 Light Green body, Mid-Green chassis, 'Robin Starch' adverts........**£8-15**

'ASHTON-under-LYNE'
1990 Blue body, Black chassis, 'Swan Fountpens' adverts.
Passport Scheme model available in framed cabinet only **£60-70**

'CITY of COVENTRY'
1991 Maroon body, Black chassis, 'Newcastle Brown Ale' adverts **£8-12**

Y6-1 1916 AEC 'Y' type Lorry

Scale 1:100. **'OSRAM LAMPS'**

1957 Pale Blue cab, body and chassis, Grey metal wheels,
crimped axles, Gold or Silver radiator...............................**£1,800-2,000**
Mid Blue cab, body and chassis, Grey metal wheels,
crimped axles, Silver radiator...**£1,800-2,000**
Light Grey cab, body and chassis, Grey metal wheels,
crimped axles, Gold radiator...**£100-120**
Same but with Silver radiator...**£80-100**
1958 Dark Grey cab, body and chassis, Grey metal wheels,
crimped axles, Silver radiator **£140-160**
Same but with riveted axles..**£120-140**
1961 Dark Grey cab, body and chassis, Black plastic wheels,
riveted axles, Silver radiator **£1,500-1,750**
riveted axles, Silver radiator **£1400-1500**

Y6-2 1935 Type 35 Bugatti

Scale 1:48. Model has a black baseplate and gold 8-spoke wheels with a spare
on the nearside. Racing number '6' may be upside-down and appear as '9'.

1961 French Blue body, Gold radiator grille, Red dashboard,
Grey knobbly tyres...**£100-120**
Same but with Black knobbly tyres **£30-40**
Same but with smooth Black tyres **£20-30**
With French Blue body and grille, Black knobbly tyres **£150-175**
Same but with smooth Black tyres **£150-175**
1965 French Blue body, Gold radiator grille, White dashboard........**£350-400**
Italian Racing Red body, Gold radiator grille, White dashboard ...**£20-30**
Same but with Italian Racing Red radiator grille **£150-175**
Italian Racing Red body, Gold grille, Black dashboard **£400-450**

Y6-3 1913 Cadillac

Scale 1:48. Except where noted, the model has 12-spoke wheels.

1968 Light Gold body, smooth Dark Red roof, no lug on windscreen,
no seat pin cut outs, no pips on hood **£100-120**
Same but with pips on hood **£40-50**
Same but with lug on windscreen....................................**£30-40**
Same but with seat pin cut outs **£20-25**
Light Gold body, smooth Dark Red roof, lug on windscreen,
seat pin cut outs, pips on hood, smaller (11mm dia.) wheels....**£50-60**
1970 Dark Gold body, textured Dark Red roof **£80-100**
Same but with smooth Dark Red roof **£15-25**
1975 Dark Gold body, Chrome 12-spoke wheels,
thick spare tyre carrier **£80-100**
Green body, textured Black roof, thin spare tyre carrier **£80-100**
Same but with thick spare tyre carrier, Chrome 12-spoke wheels **£5-10**
Same but with Chrome 24-spoke wheels..........................**£10-15**
Same but with Red or Yellow 12-spoke wheels **£10-15**

Y6-4 1920 Rolls-Royce Fire Engine

Scale 1:48. Except where noted, the chassis is the same colour as the body.

1977 Bright Red body, White ladder with small lugs,
no lugs on body for label **£100-150**
Same but with Brown or Orange ladder with small lugs **£80-120**
Same but with 12-spoke Gold wheels **£70-100**
Bright Red body, Brown or Orange ladder with small lugs, lugs
on body for label, Gold 12-spoke or Chrome 24-spoke wheels....**£15-25**
1978 Bright Red body, White, Brown or Orange ladder with large lugs,
Gold 12-spoke wheels **£7-15**
Same but with Chrome 24-spoke or Red 12-spoke wheels...........**£15-20**
1983 Red body, Red seats, White, Brown or Orange ladder,
bronzed metal side seats or Black plastic side seats.................**£250-350**
1984 Darker Red body, Black chassis, Black seats, White ladder,
Gold 12-spoke or Chrome 12-spoke wheels......................**£5-15**

Y6-5 1932 Mercedes-Benz L5 Lorry

Scale 1:69. **'STUTTGARTER HOFBRAU'**
1988 Cream body and cab, Black steps and mudguards, Grey chassis,
deep body planking **£5-10**
1989 Same but with shallow body planking **£5-10**

Y7-1 1918 Leyland 4-ton Van

Scale 1:100. **'W. & R. Jacob & Co. Ltd.'**

1957 Dark Brown body, bare metal wheels, White roof **£100-120**
Same but with Cream roof **£80-110**
Lighter Brown body, bare metal wheels, Cream roof,
middle line of body transfers missing................................**£750-1,000**
Same but with complete transfer **£75-100**
1959 Reddish Brown body, bare metal wheels, Cream roof **£75-100**
1960 Same but with Black plastic wheels, 24-tread pattern on
front wheels, 32-tread pattern on rear wheels.......................**£750-1,000**

Y7-2 1913 Mercer Raceabout type 35J

Scale 1:46.

1961 Pale Lilac body and chassis, Black knobbly tread tyres.................**£25-65**
Pale Lilac body and chassis, Grey knobbly tread tyres..............**£75-100**
1963 Light Lilac body and chassis, Black fine tread tyres....................**£25-30**
1965 Yellow body and chassis, Gold radiator **£25-30**

Same but with Yellow radiator £30-50

NB On 1961-1963 issues, colour can vary from almost Silver (early issues) to Light Lilac (late issues).

Y7-3 1912 Rolls-Royce

Scale 1:48.

1968 Silver body and bonnet, Dark Red chassis and smooth roof,
Brass 12-spoke wheels, Dark Red seats £15-20
Same but with Yellow seats..£650-750
1969 Silver body and bonnet, Dark Red chassis, Grey ribbed roof,
Brass 12-spoke wheels, Dark Red seats £60-80
Same but with Dark Red ribbed roof.................................£10-20
1974 Silver body and bonnet, Dark Red chassis and ribbed roof,
Dark Red seats, Chrome 12-spoke wheels...................£75-125
Gold body, Silver bonnet, Red chassis and ribbed roof,
Dark Red or Black seats, Brass 12-spoke wheels £75-125
Gold body and bonnet, Red chassis and ribbed roof,
Dark Red or Black seats, Chrome 12-spoke wheels.........£5-10
Same but with Chrome 24-spoke wheels.............................£10-20
Gold body and bonnet, Red chassis and ribbed roof,
Green seats and grille, Chrome 12-spoke wheels.......£250-300
1979 Yellow body and bonnet, Red chassis, Black ribbed roof
and seats, Gold 12-spoke wheels...................................£300-350
Yellow body and bonnet, Black chassis, roof and seats,
Gold or Chrome 12-spoke wheels £8-12
Same but with Red 12-spoke or Chrome 24-spoke wheels...........£12-18

Y7-4 1930 Ford Model 'A' Breakdown Truck

Scale 1:40.

'BARLOW MOTOR SALES'
1985 Orange body, Black chassis and roof, Green crane,
'Made in England' base £5-10
Same but with 'Made in Macau' base £25-30

'SHELL'
1988 Yellow body, Black chassis and roof, Light Green crane................£5-10
Same but with Grey crane..£15-20

Y8-1 1926 Morris Cowley

Scale 1:50.

1958 Tan body, Dark Brown chassis, Silver or Light Copper wheels.....£60-90

Y8-2 1914 Sunbeam Motorcycle and Sidecar

Scale 1:34

1962 Chrome plated motorcycle and sidecar, bare metal wheels,
Black motorcycle seat, Dark Green sidecar seat £35-60
Same but Pale Gold plated motorcycle and sidecar £600-750
1967 Chrome plated motorcycle and sidecar, bare metal wheels,
Black motorcycle seat, Emerald Green sidecar seat..................£250-350
or Black sidecar seat £600-750

Y8-3 1914 Stutz Roadster

Scale 1:48.
1969 Dark Red body and chassis, smooth Tan roof £10-20
Same but with textured Tan roof £30-35
1973 Blue body and chassis, Black textured roof,
White seats and grille...£10-20
Same but with Bright Red seats and grille £35-45

Y8-4 1945 MG 'TC'

Scale 1:35.

1978 Dark Green body and chassis, Tan roof, Chrome 24-spoke wheels,
Red seats £10-15
Same but with Tan seats...£25-35
Same but with Red seats, Green 12-spoke wheels £15-20
Same but with Red seats, Red 12-spoke wheels £25-35
1981 Bright Red body and chassis, Chrome 24-spoke wheels,
Tan or Rust Brown top, Black seats £5-10
Same but with Tan top, Red seats......................................£20-25
With Tan roof, solid wheels £10-15
1982 Darker Red body and chassis, Chrome 24-spoke wheels,

Tan or Rust Brown top, Black seats £5-10
Same but with Tan top, Red seats......................................£20-25
1983 Blue body and chassis, Chrome 24-spoke wheels,
Tan or Rust Brown top, Tan seats.......................................£5-10
Same but with Rust Brown top and Black seats.................£10-15
1984 Cream body and Dark Brown chassis, Chrome 24-spoke wheels,
Tan or Rust Brown top, Tan or Black seats..........................£5-10

Y8-5 1917 Yorkshire Steam Wagon

Scale 1:61.

'JOHNNIE WALKER'
1987 Strawberry Red cab and body, Black chassis, Bright Red
lettering on truck canopy, 2 rivets in cab roof £125-150
Same but with 3 rivets in cab roof....................................£45-50
Same but Maroon lettering on canopy, 3 rivets in cab roof £8-12

'SAMUEL SMITH'
1989 Green cab and body, Black chassis. Passport Scheme model,
available in framed cabinet with nickel-plated components £60-80

'WILLIAM PRITCHARD'
1989 Dark Blue cab and body, Black chassis...............................£5-10

'FYFFES'
Yellow cab and bonnet, Navy Blue chassis....................................£5-10

Y9-1 1924 Fowler Showman's Engine

Scale 1:80. **'Lesney's Modern Amusements'**.

1958 Dark Maroon body, Cream roof, Yellow wheels,
Gold cylinder block...£150-200
Same but with Dark Maroon cylinder block £80-140
Light Purple body, Cream roof, Yellow wheels,
Gold cylinder block..£250-350
Same but with Light Purple cylinder block £250-350
1960 Maroon body and cylinder block, Yellow wheels, Cream roof.....£65-85
Same but with White roof..£100-120
1965 Bright Red body and cylinder block, Yellow wheels,
Cream roof £100-120
Same but with White roof..£80-100

Y9-2 1912 Simplex

Scale 1:48. Except where noted, the model is fitted with 12-spoke wheels.

1968 Lime Green body and chassis...£25-35
1969 Mid Green body, Bright Red seats, smooth Tan roof.................£10-15
Same but with Light Yellow seats....................................£300-350
Same but with Bright Red seats, textured Tan roof..........£25-40
1970 Gold body, Dark Red chassis, Black textured roof, Brass wheels..£20-35
Same but with Chrome 12-spoke wheels..........................£30-45
Same but Brass 12-spoke wheels and Bright Red chassis.........£175-225
1975 Red body & chassis, Black textured roof, Chrome or Red wheels ..£8-20
1979 Dark Red body, Black chassis, Black textured roof,
Bright Yellow seats, Red or Chrome 12-spoke wheels
or Chrome 24-spoke wheels...£8-12
1983 Dark Red body, Black chassis, Yellow textured roof,
Yellow seats, Red 12-spoke wheels...................................£8-12
Same but with Orange-Yellow textured roof.....................£10-15
Same but with Orange-Yellow textured roof and seats £10-20
1986 Yellow body and chassis, gloss Black chassis, plastic diorama
in box, 'Made in England', Yellow or Black textured roof............£8-10
1988 Darker Yellow body and bonnet, gloss Black chassis, diorama in
box, 'Made in Macau', Yellow or Black textured roof £275-300

Y9-3 1920 Leyland 3-ton Lorry

Scale 1:62.

1985 Dark Green cab and truck body, Bright Red chassis....................£15-20

Y9-4 1936 Leyland Cub Fire Engine FK-7

Scale 1:49. 'Special Limited Edition' model, 1989.

1989 Bright Red cab and body, Black roof, Red escape ladders,
'Made in Macau' £40-50

Y10-1 1908 'Grand Prix' Mercedes

Scale 1:54.

1958 Cream body, Black baseplate, Light Green seats £60-95
Same but with White body..£150-220
1959 Cream body, Black baseplate, Dark Green seats £60-95
Same but with White body..£150-220

Y10-2 1928 Mercedes-Benz 36-220

Scale 1:52

1963 White body and chassis, twin spare wheels, 2 holes in base,
Black seats and folded top £1500-1800
Same but with Red seats and folded top....................................£40-50
White body and chassis, single spare wheel, 2 holes in base,
Red seats and folded top £30-35
Same but with twin spare wheels, no holes in base.........................£55-60
Same but with single spare wheel, no holes in base........................£20-30

Y10-3 1906 Rolls-Royce Silver Ghost

Scale 1:51.

1969 Lime Green body, Bronze chassis, Dark Red seats and grille........£15-25
1974 White body, Purple or Ruby Red chassis, Black seats and grille,
Chrome 12-spoke wheels £8-12
With Chrome 24-spoke wheels or Red 12-spoke wheels £15-18
1979 Silver body, Purple chassis, Black seats and grille,
Chrome 12-spoke wheels £350-400
Silver body and chassis, Black seats and grille,
Chrome 12-spoke wheels or Red 12-spoke wheels £5-10
1980 Silver body and chassis, Dark Reddish Brown seats and grille,
Red 12-spoke wheels or Chrome 12-spoke wheels £5-10
1981 Silver body and chassis, Yellow seats, Black grille,
Red 12-spoke wheels £15-30
Same but with Chrome 12 or 24-spoke wheels £35-50
1983 Silver body and chassis, Off-White seats, Black grille,
Red 12-spoke wheels £350-400

Y10-4 1957 Maserati 250F

Scale 1:35.

1986 Red body and chassis, no copyright date on base,
Chrome 24-spoke wheels or Aluminium 24-spoke wheels £10-15
Same but with copyright date cast on base..............................£5-10

Y10-5 1931 'Diddler' Trolley-Bus

Scale 1:76. **'London Transport'**. 'Special Limited Edition' model, 1988.

1988 Red body and Black chassis, 'Ronuk' adverts £15-25

Y11-1 1920 Aveling & Porter Steam Roller

Scale 1:80.

1958 Mid-Green body, boiler and roof, Black roof supports £70-90
Same but with Mid-Green roof supports £70-90
Mid Green body, boiler, roof and roof supports,
Gold makers plate (on front of cylinder housing) £200-250

Y11-2 1912 Packard Landaulet

Scale 1:50.

1964 Dark Red body and chassis, Black bonnet,
4-prong spare tyre carrier £15-40
Same but with 3-prong spare tyre carrier £15-20
1971 Orange-Red body and chassis, Black bonnet,
3-prong spare tyre carrier...£20-30
1984 Cream body and bonnet, Black roof, very Dark Brown chassis.
Only available in 'Connoisseur Collection'...................................GSP

Y11-3 1938 Lagonda Drophead Coupé

Scale 1:43. Except where noted, this model is fitted with 24-spoke wheels.

1972 Gold body, Black seats, floor etc, with Purple chassis.............£700-750
With Dark Red chassis £175-250

With Strawberry Red chassis £125-175
With Light Maroon chassis..£150-200
With Dark Maroon chassis..£20-30
1974 Orange body, Gold chassis, Black seats,
Brass (narrow section) 24-spoke wheels £125-150
Same but with Chrome (wide section) 24-spoke wheels.................£7-15
1975 Copper body, Gold chassis, Black seats, Chrome wheels £7-15
Same but with Red or Chrome 12-spoke wheels........................£12-20
1978 Copper body, Gold chassis, Maroon seats, Chrome wheels...........£7-15
Same but with Chrome solid wheels..................................£12-20
Copper body, Gold chassis, Bright Red seats,
Chrome 24-spoke wheels £250-300
1979 Copper body, Black chassis, Maroon seats,
Chrome solid wheels..£200-250
Dark Cream body, Gold chassis, Maroon seats,
Chrome 24-spoke wheels £200-250
Dark Cream body, Black chassis, Maroon seats,
Chrome 12 or 24-spoke wheels or Red 12-spoke wheels £7-15
Same but with Chrome solid wheels £5-10
1983 Dark Cream body, Black chassis, Black seats,
Chrome solid wheels or Chrome 24-spoke wheels £25-35
1985 Maroon body and chassis, Gold 24-spoke wheels,
Black or Maroon seats. In 1985 'Fathers Day' Set ....GSP

Y11-4 1932 Bugatti type 51

Scale 1:35.
1986 Blue body, Brown seats, Aluminium wheels, Black RN '4' £5-10

Y11-5 1927 Bugatti type 35

Scale 1:35
1990 Light Blue body, Black seats, Chrome wheels, White RN '6' £5-10

Y12-1 1899 Horse-drawn Bus

Scale 1:100.

1959 Red body and chassis, Brown horses, drawbar fixed to body
with single rivet (narrow end)..£70-90
Red body and chassis, Dark Brown horses, drawbar fixed to
body with double rivets (square end)....................................£60-75

Y12-2 1909 Thomas Flyabout

Scale 1:48.
1967 Blue body and chassis, smooth Tan roof, Yellow seats and
grille, roof - to - body pins...£1,250-1,500
Same but with Dark Red seats and grille...................................£15-25
Blue body and chassis, Dark Red seats and grille,
roof - to - seat pins, smooth Tan roof £10-20
Same but with textured Tan roof £20-30
1975 Purple-Red body and chassis, Off-White seats, Black grille,
textured Black roof, Chrome 12-spoke wheels...........................£10-20
Same but with Chrome 24-spoke wheels..................................£15-25
Ruby Red body and chassis, Off-White seats, Black grille,
textured Black roof, Chrome 12-spoke wheels...........................£10-20
Same but with Chrome 24-spoke wheels..................................£15-25

Y12-3 1912 Ford Model 'T' Van

Scale 1:35.

'COCA COLA'
1979 Off-White body, Black chassis, 5 vertical Red printed lines,
Chrome trim £350-400
Same but with Gold trim..£350-400
Off-White body, Black chassis, 4 vertical Red printed lines,
Black seats, Red 12-spoke wheels £25-30
Same but with Tan seat £50-60
Same but with Black seats, Chrome 12 or 24-spoke wheels........£35-45
With Black seats and Light Gold 24-spoke wheels £35-45

'COLMANS MUSTARD'
1979 Yellow body, Black chassis, matt Black roof, Red single line
rear doors, 'No, Y12' cast on base, Red 12-spoke wheels..............£5-10
Same but with Chrome 12 or 24-spoke wheels £20-25
1981 Yellow body, Black chassis, matt Black roof, Red double lines
on rear doors, 'No,Y12' not cast on base, Red 12-spoke wheels.....£5-15
Same but with Gold 12-spoke wheels £20-25
Same but with Red 12-spoke wheels and gloss Black roof..........£35-45

'TAYSTEE'
1980 Yellow body, Black chassis, matt Black roof, Red single line
    rear doors, 'No. Y12' cast on base, Red 12-spoke wheels.........**£375-500**
NB There are known to be fakes which have the smaller labels as
    used on the Y5-4 Talbot Van. Genuine 'Taystee' labels for the
    Ford Model 'T' Van measure 29mm end to end of 'Taystee' oval
    and 11mm top to bottom of the oval.

'SUZE'
1980 Yellow body, Black chassis, matt Black roof, Black single line
    on rear doors, 'No. Y12' cast on base, Red 12-spoke wheels..........**£5-10**
    Same but with Chrome 12 or 24-spoke wheels **£20-25**
1981 Yellow body, Black chassis, matt Black roof, Black double lines
    on rear doors, 'No. Y12' not cast on base, Red 12-spoke wheels **£5-10**
    Same but with Gloss Black roof, Black double lines rear doors....**£35-40**
    Same but with Gloss Black roof, Red double lines rear doors...**£135-150**

'SMITHS CRISPS'
1981 Blue body, Black chassis, White roof, single line White rear doors,
    'No. Y12' cast on base, Tan seats......................................**£5-10**
    Same but with Black seats **£15-20**
    Blue body, Black chassis, White roof, 'No. Y12' cast on base,
    Tan seats, double lines White rear doors **£15-20**
    Same but with 'No. Y12' not cast on base **£5-10**
    Blue body, Black chassis, White roof, 'No. Y12' not cast on base,
    Black seats, double lines White rear doors.......................**£15-25**

'25 YEARS SILVER JUBILEE'
1981 Light Green body, Dark Green chassis, Grey roof, Yellow
    12-spoke wheels, 'No. Y12' cast on base,
    Silver single line rear doors **£350-400**
    Same but with Silver double lines rear doors...................**£15-20**
    Light Green body, Dark Green chassis, Grey roof, 'No. Y12' not
    cast on base, Silver double lines rear doors,
    Yellow 12-spoke wheels **£5-10**
    Same but with Chrome or Red 12-spoke wheels...............**£10-15**
    Same but with Yellow 24-spoke wheels.........................**£70-75**

'BIRDS CUSTARD'
1982 Blue body, Black chassis, Yellow roof, Red 12-spoke wheels,
    Yellow double lines rear doors, Black or Tan seats...........**£5-12**
    Metallic Blue body, Black chassis, Yellow roof, Red 12-spoke
    wheels, Yellow double lines rear doors, Black seats........**£80-120**
    Blue body, Black chassis, Yellow roof, Yellow 12-spoke wheels,
    Yellow double lines rear doors, Back seats **£25-35**
    Blue body, Black chassis, Yellow roof, cast rear doors outline,
    Black or Tan seats, Red 12-spoke wheels **£5-12**
    Same but with Chrome 12-spoke wheels.......................**£25-30**

'CEREBOS'
1982 Light Blue body, Black chassis, Yellow roof, Gold components,
    Red 12-spoke wheels **£200-250**
    With Chrome components, Red or Gold 12-spoke wheels **£200-250**
    Light Blue body, Black chassis, White roof, Gold components,
    Black seat, Gold 12-spoke wheels **£5-12**
    Same but with Tan seat **£45-60**
    With Black seat and Red or Chrome 12-spoke wheels **£5-12**

'ARNOTTS'
1982 Bright Red body, Black chassis, gloss Black roof.....................**£125-145**
    Same but with matt Black roof **£110-120**
NB This model can have double labels applied on one or both
    sides. Such examples usually attract a premium of **£5-10**

'HARRODS'
1982 Dark Green body, Black chassis, Khaki roof, Black seats,
    Cream double lines rear doors **£5-10**
    Same but cast rear doors outline, Black or Tan seats **£5-10**
    Same but with Pale Cream seats **£10-15**

'SUNLIGHT SEIFE'
1983 Yellow body, Black chassis, matt Black roof, Black seats,
    Red 12-spoke wheels, Red double lines rear doors.....................**£65-80**
NB 'Sunlight' models exist with fake labels. Genuine labels have a clothes
    line post to the right of the woman hanging out the washing.

'ROYAL MAIL'
1983 Bright Red body, Black chassis and roof, Yellow double lines
    rear doors, Red or Gold 12-spoke wheels................................**£210-250**
    Post Office Red body, Black chassis and roof, cast rear
    doors outline Red or Gold 12-spoke wheels..........................**£5-10**
    Same but with Chrome 12 or 24-spoke wheels **£10-15**

'CAPTAIN MORGAN'
1983 Black body and chassis, White roof, one piece label covering
    cab doors and body sides, Tan seats, Gold 12-spoke wheels **£5-10**
    Same but with Black seats **£45-50**
    With Red 12-spoke wheels and Black seats **£50-55**
1984 Black body and chassis, White roof, two piece labels, one for
    cab doors, one for body sides, Tan seats, Gold 12-spoke wheels **£5-10**
    Same but with Black seats **£45-50**
    Same but with Tan seats, cast hole in rear base of body................**£60-70**
    Same but with Black seats, cast hole in rear base of body.........**£75-100**

'HOOVER'
1983 Orange body, Black chassis and roof, Black seats,
    Black 12-spoke wheels **£5-10**
    Same but with Tan seats..**£40-50**
    With Black seats, cast hole in rear base of body **£5-10**
    With Black seats, Black 24-spoke wheels...............................**£10-15**

'PEPSI COLA'
1984 White body, Blue chassis, Red roof, Chrome 12 or 24-spoke
    wheels or with Red 12-spoke wheels..................................**£5-10**
NB This model can have either 'Lesney Products' or 'Matchbox
    International' cast on the base.

'MOTOR 100'
1985 Bronze body, Dark Brown chassis, Dull Red 12-spoke wheels,
    world globe with White land, Blue oceans, with certificate **£35-45**
    Same but without certificate..**£5-10**
    Same but with Red or Gold 12-spoke wheels **£5-10**
    With Dull-Red 12-spoke wheels, Blue land, White oceans **£700-800**

'IMBACH' (Truck)
1985 Blue body, Black chassis, Tan seat, Gold 12-spoke wheels **£5-12**
    Same but with Red 12-spoke wheels...............................**£15-25**

'HEINZ'
1986 Light Greenish-Grey body and roof, Dark Green chassis,
    'Lesney Products' base **£250-300**
    Very Pale Greenish-Grey body and roof, Dark Green chassis,
    'Matchbox International' base **£5-15**
NB Many variations of this model are known to exist with different
    wheels. All are 12-spoke design finished in Maroon, Dark Red,
    Bright Red, Dull Red or Gold. Base plates can be © 1985 or © 1986.

'ROSELLA'
    Dark Blue body, Black chassis, Yellow roof **£5-40**
NB Many variations are known to exist with different wheels.
    All are 12-spoke design finished in Maroon, Dark Red, Bright Red,
    Gold or Chrome. Base plates can be 'Lesney Products' or
    'Matchbox International Limited Edition', © 1985 or © 1986

Y12-4 1829 Stephenson's 'Rocket'

Scale 1:64 ('S' gauge).

1987 Yellow body and tender, Black chassis, 'Made in Macau'...............**£8-12**

Y12-5 1937 GMC Van

Scale 1:45.

'GOBLIN'
1988 Black body and chassis, Grey roof **£10-20**
    Same but with Black roof **£5-10**

'BAXTERS'
1989 Cream body and roof, Dark Green chassis **£5-10**

'GOANNA'
1991 Dark Blue body and roof, Black chassis **£5-8**

Y13-1 'Santa Fe' Locomotive (1862)

Scale 1:112.
1959 Dark Green cab and boiler, Dark Red chassis and smokebox........**£75-95**
NB The level of Gold trim was reduced over the years thus it is
    possible to find models with Gold chimney rim and condenser
    tops through various combinations to Dark Red chimney rim and
    Dark Green condenser tops.
    Mid Green cab and boiler, Dark Red chassis and smokebox,
    Gold chimney rim and condenser tops **£750-850**

Y13-2 1911 Daimler

Scale 1:45.

1966 Yellow body and bonnet, Black chassis, 5-spoke steering wheel,
 Black seats...**£25-35**
 Same but with Dark Red seats.................................**£15-25**
1967 Yellow body and bonnet, Black chassis, 4-spoke steering wheel,
 Black seats...**£25-35**
 Same but with Dark Red seats.................................**£10-18**
1984 Blue body, Powder Blue chassis, 4-spoke steering wheel,
 Brown seats. In 'Connoisseur Collection' ....GSP

Y13-3 1918 Crossley Lorry

Scale 1:47. **'RAF' Tender**

1975 RAF Blue cab, body and chassis, Tan canopy and tilt,
 no brake between front mudguards and chassis,
 Dull Dark Red seats..**£250-400**
 Same but with Milky White seats......................**£300-350**
1976 RAF Blue cab, body and chassis, Tan canopy and tilt, brace
 between front mudguards and chassis, Milky White seats.............**£10-30**
 Same but with Dull Dark Red seats.................**£150-200**
 Same but with Green seats...............................**£150-200**
 RAF Blue cab, body and chassis, Tan canopy and tilt,
 Milky White seats and grille.............................**£100-150**
 Same but with Olive Green canopy and grille.............**£45-70**
 Same but with Dark Charcoal Grey canopy and grille.............**£250-300**
 NB Almost all above variations can have Chrome 12 or 24-spoke wheels.

Y13-4 1918 Crossley Lorry

Scale 1:47.

'EVANS Bros.'
1979 Dark Red cab and body, Black chassis, 'RAF Tender' base,
 Red 12-spoke wheels or Chrome 12 or 24-spoke wheels **£10-15**
1980 Same but without 'RAF Tender' on base **£10-15**
1982 Bright Red cab and body, Black chassis, Red 12-spoke wheels **£5-10**

'CARLSBERG'
1983 Cream cab and body, Black chassis, Light Green canopy and tilt,
 'Lesney Products' base, Chrome or Gold 12-spoke wheels.............**£45-55**
 'Matchbox Toys Ltd' base, Chrome or Gold 12-spoke wheels.............**£5-8**
1984 'Matchbox Toys Ltd' base, Darker Green canopy and tilt **£5-8**
 'Matchbox Toys Ltd' base, Ice Blue canopy and tilt...................**£80-125**

'WARING and GILLOW'
1985 Dark Green body, Black chassis, White or Cream canopy and tilt ..**£5-10**

'KOHLE and KOKS'
1988 Lemon cab and body, Black chassis, Black 12-spoke wheels.............**£5-10**
 Same but with Dark Green 12-spoke wheels.................................**£45-50**

Y14-1 Duke of Connaught' Locomotive (1903)

Scale 1:130.

1959 Dark Green cab and boiler, Dark Brown chassis,
 with Gold boiler door...**£75-130**
 With Silver boiler door **£100-150**

Y14-2 1911 Maxwell Roadster

Scale 1:49.

1965 Turquoise body and chassis, Brass petrol tank **£120-150**
 Same but with Copper petrol tank...**£15-20**
1984 Dark Cream body, Dark Green chassis, Copper petrol tank.
 In 'Connoisseur Collection' ....GSP

Y14-3 1931 Stutz Bearcat

Scale 1:44.

1974 Lime Green body, Dark Green chassis, Bright Red seats **£8-12**
 Same but with Dark Red seats...**£50-75**
1979 Cream body, Bright Red top panels, Darker Red chassis,
 Bright Red seats..**£30-45**
 Same but with Black seats **£5-10**
1981 Cream body and top panels, Emerald Green chassis,

 Chrome 24-spoke wheels...**£5-10**
 Same but with Red 12-spoke wheels...................................**£20-25**
1985 French Blue body, Dark Grey chassis.....................................**£5-8**
1990 Dark Blue body and chassis, Cream panels, Dark Blue chassis **£8-12**
1995 Bright Red body, Black chassis **£8-10**

Y14-4 1936 ERA type R1-B

Scale 1:35.

1986 Gloss Black body and chassis..**£10-15**
1988 Blue body, Yellow chassis, 'Made in Macau' **£8-10**
1991 Blue body, Yellow chassis, 'Made in China'...............................**£10-15**

Y15-1 1907 Rolls-Royce Silver Ghost

Scale 1:55.

1960 Light Green body and chassis, Black seats,
 Silver 12-spoke wheels, Grey knobbly tyres **£45-55**
 Same but with Black knobbly tyres.......................................**£25-30**
 Same but with Brass 12-spoke wheels, Black knobbly tyres.........**£15-30**
 Same but with Silver 12-spoke wheels, Black smooth tyres.........**£15-30**
 Light Green body and chassis, Brass 12-spoke wheels,
 Black smooth tyres, Dark Green seats.......................................**£60-70**

Y15-2 1930 Packard Victoria

Scale 1:46.

1969 Brownish-Gold body, Dark Brown chassis,
 Dark Red seats and roof...**£10-20**
1974 Lime Gold body, Dark Brown chassis, Dark Red seats and roof,
 or Black roof, narrow cast coachline to rear side panels.................**£10-15**
 With Black roof and wide cast coachline to rear side panels.........**£40-60**
1979 Gloss Black body and chassis, Dark Red side panels,
 Black or White roof **£5-10**
1984 Dark Sand body, Dark Brown chassis, Brown or White roof **£5-8**
 Same but with Orange-Brown roof.......................................**£75-100**

Y15-3 1920 'Preston type' Tram Car

Scale 1:87.

'LONDON TRANSPORT'
1987 Red body, White window frames, 'Swan Vestas' side adverts **£5-10**
 'Passport Scheme' version in cabinet plus extra components........**£60-70**

'DARLINGTON CORPORATION'
1988 Blue body, Off-White window frames, 'Swan Soap' side adverts...**£5-10**

'PAISLEY DISTRICT'
1989 Orange body, Cream window frames, 'Golden Shred' side adverts **£5-12**

'NEWCASTLE CORPORATION'
1991 Dark Brown body, Pale Cream window frames,
 'Zebra Grate Polish' side adverts...**£5-10**

Y16-1 1904 Spyker

Scale 1:45.

1961 Pale Cream body and chassis, Grey knobbly tyres....................**£300-350**
 Pale Lemon body and chassis, Grey knobbly tyres....................**£50-70**
 Same but with Black knobbly tyres **£30-40**
 Same but with smooth tyres..**£20-30**
 Pale Lemon body and chassis, 2 cast holes in base **£110-130**
 Maroon body and chassis, Black knobbly or smooth tyres....**£1750-2000**
1968 Pale or Mustard Yellow body and chassis **£15-25**

Y16-2 1928 Mercedes-Benz SS Coupé

Scale 1:45.

1972 Silver body, Red chassis, cast rear axle differential casing..........**£75-100**
 Same but rear axle differential not cast **£15-25**
1974 Lime Green body and chassis, separate cast exhaust underneath,
 Black roof and seats..**£15-30**
 Same but with Dark Green roof and seats...............................**£30-45**
 Lime Green body, Dark Green chassis (as Y14-3 Stutz),
 Black roof and seats..**£175-225**

Lime Green body and chassis, exhaust cast as ridge
on baseplate, Dark Green roof and seats £25-35
Same but with Black roof and seats.................................£10-20
1979 White body and chassis, Black roof and seats...............................£10-15
White body, Black chassis, Black roof and seats £370-450
1981 Blue body and chassis, Mid-Grey side panels.................................£5-15
Same but with Duck Egg Blue side panels....................................£45-60
With Milky White side panels £75-100
With Beige side panels...£5-15
1985 Red body, Silver chassis, top in folded position............................£5-10
1990 Pinkish-Grey body, Black chassis, Black roof (closed) and seats ..£12-15

Y16-3 1960 Ferrari Dino 246 V12

Scale 1:35.

1986 Red body and chassis, Chrome 24-spoke wheels............................£5-10
Same but with Aluminium spoked wheels £10-18

Y16-4 1923 Scania-Vabis Post Bus

Scale 1:49. 'Special Limited Edition' model, 1988.

1988 Yellow body, gloss Black chassis, Grey roof, Brown interior........£10-20
Same but with Black interior £250-300

Y16-5 Scammell 100-ton Truck and Trailer

Scale 1:64. 'PICKFORDS'. 'Special Limited Edition' model, 1989.

1989 Blue prime mover and trailer, White cab roofs and 'PICKFORDS'
logo, Red chassis and wheels. Very dark Blue E4 Class 2-4-0
locomotive in G.E.R. livery, Gold trim and number '490' £75-95

Y17-1 1938 Hispano-Suiza

Scale 1:48.

1975 Dark Red body, Black chassis, Chrome 24-spoke wheels...............£7-15
Same but with Chrome 12-spoke wheels....................................£15-25
1980 Pale Blue body and chassis, Powder Blue side panels,
Chrome 24-spoke or solid wheels..£7-12
Pale Blue body, Black chassis, Powder Blue side panels,
Chrome 24-spoke wheels...£15-25
Same but with Chrome solid wheels £7-12
1981 Silver body, Silver or Black chassis, Powder Blue side panels,
Chrome solid wheels...£110-125
1986 Mid-Green body, Dark Green chassis, Gold 24-spoke wheels,
'Lesney Products' base £5-15
Same but with 'Matchbox Int'l England' base...........................£75-100
Same but with 'Matchbox Int'l Macau' base £7-10
1990 Light Green body and chassis, Lime Green side panels.................£10-15
1995 Navy Blue body and chassis, Gold 24-spoke wheels....................£12-15

Y18-1 1937 Cord 812

Scale 1:48.

1979 Red body and chassis, White roof and seats,
Chrome 24-spoke wheels or Red or Chrome solid wheels £5-10
1981 Darker Red body and chassis, White roof and seats,
Chrome solid wheels...£10-15
1983 Plum Red body and chassis, White roof and seats,
Chrome solid wheels...£10-15
Same but with Chrome 24-spoke wheels....................................£15-20
1990 Pale Yellow body and chassis (Black baseplate),
Brown roof and seats £15-20
Same but with in plain White box £20-25
1995 Rich Cream body, chassis and base, Tan hood,
Dark Brown seats...£15-20

Y18-2 1918 Atkinson 'D' type Steam Wagon

Scale 1:60.

'LAKE GOLDSMITH'
1985 Green body, Red chassis, Green and-spoke wheels.......................£12-20

'BLUE CIRCLE CEMENT'
1986 Yellow body, Black chassis, Yellow 8-spoke wheels £7-10

'BASS & Co.'
1987 Dark Blue body, Black chassis, Red 8-spoke wheels,
7 barrel load, posts and chains to truck body £10-20

'BURGHFIELD MILLS'
1988 Red body, Black chassis, Red 8-spoke wheels, sacks load £5-8

Y19-1 1936 Auburn Speedster

Scale 1:42.

1979 Beige body and bonnet sides, Light Brown top panels,
Dark Brown chassis, solid Red, Cherry Red or Chrome wheels £5-10
1983 Creamy White body and bonnet sides and tops, Black chassis,
Red solid or 12-spoke wheels...£8-15
1985 White body, bonnet and chassis, Blue side panels,
Blue 24-spoke wheels £5-10
1990 Dark Tan body, bonnet and chassis, Cream side panels,
Chrome 24-spoke wheels £12-18
Same but in plain White box £20-25

Y19-2 Fowler B6 Showman's Engine

Scale 1:68. 'Heigh-Ho, Come to the Fair'. 'Special Limited Edition', 1986.

1986 Blue body and boiler, Black smokebox, Off -White roof £25-35

Y19-3 1929 Morris Cowley Van

Scale 1:39. All Y19-3 models have 12-spoke wheels.

'BRASSO'
1987 Dark Blue body, White roof, Black chassis, 'Macau'
baseplate, Red 12-spoke wheels £5-10
Same but with Chrome wheels £15-25
Same but with Red wheels, 'China' baseplate £10-15

'MICHELIN'
1988 Dark Blue body, Yellow roof, Black chassis, Chrome wheels........£5-10

'SAINSBURY'
1990 Dark Brown body, White roof, Black chassis, Chrome wheels £5-10

Y20-1 1937 Mercedes-Benz 540K

Scale 1:45.

1981 Silver body, Black chassis, seats ranging in colour from
Amber to Red, Chrome 24-spoke wheels................................£5-15
Same but with Red 12-spoke wheels £15-20
1985 White body and chassis, Red seats, Red 24-spoke wheels................£5-8
1987 Red body and chassis, Brown seats, Chrome 24-spoke wheels £5-10
1990 Black body and chassis, Maroon seats, Tan steering wheel,
Chrome 24-spoke wheels £5-8
1995 Black body and chassis, Bright Red seats, Black steering wheel,
Chrome 24-spoke wheels £10-15

Y21-1 1930 Ford Model 'A' Woody Wagon

Scale 1:40.

1981 Yellow bonnet, Dark Brown chassis, Red seats,
Chrome 24-spoke wheels, 'Lesney' base £5-30
Same but with 'Matchbox Int'l' base £5-25
1983 Copper bonnet, Dark Brown chassis, Red seats,
Chrome 12-spoke wheels, 'Lesney' or 'Matchbox Int'l' base £5-10
1985 Orange bonnet, Dark Brown chassis, Red seats,
Chrome 12-spoke wheels, 'Lesney' or 'Matchbox' base £10-15

Y21-2 1930 Ford Model 'A' Woody Wagon

Scale 1:40

'A. & J. BOX'
1983 Copper bonnet, Dark Brown chassis, Off-White seats,
Chrome 12-spoke wheels, 'Lesney' base £5-15
Same but with 'Matchbox Int'l' base £5-10
1984 Orange bonnet, Dark Brown chassis, Off-White seats,
Chrome 12-spoke wheels, 'Lesney' or 'Matchbox Int'l' base £5-10
Yellow bonnet, Black chassis, Off-White or Red seats,
Chrome 24-spoke wheels, 'Lesney' base £40-50

'CARTERS SEEDS'
1985 Blue bonnet, Black chassis, Off-White seats,
Chrome 12-spoke wheels, 'Lesney' base £15-25
Same but with 'Matchbox Int'l' base £5-10

Y21-3 Aveling and Porter Road Roller

Scale 1:60. **'James Young & Sons, Edinburgh'**. 'Special Ltd. Edition' 1987.

1987 Green body and Boiler, Black firebox and smokebox, no cast
lettering on underside of roof, very Pale Grey rear 'tyres' £450-500
Same but with Mid-Grey rear 'tyres'.................................£150-200
Same but with cast lettering on underside of roof and
with Mid-Grey rear 'tyres'..£20-25

Y21-4 1955 BMW 507

Scale 1:38.

1988 Blue body, Black roof, Red seats.......................................£5-10

Y21-5 1926 Ford Model 'TT' Van

Scale 1:41.

'OSRAM'
1989 Dark Green body, Black chassis, Red roof, Chrome grille £10-15
Same but with Black radiator grille £5-10

'MY BREAD'
1990 Sandy Beige body and roof, Black chassis, riveted axle ends £5-10
Same but with wheels press-fitted onto axles...............................£10-15

'DRAMBUIE'
1992 Black body, roof and chassis, Brass 12-spoke wheels...................£10-20

Y22-1 1930 Ford Model 'A' Van

Scale 1:41.

'OXO'
1982 Red body, Black chassis, Red seats and interior, 'Lesney' base £130-150
Red body, Black chassis, Fawn seats and interior, 'Lesney' base,
matt Black van roof..£5-10
Same but with gloss Black van roof £15-20
Same but with matt Black van roof, 'Matchbox Int'l' base £20-25

'MAGGI SOUPS'
1984 Yellow body, Black chassis, Red roof, Chrome 24-spoke wheels,
'Lesney' base £25-35
Same but with Red 12-spoke wheels......................................£25-35
1985 Yellow body, Black chassis, Red roof, Chrome 24-spoke wheels,
'Matchbox Int'l' base £5-8
Same but with Chrome 12-spoke wheels...................................£5-15

'TOBLERONE'
1984 Beige body, Dark Brown chassis, Red roof, 'Matchbox Int'l' base...£5-8

'PALM TOFFEE'
1984 Light Cream body, Red chassis and roof, Dark Green colour in
logo, Gold 24-spoke wheels..£5-8
Same but with Chrome 24-spoke wheels..................................£10-15
Same but Gold 24-spoke wheels, Light Green Colour in logo £8-12

'CANADA POST'
1984 Red body, Black chassis and roof, Black 24-spoke wheels,
'Postes Canada Post' on box..£10-15
Same but with regular box (no 'Postes Canada Post' printed)...........£5-8
Same but with Chrome 24-spoke wheels (regular box) £10-15

'SPRATTS'
1986 Brown body, Dark Brown chassis, Off-White roof,
Chrome 24-spoke wheels..£5-12
Same but with Gold 12-spoke wheels £15-20

'LYONS TEA'
1987 Blue body, Black chassis, White roof, 'Matchbox Int'l',
'Made in Macau' base, Chrome or Red 12-spoke wheels...............£5-10
Same but with Light Gold 12-spoke wheels...................................£8-12
1991 Blue body, Black chassis, White roof, Chrome 12-spoke wheels,
'Matchbox Int'l, Made in China' base.......................................£15-20

'CHERRY BLOSSOM'
1989 White body, Black chassis and roof, riveted axle ends,
'Matchbox Int'l, Made in Macau' base...................................£5-10
1991 White body, Black chassis and roof, wheels press-fitted on axles,
'Matchbox Int'l, Made in China' base......................................£15-20

'PRATTS'
1991 White body, Black chassis and roof, Orange solid wheels...............£5-10

Y23-1 1922 AEC Omnibus

Scale 1:72.

'SCHWEPPES'
1983 Red body, gloss Black chassis, side adverts in White with
Red printing, Light Tan, Fawn or Dark Brown seats and panels ...£65-80
Same but with side adverts in White with Black printing..............£5-15
1984 Red body, gloss Black chassis, Fawn seats and side rails,
side adverts in Yellow with Black and White printing.................£5-15

'R.A.C.'
1985 Red body, gloss Black chassis, Fawn seats and side rails, 'RAC' ...£5-10

'MAPLES'
1985 Red body, Gloss Black chassis, Fawn seats and side rails, 'Maples'.
This model was only available in 'Fathers Day' Set........................GSP

'HAIG'
1986 Dark Brown body, gloss Black chassis, Cream upper deck,
Dark Brown seats, Dark or Bright Red 12-spoke wheels................£5-10

'RICE KRISPIES'
1988 Red body, gloss Black chassis, Pinkish-Tan seats £5-10

'LIFEBUOY'
1989 Blue body, Light Cream upper deck, Dark Brown seats £5-10

Y23-2 Mack Bulldog Tanker

Scale 1:60.

'TEXACO'
1989 Red cab and tank, Black chassis, Red wheels £5-12
Same but with Gold wheels...£50-75

'CONOCO'
1991 Red cab, White tank, Black chassis, 'Made in Macau' base.........£65-75
Same but with 'Made in China' base.......................................£5-10
With 'Made in China' base, Gold wheels..................................£50-75

Y24-1 1928 Bugatti T44

Scale 1:72.

1983 Black body and chassis, Bright Yellow side panels, Beige seats £5-10
Same but with Brown, Green or White seats £200-250
1984 Black body and chassis, Lemon side panels with Black stripe below
door windows, Chrome 24-spoke wheels, Beige seats....................£5-10
Same but with White seats..£75-100
Same but with Black seats..£15-20
With Black seats and Chrome 12-spoke wheels............................£75-100
1987 Light Grey body, Red chassis, Dull Red side panels, Beige seats,
Chrome solid wheels..£5-10
1990 Black body and chassis, Red side panels, Light Brown seats,
Chrome 24-spoke wheels...£5-10
1995 Black body and chassis, Khaki wicker-work printed side panels,
Light Tan seats, Chrome 24-spoke wheels £8-12

Y25-1 1910 Renault 'AG' Van

Scale 1:38.

'PERRIER'
1983 Green body, Dark Green chassis, White seats, roof rack with
only 3 side struts, right hand sidelight with protruding lens,
Gold 12-spoke wheels...£220-250
NB The following models have roofs with rack with 4 side struts.
1983 Green body, Dark Green chassis, White or Dark Red seats,
right hand sidelight with protruding lens, Gold 12-spoke wheels....£5-10
Same but with Red 12-spoke wheels..£10-15

With flat lens to right hand sidelight £5-10
With Chrome 12-spoke wheels £5-10

'JAMES NEALE'
1985 The basic model has a Yellow cab and body with a White roof.
Mounted on Royal Blue chassis with closed grab handles £15-20
Same but with cast hole in cab floor £25-30
With cast hole in cab floor, open grab handles..............................£25-45
Mounted on Navy Blue chassis with closed grab handles £60-80
Same but with cast hole in cab floor £35-50
With cast hole in cab floor, open grab handles..............................£30-45
NB The 12-spoke wheels can be Light or Dark Yellow or Orange-Yellow,
but these differences do not usually attract further premiums.

'DUCKHAMS'
1985 Silver body, Navy Blue chassis, open grab handles £10-15
Same but with closed grab handles..£50-60
NB Although sometimes for sale as individual models, the Duckhams
Van was only issued as part of the 1985 'Fathers Day' Set ....GSP

'EAGLE PENCILS'
1985 Blue body, Navy Blue chassis, Gold 12-spoke wheels,
open grab handles, 'Matchbox © 1983' base £5-10
Same but with closed grab handles..£50-60
Open grab handles, Chrome 12-spoke wheels.................................£5-10
Open grab handles, 'Matchbox © 1986' base £5-10
Open grab handles, 'Matchbox © 1986 Limited Edition' base......£15-20

'BRITISH RED CROSS'
1986 Army Green body, Black chassis, 'Matchbox © 1986' base £12-18
Same but with 'Matchbox © 1986 Limited Edition' base £12-18

'TUNNOCKS'
1987 Bright Red body, Black chassis, Black 12-spoke wheels,
'Matchbox Int'l © 1983' or 'Matchbox Int'l © 1986' base............£5-10
Same but with Gold 12-spoke wheels £10-15
With closed grab handles £25-35
With 'Matchbox © 1986 Limited Edition' base £10-15

'DELHAIZE'
1987 Dark Green body, Black chassis, Gold 12-spoke wheels,
'Matchbox © 1986' base £5-10

'SUCHARD'
1989 Pale Lilac body, Black chassis, Gold 12-spoke wheels,
'Matchbox © 1986' base £5-10

Y26-1 Crossley Delivery Truck

Scale 1:47.

'LOWENBRAU'
1984 Powder Blue body, Black chassis, Red solid wheels, Tan roof,
Brown barrels, 'Renault Y25' base..£225-250
Same but with 'Crossley Y13' base..£40-50
Same but with 'Crossley Y13/Y26' base..£5-10
1985 Powder Blue body, Black chassis, Red solid wheels, Light Tan
roof, Brown barrels, 'Crossley Y13/Y26' base £5-10
Same but with Red 12-spoke wheels..£20-25
1986 Powder Blue body, Black chassis, Red solid wheels, Cream roof,
Dark Brown barrels, 'Crossley Y13/Y26' base £5-10
Same but with Light Olive Green roof £20-25

'ROMFORD BREWERY'
1986 Black body, Mid Brown chassis, Light Brown seats, Black grille...£5-10
Same but with Ruby Red seats £10-20
Same but with Ruby Red seats and radiator grille £10-20

'GONZALEZ BYASS'
1987 White body, Ruby Red chassis, Gold 12-spoke wheels,
with or without tampo print on barrels.......................................£5-10
Same but with Chrome 12-spoke wheels..£15-20

Y27-1 1922 Foden Steam Lorry

Scale 1:72.

'PICKFORDS'
1984 Blue body, Red chassis, Light Grey cab roof and canopy,
'© 1984' base, truck body butts up to cab sides £15-25
Same but truck body overlaps cab sides...£70-80
Same but truck body overlaps cab sides with full-length bearer......£5-10

NB The following issues have truck body overlapping cab sides with
full-length bearer.
1985 Blue body, Red chassis, Dark Grey cab roof and canopy,
'© 1984' or '© 1986' base £10-15
Same but with Light Grey cab roof and canopy, '© 1986' base......£5-10
1986 Blue body, Red chassis, Light or Dark Grey cab roof and canopy,
'© 1986' base, with tow hook £10-15
Blue body, Red chassis, Light or Dark Grey cab roof and canopy,
'© 1986' base, with rivet only (no hook)..................................£125-150

'HOVIS'
1985 Dark Brown body, Black chassis, Yellowish-Cream or
Light Yellowish-Cream cab roof, canopy and wheels....................£10-15

'TATE and LYLE'S'
1986 Brown body, Black chassis, body side panel cast relief as the 'Hovis',
'© 1984' base, Jet Black cab roof and canopy £25-35
Same but with Charcoal Grey cab roof and canopy.........................£50-60
Brown body, Black chassis, shallower side panel cast relief,
Jet Black cab roof and canopy, '© 1984' or '© 1986' base...........£10-15

'FRASERS' (Lorry and Trailer)
1986 Dark Green bodies, Black chassis, White cab roof and canopies ..£20-25

'SPILLERS'
1987 Pale Cream body, Green chassis, Dark Cream sacks load,
with tow hook rivet £15-20
Same but without tow hook rivet...£10-15
NB The colour of the truck body side panels can range from very
Dark Green to Emerald Green, all with or without tow hook rivets.

'GUINNESS'
1989 Dark Blue body, Black chassis, Dark Brown barrels £15-25

'JOSEPH RANK'
1990 Dark Green body, Light Brown chassis, Off-White sacks,
2 cast holes in bed of truck body..£15-25
Same but without cast holes in bed of truck body..........................£10-15
NB The wheels can have open ended or closed ended hub centres.

'McMULLEN'
1992 Black body, Red chassis, 5 Dark Brown barrels £15-25

Y28-1 1907 Unic Taxi

Scale 1:42.

1984 Dark Red body, Black chassis, Black hood and roof,
Brown seats, Red, Maroon or Gold 12-spoke wheels....................£5-12
1987 Dark Blue body, Black chassis, Black hood and roof,
Brown seats, Red, Maroon or Chrome 12-spoke wheels £5-10
1991 White body, Black chassis, Black hood, roof and seats £10-15

Y29-1 1919 Walker Electric Van

Scale 1:51.

'HARRODS'
1985 Khaki Green body, Black chassis, Cream canopy and tilt...............£5-10

'JOSEPH LUCAS'
1986 Bright Green body, Black chassis, Bright Green canopy and tilt.....£5-10
NB The surface of the canopy/tilt can vary from fine texture to
eggshell effect.

'HIS MASTERS VOICE'
1988 Dark Blue body, Black chassis, Pinkish-Beige canopy and tilt........£8-12

'HARRODS BREAD'
1989 Khaki Green body, Black chassis, Dark Green canopy and tilt £8-12

Y30-1 1920 Mack Truck

Scale 1:60.

'ACORN STORAGE'
1985 Cambridge Blue body, Dark Blue chassis and cab steps,
Dark Grey cab and van body roof, 'Made in England' base............£8-15
1986 Same but with Dark Grey cab steps..£10-15
1987 Aqua Blue body, Dark Blue chassis and cab steps, Pale Grey cab,
Charcoal Grey van body roof, 'Made in Macau' £350-400

'CONSOLIDATED'
1985 Yellow body, Dark Brown chassis, Yellow cab and roof,
Dark Tan truck body cover **£5-10**
Same but with very Pale Olive Truck body cover.......................**£80-100**

'ARCTIC ICE CREAM'
1987 Cream body, Dark Green chassis, Beige Van body roof **£5-8**

'KIWI'
1988 Red body, Black chassis, Beige van body roof **£5-10**
NB The Kiwi bird etc., can be Light, Mid or Dark Brown.

Y31-1 1931 Morris Courier Van

Scale 1:59.

'KEMPS'
1990 Red body, Black chassis, Off-White roof, full-length van body cast
horizontal lines **£70-75**
Same but cast horizontal lines are 2mm short of full-length...........**£5-10**

'WEETABIX'
1992 Yellow body and roof, Black chassis..**£5-10**

Y32-1 Yorkshire Steam Wagon

Scale 1:54.

'SAMUEL SMITH'
1990 Maroon cab and body, Black chassis, 'Y8' cast on base................**£5-10**
Same but with 'Y32' cast on base **£10-15**

Y33-1 1920 Mack 'AC' Truck

Scale 1:60.

'GOODYEAR'
1990 Cambridge Blue body, Dark Blue chassis, Dark Grey roof **£5-10**

Y34-1 1933 Cadillac V16

Scale 1:48.

1990 Navy Blue body and chassis, White hood, 'Macau Y34' base **£5-10**
1992 White body, Navy Blue chassis, Black hood,
'China YY46, Y34' base...**£8-12**

Y35-1 1930 Ford Model 'A' Pick-up Truck

Scale 1:40.

'W. CLIFFORD & SONS'
1990 Cream cab and body, Black chassis, Black roof.............................**£5-10**

'AMBROSIA'
1992 Blue cab and body, Cream chassis and roof **£5-15**

Y36-1 1936 Rolls-Royce Phantom I

Scale 1:46.

1990 Dark Red body, Black chassis and roof, Dark Red seats **£5-15**
1992 Blue body, Black chassis and roof, Maroon seats **£5-10**
1994 Dull Dark Red body, Black chassis, Dark Brown seats **£5-10**

Y37-1 1931 Garrett Steam Wagon

Scale 1:59.

'CHUBB'S SAFE DEPOSITS'
1990 Pale Blue cab and body, Navy Blue chassis, White/Cream roof,
'Garrtt' cast on base..**£80-100**
'Garrett' cast on base **£10-15**

'MILKMAID MILK'
1992 Cream body, Navy Blue cab and chassis and cab roof,
White Van body roof, Pale Blue wheels.......................................**£35-40**
Same but with Red wheels..**£10-15**

Y38-1 1920 Rolls-Royce Armoured Car

Scale 1:48. 'HMAC Ajax'.

1990 Sand body, turret and chassis...**£15-20**

Y39-1 1820 Passenger Coach

Scale 1:43. 'York to London'.

1990 Black body, Red chassis, Black roof, 4 horses, 6 figures...............**£35-40**

Y40-1 1931 Mercedes-Benz 770

Scale 1:48.

1991 Grey body and chassis, Dark Blue roof, Maroon seats **£10-15**

Y41-1 1932 Mercedes-Benz 'L5' Lorry

Scale 1:69. 'HOWALDTSWERKE A.G.'

1991 Dark Green cab and body, Dark Grey chassis, Black mudguards and
steps, Dull Silver radiator **£10-15**
Same but with Bright Chrome radiator..**£5-10**

Y42-1 1939 Albion 'CX7' 10-ton Lorry

Scale 1:60. 'LIBBYS'

1991 White cab, Blue body, Navy Blue chassis, Dull Silver radiator.....**£10-15**
Same but with Bright Chrome radiator..**£5-10**

Y43-1 1905 Busch Steam Fire Engine

Scale 1:43. 'Special Edition', 1991 model

1991 Dark Green body and crew area, 5 figures/crew,
Copper boiler pipes etc. **£80-100**
Same but with Brass boiler pipes..**£40-45**

Y44-1 1910 Renault 'T45' Bus

Scale 1:38.

1991 Yellow body, Black chassis and Black roof...................................**£5-15**
Same but with Red roof **£55-70**

Y45-1 1930 Bugatti Royale 'Napoleon'

Scale 1:46.

1991 Black body, bonnet and chassis, Dark Blue side panels,
Dark Blue seats **£10-15**
1994 Same but with Lilac-Blue seats **£10-15**

Y46-1 1868 Merryweather Fire Engine

Scale 1:43. 'Special Edition', 1991 model.

1991 Red body, Brass boiler etc, 2 White horses, 4 figures/crew...........**£35-60**

Y47-A 1929 Morris Cowley Van

Scale 1:39. 'CHOCOLAT LINDT'

1991 Black body and chassis, Yellow roof...**£5-10**

Y61 1933 Cadillac Fire Engine

Scale 1:46. 'FEUEWEHR AARU'

1992 Red body and chassis, Light Brown ladder **£10-20**

Y62 1932 Ford Model 'AA' Truck

Scale 1:46. 'PEACOCK'

1992 Light Green cab and body, Black chassis, Light Grey roof,
Light Brown sacks **£10-15**

Y63 1939 Bedford 'KD' Truck

Scale 1:46. 'G. FARRAR'

1992 Red cab, Light Brown body, Black chassis, loose stones..............**£25-35**

Y64 1938 Lincoln Zephyr

Scale 1:43.

1992 Cream body and mudguards, Black running boards, Brown seats,
Dark Cream folded top...**£20-25**
1995 Maroon body and mudguards, Silver running boards,
Light Brown seats, Off-White folded top.......................................**£15-20**

Y65 1928 Austin 7 (Set)

Scale 1:43. 'Special Limited Edition' Set.

1992 Austin 7 Van; Red body, Black chassis, 'Castrol' logo,
Rosengart Saloon; Blue body, Black chassis, textured Black plastic roof,
BMW Dixie open tourer; White body, Black chassis, Black folded top
....**£40-50**

Y66 State Coach

Scale 1:100. 'Special Limited Edition', 1992.

1992 Gold coach and wheels, 8 horses (in pairs) with 4 riders..................**£4-7**
Same but with Brass coach and wheels..**£4-10**

Models of Yesteryear Gift Sets

G 6	1960	**Gift Set** ....Contains Nos. 1, 2, 5, 10 and 13. Lesney line-drawing box	**£325-375**
G 7	1960	**Gift Set** ....Contains Nos 3, 8, 9, 12 and 14. Lesney line-drawing box	**£325-375**
G 6	1962	**Veteran & Vintage Car Set** Contains Nos 5, 6, 7, 15 and 16. Lesney picture box..	**£325-375**
G 7	1962	**Gift Set** ....Contains Nos 3, 4, 11, 12 and 13. Lesney picture box..	**£325-375**
G 7	1965	**Veteran & Vintage Set** ....Contains Y2, Y5, Y10, Y15 and Y16. Picture box..	**£100-125**
G 7	1966	**Gift Set** ....Y1-2 Model T Ford, Y3-2 Benz, Y11-2 Packard, Y14-2 Maxwell. Picture box...........................	**£75-100**
G 5	1968	**Gift Set** ....Y4-3 Opel, Y6-3 Cadillac, Y9-2 Simplex, Y9-2 Simplex	**£55-65**
G 5	1970-72	**Gift** Set ....Contains Y8-3 Stutz Red, Y14 Maxwell, Y16-1 Spyker (Dark Yellow), Y7-3 Rolls-Royce Silver and Red. Picture box..	**£45-55**
Y-50	1982	**Gift Set** ....Contains Y3-4 'BP' Tanker, Y5-4 Talbot Van 'Chivers', Y10-3 Rolls Royce, Y12-3 Model 'T' Van, Y13-3 Crossley Coal Lorry	**£20-30**
	1984	**'Connoisseur Collection'** ....Contains Y1-2 Black 1911 Model 'T' Ford, Y4-3 Red/Beige 1909 Opel, Y3-2 Blue/Black 1910 Benz Limousine, Y11-2 White/Black 1912 Packard Landaulet, Y13-2 Blue 1911 Daimler, Y14-2 Beige/Black 1911 Maxwell. 30,000 certificated and numbered sets issued in beechwood display case	**£80-100**
	1985	**'Fathers Day' Set** ....Y11-3 Lagonda, Y23-1 'MAPLES' Bus, Y25-1 Renault Van 'DUCKHAMS'	**£20-30**
	1987	**30 years Set** (A) ....Y6-4 Rolls-Royce Fire Engine, Y25-1 'Eagle Pencils', Y29-1 'Harrods'...................................	**£15-20**
	1987	**30 years Set** (B) ....Y4-4 Blue Duesenberg, Y28-1 Red Unic Taxi, Y29-1 'Harrods' Van	**£15-20**
	1987	**Starter Kit**................................(5 for 4 Set) Australian Gift Set	**£25-30**
Y65	1992	**1928 Austin 7** (Set) ....A Special Limited Edition Set comprising Austin 7 Van (Red body, 'CASTROL'), BMW Dixi 3/15 (Blue body, Black roof) ROSENGART 3-seater Tourer (White body). All three have Black chassis, Tan seats and Chrome wheels Scale 1:43	**£40-50**

Models of Yesteryear plated souvenir and giftware models

Models specially plated to adorn giftware (e.g., cigarette boxes, ashtrays, penstands, boxes and pipestands. Non-plated versions of the models listed will also be found with the two baseplate holes used for fixing the plated models to the various items.

SILVER PLATED MODELS

Y1-2	1911	Model 'T' Ford **£20-30**
Y2-2	1911	Renault 2 seater...................**£20-30**
Y2-3	1914	Prince Henry Vauxhall........**£20-30**
Y3-3	1934	Riley MPH **£20-30**
Y4-3	1909	Opel Coupé **£20-30**
Y5-2	1929	4½ Litre Bentley **£30-40**
Y6-2	1926	Type 35 Bugatti **£75-95**
Y7-2	1913	Mercer Raceabout..............**£45-65**
Y7-3	1912	Rolls-Royce **£20-30**

Y10-2	1928	Mercedes-Benz 36-220 ......**£30-40**
Y10-3	1906	Rolls-Royce **£20-30**
Y12-2	1909	Thomas Flyabout **£20-30**
Y13-2	1911	Daimler **£20-30**
Y13-3	1918	Crossley **£175-225**
Y14-2	1911	Maxwell Roadster...............**£15-20**
Y15-1	1907	Rolls-Royce Silver Ghost ...**£15-20**
Y16-1	1904	Spyker.................................**£20-30**

GOLD PLATED MODELS

Y1-2	1911	Model 'T' Ford **£30-40**
Y2-3	1914	Prince Henry Vauxhall........**£15-20**
Y3-2	1910	Benz Limousine **£250-300**
Y4-3	1909	Opel Coupé **£15-20**
Y5-2	1929	4½ Litre Bentley **£35-40**
Y7-2	1913	Mercer Raceabout..........**£100-120**

Y7-3	1912	Rolls-Royce **£15-20**
Y10-2	1928	Mercedes-Benz 36-220 ......**£75-95**
Y10-3	1906	Rolls-Royce **£20-30**
Y12-2	1909	Thomas Flyabout **£20-30**
Y13-2	1911	Daimler **£20-30**
Y13-3	1918	Crossley **£200-250**
Y14-2	1911	Maxwell Roadster...............**£15-20**
Y15-1	1907	Rolls-Royce Silver Ghost ...**£40-50**

GOLD PLATED SETS
Golden Veteran Set with 3 models:
Y7-3, Y13-2, Y14-2....................................**£50-65**
Heritage Gifts, 2 models: Y7-3, Y10-3 ......**£35-50**

Lesney 'Pub Signs'

A series of plated figurines made for attachment to giftware. The base of each is marked 'Lesney Co. Ltd. 1975'. They have 'spurs' underneath to aid fixing to such items as ashtrays, etc. The Editor would be pleased to receive more details. NGPP.

'The Cock'......................	'The Swan'	'The Bull'	'Pig & Whistle'	'Dick Turpin'	'The Volunteer' ....
'The Lion'......................	'The Unicorn'	'Rose & Crown'	'George & Dragon'	'Sherlock Holmes'..........	'Britannia'......................

Since Matchbox Collectibles was established worldwide in 1992, the brand name owners have produced Yesteryears exclusively for seminars, expositions, conventions, and U.S. department stores, which have become very collectable. These issues have mostly been standard models with additional tampo decoration, but have been produced exclusively and entirely by the brand owners or their contractors. These models have been made available to people other than the brand name owner employees, albeit in limited numbers and mostly at one day events. The majority of collectors feel that, as these models were produced entirely by the brand name owners or their contractors, they cannot be classified as 'Code 2' models. These collectors are of the opinion that these models can only be categorised as 'Code 1 Promotionals'. Models that were produced under the same criteria, prior to the establishment of Matchbox Collectibles, have also been included in this listing.

1976 **Y1-2 1911 Ford model 'T' car.** Black body, chassis, seats, grille and textured roof, chrome 12-spoke wheels. Distributed to members of the U.S.A. Matchbox Club, 900 ....**£215-255**

1979 **Y13-3 1918 Crossley Lorry.** 'U.K. MATCHBOX CLUB'. Red body, Black chassis, Yellow roof and rear tilt. Distributed to members of that club, 930 ....**£175-200**

1983 **Y12-3 1912 Ford model 'T' van.** 'HOOVER'. Aral blue body, Black chassis, White roof, brass radiator, windscreen and 12-spoke wheels, tampo print in Gold. Distributed by Hoover management, 500 (with certificate) **£650-800**
Same, 50 (no certificate) **£400-450**

1991 **Y47-1 1929 Morris light van.** 'B.B.C. ANTIQUES ROADSHOW, GOING LIVE' (labels). Black body and chassis. 6 given to the BBC for prizes, 18 given to Matchbox staff, (24)..................**£750-1,000**

1992 **Y21-5 1926 Ford model 'TT' van.** 'B.B.C. ANTIQUES ROADSHOW, THE NEXT GENERATION' (transfers). Black body and chassis. 6 given to the BBC for prizes, 18 given to Matchbox staff, (24)..................**£750-1,000**

1992 **Pair of Y21-5 1926 Ford model 'TT' vans.** 'MODELS OF AUSTRALIAN ART'. 'Jenny Kee' model with Royal Blue body, 'Pro Hart' model with dark Green body. Sold to winners, in Australia and New Zealand only, of a postal ballot organised by Matchbox Collectibles Pty. (Australia), 1,000.....................**£550-750**

1995 **Quartet of Y65-1 1928 Austin 7 vans.** 'F.A.O. SCHWARTZ' (USA), 1 Red, 1 Yellow, 1 Aquamarine, and 1 Purple. Sold exclusively through F.A.O. Schwartz toy stores and their mail-order catalogue, 7,500.............................**£15-25**

1998 **YMC01 1970 Chevelle SS454.** 'MATTEL ANNUAL OPERATIONS MEETING 1998'. Red body with Black stripes. Given to attending independent sales reps, 50.........................**£195-245**

1998 **Y18-1 1937 Cord 812.** 'MATCHBOX COLLECTIBLES 1998 DEALER CONFERENCE, MELBOURNE.' (Australia). Cream body. Given to invited 'Collectibles Centres' dealers and their partners, 50................................**£450-600**

1999 **Y28-1 1907 Unic Taxi.** '25th ANNIVERSARY INTERNATIONAL COLLECTIBLE EXPOSITION. APRIL, 1999, LONG BEACH CALIFORNIA'. White body, Black chassis and roof. Given to attending dealers and visitors, 500 ....**£75-95**

1999 **YTC03 1940 Ford pick-up.** 'MATCHBOX TOYSHOW '99 HERSHEY Pa., JUNE 26-27, 1999'. dark Red body. Given to those attending the Saturday evening convention supper, 280......**£75-95**

1999 **Y28-1 Unic Taxi.** '25th ANNIVERSARY INTERNATIONAL COLLECTIBLE EXPOSITION. JUNE, 1999, ROSEMONT, ILLINOIS'. White body, Black chassis and roof. Given to attending dealers and visitors, 500.................................**£70-80**

1999 **DYM38236 1970 Chevelle SS454.** '1st ANNUAL MATCHBOX COLLECTIBLES REP. ADVISORY MEETING, DECEMBER 3-5, 1999'. Metallic dark Blue body with White stripes. Given to attending independent sales reps, 25.........................**£225-300**

2000 **YPP02/SB 1931 Morris Pantechnicon.** 'INTERNATIONAL COLLECTIBLE EXPOSITION, ATLANTA, GA. May 4-7, 2000'. Cream body, Green roof and mudguards. (Can have satin or matt grey bases). Given to attending dealers and visitors, 400 .....**£75-85**

2000 **Y64-1 1938 Lincoln Zephyr.** 'ASHLEY AVERY'S FATHER'S DAY EVENT, WESTMINSTER CO., JUNE 2000'. Maroon body. Given to regular, high spending preferred customers for Father's Day at the Ashley Avery store, 80 ....**£85-125**

2000 **YYM92093 1912 Ford model 'T' van.** 'SEE'S CANDIES, SUMMER'. (USA) White body, Black roof and chassis. Sold exclusively through See's candy stores and their Mail-Order department, (estimated) 3,000...........................**£30-35**

2000 **YTC02-M 1946 Dodge Power Wagon.** 'MATCHBOX TOYSHOW 2000, HERSHEY PA'. dark Green body. Given to those attending the Saturday evening convention supper, 210......**£70-85**

2000 **YY19B/SA. 1905 Fowler 'B' type Showman's Engine.** 'INTERNATIONAL COLLECTIBLES EXPOSITION JUNE 2000 - ROSEMONT, IL.'. Yellow body, White roof. (Can have serial number in block capitals or italics). Given to attending dealers and visitors, 500..................................**£65-75**

2000 **YYM92294 1926 Ford model 'TT' Van.** 'SEE'S CANDIES, ELECTION'. (USA). White body, Black roof and chassis. Sold exclusively through See's candy stores and their Mail-Order department, (estimated) 3,000..................................**£30-35**

2000 **YYM92296 1937 GMC Van.** 'SEE'S CANDIES, CHRISTMAS'. (USA). White body, Black roof and chassis. Sold exclusively through See's candy stores and their Mail-Order department, (estimated) 3,000.........................**£30-35**

2000 **YTC01-M 1941 Chevrolet Pick-up.** 'HOPE SPRING 2000 CANCER SUPPORT CENTRE'. Blue body. Sold via Joe Recchia (MICA N. America) and MICA auctions, 45 ....**£185-215**

2001 **YFE14 1953 Ford Fire Truck.** 'MATCHBOX COLLECTIBLES NEW YORK TOY FAIR 2001'. Red body. Given to attending dealers, 100..**£175-200**

2001 **YFE14 1953 Ford Fire Truck.** 'MATCHBOX COLLECTIBLES TUCSON TOY FAIR 2001'. Red body. Given to attending dealers, 100..**£175-200**

2001 **Set of 6 Pick-up Trucks;**
'HOPE SPRING 2001 CANCER SUPPORT CENTRE'.
YTC01-M 1941 Chevrolet (in Blue),
YTC02-M 1946 Dodge Power Wagon (in dark Green),
YTC03-M 1940 Ford (in dark Red), **YTC04-M Reo** (in Cream),
YTC05-M 1938 Studebaker (in Yellow), and
YTC06-M International 'C' Series (in Brownish Maroon),
Sold via Joe Recchia (MICA N. America) and MICA auctions,
13 sets..each set: **£900-1,100**
Individual models ....each model: **£125-155**

Matchbox Collectibles Code 1 (Factory-produced) privately commissioned Limited Edition models (see page 236)
YY039SC Ford 'TT' Van, 'Matchbox USA 20th Year' YHN01SA Holden Van, 'Auto One' Y19 Fowler 'Billy Smarts'

A system of categorising models has evolved among collectors to distinguish between authentic manufacturers' output and acceptable but unauthorised alteration of their models for later resale. The explanation which follows refers to a coding system adopted generally (but not officially) throughout the model collecting fraternity in the UK and elsewhere, and may he applied to models produced by any manufacturer.

CODE 1 Applies to models which have been originated and totally produced by an established manufacturer.

CODE 2 As CODE 1, but labelled or finished outside the factory WITH the manufacturer's permission.

CODE 3 Same as CODE 2, but model re-labelled, altered or re-worked WITHOUT authorisation or permission from the manufacturer.

Y1-2 76 **1911 Ford Model 'T' Car**. Black body, textured roof, grille and seats, Chrome 12-spoke wheels, brass trim, bare windscreen frame. 900 models made for the USA **£215-255**

Y3-4 **1912 Ford model 'T' tanker**
98 'HAINES GAS SERVICES', White cab roof, 600 ....
Same but with dark Blue cab roof, 50.............................**£90-140**

Y4-4 **1930 Duesenberg model J town car** (YY0044/C)
00 (MICA U.K. 15th Convention), White body, dark Orange chassis, Yellow painted roof and seats, 800 ....**£35-40**

Y5-4 78 **1927 Talbot Van** with 12-spoke wheels and Chrome trim.
'2nd AIM CONVENTION', Dark Green body and wheels, 'Toy Show, Harrisburgh PA May 27/28, 1978' **£80-100**
81 'CRAWLEY SWAPMEET 1981', Royal Blue body, Black roof and chassis, 'Follow Us To Crawley' **£140-150**
81 'VARIETY CLUB'
1: Yellow body and chassis, Black roof, Red wheels, 'Sunshine Coach Appeal'...**£180-200**
2: As 1 but with Black chassis **£180-200**
80 'MERITA BREAD', Yellow body, Black roof, Red wheels, 'Old Fashioned Enriched Bread....................**£40-45**
80 'LANGENDORF', Yellow body, Black roof, Red wheels, 'Old Fashioned Enriched Bread'..............**£40-45**
80 'TAYSTEE BREAD', Yellow body, Black roof, Red wheels and Pale Yellow 'Taystee' on Red oval **£70-80**
81 'IRONBRIDGE' 1: Yellow body, matt Black roof, Red wheels, 'The World's First Iron Bridge' **£160-180**
2: As 1 with gloss Black chassis and mudguards...........**£160-180**
81 'BEES' 1: Yellow body, Black roof, Red wheels, plain or White-wall tyres, 'Bees Art & Model Service' **£90-110**
2: As 1 but Black chassis and mudguards........................**£80-100**
81 'DUTCH MATCHBOX MEET'.
lst Matchbox meeting in Holland on 4th October 1981.
1: Blue and Grey body, Black roof and chassis, 'Stoevclaar', with Certificate **£250-300**
2: Yellow and Red body, Black roof and chassis, 'Stoevclaar', 72 only presented to stallholders **£500-600**
81 LAWRENCE FRASER TOYS', Blue body....................**£200-300**
95 'AIM COLLECTORS EXCHANGE CLUB'.
25th Anniv. model in Black and Yellow. 600 only **£70-80**

Y5-5 92 **Leyland Titan Bus**. 'MICA, 'City of Chester'. 5,000 ......**£35-40**

Y7-3 82 **1912 Rolls-Royce**. Wedding of Prince Charles and Princess Diana. Bright Yellow and Black, Red wheels, 600........**£160-180**

Y12-3 81 **Ford Model 'T' Van**
'BANG & OLUFSEN', White/Red/Black, certificate **£350-400**
81 'RAYLEIGH SWAPMEET', Yellow body, Black roof......**£60-90**
82 'CADA TOYS Have Moved', Yellow/Black, 600 ....**£180-200**
82 'DEANS of LEEDS', Yellow body, Black roof, Red 'Deans for Toys', telephone no. on some, 800 ......**£120-130**
80 'CAMBERLEY NEWS', Yellow/Black, '75th', 750 ......**£120-140**
83 'HOOVER', Blue body, White roof, Black chassis,
1: With certificate, 500 ....**£650-800**
2: Without certificate, 50 ....**£400-450**
YGB19 97 'MICA MEMBERS MEET AT HERSHEY', PA, June 28th/29th 1997, Chocolate Brown, 464 ....**£30-40**
36 exist with a Y12 base and much smaller decals..........**£80-100**
YGB14 97 'Dueschland Matchbox Club', Cream roof, 2,000 ....**£30-35**
Same but with Dark Blue roof, 20.............................**£200-250**

Y12-5 **1937 GMC van**
94 GMC Van 'MSS SECURITY', White/Black, 2,000 ....**£40-50**
95 'MICA 2nd European Convention' '10 Sept 1995'.

Bright Yellow body, Blue chassis. 600..............................**£50-60**
YGB08 Same but with Pale Yellow body, Blue chassis. 600..........**£40-50**
Y12-5 98 'WEET-BIX'. Green and White body, White roof (no header board). 600................................**£85-105**
YWG04 99 'GERMAN MATCHBOX COLLECTORS CLUB MEETING, HAMBURG 11-04-1999'.
White body, dark Green roof and base, 500....................**£40-50**
YY034/SA Powder Blue body and roof, dark Blue base, 100 ....**£85-105**
YWG04 99 Same but Green roof, White header board, 300.................**£65-80**
YPP07 00 'MICA ROCKS BLACKPOOL, 18.03.2000', 300............**£40-50**

Y13-2 00 **1911 Daimler Type A12 car** 'OLD CAR AUTOMOBILE MUSEUM OF CANADA' 250 ....**£50-65**

Y13-3 **1918 Crossley**
79 'UK M'BOX CLUB', Red/Yellow, '800 Members' **£180-200**
81 'ASPECTS and IMAGES', Red/Light Brown **£160-180**
81 'SURREY MODEL FAIR', Red body, 'Tangley Model Workshop' on rear of Grey canopy only, 500 ....**£150-180**

Y19 **Morris Cowley Van**
95 'CHURTON'S WHISKEY', 1,200................................**£40-50**
97 'VITACRAFT'. Multicoloured body.
1,000 with windows rear of cab, 1,000 without.................**£40-50**
Same but with body side window and White roof, 50....**£200-250**
97 '12th MICA CONVENTION, ALDERSHOT, 15th March. 1997.' (see M3 Set),
White body, Maroon roof, 'Macau' base. 1,000 ....**£40-50**

Y18-2 **1918 Atkinson model 'D' Steam Wagon**
YGB03 01 Czech Matchbox Collectors Club model, 'PRAGUE GOLDEN CITY', with Czech language printing, 50........**£80-120**
Same but with English language printing, 200 ....**£40-50**

Y20-1 00 **Mercedes-Benz 540K** 'MICA. HERSHEY JUN. 24, 2000.'
Maroon body, Silver chassis, 50...................................**£135-175**
Metallic Silver body, Maroon chassis, 12 ....**£185-215**
Metallic Silver body, dark Red chassis, 250 ....**£50-60**
Yellow body, Black chassis, 50 ....**£160-185**

Y21-5 **1926 Ford Model 'TT' Van**
95 'CLASSIC TOYS MAGAZINE'. Green body, Cream roof, Gold wheels, magazine pictured on sides, 1,500 .....**£40-50**
YGB14 96 '3rd MICA CONVENTION, SYDNEY 1996'.
Dark Blue body, Cream roof, 1,100 ....**£40-50**
Same but PaleBlue body, 100.......................................**£60-80**
96 'BARCLAY'S PROPERTY HOLDINGS Ltd'.
120 certificated models..**£600-700**
YGB13 97 'ROYAL AUTOMOBILE CLUB of VICTORIA',
Dark Blue, Cream roof, Copper wheels, 200 ....**£250-300**
Dark Blue, Cream roof, Gold wheels, 100...................**£300-400**
YCH2-1 97 'RONALD McDONALD HOUSE CHARITIES',
'Magical Million 11th Annual Ball', 300.......................**£250-300**
99 'ACME' Yellow body, Blue roof, Black chassis, 20.......**£125-155**
YY039/SC Same but with Blue chassis, 290.................................**£40-50**
YY039/SC Same (Blue chassis), but 'Wiley Coyote' cartoon character on rear doors, 10 ....**£200-225**

Y22-1 **1930 Ford model 'A' van**
95 'BRAVO - COLONEL GOLF BALLS'.
Orange body, Blue chassis, Black roof. 2,000 ....**£45-50**
95 'MATCHBOX and LESNEY TOY MUSEUM', USA.
Brown body, White roof. 2,000 ....**£45-50**
YPP08 97 'MATCHBOX USA 16th Annual Convention, 250..........**£50-60**
98 'MICA AT HERSHEY' (Red and Black decals), White body and roof, dark Brown chassis, chrome 24 spoke wheels, 25...**£75-95**
Same but Black chassis, Chrome 24 spoke wheels, 30......**£75-95**
Same but Black chassis, Red 12 spoke wheels, 5 ....**£95-125**
98 'MICA AT HERSHEY', (Orange / Black decals), White body and roof, Black chassis, Orange solid wheels, 300....**£40-50**
YGB01 00 '8th MICA EUROPEAN CONV', 8 & 9 SEPT. 2000', Aquamarine body, Black roof and chassis, 275 ....**£40-50**

Y23 **Mack AC Tanker**
97 'SUPERTEST PETROLEUM' (White lettering), 100........**£60-80**
'SUPERTEST PETROLEUM' (Black lettering), 400 ....**£40-60**
98 Canadian Military, Desert Brown, 400..........................**£40-50**
Same but with Grey land colour, 100................................**£80-100**

Y25-1   **1910 Renault type 'AG' van**
YPP01   99   'MICA 15 YEARS, 1984-1999', Yellow body,
     dark Navy Blue roof, Blue bonnet and chassis, 1,500 ....**£38-42**
YGB07   00   'MICA 2000 15 YEARS OF MICA' (N. America), White
     body, Red roof, dark Blue chassis, riveted base, 205........**£45-55**
     Same but screwed base, 45 ....**£65-75**
Y25-1   00   'MICA 2000 15 YEARS OF MICA' (N. America),
     White body and roof, mid Blue chassis, 10 ....**£125-135**
     Same but Navy Blue chassis, 15 ....**£105-120**
     Same but Red roof, mid Blue chassis, 10 ....**£125-135**
     Same but Red roof, Navy Blue chassis, 15 ....**£105-120**

Y26   **Crossley Lorry**
   95   'De BORTOLI WINE', White / Maroon, 2,000...................**£45-50**
   96   '11lth MICA CONVENTION 13th April 1996 TELFORD'
     Maroon/Cream, Maroon seats. 1,500 ....**£35-40**

Y27   **Foden Steam Lorry**
   98   YGB11 Foden (red chassis) 'MICA 13th Conv.', 1,000.....**£50-60**

Y33-1   **1930 Mack 'AC' truck**
   99   '18th MATCHBOX U.S.A. CONVENTION & TOY SHOW',
     White body & cab, Red roof, Blue base & wheels, 196 .....**£40-50**
YGB09   Same but Blue roof, Red base and wheels, 98 ....**£85-95**
YPP06   01   '16th MICA UK CONVENTION 7 & 8 APRIL 2001',
     Red body, light Blue roof, Navy Blue side labels, 300.....**£30-40**

Y37-1   **Garrett Steam Wagon**
   94   'MICA'. 1: Grey and Yellow body, 'Year Ten 1984-1994'
     on n/s. 3,000 ....**£60-70**
     2: Blue and Silver body, 'Year Ten 1984-1994' on o/s.
     Presented to each of the members who had attended ten
     MICA Conventions. 52 only **£300-400**
YY048SB
   98   Grey roof, 'MICA 6th European Convention', 1,000.........**£40-50**
   98   Dark Blue cab, 'MICA 14th Convention', 1,000................**£40-50**

Y47-A   **1929 Morris Van**
   95   'CHURTONS WINE IMPORTERS'.
     Black body, Yellow roof. 1,200...**£40-45**

Y65   **Austin 7 Van**
   96   'The YESTERYEAR BOOK'. Dark Green base,
     Light Green top (4 shades), White or Cream print,
     White or Dark Blue seats. 1,500 ....**£45-55**
YSC01   97   '1st GERMAN COLLECTOR CLUB MEETING',
     'Eriangen 23-03-1997', 2,000...**£25-30**
YCC02   98   'MICA 13th Convention', (white seat), 1,000 ....**£50-60**
YCC02   98   'MICA 6th European Convention', (white seat), 600.........**£30-40**
YCC02   98   'MICA 14th Convention', (white scat), 1,000 ....**£30-40**
YCC1   98   1st GERMAN MATCHBOX CLUB CONVENTION,
     STUTTGART, 9th JUNE, 1998', 600............................**£35-40**
YCC1   99   '4th MICA AUSTRALIAN CONVENTION. 3 JULY 1999',
     Orange and dark Cream body, 300 ....**£40-50**
YCC1   99   '7th MICA EUROPEAN CONVENTION. 23.10.1999',
     Red and light Cream body, 300 ....**£45-65**

YCH11   **1951 Holden 50/2106 Utility (pick-up) Truck**
   00   'AUSDEN RESTORATIONS', (Australia), 500 ....**£40-50**
   01   '12th SUPER SOUTHERN SWAPMEET, BALLARAT,
     2001', Blue tarpaulin cover, 150 ....**£55-75**

YHN01   **1955 Holden FJ/2104 Panel Van**
   00   '4th GERMAN MATCHBOX COLLECTORS MEETING,
     CHOZEUZ 20/21 MAY 2000', Blue and Silver, 100 .....**£150-175**
     Same but Green and White, 400.....................................**£40-45**
   00   'BENDIGO, VICTORIA. 2000 BENDIGO NATIONAL
     SWAPMEET', 100 ....**£90-120**
/SB   00   'WERKSFEURERWEHF', 400 ....**£40-50**
/SA   98   Australian Collectors Club' '98, no wing mirrors, 500 .....**£50-60**
     Same but with wing mirrors, 50..**£70-80**
/SC   'Ronald McDonald' 'Love Boat', 12th Annual Ball,
     with date on rear doors, 300 ....**£200-250**
     Same but with date on body side, few only **£300-350**
/SC   'DEPENDABLE PLUMBING', 500 ....**£40-50**

YGB16   **1932 Ford 'AA' Truck**
   00   'THE YESTERYEAR BOOK 3rd ISSUE 1956-2000'
     Gold body, cab and tilt, 400 ....**£40-50**
     Same but Silver body, cab and tilt, (only available with
     special 'Contributors Edition' book), 30........................**£135-155**

YGB24   **1939 Bedford 'KD' Truck**
   99   '7th MICA EUROPEAN CONVENTION 23.10.1999',
     Black and White decals on tank, 300 ....**£45-55**

YTF5   **Citroën 'H' Van**
   96   'BRISBANE INTERNATIONAL MOTOR SHOW 1996'.
     Silver/Cream/Maroon. 2,000 ....**£35-40**
     Same but with larger decals extending over door, 50 .....**£100-150**
   96   'MATCHBOX 15th USA CONVENTION,
     June 15-16 1996', Cream body, Red roof. Blue or Red
     wording and decals. 500 of each **£60-80**
     Same but in Silver/Maroon/Cream. Rear doors have 11
     names of attendees of all 15 events. 15 only **£200-300**

YPP02   **1931 Morris Courier van**
/SB   99   '4th MICA AUSTRALIAN CONVENTION. 3 JULY 1999',
     Cream body, Green roof and mudguards, 300 ....**£45-65**
YPP02   00   'FARNHAM MALTINGS, WHERE MATCHBOX
     COLLECTORS MEET', 250 ....**£40-50**
     Same but 'WHERE MODELS OF YESTERYEAR
     COLLECTORS MEET', 250 ....**£40-50**

YPP03   **Mercedes L5 Lorry**
   98   '2nd German Matchbox Conv.', Black cab roof, 750 ....**£40-60**
     Same but with Grey cab roof, in wooden box, 80 ....**£130-150**

YPP04   **Dodge Route Van**
MSM01 96   'THE HERSHEY HERALD', MICA Meet at Hershey,
     1: Black body, Silver grille, 300.....................................**£50-60**
     2: Black body, Black grille, 50..**£80-90**
     3: Red body, Silver grille, 150..**£140-150**
     4: Silver body, Silver grille, 10......................................**£400-500**
   98   'COCA-COLA, Bright Red, 300.......................................**£80-100**
/SA   00   '14th McDonald's annual ball'
     'A NIGHT AMONGST THE STARS', 250 ....**£55-85**

CODE-2 SETS
M1 Set   96   Y26 **Crossley** (Maroon seats) and **MB38 Ford 'A' Van**
     'MICA llth Convention, Telford', 210 ....**£90-100**
     Same but Crossley Lorry has Brown seats, 40................**£80-110**
M3 Set   97   Y19 **Morris Cowley Van** ('China' base) and YCC02
     Austin 7 Van '12th MICA CONVENTION', 250 ....**£90-100**
M5 Set   98   YGB11 **Foden** (black chassis) and YCC02 **Austin 7 Van**
     (blue seat), 'MICA 13th Convention', 200......................**£90-110**
M6 Set   98   YY048SB **Garrett** (grey roof) and YCC02 **Austin 7 Van**
     (blue scat), 'MICA 6th European Convention', 200.........**£90-110**
M7 Set   99   YY048SB **Garrett** (grey cab) and YCC02 **Austin 7 Van**
     (blue seat), 'MICA 14th Convention', 200......................**£90-110**
---   00   YRS05 **Chevrolet Pick-up Truck** and YCC1 **Austin 7 Van**.
     2000 'MICA AUSTRALIA 2000 MEMBERSHIP DRIVE',
     Blue Chevrolet truck; Red Austin 7 van within, 150.........**£75-95**
     Same but Cream Austin 7 van, 100...............................**£80-100**
     Same (Cream Austin 7 van) but with web-site address
     on the Blue Chevrolet, 250...**£40-50**
M8 Set   99   YPP02/SB **Morris Courier** van Cream / Black and YCC1
     Austin 7 van Red / Black, '4th MICA AUSTRALIAN
     CONVENTION, 3 JULY 1999', 200 ....**£95-125**
M9 Set   99   YGB24 **Bedford KD truck** Red / White and YCC1
     Austin 7 van Red / Cream, 'E7C MICA 7th EUROPEAN
     CONVENTION 23.10.1999', 200 ....**£85-105**
M10 Set   00   YPP07 **GMC van** 'MICA ROCKS BLACKPOOL
     18.03.2000' and Y4/YY004C **Duesenberg** model 'J'
     White body, dark Orange chassis, Yellow (painted) roof
     and seats, 200...**£85-105**
M11 Set   00   YGB01 **Ford model 'A' van** Black / Aquamarine '8th
     MICA EUROPEAN CONV. 8 & 9 SEPT. 2000', plus
     DINKY YMC05/B **Ford 'Boss' Mustang** (Black), 200 ..**£85-105**
M12 Set   01   YPP06 **Mack 'AC' lorry** Yellow / White '16th MICA UK
     CONVENTION 7 & APRIL 2001', plus DINKY
     DYM36840 Citroën 2cv in Turquoise), 200 ....**£85-105**

Thematic models based on 'Models of Yesteryear' castings from 1993.

'TASTE OF FRANCE' SERIES issued 1993:
1947 Citroën Type 'H' Van
YTF01 'EVIAN MINERAL WATER.....................................£12-15
YTF02 'MARTELL COGNAC'...£12-15
YTF03 'YOPLAIT YOGHURT'...£12-15
YTF04 'MARCILLAT BRIE'..£12-15
YTF05 'TAITINGER CHAMPAGNE'..................................£12-15
YTF06 'POMMERY MUSTARD'.......................................£12-15
YTF501 Two models set on wooden plinth.....................£24-27

'GREAT BEERS OF THE WORLD' SERIES issued 1993 / 1994:
YGB01 Ford 'A' Van, 'CASTLEMAINE XXXX' (Australia)
         Red metal roof...£10-12
         Red plastic roof...£10-12
YGB02 Ford 'TT' Van, 'BECKS' (Germany)
         With body side window...................................£10-12
         Without body side window...............................£10-12
YGB03 Atkinson Steam, 'SWAN' (Australia).....................£10-12
YGB04 Morris Van, 'FULLERS' (England).........................£10-12
YGB05 Ford 'AA' Van, 'CARLSBERG' (Denmark)................£10-12
YGB06 Mercedes Truck, 'HOLSTEIN' (Germany)................£13-17
YGB07 Renault Van, 'KRONENBOURG' (France)..................£10-12
YGB08 GMC Van, 'STEINLAGER' (New Zealand),
         Large tampo print (roof to wheel arches).........**£700-750**
         Small tampo print (top half of van body sides only)......£10-12
YGB09 Mack AC, 'MOOSEHEAD' (Canada).......................£10-12
YGB10 Talbot Van, 'SOUTH PACIFIC' (New Guinea)............£10-12
YGB11 Foden Steam Wagon, 'WHITBREAD' (England)........£10-12
YGB12 Yorkshire Steam Wagon, 'LOWENBRAU' (Germany)...£10-12
Issued in 1995:
YGB13 Ford 'TT' Van 'ANCHOR' (USA).............................£10-12
YGB14 Ford Model 'T' Van 'KIRIN' (Japan)......................£10-12
YGB15 Garrett Steam Wagon 'FLOWERS' (England).............£10-12
YGB16 Ford 'AA' Van 'CORONA' (Mexico).......................£10-12
YGB17 Mercedes-Benz 'HENNINGER' (Germany)................£10-12
YGB18 Morris Van 'CASCADE' (Australia)........................£10-12
YGB19 Ford Model 'T' 'YUENGLING' (USA)......................£10-12
YGB20 Ford 'AA' Van 'STROHS' (USA)............................£10-12
YGB21 Mercedes-Benz 'DAB' (Germany).........................£10-12
YGB22 Atkinson Steam 'BEAMISH' (Ireland)....................£10-12
YGB23 Mack Truck 'TSING TAO' (China).........................£10-12
YGB24 Bedford Truck 'TOOHEYS' (Ausualia)...................£10-12
YGB501 Twin model issue on Plinth...............................£25-28

'HORSE DRAWN CARRIAGE' SERIES issued 1993:
YSH 1 1900 Gypsy Caravan..£35-45
YSH2 1886 London Omnibus..£30-35
YSH3 1875 Wells Fargo Stage Coach...............................£30-35

'THE GRAND CLASSICS COLLECTION' issued 1994:
YI-3 1936 SS Jaguar, Red with Black folded hood................£12-15
Y2-4 1930 Supercharged 4½ litre Bentley, Dark Blue............£12-15
Y4-4 1930 Duesenberg Town Car, Blue, Cream hood.............£12-15
Y34-1 1933 Cadillac 452 V16 Town Car, White/Black.............£12-15
Y36-1 1925 Rolls-Royce Phantom 1, Red and Black...............£12-15
Y40-1 1931 Mercedes-Benz 770, Grey body, Blue hood...........£12-15
Y45-1 1930 Bugatti Royale, Black/Royal Blue......................£12-15

'FIRE ENGINE' SERIES issued 1994 – 1998:
YFE01 1920 Mack Fire Engine (1995),
         'YFE01' on base...£18-22
         'YGB09' on base...£75-100
YFE02 1952 Land Rover Auxiliary and Trailer
         with Red wheels (1994)...................................£40-45
         re-run with Silver wheels (1995)........................£18-22
YFE03 1933 Cadillac V16 Fire Wagon (1995)....................£18-22
YFE04 1939 Bedford KD Tanker Truck (1995)....................£18-22
YFE05 1932 Mercedes-Benz L5 Ladder Truck (1995)...........£18-22
YFE06 1932 Ford AA Fire Engine (1995).........................£18-22
YFE07 1938 Mercedes-Benz KS 15 Fire Truck (1996)..........£18-22
YFE08 1936 Leyland Cub FK7 (1995)............................£30-35
YFE09 1932 Ford 'AA' Open Cab (1996)..........................£18-22
YFE10 1937 GMC Rescue Squad 4th Precinct (1996)..........£18-22
YFE11 1923 Mack 'AC' Water Tanker (1996)....................£18-22
YFE12 1930 Ford 'A' Batallion Chief's Vehicle (1996)..........£18-22

YFE13 Citroën 'H' Van 'LONGUEVILLE' (1997)...................£18-22
YFE14 1953 Ford Pick-Up 'GARDEN CITY' (1997)..............£18-22
YFE15 1923 Mack 'AB' Open Cab (1997).........................£18-22
YFE16 1948 Dodge 'Route' Canteen Support Truck (1997).....£18-22
YFE17 1939 Bedford Pump Truck 'City of Manchester' (1997)...£18-22
YFE18 1950 Ford E83W Van and Auxiliary Trailer (1997).......£18-22
YFE19 1904 Merryweather, Finchley Fire Brigade (1998).......£28-32
YFE20 1912 Mercedes-Benz Motor Spritze Fire Engine (1998)...£28-32
YFE21 1907 Seagrave AC53, VFD Fire Dept. (1998).............£28-32
YFF22 1916 Ford Model 'T' Fire Engine (1998)..................£28-32
YFE23 1906 Waterous SP Pumper, Radnor Fire Co. (1998)......£28-32
YFE24 1911 Mack Fire Pumper, UFALM Fire Dept. (1998)......£28-32
YSFE01 1930 Ahrens-Fox Quad, mounted on plinth (1994).....£60-70
YSFE02 1936 Leyland Cub (YFE08) on wooden plinth (1995)...£40-45
YSFE03-M Busch Fire Engine. White pipes, no figures (1996)....£55-60
YSFE04-M Ahrens-Fox NS4, Lockheed, mounted on plinth (1997)...£60-70
YSFE05-M 1880 Merryweather Horse-Drawn, on plinth (1997)...£55-60
YYM35193 1930 Ahrens-Fox, Coca-Cola, Xmas Holiday (1999)...£60-70
Issued 1999 / 2000:
YYM35187 (YFE25) 1954 Ford F100, 'RESCUE SERVICE'..........£28-30
YYM35188 (YFE26) 1952 Land Rover, 'ROYAL NAVY RESCUE'....£30-33
YYM35189 (YFE27) 1941 Chevrolet, 'U.S. ARMY FIRE TRUCK'....£28-30
YYM35190 (YFE28) 1932 Ford 'AA', 'FOREST FIRE TRUCK'......£28-30
YYM35191 (YFE29) 1939 Bedford, 'BRISTOL AEROPLANE Co.'...£35-40
YYM35192 (YFE30) 1937 G.M.C., 'AMBULANCE'..................£28-30
YYM37631 1948 G.M.C. CoE pumper, 'PORT VINCENT'..........£20-22
YYM37632 1932 Mercedes-Benz searchlight truck, 'HILDEN'....£20-22
YYM37633 1920 Mack AC water tower truck......................£20-22
YYM37634 1932 Ford 'AA' high pressure hose truck, 'G.C.F.D.'...£20-22
YYM37635 1935 Leyland Cub open cab, 'DEVON COUNTY'......£30-35
YYM37636 1946 Dodge power wagon, 'PORT VINCENT'..........£20-22

YCC01 **'CHRISTMAS TREASURES' SET issued 1994**:
Four 1938 Austin 7 models in Christmas '1994' liveries of Red,
Metallic Green, White/Blue and Blue (5,000).................£25-30
YCC02 **1995 Set**. Red, Gold, White, Metallic Green..........£25-30

'POWER OF THE PRESS' SERIES issued 1996:
YPP01 Renault AG Van 'LE FIGARO' (France).....................£14-16
YPP02 Morris Courier 'THE TIMES' (Great Britain)...............£14-16
YPP03 Mercedes Truck 'MORGENPOST' (Germany)..............£14-16
YPP04 Dodge RT Van 'NEW YORK TIMES' (USA)................£14-16
YPP05 Ford Truck 'LOS ANGELES TIMES' (USA).................£14-16
YPP06 1923 AC Mack Truck 'PRAVDA' (Russia)..................£14-16
YPP07 GMC Van 'The AUSTRALIAN' (Australia)...................£14-16
YPP08 Ford 'A' Van 'WASHINGTON Post' (USA).................£14-16

'STEAM POWERED VEHICLES' Collection, issued 1996 / 1997:
YAS01 Stephenson's Rocket, (1996)................................£18-22
YAS02 Foden 'C' Steam Truck 'HULTON COALS', (1996)........£18-22
YAS03 Aveling & Porter Steam Roller 'COULSON', (1996),
         with 'COULSON' in Blue....................................£18-22
         with 'COULSON' in Green.................................£350-400
YAS04 Yorkshire Steam Wagon 'de SELBY QUARRIES', (1996)...£18-22
YAS05 Fowler Showman's Engine 'JOHN HOADLEY', (1996)......£22-25
YAS06 Atkinson Logger 'J.B. KIND Ltd', (1996),
         'Models of Yesteryear' cast on base...................£40-50
         'Models of Yesteryear' **not** cast on base...........£18-22
YAS07 Fowler Crane Engine 'MARSTON'S', (1997)................£22-25
YAS08 Burrell Road Tractor 'WOODS MOORE', (1997)...........£22-25
YAS09 Garrett Steam Lorry, 'RAINSFORD'S', (1997)............£18-22
YAS10 Atkinson Steam Lorry, 'CITY of WESTMINSTER', (1997)...£18-22
YAS11 Yorkshire Steam Lorry, 'GWR', (1997)...................£18-22
YAS12 Foden 'C' Steam Lorry, 'R. BRETT', (1997)..............£18-22

'TROLLEYS, TRAMS & BUSES' Collection, issued 1996:
YET01 1920 Preston type Tram Car, Birmingham.................£16-18
YET02 1921 Leyland Titan Bus, Glasgow..........................£16-18
YET03 1931 Diddler Trolley Bus, London United.................£16-18
YET04 1923 Scania Post Bus, Stockholm..........................£16-18
YET05 1922 AEC Omnibus, Dublin.................................£16-18
YET06 1910 Renault Motor Bus, Paris.............................£16-18

'GRAND MARQUES' Collection, issued 1966:
YY014AC 1931 Stutz Bearcat, Red.................................£18-20
YY017AD 1938 Hispano-Suiza, Dark Blue........................£18-20
YY018AC 1937 Cord, Cream.......................................£18-20
YY020AD 1935 Mercedes-Benz 500K, Black......................£18-20
YY024AD 1928 Bugatti T44, Black.................................£18-20
YY064AC 1939 Lincoln Zephyr, Maroon...........................£18-20

'The ANNIVERSARY COLLECTION', issued 1996:
All the models in this range have Gold coachlining.
YMS01 1911 Ford Model 'T', Black, Dark Brown seats.........................**£16-18**
YMS02 1910 Benz Limousine, Navy Blue body, Black roof,
    Dark Brown seats..**£16-18**
YMS03 1909 Opel Coupé, Yellow, Black hood, Black seats...................**£16-18**
YMS04 1912 Packard Laundaulet, White, Black roof, Black seats.......**£16-18**
YMS05 1911 Daimler, Maroon, Brown seats.......................................**£16-18**
YMS06 1911 Maxwell Roadster, Red, Black hood, Brown seats...........**£16-18**
YMS07 1914 Prince Henry Vauxhall, Dark Green/Silver, Brown seat....**£16-18**
YMS08 1912 Simplex, Red, Black hood, Black seats **£16-18**

'FABULOUS FIFTIES - ROAD SERVICE COLLECTION'
Series 1, issued in 1996:
YRS01 1955 Chevy 3100 'AAA Towing and Service' **£18-22**
YRS02 1953 Ford F100 'Flying 'A' Tire Service' **£18-22**
YRS03 1956 Chevy 3100 'Mobil Battery Service' **£18-22**
YRS04 1954 Ford F100 'Sinclair' Snow Plough **£18-22**
YRS05 1957 Chevy 3100 'Dixie Gas Parts and Service' **£18-22**
YRS06 1955 Ford F100 'Red Crown', 'Route US 66' on tilt..................**£30-35**
YRS06BM 1955 Ford F100 'Red Crown', 'Route US 83' on tilt **£18-22**
Series 2, issued in 1997:
YIS01M 1955 Chevy 3100 'Harley Davidson' **£18-22**
YIS02M 1955 Ford F100 'Caterpillar'...**£18-22**
YIS03M 1955 Chevy 3100 'GM Parts' **£18-22**
Y1S04M 1957 Chevy 3100 'American Airlines' **£18-22**
YIS05M 1954 Ford F100 'Pennsylvania Rail Road'..............................**£18-22**
YIS06M 1953 Ford F100 'Parts & Service'..**£18-22**

'AMERICAN MUSCLE CARS'. Issued in 1996:
YMC01 1971 Chevelle SS454...**£15-20**
YMC02 1971 Plymouth 'Cuda 440 6-Pack **£15-20**
YMC03 1967 Pontiac GTO **£15-20**
YMC04 1970 Plymouth Road Runner Hemi **£15-20**
YMC05 1970 Ford Boss Mustang **£15-20**
YMC06 1968 Camaro SS396 ....**£15-20**
YMC07 1970 Plymouth Road Runner GTX **£15-20**
YMC08 1966 Chevelle SS396 ....**£15-20**
YMC09 1966 Ford Fairlane XL..**£15-20**
YMC10 1969 Dodge Charger **£15-20**
YMC11 1970 Oldsmobile 442 ....**£15-20**
YMC12 1971 Dodge Challenger **£15-20**

'XMAS SPECIALS' 1996
YSC01-M **Scania-Vabis Bus** White body, Xmas tree on roof.
    5,000 total of which 1,236 shorter trees made in China **£35-40**
YSC02-M **Chevy 3100 Pickup.** Red body, Xmas tree, sleigh,
    reindeer, etc., in back. 7,500 worldwide...........................**£30-35**
YSC03-M **Holiday Fire Engine.** Ford 'AA' Open Cab as YFE09 model
    but with White chassis. Santa Claus and sack of presents.
    7,500 worldwide **£30-40**
YY21A/SA-M **Ford Woody Wagon.** Blue/Cream, with
    'Drink Pepsi-Cola' and 'Smith's Apothecary' **£18-22**
YY004/C-M **Duesenberg Town Car.** Brown body, Tan chassis
    and seats, Black hood. 7,500 worldwide **£25-30**
MB289/SA-M **Pontiac GTO.** Purplish Black, 5,000...........................**£15-20**

The 'WHISKEY COLLECTION' Issued in 1997:
YWG01M 1930 Ford Model 'A' Van, 'BALLANTINE'S' **£16-18**
YWG02M 1930 Ford Model 'TT' Van, 'LONG JOHN' **£16-18**
YWG03M 1929 Morris Van, 'CUTTY SARK' **£16-18**
YWG04M 1937 GMC Van, 'LAPHROAIG' **£16-18**
YWG05M 1912 Ford Model 'T' Van, 'SHEEP DIP'................................**£16-18**
YWG06M 1932 Ford Model 'AA' Truck, 'TEACHERS'........................**£16-18**

The 'COCA-COLA COLLECTION' Issued in 1998:
YPC01M 1957 Chevy Pick-up, 'Vending Service & Repair' **£24-26**
YPC02M 1937 GMC Van, 'Nine Million Drinks a Day'.........................**£24-26**
YPC03M 1920 Mack AC Truck, 'Stoneleigh Pharmacy' **£24-26**
YPC04M 1912 Ford Model 'T' Van, 'Ice Cold Coca-Cola Sold Here'...**£24-26**
YPC05M 1930 Ford Model 'A' Pick-up, 'Parts & Maintenance' **£24-26**
YPC06M 1932 Ford Model 'A' Truck, 'Delicious and Refreshing' **£24-26**

'The 30's and 40's PICK-UP COLLECTION' issued in 1998:
YTC01 1941 Chevrolet Model AK, Blue, Black chassis **£22-24**
YTC02 1946 Dodge Power Wagon WDX, Dark Green **£22-24**
YTC03 1940 Ford De-luxe, Red, Black fenders **£22-24**
YTC04 1939 Reo Speed Delivery Vehicle, White, Red stripe................**£22-24**
YTC05 1938 Studebaker Coupé Express, Yellow, Silver stripe..............**£22-24**
YTC06 1934 International Harvester 'C' Series. Maroon/Black **£22-24**

The 'BUDWEISER Vintage Delivery Truck Collection'. Issued in 1999:
YYT01 (YYM35253) 1932 Diamond-T Truck, Red/White/Brown.........**£22-24**
YYT02 (YYM35254) 1937 Dodge Airflow Refrigerated Van................**£22-24**
YYT03 (YYM35255) 1926 Ford TT Delivery Van, Black/Red...............**£22-24**
YYT04 (YYM35256) 1955 Chevy 55 Pick Up Truck, Red/White.........**£22-24**
YYT05 (YYM35257) 1940 Ford Pick Up Truck, Red and Black **£22-24**
YYT06 (YYM35258) 1948 GMC Refrigerated Truck. Red/White **£22-24**

'THE WORLD'S LEGENDARY SPIRITS COLLECTION'
Issued 1999 / 2000:
YYM37788 1948 GMC CoE truck, 'JIM BEAN' **£20-22**
YYM37789 1926 Ford 'TT' van, 'BACARDI' **£20-22**
YYM37790 1937 Dodge Airflow van, 'JACK DANIEL'S' **£20-22**
YYM37791 1929 Morris light van, 'CUTTY SARK' **£20-22**
YYM37792 1910 Renault 'AG' van, 'DEWARS WHISKY' **£20-22**
YYM37793 1929 Morris light van, 'BEEFEATER GIN' **£20-22**

'INTERNATIONAL RED CROSS COLLECTION' Introduced to celebrate
the world wide operation of the Red Cross Society. **Issued in 2000:**
YYM38057 1912 Ford 'T' van, 'AMERICAN FIELD SERVICE' **£20-22**
YYM38058 1937 GMC van, 'MERCY HOSPITAL' **£20-22**
YYM38059 1947 Citroën 'H' van, 'AMBULANCE HOPITAUX'.........**£20-22**
YYM38060 1950 Ford 'E83W' van, 'AMBULANCE' **£20-22**
YYM38061 1955 Holden 'FJ' van, 'MELBOURNE DISTRICT'..........**£20-22**
YYM38062 1959 Mercedes-Benz 'L408' van, 'AMBULANCE' **£20-22**

'SMALL TOWN PICK-UP TRUCKS' This set of models all have
'cold-cast' loads in their truck bodies. **Issued 2000:**
YYM38035 1951 Holden 'FX', 'Mr FIXIT'.......................................**£20-22**
YYM38038 1953 Ford F100, 'CUSTER DRY GOODS' **£20-22**
YYM38039 1934 International 'C', 'WILSONS GRAIN & FEED' **£20-22**
YYM38040 1940 Ford, 'MURDOCK LUMBER MILL WORK'.........**£20-22**
YYM38041 1939 Reo, 'FORGIONE STONE & BRICK MASON' **£20-22**
YYM38042 1941 Chevrolet, 'KENTS DAIRY'....................................**£20-22**

'PIONEERS OF PROGRESS'
Issued 2000:
YYM36831 1934 Scammell rigid 4 wheel lorry, 'GWR' **£30-35**
YYM36832 1920 Mack 'AC' truck, 'THREE M's'................................**£20-22**
YYM36833 1937 International DR60 truck, 'HARLEY DAVIDSON'...**£20-22**
YYM36834 1937 Dodge Airflow tanker, 'TEXACO' **£20-22**
YYM36835 1933 Diamond 'T' low-wall truck, 'CATERPILLAR' **£20-22**
YYM36836 1948 GMC CoE dump truck, 'US STEEL'.........................**£20-22**

'THE FIRST GREAT 4 x 4 COLLECTION'
Issued 2000:
YYM35053 1946 Dodge Power Wagon, Red and Black **£20-22**
YYM35054 1948 Series I Land Rover, Green and Fawn **£20-25**
YYM35055 1945 Jeep CJ2A, Khaki and Rust Brown **£20-22**
YYM35056 1961 Scout 80, pale Primrose Yellow and White................**£20-22**
YYM35057 1966 Ford Bronco, metallic Bottle Green and White..........**£20-22**
YYM35058 1969 Chevy K5 Blazer, dark Orange and White................**£20-22**

'COCA-COLA: THE VINTAGE VENDING MACHINES EDITION'
These models were decorated with pictures of vintage vending machines, the
type of which is referred to in the description. **Issued in 2000:**
YYM96504 1948 GMC CoE, 'WESTINGHOUSE 3 CASE'................**£20-22**
YYM96505 1937 Dodge Airflow van, '1951 CAVALIER C102' **£20-22**
YYM96506 1932 Mercedes-Benz L5, 'WESTINGHOUSE MASTER' .**£20-22**
YYM96507 1932 Ford 'AA' van, 'VENDO STANDARD 1941' **£20-22**
YYM96508 1929 Morris light van, 'GLASCOCK STANDARD' **£20-22**
YYM96509 1926 Ford 'TT' van, 'MULTIPLEX DISPENSER'............**£20-22**

'THE STATE POLICE INTERCEPTOR SERIES'
This series of 'State Highway Patrol' cars, despite having 'DYM' serial
numbers, all had 'Models of Yesteryear' printed on their bases and as such
have been classified as 'Yesteryears'. **Issued 2000:**
DYM96659 1966 Chevrolet Chevelle, 'ARIZONA' **£20-22**
DYM96663 1971 Dodge Challenger, 'TEXAS' **£20-22**
DYM96664 1970 Plymouth Roadrunner, 'NEW YORK' **£20-22**
DYM96665 1966 Ford Fairlane, 'FLORIDA' **£20-22**
DYM96666 1957 Chevrolet Bel-Air, 'OHIO' **£20-22**
DYM96667 1970 Ford Boss Mustang, 'NEVADA' **£20-22**

'US POST OFFICE COLLECTION'
Identification is the 'fleet number' and the title of the featured advertisement
on the side of the model. **Issued 2000:**
YYM38237 1912 Ford 'T van, '11620', 'I WANT YOU' **£20-22**
YYM38238 1920 Mack 'AC' truck, '6571', 'JOIN THE NAVY'..........**£20-22**
YYM38239 1932 Ford 'AA' truck, '18351', 'AIR MAIL NOW 5c' **£20-22**
YYM38240 1937 GMC van, '39250', 'WE CAN DO IT!' **£20-22**

Matchbox Collectibles

YYM38241 1948 Dodge 'RT' van, 'PREVENT FOREST FIRES'........**£20-22**
YYM38242 1961 Scout 80, '717104', USE ZIP CODE' **£20-22**

'THE GREAT OUTDOORS COLLECTION'
Issued 2000:
YYM38051 1946 Dodge power wagon, 'WHITE TAIL RESERVE' **£20-22**
YYM38052 1948 series 1 Land Rover, 'UK PHEASANT CLUB' **£20-22**
YYM38053 1945 Jeep CJ2A, 'BASS HEAVEN' **£20-22**
YYM38054 1961 Scout 80, 'MATAURA BROWN TROUT'................**£20-22**
YYM38055 1966 Ford Bronco, 'MARLIN ADVENTURES'................**£20-22**
YYM38056 1969 Chevy K5 Blazer, 'MALLARD ACRES' **£20-22**

SINGLE (STAND ALONE) ISSUE MODELS
Prior to the establishment of 'Matchbox Collectibles', all models, Limited
Editions or not, were single, non-thematic, issues. Since 1999, there has been a
return to producing some Yesteryears as single issue (non-Limited Editions /
Exclusive Collectors Editions / Privately Commissioned) models.
They are as follows;
Issued 1999:
YYM37799 Chevy 3100 wrecker truck, White and Red, 'TEXACO' **£25-30**
YYM38298 Chevy 3100 service truck, Green and Black, 'TEXACO' ..**£25-30**
YYM38044 Mack 'AC' tanker, Red and Black, 'THE TEXAS Co' **£30-35**
YYM26108 Chevy 3100 wrecker, 'MATCHBOX COLLECTIBLES' **£30-35**
YYM35810 1956 Mack B-95 pumper, 'EVANS CITY PA FIRE Dept'..**£60-65**
YYM36400 1952 Land Rover and trailer, 'SURF PATROL'..................**£40-45**
The next two models were, initially, only available from the Matchbox
Collectibles (USA) website and are now commonly referred to as 'website
models':
YYM38182 Ford 'AA' fire engine, Red, White, and Black, 'FDNo1' **£25-30**
DYM38236 1970 Chevelle SS454 (car), metallic dark Blue **£25-30**
Issued 2000:
YYM38336 1956 Holden FJ van, 'OLYMPIC TORCH RELAY' **£20-22**
YYM92087 International 'C' series, 'JACK DANIELS' safe truck........**£20-22**
YYM96652 1941 Chevrolet pick-up, 'HARLEY-DAVIDSON'.............**£20-22**
YYM96546 1948 GMC CoE , 'COCA-COLA' bottle lorry **£20-22**
YYM92014 1937 GMC van, 'COCA-COLA', Yellow and Black **£20-22**

'OLYMPICS' Set, issued 2000:
HNLP013   Set of 3 Holden FJ models, '2000 OLYMPICS';
          FJ sedan (Gold), FJ van (Silver), FJ pick-up (Bronze)........**£58-70**

SPECIAL LIMITED EDITIONS
(Year of introduction and quantity produced shown in brackets)
YCH04M 1929 Morris Van, RSPCA, Cream/Blue............(1997, 5,000) **£20-25**
YHN01M 1955 Holden FJ 2104 Panel Van, Grey.............(1997, 5,000) **£30-35**
YHN02M 1954 Holden FJ 2106 Pick-up, Black.............(1997, 5,000) **£30-35**
YHN03M 1951 Holden FX 2106 Pick-up, Fawn ....(1997, 5,000) **£30-35**
YRS05SA 1957 Chevy 3100 Pick Up, 'The Classic 1957 Chevrolet
          40th Anniversary Collection'.....................(1998, 5,000) **£30-40**
YRS6SAM 1955 Ford F100 Pick Up, 'Fire Marshall' ......(1998, 9,500) **£50-55**
YRS07SAM Ford F100 Pick Up. 50th Ann. Special Ed...(1998, 9,500) **£36-38**
YSC0IM 1922 Scania-Vabis Half Track Post Bus, White,
          Xmas tree on roof.................................(1995, 7,000) **£110-150**
YSC02M 1955 Chevy 3100 Pick Up, Red tree ....(1996, 7,500) **£40-50**
YSC03M 1932 Ford 'AA' Fire Engine, Santa, presents....(1996, 8,000) **£34-36**
YY062A/B 1932 Ford 'AA' Truck, 'Clayton Grain'.........(1997, 9,500) **£28-30**
YSC04M Ford Fire Engine, Santa and Mrs Claus...........(1997, 8,000) **£34-36**
YY004CM 1930 Duesenburg Town Car, Maroon/Tan ......(1996, 7,500) **£28-30**
YY012SBM Ford 'T' Field Ambulance, UK Khaki ....(1997, 5,000) **£28-30**
YY013SAM 1918 Crossley Truck, 'Sherwood Florists' ....(1998, 9,500) **£30-35**
YY17ASAM 1938 Hispano-Suiza, Green and Tan ....(1997, 9,500) **£28-30**
YY0I8ESA 1918 Atkinson Steam Wagon, 'Conybeare' ...(1997, 9,500) **£40-50**
YY19BSCM Fowler Showmans Eng. 'J.Searle & Sons' ..(1997, 9,500) **£30-35**
YY020SA 1937 Mercedes 540K Special, Red ....(1997, 7,500) **£35-40**
YY21ASAM 1932 Ford 'A' Woody Wagon, 'Pepsi'.........(1996, 5,000) **£18-20**
YY027SA 1922 Foden 'C' Type Steam Wagon. 'Fullers' (1995, 7,000) **£20-25**
YY027SC 1922 Foden Steam Wagon, Maroon,
          'F. Parker & Co. Timber Importers' ....(1997, 5,000) **£120-140**
YY30ASAM 1920 Mack AC Truck, Red, 'Allentown' ....(1997, 5,000) **£20-22**
YY30ASBM 1920 Mack Truck, 'Fishermans Wharf' ......(1998, 9,500) **£30-34**
YY032ASA Mercedes L5 Lorry, Green, 'O'Neil Farm' .(1997, 12,500) **£28-30**
YY033SBM 1957 BMW 507 Special, Cream Black top ..(1998, 7,500) **£24-26**
YY0345CM 1937 GMC Ambulance, US Army Green.....(1997, 5,000) **£28-30**
YY035 Scania-Vabis, 'Snow Mountain Ski Lodge' ....(1997) **£70-90**
YY039SF 1913 Ford 'TT' Van, 'Jack Daniels' ....(1997, 12,500) **£28-30**
YY047SA Morris Van, 'Fullers', Green, Red roof,
          differences to YGB04 ....(1995, 7,000) **£18-20**
YY052B Mack Truck, 'Matchbox Collectibles' Club Model ......(1998) **£28-30**
YY053SAM Mercedes 770K Special Ed., Red/Black.......(1998, 9,500) **£24-26**
YYM36791 Horse Drawn Wagon, 'Anheuser Busch'.......(1998, 7,500) **£38-40**

YYM36793 Scania-Vabis Post Bus, 'North Pole Mail'.....(1998, 5,000) **£28-30**
YYM36839 Dodge Van. 'McDonalds Courtesy Wagon' ..(1999, 9,500) **£36-38**
Issued 1999 / 2000:
YYM37797 1920 Preston type tram, 'COCA-COLA' ....(12,500) **£20-22**
YYM38030 1926 Ford 'TT' van, 'MATCHBOX COLLECTORS
          GUILD' (2nd Annual Edition, 1999), red seats **£25-30**
          Same but dark grey seats **£60-70**
YYM36837 Fowler B6 crane engine, 'LONDON TRACTION' .(5,000) **£25-30**
YYM38259 1920 Mack AC fire engine, Red and Black...........(10,000) **£25-30**
YYM38289 1938 Studebaker pick-up truck, 'TEXACO' ....(10,000) **£35-40**
YYM95166 1939 Bedford pumper, 'MATCHBOX COLLECTORS
          GUILD' (4th Annual Edition, 2001)...............................**£30-£35**

Matchbox Collectibles Code 1 (Factory-produced) privately
commissioned Limited Edition models
Y5-5 Leyland Titan Bus, 'Chester', 'MICA' model ....(1992, 5,000) **£25-30**
Y19 Fowler Showmans Engine, 'Billy Smarts'................(1997, 3,500) **£30-35**
Y19 Fowler Showmans Engine, 'Lesney' ....(1997, 3,000) **£30-35**
Y21 Aveling & Porter Roller, 'Fred Dibnah'...................(1997, 3,500) **£30-35**
YY48 Garrett Steam Wagon, 'Chester Plays'...................(1998, 3,000) **£30-35**
YCH01 Ford 'T' Van, 'Ronald McDonald House'............(1995, 5,000) **£60-75**
YCH02 Collectors Set. Ford 'T' Van, 'Ronald McDonald
          Charities' (Red with Yellow roof) and Ford
          Model 'A' Van, 'Camp Quality Kids Support'
          (Lt. Blue, Dark Blue chassis and roof).........(1997, 5,000) **£50-60**
YCH02 As above but with All-Red and
          All-Light Blue models ....(1997, 500) **£125-175**
YCH06 Mack Truck, 'Ronald McDonald', 'Perth' ....(1998, 5,000) **£25-30**
YCH07 Ford 'A' Van, 'Ronald McDonald', 'Tasmania' ..(1998, 5,000) **£25-30**
YCH08 Mercedes L5, 'Ronald McDonald', 'Brisbane' ..(1998, 5,000) **£25-30**
YCH09 Morris Courier, 'Ronald McDonald', 'Adelaide' .(1998, 5,000) **£25-30**
YCH010 Holden Van, 'Ronald McDonald', 'Sydney' .....(1998, 5,000) **£25-30**
YCH011 Holden Van, 'Ronald McDonald', 'Melbourne' .(1998, 5,000) **£25-30**
YFE04B Bedford KD Tanker, 'Belrose Bush Fire'..........(1995, 5,000) **£60-80**
YFE02B Land Rover & Trailer, 'Londonderry Fire'.........(1996, 3,000) **£60-80**
YFE05SA 1932 Mercedes L5 Fire Truck, 'Solingen' ......(1997, 3,500) **£30-35**
YFE07SA 1938 Mercedes Fire Wagon, 'Oberndorf' ....(1997, 3,500) **£30-35**
YFE10SA GMC Van, white/yellow, 'Cessnock Rescue' ..(1997, 3,500) **£30-35**
YHN01SA 1955 Holden FJ Van, 'Auto One' ....(1997, 3,500) **£30-35**
YHN01SB Holden FJ 2104 Van, 'Temora Ambulance' ....(1997, 3,500) **£30-35**
YHN01SC Holden Van, 'Automodel Solingen/Sydney' ...(1998, 3,000) **£30-35**
YPP02SA Morris Courier Van, 'Classic Toys' ....(1996, 3,000) **£35-40**
YPP02SB Morris Courier Van, 'Lesney Prodocts' ....(1996, 3,000) **£30-35**
YPP04SA 1948 Dodge Route Van, 'Express Delivery' ...(1996, 3,000) **£35-45**
YY0I2SA Ford 'T' Van, 'Junior Collectors Club'.............(1996, 3,000) **£25-30**
          Within the 3,000 exist 36 with Blue roof
          (normally Green)..(1996, 36) **£300-400**
YY027SB Foden Steam Wagon, 'MICA' Club Model......(1996, 3,000) **£40-50**
YY034SA GMC Van, 'Chester Toy Museum' ....(1996, 3,000) **£25-30**
          Within the 3,000 exist 36 with 6-spoke
          Copper wheels (normally Silver solid).........(1996, 36) **£300-400**
YY039SC Ford 'TT' Van, 'Matchbox USA 20th Year' ....(1997, 3,500) **£30-35**
YY048SA Garrett Steam Wagon, 'Pickfords' ....(1997, 3,500) **£30-40**
YY065SB Austin 7 Van, '4th European Convention' ....(1996, 1,400) **£45-50**
YY065SC Austin 7 Van, 'MICA 12th UK Conv.'.............(1997, 1,400) **£45-50**
YY065SD Austin 7 Van, 'MICA 5th European Conv.'.....(1997, 1,400) **£45-50**

Collectors notes

236

The 'PLATINUM' Range

In 2000, Matchbox Collectibles launched the new brand name, 'Platinum', onto the collectors market. This range of models was made mostly from existing Models of Yesteryear and Dinky tooling and was created mainly for the American market to differentiate more markedly between the bargain priced '1:43 Retail' series (also made from the same tooling) and the costlier regular Yesteryears and Dinkys. The words 'Models of Yesteryear' and 'Dinky' on the baseplates were replaced by the word 'Platinum', but 5 digit serial numbers were retained. The majority of these Platinum models were put into 6 piece 'themed sets', but some were stand alone 'Special Issues'. The packaging was the same as for the regular Yesteryears and Dinkys, except that the outside of the boxes were coloured in black and silver and the Platinum name was featured.

'JACK DANIELS 150th BIRTHDAY WHISKEY COLLECTION'
Issued 2000
92155 1948 GMC CoE truck, 'PORTRAIT', Red and Black.................**£19-22**
92156 1932 Ford 'AA' truck, 'OLD No. 7', Black and Tan.................**£19-22**
92157 1937 GMC van, 'WHITE RABBIT SALOON', Red and Black .**£19-22**
92158 1926 Ford 'TT' van, 'OLD TIME', Black and Tan....................**£19-22**
92159 1912 Ford 'T' van, 'GOLD MEDAL', Red and Black.................**£19-22**
92160 1930 Ford 'A' van, SINGLE BARREL', Red and Tan................**£19-22**

'TEXACO VINTAGE DELIVERY TRUCKS COLLECTION'
Issued 2000
92119 1955 Chevrolet '3100', wrecker truck, Red and Black **£19-22**
92121 1941 Chevrolet ½ ton pick-up, Green, White and Red...............**£19-22**
92122 1940 Ford pick-up, Red, White and Green **£19-22**
92123 1920 Mack 'AC' truck, Red, White and Black................**£19-22**
92124 1934 International 'C' series pick-up, Black and Red.................**£19-22**
92125 1930 Ford 'A' pick-up, Red and White.......................................**£19-22**

'HERSHEY (small scale) TRACTOR/TRAILER COLLECTION'
Issued 2000
92167 1939 Peterbilt 'VALENTINES GREETINGS' **£19-22**
92168 Kenworth 'HAPPY EASTER' **£19-22**
92169 Kenworth 'MOTHERS DAY' **£19-22**
92171 1939 Peterbilt 'INDEPENDENCE DAY' **£19-22**
92172 Mack 'CH600' 'TRICK OR TREAT'...**£19-22**
92173 Ford 'Aero-Max' 'SEASONS GREETINGS' **£19-22**

'LEGENDARY `PLANES COLLECTION'
Issued 2000/2001
92098 P-51 D Mustang, Silver, Black and Red **£19-22**
92099 F4 U-1A Corsair, Black with White star, No. '86' **£19-22**

92101 Grumann Hellcat, Black with White star, No. '59' **£19-22**
92102 Spitfire Mk.1A, R.A.F., camouflage **£19-22**
92103 P-40 Curtiss, Khaki with White star **£19-22**
92104 P-38J Lightning, Silver, Black and Yellow **£19-22**

'U.S. POSTAL SERVICE COLLECTION' (Series 2)
Issued 2001
92546 1912 Ford 'T' van 'JIM THORPE', Cream and Black.................**£20-22**
92547 1926 Ford 'TT' van 'MARGARET MEAD', lt. Blue / Black **£20-22**
92548 1930 Ford 'A' van 'JESSE OWENS', pale Blue and Red...........**£20-22**
92549 1937 Dodge Airflow van 'F.D. ROOSEVELT', pale/dark Blue...**£20-22**
92552 1948 GMC CoE truck 'HARRY TRUMAN', dk. Blue / White...**£20-22**
92553 1955 Ford F100 'R. MARCIANO', Cream, dk.Blue and Black ..**£20-22**

'U.S. CLASSIC CARS SERIES' (Each model finished in the original car manufacturer's paint colour. Models presented in tin boxes.)
Issued 2001
92686 1968 Chevrolet Camaro SS396, White **£25-27**
92687 1970 Ford Boss 429 Mustang, mid Blue **£25-27**
92688 1971 Plymouth Barracuda 440/6 PK, Lime Green and Black......**£25-27**
92689 1959 Cadillac Coupe de Ville, bright Red **£25-27**
92692 1955 Ford Thunderbird, bright Yellow **£25-27**
92696 1958 Studebaker Golden Hawk, Gold with White roof...............**£25-27**

Individual 'SPECIAL EDITION' models
Issued 2000
96769 1956 Mack B61 lorry, 'JACK DANIELS', Black with barrels **£40-42**
92024 1956 Mack B61 lorry, 'BUDWEISER', Red with crates **£40-42**
92312 1948 GMC CoE truck 'MATCHBOX COLLECTORS GUILD
    (3rd Annual Edition, 2000)'..**£25-27**
92554 Peterbilt tractor/trailer, 'COCA-COLA XMAS TREE FARM'.**£55-58**
38100 1999 VW Beetle (1:18 scale), 'COCA-COLA', Red andWhite ..**£30-33**
92174 Kenworth tractor/trailer (tanker), 'TEXACO', Black and Silver .**£55-58**
92175 1926 Ford 'TT' van, 'CAMPBELL'S SOUPS', Grey and White .**£20-22**
92544 1964½ Ford Mustang convertible, Cream....................................**£20-22**
92541 1932 Ford 'AA' truck, 'BUDWEISER XMAS BREW'..............**£20-22**
38045 Mack B61 tractor/trailer, 'YESTERYEAR DESIGN SMTT' **£20-22**
Issued 2001
38049 Daf LGTT tractor/trailer, 'SCUDERIA FERRARI', Red............**£55-57**
92545 1900 Horse drawn wagon, 'HERSHEY CHOCOLATES' **£25-30**
92540 1912 Ford 'T' van, 'JACK DANIELS LYNCHBURG',
    Black, Red andWhite..**£20-22**
38046 1968 VW Beetle, 'COCA-COLA' **£20-22**
92542 1955 Ford Thunderbird, Turquoise **£20-22**

YYM37788 GMC Truck, 'JIM BEAN'   YYT01 (YYM35253) Diamond-T 'BUDWEISER'   YYM35055 Jeep CJ2A

In 1986, Matchbox Toys Ltd. (UK) began negotiations with Kenner Parker, who owned Airfix, to buy the Dinky Toys trademark. By early 1987, Matchbox had acquired the Dinky name, due in part to Airfix going into liquidation and Kenner's need for cash. Matchbox decided that the new Dinkys would be made, with very few exceptions, to the universally accepted model scale of 1:43. The range would, almost exclusively, feature cars only. The first prototypes were shown to the trade at the January 1988 Harrogate Toy Fair, but it was not until the end of that year that the first dedicated 'Matchbox Dinky' appeared in the shops.
Manufactured by Matchbox International Ltd., in Macau and China.

1967 Jaguar 'E'-type series 1½ soft-top
DY-1	1988	Dark Green body, Black soft-top	**£8-12**
DY-1B	1991	Yellow body, Black soft-top	**£8-12**
DY921	1992	Model cast entirely in pewter (on wooden plinth)	**£18-22**

1957 Chevrolet Bel-Air
DY-2	1989	Red body, White roof, light grey base	**£8-12**
		Same but Black base	**£40-50**

1965 MGB GT
DY-3	1989	Teal blue body, Black sun roof	**£8-12**
DY-3B	1992	Orange body and roof	**£8-12**

1950 Ford E83W van
DY-4	1989	'HEINZ', Yellow body, Black wings, riveted base	**£8-12**
		Same but screwed base	**£18-22**
DY-4B	1989	'RADIO TIMES',	
		Olive Green body, matt Black roof	**£10-12**
		Same but gloss Black roof	**£28-32**

1949 Ford V8 Pilot
DY-5	1989	Black body, Black sun roof	**£8-12**
DY-5B	1991	Silver body, Black sun roof	**£8-12**
DY-5C	1992	Beige Sandalwood body, Black sun roof	**£8-12**

1951 Volkswagen 'Beetle' De-luxe Sedan
DY-6	1989	Pale Blue body, mid Grey sun roof	**£8-12**
		Same but charcoal Grey roof	**£18-24**
DY-6B	1991	Black body, dark Grey sun roof	**£10-15**
DY-6C	1992	Red body, dark Grey sun roof	**£8-12**

1959 Cadillac Coupe-de-Ville
DY-7	1989	Ruby red body, Cream roof	**£10-15**
DY-7B	1991	Pink body, Cream roof	**£10-15**

1948 Commer 8cwt Van
DY-8	1989	'SHARP'S TOFFEE', Red body	**£8-12**
DY-8B	1991	'HIS MASTER'S VOICE', Navy Blue body	**£8-12**

1948 Land Rover 1st Series
DY-9	1989	Dark Green body, Tan canvas roof	**£22-27**
DY-9B	1991	'AA', Yellow body, Black chassis and front wings	**£8-12**

1950 Mercedes-Benz Konferenz type 0-3500 Bus
DY-S10	1990	Cream body, Blue bonnet and side stripe	**£28-32**

1948 Tucker Torpedo
DY-11	1990	Metallic dark Red body,	
		'Made in Macau' cast on base	**£8-12**
		'Made in China' cast on base	**£33-38**
DY-11B	1992	Metallic Azure Blue body	**£8-12**

1955 Mercedes-Benz 300SL
DY-12	1990	Cream body	**£8-12**
DY-12B	1992	Black body	**£8-12**

1955 Bentley 'R' type Continental
DY-13	1990	Metallic steel Blue body	**£8-12**
DY-13B	1992	Dark Blue body	**£8-12**

1946 Delahaye 145
DY-14	1990	Metallic dark Blue body	**£8-12**
DY-14B	1992	Dark Red body	**£8-12**

1953 Austin A40 van
DY-15	1990	'BROOKE BOND TEA', Red body	**£8-12**
DY-15B	1991	'DINKY TOYS', Yellow body	**£8-12**

1967 Ford Mustang Fastback 2+2
DY-16	1989	Green body, 'Made in Macau' cast on base	**£8-12**
		Same but 'Made in China' cast on base	**£33-38**
DY-16B	1992	White body	**£8-12**

1939 Triumph Dolomite
DY-S17	1990	Red body, Black (removable) soft-top	**£13-18**

1968 Jaguar 'E'-type series 1½
DY-18	1990	Red body, Black folded-down hood	**£8-12**

1973 MGB GT V8
DY-19	1990	Damask Red body and roof	**£8-12**

1965 Triumph TR4A-IRS
DY-20	1990	White body, Black folded-down hood	**£8-12**

1964 Austin Mini Cooper 'S'
DY-21	1991	Cream body, Black roof	**£8-12**

1952 Citroën 15cv
DY-22	1991	Black body, base with **rear-wheel** drive cast detail	**£8-12**
		Same but base with **front-wheel** drive cast detail	**£75-80**
	1992	Cream body	**£8-12**

1956 Chevrolet Corvette
DY-23	1991	Bright Red body with Cream side flash	**£10-15**
DY-23B	1992	Metallic Copper body with Cream side flash	**£8-12**

1973 Ferrari Dino 246 GTS
DY-24	1991	Red body with Black removable roof	**£8-12**

1958 Porsche 356A Coupé
DY-25	1991	Silver body	**£8-12**

1957 Studebaker Golden Hawk
DY-26	1991	Gold body with Cream rear fin panels	**£10-15**

1957 Chevrolet Bel-Air Convertible
DY-27	1991	Light Blue body, White and Blue seats	**£10-15**
		Same but Brown and Blue seats (qty. 1,100)	**£75-85**

1969 Triumph Stag
DY-28	1992	White body (open top)	**£10-15**

1953 Buick Skylark
DY-29	1992	Light Blue body (open top)	**£10-15**

1956 Austin-Healey 100 BN2
DY-30	1992	British Racing Green body (open top)	**£10-15**

1955 Ford Thunderbird
DY-31	1992	Red body (open top)	**£18-25**

1957 Citroën 2cv
DY-32	1992	Grey body and sun roof	**£10-15**

European Sports Cars Set
DY-902	1991	Three sports cars in colours unique to this set, mounted on a wooden plinth. Comprised of: DY-12 1950 Mercedes-Benz 300SL in Silver, DY-24 1973 Ferrari Dino in metallic Blue, DY-25 1956 Porsche 356A in Red	**£30-35**

British Sports Cars Set
DY-903	1992	Three sports cars in colours unique to this set, mounted on a wooden plinth. Comprised of: DY-18 1968 Jaguar 'E'-type Series 1½ in Cream, DY-20 1965 Triumph TR4 IRS in Red, DY-30 1956 Austin-Healey 100 BN2 in steel Blue	**£30-35**

The name of Matchbox International Ltd.'s marketing division in Australasia was 'Matchbox Collectibles'. They not only supplied models to shops, but also operated a successful mail-order system supplying models direct to collectors. In October 1992, Tyco Toys Inc. of the USA bought the Matchbox brand name from Universal Toys. The title 'Matchbox Collectibles' and its way of selling the Matchbox range of models was adopted for worldwide distribution by Tyco Toys. As with the 'Models of Yesteryear' range, Dinkys were grouped into 6-piece 'Thematic Sets', but due to a two year break in production, few sets were produced under Tyco's stewardship.

In September 1997, Mattel Inc., the world's No.1 toy maker and also of the USA, began merger talks with Tyco, and by 31st March, 1998, the deal was completed. The 'Matchbox Collectibles' division was unaffected by this change of ownership and the 'Thematic Sets' continued whilst the range was expanded to include models made from the Kingsize and Convoy ranges tooling. All cars that had been previously in the Yesteryear range were to be produced only as Dinkys, and new tooling introduced 1:48 scale American tractor/trailers, some minus their trailers, into the range. More new tooling resulted in 'World War 2' military tanks and fighter 'planes. Additional cars were produced from other toy companies (mainly Vitesse) tooling to swell the range. Single (stand alone) and 'Special Limited Edition' models were also introduced.

In 2001, the mail-order operation was terminated at the end of March as all 'Matchbox Collectibles' product was to be sold henceforth via the existing chain of 'Collectibles Centres' and other 'High Street' outlets. These models were manufactured in China.

'The Golden Age of Sports Cars' (1995)
DY001/C 1967 **Jaguar 'E'-type** soft top, Black body and hood £23-28
DY019/B 1973 **M.G.B. GT V8**, Tartan Red body and roof £23-28
DY028/B 1969 **Triumph Stag**, metallic dark Green body (open top) .£23-28
DY033/A 1962 **Mercedes-Benz 300SL**, dark Blue body (open top) ..£23-28
DY035/A 1968 **Volkswagen Karmann-Ghia**, Red body (open top)...£23-28
DY036/A 1960 **Jaguar XK150 Coupé**, Ivory body,
(open top, 'Dinky' cast on base)..............................£28-35
Same but Cream body ('Dinky' not cast on base)...............£28-35

'American Classics, Stars of the Silver Screen' (1995)
This was a series of 8 American cars in colours in which they had previously appeared as individual models. However, they all featured additional 'enhanced' painted detailing such as coloured rear light lenses and highlighted internal fittings.
DY007/C 1959 **Cadillac Coupé-de-Ville**, (lighter) Pink body,
Cream roof...£23-28
DY011/C 1948 **Tucker Torpedo**, metallic Azure Blue body and roof £23-28
DY016/C 1967 **Ford Mustang Fastback 2+2**, metallic Green £23-28
DY023/A 1956 **Chevrolet Corvette**, (darker) Red body,
Cream side flash..£23-28
DY026/B 1957 **Studebaker Golden Hawk**, metallic dark Gold body,
light Cream rear fin panels.....................................£23-28
DY027/B 1957 **Chevrolet Bel-Air**, light Blue, (open) ..£23-28
DY029/B 1953 **Buick Skylark**, pale Blue body (open top) £23-28
DY031/B 1955 **Ford Thunderbird**, (lighter) Red body (open top) £32-38

1995 witnessed the withdrawal of the familiar blue and white 'window' boxes. The generic enclosed boxes that were initially introduced for the Yesteryear range were adopted for the Dinky range in 1996. Also, the enhanced painted and printed detailing that was introduced for the 'Stars of the Silver Screen' models became the norm for all subsequent issues.

'Oldies But Goodies' Series 1 (1996)
DYG01 1967 **Ford Mustang Fastback 2+2**, dark Blue body £19-22
DYG02 1967 **Chevrolet Bel-Air**, dark Red body, Ivory White roof £19-22
DYG03 1958 **Studebaker Golden Hawk**, Petrol Blue body £19-22
DYG04 1953 **Buick Skylark**, light Yellow body £19-22
DYG05 1959 **Cadillac Coupé-de-Ville** open-top, Black body £19-22
DYG06 1956 **Chevrolet Corvette**, Black body and removable top..£19-23
DYG07 1948 **Tucker Torpedo**, dark Green body £19-22
DYG08 1955 **Ford Thunderbird**, Turquoise body, Ivory top £19-22

'Oldies But Goodies' Series 2 (1997)
DYG09-M 1959 **Chevrolet Impala**, White body, Black soft-top £19-22
DYG10-M 1947 **Chrysler Town and Country**, dark Beige body/top ..£19-22
DYG11-M 1958 **Buick Special**, metallic dark Green body, Ivory top ..£19-22
DYG12-M 1956 **Ford Fairlane**, Blue and White body, Blue roof £19-22
DYG13-M 1953 **Cadillac Eldorado**, Black body, White soft-top £19-22
DYG14-M 1948 **De Soto**, Maroon body and roof £19-22
DYG15-M 1958 **Nash Metropolitan**, Turquoise and White body........£19-22
DYG16-M 1955 **Chevrolet Bel-Air**, Red and Ivory body, Ivory roof...£19-22

'Classic European Economy Cars' (1997)
VEM01-M 1949 **Volkswagen Cabriolet**, Black + Red side panels....£14-16
VEM02-M 1959 **Austin 7 Mini**, Red body and roof.........................£14-16
VEM03-M 1949 **Citroën 2cv**, Steel Grey body, dk.Grey (open) top..£14-16
VEM04-M 1955 **Messerschmitt KR200**, Yellow and Black body £14-16
VEM05-M 1962 **Wolseley Hornet**, dark Maroon body, Ivory roof....£14-16
VEM06-M 1966 **Fiat 500**, light Green body, Cream (open) sun roof.£14-16
VEM07-M 1962 **Renault 4L**, light Blue body, Black sun roof..........£14-16

'The Classic British Sports Car Collection' (1998)
DYB01 1959 **Triumph TR3A**, British Racing Green body,
light Brown soft-top..£14-16
DYB02 1967 **Jaguar 'E'-type**, bright Red body,
Brown folded-down hood..................................£14-16
DYB03 1955 **Morgan 4/4**, Black body, Rust Brown tonneau £14-16
DYB04 1956 **Austin Healey**, Cream body, Black folded hood £14-16
DYB05 1967 **MG B**, pale Yellow body, Black soft-top £14-16
DYB06 1962 **Aston-Martin DB4**, Silver body and roof..............£14-16
DYB07 1961 **Lotus Super Seven**, Red body, Black hood........£110-170
DYM38304 1960 **Jaguar XK150**, Silver body, Black folded hood £45-60

'The Classic 1957 Chevrolet 40th Anniversary Collection' (1998)
This set was limited to 5,000 pieces of each model.
DYG02/SA 1957 **Chevrolet Bel-Air**, Dusk Pearl body,
Imperial Ivory roof..£25-35
DY027/SB 1957 **Chevrolet Bel-Air Convertible**, Matador Red body £25-35
VCV01 1957 **Chevrolet Nomad**, Black body, Imperial Ivory roof.£55-65
CCV03 1957 **Chevrolet Corvette**, Cream body, Silver flash £25-35
One other model was included in this 5-piece set, the **1957 Chevrolet 3100 Pick-up Truck** which was issued as a 'Models of Yesteryear'.

'Coca-Cola Cruisers' (1998)
These 6 models were decorated with well-known Coca-Cola advertising slogans.
CCV06-BM 1953 **Chevrolet Corvette**, Red and Yellow,
'Dependable as Sunshine' £17-20
DYG08-BM 1955 **Ford Thunderbird**, Red and Black,
'Americans Prefer Taste'..£17-20
DYG02-BM 1957 **Chevrolet Bel-Air Convertible**,
Yellow and Red, 'Sign of Good Taste' £17-20
YMC03-BM 1967 **Pontiac GTO**, Red and Black,
'Coke after Coke after Coke' £17-20
YMC06-BM 1968 **Chevrolet Camaro**, Black and Yellow,
'It's Twice Time'..£17-20
YMC05-BM 1970 **Ford 'Boss' Mustang**, Red and Yellow,
'It's the Real Thing' £17-20

'Cars of the Rich and Infamous' (1998)
This set of 6 models was originally planned to be included in the 'Yesteryear' range and was promoted as such, however when they were released, DYM serial numbers and the name 'Dinky' had been printed on their bases.
DYM35178 1937 **Cord 812 Viton**, dark Blue body, White roof £17-20
DYM35179 1931 **Stutz Bearcat**, Yellow body, Black chassis......£17-20
DYM35180 1938 **Lincoln Zephyr**, pearlescent pale Pink.............£25-30
DYM35181 1933 **Cadillac V16**, dark Green body, Cream roof £17-20
DYM35182 1930 **Duesenberg 'J'**, dark Red body, White roof.......£17-20
DYM35185 1931 **Mercedes-Benz 770**, Black body, Grey roof......£17-20

The 'Austin Powers' collection (1999)
Released to coincide with the release of the 2nd Austin Powers movie.
DYM37905 1967 **Jaguar 'E'-type series 1½** open-top, body with
Union flag decoration in Red, White and Blue...........£30-40
DYM37905 1999 **Volkswagen Concept Convertible**,
Multi-coloured body..£30-40

'The Anheuser-Busch Sports Cars Collection' (1999)
These 6 models were all given multi-coloured finishes and graphics portraying the different beers produced by this company and the sports they sponsor.
DYM37597 1959 **Cadillac Coupé-de-Ville**, 'Michelob Golf' £17-20
DYM37598 1969 **Dodge Charger**, 'Bud Racing' £17-20
DYM37599 1971 **Plymouth Barracuda**, 'Budweiser Fly-Fishing'£17-20
DYM37600 1957 **Chevrolet Bel-Air**, 'Budweiser Boxing'...........£17-20
DYM37619 1964 **Ford Mustang** open-top, 'Bud Light Rodeo' £17-20
DYM37622 1968 **Volkswagen Beetle**, 'Budweiser Bowling' £17-20

'The Vintage Police Car Collection' (1999)
Despite the title of this series, two of the models were in fact vans from the 'Models of Yesteryear' range.
DYM38019 1912 **Ford 'T' Van**, Black body and roof, 'Dallas' £17-20
DYM38020 1966 **Ford Fairlane**, White/Green, 'Miami' £17-20

DYM38021	**1933 Cadillac V16**, Black body, 'Salt Lake City'	**£17-20**
DYM38022	**1970 Plymouth Roadrunner**, White, 'Denver'	**£17-20**
DYM38023	**1957 Chevrolet Bel-Air**, Black/White, 'Atlanta'	**£17-20**
DYM38024	**1926 Ford 'TT' Van**, Green/Black, 'New York City'	**£17-20**

'On the road with Anheuser-Busch' (1999)
A set of 6 small scale (SMTT) modern American Tractor/Trailer units decorated with the graphics of Anheuser-Busch's best known beers.

DYM36670	**Peterbilt**, Red, 'Budweiser'	**£17-20**
DYM36671	**Kenworth**, Black, Red and Gold, 'Michelob'	**£17-20**
DYM36672	**Mack CH600**, Blue and Silver, 'Bud Light'	**£17-20**
DYM36674	**Ford Aeromax**, Green and Yellow, 'O'Doul's'	**£17-20**
DYN36675	**Kenworth**, Blue/White/Yellow/Red, 'Busch Beer'	**£17-20**
DYM36677	**Peterbilt**, Blue, Silver, Red and Yellow, 'Bud Ice'	**£17-20**

'The Classic 50's Automobilia Collection' (1999)
This set was comprised of vintage SMTT American tractor/trailer units, decorated with suitable vintage graphics of some famous automotive products.

DYM35265	**1956 Mack 'B'**, Yellow and Black, 'Pennzoil'	**£17-20**
DYM35266	**1953 Mack 'B'**, Green, Black and Red, 'Fire Chief Gasoline'	**£17-20**
DYM35267	**1939 Peterbilt**, Red and light Blue, 'Pep Boys'	**£17-20**
DYM35268	**1956 Mack 'B'**, Blue and Yellow, 'Champion'	**£17-20**
DYM35269	**1939 Peterbilt**, Blue, White and Yellow, 'Michelin'	**£17-20**
DYM35270	**1939 Peterbilt**, Red and black, 'Sinclair'	**£17-20**

'Masters of the Highway' (1999)
Set of 4 (only) modern SMTT American tractor/trailer units, decorated with the graphics of some of the largest haulage companies in the USA.

DYM38007	**Ford Aeromax**, Orange, Blue and White, 'Roadway Express'	**£17-20**
DYM38008	**Ford Aeromax**, White, Green and Red, 'Consolidated Freightways'	**£17-20**
DYM38009	**Ford Aeromax**, Silver and Blue, 'Overnight'	**£17-20**
DYM38010	**Mack CH600**, Yellow, White and Yellow, 'Yellow'	**£17-20**

'Vintage Big-Rigs – The Pioneers of Trucking' 1999
A set of 3 vintage tractor units in 1:43 scale.

DYM35214	**1956 Mack B61**, Orange and Black	**£29-32**
DYM35216	**1948 Diamond 'T'**, Blue, Black and White	**£29-32**
DYM35217	**1939 Peterbilt**, Red and Black	**£29-32**

'Great Tanks of the World Collection' (2000)
This set included 8 of the best known tanks that featured in various WW2 theatres of action. The turrets rotate, but the tracks do not. They were given appropriate camouflage finishes.

DYM37579	**Sherman M4 A3 76mm**, dark Green	**£19-22**
DYM37580	**Panzer 1V (SDKFZ 161) AUSF F1**, charcoal Grey	**£19-22**
DYM37581	**Panzer V Panther AUSF A**, Sand and Brown	**£19-22**
DYM37582	**Wirbelwind Flakpanzer 1V**, Sand/Brown/Green	**£19-22**
DYM37583	**(Russian) T34/76**, drab Green and Brown	**£19-22**
DYM37584	**Churchill Mk.4**, drab Green	**£19-22**
DYM37585	**Sherman M4 A3 105mm Howitzer**, drab Green/Sand	**£19-22**
DYM37586	**Panzer 1V (SDKFZ 161) AUSF H/J**, Sand/Brown	**£19-22**

'The Coca-Cola Vintage Tractor/trailer Collection'.
This was a set of SMTT models with multi-colour finishes featuring appropriate advertising graphics.

DYM96653	**1956 Mack B61**, 'Sunshine'	**£19-22**
DYM96654	**1939 Peterbilt**, 'Bowling'	**£19-22**
DYM96655	**1956 Mack B61**, 'Beach'	**£19-22**
DYM96656	**1939 Peterbilt**, 'Baseball'	**£19-22**
DYM96657	**1956 Mack B61**, 'Refreshing'	**£19-22**
DYM96658	**1939 Peterbilt**, 'Sprite Boy'	**£19-22**

Single and Special Limited Edition (stand alone) models
There have been many single edition models, some in limited quantities and some not. Where a model was a 'Limited Edition', the quantity that was produced is given.

Issued in 1997:

DY016/D-M	**1967 Ford Mustang Fastback 2+2**, Red, White stripes, 5,000	**£30-40**
DY002/SA	**1957 Chevrolet Bel-Air 'Hot-Rod'**, Black with flame decoration, 5,000	**£55-65**

Issued in 1998:

DY011/SA-M	**1948 Tucker Torpedo**, Primrose Yellow, 9,500	**£25-30**
DY014/SA	**1946 Delahaye 145 Chapron**, Pea Green, 7,500	**£25-30**

Issued in 1999:

DYM36840	**1957 Citroën 2cv**, Yellow and Black, 10,000	**£25-30**
DYM37798	**1953 Buick Skylark**, Balsam Green, 7,500	**£25-30**

All the following models are tractor/trailer units unless otherwise stated.

DYM34577	**1955 Mack B61**, 'McDonalds', Red and Yellow	**£55-60**
DYM36097	**Ford Aeromax SMTT**, 'Jack Daniels', Blackand Grey, 9,500	**£20-25**
DYM36838	**Kenworth (tanker) SMTT**, 'Gulf Oil', White, Red and Blue, 9,500	**£25-30**
DYM37040	**Peterbilt**, 'Harley-Davidson', Black	**£55-60**
DYM37796	**Mack CH600**, 'Matchbox Collectibles Millennium', 7,500	**£65-75**
DYM37904	**1948 Kenworth W900**, 'Jack Daniels', Black	**£55-60**
DYM38050	**1939 Peterbilt**, 'Coca-Cola', Yellow and Red	**£55-60**
DYM38233	**1948 Diamond 'T'**, 'Budweiser', Red, 10,000	**£55-60**
DYM38258	**Peterbilt 359**, 'Holiday (Xmas) Greetings from Budweiser'	**£55-60**
DYM38277	**Freightliner CoE**, 'Hershey's Milk Chocolate Centenary'	**£55-60**
DYM38314	**Freightliner CoE**, 'McDonalds, 45 Years'	**£55-60**

Issued in 2000:

DYM38179	**Auburn 851 Speedster**, White, Red stripe, 5,000	**£25-30**
DYM92013	**1968 VW Beetle**, 'McDonald's', Blue/Red/Yellow	**£20-25**
DYM92139	**1957 Chevrolet Corvette**, Arctic Blue	**£20-25**

All the following models are tractor/trailers units unless otherwise stated.

DYM38337	**1939 Peterbilt**, 'Campbell's Soups'	**£55-60**
DYM92015	**1948 Diamond 'T'**, 'Jack Daniels', White/Black	**£55-60**
DYM92058	**1939 Peterbilt**, 'Hershey Chocolates', Cream body	**£55-60**
DYM92127	**Peterbilt 359**, 'Matchbox Collectibles Anniversary Tractor Trailer', Blue and Yellow tractor/trailer	**£58-63**

Matchbox Dinky 'Code 1 Commemorative Models'
These models were made by Matchbox's Research and Development department to commemorate special occasions.
When the 'R&D' department had completed their research work on the 1964 Austin Mini Cooper, they painted four of the models in the original colours of the actual vehicle used for their research and presented them to the owner of the vehicle.
1964 Austin Mini Cooper

DY-21	1991	Fiesta Yellow body, Cream roof. Quantity 4	**£1,000-1,100**

When Matchbox closed their Office and Warehouse facility in Rugby, Warwickshire, fifty of the Austin A40 'Dinky' vans were decorated with labels commemorating the closure and were presented to staff members.
1953 Austin A40 van

DY-15B	1996	'Matchbox at Rugby, 1990 to 1996.', Yellow body. Quantity 50	**£325-375**

In 1999, the Matchbox (UK) Research and Development department closed, ending almost 50 years of service and tradition. To commemorate this sad event, thirty Studebaker Golden Hawks were re-coloured and mounted on black MDF plinths that had brass plaques affixed stating, 'To commemorate the closure of the Matchbox UK R and D department October 1999. John Torrance, The Dinky Collection 1989-1996.'
1958 Studebaker Golden Hawk

DYG03	1999	'Closure of the Matchbox R and D dept.', Orange body, dark Red roof, Yellow seats. Qty. 30.	**£350-400**

Matchbox Dinky 'Code 2' Models

DY-2	**Mini-Cooper**, 'Classic Car Show' (1991), qty. 1,000	**£70-80**
DY-8	**Commer Van**, 'Motorfair 91' (1991), qty. 2,300	**£30-35**
DY-28	**Triumph Stag**, 'Classic Car Show' (1992), qty. 2,000	**£40-50**
001	**Mini-Cooper**, 'Police' panda car, (1994), qty. 2,000	**£70-80**
N01	**Commer Van**, 'Classic Toys', (1994), qty. 2,000	**£70-80**
DDS003	**Ford E83W Van**, 'I'm a Dinky', (1995), qty. 300	**£225-275**
DY073	**Cadillac Coupé de Ville**, 'Dinky Toy Club of America', (1995), quantity 200	**£60-80**
002	**Commer Van**, 'Bentalls', (1996), qty. 1,500	**£60-70**
003	**Mini Cooper**, '13' Bathurst racer, (1995), qty. 1,500	**£60-70**
004	**Austin A40 Van**, 'Major Print', (1996), qty. 1,200	**£60-70**
DY033A	**Mercedes-Benz 300SL**, 'Dinky Toy Club of America', (1996), quantity 200	**£60-70**
005	**Austin A40 Van**, '4th Mica European Convention', Black wheels, (1996), quantity 250	**£50-60**
DY-31	**Ford Thunderbird**, 'Maple Leaf Thunderbird Club, 1995-1996', Black body, Red and White interior, (1996), quantity 12	**£425-475**
	Same but Silver body, Red and White interior, (1996), quantity 42	**£275-325**

DY031/B Same (Silver body) but Red, White and Silver interior,
(1996), quantity 6 ....**£475-525**

DY-31 **Ford Thunderbird**, 'Maple Leaf Thunderbird Club,
1996-1997', Yellow body, Red and White interior,
(1997), quantity 6 ....**£475-525**
Same but White body, Red and White interior,
(1997), quantity 10 ....**£425-475**

DYG08 Same but White hood fitted, Turquoise, White and
Silver interior, (1997), quantity 50 ....**£275-325**

DYG08 Same but Turquoise body and fitted hood, (1997), 280 ......**£40-50**

006 **Ford E83W Van**, '5th MICA European Convention',
Silver wheel hubs, (1997), quantity 250 ....**£50-60**

DY-30 **Austin-Healey BN2**, 'Dinky Toy Club of America'
(1997), quantity 150 ....**£60-65**

DY033/A **Mercedes-Benz 300SL**, 'The Dinky Book' (1997),
Cream body. Only available in special box with hard-back
edition of the book. Quantity 24 ....**£400-450**
Same, but Silver body (soft-back edition of book). 600......**£60-65**

DY-016/D-M **Ford Mustang Fastback 2+2**,
'Dinky Toy Club of America' (1998), quantity 150 ....**£60-65**

DY-308 **Austin-Healey 100 BN**, 'Austin-Healey Club (UK)' (1998)
Black body, Ivory interior, quantity 8 ....**£400-450**
Same but Red body, Ivory interior, quantity 210 ....**£40-45**

DY-30 Same (Red body), but Black interior, quantity 8 ....**£400-450**
Same but White body, Black interior, quantity 17 ....**£350-400.**

DY-23 **Chevrolet Corvette**, 'France, Dutch and German
Dinky Society', Yellow body and roof, (1999), 500......**£45-55**

DY-27 **Chevrolet Bel-Air hard-top**, 'The 2nd Dinky Book' (1998),
Dark Blue body. Only available with book with dark
Blue cover, quantity 25 ....**£350-400**
Same but White body (book with White cover), qty. 475 ....**£60-70**

007 **Jaguar 'E'-type**, 'Trillium Jaguar Club (Canada)' (1999),
Bluish-Grey body, quantity 200 ....**£50-55**
Same but metallic Maroon body, quantity 15 ....**£325-375**

008 **Studebaker Golden Hawk**, 'Binns Road, 1934-1979'
(1999), quantity 500 ....**£55-65**

009 **Chevrolet Corvette**, 'MICA Hershey, June 25-27, 1999',
dark Blue body, quantity 50 ....**£150-175**
Same but Silver body, quantity 250 ....**£45-55**

DY035/A **VW Karmann Ghia**, 'Dutch Dinky Society 3rd Convention'
(1999), Yellow body, quantity 175.......................**£65-75**
Same but metallic Blue body, quantity 300 ....**£40-45**

010 **Triumph TR4A-IRS**, Triumph Power Club of Canada
1999 Rally, Yellow body, Red wheels, No. '21', qty. 15..**£400-425**
Same but Navy Blue body, White wheels, No.'4', 200.......**£50-60**

DY921 **Jaguar 'E'-type**, 'Matchbox USA. The Millennium
Convention, June 3, 2000, Parsippany, NJ.',
pewter model, quantity 20 ....**£200-250**

DY-1B Same but Yellow body, Black hood, quantity 180 ....**£95-105**

DY-1 Same but 'Matchbox USA, The Millennium Toy Show,
June 4, 2000, Parsippany, NJ.', Green body, Black hood,
quantity 160 ....**£50-60**

011 **Ford 'Boss' Mustang 429**, '8th MICA European
Convention, Cologne, 8-9 September, 2000.'
Aquamarine body, Red decals, quantity 300.......................**£40-50**

DY-25 **Porsche 356A Coupé**, 'Supplement Dinky Book', metallic
lt. Blue body. Only available with Supplement book, 20.**£250-300**
Same but White body, quantity 480 ....**£60-65**

DYM36840 **Citroën 2cv**, 'MICA 16UK, 7.4.2001, Hilton Hotel,
Warwick', Black Body, light Blue roof and wings, 300 ......**£30-40**

Matchbox Dinky 'Code 2' Gift Sets

M2 Set **Austin A40 Van**, '4th MICA European Convention',
Red wheels. (plus YY65 Austin 7 van from the
Yesteryear range), quantity 250..................................**£90-110**

M4 Set **Ford E83W Van**, '5th MICA European Convention',
Yellow wheel hubs, (plus YY65 Austin 7 van from the
Yesteryear range), quantity 250...................................**£90-110**

M11 Set **Ford 'Boss' Mustang 429**, '8th Mica European
Convention, Cologne, 8-9 September, 2000', Black body,
Red decals, (plus Y22 Ford 'A' van from the Yesteryear
range), quantity 2,000..**£90-110**

M12 Set **Citroën 2cv**, 'MICA 16UK, 7.4.2001, Hilton Hotel,
Warwick', light Blue body, Black roof and wings,
(plus YPP06 Mack 'AC' truck from the Yesteryear
range), quantity 200...**£85-95**

Models in 'The Dinky Collection' range:

DY-8B Commer Van 'His Master's Voice'   DY-4 Ford E83W Van 'Heinz'   DY-15 Austin A40 Van 'Brook Bond Tea'

Morestone, Modern Products, Budgie Toys and Seerol

The following history and listings have been provided by Robert Newson.

The history of these makes is a fascinating story of inter-linked companies, take-overs and bankruptcies reflecting the ups and downs of the toy trade. In the late 1940s Morris & Stone was a toy wholesaler selling the products of many small toy manufacturers including those from Modern Products who had started as die-casters. Morris and Stone decided to have their own exclusive 'Morestone' branded lines and some were made by Modern Products, who increasingly relied on Morestone for the sole marketing and distribution of their toys. Morestone continued to use several suppliers but in 1954 set up a die-casting company jointly with Rodney Smith (one of the founders of Lesney Products).

From the mid-1950s to 1966 the Morestone and Budgie ranges contained models that came either from the in-house factory or from Modern Products. Morestone's production expanded with new ranges of models, such as the 'Noddy' and 'Big-Ears' vehicles in 1956 and the Esso Petrol Pump Series of miniatures, launched at Christmas of that year. In 1958, the 'Trucks of the World International Series' was introduced, but only ran to three models.

Some of the earlier Morestone and Modern Products models were re-issued as part of the Budgie range which was introduced in 1959. Model numbers were allocated in 1960 and new additions to the range continued every year up to 1966. During 1961, Morris & Stone was taken over by S. Guiterman & Co. Ltd., who changed the name of their new subsidiary to Budgie Models Ltd. Although the range included many interesting and unusual subjects, they failed to compete with Corgi, Dinky and Matchbox, and losses in Budgie Models Ltd. contributed to losses in the Guiterman group. In March 1966 these companies went into voluntary liquidation.

Modern Products was badly hit by this but eventually were able to set up a new company called Budgie Models (Continuation) Ltd and purchase the Budgie trade mark from the receiver. They wanted the Budgie dies as well, but these were destroyed in a fire while negotiations were in progress. The only dies to survive were those in their own factory.

Thus the main range of Budgie commercial vehicles came to an end in 1966. Modern Products continued to produce the Budgie miniatures, mainly for the USA, until 1969 when the stronger competition this time was from Mattel's 'Hot Wheels'. Modern Products direction for the 1970s was to produce models for H. Seener Ltd., distributors of toys and souvenirs to London's tourist shops. The old Budgie Routemaster bus was reintroduced for Seener, followed by a new FX4 Taxi and Rolls-Royce Silver Cloud.

In 1983, following the death of one of the partners in Modern Products, the business was sold to a neighbouring engineering company called Starcourt Ltd (some boxes say Merracroft Ltd - an associated company of Starcourt). The new owners reintroduced several models from the original moulds, starting with the Aveling Barford Road Roller. However, a disagreement developed with Seener who withdrew the dies for the Taxi and Rolls-Royce (which he had paid for), and arranged for these to be made by Corgi together with a completely new Routemaster bus. These 'Seerol' models appeared in 1985 and are still available. Starcourt ceased toy production in 1985.

Some unpainted castings for no.204 Volkswagen Pick-Up and some empty boxes were sold to a Dutch firm and have since appeared in various liveries. These are classed as 'Code 3' models and have not been listed. The die-casting moulds were sold to Autocraft (Dave Gilbert) in 1988, and these include most of the 1950s Modern Products and part of the 1960s Budgie range. Autocraft are now in the process of adapting dies for a range of some 35 various models. Only one model has so far been reintroduced - a run of 1000 of no.258 Daimler Ambulance in kit form.

A complete history of these companies and their products is contained in the book 'Budgie Models' by Robert Newson. This hardback book also has full descriptions of all the models, 58 pages of colour photographs illustrating over 180 models, and reproductions of Budgie leaflets.

NB See the 'Miscellaneous Models' colour section for pictures.

Morestone and Modern Products

Ref	Year(s)	Model name	Colours, features, details	Market Price Range
-	c.1946	**Racing Car**	Red, Dark Blue, Dark Green or Light Brown. One piece casting including driver. No identification on model. 135 mm	**£30-40**
-	c.1947	**Stage Coach with Four Horses**	English mail coach with driver and trunk, Yellow body, Red wheels, 173 mm. 'Ye Olde Coach and Four' on box.	**£100-150**
-	c.1948-56	**Fire Escape** (large)	Brass bell and wheel hubs. Base consists of sump and prop shaft only. Extending wheeled escape ladder. 108 mm. (excluding ladder)	**£60-80**
-	c.1950	**Fire Escape** (smaller)	Plain flat base, wheeled escape ladder, 66 mm. (excluding ladder)	**£60-80**
-	c.1948	**Fire Engine**	Clockwork motor and bell underneath, 'Morestone Series' cast-in, 135 mm	**£80-90**
-	c.1948-58	**0-6-0 Tank Locomotive**	Green or Red, 'British Railways' cast in, re-issued as Budgie 224, 119 mm	**£25-35**
-	1949-51	**Horse Drawn Snack Bar**	'SAM'S' cast on side below counter, removable roof, separate man, tea urn and two mugs, 117mm. Wide range of colours	**£65-85**
-	1949-59	**Horse Drawn Hansom Cab**	Black / Yellow, driver, elastic band for reins, 118 mm. (re-issued as Budgie 100)	**£50-70**
-	c.1948-61	**Horse Drawn Covered Wagon with Four Horses**	Green, Red or Orange, driver, cloth canopy plain or printed with *'Thundering Hooves and Blazing Guns on the Western Trail'*, or *'Walt Disney's Davy Crockett Frontier Wagon'* or *'Last of the Mohicans Chingachgook Hawkeye'*, later with two barrels, 'Made in England' cast transversely under, 190 mm. (Budgie 404).	**£70-90**
-	1949	**'Wells Fargo' Stage Coach with two 'Galloping' Horses**	Brown / Yellow, driver and guard, eccentric wheel for 'galloping' effect, some with 'Copyright F.W. Birch & Co.' cast inside, 164 mm	**£70-90**
-	c.1950	**'Wells Fargo' Stage Coach**	Various colours, four horses, driver, 172 mm	**£70-90**
-	1952-58	**Stage Coach with Two Horses**	Red or Orange (no lettering), Black plastic horses, wheels and figures,165 mm	**£70-90**
-	1954-59	**Horse Drawn Covered Wagon with Six Horses**	Red, Yellow wheels, printed cloth canopy *'The Wild West Land of Buffalo and Covered Wagon'*, driver, two barrels, 'Made in England' cast transversely underneath, 265mm	**£70-90**
-	1950-51	**Road Sweeper**	'City Cleansing Dept.' cast-in, clockwork motor in some, 91 mm	**£80-100**
-	c.1950	**Compressor**	With man and pneumatic drill. No identification cast on model. 76 mm	**£40-50**
-	1953	**State Landau with Six Horses**	Coronation souvenir, three figures cast-in. No identification cast on model. 111 mm	**£30-40**
-	1953	**Prime Mover with Trailer**	Red prime mover, 'British Road Services', 'NO 311' and 'MAX 20 MPH' cast-in, Black plastic wheels, 83 mm. Orange plastic trailer, 136 mm	**£100-125**
-	1953	**Sleigh with Father Xmas**	One reindeer. No identification on model. About 140 mm	**£65-85**

-	1953-55	**RAC Motorcycle and Sidecar**	Cast wheels / tyres and rider, no windscreen, hinged lid on sidecar, 70 mm	**£75-100**
-	1954-55	**A.A. Motorcycle and Sidecar**	Cast wheels / tyres and rider, windscreen, non-opening sidecar, separate rails	**£75-100**
-	1956-57	**RAC Motorcycle and Sidecar**	Cast rider, windscreen, separate rails and hinged lid on sidecar, steering front forks, rubber tyres, plain number plates, 82 mm	**£75-100**
-	1956-57	**A.A. Motorcycle and Sidecar**	Cast rider, windscreen, separate rails and hinged lid on sidecar, steering front forks, rubber tyres, plain number plates, 82 mm	**£75-100**
-	1956-57	**Solo Motorcycle**	Cast rider, steering front forks, rubber tyres, plain number plates, 82 mm. There are four versions: Police Patrol, Despatch Rider, GPO Messenger and TT Rider. Each	**£50-75**
-	?	**Police Motorcycle and Sidecar**	Black machine, Dark Blue sidecar, Black uniformed figures, cast wheels	**£50-75**
-	1954-55	**Horse Drawn Gipsy Caravan**	Yellow / Green, tinplate roof and base, separate driver and rear steps, 190 mm	**£300-350**
-	1954-56	**Bedford Dormobile**	Red or Green body. 90 mm	**£100-125**
-	1955-58	**Leyland Double Deck Bus**	'Finest Petrol - ESSO - in the World', Red or Green, route '7', 103 mm	**£70-80**
			'ESSO - for Happy Motoring - ESSO', Red body, route '7', 103 mm	**£70-80**
			'Motor Oil - ESSO - Petrol', Red body, route '7', 103 mm	**£70-80**
-	1955-56	**Aveling-Barford Road Roller**	Green, Yellow or Red, with driver, 117 mm. Re-issued as Budgie 701	**£40-50**
-	1955-59	**Wolseley 6/80 Police Car**	Black, loudspeaker, aerial, 113 mm. No maker's name. (Budgie 246)	**£50-60**
1	1955-57	**Foden 8-wheel Petrol Tanker**	Red body, 'Motor Oil Esso Petrol' transfers, leaflet, 136 mm	**£175-200**
2	1955-56	**Foden 8-wheel Open Lorry**	Light brown cab and chassis, Red truck body, leaflet, 138 mm	**£150-200**
3	1955-56	**Foden Flat Lorry with Chains**	Green cab and 8-wheel chassis, Beige flatbed, brass chain, leaflet, 138 mm	**£150-200**
4	1955-57	**Foden 8-wheel Flat Lorry**	Yellow or Orange cab and chassis, Grey flatbed, leaflet, 138 mm	**£150-200**
-	1956-57	**Bedford Car Transporter**	Orange cab, Grey trailer, collapsible top deck, two loading ramps, 243 mm	**£110-130**
-	1956	**Daimler Ambulance**	White or Cream body (no transfers), Silver base, opening rear doors, no maker's name, 110 mm. Re-issued as Budgie 258	**£110-130**
-	1955-57	**A.A. Land Rover** (large)	Yellow / Black, 'AA ROAD SERVICE' cast-in, opening rear doors, driver, passenger, 108 mm	**£125-150**
-	1957-58	**A.A. Land Rover** (medium)	Yellow / Black, driver, 79 mm. 'AA ROAD SERVICE' transfers, no rear windows	**£125-150**
			Same but 'AA ROAD SERVICE' cast-in, two rear windows	**£125-150**
-	1958	**Military Police Land Rover**	Olive Green, driver, 'MP Military Police' cast on sides, 79 mm	**£150-200**
-	1958	**Breakdown Service Land Rover**	Red body, driver, 'Breakdown Service Unit' cast on sides, 79 mm	**£100-125**
-	1958	**Foden Dumper**	Orange cab and chassis, Grey dumper, 108 mm. Re-issued as Budgie 226	**£40-50**

Morestone 'Trucks of the World International' Series

-	1958	**Klöckner Side Tipper**	Red cab, Black chassis, Cream tipper, 81 mm. (with 'Driving Licence')	**£40-50**
-	1958	**Scammell Articulated Tanker**	Orange cab, Cream tank. 'LIQUID IN BULK' cast on sides, 114 mm	**£35-45**
-	1958	**International Articulated Refrigerator Lorry**	Red / Blue cab, Silver trailer, 'COAST to COAST REFRIGERATION' transfers, 153 mm. Re-issued as Budgie 202	**£40-50**

'Noddy' items by Morestone and Budgie

The 'Noddy' items were given numbers when incorporated in the Budgie range around 1960.

301	1956-61	**Noddy and his Car** (large)	Yellow / Red, windscreen, solid rubber wheels, metal or plastic 'Noddy', 98 mm	**£100-150**
-	1957-58	**Big Ears on Bicycle** (large)	Red bicycle (64 mm.), metal 'Big Ears' with legs that move as the model is pushed along. No maker's name on model	**£125-175**
-	c.1959	**Clown on Bicycle** (large)	Metallic Light Brown bicycle (64 mm. as previous model), metal clown figure with moving legs. No maker's name on model	**£100-125**
-	1958	**Noddy's Garage Set**	331 Noddy's Car and 'Esso' series nos. 7, 13, 16 and 20. Box folds into garage	**£150-175**
303	c.1961	**Noddy and his Car** (large) with Big Ears	As 301 but with additional metal Big Ears Figure	**£125-175**
305	1959-61	**Noddy's Gift Box**	Contains numbers 331, 333 and plastic Mr. Plod the Policeman	**£150-200**
307	1959-61	**Locomotive and Wagon with Noddy and Big Ears**	Yellow loco with red cab. Red wagon. Plastic figures, 104 mm	**£100-125**
309	c.1961	**Noddy and Locomotive**	As no.307 but without wagon, 57 mm	**£60-80**
311	1960-61	**Noddy on Bicycle with Trailer**	Yellow bicycle, red trailer, plastic figure, 81 mm	**£80-100**
331	1958-61	**Noddy and his Car** (small)	Yellow car, red base and wheels, plastic figure, 52 mm	**£80-100**
333	1958-61	**Big Ears on Bicycle** (small)	Red. No maker's name on model, plastic figure, 48 mm	**£80-100**

Packed in 'Esso' Petrol Pump boxes from 1956 to around 1959, then in Budgie bubble packs (yellow backing card) till 1964, and from 1965 in bubble packs with blue backing card. In early 1960s conventional boxes marked 'Mobile Vehicle Series' or 'Modern Vehicle Series' were also used.

1	1956-58	**A.A. Motorcycle and Sidecar**	Rider, separate windscreen, 'MADE IN ENGLAND' under lid, 46 mm	**£30-40**
2	1956-58	**RAC Motorcycle and Sidecar**	Rider, separate windscreen. 'MADE IN ENGLAND' under lid, 46 mm	**£30-40**
3	1956-58	**A.A. Land Rover**	'AA ROAD SERVICE' cast-in, spare wheel (on bonnet) on some, 54 mm	**£35-45**
4	1956-58	**A.A. Bedford Van**	AA badge and 'ROAD SERVICE' cast-in, 57 mm	**£35-45**
5	1956-70	**Wolseley 6/80 Police Car**	Black or green body, 65 mm	**£20-30**
6	1956-58	**Cooper-Bristol Racing Car**	Blue or Dark Blue body, Off-White base and driver, 58 mm	**£15-20**
7	1956-65	**Mercedes-Benz Racing Car**	Silver body, Red base and driver, 60 mm	**£15-20**
8	1956-70	**Volkswagen 1200 Saloon**	Metallic Light Blue body, 58 mm	**£15-20**
9	1956-58	**Maudslay Horse Box**	Red body, 'HORSE BOX SERVICE' cast-in, 57 mm	**£30-35**
10	1956-58	**Karrier GPO Telephones Van**	Dark green body, 57 mm	**£30-35**
11	1957-65	**Morris Commercial Van**	Red body, 'ROYAL MAIL' and 'E-II-R' cast-in, 58 mm	**£30-40**
12	1957-70	**Volkswagen Microbus**	Light Brown, Pale Blue or Metallic Dark Blue, 61 mm	**£15-20**
13	1957-64	**Austin FX3 Taxi**	Black body, Silver base and driver, 58 mm	**£15-20**
14	1957-70	**Packard Convertible**	Beige or Metallic Lt.Blue body, Red base/seats, Lt. Brown or Gold driver	**£15-20**
15	1957-70	**Austin A95 Westminster Countryman**	Blue or Orange, (Silver flash on some); or Metallic Mauve, 66 mm	**£15-20**
16	1957-64	**Austin-Healey 100**	Red body, Off-White base and driver, 57 mm	**£30-40**
17	1957-58	**Ford Thames 5 cwt. Van**	Blue body, 60 mm	**£40-50**
18	1957-66	**Foden Dumper**	Red cab and chassis, Lemon-Yellow or Grey dumper, 60 mm	**£15-20**
19	1957-70	**Rover 105R**	Green or Gold body, 65 mm	**£15-20**
20	1957-64	**Plymouth Belvedere Convertible**	Pale Pink or White body, Red base and driver, 64 mm	**£20-30**
20	1968-70	**Austin A95 Emergency Vehicle**	As 15 but White with Orange beacon, 'EMERGENCY' transfer, Red base	**£35-45**
21	1963-66.	**Bedford TK Tipper Lorry**	Dark Green tipper. Yellow, Off-White or Orange cab, 58 mm	**£15-20**
21	1968-70	**Oldsmobile Town Sedan**	Gold body, 66 mm	**£20-25**
22	1963-66	**Bedford TK Crane Lorry**	Dark Green cab, Orange crane, Orange or Dark Green platform, 56 mm	**£15-20**
22	1968-70	**Cattle Transporter**	Adapted from no.58. Light Brown body, Dark Brown rear door, 61 mm	**£20-25**
23	1963-66	**Bedford TK Cement Mixer**	Off-White mixer. Green, Yellow, Red or Orange cab and chassis, 59 mm	**£15-20**
24	1963-66	**Bedford TK Refuse Lorry**	Green, Orange, Red or Yellow cab, Silver back, 59 mm	**£15-20**
25	1963-66	**Bedford TK Cattle Lorry**	Light brown body. Off-White, Orange or Yellow cab, 58 mm	**£15-20**
26	1963-66	**Aveling-Barford Road Roller**	Similar to Lesney Matchbox no.1c. Green body, Red wheels, 55 mm	**£15-20**
27	1963-70	**Wolseley 6/80 Fire Chief Car**	Same as no.5 with altered base lettering. Red body, 65 mm	**£25-35**

Models 50 - 55 were designated the 'Road Tanker Series'.

50	1963-66	**'BP Racing Service' Tanker**	Green with White tank, 61 mm	**£20-30**
51	1963-66	**'Shell' Tanker**	Yellow, 61 mm	**£20-30**
52	1963-64	**'Shell BP' Tanker**	Green or Yellow; White tank, 61 mm	**£20-30**
53	1963-66	**'National' Tanker**	Blue with Yellow tank, 61 mm	**£20-30**
54	1963-66	**'BP' Tanker**	Green with White tank, 61 mm	**£20-30**
55	1963-66	**'Mobil' Tanker**	Red body, 61 mm	**£20-30**
56	1966-70	**GMC Box Van**	'HERTZ TRUCK RENTAL' transfers and 'TRUCK RENTAL' cast-in. Light Green or Pale Blue body, 61 mm	**£20-30**
57	1966-70	**International Parcels Van**	Green body, sliding door. 'REA EXPRESS' transfers, 67 mm	**£20-30**
58	1966-70	**'Modern Removals' Van**	'MODERN REMOVALS' transfers. Light Brown or Metallic Green, 61 mm	**£20-30**
59	1967-70	**AEC Merryweather Fire Engine**	Copied from Lesney Matchbox no.9c. Red body, Gold ladder, 65 mm	**£20-30**
60	1966-70	**Rover 105R Squad Car**	As no.19 but with altered base lettering. Black or Red body, 65 mm	**£20-30**
61	1966-70	**Austin A95 'Q Car'**	As no.15 but with altered base lettering. Black or Metallic Dark Blue body	**£20-30**

Sets of three vehicles (bubble-packed)

94	1966	**Interpol Set**	Intended to contain no.5 Police Car, 60 Squad Car, 61 'Q' Car. Not issued	NPP
95	1966	**Road Haulage Set**	Intended to contain 56 Hertz Van, 57 REA Van, 58 Removals Van. Not issued	NPP
96	1965-66	**Road Construction Set**	Contains no.18 Dumper, 23 Cement Mixer, 26 Road Roller	**£50-75**
97	1965-66	**Truck Set**	Contains no.21 Tipper, 22 Crane, 25 Cattle Lorry	**£50-75**
98	1965-66	**Utility Vehicle Set**	Contains no.12 VW Microbus, 24 Refuse Lorry, 55 Mobil Tanker	**£50-75**
99	1965-66	**Traffic Set**	Contains no.8 Volkswagen, 15 Austin, 27 Fire Chief	**£50-75**
95	1968-70	**Town Set**	Contains no.20 Emergency Vehicle, 21 Oldsmobile, 56 Hertz Van	**£50-75**
96	1967-70	**Service Set**	Contains no.5 Police Car, 19 Rover, 59 Fire Engine	**£50-75**
97	1967-70	**Truck Set**	Contains no.12 VW Microbus, 57 REA Van, 58 Removals Van	**£50-75**
98	1967-70	**Utility Vehicle Set**	Contains no.27 Fire Chief, 60 Squad Car, 61 Q Car	**£50-75**
99	1967-70	**Traffic Set**	Contains no.8 Volkswagen, 14 Packard, 15 Austin	**£50-75**

Gift Sets

	1962	**Gift Set No.8**	Contains numbers 5, 8, 11, 12, 13, 15, 18 and 19	**£100-130**
	1962	**Gift Set No.12**	Contains 5, 7, 8, 11, 12, 13, 14, 15, 16, 18, 19 and 20 (Plymouth)	**£120-150**

Morestone Leyland Double Decker Bus
with 'ESSO' advertising

Budgie Models No. 272 'Supercar'
with plastic canopy and retractable wings

Budgie Toys No. 216 Renault Truck
with 'Fresh Fruit' advertising on the removable cloth hood

Budgie Toys No. 296 Motorway Express Coach
in light blue and white 'Blue Line Sightseeing' livery

Various 'Noddy' items by Morestone
Big Ears with Bicycle – Noddy and his Car – Noddy on Bicycle with Trailer

Morestone No. 2 'RAC Patrol'
'Made in England' is cast under the sidecar lid

Photos: Swapmeet Publications

Ref	Year(s)	Model name	Colours, features, details	Market Price Range
100	1972-84	Horse Drawn Hansom Cab	With driver, elastic band for reins. Re-issue of a Morestone/Modern Products model. 'Gold' plated or Metallic Light Brown, 118 mm	£15-20
101	1977-84	Austin FX4 Taxi	Also issued as no.703. Re-issued by Seerol. Black or Maroon. 106 mm	£15-20
101	1984	Austin FX4 Taxi	Silver body, 'LONDON VINTAGE TAXI ASSOCIATION'. Limited (1,000) commemorative marking 25 years of the FX4. Normal box	£20-25
102	1981-84	Rolls-Royce Silver Cloud	Re-issued by Seerol. Gold (painted or 'plated'), Black, Silver, Cream, Red, Blue, Metallic Lt.Blue, Metallic Turquoise or Metallic Dark Pink, 107 mm	£15-20
202	1959-66	International Articulated Refrigerator Lorry	Re-issued 'Trucks of the World' model. Red / Blue or Red cab (windows later). Silver trailer, 'COAST TO COAST REFRIGERATION', 153 mm	£40-50
204	1959-64	Volkswagen Pick-Up	Blue body, Cream base, cloth tilt 'EXPRESS DELIVERY', 92 mm	£35-45
206	1959-64	Leyland Hippo Coal Lorry	Green or Orange cab, Light Brown body, 'COAL AND COKE' cast-in, coal load, 92 mm	£45-55
208	1959-61	RAF Personnel Carrier	RAF blue, roundels, White tilt. 'A MORESTONE PRODUCT', 104 mm	£90-120
210	1959-61	US Army Personnel Carrier	As 208 but Army brown body with star, Light Brown tilt, 104 mm	£90-120
212	1959-61	British Army Personnel Carrier	As 208 but Dark Green with Red / Yellow square, Light Brown tilt	£90-120
214	1959-64	Thornycroft Mobile Crane	Red cab and chassis, Yellow crane engine, Light Blue crane, 100 mm	£50-60
216	1959-64	Renault Truck	Yellow cab, Red body. Cloth tilt 'FRESH FRUIT DAILY', 103 mm	£35-45
218	1959-63	Seddon 'Jumbo' Mobile Traffic Control Unit	Yellow cab and trailer with Black flash and catwalk. 'AUTOMOBILE ASSOCIATION' and AA badge transfers, 168 mm	£100-120
220	1959-66	Leyland Hippo Cattle Transporter	Orange cab, Light Brown body, Dark Brown base and ramp, 97 mm	£35-45
222	1959-65	International Tank Transporter with Centurion Tank	Army brown with star transfers. Cab as no.202. 155 mm. (with ramps up)	£45-55
224	1959-66	0-6-0 Tank Locomotive	As Modern Products model. Red, 'BRITISH RAILWAYS' cast-in, 119 mm	£25-35
224	1971-84	0-6-0 Tank Locomotive	Red, Metallic Brown, Black or Dark Green, 'BRITISH RAILWAYS' on transfers or labels	£10-15
226	1959-66	Foden Dumper	Re-issue of a Morestone model. Orange cab and chassis, Grey dumper. 'BUD 123' number plate transfers, 108 mm	£30-40
228	1959-64	Karrier Bantam Bottle Lorry	Orange-Yellow, 12 maroon plastic crates. 'DRINK COCA-COLA' transfers, 'COMMER LOW LOADER' cast underneath, 134 mm	£120-140
230	1959-66	Seddon Timber Transporter	Orange cab (no windows), or Green cab (with windows), Yellow trailer, five 'logs', 178 mm	£45-55
232	1960-66	Seddon Low Loader	Red cab (windows later), Orange trailer, 3 wooden cable drums. 167 mm	£60-70
234	1960-65	International Low Loader with Caterpillar Tractor	Orange cab, Light Brown trailer, Orange tractor, 155 mm. (with ramps up)	£40-50
236	1960-66 and 1969-84	AEC Routemaster Bus	Also issued as nos.704, 705 and 706. All models have destination transfers for route '9' and and 'LONDON TRANSPORT' transfers or labels. They were available with or without windows. 108 mm.	
			Red, 'Esso GOLDEN Esso'	£25-35
			Red, 'Esso UNIFLO - the tuned motor oil'	£25-35
			Red, 'GO ESSO - BUY ESSO - DRIVE ESSO'	£25-35
			Red, 'UNIFLO sae 10W/50 Motor Oil'	£25-35
			Red, Green or Gold, 'Houses of Parliament Tower Bridge'	£15-20
236	1973	Promotional issue:	Red body (with windows), 'Sheraton-Heathrow Hotel' on sides, 'OPENING 1st FEBRUARY 1973' on roof, Special box	£70-80
238	1960-63	Scammell Scarab Van	Crimson / Cream body. 'BRITISH RAILWAYS' and 'CADBURYS', 150mm. Note: Chocolate Bar picture may be vertical or horizontal	£80-100
238	1964-66		Yellow cab, Black chassis, Yellow trailer. 'Railfreight', 'CADBURYS'	£80-100
238	1985		Maroon cab, Maroon / Cream trailer. 'BRITISH RAILWAYS' and 'CADBURYS'.	£15-20
			Yellow cab and trailer. 'Railfreight' and 'CADBURYS' transfers. Most of these were issued in original 1960s boxes. 150 mm	£15-20
240	1960-64	Scammell Scarab Wagon	Red / Cream cab, Yellow chassis, Red trailer, Green cloth tilt, 150 mm	£55-65
242	1960-66	Euclid Dumper	Red cab, Orange chassis and dumper. 114 mm	£35-45
244	1961-65	Morris Breakdown Lorry	Blue body, Yellow base, tool box and jib. 'BUDGIE SERVICE', 120 mm	£45-55
246	1960-63	Wolseley 6/80 Police Car	Re-issued Modern Products model. Black, loudspeaker, aerial, 'BUDGIE TOYS' cast under, 'POLICE' transfers on grille and boot, 113 mm	£35-45
246	1983	Wolseley 6/80 Police Car	Light Blue, 'POLICE' labels, spotlights and roof sign replace the loudspeaker and aerial. Trial run only - did not go into full production	£45-55
248	1961	Stage Coach with Four Horses	Listed on this number as 'available later', but issued as no. 434.	
250	------	Pack reference	This number was used for packs of one dozen of the Budgie miniatures.	
252	1961-63	Austin Articulated Lorry with Railway Container	Crimson / Cream cab, windows, Crimson trailer / container, 'BRITISH RAILWAYS' transfers	£65-75
252	1964		Crimson cab / trailer, windows, Blue container, 'Door to Door' transfers	£75-85
254	1961-64	AEC Merryweather Fire Escape	Red, windows, Silver extending turntable ladder. 97 mm. (excl. ladder)	£65-75
256	1961-64	Foden Aircraft Refuelling Tanker 'Pluto'	Red, with windows. 'ESSO AVIATION PRODUCTS' transfers, 149 mm	£100-125
258	1961-63	Daimler Ambulance	Re-issued Modern Products model. Cream with Red base ('BUDGIE TOYS' cast-in), 'AMBULANCE' and 'EMERGENCY' transfers, 110 mm	£65-75

258	1991	Daimler Ambulance Kit	Re-issued as a kit of unpainted castings (by Autocraft)	£10-20
260	1962	Ruston-Bucyrus Excavator	Yellow / Red cab, '10-RB', Beige or Olive-Green base and jib, 73 mm	£100-125
262	1962-64	Racing Motorcycle	No maker's name. Unpainted cycle, tinplate fairing in Metallic Blue, Metallic Lilac, Metallic Brown or Lime Green, Black plastic rider, 104 mm	£75-100
264	1962-64	Racing Motorcycle and Sidecar	Cycle as 262, sidecar and fairing in Metallic Blue, Metallic Pinkish-Red, Metallic Green, Metallic Lilac, Metallic Brown or Lime Green. Black plastic rider / passenger, no maker's name, 104 mm	£75-100
266	1962-64	Motorcycle and Delivery Sidecar	Blue cycle as 262, Red sidecar, 'EXPRESS DELIVERY' cast-in, no maker's name, Black plastic rider. 108 mm	£75-100
268	1962-64	A.A. Land Rover	Different from Morestone AA Land Rovers. Yellow body, Black roof, windows, opening rear doors, 'AA ROAD SERVICE' transfers, 97 mm	£125-150
270	1962-66	Leyland Articulated Tanker	Red, windows, 'ESSO PETROLEUM COMPANY LTD' labels, 132 mm	£60-75
272	1962-64	Supercar	From TV series. Red / Silver body, Red wings (or colours reversed), clear plastic canopy, 'SUPERCAR' transfers, 122 mm	£175-225
274	1962-66	Ford Thames Refuse Lorry	Blue cab / Silver body, or Yellow cab / Metallic blue body, windows	£45-55
276	1962-66	Bedford LWB Tipper	Red cab with windows, Yellow tipper, 'HAM RIVER GRIT'	£40-80
278	1963-64	RAC Land Rover	Casting as 268, Blue, windows, 'RAC RADIO RESCUE' transfers, 97 mm	£125-150
280	1963-64	AEC Super Fueller Tanker	White cab and trailer, windows, Green base and canopy, 'AIR BP', 219 mm	£300-400
282	1963-66	Euclid Scraper	Yellow or Lime Green, windscreen, 'EUCLID', Black plastic wheels, 163 mm	£35-45
284	1962	Euclid Crawler Tractor	Not issued	NPP
286	1962	Euclid Bulldozer	Not issued	NPP
288	1963-66	Leyland Bulk Flour Tanker	Red cab, windows, Off-White silos, Yellow hopppers, 'BULK FLOUR', 107 mm	£45-55
290	1963-64	Bedford Ice Cream Van	No maker's name on model. Blue body and base, windows, 'Tonibell' transfers, Pink plastic cow on roof, 103 mm	£85-110
292	1963-66	Leyland Bulk Milk Tanker	Blue or Red cab, windows, White tank, 'MILK', 107 mm	£45-55
294	1963-66	Bedford TK Horse Box	Off-White cab, windows, Brown body, Light Brown doors. two Brown plastic horses. 'EPSOM STABLE' transfer, 109 mm	£60-70
296	1963-66	Motorway Express Coach	Midland Red livery: Red body, Black roof, 'BIRMINGHAM-LONDON MOTORWAY EXPRESS' transfers, windows, 121 mm	£70-85
	USA livery:		Light Blue body, Cream roof, 'WASHINGTON D.C.' and 'BLUE LINE SIGHTSEEING CO.' transfers, phone number 'LA9-7755' at rear	£300-400
298	1963-66	Alvis Salamander Crash Tender	Red body, windows, Silver plastic ladder, Yellow engine cover at rear, Black plastic wheels. 'FIRE SERVICE' transfers, 92 mm	£100-125
300	1963-65	Lewin Sweepmaster	Blue / Silver, windows, Black plastic wheels, Black sweeping brush	£60-75
302	1963-66	Commer Cabin Service Lift Truck	Blue cab, windows, Silver body, 'BOAC CABIN SERVICES', 104 mm	£60-75
304	1964-66	Bedford TK Glass Transporter	Off-white cab and chassis, windows, Green body. 'TOWER GLASS CO.' transfers. Four clear plastic 'glass' sheets, 108 mm	£45-55
306	1964-66	Fiat Tractor with Shovel	Orange tractor, Metallic Blue shovel, 108 mm	£75-100
308	1964-66	Seddon Pitt Alligator Low Loader	Green cab, windows, Yellow trailer with Black ramp, 163 mm	£45-55
310	1964-66	Leyland Cement Mixer	Orange cab, windows, Silver mixer, 'INVICTA Construction Co.', 98 mm	£45-55
312	1964-66	Bedford Super Tipmaster	Dark Green cab, windows, Silver tipper. 'SUPER TIP-MASTER', 127mm	£45-55
314	1965-66	Fiat Tractor with Dozer Blade	As 306 but enclosed cab, Orange tractor, Metallic Blue blade, 81 mm	£45-55
316	1965-66	Albion Overhead Maintenance Vehicle	Green body, windows, Silver / Black boom assembly, 107 mm	£40-50
318	1965-66	Euclid Mammoth Articulated Dumper	Modified from no.242. Green cab, Yellow chassis, Orange tipper, 201 mm	£75-95
322	1965-66	Scammell Routeman Pneumajector Transporter	Light Blue cab, Cream or White tank, 'THE ATLAS CARRIER CO.', 111 mm	£50-60
324	1965-66	Douglas Prospector Duomatic Tipper	Tips in two directions. Blue cab and chassis, windows, Grey tipper, 112 mm	£55-65
326	1965-66	Scammell Highwayman Gas Transporter	Green cab, windows, Dark Green trailer, 6 White / Red gas cylinders, 146 mm	£125-150
328	1966	Scammell Handyman Artic	Planned but not issued	NPP
330	1966	Land Rover	Modified 268, planned but not issued	NPP
332	1966	'Kenning' Breakdown Lorry	Planned but not issued	NPP
334	1966	Austin Gipsy Fire Tender	Planned but not issued	NPP
404	1960-61	Horse Drawn Covered Wagon	with Four Horses. For details see Morestone and Modern Products entry.	
410	1961	Stage Coach with Four Horses	Blue or 'Gold' plated coach, no lettering cast on sides but 'WELLS FARGO STAGE COACH' and 'A BUDGIE TOY' cast underneath, plastic horses and driver, bubble-packed, 118 mm	£70-90
430	1960-61	Wagon Train Set	Contains 3 of no. 432 plus two more horses with riders, bubble-packed	£100-150
432	1960-61	Horse Drawn Covered Wagon with Two Horses	Red wagon, ('A BUDGIE TOY' on floor), Grey, White or Lemon metal canopy, 2 barrels, plastic horses, driver, passenger, bubble packed, 82 mm	£35-45
434	1961	Stage Coach with Four Horses	'WELLS FARGO' above windows, 'STAGE LINES' on doors, luggage cast on roof, Red or Blue, plastic horses and driver, 189 mm	£70-90
452	1958-63	A.A. Motorcycle and Sidecar	Initially in Morestone box. Windscreen, plastic rider, integral rails and hinged lid on sidecar, steerable, rubber tyres, plain number plates, 82 mm	£75-100
452	1964-66	A.A. Motorcycle and Sidecar	New design. Sidecar with transfers and 'BUDGIE' underneath, plastic rider, windscreen and leg guards, plain number plates, 84 mm	£75-100
454	1958-63	RAC Motorcycle and Sidecar	Initially in Morestone box. Windscreen, plastic rider, integral rails and hinged lid on sidecar, steerable, rubber tyres, plain number plates, 82 mm	£75-100
454	1964-66	RAC Motorcycle and Sidecar	New design. Sidecar with transfers and 'BUDGIE' underneath, plastic rider, windscreen and leg guards, plain number plates, 84 mm	£75-100

Budgie Toys and Models

456	1958-66	**Solo Motorcycle**	Initially in Morestone boxes. Two casting versions as 452 and 454 but 'Silver plated'. Plastic riders:	
			Police Patrol (Blue uniform)..	**£40-50**
			Despatch Rider (Light Brown uniform)..	**£40-50**
			GPO Messenger (Light Blue uniform)...	**£40-50**
			'Tourist Trophy' Rider (White racing overalls)....................................	**£40-50**
701	1983	**Aveling-Barford Road Roller**	Re-issued Modern Products model. Dark Green body, Silver / Red wheels, Dark Blue driver...	**£10-15**
702	1984-85	**Scammell Scarab Vans**	Re-issue of 238. Very Dark Blue cab and trailer, White 'RN' on doors, 'ROYAL NAVY' on tilt	**£15-20**
			Very Dark Blue cab and trailer, 'HALLS MENTHO-LYPTUS' labels	**£15-20**
			Maroon cab and trailer, 'LMS LIVERPOOL ROAD' transfers................	**£15-20**
			Maroon cab and trailer, 'SPRATTS BONIO' transfers........................	**£15-20**
			Maroon cab and trailer, 'REA EXPRESS' transfers............................	**£15-20**
703	1984	**Austin FX4 Taxi**	As no.101 but in window box. Black, Silver, Met.Dk.Pink, Gold, Dark Green, Grey or White...	**£15-20**
704	1984	**AEC Routemaster Bus**	Yellow / Red body with windows, 'SHOP LINKER' labels, casting as 236	**£15-20**
705	1984	**AEC Routemaster Bus**	Silver body with windows, '25 FAITHFUL YEARS' labels, casting as 236	**£15-20**
706	1984	**AEC Routemaster Bus**	Yellow / Red with windows, 'Watford FA Cup Final 84' labels, 236 casting	**£15-20**

Budgie Gift Sets

No. 4	1961	**Gift Set No.4**	Contains four models. Price depends on contents which vary	**£125-165**
No. 5	1961	**Gift Set No.5**	Contains five models. Price depends on contents which vary................	**£150-200**

Seerol Models

-	1985	**Austin FX4 Taxi**	Re-issue of Budgie no.101 with amended base lettering and low friction wheels. Black body, 106mm. Still available.	**£5-10**
-	1985	**Rolls-Royce Silver Cloud**	Re-issued Budgie 102, amended lettering, low friction wheels. Black, Silver, White, Yellow, Dark Blue, Pink or Maroon, 107 mm. Still available	**£5-10**
-	1985	**AEC Routemaster Bus**	New design, 1:76 scale, 108 mm. Was available from London souvenir outlets till the late 1990s.	
-			Red, Light Green or Dark Green, 'Houses of Parliament Tower Bridge' labels	**£10-15**
-			Red, 'The Original London Transport Sightseeing Tour' labels..............	**£10-15**
-			Red, 'Greetings from London' tampo print	**£5-10**
-			Red, 'Tower of London' tampo print	**£5-10**
-			Red, 'Petticoat Lane' tampo print	**£5-10**
-			Red, 'Buckingham Palace' tampo print	**£5-10**

Budgie Leaflets and Catalogues

A leaflet was included in the box with most Budgie Toys. Dates are not shown on any except the 1963 and 1964 catalogues.

-	1959	**Leaflet**	Printed on one side only. 'Budgie Toys Speak for Themselves' at top.	
		1st version:	Includes the Six-horse Covered Wagon..	**£10-20**
		2nd version:	Timber Transporter replaces the Covered Wagon	**£10-20**
-	1960	**Leaflet**	'Budgie Toys Speak for Themselves' on front, 'Budgie Toys for Girls and Boys' on reverse....	**£10-20**
-	1961	**Leaflet**	'Budgie Toys Speak for Themselves' on Black background	**£10-15**
	1961	**Trade catalogue**	Fold-out leaflet showing Noddy items, Wagon Train and Budgie miniatures as well as the main Budgie range. Separate price list marked 'Price List 1961' showing wholesale and retail prices..	**£30-40**
-	1962	**Leaflet**	'Die-Cast Models by Budgie They Speak for Themselves' on Black background.	
		1st version:	268 AA Land Rover on front, 258 Daimler Ambulance on reverse........	**£10-15**
		2nd version:	214 Mobile Crane on front, 266 Express Delivery Motorcycle on reverse....	**£10-15**
-	1963	**Leaflet**	'Die-Cast Models by Budgie They Speak for Themselves' on Black background.	
		1st version:	278 RAC Land Rover on front, 258 Daimler Ambulance on reverse.......	**£10-15**
		2nd version:	278 RAC Land Rover on front, 266 Express Delivery Motorcycle on reverse.....	**£10-15**
-	1963	**Trade Catalogue** (8 pages)	Landscape format, includes retail price list....................................	**£30-40**
-	1964	**Trade Catalogue** (8 pages)	'Budgie Models' on cover (portrait format). Includes retail price list........	**£30-40**

Collectors notes

The 'River Series'

A trademark owned by M/s Jordan and Lewden of Homerton, London E9. Note that, while 'River Series' models were cast using tools supplied by DCMT, they had no other connection with DCMT. The Jordan and Lewden company started to offer diecast toys to the toy trade from about 1953 and continued to do so for only a few years. Dies were eventually sold to the Habonim firm in Israel and models subsequently appeared in the 'Gamda' series of toys. Some examples are known to have been produced in New Zealand by Lincoln Industries (who were also responsible for some 'lookalike' Matchbox models). Only 'Made in England' and the car name appear on the diecast

base of each model. None of the models acquired window glazing while made as 'River Series' – some did when produced as 'Gamda' toys.

These car models came in various colours and had cast hubs / rubber tyres where friction-motor fitted, otherwise one-piece rubber wheels.
Ford Prefect ....NGPP
American Buick ....NGPP
Daimler Conquest......................................NGPP
Austin Somerset ....NGPP
Standard Vanguard II Saloon ....NGPP
Standard Vanguard Estate ....NGPP

These larger items were also available in various colours, some have clockwork motor, most have one-piece cast wheels, and some were boxed.
Cattle Truck ....NGPP
Car Carrier...NGPP
Excavator Truck ....NGPP
Tower Wagon ....NGPP
Cattle Truck ....NGPP

The Editor would welcome any additional information on the 'River Series'.

'River Series' American Buick

'River Series' Austin Somerset

Scamold Racing Cars

Manufactured between 1939 and 1950 by Scale Models Ltd from whose title the model name was obtained. The models are extremely accurate 1/35 diecast scale models, with their original measurements being taken from the real racing cars at the famous Brooklands race track. Pre-war boxes state 'MANUFACTURED BY SCALE MODELS LTD, BROOKLANDS TRACK, WEYBRIDGE, ENG.'. This was dropped after the war. The proprietor of Scale Models Ltd was a Mr Tilley who wound up the business in the 1960s.

The model detail and castings are outstanding, with features such as removeable exhausts, spring suspension, steering wheels and dashboards. In addition the back axle could be exchanged for one containing a clockwork motor which was

wound up by a long starting handle. The wheel axles were crimped and the hubs were either brass (early) or aluminium (later) with black treaded rubber tyres.

Scamold kits were also available. The kit models had detailed features similar to the production issues including a working differential gear. In addition, it was also possible to fit a flywheel type motor which was activated by turning a 'starting handle'.

This information on Scamold models and kits has been kindly provided by Mr R.N. Eason-Gibson. The Editor would welcome additional information on this small but fascinating range.

PRODUCTION MODELS

101	1939-50	**ERA Racing Car**.................Blue (Light or Dark), Green (Light or Dark), Yellow, White or Black body **£90-120**
103	1939-50	**Maserati Racing Car**...........Red, Blue, Green (Mid or Dark), Silver body **£90-120**
105	1939-50	**Alta Racing Car**...................Green (Mid or Dark), Silver, White or Blue...**£90-120**

SCAMOLD KITS
Austin 7 Single-seater 750cc, Bugatti Type 35, 'E'-type E.R.A. (prototype only), Brooklands Riley, MG (planned type not known), Bentley LeMans Tourer and Maserati Racing Car.

Mobil Midget Fun-Ho! Series

Manufactured and distributed by the Underwood Engineering Co. Ltd, Mamaku Street, Inglewood, New Zealand.

Market Price Range. Most small cars and trucks etc. **£20-30**. Exceptions: No.7 BOAC Observation Coach **£40-50**, No.9 VW Beetle **£40-50**, No.11 Morris Mini Minor **£80-90**, No.2 Vauxhall Velox **£30-40**, No.? Morris 1100 **£40-50**, No.17 Austin Mini **£80-90**, No.23 Mark 10 Jaguar **£80-90**, No.25 MG Sports **£80-100**; No.43 E Type Jaguar **£80-90**.
Larger Commercials/Emergency vehicles etc.:
Nos.18, 21, 22, 27, 31, 35, 36, 40 **£30-40**.

Technical Information. Models from No.10 are 1:80 scale. Early models 1-32 1963-66 were all either chrome or copper plated. Painted finishes were introduced in 1966. Boxed models 1-18 include a folded leaflet in black and white giving details of the first 18 models and all have Black plastic wheels. Similarly the later issues contained leaflets showing the complete 1-46 model range as per the above leaflet.

'Fun Ho!' Mighty Mover Sets
1 Army Construction Battalion Kit Set: Contains six Military models, Bulldozer, Cement Mixer, Road Roller, Earth Mover, JCB, Land Rover, Brown display box **£50-60**
2 Civilian Road Construction Set: Yellow/Silver Bulldozer, Red/Silver Bedford Lorry, Green Aveling Road Roller, Blue Earth Mover, Red/Blue Ford Sand Dumper, Yellow JCB, Red window display box **£50-60**
3 Fire Service Kit Set: Contains six Red models, 21 Fire Engine, Jeep, Pick Up, Artic Lorry, Rescue Truck, Fire Van with Blue light, Red window display box **£50-60**

Later issues (c.1965?) Window Boxes
48 Ford, Brown/Green, Two-tone Green or Maroon White body **£10-15**,
49 Ford Sand Dumper, Red/Blue body **£10-15**, 50 Ford Dumper **£10-15**,
51 Ford Articulated Truck **£15-20**, 52 Sand Dumper Trailer **£5-10**

Shackleton Models

The company was formed by Maurice Shackleton and traded as James Shackleton & Sons Ltd. from 1939 to 1952. They had premises in Cheshire and originally produced wooden toys such as lorries and dolls houses. The toy lorries were only made pre-war and had four wheels, a simple wooden chassis and body with a green name badge on the rear of the cab, and were fitted with a highly detailed aluminium radiator grille. Known models are a Chain Lorry, Breakdown Lorry and a Sided Wagon. Their price today is around £100 each.

In 1948 having expanded its staff to nearly 40 people, the company started to produce diecast constructional models based on the Foden FG six-wheel platform lorry. The models consisted of separate parts all of which were, incredibly, made 'in house', including the clockwork motor, its key, and the wheels and tyres. The models were advertised in the 'Meccano Magazine' with the slogan 'You can dismantle it - Just like the real thing', and they were originally priced at £2/19/6. Eventually the range was extended to include a Dyson Drawbar Trailer and a Foden Tipper. Each model was packed in its own distinctive box which displayed a black and white picture of the model inside.

In 1952, whilst in the midst of producing the David Brown Trackmaster 30 Tractor, a shortage of materials coupled with difficult trading conditions brought about the end of the company. Some remaining models from this period were acquired and distributed by Chad Valley. The unique models produced by the Shackleton company are now highly collectable and difficult to find.

---	1948-52	**Foden FG 6-wheel Platform Lorry**	Yellow, Blue, Grey or Green body with Red wings, Grey chassis and Red or Grey fuel tanks, 12½ inches (305 mm.) long, initially in Blue/Yellow box, later in mottled Green box, (20,000 made)	£200-300
			Same colours as above but with Grey or Black wings and Red chassis	£300-400
			Same casting but with Red, Orange or Brown cab	£300-400
		NB Box difficult to find:	Blue box with paper label having picture of chassis.	
---	1949-52	**Dyson 8-ton Drawbar Trailer**	Yellow, Blue, Grey or Green body, packed in Red and Yellow box, (15,000)	£100-150
---	1950-52	**Foden FG 6-wheel Tipper Lorry**	Yellow, Blue, Grey or Green body with Red wings, Grey chassis and Red or Grey fuel tanks, Silver wheels, (5,000)	£300-400
			As previous models but with Grey wings and Red chassis	£300-400
			As previous models but with Blue wings, Grey chassis, Grey wheels	£300-400
			Orange or Red body	£300-400
---	1952	**David Brown Trackmaster 30 Tractor**	Red body, Black rubber tracks, 10 inches long, boxed. Only 50 models thought to exist	£750-950
		Note: It is known that some prototype models were made of Ploughs and Harrows, though it is not known if any were produced for sale.		
---	1958-60	**Foden S21 8-wheel Platform Lorry**	Dark Blue, Dark Green or Light Turquoise fibreglass cab with Red metal chassis and wheels, wooden flatbed, length overall 18½ inches (470 mm), plastic injection moulded springs and axle parts, powered by 'Minimax' electric motor. (250 made as a promotional for Foden)	£750-950

The information in this listing has been taken from an original article written by John Ormandy in the 'Modellers World' magazine, Volumes 12 and 13, and is used by kind permission of the Editors, Mike and Sue Richardson. Robert Taylor provided additional information. Gary Irwin contributed information on the DB Trackmaster.

Foden FG 6-wheel Platform Lorry with a **Shackleton Dyson 8-ton Drawbar Trailer**
(Models sold by Romsey Model Auctions, Romsey, Hampshire; picture used by their kind permission)

Taylor and Barrett

Taylor and Barrett Lead Vehicles and the Postwar Re-issues

by Mike Richardson

The firm of Taylor and Barrett dates from the early 1920s when they started producing mainly figures but with a few odd carts. The vehicles themselves were only introduced in about 1935. These were rather crude by comparison with the Dinky Toys of the day as the lead gravity casting process was incapable of working to the fine limits possible with pressure diecasting as used by Meccano Ltd. The majority of the vehicles use a basic chassis incorporating the bonnet and wings. Different bodies are attached to this base unit by tabs and a radiator is plugged into the front. Some versions have the grille cast integrally with the bonnet, and most of these use plain metal wheels instead of having rubber tyres. These vehicles have a tremendous amount of charm as toys while they are only a generic representation of the types of vans and small trucks of the time.

A wide variety of types were made including petrol tankers, a pick-up truck and a couple of mail vans. The breakdown truck is particularly attractive with a working crane on the rear. These toys were made until the production was halted in 1940 when the factory was bombed out of existence. All salvageable tools, moulds and stock was moved to a new location in North Finchley but production stopped very soon after because of the munitions requirements of the war effort.

During the war the tools were split between the Taylors and the Barretts for safe keeping but they did not join up again afterwards and two separate companies, F.G.Taylor & Sons and A.Barrett & Sons, started up in 1945. The main part of the range, the small commercial vehicles and the cars, does not seem to have survived the War, only the trolley buses, which became Barretts, and the Leyland coach which appeared in one-piece casting form as a Taylor. It is interesting to note that the trolleybus carries a route board '621 Finchley' which probably means that they went past the factory.

A range of very nice fire engines came along in the late 1930s with a super turntable ladder appliance as the top of the range. These were longer than the main range and had many parts. To mark the advent of the Home Office Fire Precautions scheme (where fire appliances were made available to local areas by central government), Taylor and Barrett painted their range in grey as well as the more traditional red. These grey models are highly sought after now.

Personnel were also available to go with these fire engines. A 'Decontamination Squad' being a particular favourite with their gas masks and chemical-proof overalls. There is also a fire engine in the short chassis range but it is not very impressive.

The trolley buses came in two sizes. The large one has a separate driver figure (and conductor as well in the T & B version but not the later Barrett), and the body is in two pieces, upper and lower decks. The small one is in one piece and has no driver. Needless to say there is a vast difference in the values of the two sizes.

There are generic cars, roadster, coupé, saloon, on the short base but there is also quite a good model of the 1935 Singer Airstream saloon. This is also the poor man's Chrysler Airflow but never really caught on, the styling made the car look too tall to be appealing. A rather crude one-piece Austin Seven racer was the final car but this was to a larger scale.

Dinky Toys were not the only factory to make a model of the Air Mail Service Car based on the Morris Commercial chassis. T & B also made one and a nice chunky toy it is too. A couple of aeroplanes, a De Havilland Comet and an air liner, completed the range of powered vehicles. A modified version of the Comet seems to have been made by Barrett later but it differs a lot from the T & B, which is a much better model.

Some of the moulds were still around a few years ago and some attempts were made to make models again. These were fairly unsuccessful as casting techniques had changed and the new metals did not have the same flow characteristics as the early lead. Some models are definitely known to have been re-made as they have been seen at a swapmeet some time back, so collectors are advised to be wary.

Editor's note: All the models are rare - any auction prices that become available will be published in subsequent editions of this Catalogue.

The following listing is of models issued by Taylor and Barrett between 1920 and 1939. Post war production was split between F. G. Taylor & Sons and A. Barrett & Sons, each firm inheriting some moulds and continuing to make some but not all of the models until about 1952.
(FGT) = produced by F. G. Taylor after 1945, **(AB)** = produced by A. Barrett after 1945, **(-)** = date and company not known for certain, **NGPP** = no price grading possible at present.

14	**Trotting Pony Racer** (FGT)	**£55-65**
15	**Turntable Fire Escape** (AB)	**£55-65**
16	**Fire Engine and Escape** (FGT)	**£100-150**
17	**Fire Engine and Men** (FGT)	**£200-300**
20	**Horse Drawn Water Cart** (FGT)	**£300-400**
21	**Horse Drawn Brewer's Cart** (FGT)	**£100-200**
22	**Horse Drawn Window Cleaner's Cart** (FGT)	**£100-200**
23	**Horse Drawn Baker's Cart** (FGT)	**£100-200**
26	**Roman Chariot** (FGT)	**£25-35**
27	**Donkey Drawn Coster Cart with Dog and Boy** (FGT)	**£50-60**
28	**Donkey Drawn Coster Cart, Plants load, Walking Coster** (FGT)	**£50-60**
28a	**Donkey Drawn Coster Cart, Vegetable load, Walking Coster** (FGT)	**£50-60**
29	**Ice Cream Bicycle**, 'ICE BRICKS' (FGT)	**£200-300**
36	**Milk Float and Milkman**, 'EXPRESS DAIRY' (AB)	**NGPP**
42	**Fire Escape and Team of Firemen** (FGT)	**£150-200**
43	**Air and Land Postal Service Set** (-)	**£150-200**
49	**Street Cleaning Barrow with two Bins** (FGT)	**NGPP**
92	**Llama Cart** (FGT)	**£20-30**
92a	**Donkey Cart** (FGT)	**£20-30**
109	**Pony Drawn Governor's Cart** (AB)	**£20-30**
109a	**Pony Drawn Cart** (AB)	**£20-30**
111	**Saloon Car** (-)	**£80-100**
112	**Transport Lorry** (-)	**£20-30**
113	**'ROYAL MAIL' Van** (-)	**£150-200**
114	**'AMBULANCE'**, Grey (Wartime civilian) (-)	**£150-200**
114a	**'AMBULANCE'**, Khaki (Army) (-)	**£150-200**
115	**Sports Car** (-)	**£100-200**
116	**Coupé** (-)	**£100-200**
117	**'AMBULANCE'**, (Street, civilian) (-)	**£150-200**
119	**Racer** (AB)	**£20-30**
120	**Fire Engine** (AB)	**£50-60**
123	**Atlanta Touring Plane** (AB)	**£50-75**

124	**'AIR MAIL' Van** (AB)	**£100-200**
128	**Petrol Tanker** (-)	**£100-200**
129	**Breakdown Lorry** (-)	**£100-120**
137	**DH 'Comet' Aeroplane** (AB)	**£50-60**
138	**'AIR MAIL' Streamline Van** (-)	**£100-120**
139	**Saloon Car** (-)	**£50-60**
152	**Streamline Motor Coach** (-)	**£100-200**
163	**Streamline Fire Engine** (-)	**£50-60**
197	**Trolley Bus (small)** (AB)	**£200-250**
204	**Trolley Bus (large)** (AB)	**£300-400**
302	**Horse Drawn Covered Wagon** (-)	**£50-60**
304	**Sledge and Dogs** (FGT)	**£50-60**
306	**Aeroplane Set** (Comet, Atlanta and pilots) (FGT)	**£100-120**
307	**Fire Brigade Set** (-)	**£300-400**
310	**Rickshaw pulled by Chinese Coolie** (FGT)	**£100-150**
311	**Light Trailer Fire Pump in Action Set** (-)	**£100-150**
?	**Space Ship** (-)	**NGPP**
?	**Coronation Coach (small)** (AB)	**£20-30**
?	**State Landau Coach** (-)	**£30-40**
?	**Farmer's Gig** (FGT)	**£30-40**
?	**Farm Cart with Trotting Horse** (-)	**£30-40**
?	**Mobile Animal Trailer and Vet** (-)	**£60-70**
---	**Racing Car**, Red body with 'MG Magnette' cast into side, 110 mm. 'FGT & SONS'	**£60-70**
---	**Petrol Pumps**, Black/White with rubber hoses (T&B)	**£25-35**
---	**Village Blacksmith Set**, contains blacksmith, forge with hood, anvil, Shire horse. In 2-part card box	**£120-150**

The listing has been compiled from original manufacturer's records by Mr Norman Joplin to whom the Editor would like to express his grateful thanks. Thanks are also due to Mr J.R. Anderson of Queensland, Australia and Ross Kennett of Roscoes Relics, South Australia, Australia for kindly sending new model information.

Timpo Toys

Robert Newson has provided this history and listing of cast metal Timpo motor vehicles.

The name Timpo comes from 'Toy Importers Ltd'. It was only with the outbreak of war in 1939 that Timpo started to manufacture their own lines, when importing became impossible. A few vehicles were made in 1940-41, but the main Timpo range started in 1946. The models were cheap and sturdy, if somewhat crude, and many have survived. Relatively few suffer from metal deterioration. In 1949 Timpo advertised 'faithful replicas of famous delivery services' and introduced several vans with attractive advertising liveries. An AEC Monarch lorry in the livery of Vaux brewery was introduced around 1950, and this was a far better model than the earlier toys. Sadly it was not the first of a new range - the 1951-2 ban on the use of zinc meant that Timpo discontinued all their diecast vehicles. Some of the dies were subsequently sold to Benbros, including the AEC lorry.

Timpo Toys are very rarely seen in mint condition, and prices are therefore quoted for good original condition. Dates given are the approximate year of introduction.

NB See the 'Miscellaneous Models' colour section for a picture of a Timpo model.

Ref	Year(s)	Model name	Colours, features, details	Market Price Range
	1940	MG Record Car	Hollow-cast lead. Red, 'TIMPO TOYS' cast on side, 98 mm	£40-50
	1940	Streamlined Saloon	Separate body and chassis. 'Timpo' in script underneath. 99 mm	£30-40
	1940	Pick-Up Truck	Separate body and chassis. 'Timpo' in script underneath.	
			Re-issued post-war with name blanked out. 97 mm	£30-40
	1940	Four-light Saloon	Possibly re-issue of a Goody Toy. Details unknown	NGPP
	1946	MG Record Car	Zinc diecast. 'TIMPO TOYS' cast at rear on offside. 97 mm	£40-50
	1946	'American Star' Racer	Star transfer on each side, 101 mm	£40-50
	1946	'Timpo Saloon'	Possibly a Morris 8. 93 mm	£40-50
	1946	Austin 16 Saloon	Black. 'TIMPO TOYS' underneath. 96 mm	£40-50
			Re-issued by Betal in four versions:	
			1. No name on model, brass wheel hubs	£30-40
			2. 'A BETAL PRODUCT' under roof, tin base with friction motor, brass wheel hubs	£30-40
			3. As 2. but with plastic body rather than diecast	£30-40
			4. As 3. but with clockwork motor and solid metal wheels	£30-40
	1946	MG Midget	Composition wheels. 82 mm	£30-40
	1946	Packard Saloon	Fitted with aluminium baseplate and friction motor from 1948. 113 mm	£30-40
	1946	'Speed of the Wind' Record Car	Similar to the Dinky Toy. 99 mm	£40-50
	1946	'Arctic' Set	Contains Sledge, Dog Team, 2 men, 2 seals, 2 penguins, polar bear, snowy hedge. Orange box	£150-175
	1947	Alvis 14 Saloon	A big four-light saloon. 106 mm	£30-40
	1947	Utility Van	With aluminium baseplate and friction motor from 1948. (Early casting 102mm, later 104mm).	
			1. No transfers, numerous colours, without motor	£10-15
			2. Black, 'TYRESOLES SERVICE' transfers, no motor	£150-200
			3. 'HIS MASTER'S VOICE' transfers, pale Yellow, Orange-Yellow, pale Blue or Green, with or without motor	£150-200
	1947	Articulated Petrol Tanker	No transfers. Re-issued by Benbros. 149 mm	£30-40
	1947	Lincoln Convertible	A very approximate model of the 1942 Lincoln. Aluminium baseplate and windscreen. Most models in single colours (many different). Late version in cream with blue seats. 115 mm	£30-40
	1947	Armstrong-Siddeley Hurricane	A coupe with top up. 105 mm	£30-40
	1947	Streamlined Fire Engine	Red, two Yellow aluminium ladders. With aluminium baseplate and friction motor from 1949. 105 mm	£30-40
	1947	Articulated Box Van	Re-issued by Benbros. 146 mm. Models were boxed.	
			1. Green, Blue or Red trailer with 'TIMPO TOYS' transfers	£140-160
			2. Black cab and trailer with Grey roof, Red wheel hubs, 'PICKFORDS' transfers	£120-140
			3. Orange cab and trailer, Black roof, 'UNITED DAIRIES' transfers	£120-140
			4. Light Blue cab, Light Blue and Cream trailer, 'WALL'S ICE CREAM' transfers	£120-140
			5. Dark Blue cab and trailer with off-White roof, 'LYONS TEA' transfers	£120-140
			6. Pale Yellow cab and trailer, transfers with 'BISHOPS MOVE' logo and 'BISHOP & SONS DEPOSITORIES LTD. 10-12 BELGRAVE ROAD LONDON, S.W.1'	£120-140
			7. Pale Yellow cab and trailer, transfers with 'BISHOPS MOVE' logo and 'JOHN H. LUNN LTD. 6 HOPE CRESCENT EDINBURGH'	£120-140
	1947	London Taxi	Cast in two parts. 94 mm	£20-25
	1947	Alvis 14 Police Car	Police sign and loudspeakers at front of roof, wire aerial behind. Black. 106 mm	£50-75
	1947	Articulated Low Loader	Re-issued by Benbros. 168 mm	£10-15
	1947	Buick Saloon	A very crude model. Composition wheels. 99 mm	£10-15
	1947	Pick-Up Truck	With eight cast-in barrels. 104 mm	£15-20
	1947	Forward Control Tipper Lorry	Cream cab and chassis, Red tipper. 101 mm	£15-20
	1947	Forward Control Luton Van	Same chassis as the tipper. 97 mm. Models were boxed.	
			1. No transfers, Black lower half, Light Blue upper half	£15-20
			2. Dark Blue, 'SMITH'S CRISPS' transfers	£100-120
			3. Brown, 'W.D. & H.O. WILLS' transfers	£100-120
	1949	Forward Control Box Van	Same chassis as above. Re-issued by Benbros. 96 mm. Dark Blue, 'CHIVERS JELLIES' transfers	£100-120
	1949	Normal Control Box Van	Later models with aluminium baseplate and friction motor. 105 mm. Models were boxed.	
			1. Dark Blue with White roof, 'EVER READY' transfers, with or without motor	£100-120
			2. Green, 'GOLDEN SHRED' transfers, with motor	£100-120
			3. Green, 'MELTONIAN SHOE CREAM' transfers, with motor	£100-120
	1949	Normal Control Petrol Tanker	Red, paper labels reading 'MOTOR OIL ESSO PETROL'. Re-issued by Benbros. 116 mm	£100-120
	1950	AEC Monarch Brewery Lorry	Red. 'VAUX' cast on headboard behind cab, 'SUNDERLAND' cast on cab sides. Models were boxed. Brown hollow-cast barrels with 'VAUX' cast on ends. Re-issued by Benbros without the headboard and with other changes. 129 mm	£100-120
	?	Petrol Station No.2 Set	Contains Saloon Car and Racing Car plus 3 Personnel and 5 Pumps. Pictorial box lid states: 'THE FAMOUS TIMPO CARS'	£100-150
	1940s	Bomber Station Set	3 x twin-fuselage aircraft, 2 x twin-engined, single-fuselage aircraft and a single-engined fighter. Box has a pictorial label on its lift-off lid	£100-150

MARKET PRICE RANGE   Please note that for Price Range purposes, the models have been assumed to be boxed where appropriate and in good condition.

Tri-ang Minic Ships

Minic ships are accurately detailed waterline models made between 1958 and 1964 to a scale of 1:1,200 (1in to 100ft).
Six sales catalogues were published which nowadays are quite hard to find.
No single catalogue shows the full range.
Minic ships re-introduced in 1976 were fitted with wheels and have 'Hong Kong' on the base.

Ocean Liners

Ref	Year(s)	Model name	Colours, features, details	Market Price Range
M701		RMS 'Caronia'	Green body, one plain Red/Black or detailed funnel, one mast, 178 mm. 'Painted in the correct Cunard green she is a most striking vessel'.	£45-55
M702		RMS 'Queen Elizabeth'	Black/White, 2 plain Red/Black or detailed funnels, 2 masts, 262 mm. 'The worlds largest ship and the pride of the Cunard fleet'.	£55-65
M703		RMS 'Queen Mary'	Black/White, plain Red/Black or detailed funnels, 2 masts, 259 mm. 'Her three funnels make her the most easily recognisable'.	£45-55
M704		SS 'United States'	Black/White body, two Red/White/Blue funnels, 252 mm. 'The present holder of the Blue Riband of the Atlantic'.	£45-55
M705		RMS 'Aquitania'	Black/White body, four Red/Black funnels, two masts, 231 mm.	£80-100
M706		SS 'Nieuw Amsterdam'	Grey/White body, two Yellow funnels, two masts, 192 mm.	£45-55
M707		SS 'France'	Black/White, 2 Red/Black funnels, 5 masts, 262 mm. 'The longest ship in the world – 1035ft, being 4ft longer than Queen Elizabeth'.	£80-100
M708		RMS 'Saxonia'	Black/White body, one Red/Black or detailed funnel, nine masts, cargo handling gear on stern	£40-50
M708/2		RMS 'Franconia'	Green body, one Red/Black funnel, nine Green masts, 155 mm, swimming pool on stern.480 made	£500-550
M709		RMS 'Ivernia'	Black/White or Green body, 155mm, cargo handling gear on stern.	£40-50
M709/2		RMS 'Carmania'	Green body, one Red/Black funnel, nine Green masts, 155 mm, swimming pool on stern.480 made	£500-550
M710		RMS 'Sylvania'	Black/White, one Red/Black funnel, nine masts, 155 mm.	£35-45
M711		RMS 'Carinthie'	Black/White, one Red/Black funnel, nine masts, 155 mm.	£35-45
M712		NS 'Savannah'	White, no funnels (nuclear powered), four masts, 149 mm.	£45-55
M713		SS 'Antilles'	Black/White, one Red/Black funnel, ten masts, 152 mm. All White body, one Red/Black funnel, ten masts	£45-60 £65-70
M714		'Flandre'	Black/White, one Red/Black funnel, ten masts, 152 mm. All White body, one Red/Black funnel, ten masts	£35-45 £45-55
M715		RMS 'Canberra'	White body, one Yellow funnel, three masts, 189 mm.	£55-65
M716		MS 'Port Brisbane'	Grey/White, one Red/Black funnel, eight masts, 140 mm.	£90-110
M717		SS 'Port Auckland'	Grey/White, one Red/Black funnel, seven masts, 140 mm.	£90-120
M718		RMS 'Amazon'	White, Yellow funnel, 19 masts, 10 lifeboats, 149 mm.	£115-130
M719		RMS 'Arlanza'	White, Yellow funnel, 19 masts, 149 mm.	£130-150
M720		RMS 'Aragon'	White, Yellow funnel, 19 masts, 149 mm.	£115-130
M721		RMS 'Britannia'	The Royal Yacht. Blue/White body, Yellow/Black funnel, 3 masts, 105 mm.	£20-25
M721/H		RMS 'Britannia'	Hospital Ship. White body, three masts, 105 mm.	£20-25

Smaller craft

CHANNEL ISLANDS STEAMERS (78mm long)

M722	'Isle of Jersey'	Black/White, 2 Yellow/Black funnels, 2 masts	£18-24
M723	'Isle of Guernsey'	Black/White, 2 Yellow/Black funnels, 2 masts	£18-24
M724	'Isle of Sark'	Black/White body, 2 Yellow/Black funnels, 2 masts	£18-24
M726	'PILOTS' Boat	Black/White/Yellow, 45 mm	£65-75
M727	Lifeboat	Blue body	£15-20

PADDLE STEAMERS (all are 78 mm long)

M728	'Britannia'	Black/white, 2 funnels (black/blue, red/black or yellow/black), 2 masts	£20-25
M729	'Bristol Queen'	Black/white, 2 funnels (black/blue, red/black or yellow/black), 2 masts	£20-25
M730	'Cardiff Queen'	Black/White, 2 funnels (Black/Blue, Red/Black or Yellow/Black), 2 masts	£20-25

OIL TANKER

M732	SS 'Varicella'	Black/White body, Black/Yellow funnel ('SHELL' logo), 2 masts, 169 mm.	£30-40

WHALE FACTORY SHIPS

M733	TSS 'Vikingen'	Grey body, six masts, 125 mm.	£25-30
M734	Whale Chaser	Grey, Yellow/Black funnel, 39 mm.	£12-15

TUGBOATS (all except 'Turmoil' are 38mm long)

M731	Tugboat	Black/Grey/Red, Red/Black funnel	£5-7
M731	Tugboat	Black/Grey/Red, Yellow/Black funnel	£5-7
M731	Tugboat	Black/Blue/Red, Yellow/Black funnel	£5-7
M731	Tugboat	Black/Grey/Yellow, Yellow/Black funnel	£5-7
M740	Barge	Intended to match M731, but not issued	NPP
M810	Navy Tug HMS 'Turmoil'	Black/Blue or Grey, Black funnel, 50 mm.	£10-15

LIGHTSHIPS (all are 33mm long)

M735	'SUNK'	Red body, White logo/name	£10-15
M736	'SHAMBLES'	Red body, White logo/name	£10-15
M737	'CORK'	Red body, White logo/name	£10-15
M738	'VARNE'	Red body, White logo/name	£10-15
M739	'St GOWAN'	Red body, White logo/name, no number on base	£10-15

BATTLESHIP
M741   HMS 'Vanguard' .....Grey or Blue, two masts, 206 mm **£30-40**

AIRCRAFT CARRIERS
M751   HMS 'Bulwark' ....Grey or Blue, one mast, 186 mm **£25-35**
M752   HMS 'Centaur' ....Grey or Blue body with one mast **£25-35**
M753   HMS 'Albion'..........Grey or Blue body with one mast **£25-35**

COMMANDO SHIP
M754   HMS 'Albion'..........Grey ship with 12 Cream or Brown plastic
        helicopters. 1000 models issued and given to H.M.S. 'Albion' crew
        members (Capt. Adams in command) **£400-500**

CRUISERS
M761   HMS 'Swiftsure' .....Blue or Grey, one crane jib, 145 mm **£15-18**
M762   HMS 'Superb'.........Blue or Grey, one crane jib, 145 mm **£15-18**

DESTROYERS, FLEET ESCORT, 'DARING' CLASS
M771   HMS 'Daring' ....Blue or Grey, one mast, 98 mm **£10-15**
M772   HMS 'Diana' ....Blue or Grey, one mast, 98 mm **£10-15**
M773   HMS 'Dainty'..........Blue or Grey, one mast, 98 mm **£10-15**
M774   HMS 'Decoy'...........Blue or Grey, one mast, 98 mm **£10-15**

DESTROYERS, FLEET, 'BATTLE' CLASS
M779   HMS 'Alamein'.......Blue or Grey, one mast, 97 mm **£10-15**
M780   HMS 'Jutland' ....Blue or Grey, one mast, 97 mm **£10-15**
M781   HMS 'Anzac'...........Blue or Grey, one mast, 97 mm **£10-15**
M782   HMS 'Tobruk'.........Blue or Grey, one mast, 97 mm **£10-15**

DESTROYERS, GUIDED MISSILE, 'COUNTY' CLASS
M783   HMS 'Hampshire' ...Grey body with two masts, 136 mm **£25-35**

M784   HMS 'Kent'.............Grey body with two masts, 136 mm **£30-35**
M785   HMS 'Devonshire' ...Grey body with two masts, 136 mm **£30-35**
M786   HMS 'London'........Grey body with two masts, 136 mm **£30-35**

FRIGATES, FAST ANTI-SUBMARINE, 'V' CLASS
M787   HMS 'Vigilant'........Blue or Grey, one mast, 92 mm **£10-15**
M788   HMS 'Venus' ....Blue or Grey, one mast, 92 mm **£10-15**
M789   HMS 'Virago'.........Blue or Grey, one mast, 92 mm **£10-15**
M790   HMS 'Volage'.........Blue or Grey, one mast, 92 mm **£10-15**

FRIGATES, ANTI-SUBMARINE, 'WHITBY' CLASS
M791   HMS 'Whitby' ....Blue or Grey body, 94 mm **£10-15**
M792   HMS 'Torquay'......Blue or Grey body, 94 mm **£10-15**
M793   HMS 'Blackpool'....Blue or Grey body, 94 mm **£10-15**
M794   HMS 'Tenby'.........Blue or Grey body, 94 mm **£10-15**

MINESWEEPERS, 'TON' CLASS
M799   HMS 'Repton'........Blue or Grey body **£10-15**
M800   HMS 'Dufton' ....Blue or Grey body **£10-15**
M801   HMS 'Ashton'........Blue or Grey body **£10-15**
M802   HMS 'Calton'........Blue or Grey body **£10-15**
M803   HMS 'Picton' ....Blue or Grey body **£10-15**
M804   HMS 'Sefton' ....Blue or Grey body **£10-15**
M805   HMS 'Upton'........Blue or Grey body **£10-15**
M806   HMS 'Weston'.......Blue or Grey body **£10-15**

SUBMARINES, 'A' CLASS
M817   Sub 'A' Class............Blue or Grey body, 61 mm **£5-7**
M818   Sub Recon.................Blue or Grey body, 61 mm **£7-10**

Accessories, Gift Sets, Hong Kong issues and Catalogues

DOCKSIDE ACCESSORIES

M827	**Breakwater Straights**, Grey	**£3-4**
M828/L	**Breakwater Angle**, Left, Grey	**50p**
M828/R	**Breakwater Angle**, Right, Grey	**50p**
M829	**Breakwater End**, Grey	**50p**
M836	**Quay Straights**,Tan	**£3-4**
M837	**Crane Units**, Tan, Brown or Green cargo	**£3-4**
M838	**Storage Tanks**, Grey/Silver and Red	**£2-3**
M839	**Customs Shed**, Green	**£3-4**
M840	**Warehouse**, Brown	**£3-4**
M841	**Ocean Terminal**, White with Black windows	**£5-6**
M842	**Swing Bridge**, Red, no description on base	**£2-3**
M843	**Terminal Extension**, White with Black windows	**£5-6**
M844	**Lock Gates** (pair), Brown	**£1-2**
M845	**Landing Stages**, Cream 'L' shaped, 1in long	**£1-2**
M846	**Lift Bridge**, Silver/Tan	**£2-3**
M847	**Pier centre section**, White	**£2-3**
M848	**Pier entrance section**, White	**£2-3**
M849	**Pier head**, White	**£12-14**
M850	**Pier Shelter**, Green, 35 mm	**£5-6**
M851	**Pier archways**	**£2-3**
M852	**Pier Building**, White/Blue/Green, Silver Cupola, 'RESTAURANT' plus 'DANCING TONIGHT'	**£2-3**
M853	**Factory Unit**, Pink and Buff, Black chimneys	**£25-30**
M854	**Tanker Wharf Straight**, Cream and Red	**£65-75**
M855	**Tanker Wharf Berth**, Red and Green or Cream and Green, Black plastic pipeline	**£2-3**
M857	**26in Sea**, Blue plastic	**£14-18**
M857	**52in Sea**, Blue plastic	**£25-30**
M861	**Lifeboat set**, Grey, Blue shed, one lifeboat	**£35-40**
M878	**Lighthouse**, White	**£1-2**
M880	**Whales**, White or plain Grey	**£12-15**
M882	**Beacon**, White/Red or Green	**£1-2**
M884	**Statue of Liberty**, Green	**£15-20**
M885	**Floating Dock**, Grey, 4 Black plastic cranes	**£20-25**
M -	**Helicopter**, Cream or Brown plastic	**£20-25**

GIFT SETS and SPECIAL PRESENTATION PACKS

M891	**'Queen Elizabeth'** Gift Set	**£75-100**
M892	**'United States'** Gift Set	**£150-175**
M893	**'Task Force'** Gift Set	**£30-40**
M894	**'Royal Yacht'** Gift Set	**£80-100**
M895	**'Nieuw Amsterdam'** Gift Set	**£600-700**
M702s	**'Queen Elizabeth'** Presentation Set	**£80-100**
M703s	**'Queen Mary'** Presentation Set	**£100-120**
M704s	**SS 'United States'** Presentation Set	**£100-120**
M705s	**RMS 'Aquitania'** Presentation Set	**£125-150**
M707s	**SS 'France'** Presentation Set	**£125-150**
M741s	**HMS 'Vanguard'** Presentation Set	**£50-60**

HONG KONG 'BLUE BOX' MODELS (1976-80)

These models are slightly larger than the original issues, e.g., Canberra is 207mm.
'Queen Mary', 'Queen Elizabeth', 'United States', 'Canberra',
HMS 'Vanguard', HMS 'Bulwark', 'Missouri', 'Bismark',
'Scharnhorst', 'Yamato'. Each, boxed **£15-20**
RMS 'Canberra, boxed **£25-30**

HONG KONG SETS of MODELS

1	**Fleet Anchorage Set**	**£25-30**
2	**Quay Set**	**£25-30**
3a	**Ocean Terminal**, lid shows stern of RMS 'Queen Mary'	**£45-50**
3b	**Ocean Terminal**, lid shows bow of RMS 'Queen Mary'	**£35-40**
4	**Naval Task Force**, with HMS 'Bulwark' and 'Vanguard'	**£35-40**
5	**Naval Task Force**, with 'Bismark' and 'Scharnhorst'	**£50-55**

MINIC CATALOGUES 1958-64

1	**Leaflet** ....with first Minic Ships listed	**£75-100**
2	**Booklet** ....with first Minic Ships listed	**£25-30**
3	**Booklet** ....with Ships and other Tri-ang products	**£60-75**
4	**Booklet** ....with Minic Ships only	**£25-30**
5	**Booklet** ....with Minic Ships only	**£25-30**
6	**Booklet** ....with Tri-ang range	**£30-35**
M862	**Leaflet** ....Minic illustrated leaflet	**£10-15**

Tri-ang
Spot-On models

Introduction

Spot-On Models were introduced in 1959 by Tri-ang Toys to gain a foothold in the diecast market dominated at the time by Dinky Toys and their recently established rivals Corgi Toys.

Tri-ang realised that they had to offer not only a range of features similar to those of their competitors' products but something more besides. They decided that collectors would appreciate models that were all made to the same precise scale right across the range.

The models would thus look right together and qualify as such rather than toys. Much of the Dinky and Corgi cars range was made to a scale of around 1:45 (with a few exceptions).

Tri-ang advertised the precise nature of their (larger) chosen scale as being 'spot-on' at 1:42.

A large modern factory was set up in Belfast, Northern Ireland to produce the models. A coloured picture of the real vehicle was included in the box of most early issues.

Well over a hundred different models were designed, the range being extended to include scale buildings and road signs. Production continued till the time that Tri-ang bought up Dinky Toys in 1967. After the cessation of UK production, some of the Spot-On dies went to New Zealand where some interesting versions were produced for a couple of years.

All Spot-On models are highly collectable today particularly commercial vehicles, buses and the Presentation and Gift Sets.

NB See the 'Miscellaneous Models' colour section for pictures.

Spot-On model identification

Makers Name and Trade Mark are clearly marked on base of the model ('SPOT-ON' and 'Models by Tri-ang'). Some New Zealand produced versions have nothing at all on the base.

Model Name is shown on the base (except some New Zealand versions) while the **Model Number** is usually shown on box but not always on the model.

Baseplates can be any of a variety of colours: black, silver, grey - even green has been observed on the base of a maroon version of No. 155 Taxi !

Scale of models is 1:42 (with very few exceptions) and is usually (but not always) shown on the base.

Wheel hubs on cars are usually turned aluminium with a raised 'hub cap'. Truck models usually have diecast and more accurate representations of real hubs. **Tyres** are mostly black rubber (occasionally plastic) on all the vehicle models. Rear twin wheels have special 'double tyres'.

Number plates are represented on most Spot-On models with the exception of those having plastic chassis (such as 266 Bull Nose Morris and 279 MG Midget). A large range of

registration numbers were available to factory production staff and were applied randomly to most models. Different number plates are therefore to be expected on different examples of the same model and do not have any effect on the price.

Windscreens and windows are included in all vehicle models.

Other features include seats and steering wheel on most models, suspension on most cars, driver, other figures and lorry loads with some. Very few 'decals' or 'frills' is the norm.

Colours are all listed where known though different and previously unknown colours still come to light occasionally.

Prices shown in the 'Market Price Range' column are for mint models in pristine boxes. These models are rare, hence their high market prices. The condition of models generally encountered tends towards the average and consequently command lower prices. Similarly, rare colours or combinations of colours puts the price into the higher part of the range with common colours achieving a more moderate price level.

Spot-On Cars

Ref	Year(s)	Model name	Colours, features, details	Market Price Range
100	1959	**Ford Zodiac** (without lights)	Red / Cream or Blue / Cream body, 107 mm	£70-90
			Red body	£80-100
			Cream body	£70-90
			Yellow body	£110-140
			Light Blue, Salmon-Pink or Green body	£70-90
			Bluish-Grey and Brownish-Pink body	£75-100
			Light Blue over Grey body, Red interior	£100-120
100sl	1959	**Ford Zodiac** (with lights)	Grey/Turquoise or Grey/Pink body	£100-120
			Grey/White, Grey/Light Blue, or Green/White body	£100-120
			Yellow/White, Grey/Green, or Two-tone Blue body	£100-120
101	1959	**Armstrong Siddeley 236 Sapphire**	Blue / Grey, Turquoise / Black, Blue / Black,	
			Pink or Mauve body	£100-130
			Salmon body, Black roof	£150-175
			Mid-Green body, Dark Green roof	£150-200
			Light Blue body, Dark Blue roof	£150-175
			Powder Green, Metallic Green / Black, or Bluish-Grey	£75-100
			Light Blue body	£100-120
			Light Blue / Black, Grey / Black	£95-125
			Pale Green / Metallic Charcoal, or Deep Lilac / Black roof	£160-190
			Cream / Metallic Charcoal or Metallic Blue / Black	£75-100
			Yellow body, Black roof	£150-175
102	1959	**Bentley Continental 4-door Sports**.	Metallic Green / Silver, or Metallic Grey / Blue. 127 mm	£80-125
			Metallic Maroon / Silver	£150-175
			Two-tone Grey, Silver / Grey or Green / Grey	£95-125
			Silver / Light Blue or Grey / Light Blue body	£120-150
103	1959	**Rolls Royce Silver Wraith**	Metallic Silver and Maroon body, White seats, 131 mm	£200-300
			Metallic Silver and Metallic Light Blue (Cream seats), or	
			Metallic Silver and Metallic Green body	£125-150
104	1959	**M.G. 'MGA' Sports Car**	Beige body, 95 mm	£150-175
			Red body (Grey seats), Mid-blue or Pale Blue body (White seats)	£130-160
			Turquoise or Cream body (White seats)	£130-160
			Salmon Pink (Grey seats) or Bluish-Green (Lemon seats)	£150-200
			Greenish-Grey (Turquoise seats)	NGPP
			Deep Green body (White seats)	£150-175
			Metallic Steel Blue body (Grey seats)	£130-160
105	1959	**Austin-Healey 100/6**	Yellow (White or Grey seats), Grey (Red seats), Beige (Grey seats)	£140-200
			Red / Cream or Metallic Blue / Cream	£200-300
			Blue, Green, Cream, Turquoise, Metallic Blue, Metallic Green, or Pink	£130-170
			Light Blue body (Royal Blue seats) or Turquoise (Light Grey seats)	£150-180
107	1960	**Jaguar XK-SS**	Metallic Blue body, Lemon seats, Black folded hood	£150-175
			Cream, Beige, Red or Light Green body	£150-175
			Dark Olive (Light Grey seats / hood), or	
			Pale Blue (Pale Grey seats / hood)	£150-175
			Lilac body with Grey seats, Black folded hood	£150-175
			Light Blue with Dark Blue seats and folded hood	£150-175
			Light Grey body, Pale Blue seats and folded hood	£150-200
			Fawn body, cast hubs have 'stick-on' wheel trims that create a	
			spoked wheel and white-wall tyre effect.	NGPP
108	1960	**Triumph TR3a Sports**	Light Blue with Dark Blue seats, 88 mm	£150-200
			Cream body with Dark Brown seats	£150-200
			Light Brown (White seats), Pale Green (Off-White seats) or Apple Green (Cream seats)	£140-170
			Red or Sea Green body with Grey seats	£120-150
			Grey body (White seats), or Metallic Green (Lemon seats)	£125-175
			Pale Blue body with Pale Grey seats	£125-175
			Mid-Blue body with Mid-Grey seats	£125-175
			Note: Two baseplate castings are known with this model.	
			One exposes the axle ends near to the wheels, while the	
			other completely hides the axles.	
112	1960	**Jensen 541**	Grey, Mauve, Pink, Maroon / Black or Metallic Green body, 106 mm	£100-125
			Light Blue or Pale Green or Metallic Blue body	£100-125
			Lemon body (Black roof), or Yellow body (Red seats)	£100-125
113	1960	**Aston-Martin DB3 Saloon**	Light Blue, Grey, Red, Light Green, Dark Green, 104 mm	£125-150
			Maroon body	£200-250
			Very Pale Pink or Deep Pink body, Cream interior	£130-160
			Deep Lilac or Light Brown body	£130-170
			White or Metallic Dark Green body	£130-160
			Metallic Silver Blue body	£130-160
			Yellow body, Lemon interior, Red steering wheel	£175-225
114	1960	**Jaguar 3.4 Mark 1 Saloon**	Metallic Blue, Maroon, Mauve, Metallic Green, or Pink, 108 mm	£125-150
			Light Grey or Mid-Green body	£140-180
			Light Blue or Yellow body	£110-150
			White or Dark Red body	£150-180
			Very Pale Pink or Deep Pink body	£150-200

115	1960	**Bristol 406 Saloon**	Orange or Red body, 116 mm	£100-130
			Metallic Dark Steel body	£140-160
			Yellow or Metallic Green body	£100-160
			Grey body, Black roof, Cream seats	£100-130
118	1960	**BMW Isetta Bubble Car**	Pale Blue, Beige, Grey or Turquoise, 56 mm	£75-100
			Green or Metallic Green, Red, Pink or Yellow	£75-100
			Yellow body	£120-160
119	1960	**Meadows Frisky Sport**	Orange / Grey, Blue / Grey or Turquoise / Black	£60-80
			Red / Light Grey, Red / Black, or Light Blue / White, 69 mm	£75-100
			Pale Blue / Black or Red / White	£100-125
120	1960	**Fiat Multipla Estate**	Blue (Cream seats), or Mauve (Red seats), 85 mm	£70-80
			Pink, Light Blue, Yellow, Red, Dark Red, Sea Green or Pale Green	£100-125
			White (Off-White seats)	£100-125
131	1960	**Goggomobil Super Regent**	Grey / Black, Yellow / Black, Mauve / Black, Blue / Grey, Blue,	
			Green, or Grey	£50-75
			Metallic Green, Beige, Light Grey, Pink, Deep Salmon Pink,	
			Red or Turquoise	£50-75
			Light Blue / Black, Red / Black, Dark Blue / Black, Green / Black	£50-75
154	1961	**Austin A40 Farina Saloon**	Green, White, Light Blue/White or Grey/Blue	£50-70
			Light Grey, Metallic Blue, Beige, Light Blue, Navy or Turquoise body	£50-75
			Pale Grey body, White interior	£100-125
			Metallic Green body, Cream interior	£80-100
			Red / Black, Blue / Black, Green / Black, Lavender / Black	£60-80
	1966	**'MAGGI' Promotional**	Red body, Cream interior, 'MAGGI' in yellow on front doors.	
			Housed in special red / yellow box with leaflet	£200-300
157	1963	**Rover 3-litre** (without lights)	Mid Blue, Mauve, Beige or Yellow	£100-120
			Mid-Grey, Dark Grey, Pale Grey, Sea Green, Dark Green,	
			Light Blue or Deep Pink	£90-120
			Dark Blue body	£150-175
			White body	£95-125
157sl	1963	**Rover 3-litre** (with lights)	Mid Blue, Mauve, Beige, Red or Yellow	£90-120
			Grey, Pale Grey, Sea Green, Dark Green, Light Blue	£90-120
			Dark Blue or Dark Grey	£120-150
			White body	£95-125
165/1	1961	**Vauxhall PA Cresta Saloon**	Beige, Red, Maroon, Pink, Turquoise or Yellow, 115 mm	£80-100
			Blue, Light Blue, Grey or Light Grey	£90-120
			Plum Red or Sea Green body	£100-125
165/2	1961	**Vauxhall PA Cresta with roof rack**	Beige, Red, Maroon, Pink, Turquoise or Yellow, 115 mm	£80-100
			Blue, Light Blue, Grey or Light Grey	£90-120
			Plum Red or Sea green body	£110-150
166	1962	**Renault Floride Convertible**	Blue, Green or Grey body, 101 mm	£80-100
			Dark Red, White or Yellow body	£80-100
183	1963	**Humber Super Snipe Estate**	Beige / White, Blue / White, Green / White, Blue / Black, Beige, Blue,	
			Metallic Bronze or two-tone Blue, wing mirrors on some	£75-100
184	1963	**Austin A60** (with skis)	Beige, Green or White body, 2 figures, roof rack, 106 mm	£80-10
			Red, Light Blue or Light Grey (Grey rack)	£75-100
			Lime Green or Greyish-Blue (Black or Grey roof-rack)	£90-120
185	1963	**Fiat 500**	Light Blue, Green, Red or Grey body	£80-100
			Yellow or Dark Blue	£120-150
191	1963	**Sunbeam Alpine Convertible**	Beige, Mid-Blue, Green, Red, Mauve or Pink, 95 mm	£90-120
			Turquoise or Grey (Cream seats), or Light Blue (White seats) ..	£90-120
			Deep Salmon Pink or White with Red seats; Yellow with Cream seats	£100-130
191/1	1963	**Sunbeam Alpine Hardtop**	Red / White, Turquoise / White, Blue / Black, Blue / Cream,	
			White / Black, Beige / White, Grey / Black body and hardtop ..	£100-130
			Dark Green (Red seats), or Metallic Green / Black	£100-130
			Pink (Cream seats)	£90-120
			Mauve (Cream seats), or Yellow body (Cream seats)	£120-150
			Light Blue, Light Blue/White, Pale Blue/White	£80-110
193	1963	**N.S.U. Prinz**	Turquoise, Beige, Pale Blue, Light or Dark Blue,	
			Cream, Grey or Red	£50-70
			White body	£80-90
195	1963	**Volkswagen Rally Car**	Beige, Cream, Maroon, or Orange body, roof light,	
			flags on bonnet, racing number '9' or '23'	£150-175
			Red body, racing number '11', or Metallic Bronze	£200-300
			Light Blue ('6'), Turquoise ('9')	£150-175
210	1960	**Morris Mini Minor**	Shown in catalogue but not issued	NPP
211	1963	**Austin Seven** (Mini)	Light Blue, Grey, Red or Yellow body, 73 mm	£125-150
			Pink body	£200-250
			White body	£160-180
213	1963	**Ford Anglia Saloon**	Beige, Grey, Yellow or White body, 95 mm	£130-160
			Turquoise, Light Blue, Dark Blue, Red or Pink	£130-160
215	1961	**Daimler Dart SP250**	Beige, Green or Yellow body, 75 mm	£90-120
			White (Red seats), or Light Blue (Blue seats)	£140-160
			Turquoise (White seats), Red (Cream seats) or	
			Grey (Cream seats)	£100-125

216	1963	**Volvo 122s**	Red, Orange, Blue or Turquoise body, sliding roof...	£90-120
			Grey, Bright Yellow or Dark Green...	£100-125
			Lime Green, White interior..	£125-150
217	1963	**Jaguar 'E' Type**...............................	Beige, Cream, Light or Dark Green, Red,	
			White or Yellow / Black..	£90-120
			Mid-Blue or Light Grey body..	£100-130
			Light Blue body..	£200-250
218	1963	**Jaguar Mk.10**	Metallic Brown or Blue, 122 mm..	£90-120
			Dark or Mid-Green, Bronze or White...	£120-150
219	1963	**Austin-Healey Sprite Mk.III**		
		(with driver figure)	Red (White seats), Blue (Red seats), Beige (White seats)...	£100-125
			Off-White or Light Blue body	£100-125
259	1963	**Ford Consul Classic**	White (Blue seats), Beige (White seats); or Blue, Light Blue,	
			Red, Grey or Green body, 105 mm...	£80-100
260	1963	**Royal Rolls-Royce Phantom V**	Maroon body, Blue interior, two flags on roof, Queen and Prince	
			Philip in rear seats, driver and attendant in front...	£200-300
261	1963	**Volvo P1800**	Two versions of this model exist (no price difference):	
			1: the bonnet and boot open and a spare wheel is supplied;	
			2: only the bonnet can be opened.	
			Light Blue, Mid-Blue, Red, Turquoise, Grey or Met. Bronze...	£80-100
			Tan body..	£100-130
			Red body, Grey interior..	£125-150
262	1963	**Morris 1100**	Dark Blue or Red (Grey seats), Green or Beige (Red seats)..	£70-90
			Lime Green or Light Blue body..	£70-90
263	1964	**Bentley 4½ Litre** (Supercharged).....	Green body, Union Jack, racing number '27', '11' or '15'...	£80-100
266	1965	**'Bull Nose' Morris** 1923	Red / Black or Yellow / Black, Brown driver, (scale 1:48)...	£70-80
267	1964	**M.G. 1100 Saloon**	White / Dark Green (Red seats), Red (Cream seats),	
			Green (Red seats) or Red / White (Red interior), 88mm...	£100-125
			Royal Blue / White, Red interior...	£350-450
268	1965	**Vauxhall PB Cresta**.........................	Shown in catalogue but not issued under this number, see 280	NPP
270	1965	**Ford Zephyr 6 Mk.III**	Pale Blue (Red seats), Cream, Green, Greyish-Green or Grey (Red seats); or	
			Red (Grey seats), with poodle..	£100-125
274	1965	**Morris 1100 and Canoe**	Green, Grey, Light Blue, Dark Blue or Red car, Brown canoe on roof...........................	£70-80
			Light Blue or Two-tone Blue (Red canoe) or Red (Red / White canoe)...........................	£70-80
			Light Blue car with Blue / Red canoe, Orange paddle (Set 703)......................................	GSP
276	1964	**Jaguar 'S' type**	Metallic Bronze body, 114 mm., 2 figures..	£120-150
			Metallic Blue or Metallic Green body, Red interior, 2 figures...	£120-150
			Silver body, 2 figures..	£180-220
			Greyish Green body, Red interior, 2 figures..	£150-175
278	1965	**Mercedes-Benz 230 SL**	Metallic Red, Cream, or Maroon body, 100 mm., 2 figures...	£80-100
			Metallic Blue or Metallic Bronze..	£90-120
279	1965	**M.G. PB Midget** 1935 (scale 1:48)..	Dark Blue or Red body, Black wings and seats..	£70-80
280	1963	**Vauxhall PB Cresta**.........................	Beige / Red, Dark Blue / White or Grey / Green body	£100-125
281	1966	**M.G. Midget Mk.II**	Blue or Red body, White interior, driver with scarf, policeman figure, 83 mm	£120-140
286	1965	**Austin 1800**	Light or Dark Blue, Cream, Green or Beige (all with Red seats); or Red (Grey seats).............	£70-85
287	1965	**Hillman Minx**		
		(with Roof Rack and Luggage)	Pale Green, Beige, Cream or Green (all with Red seats),	
			Red (Grey seats) or Greyish-Green body. Two brown suitcases.	£80-100
287/1	1965	**Hillman Minx** (with Roof Rack)......	Same details as 287.	£80-100
289	1963	**Morris Minor 1000**	Metallic Blue or Light Blue body	£120-150
			Red or Metallic Green body	£160-200
304	1967	**VW Variant Estate Car**	Mid-Blue body and plastic opening tailgate. See also 401/1...	NGPP
306	1964	**Humber Super Snipe Estate**	Same casting as 183 but with roof-rack and two suitcases.	
			Beige, Blue, Green or Red or Metallic Bronze body..	£120-150
			Light Blue (White roof-rack) or Turquoise (White roof-rack)..	£85-100
			White and Turquoise body, Grey roof-rack..	£100-120
			Blue body, White roof...	£80-95
307	1965	**Volkswagen Beetle 1200**	Metallic Blue or Metallic Dark Red body...	£200-250
308	1965	**Land Rover and Trailer**	Green (Tan plastic canopy), trailer has Brown plastic body..	£80-100
401/1	1967	**VW Variant Estate Car**	Dark Blue body, White plastic opening tailgate...	£300-500
405	1966	**'BEA' Vauxhall Cresta**	Dark Grey body with Red 'BEA' logo...	£100-125
407	1966	**Mercedes-Benz 230 SL**	Brown body, Red interior, boot rack and luggage..	£70-80
408	1966	**Renault Caravelle**	Not issued	NPP
410	1966	**Austin 1800 and Rowboat** (on roof)	Green, Blue, Beige or Red car with Red or Orange boat..	£80-100

'Magicar' series

501	1965	**Jaguar Mk.10** ....Blue or Green body..	£70-90
502	1965	**Rolls-Royce Silver Cloud Mk.III** ....Blue or Red body	£100-125
503	1965	**Bentley S3 Saloon** ....Blue or Red body...	£80-110
504		**Ferrari Superfast** ....Blue or Red...	£80-110
505	1966	**Batmobile** ....Black body with Batman and Robin figures............	£150-175
?	?	**Tric-Trac car** ....Plastic bodied racing car..	£80-110
MG1	?	**Magicar** ....no details...	NGPP
MG2	?	**Magicar** ....no details...	NGPP
MG3	?	**Magicar** ....no details...	NGPP

Ref	Year(s)	Model name	Colours, features, details	Market Price Range
106a/0c	1960	Austin Articulated Flatbed Lorry with MGA in Crate	Light Blue, Dark Blue, Red or Orange cab, 234 mm	£250-400
106a/1	1959	Austin Articulated Dropside Lorry	Light Blue, Green or Orange cab and body, 234 mm	£200-250
106a/1c	1960	Austin Articulated Flatbed Lorry with Crate Load	Light Blue, Light Green or Orange cab, seven black plastic crates	£200-250
			Turquoise or Dark Blue body	£300-350
CB106	1961-62	Four Wheel Trailer	Turquoise or Red body, for use with ERF and AEC lorries	£90-110
109/2	1960	E.R.F. 68g Flatbed Lorry	Turquoise, Light Grey or Blue body, 210 mm	£160-190
			Maroon body	£350-400
109/2p	1960	E.R.F. 68g Flatbed Lorry with Planks	Turquoise (with or without Black cab roof), 210 mm	£200-250
			Yellow body	£300-400
109/3	1960	E.R.F. 68g Dropside Lorry	Dark Blue cab with Pale Blue or Silver truck body	£300-400
			Yellow body (Metallic Grey roof), Light Green body (Green roof), Blue body or Green body (Black roof)	£160-190
			Deep Blue body, Silver chassis	£250-350
			Orange-Red body, Light Grey chassis	£350-450
			Lemon, Pale Green or Turquoise body, Silver chassis	£190-225
109/3b	1960	E.R.F. Dropside Lorry with Barrel load	Turquoise, Light Blue or Red body (Silver truck bed on some), hinged tailboard, ten Brown plastic barrels	£250-350
110/2	1960	A.E.C. Mammoth Major 8 Flatbed Lorry	Red body (with or without Black roof), 210 mm	£170-200
			Maroon or Dark Blue body	£450-500
110/2b	1960	A.E.C. Lorry 'London Brick Co Ltd'	Red body, Black cab roof, 'brick' load, 'Phorpes Bricks'	£200-250
110/3	1960	A.E.C. Lorry 'British Road Services'	Red body, with or without Black cab roof, Silver chassis and back, barrels load	£400-500
110/3d	1962	A.E.C. Lorry with Oil Drums Load	Red body, Black cab roof, Silver trim	£225-300
110/4	1961	A.E.C. Tanker 'SHELL-BP'	Green cab, Red tank, Black chassis and catwalk	£300-400
			Yellow cab, White/Yellow tank, Silver chassis / catwalk	£500-750
111/30g	1962	Ford Thames with Garage Kit	Orange cab and truck body, Silver chassis, 219 mm	£300-350
			Light Blue cab and truck body, White garage	£250-300
111/a0t	1961	Ford Thames Trader with Three Log Load	Dark Blue or Red cab and truck body, 3 logs	£275-325
			Light Blue cab and truck body	£200-275
			Light Yellow cab and truck body	£250-300
111a/1	1959	Ford Thames Trader 'British Railways'	Maroon and White body, '4884 BGM', 'M 1741 GT6'	£225-300
111a/1	1960	Ford Thames Trader 'R.Hall & Son'	Green body, logo on door. Doubtful if model issued	NPP
111a/1s	1960	Ford Thames with Sack Load	Light Blue and Silver, twelve brown plastic sacks	£250-325
			Dark Green body	£300-350
			Two-tone Blue body	£300-400
			Strawberry and Cream body	£300-400
116	1959	'CATERPILLAR' Tractor D9	Brown / Silver body, Black rubber tracks, 'CAT D9'	£500-750
117	1963	'JONES' Mobile Crane	Cream cab and jib, Red body and wheels, Black chassis, Grey base	£150-200
			Dark Red cab / body, White jib, Light Grey chassis, Silver wheels	£300-400
122	1961	'UNITED DAIRIES' Milk Float	Red / White body, chains, 'Lada and New Yoghurt'	£90-120
123	1959	Bamford Excavator	Red / Yellow, 'J.C.B.'. Intended model but not issued	NPP
137	1962	'MASSEY FERGUSON 65' Tractor	Red / Grey body, Orange engine cover, yellow wheels	£350-500
158a/2	1961	Bedford 'S' Type 2000 Gallon 'SHELL-BP' Tanker	Green cab, Red tank, Black chassis, 'P33A37' logo	£400-500
			Yellow cab, White tank, 'P33A37' logo, 202 mm	£700-1000
			Dark Metallic Green cab, Red tank, Black chassis	£500-600
158a/2C	1961	Bedford Low Loader	Red low-loader with cable drum load. Doubtful if issued	NPP
161	1961	Land Rover (long wheel base)	Grey / White, Light Grey / White or Blue / White	£65-80
210	1961	Morris Mini Van	Bright Yellow, seats / steering wheel, suspension	£90-120
210/1	1962	Morris Mini Van 'Royal Mail'	Red body, Post Office crest, 'E-II-R', suspension	£70-90
210/2	1962	Mini Van 'P.O. Telephones'	Olive-Green body, White interior, Gold crown logo and 'TELEPHONE MANAGER'	£140-160
258	1963	'R.A.C.' Land Rover	Dark Blue body, 'RADIO RESCUE', 108 mm	£100-125
265	1964	'TONIBELL' Ice Cream Van	Blue body, thick Red flash, attendant, 'Tonibell' on doors	£90-135
271	1965	'EXPRESS DAIRIES' Milk Float	Blue / White, 3 wheels, driver, 'Drink Express Milk'	£100-125
273	1965	Commer Van 'SECURITY EXPRESS'	Green / Gold, driver and seated guard, coin slot in roof	£100-130
308	1965	Land Rover and Trailer	Green (Tan plastic canopy), trailer has Brown plastic body	£80-100
315	1965	'GLASS & HOLMES' Commer Van	Blue / Yellow, ladder, figures, 'Window Cleaning Co. Est 1891'	£160-190
402	1966	Crash Service Land Rover	Orange body, 'MOTORWAYS CRASH SERVICE' in Blue	£100-120
404	1966	Morris Mini Van	Yellow body, suspension, ladder, figure, 79 mm	£300-350
404/1	1966	Morris Mini Van 'SHELL'	As previous model but without ladder and figure	£400-500
404/2	1966	Morris Mini Van 'AA'	Shown in 1966 catalogue but never seen	NGPP

Buses, Coaches and Taxis

145	1963	Routemaster Bus	Red 'London Transport' bus, route '284', 'Ovaltine - The Worlds Best Nightcap'.
			1st type has chrome moulded radiator	£300-400
			2nd type has transfer print on plastic background	£300-400
155	1961	Austin FX4 Taxi	Maroon body, Cream steering wheel, Green base, tin-plate hubcaps	£300-400
			Black body, Red steering wheel, Grey base	£65-80
156	1961	Mulliner Luxury Coach	Pale Blue / Grey, Red flash, 'Tri-ang Tours' rear logo, 213 mm	£200-300
			Yellow / White body, Brown side flash	£900-1,200
			Sea Green / Cream, Red flash	£800-1,000
			Silver / Red / Dark Blue	£250-350
			Sky Blue / White body, Red flash	£500-600

Military models

415	1965	R.A.F. Land Rover	Blue/Grey, R.A.F. roundel, hose/pump/attendant, 111 mm	£80-100
416	1965	Leyland Army Ambulance	Olive Green body. Not issued	NPP
417	1965	Military 'FIELD KITCHEN'	Olive Green body, squadron markings, suspension, 108 mm	£100-125
418	1965	Leyland Military Bus	Olive Green body, 'Army Personnel'. Not issued	NPP
419	1965	Land Rover and Missile Carrier	Olive Green body, three White missiles	£200-250

Emergency vehicles

207	1964	Wadham Ambulance	Cream body without Red crosses, with stretcher and patient	£200-300
			White body with Red crosses, with stretcher and patient	£300-400
256	1966	Jaguar 3.4 'POLICE' Car	White or Black. Very few exist with undamaged aerial or roof sign	£200-275
258	1963	'R.A.C.' Land Rover	Dark Blue body, 'RADIO RESCUE', 108 mm	£100-125
309	1965	Police 'Z' Car	Ford Zephyr police car from the BBC-TV series 'Z-Cars'.
			1st type with aerial and 'POLICE' sign, White body	£130-160
			2nd type with no aerial or police sign. Black body	£300-400
			2nd type (no aerial or police sign), White body	£300-400
316	1966	'FIRE DEPT' Land Rover	Red body, suspension, two firemen, 112 mm	£125-150
402	1966	Land Rover 'MOTORWAYS'	Orange / Blue body, hook, Blue 'CRASH SERVICE' logo	£100-125
409	1966	Leyland 'Black Maria'	Blue body, 'Police', policeman and villain. Not issued	NPP

Caravans, Boats, Motor Scooter

135	1961	14ft Sailing Dinghy and Trailer	Blue / Grey, Dark Blue / Red, Dark Blue / White, or
			Red / White boat (with or without cover), plastic trailer	£40-55
135	1964	14ft GP Sailing Dinghy	Brown or Yellow boat on trailer, 128 mm	£35-45
139	1960	Eccles E.16 Caravan	Blue body, White roof, 146 mm	NPP
229	1966	Lambretta	Pale Grey body, Red or White side panels, Black seat	£175-225
264	1962	Tourist Caravan	Blue body, White roof, 152 mm	£90-120
			Yellow body, White roof	£70-90
			Tan body, White roof	£80-125

Collectors notes

Garages and Equipment, Road Signs and Accessories

Garages and equipment

L146	'SHELL' lamp standard	**£10-15**
L147	'SHELL' sign	**£10-15**
L148	'SHELL' petrol pump	**£10-15**
L148	Trade pack, Blue card box of 6 of L148 pumps	**£80-100**
L149	Oil Dispenser Rack	**£10-15**
L159	'BP' Lamp Standard	**£10-15**
162	'BP' or 'SHELL' Filling Station	**£35-45**
162/1/2/3	Garages, each	**£15-20**
163	'BP' Petrol Pump	**£10-15**
164	'BP' Forecourt Sign	**£10-15**
172a	'SHELL' Garage Set	**£50-75**
172b	'BP' Garage Set	**£50-75**

Road signs and accessories

L208/B	**Road Traffic Signs**: 20 different signs issued, each	**£5-10**
L1271/	**Road Direction Signs**: /1 Portsmouth, /2 Guildford, /3 Bristol, /4 Birmingham, /5 Biggar, /6 Dumfries	**£10-15**

Bus Stops: No details available **£10-15**
Road sections: Straights, curves, T-junctions. Each **£6-8**

Plastic Figures: In groups set on a card. Figures include: Garage Personnel, Newspaperman/Milkman/Postman, Doctor/Parson/Schoolmaster, 2 Policeman and an RAC Man, 3 Schoolboys, 2 Children and a Man (in country clothes), 3 Roadmen and Brazier or 3 Roadmen and Road Drill/Planks/Walls
Per card **£5-10**
Retailer's sheet of any six cards of figures **£75-95**

Spot-On Presentation and Gift Sets

Ref	Year(s)	Set name	Contents	Market Price Range

Colours of individual items are not listed. It is possible to find virtually any factory colour that was available at the time of manufacture in Spot-On Gift Sets. Early sets should contain Picture Cards, Fleet Owners leaflets and Magazine Club leaflets.

Ref	Year(s)	Set name	Contents	Market Price Range
A	1960	Presentation Set 'A'	102 Bentley, 108 Triumph TR3, 114 Jaguar 3.4, 118 BMW Isetta, 154 Austin A40	£350-450
No.0	1960	Presentation Set	106a/1 Austin Articulated Dropside Lorry, 100 Ford Zodiac, 103 Rolls-Royce Silver Wraith, 104 MGA and 113 Aston Martin	£400-500
No.1	1960	Presentation Set	100 Ford Zodiac, 101 Armstrong-Siddely, 103 Rolls-Royce and 104 MGA	£500-600
No.2	1960	Presentation Set	109/3 ERF Dropside Lorry, 101 Armstrong-Siddely, 102 Bentley Continental and 105 Austin-Healey 100/6	£500-600
No.3	1960	Presentation Set	Contains 111a/1 Ford Thames Trader, 101 Armstrong-Siddely, 104 MGA, 108 Triumph TR3a, 112 Jensen 541, 113 Aston Martin, 114 Jaguar 3.4	£500-600
No.4	1960	Presentation Set	106a/1 Austin Articulated Dropside Lorry, 109/3 ERF Dropside Lorry, 100 Ford Zodiac, 107 Jaguar XK-SS, 112 Jensen 541	£500-600
No.4a	1963	Presentation Set	104 MGA, 105 Austin-Healey, 107 Jaguar XK-SS and 108 Triumph TR3a	£300-400
No.5		Presentation Set	118 BMW Isetta, 119 Meadows Frisky Sport and 131 Goggomobil Super Regent	£250-300
No.6		'Miniature' Presentation Set	131 Goggomobil, 185 Fiat 500, 193 NSU Prinz and 211 Austin Seven	£300-400
			Variation with 210/1 *ROYAL MAIL* Van instead of 193 NSU Prinz	£300-400
No.6a		'Miniature' Presentation Set	131 Goggomobil, 185 Fiat 500, 119 Meadows Frisky and 211 Austin Seven	£300-400
No.7		Rally Presentation Set	Contains 166 Renault Floride, 191 Sunbeam Alpine, 211 Austin Seven, 213 Ford Anglia, 215 Daimler Dart, 217 Jaguar 'E'-type	£500-600
No.8		Presentation Set	157 Rover, 191 Sunbeam, 213 Ford Anglia, 216 Volvo, 258 RAC Land Rover	£500-600
No.9		Presentation Set	122 Milk Float, 145 Routemaster Bus, 193 NSU Prinz, 207 Wadham Ambulance, 211 Austin Seven, 256 Jaguar Police Car	NGPP
No.10		Presentation Set	122 Austin Seven, 145 Routemaster Bus, 157 Rover 3 litre, 158a/2 Bedford Tanker, 185 Fiat 500, 165 Vauxhall Cresta, 166 Renault Floride, 211 Austin Seven, 215 Daimler Dart and 262 Morris 1100	£400-500
No.14		Presentation Set	211 Austin 7 Mini, 154 Austin A40, 156 Mulliner Coach, 191/1 Sunbeam (Hardtop), 122 'UNITED DAIRIES' Milk Float, 157sl Rover 3 Litre with lights	£500-600
173		Terrapin Building Set	A constructional set	£20-30
208/a		Road Construction Set	4 workmen, brazier, hut, poles, road sections and 18 other small items	£125-175
259		Garage Set	A constructional set	£20-30
701		'His, Her's, Junior's' Set	219 Austin-Healey Sprite, 267 MG 1100, 280 Vauxhall Cresta, in 'window' box	£200-250
702		Gift Set 702	270 Zephyr Six, 274 Morris 1100 and canoe, 286 Austin 1800 and 135 Dinghy	£200-250
702(a)		Gift Set 702	195 VW Rally, 217 Jaguar 'E' type, 261 Volvo P1800, 287 Hillman Minx	£300-350
212	1963	Car, Dinghy and Trailer Set	Contains 165 Vauxhall PA Cresta and 135 GP Dinghy	£125-150
269	1965	Ford Zephyr and Caravan	Contains 270 plus 264 Caravan	£125-175
308	1965	Land Rover and Trailer	Green bodywork, Fawn cover, 170 mm	£65-85
406	1966	Hillman Minx and Dinghy	Contains 287 Hillman Minx and 135 GP Dinghy and trailer	£70-95
MG1	1966	'Magicar Motoring' Set	501 Jaguar Mk.10 and 502 Rolls-Royce, roadway sections and traffic cones	NGPP
MG2		'Magicar Motoring' Set	503 Bentley S3 and 504 Ferrari Superfast, roadway sections and traffic cones	NGPP

'Tommy Spot' Gift Sets

All include a building kit and Tommy Spot figure.

801	'Home with Tommy Spot'	287 Hillman Minx (with Mr Spot), 270 Ford Zephyr Six with driver, pictorial stand	£200-275
802	'Cops 'n' Robbers with Tommy Spot'	309 BBC-TV 'Z-Car' with driver and criminal, 276 Jaguar and driver, pictorial stand	£275-350
803	'Superville Garage with Tommy Spot'	286 Austin 1800 with driver, 279 MG Midget, two garage workers, pictorial stand	£200-275
804	'Sailing with Tommy Spot'	280 Vauxhall PB Cresta and sailing dinghy with Tommy and Mr Spot, pictorial stand	£150-225
805	'Fire with Tommy Spot'	316 Fire Dept Land Rover and trailer, two firefighters, pictorial stand	£195-260
806	'Royal Occasion with Tommy Spot'	260 Royal Rolls-Royce with chauffeur and royal passengers, 6 guardsmen, pictorial stand	£450-650
807	'Pit stop with Tommy Spot'	Mercedes-Benz 230 SL and Jaguar 'S', two racing drivers, pictorial stand	£300-400
808	'Motorway Rescue with Tommy Spot'	402 'Crash Service' Land Rover and mechanic, A.A. van and man, pictorial stand	£400-500

Catalogues, Leaflets and Pictures

Ref	Issued	Publication	Cover, features, contents	Market Price Range
---	1959	**Early issue**	Red cover featuring a Target plus the dividers and diagram of Rolls Royce 'LTP 103'. Wording: '1/42' and 'SPOT-ON MODELS BY TRI-ANG'. Contains 8 pages	**£30-40**
---	1959	**'1st Edition'**	Village scene with Spot-On buildings and models, 'Tri-ang' logo in bright red, '6d', 'dividers' mark, 'SCALE 1/42'. Thick numbered pages with superb pictures	**£30-40**
---	1960	**'2nd Edition'**	As 1st Edition but 'Tri-ang' logo in maroon and pages not numbered	**£30-40**
100M/C.P.C./6.61	1961	**'3rd Edition'**	Same as 2nd Edition	**£25-35**
5a7383/DP	1963	**'4th Edition'**	Royal Rolls-Royce on cover, '3d', Page 19 shows the new Presentation Sets 5-10 and 14	**£20-30**
---	1964	**'5th Edition'**	Blue Austin 1800 (286) on cover, '2d', concertina type leaflet featuring new type of Black/Red window boxes for Gift Sets and single models	**£20-£30**
---	1965	**'6th Edition'**	Cover again features 286 Austin 1800 plus 289 Morris Minor, '2d', concertina type leaflet which includes 'Tommy Spot' and 'Magicar' listings and pictures	**£20-30**
---	1966	**'7th Edition'**	Booklet type featuring 407 Mercedes 230 SL and 287 Hillman Minx, '6d', 'Tommy Spot' featured with 'Royal Occasion' set and Car Spotters guide	**£20-30**

Leaflets and Model Pictures

The early 'blue boxes' for cars and small commercial vehicles and the early card boxes for the large commercial vehicles contained a model picture and a yellow / blue / white leaflet listing the models available. Prices of model picture cards can vary depending on the rarity of the model itself within a price range from **£5 to £25**.
Spot-On 'Picture wallets' are to be found at **£15-20**.
It should be noted that no 'blue box' model or early large commercial boxed model is complete without the model picture.
Leaflets are not uncommon and may be obtained for **£2-3**.

Trade Display Material

---	---	Electric revolving Trade Display Unit	**£300-400**
---	---	Glass shop-sign with 'SPOT-ON MODELS' in red/black/yellow design, 25 inches long	**£150-200**

Spot-On New Zealand issues

When Tri-ang took over the production of Dinky Toys in 1967 they stopped production of Spot-On Models in the United Kingdom. Fourteen models were subsequently produced by the Tri-ang Pedigree company of New Zealand from the original dies sent out from the U.K.

New Zealand production lasted just two years and ceased in 1969 / 70. The New Zealand model reference numbers were different to their UK counterparts

as listed in the Spot-On 7th Edition catalogue. Extras such as roof racks and luggage were not included with NZ issues and the models were housed in New Zealand yellow cellophane 'window' boxes. The following listing first appeared in 'Mini Cars' ('The News Sheet for Caledonian Autominologists'), dated September 1972 and was prepared by Eric Brockie in New Zealand. Thanks are due to James McLachlan (Club Secretary) for his kind permission to reproduce the listing.

UK no.	NZ no.	Model name	Difference from UK version	NZ colour	Market Price Range
289	101	**Morris Minor 1000**	Not manufactured in New Zealand	-	NPP
219	102	**Austin-Healey Sprite**	Colour only	White body, Red seats	**£200-300**
281	103	**MG Midget**	No Policeman included	Dark Green or Red, White seats	**£200-300**
404	104	**Morris Mini Van**	No 'Shell' logo, ladder or mechanism	Yellow	**£100-150**
267	105	**MG 1100**	Single colour only	Green	**£100-150**
262	106	**Morris 1100**	Same as UK issue	Blue	**£100-150**
287/406	107	**Hillman Minx**	No roof rack or dinghy	Green	**£100-150**
280	108	**Vauxhall Cresta**	Single colour only	Blue	**£100-150**
276	109	**Jaguar 'S' type**	Same as UK issue	Blue	**£200-300**
286	110	**Austin 1800**	No lady driver or schoolboy	Light Brown	**£100-150**
270	111	**Ford Zephyr 6**	Same as UK issue	White	**£100-150**
308	112	**Land Rover**	No trailer included	Olive Green body, Pale Green tilt	**£100-150**
407	114	**Mercedes-Benz 230 SL**	Not manufactured in New Zealand	-	NPP
401	115	**Volkswagen Variant**	No roof rack or skis	Dark Blue, Red int., White hatchback	**£200-300**
279	116	**MG PB Midget**	Same as UK issue	Blue, Black	**£150-200**
265	117	**'TONIBELL' Ice Cream Van**	Same as UK issue	Turquoise	**£200-300**
402	118	**Crash Service Land Rover**	Same as UK issue	Orange, Blue	**£100-150**
316	119	**Fire Dept Land Rover**	No Firemen	Red	**£100-150**
415	120	**RAF Land Rover**	Not manufactured in New Zealand	-	NPP

The 'Cotswold Village' series

The 'Cotswold Village' items are rare and it is suggested that larger buildings (church, shop, etc) are likely to be in the region of **£100 - £150**, while smaller items might be anything from **£10 - £50** depending on size, complexity, etc.
These price levels can only be applied

to pristine items in perfect original boxes.

1 School
2a Haystack
3 'Cornerstones' Cottage
4 'Fourways' Cottage
4b 'The Cot' Cottage

5 Antique Shop
6 General Store
7 Bourton Town Hall
8 Barn
9 Public House
10 Farm House
11 Manor House
12 Post Office

13 Church
14 Forge
15 Memorial Stone
16 Water Well
16a Stocks
- Set of Trees
- Bridge Sides

Illustrations on opposite page   **Top**: Tri-ang Spot-On Models were advertised regularly in the 'Eagle' comic; this example is from the 19 March 1960 edition. **Below**: Page 109 of Gamages of Holborn 1961 'Model Book'

All Spot-On 1/42 Scale models by Tri-ang are to scale in all dimensions. Only Spot-On offers a complete highway system—roadway sections, signs and model buildings. Ask your dealer for details.

SPOT-ON models by Tri-ang

Scale : 1/42

Each model is true to scale, 1/42nd of the size of the original vehicle, and built to the same high standard. Every perfect miniature is a collectors' item and justly deserves pride of place in your collection. Many Spot-on models have Independent Suspension, Plated Radiators and Bumpers, also Windows, Number Plates, Seats, Steering Wheels and beautiful duo-tone finish.

No. 118 BMW ISETTA. Length 2¼" — 2/9

No. 113 ASTON MARTIN D.B.3. Length 4⅛" — 3/6

No. 115 BRISTOL 406 with independent suspension. Length 4⅜" — 4/9

No. 131 GOGGOMOBIL 'SUPER'. Length 2¼" — 2/11

No. 154 AUSTIN A40 with independent suspension. Length 3½" — 3/9

No. 157 ROVER 3 Litre, with independent suspension, plated radiator, etc. Length 4⅞" — 5/3

No. 155 AUSTIN TAXI with independent suspension. Length 4⅜" — 4/6

No. 117 JONES CRANE KL 10/10. Length 11⅛" — 24/11

No. 110/2B AEC MAMMOTH MAJOR 8, with brick load. Finished in London Brick Co. livery. Length 8¼" — 14/11

No. 165 VAUXHALL CRESTA, with indedent suspension, plated radiator, etc. Length 4⅞" — 4/11

GAMAGES. HOLBORN, LONDON, E.C.I.   HOLborn 8484

Gamages Convenient Payment Plan—See Page 3

Corgi Classics
Corgi 'Original Omnibus Company'
Corgi Toys
Exclusive First Editions
Lledo 'Days-Gone'
Lledo 'Vanguards'
Oxford Die-Cast

Introduction

The diecast models in this section have been produced mainly for adult collectors. Consequently, they are very different from the traditional toy models aimed at the younger end of the market.

These modern issues are not toys that will ultimately become collectors items – they are high quality scale models that are produced as collectors items from birth.

The scarcity levels and prices of the older traditional toys are largely determined by factors such as how many have survived in good condition and their auction price track records.
These factors are totally irrelevant in respect of modern diecasts, i.e., they will all be carefully stored or displayed and no auction price track records exist.

As a consequence, the scarcity levels and retail prices are simply determined by:

- the number of models making up a 'limited edition' production run
- the collectability of individual models
- manufacturers' suggested retail prices
- trade mail order prices
- the laws of supply and demand

As a result of these factors, the asking prices of popular short-run issues often escalate, and it may be two or three years before a reasonable Market Price Range can become established.

The Market Price Range information provided by the Catalogue has endeavoured to take into consideration all the foregoing factors and reflect the market. The figures provided are in respect of RETAIL PRICES that a collector might reasonably expect to pay for a model as September 2001. They do not represent an indication of the value of individual models and the information is given solely for guidance purposes only.

In conclusion, the Catalogue's position on collecting modern diecasts is that they should be collected for the enjoyment they provide. If, over a period of time, they should happen to increase in value, this is indeed a bonus.

NB – Matchbox Collectibles issues. In the 8th Edition of the Catalogue, Matchbox Collectibles issues were listed in this 'Modern Diecasts' section. They have been re-organised in this Edition to logically follow the Models-of Yesteryear listings and will be found beginning on page 234.

Corgi Classics and Corgi Toys

History

The models were introduced in 1987. Today the models are manufactured in China by Corgi Classics Ltd., which was formed in 1995 following a management buy-out from Mattel. Late in 1999, ownership of the company passed into the hands of the Hong-Kong diecasting giant Zindart. Shortly after, they also acquired the failed Lledo brand which has now been revitalised through the application of Corgi's expertise.

The model range

Corgi Classics have developed into a superb range of models by concentrating on 1/43rd and 1/50th scales for cars coaches, buses and commercial vehicles; 1/76th scale for 'Original Omnibus Company' buses and coaches, and even 1/18th scale cars. Buses remain popular – so much so that the Corgi Collector Club have a separate 'OOC' Club for bus devotees. And a third Club has recently been added – the 'Aviation Archive' Club for collectors of Corgi's excellent aircraft models in scales of 1/72nd and 1/144th.

Basis of Market Price Range

The figures shown represent a guide to the retail price that a collector might reasonably expect to pay for a model at a Corgi Collector Centre. It must be stressed that the figures shown are RETAIL ASKING PRICES. They are NOT an indication of the value of the models.

The high retail prices of some of the models reflect low production runs, eg, Premium Edition (PE) models where only 2,000 pieces have been manufactured.

The Editor would like to thank Susan Pownall of the Corgi Collector Club, Adrienne Fuller of Corgi and Chris Brierley of the Corgi Heritage Centre for their valuable assistance in updating the listings. Details of the Corgi Collector Club (plus a handy Membership Application Form) are to be found on page 32.

Contents of Corgi Classics section

Contents of Corgi Toys section

A page from Corgi's 2001 catalogue showing the 'Café Connection' series of models and buildings

A page from Corgi's 2001 catalogue showing the 'Café Connection' series of models and buildings

Corgi Classics Commercials

Sections are listed alphabetically.
Models are listed numerically.

Gift Set models are listed here individually
only if they have a different reference number
from the set that contains them. The Classics
Gift Sets listing includes additional details.

See also 'Corgi Classics Fire Service Vehicles',
'Corgi Classics TV and Film Vehicles' and
'Collection Heritage'.

PE = Premium Edition (limited to 2,000)
LT or L.T. = London Transport
MPR = Market Price Range
NGPP = No guide price at present

Accessories and Kits

Ref	Intro	Model name, details	MPR
31601	97	Log load	£6-7
31602	97	Cement load	£6-7
31603	99	Brick load	£6-7
31604	99	Pipes load	£6-7
31605	99	Planks load	£6-7
31606	99	Sacks load	£6-7
31607	99	Hessian bags load	£6-7
31801	97	'EDDIE STOBART' Depot	£7-9
31802	97	'British Road Services' Depot	£7-9
31803	97	Fire Service Depot	£7-9
31804	97	Bus Depot	£7-9
31903	98	'Construction' set of 4 figures	£15-17
31904	99	3 'SHELL' pumps + attendant	£15-17
31905	99	3 'BP' pumps + attendant	£15-17

AEC Cabover Box Vans

Ref	Intro	Model name, details	MPR
897/1	87	'CARTER PATERSON'	£12-15
897/2	87	'JOHN KNIGHT'	£12-15
897/3	87	'LMS EXPRESS PARCELS'	£50-60
897/4	88	'DUCKHAMS WEARCURE'	£9-12
897/5	88	'AMPLION RADIO'	£9-12
897/6	88	'WEETABIX'	£9-12
897/7	88	'MARS'	£20-25
897/8	88	'HIS MASTERS VOICE'	£20-25
897/9	88	'INTERNATIONAL'	£9-12
897/10	88	'POTTERS ASTHMA CURE'	£12-15
897/11	88	'JOHN BARKER'	£12-15
897/12	89	'ROYAL MAIL'	£35-40
987/13	89	'GPO TELEPHONES'	(see GS D15/1)
897/14	90	'G.W.R.'	£10-12
987/15	90	'UNITED DAIRIES'	(see GS D67/1)
97140	91	'SOUTHERN RAILWAY'	£12-15
97754	93	'LMS RAILWAY'	(see Set 97754)

AEC Cabover Tankers

Ref	Intro	Model name, details	MPR
945/1	87	'FLOWERS BREWERY'	£15-20
945/2	87	'GAYMERS CIDER'	£12-15
945/3	88	'CARLESS CAPEL'	£12-15
945/4	88	'DUCKHAMS OILS'	£12-15
945/5	88	'SOMERLITE OIL'	£10-15
945/6	89	'REDLINE GLICO'	£12-15
945/7	90	'SHELL'	(see Gift Set D9/1)
945/8	90	'MOBILGAS'	£12-15
945/9	90	'MOBILGAS'	£12-15
945/10	88	'BP', promotional	£15-20
945/12	90	'UNITED DAIRIES'	(see GS D67/1)

AEC Trucks and Tankers

Ref	Intro	Model name, details	MPR
10301	01	'WILLMOTTS' Sheeted Flatbed	£35-40
10302	01	'BRS', Ergomatic platform lorry, dolly and girder load	£45-50
10303	01	'FRED HARRIS' Ergomatic Showman's Pole Truck	£35-40
11501	01	'SIDDLE COOK', Mk.V platform + 'Lazy Trout' Café	£35-40

Ref	Intro	Model name, details	MPR
11502	01	'SHELL-BP' tanker (PE)	£35-40
11503	01	'BRS' Mandator Flatbed (PE)	£40-45
20801	97	'JOHNNIE WALKER', tanker	£25-30
20901	96	'TRUMANS', flatbed/chains	£25-30
20903	99	'EDDIE STOBART' platform	£25-30
21101	00	'GUINNESS' Ergomatic tanker	£35-40
21201	96	'MACKINTOSH'	£10-12
21301	96	'FERRYMASTERS', trailer	£15-20
21302	97	'CALEDONIAN', trailer	£20-25
21303	97	'BELL'S', trailer	£20-25
21401	96	'WALLS' refrig. box trailer	£20-25
21402	96	'DANIEL STEWART', trailer	£20-25
21601	00	'EDDIE STOBART' tipper	£35-40
21701	96	'CODONA'S', circus closed truck / pole trailer	£30-40
22201	00	'BRS' Ergomatic + tilt trailer	£30-35
26701	00	'GUINNESS' Major tanker	£35-40
26401	00	'LONDON BRICK' + brick load	£35-40
26402	00	'BRS' platform + sheeted load	£35-40
26403	00	'H. LONG' + Shap Memorial	£40-45
26404	00	'EDDIE STOBART' platform	£35-40
26601	00	'ANDERSON' + Lea Clock	£40-45
31003	97	'CHRIS MILLER Ltd' AEC+ low-loader + Scammell Crane	£35-40
97328	96	'MAJOR', elliptical tanker	£18-22
97370	95	'FEDERATION', flatbed	£15-20
97369	96	'EDDIE STOBART', flatbed	£35-40
97891	93	'BILLY SMARTS', trailer	£40-50
97892	93	'S.HOUSEMAN', trailer	£40-50
97893	93	'J.AYERS', trailer	£40-50
97894	94	'PICKFORDS', box van	£65-75
97895	94	'BRS', truck and trailer	£35-40
97931	95	'GREENALL WHITLEY'	£35-45
97932	96	'N. E. GAS BOARD', tanker	£18-22

Albion Trucks

Ref	Intro	Model name, details	MPR
11602	01	'BRS', Victor platform lorry	£20-25
11603	01	'MALCOM' platform + Café	£40-45
21001	97	'WHITE HORSE'	£15-20
23602	00	'EDDIE STOBART' platform	£30-35
23801	00	'LONDON BRICK' + brick load	£30-35
26001	97	'BALLANYTINE'S'	£22-28
26101	99	'D. W. WARD', platform	£28-33
26201	99	'T. W. DAVIDSON', platform	£28-33

Atkinson Trucks

Ref	Intro	Model name, details	MPR
12501	01	'RIDINGS' Tautliner	£50-55
12502	01	'EDDIE STOBART' flatbed	£50-55
12503	01	'GIBBS' Borderer fridge van	£50-55
12504	01	'POLLOCK' Borderer + trailer	£50-55
27201	96	'FINA FUEL OILS', tanker	£20-25
27301	96	'BULWARK', tanker	£20-25
27501	97	'A. HENSHALL', flatbed	£20-25
27601	96	'F.B. ATKINS', flat / trailer	£30-35
27602	96	'CROW'S', flatbed / trailer	£30-35
27701	96	'WHITBREAD', horsebox	£24-28
27801	96	'ANDERTON & ROWLANDS' circus pole truck	£24-28
27901	96	'VAUX BEERS', artic. tanker	£24-28
28001	97	'SUTTONS', covered artic.	£24-28
28101	97	'SMITH of WISHAW' flatbed	£18-22
28201	97	'GIBB'S', refrig. box trailer	£24-28
97162	95	'POLLOCK', tanker	£24-28
97327	96	'EDDIE STOBART', flatbed	£30-35
97334	95	'LUCOZADE', flatbed	£24-28
97366	95	'TENNANT'S', with trailer	£35-40
97372	95	'MACKESON', tanker	£24-28

Bedford 'CA' Vans

Ref	Intro	Model name, details	MPR
981/1	89	'PICKFORDS'	(see Set D74/1)
981/2	89	'CAMBRIAN NEWS'	£6-9
981/3	90	'A.A.'	£6-9
981/4	89	'EXPRESS DAIRIES'	£6-9
981/5	89	'DANDY'	(see Set D14/1)
981/6	89	'BEANO'	(see Set D14/1)
981/7	90	'COLLECTOR CLUB 1990'	£12-15

Ref	Intro	Model name, details	MPR
981/9	90	'EVENING NEWS'	£6-9
981/10	90	'EVENING STANDARD'	£6-9
981/11	90	'The STAR'	£6-9
981/12	90	'GAS'	(see GUS Set D54/1)
05601	96	'KODAK'	£10-12
05602	96	'OVALTINE'	£10-12
05603	97	'KLG PLUGS'	£10-12
05605	97	'ROYAL MAIL'	£10-12
05607	99	'RAC SIGN SERVICE'	£10-12
05706	97	'BEATLES' grafitti van	£15-20
96900	91	'MANCHESTER Eve. News'	£6-9
96904	94	'RAC RADIO RESCUE'	£8-10
96905	95	'CHIPPERFIELDS' Booking Office	£25-30
97740	91	'The TIMES'	(see Set 97740)
96903	91	'PICKFORDS' (D981/1)	£15-18
98105	92	'AA SERVICES' (D981/3)	£8-10
98106	95	'POLICE'	£7-9
98754	91	'The ADVENTURE'	£10-15
98906	95	'BLACKBURN FIRE Brig.'	£10-12
98965	91	'The EAGLE'	(see Set 98965)
99805	91	'CAMBRIAN NEWS' (D981/2)	£7-9

Bedford Dormobiles

Ref	Intro	Model name, details	MPR
982/1	89	Cream / blue	£10-12
982/2	89	Red / cream	£10-12
982/3	90	Cream / green	£10-12
982/4	91	Brown / cream	£10-12
96920	91	'POLICE', (99806)	£10-12
96923	94	'St.JOHN AMBULANCE'	£10-12
99806	92	'POLICE', (96920)	£10-12

Bedford 'O' Articulated Trucks

Ref	Intro	Model name, details	MPR
18401	96	'BRITISH RAIL'	£18-22
18402	97	'TERRY'S CHOCOLATES'	£15-18
18403	98	'BRITISH RAILWAYS'	£18-22
18404	99	'H. E. MUSGROVE' (PE)	£45-55
97300	93	'BILLY SMARTS'	£75-90
97301	94	'LONDON BRICK Co Ltd'	£26-30
97303	94	'CHIPPERFIELD'S', trailer	£80-100
97329	95	'BRS'	£26-30
97887	95	'CHIPPERFIELD'S' Horse Box	£30-40

Bedford 'OB' Box Vans

Ref	Intro	Model name, details	MPR
822/1	88	'PERSIL'	£15-20
822/2	88	'TATE & LYLE'	£15-20
822/3	88	'GILLETTE'	£15-20
822/4	89	'CARTER PATERSON', green body, green roof	£15-20
		green body, red roof	£45-50
822/5	89	'MILLERS', cream/green, red wings	£15-20
		with black wings	£20-25
		same, logo partly hidden	£40-45
822/6	90	'SHELL'	(see GS D17/1)
	90	same but 5 rivet base	(see GS D17/1)
822/7	89	'CADBURYS'	£15-20
822/8	89	'MALTESERS'	£20-25
822/9	89	'ROYAL MAIL'	(see GS D7/1)
822/10	90	'TERRYS OF YORK'	£20-25
822/11	90	'L.N.E.R.'	£12-15
	90	no front body print	NGPP
822/12	90	'TOYMASTER'	£15-20
822/13	90	'BRITISH RAILWAYS'	(see GS D46/1)
822/16	90	'WHITBREAD'	(see GS D94/1)
18401	96	'BRITISH RAIL'	£12-15
97120	91	'LMS'	£12-15
97123	91	'NSPCC'	£15-20
97125	93	'GPO Telephones'	£15-20
97126	93	'NATIONAL COAL BOARD'	£10-15
97371	96	'CAMERON BREWERIES'	£15-20
---	93	'HOLLAND'S PIES', (unique)	NPP

Bedford 'OB' Pantechnicons

Ref	Intro	Model name, details	MPR
953/1	87	'PICKFORDS'	£35-40
953/1	89	Same but no number	(in Set D74/1)

267

953/2	87	'WARING & GILLOW'	**£50-60**
953/3	87	'FRASERS of IPSWICH'	£35-45
953/4	87	'STEINWAY & SONS'	**£30-35**
953/5	88	'GRIFF FENDER'	**£20-25**
953/6	88	'DUCKHAMS'	**£15-20**
953/7	88	'CAMP HOPSON'	£25-35
Q953/8	90	'MICHAEL GERSON',	
		with certificate	**£35-40**
		without certificate	**£20-25**
953/9	89	'STYLO'	**£20-25**
953/10	89	'WEETABIX'	**£20-25**
953/11	90	'SHELL'	(see Set D17/1)
953/12	89	'BISHOPS MOVE'	**£30-35**
953/13	90	'WYLIE & LOCKHEAD'	**£20-30**
953/14	90	'ARTHUR BATTY'	**£10-15**
953/15	90	'YORK FAIR'	(see Set Q55/1)
953/16	90	'LEE BROS', silver wheels	**£20-25**
	90	with standard wheels	**£15-20**
953/17	90	'SLUMBERLAND'	(see Set Q57/1)
953/18	90	'BLACKPOOL CIRCUS'	see 97083
953/19	90	'BREWER & TURNBULL'	see 97081
953/20	90	'CORGI ON THE MOVE'	(Set D82/1)
18301	96	'WATTS Bros'	£15-18
18302	96	'ELITE INTERNATIONAL'	**£10-15**
97080	91	'JOHN JULIAN'	**£10-15**
97081	91	'BREWER & TURNBULL'	**£15-20**
97082	91	'PICKFORDS' (John Ayrey)	**£15-20**
97083	91	'BLACKPOOL CIRCUS'	**£15-20**
97084	91	'GRATTANS', mail order	£12-15
97085	91	'SLUMBERLAND BEDS'	**£15-20**
97086	92	'FREEBORNS'	**£15-20**
97087	92	'BARNARDO'S'	**£15-20**
97088	93	'WHITE & Co.', 'Portsmouth'	**£15-20**
97089	93	'JOHN MASON', Liverpool	**£15-20**
97090	93	'RILEY'S BILLIARD TABLES'	**£15-20**
97091	93	'G.H.LUCKING & SONS'	**£15-20**
---	95	'GOING FOR GOLD',	
		gold plated model	£50-70
97092	95	'CHIPPERFIELD'S'	**£30-35**
97093	95	'HAPPY BIRTHDAY'	NGPP
	94	Corgi Heritage Centre version	
		'1st Birthday' (250 issued)	**£30-35**
97195	92	'HOWELLS & SON'	**£15-20**

Bedford 'S' type Vehicles

19301	96	'LYON'S'	**£12-15**
19302	96	'WEETABIX'	**£12-15**
19303	96	'SPRATTS'	**£12-15**
19304	97	'WALL'S' box van	**£12-15**
19306	97	'EDDIE STOBART' box van	**£14-18**
19401	96	'KEN THOMAS Ltd'	**£12-15**
19601	96	'BASS', bottle truck	**£12-15**
19701	96	TETLEY'S, canvas back	**£12-15**
19801	97	'EDDIE STOBART' artic.	**£20-25**
19802	97	'J. W. RICHARDS' artic.	**£20-25**
19901	97	'BRS' covered artic.	**£12-15**
20001	97	'W. & J. RIDING' dropside	**£12-15**
20202	97	'MILK' tanker	**£12-15**
20401	99	'LAING' tipper, 1,000 issued	**£20-25**
31008	98	'WIMPEY' + Shovel	GSP

Bedford 'TK' and 'KM' Trucks

11401	01	'PICKFORDS', Fruehauf trailer	**£40-50**
18801	98	'EDDIE STOBART' KM	**£30-35**
18901	98	'Soldier, Soldier' + figures	**£20-25**
22401	98	'BRITISH RAILWAYS' TK	**£30-35**
22502	98	'MACBRAYNES' TK artic.	**£25-30**
22503	98	'GUINNESS', artic. platform	**£45-55**
22504	00	'GUINNESS' TK + trailer	**£40-50**
22601	98	'CADBURY' TK tanker	**£18-22**
22702	98	'EDDIE STOBART' TK box	**£20-25**
22704	99	'GUINNESS' TK box van	**£18-22**
22706	00	'GUINNESS' TK box van	**£20-25**
22801	98	'SHELL-BP' TK tanker and	
		'SHELL' petrol pump	£28-33
22901	99	'TARMAC' TK	**£18-22**
22902	00	'BLUE CIRCLE' TK tipper	**£20-25**
23203	99	'EDDIE STOBART' TK	**£18-22**

Chipperfield's Circus (1995-97)

07202	97	Land Rover PA, clowns	**£20-25**

11201	97	ERF, Cage Trailer, animals	**£35-40**
14201	97	Foden S21, Hippo Tank	**£35-40**
17801	97	Scammell Cannon, Ringmaster	£25-30
31901	97	Mary Chipperfield's	
		Liberty Horses	**£20-25**
31902	97	Foden S21 Elephant Truck	
		and Trailer	**£35-40**
56901	96	Cameos Set of 10 vehicles in	
		'Chipperfields' livery	**£20-25**
96905	95	Bedford 'CA' Booking Office	**£30-35**
97022	95	AEC Regal Living Coach	**£35-40**
97092	95	Bedford 'OB' Pantechnicon	**£30-35**
97303	95	Bedford 'OB'. Artic. Truck	£80-100
97885	95	Scammell, Pole Trailer	
		and Caravan	**£50-60**
97886	95	Scammell Crane Truck	**£35-40**
97887	95	Bedford 'O' Artic. Horsebox	**£35-40**
97888	95	Foden Pole Truck + Caravan	**£45-50**
97889	95	AEC Animal Truck + Trailer	£35-45
97896	95	AEC Pole Truck	**£30-35**
97915	95	Scammell and two Trailers	£65-75
97957	95	ERF Flatbed Lorry	**£45-50**
NB.		If traded as a collection (as one lot),	
		items 96905 - 97957 would be	
		expected to realise	£500 - £600

Diamond-T Vehicles

31007	97	'ANNIS' girder trailer + loco	£45-55
31009	98	'WYNN'S' trailer + boiler	GSP
52902	00	'TEXACO' dropside, oil drums	£18-22
52903	00	'GUINNESS' dropside + crates	£18-22
52904	01	'OCHS TREE FARM' + trees	£20-22
55103	01	'GEROSA' + transformer	£65-75
55104	02	'Fred HARRIS' generator	**£35-45**
55401	98	'PINDER' circus box trailer	**£50-60**
55501	98	'ELLIOT' trailer + generator	£28-33
55601	98	'USAF' wrecker	**£20-25**
55602	98	'De LORNE' fire wrecker	£35-45
55604	98	'BRS' wrecker	**£25-30**
55605	98	'BLACKPOOL' wrecker	£18-22
55606	99	'PUBLIC SERVICE' wrecker	£25-30
55607	99	'RENAULT' wrecker	£35-45
55610	00	'TEXACO' T980 Wrecker	£28-33
56203	99	'SUPERTEST' tanker	**£20-25**
56204	00	'TEXACO' semi skirted tanker	£25-30
56301	98	'RICHFIELD' artic. with load	£28-33
56401	98	'SCHLITZ' beer delivery van	£20-25
56402	99	'BRUNCKHORST'S' van	**£20-25**
? (US)	01	'MOOSEHEAD' box van	**£20-25**

ERF Trucks and Tankers

09601	99	'BRS', platform (PE)	**£50-60**
09701	96	'ERF Parts Dept.', flatbed	**£35-40**
09801	96	'JOHN SMITHS' flatbed	**£20-25**
09802	96	'CORGI CLASSICS', flatbed	**£20-25**
09803	00	'BRS' platform + pallets	**£40-45**
09804	97	'HOLDEN' + Hook Clock	**£40-45**
09901	96	'PAT COLLINS' circus	
		dodgem truck and trailer	**£30-35**
10001	00	'McEWANS' + trailer + barrels	£35-40
10101	97	'BRS' 8 wheel dropside	**£30-35**
10102	97	'GWYNNE BOWEN'	£28-33
10201	98	'BRS' grey 'V' tipper	**£25-30**
10201	01	'BRS' 'V' + Trailer (PE)	**£40-45**
10202	01	'PICKFORDS' 'V' artic.	**£35-40**
10501	01	'READ', + 'Coronation Café'	**£40-45**
11001	97	'EDDIE STOBART'	**£35-40**
11101	97	'MOORHOUSE'S JAMS'	**£15-20**
11201	97	'CHIPPERFIELD'S', cage	**£35-40**
11301	97	'RUSSELL of BATHGATE'	£25-35
11401	97	'BLACK & WHITE' + trailer	£22-28
11501	98	'SHELL-BP' KV tanker and	
		'SHELL' petrol pump	£28-33
11601	98	'EDDIE STOBART' artic.	**£30-35**
11701	99	'BLOWERS' KV Tipper	**£35-40**
11802	00	'BASS' + barrels	**£35-40**
11803	00	'BRS' 8-w platform lorry	**£35-40**
11901	01	'BRIAN HARRIS' artic.	**£45-50**
11902	01	'CASTLE MULTICEM' c/side	**£45-50**
11904	01	'REDLAND' EC Powder Tanker	**£55-60**
11905	01	'J. MILLICAN' EC Log Trailer	**£55-60**

12701	01	'ERF' ECS curtainside	**£55-60**
31011	98	'R. WALKER' KV low-loader	**£30-35**
59529	99	'GUINNESS', curtainside, 1:64	**£14-16**
59539	00	'BASSETT & SONS, 1:64	**£14-16**
59559	00	'ELLIS' curtainside, 1:64	**£14-16**
74901	99	'RUGBY CEMENT', tanker	£65-75
74902	99	'A. SMITH', powder tanker	£55-60
74903	00	'CASTLE CEMENT' tanker	£55-60
74904	00	'W.R. WOOD' powder tanker	£40-50
75101	98	'GULF' tanker	**£40-45**
75102	98	'SHELL' tanker	**£40-45**
75103	98	'BP' artic. tanker	**£40-45**
75104	98	'ESSO' artic. tanker	**£40-45**
75201	98	'EDDIE STOBART'	**£40-45**
75202	98	'BODDINGTONS' curtainside	**£40-45**
75203	98	'RICHARD READ' c/side	**£40-45**
75204	98	'JACK RICHARDS' c/side	**£40-45**
75205	99	'POLLOCK' curtainside	**£40-45**
75206	99	'MASSEY WILCOX' c/side	**£40-45**
97319	96	'BASS' cylindrical tanker	£27-32
97930	94	'BLUE CIRCLE', tanker	**£40-45**
97940	95	'EDDIE STOBART', flat	£130-140
97942	95	'FLOWERS', flatbed	**£28-32**
97957	95	'CHIPPERFIELD'S', flatbed	**£45-50**
97980	94	'ESSO', tanker	**£40-50**

Foden Trucks and Tankers

10801	01	'CULLIMORE' S21 + Café	**£40-45**
10802	01	'Fred HARRIS' + Trailer	**£40-45**
12101	98	'CADBURY'S' FG tanker	**£25-30**
12301	97	'MOTOR PACKING', flatbed	**£28-32**
12302	99	'EASTWOODS' (PE)	£55-65
12401	96	'FREMLINS ALES', chains	**£25-30**
12501	96	'BLUE CIRCLE', flatbed	**£15-20**
12601	96	'SILCOCK'S', pole truck	**£25-30**
12801	97	'EDWARD BECK' artic.	**£28-32**
13501	97	'G. C. MUNTON' S21 artic.	**£28-32**
13601	97	'EDDIE STOBART' S21 van	**£35-40**
13602	97	'C.W.S.' box van	£15-18
13701	97	'ARROW' S21 tanker	**£25-30**
13901	97	'BASSETTS' S21 flatbed	**£25-30**
13902	98	'KNOWLES' S21 tank load	£28-33
13903	98	'BRITISH RAILWAYS' S21	£28-33
13904	99	'BLUE CIRCLE' S21	£28-33
13905	00	'RUGBY CEMENT' platform	**£35-40**
14001	97	'BERESFORD', 6w dropside	**£25-30**
14101	97	'TUBY'S, S21 dodgem	
		truck and trailer	**£30-35**
14201	97	'CHIPPERFIELDS', hippo tank.	**£35-40**
14401	98	'HOVERINGHAM' S21	**£28-32**
14501	98	'BLUE CIRCLE' S21	**£28-32**
31012	98	'MICKEY KIELY', FG Pole	
		Truck, Living Van, Boxing	
		Pavilion, figures, etc.	£60-70
31902	97	'CHIPPERFIELD'S'	
		Elephants Trailer	£40-50
97309	96	'BRS' flatbed with load, (Classic	
		Toys magazine promotional.	
		Limited Edition, 5,000)	**£45-55**
97317	96	'Scottish & Newcastle'	**£30-35**
97950	93	'GUINNESS',	
		with normal cab/tank gap	£110-130
		smaller cab/tank gap (500)	£20-150
97951	93	'MILK'	**£30-35**
97952	93	'HOVIS'	**£30-35**
97955	94	'GUINNESS', with chains	£90-120
97956	95	'PICKFORDS' flatbed	£60-80
97970	95	'REGENT', elliptical tanker	**£45-55**
97971	94	'ROBSONS', flatbed	**£40-45**

Ford Model 'T' Vans

865	86	'LYONS TEA', white roof	**£10-15**
865/1	87	'NEEDLERS'	**£10-15**
865/2	86	'LYONS TEA', black roof	**£35-40**
865/2	87	'DRUMMER DYES'	**£10-15**
865/3	87	'KALAMAZOO'	**£10-15**
865/4	87	'PEPSI COLA'	**£10-15**
865/5	87	'TWININGS'	£15-18
865/6	88	'AMBULANCE'	(see Set C88)
865/7	89	'KAYS'	**£10-15**
865/8	89	'ROYAL LAUNDRY'	(see Set C90)

?	89	'SUNLIGHT'	(see Set C90)
865/11	89	'STEIFF'	**£10-15**
865/12	89	'A1 SAUCE'	(see Set D71/1)
865/13	89	'APS MEDICINES'	(see Set D71/1)
865/14	90	'NAAFI'	£40-50
865/15	90	'JOHN MENZIES'	**£10-15**
865/17	90	'WHITBREAD'	(see Set D94/1)
873	86	'ZEBRA GRATE POLISH'	**£10-15**
874	87	'CORGI CLUB', 2nd anniv.	**£20-25**
875	86	'SCHOKOLADE GOLD'	**£10-15**
876	86	'DICKINS & JONES'	**£12-15**
877	86	'ROYAL MAIL'	**£15-20**
965	86	'FORD'S 75th', yellow letters	**£8-10**
966	86	white lettering	**£8-10**
?	87	'SWAN VESTAS'	(see Set C69)
?	87	'THE TIMES'	(see Set C49)
?	87	'KAY & Co'	(see Set C68)
?	87	'T. C. BENNETT'	(see Set C50)
?	87	'H. & C. MAILES'	(see Set C50)
?	87	'T. J. POUPART'	(see Set C50)
08101	98	'BOURNVILLE'	**£18-22**
97464	92	'CADBURYS' (Woolworths)	NGPP
97469	95	'VICTROLA', USA	**£8-10**
97751/a	92	'BASS BREWERY', (Kay's)	£8-12
97753/a	92	'TERRY'S of YORK'	£8-12

Ford Model 'T' Tankers

864	86	'PRATTS MOTOR SPIRIT'	**£8-10**
864/1	87	'STALEY SALES CORP.'	**£10-12**
864/2	87	'RIMMER BROS Ltd'	**£10-12**
864/3	87	'SAN FRANCISCO'	**£8-10**
864/4	87	'NATIONAL BENZOLE'	**£10-15**
872	86	'DOMINION'	**£9-12**
880	86	'BP MOTOR SPIRIT'	**£9-12**
864/6	88	'OLYMPIC GASOLINE'	**£8-10**
864/7	89	'TEXACO'	(see Set D71/1)
864/8	89	'SOMERLITE'	(see Set D71/1)

Ford Popular (Fordson 8) Vans

980/1	89	'S.A. PEACOCK'	**£12-15**
980/2	89	'FULLERS'	**£12-15**
980/3	89	'LUTON MOTOR Co'	**£12-15**
980/4	89	'CORGI CLUB 89'	**£15-20**
980/5	89	'SIGNSMITH'	(see Set D23/1)
980/6	89	'FRASER COOK'	(see Set D23/1)
980/7	89	'LEWIS EAST'	(see Set D23/1)
980/8	89	'C. PEARSON'	**£12-15**
980/9	89	'COLMANS'	(see Kay's Set D72/1)
980/10	89	'BOWYERS'	(see Kay's Set D72/1)
980/11	89	'PICKFORDS'	(see Kay's Set D74/1)
980/12	89	'D. SHELDON'	**£12-15**
980/13	90	'LIMA FURNITURE Ltd'	**£12-15**
980/14	90	'CAMBRIAN FACTORY'	**£12-15**
980/15	90	'ABBEYCOLOR'	**£12-15**
980/16	90	'ROYAL MAIL' (99808)	**£12-15**
980/17	90	'NCB'	(see GUS Set D54/1)
05901	97	'ROYAL MAIL'	**£12-15**
96860	91	'EASTBOURNE MOTORS'	**£12-15**
96862	91	'ROYAL MAIL'	**£12-15**
96863	93	'SUNLIGHT SOAP'	**£12-15**
96865	92	'BEEZER', 'Colonel Blink'	**£12-15**
96866	94	'GAS'	**£12-15**
98109	91	'ROYAL MAIL'	**£12-15**
98755	91	'HOTSPUR', 'Willie Wallop'	**£12-15**
99808	93	'ROYAL MAIL', (D980/16)	**£12-15**

Ford Transit Vans

58121	01	'HONG KONG POLICE'	**£15-20**

Guy Invincible

11701	01	'McCALL & GREENSHIELD' with trailer and 'Kate's Kabin'	**£40-45**
11702	01	'REGENT' Tanker	**£35-40**
29101	99	'BLUE CIRCLE', platform	**£28-32**
29102	99	'WYNNS', platform	**£28-32**
29103	99	'EDDIE STOBART', platform	**£28-32**
29104	00	'TARMAC' + bogie, beam load	**£40-50**
29105	00	'BOWKER' + Shap Clock	**£40-45**
29301	99	'A. R. DUCKETT', tipper	**£28-32**
29401	99	'DAWSONS FARGO', d/side	**£28-32**

Guy Warrior

28901	00	'BRS' platform + sheeted load	**£20-25**
29001	99	'DEE VALLEY', 6-wheels	**£28-32**
29201	99	'BRS', tractor / semi-trailer	**£28-32**

International Transtar

51401	01	'TEXACO' + Girder Trailer	**£55-60**
51402	01	'INTERNATIONAL TRANSTAR TEXACO'	**£60-70**

Kenworth Trucks

55701	00	'AMOCO' semi-tanker	not produced
55702	01	'KENWORTH' W925, boiler	**£70-75**
55703	01	'TEXACO' semi-tanker	**£50-55**
55704	01	'KENWORTH' (US)	**£70-75**
55801	00	'GUINNESS' box semi-trailer	**£50-55**

Land-Rover

(see also French 'Collection Heritage')

07101	96	Corgi Club Land-Rover	**£12-15**
07102	97	'MERSEY TUNNEL'	**£10-12**
07103	97	Gold-plated Land-Rover	**£18-22**
07104	98	'Daktari' + lion and chimp	**£18-22**
07105	00	Millennium Chrome, 1:43	**£35-40**
07202	97	'CHIPPERFIELDS' PA	**£18-22**
07301	97	'AFS' Line-layer	**£12-15**
07302	98	British Army, olive green	**£10-12**
07401	97	'ROYAL MAIL', closed	**£10-12**
07401	02	'Fred HARRIS' + trailer	**£20-25**
07402	97	'EDDIE STOBART', closed	**£10-12**
07403	98	'A.A. ROAD SERVICE'	**£10-12**
07407	98	'CITY of BATH'	**£10-12**
07408	98	'BOAC'	**£10-12**
07414	99	'RAC RADIO PATROL'	**£10-12**
07410	99	'HAMPSHIRE' fire tender	**£10-12**
07411	99	'CORNWALL' cliff rescue	**£10-12**
07412	99	'ALPES MARITIMES' fire	**£10-12**

Leyland Trucks and Tankers

11601	01	'ANDREW WISHART', with 'Silver Link' Road House	**£40-45**
11604	01	'CASTROL' LAD Tanker (PE)	**£35-40**
11605	01	'BRS' low-loader (PE)	**£40-45**
20902	99	'GUINNESS', Ergo platform	**£40-45**
22101	96	'BRS', Ergomatic / flatbed	**£25-30**
22302	00	'GUINNESS' vats + trailer	**£45-50**
23501	98	'CADBURY'S' tipper	**£28-32**
23701	00	'GUINNESS' malt, Octopus	**£35-40**
23702	00	'BRADY' + Lostock Hall Clock	**£40-45**
23901	00	'Steel, Peech and Tozer' 8-w	**£30-35**
24201	96	'McKELVIE & Co', tanker	**£20-25**
24202	97	'POWER' tanker	**£20-25**
24203	98	'SHELL-BP' tanker and 'BP Diesel' pump	**£28-32**
24301	96	'Wm. YOUNGER', tanker	**£28-32**
24302	96	'DOUBLE DIAMOND' tanker	**£28-32**
24401	96	'CODONA'S', flatbed	**£28-32**
24402	98	'EDDIE STOBART' flatbed	**£28-32**
24901	99	'GUINNESS' tanks trailer	**£45-50**
24501	96	'J & A SMITH', flatbed	**£20-25**
24503	00	'Southworth', Cape Town Clock	**£40-45**
24601	97	'BRS', Octopus + trailer	**£30-35**
24701	96	'MICHELIN', articulated lorry	**£25-30**
24801	96	'SILCOCK'S', dodgems truck + caravan	**£35-40**
25101	96	'BRS', flatbed / container	**£15-20**
25102	97	'EDDIE STOBART' Beaver	**£18-22**
25201	97	'SMITH'S of ECCLES', artic.	**£28-32**
25301	97	'HOLT LANE', Super Comet	**£25-30**
25401	00	'HANCOCK'S' + barrels	**£30-35**
87003	01	'JIMMY' (1:64 scale)	**£14-16**

Leyland-DAF Trucks

11801	01	'CLUGSTON' tanker	**£45-50**
11802	01	'GCS-JOHNSON' Jeep Dolly, Bogie and Concrete Beam	**£60-65**
73501	98	'Q8' tanker	**£40-45**
75302	99	'JET' fuel tanker	**£40-45**
75401	98	'JAMES IRLAM' curtainside	**£40-45**
75402	98	'TATE & LYLE' curtainside	**£40-45**
75404	98	'HEINEKEN' curtainside	**£40-45**
75405	99	'KNIGHTS of OLD' c/side	**£40-45**
75406	99	'KEN THOMAS', curtainside	**£40-45**
75407	99	'GUINNESS', curtainside	**£40-45**
75408	00	'T. BRADY & SON', c/side	**£25-30**
75501	98	'PARCELFORCE' box trailer	**£40-45**
75502	98	'ROYAL MAIL' box trailer	**£40-45**
75901	99	'KNOWLES', powder tanker	**£40-45**
75903	00	'HIGGINS', powder tanker	**£40-45**
75902	99	'BLUE CIRCLE', tanker	**£40-45**

Mack Trucks (see also Fire Service Vehicles)

906/1	87	'MACK PARTS'	**£10-12**
906/2	87	'SUNSHINE BISCUITS'	**£10-12**
906/3	87	'WHITE ROCK'	**£10-12**
906/4	87	'BUFFALO FIRE DEPT'	**£10-12**
906/5	87	'PEPSI COLA'	**£10-12**
906/6	88	'STANLEY TOOLS'	**£10-12**
906/7	88	'PEERLESS LIGHT'	**£10-12**
906/8	88	'BOVRIL'	**£10-12**
906/9	88	'CARNATION'	**£10-12**
906/10	88	'GULDENS MUSTARD'	**£10-12**
50601	96	AC, 'M. K. T.'	**£15-20**
50701	99	LJ, 'MERCHANTS', artic.	**£25-30**
50702	99	LJ, 'SCHAEFER', artic.	**£25-30**
50703	00	'GUINNESS' box trailer	**£40-45**
55705	01	'LITEFOOT LOGGING'	£42-48
50901	99	LJ, 'MOBILGAS', tanker	**£25-30**
51001	99	LJ, 'RICHFIELD', tanker	**£25-30**
51002	00	U, 'FLYING A' semi tanker	**£25-30**
52301	96	B, 'GREAT NORTHERN'	**£25-30**
52302	97	B, 'LIONEL CITY'	**£25-30**
52303	97	B, 'SEMI-NICKEL PLATE'	**£25-30**
52304	99	B, 'BALLANTINE'S'	**£25-30**
52307	01	B, 'TEXACO' Pumper	£22-26
52308	01	B, 'TEXACO' Wrecker	£22-26
52504	97	B, 'MILWAUKEE ROAD'	**£25-30**
52501	96	B, 'NEW YORK CENTRAL'	**£25-30**
52503	96	B, 'LIONEL CITY'	**£25-30**
52801	96	B, 'RAILWAY EXPRESS'	**£25-30**
52802	97	B, 'BURLINGTON ROUTE'	**£25-30**
53201	99	B, 'SHELL' tanker	**£25-30**
53202	98	B, 'SINCLAIR' tanker	**£25-30**
51002	00	U, 'FLYING A' semi tanker	**£25-30**
53203	00	B, 'UNION', semi-skirted tanker	**£30-35**
53502	99	B, 'CAMPBELL EXPRESS'	**£25-30**
53503	00	B, 'TEXACO', lowboy	**£45-50**
53601	98	B, 'A.N.D.' wrecker	**£20-25**
53603	99	B, 'C.A.A.' wrecker	**£20-25**
98453	95	B, 'BREYER'	**£15-20**
98454	95	B, 'WILTON FARM'	**£15-20**
98481	95	'GOODYEAR', USA	**£8-10**

M.A.N. Trucks

12001	01	'JOHN MITCHELL' c/side	**£55-60**
12002	01	'CADZOW' + crusher on trailer	**£65-70**
12003	01	'NEDERHOFF' + Trailer	**£65-70**
75701	99	'TNT', box trailer	**£40-45**
75702	00	'EDDIE STOBART' box trailer	**£65-70**
75801	99	'MAN' 'Race Power' c/side	**£45-50**
75802	99	'CONTINENTAL', c/side	**£40-45**
75804	99	'EDDIE STOBART', c/side	**£40-45**
75803	99	'GALLACHERS', curtainside	**£40-45**
75805	99	'SAFEGARD', curtainside	**£40-45**
75806	00	'W.H. MALCOLM', c/side	**£70-80**
75807	00	'John RAYMOND', curtainside	**£70-80**
76201	99	'ARAL', tanker	**£40-45**
76301	99	'RORBACH ZEMENT', tanker	**£55-60**
76801	00	'STILLER' sheeted trailer	**£55-60**
76802	00	'DUNKERLEY' bridge beam	**£50-55**

Mini-Vans

06001	97	'P. O. TELEPHONES'	**£10-12**
06002	98	'A.A. PATROL SERVICE'	**£10-12**
06003	98	'BKS AIR TRANSPORT'	**£10-12**
06004	99	'RAC ROAD SERVICE'	**£10-12**
08002	97	'EXPRESS POST' (set of 2)	**£10-12**
96950	94	'ROYAL MAIL'	**£10-12**
96951	94	'POLICE'	**£10-12**
96952	94	'RAC Radio Rescue'	**£10-12**
96953	94	'AA Road Service'	**£10-12**
96955	94	'CORGI CLASSICS' Club	**£10-12**

96956	94	'SURREY POLICE'	£10-12
97337	95	'FAWLEY REFINERY'	£10-12
97770	96	'HAMLEY'S'	£10-12
97771	96	'CAVENDISH WOODHOUSE'	£10-12
97772	95	'BURBERRY'S'	£10-12

Morris 'J' Vans

983/1	90	'P. O. TELEPHONES'	£10-12
983/2	90	'ROYAL MAIL'	£10-12
983/3	91	'CORGI CLUB 91'	£10-12
983/4	90	'Metropolitan Police'	see 96883
983/5	91	'WALLS Ice Cream' (98101)	£10-12
983/6	90	'ELECTRICITY', Set D54/1	GSP
983/7	90	'BEANO', see Set D47/1	GSP
983/8	90	'BRITISH RAILWAYS', D46/1	GSP
06201	96	'CYDRAX'	£10-12
06202	96	'OXO'	£10-12
06203	97	'ROYAL MAIL'	£10-12
06204	99	'RAC SIGN SERVICE'	£10-12
96880	91	'PICKFORDS' (99802)	£15-20
96882	91	'ROYAL MAIL'	£10-12
96883	90	'Metropolitan Police'	£10-12
96886	96	'FAMILY ASSURANCE'	£10-12
96888	96	'SOUTHDOWN'	£10-12
96887	92	'The TOPPER'	£10-12
96891	93	'MORRIS SERVICE'	£10-12
96892	93	'BOVRIL'	£15-20
96894	94	'P. O. TELEPHONES'	£10-12
96895	95	'BIRMINGHAM CITY',	
		'General Manager'	£10-12
		'Genetal Manager'	£20-25
96896	94	'FAMILY ASSURANCE'	£10-12
98101	91	'WALLS Ice Cream' (D983/5)	£10-12
98758	92	'WIZARD'	£10-12
99140	93	'GPO Telephones'	£10-12
99802	91	'PICKFORDS' (96880)	£15-20
POV21	95	'ROYAL MAIL'	£15-20

Morris Minor 1000 Pick-ups

06301	98	'DAN-AIR LONDON'	£10-12
96850	94	'WIMPEY'	£10-12
96851	95	'LONDON BRICK Co Ltd'	£10-12
96854	95	'MORRIS MOTORS' FB	£10-12
97344	95	'BLUE CIRCLE CEMENT'	£15-20
97346	95	'TARMAC'	£15-20

Morris Minor 1000 Vans

957/1	87	'ROYAL MAIL', plastic base	£18-20
	87	with metal base	£12-15
957/2	87	'GAS'	£12-15
957/3	87	'CORGI Club 3rd Anniversary',	
		1st type wheels	£15-20
		2nd type wheels	£10-12
957/4	88	'CASTROL'	£15-20
957/5	89	'MICHELIN'	£15-20
957/6	88	'FOYLES for BOOKS'	£15-20
957/7	88	'MACFISHERIES'	£15-20
957/8	89	'GRATTAN'S'	(see Set C91)
957/9	89	'TELEGRAPH & ARGUS'	(Set C91)
957/10	89	'MITCHELL'S'	(see Set C91)
957/11	89	'APPLEYARDS'	£10-12
957/12	89	'D. MORGAN'	£10-12
957/13	89	'KIMBERLEY CLARK'	£10-12
957/15	89	'POLICE'	(see Set D13/1)
957/16	89	'FRY'S COCOA'	£15-20
957/17	89	'RINGTON'S TEA'	(see Set D72/1)
957/18	89	'ROYAL MAIL'	(see Set D7/1)
957/19	89	'PICKFORDS'	(see Set D74/1)
957/20	89	'GUERNSEY POST'	£10-12
957/21	89	'7 UP'	£10-12
957/22	90	'BISHOPS'	as 96845
957/23	90	'A. DUNN & SON'	as 96844
957/24	90	'B.A.T.R.', (with cert)	£70-80
957/25	90	'ROYAL AIR FORCE'	(see Set D35/1)
957/26	90	'NAMAC 25' (Dutch),	
		'England' on base	£30-35
		'China' on base	£15-20
957/27	90	'GPO TELEPHONES'	£10-15
958/1	87	'POST OFFICE TELEPHONES',	
		with plastic base	£20-25
958	87	same but with metal base	£15-20

958/2	89	'GPO TELEPHONES'	(see Set D15/1)
959	87	'SMITHS CRISPS',	
		black interior	£15-20
	87	brown interior	£15-20
06501	96	'SHELL / BP'	£15-20
06502	96	'NESTLES'	£15-20
06503	97	'ROYAL MAIL'	£9-12
06504	97	'TV LICENCE'	£9-12
06505	98	'BRITISH CALEDONIAN'	£9-12
06506	98	'COURTLINE'	£9-12
06507	99	'BRS PARCELS' (PE)	£45-50
06508	99	'RAC ROAD SERVICE'	£9-12
06601	96	'CARTERS STEAM FAIR'	£15-20
31006	97	'WYNN'S Thames Trader	
		and Morris 1000 Van	£20-25
31704	97	'EDDIE STOBART'	see Set 31704
96744	95	'LEICESTERSHIRE POLICE'	GSP
96837	91	'MAIDSTONE & DISTRICT'	£10-12
96839	95	'ROYAL MAIL', Xmas	£10-12
96840	91	'BRISTOL WATER'	£10-12
96842	91	'P.O. TELEPHONES'	£10-12
96844	91	'A.DUNN & SON'	£10-12
96845	91	'BISHOPS REMOVALS'	£10-12
96846	92	'TIGER', 'Roy of the Rovers'	£10-12
96847	93	'COLMANS'	£10-12
96848	93	'BIRDS CUSTARD'	£10-12
96849	94	'A.A. SERVICE'	£10-12
96852	94	'CORGI CLASSICS'	
		(3rd Gaydon Show)	£15-20
96855	55	'WILTSHIRE POLICE'	£10-15
97346	95	'TARMAC'	£10-15
97541	96	'P. O. ENGINEERING'	£10-12
98104	93	'ROYAL MAIL'	£10-12
98756	97	'The ROVER'	£10-12
POV22		'ROYAL MAIL' 'Engineers'	£10-12
POV23		'ROYAL MAIL' 'Epsom'	£10-12
POV24		'GPO' 'Bristol'	£10-12

Preistman Luffing Shovel

30901	99	'PREISTMAN' 1,000 only	£20-25

Reliant Regal Vans

05201	99	'TROTTERS' ('dirty' version)	£8-12
85801	01	'EDDIE STOBART'	£8-12

Renault (vintage) Trucks & Vans

(see also French 'Collection Heritage')
(see also 'Modern Trucks' section)

823/1	85	'JULES COLARD' truck	£7-9
824	?	'MARCEL GARDET' van	£8-10
824/1	88	'HERLOIN' truck	£8-10
824/3	88	'THE LIPTON' van	£10-12
889/1	89	'STELLA ARTOIS' lorry	£8-10
902	85	'ROYAL MAIL' van	£20-30
917	86	'COURVOISIER' van	£7-9
922	86	'GALERIES LAFAYETTE'	£8-10
925	86	'GERVAIS DANONE' truck	£10-12
08705	99	'Printemps' Renault promo	NGPP
08706	99	'Au Bon Marché' Ren. promo	NGPP
08707	99	'BHV' Renault promo	NGPP
08708	99	'Samaritaine' Renault promo	NGPP
97000	91	'PERRIER WATER' van	£7-9

Renault (modern) Trucks

59557	00	'CAVEWOOD' c/side, 1:64	£14-16
59563	00	'GUINNESS'	see Set 59563
75601	99	'EDDIE STOBART' c/side	£40-45
75602	99	'MACFARLANE' curtainside	£40-45
75604	99	'KENT CONNECTION' c/side	£60-70
75605	99	'NIGEL RICE' curtainside	£40-45
75606	99	'JAMES IRLAM' curtainside	£40-45
76101	00	'DAMAC' cement tanker	£45-50
76102	00	'CANUTE' powder tanker	£45-50

Scammell (heavy) Trucks

(see also French 'Collection Heritage')

10701	01	'BOC' Highwayman Tanker	£40-45
10702	01	'MANBRE & GARTON' (PE)	£40-45
10703	01	'POINTER' low-loader (PE)	£40-45
10704	01	'WESTFIELD' cradle load (PE)	£40-45
10705	01	'Fred HARRIS' Highwayman	

		Ballast Tractor plus Caravan	£40-45
11101	01	'SIDDLE COOK' Constructor	£30-35
12301	01	'UNITED' Constructor	£30-35
12302	01	'SUNTERS' Contractor	£90-100
12601	01	'ADAMS' Crusader + Trailer	£45-50
12602	01	'ACKWORTHS' Crusader	£45-50
12603	01	'Eastern BRS', Crusader artic.	£50-55
12604	01	'WYNN'S' trailer + vessel	£60-70
12605	01	'PICKFORDS' + King Trailer	£60-70
15901	66	'ANDERTON & ROWLANDS'	
		dodgem truck and trailers	£30-35
16001	97	'JAMESON'S', + trailer	£28-32
16101	96	'CROW'S', heavy recovery	£20-25
16201	97	'PENTUS BROWN', tanker	£28-32
16301	96	'GUINNESS', artic. tanker	£55-65
16302	96	'ESSO', articulated tanker	£25-28
16303	96	'EVER-READY', artic. tanker	£25-28
16304	97	'CROW CARRYING', tanker	£28-32
16306	98	'SHELL-BP' Highwayman	
		tanker and 'BP' petrol pump	£28-32
16401	96	'S.C. COOK Ltd', + trailer	£25-30
16501	96	'CARTERS' circus truck plus	
		pole trailer and caravan	£30-35
16502	96	'PAT COLLINS' + trailer and	
		caravan	£30-35
16601	97	'PICKFORDS' Scammell	
		Highwayman and Land-Rover	£65-75
16701	97	'WREKIN' artic. low-loader	£25-30
16901	97	'HALLETT, SILBERMANN'	
		Highwayman and low-loader	£25-30
17501	97	'S. C. COOK' Constructor	£45-50
17502	00	'PICKFORDS' Constructor	£30-35
17601	97	'HILL of BOTLEY'	
		Constructor and low loader	£45-50
17602	98	'SUNTER BROS' Constructor	
		and low-loader	£45-50
17701	97	'PICKFORDS' Constructors	
		and low-loader	NGPP
17801	97	'CHIPPERFIELD'S' Cannon	£30-35
17901	99	'BRS' wrecker (PE)	£150-170
17902	99	'SUNTER' Contractor	£60-70
17903	99	'WYNNS' Contractor	£40-50
17905	00	'POINTER' Contractor	£30-35
17904	00	'PICKFORDS' 2 Contractors	£70-80
18001	99	'ECONOFREIGHT', Contractor	
		and steam turbine	£50-60
18002	99	'PICKFORDS', two Contractors	
		and casting load	£90-110
18003	00	'WYNN'S' two Contractors,	
		Nicolas trailer, bogies, and	
		stator core load	£110-130
18004	00	'SIDDLE COOKE' two Contractors	
		two Dyson Trailers, girder load	£60-70
18005	00	'PICKFORDS' two Contractors,	
		Nicolas trailer, generator load	£120-140
18006	00	'N. IRELAND' Contractor, two	
		Nicolas bogies, pressure vessel	£80-90
18007	00	'WREKIN' two Contractors,	
		girder trailer, transformer load	£90-110
31004	97	'WYNN'S' articulated low-loader	
		plus Bedford 'S' tractor unit	£40-45
31009	98	'WYNN'S' trailer + boiler	GSP
31010	98	'SHORT BROS' Highwayman	
		low-loader, Priestman Shovel	£45-50
31013	99	'A.L.E.' 2 Contractors, Nicholas	
		Bogies + pressure vessel	GSP
97637	96	'POINTER', tanker	£25-30
97638	96	'PICKFORDS', crane	£45-55
97840	95	'SHELL-MEX / BP', tanker	£28-32
97897	96	'BILLY SMARTS',	
		pole truck/trailer	£50-55
97920	94	'EDWARDS', + 2 trailers	£50-60

Scammell Scarab Trucks

15002	97	'ROYAL MAIL'	£14-18
15004	98	'BOURNVILLE'	£18-22
15005	99	'BRITISH RAILWAYS'	£14-18
15006	00	'TATE & LYLE'	£14-18
15007	00	'GUINNESS'	£14-18
15101	96	'EXPRESS DAIRY'	£14-18
15201	96	'M & B', with barrels	£14-18

15202	96	'BULMERS CIDER', barrels	**£14-18**
97318	95	'WEBSTERS', with barrels	**£14-18**
97335	96	'ESKIMO FROZEN FOODS'	**£15-20**
97910	93	'RAIL FREIGHT', yellow	**£35-40**
97911	93	'BRITISH RAILWAYS'	**£90-100**
97912	94	'ROYAL MAIL' limited ed.	**£15-20**
97913	94	'RAIL FREIGHT', grey	**£35-40**
97914	94	'BRS'	**£25-30**
97916	94	'CORGI CLUB' 10th Anniv	**£15-20**
97917	95	'WATNEYS'	**£20-25**
POV29		'ROYAL MAIL' (G. Ward)	**£20-25**

Scania Trucks

12201	01	'ANDREW WISHART' c/side	**£80-90**
12202	01	'DUKES' fridge trailer	**£45-50**
12203	01	'EDDIE STOBART' low-loader	**£60-70**
12206	01	'MacFARLANE'	**£30-35**
12207	01	'P. OSBORNE' curtainside	**£80-90**
12208	01	Van der WEIL' + Log Trailer	**£50-60**
59506	98	'EDDIE STOBART' c/side	**£10-12**
59531	99	'GUINNESS' + trailer, 1:64	**£14-16**
59534	00	'Dentressangle' tanker 1:64	**£10-12**
59536	00	'Dentressangle' artic. c/side 1:64	**£10-12**
59558	00	'PHH' curtainside, 1:64	**£10-12**
59564	00	'GUINNESS'	see Set 59564
76401	00	'POLLOCK' curtainside	**£60-70**
76402	00	'NORFOLK LINE'	**£80-90**
76403	00	'GUINNESS' curtainside	**£50-60**
76404	00	'PRESTON'S' curtainside	**£75-85**
76601	00	'H.E. PAYNE' box trailer	**£90-100**
76602	00	'EDDIE STOBART'	**£60-70**
76603	00	'D. STEVEN' box trailer	**£150-175**
86603	01	'SUNPRIDE' curtainside	**£14-16**
86604	01	'KNAUF' curtainside	**£14-16**

Thames Trader Trucks

30101	99	'WIMPEY'	**£25-30**
30102	00	'LONDON BRICK Co.'	**£20-25**
30201	96	'R.A.KEMBERY & Sons'	**£12-15**
30202	97	'EDDIE STOBART' dropside	**£15-20**
30301	97	'SLUMBERLAND'	**£12-15**
30302	97	'EVER-READY'	**£12-15**
30303	96	'HEINZ'	**£12-15**
30304	97	'ROBSON'S of CARLISLE'	**£12-15**
30306	97	'LUCOZADE' box van	**£12-15**
30308	97	'FOX'S GLACIER MINTS'	**£12-15**
30309	99	'PICKFORDS'	**£12-15**
30401	97	'GULF OIL' tanker	**£12-15**
30501	98	'PICKFORDS' artic.	**£28-32**
31006	97	'WYNN'S + Morris 1000 Van	**£20-25**
31704	97	'EDDIE STOBART'	(see Set 31704)

Thornycroft Box Vans

821	85	'WAKEFIELD CASTROL'	**£12-15**
821/1	85	'HEIDELBERGER'	**£12-15**
828	85	'GAMLEYS'	**£12-15**
830	85	'W & R JACOB'	**£30-40**
831	85	'HUNTLEY & PALMERS'	**£12-15**
832	85	'CORGI CLUB 1st Anniversary',	
		'Fforestfach Ind.Est.'	**£30-35**
		'Kingsway Ind.Est.'	**£30-35**
833	85	'MACFARLANE LANG'	**£9-12**
834	85	'LYONS SWISS ROLLS'	**£50-60**

839	85	'NURDIN & PEACOCK'	
		with A4 certificate	**£35-40**
840	85	'ALLENBURYS'	**£15-20**
841	85	'PEEK FREANS'	
		with cab scuttle	**£12-15**
		no cab scuttle	**£50-60**
842	85	'CARTER PATERSON'	**£12-15**
843	85	'EDDERSHAWS'	**£12-15**
845	85	'DUCKHAMS OIL',	
		spoked or disc wheels	**£12-15**
846	85	'IND COOPE'	**£12-15**
847	85	'KEILLERS'	**£12-15**
848	85	'NEWS OF THE WORLD'	**£12-15**
853	85	'M. A. RAPPORT'	**£12-15**
854	85	'Lincolnshire Ambulance'	**£12-15**
855	85	'Lincolnshire Fire'	**£12-15**
856	85	'Lincolnshire Police'	**£12-15**
859	86	'THORLEYS'	**£12-15**
859/1	87	'SCOTTS EMPIRE BREAD'	**£12-15**
859/2	87	'CHIVERS JAMS'	**£12-15**
859/3	87	'ARNOTTS BISCUITS'	**£45-55**
859/4	87	'GOODYEAR',	
		(USA), Tan scuttle	NGPP
		(UK), Grey scuttle	NGPP
859/5	87	'GRATTANS 75th', no scuttle	**£25-30**
859/6	87	'KAYS'	(see Set C68)
859/7	89	'LEDA SALT'	**£9-11**
859/8	88	'VOLVOLUTUM'	**£9-11**
859/9	88	'ASDA'	**£11-14**
859/10	88	'BATCHELORS PEAS'	**£12-15**
859/11	88	'LEA & PERRINS'	**£12-15**
859/12	90	'SHELL OIL'	(see Set D9/1)
859/13	89	'McDOUGALLS'	**£20-25**
859/16	90	'ASDA 25th Birthday'	**£11-14**
907	86	'HP SAUCE'	**£14-18**
910	86	'SMALL & PARKES'	**£14-18**
911	86	'PERSIL'	**£12-15**
913	86	'DEWARS WHISKY'	**£10-14**
914	86	'LIPTONS TEA'	**£10-14**
915	86	'OXO'	**£12-15**
924	86	'SAFEWAY'	**£12-15**
926	86	'DOUBLE DIAMOND'	**£18-22**
929	86	'GAMLEYS'	**£15-20**
931	86	'STEPNEY TYRES'	**£12-15**
932	86	'PURITAN SOAP'	**£12-15**
933	86	'BUY PUNCH'	**£20-25**
968	86	'RADIO STEINER'	**£20-30**
?	?	'SWANSEA BANKERS' (20)	NGPP
?	?	'MARCONI' (20)	NGPP
97150	92	'BUCKINGHAM PALACE'	**£12-15**
97151	92	'SANDRINGHAM'	**£12-15**
97152	92	'WINDSOR CASTLE'	**£12-15**
97153	92	'HOLLYROOD HOUSE'	**£12-15**
97154	92	'KENSINGTON PALACE'	**£12-15**
97155	92	'BALMORAL'	**£12-15**

Thornycroft Brewery Lorries

867	86	'THOMAS WETHERED'	**£8-10**
867/1	87	'CHARLES WELLS'	**£8-10**
867/2	87	'TOOHEYS PILSNER'	**£8-10**
867/3	87	'SWAN LAGER'	**£8-10**
867/4	88	'CARLSBERG'	**£8-10**
867/5	90	'CHARRINGTONS', Set D52/1	GSP

867/6	91	'GREENE KING', Set D51/1	GSP
882	88	'ST. WINIFREDS'	**£8-10**
883	88	'TAUNTON CIDER'	**£8-10**

Thornycroft Trucks

820/1	85	'EAST ANGLIAN FRUIT Co'	**£5-8**
827	85	'G.W.R.'	**£25-30**
836	85	'L.M.S.'	**£25-30**
837	85	'SOUTHERN RAILWAY'	**£25-30**
838	85	'L.N.E.R.'	**£25-30**
923	86	'FIELD AMBULANCE'	**£10-12**
923/2	86	'TROESCH', Swiss	**£300-500**
96970	?	'BOOTS'	**£12-15**

Trailers

19901	01	Blue Curtainside Trailer	**£20-25**

Volkswagen Vans

985/1	90	blue, plain (no logo)	**£10-15**
06901	97	red / white, plain (no logo)	**£10-15**
06902	99	'LOWENBRAU'	**£10-15**
06903	99	'BERLINER KINDL'	**£10-15**
06904	99	'HOLSTEN PILSNER'	**£10-15**
07001	98	'LUFTHANSA' mini-bus	**£10-15**
98757	91	'SKIPPER'	**£10-15**
96960	91	'BOSCH ELECTRICAL'	**£10-15**
96961	92	'The LION', 'Captain Condor'	**£10-15**
96965	92	'CORGI CLUB'	**£10-15**
96965/b	92	'The EAGLE', 'Dan Dare'	**£10-15**

Volvo Trucks

12401	01	'EDDIE STOBART' FH c/side	**£45-50**
12402	01	'OWENS' curtainside	**£50-60**
12403	01	'HEANOR' 2 Ballast Tractors,	
		Bogies and Fertiliser Dryer load	**£50-60**
12404	01	'Chris. BENNETT' Jeep Dolly	
		and King Trailer	**£50-60**
12405	01	'EDDIE STOBART'	**£20-30**
12406	01	'BANKS' + King Trailer	**£55-65**
12407	01	'Van der LINDEN' curtainside	**£50-60**
12408	01	'DOORENBOS' curtainside	**£50-60**
59507	98	'EDDIE STOBART' c/side	**£12-15**
59530	99	'GUINNESS' artic. tanker, 1:64	**£12-15**
59535	00	'Dentressangle' tanker 1:64	**£10-12**
59537	00	'Dentressangle' + trailer 1:64	**£10-12**
59562	00	'SALVESEN' c/side, 1:64	**£14-16**
59565	00	'GUINNESS'	see Set 595645
86701	01	'UNITED GLASS' curtainside	**£14-16**
86702	01	'MIRROR GROUP' c/side	**£14-16**

White Trucks and Tankers

98449	95	'PETROL CORPORATION'	**£15-20**
98452	95	'VOLUNTEER' Fire tanker	**£15-20**
98455	95	'PENNSYLVANIA' truck	**£15-20**
98456	95	'SCHEIWE'S COAL', truck	**£15-20**
98457	95	'WHITE ROCK SODA'	**£15-20**
98458	95	'JACOB RUPPERT'S BEER'	**£15-20**
98459	95	'TRIPLE XXX' bottle truck	**£15-20**

A selection of Fire Engines as they appeared in Corgi's 1999 catalogue

A page from Corgi's 2001 catalogue showing some of 'Dibnah's Choice' of steam vehicle models

Corgi Classics Fire Service Models

Accessories (sales)
POS-CC9 1999 Stepped Display Unit.............NPP

AEC (British, New Zealand)
21801	99	'BLACKPOOL' pump esc.	£28-32
22001	97	'E. YORKSHIRE', turntable	£25-30
97352	93	'STOKE-on-TRENT' ladder	£25-30
97353	94	'DUBLIN' turntable	£25-30
97355	92	'DUBLIN' pumper	£25-30
97356	92	'NOTTINGHAM' pump esc.	£25-30
97357	93	'HERTS' pump escape	£25-30
97358	93	'CLEVELAND' pump escape	£25-30
97359	94	'DUBLIN' tender	£25-30
97360	95	'ROTHERHAM' pump esc.	£25-30
97361	96	'NEW ZEALAND' ladder	£25-30
97385	93	'CARDIFF' ladder	£25-30
97386	93	'BRISTOL' ladder	£25-30

ALF (American)
51502	00	'BETHPAGE' pumper	£15-18
51503	01	'SAN FRANSICO'	£22-26

Bedford (British)
05604	97	'AFS' Personnel, ('CA')	£10-12
19201	96	'CAMBRIDGESHIRE' ('S')	£15-20
19701	97	'AFS', ('S')	£15-20
96906	95	'BLACKBURN' ('CA')	£15-20

Chevrolet (American)
51201	96	Fire Chief, 'Centerville'	£15-18
51301	96	Fire Chief, 'SAN DIEGO'	£15-18
51303	97	Fire Chief, 'NYPD'	£15-18
51304	97	Fire Chief, 'NASSAU'	£15-18
97389	94	Fire Chief, 'CHICAGO'	£15-18
97397	95	Fire Chief, 'PENSACOLA'	£15-18

Citroën type 55 (French)
74401	98	'MULHOUSE' fire ladder	£45-50
74402	99	Electro fire ventilator	£45-50

Diamond-T (French)
55602	98	'De LORNE' fire wrecker	£35-40

E-One Cyclone (American)
52201	97	Cyclone Rescue II, 'E-ONE'	£30-35
52202	97	'SCHAUMBURG'	£30-35
52204	98	'WASHINGTON DC'	£30-35
52205	99	'BOSTON'	£30-35
52206	00	'BALTIMORE'	£25-30
52207	01	'KANSAS CITY'	£32-36

52903	97	'LONG LAKE'	£30-35
54701	98	'BOSTON Fire Dept.'	£30-35
54702	99	'FORT MONROE'	£30-35
54703	99	'NEWARK Fire Dept.'	£30-35
54704	00	'SHIPPENBURG'	£25-30
54801	98	'FISHER Fire Dept.'	£30-35
54802	99	'SEATTLE'	£30-35
54901	99	Demo colours	£30-35
54902	00	'DUNCAN' 75ft ladder	£30-35
54903	99	'BARTLETT ILLINOIS'	£30-35

Ford Cortina (British)
98165	95	'LONDON TRANSPORT'	£10-15

GMC Bus (American)
54506	98	GM5300, 'PEORIA'	£30-35

La France (American)
C1143/291		La France (97320)	£40-50
51501	97	'WESTMINSTER' pumper	£20-25
51701	97	'STATEN ISLAND' pumper	£20-25
51702	97	'BALTIMORE' pumper	£20-25
51801	96	'LIONEL CITY' ladder	£20-25
51901	96	'BOSTON' ladder	£20-25
97320	91	La France open cab	£40-50
97321	92	'CENTERVILLE'	£30-40
97322	93	'CHICAGO' pumper	£20-25
97323	93	'CARNEGIE' pumper	£20-25
97324	93	'ORLANDO' ladder	£30-40
97325	93	'DENVER' pumper	£20-25
97326	94	'ORLANDO' pumper	£20-25
97387	94	'DENVER' ladder	£20-25
97393	95	'WAYNE' pumper	£15-20
97395	95	'VERO BEACH' pumper	£15-20
97398	95	'JERSEY CITY' ladder	£30-35

Land-Rover (British and French)
07102	97	'MERSEY TUNNEL'	£10-12
07106	00	'WEST SUSSEX F. B.'	
07301	97	'AFS' Line-layer	£10-12
07407	98	'CITY of BATH'	£10-12
07410	99	'HAMPSHIRE' tender	£10-12
07411	99	'CORNWALL' cliff rescue	£10-12
07412	99	'ALPES MARITIMES'	£10-12
07417	00	'LEICS. & RUTLAND'	£10-12

Leyland (British)
21901	96	'St. HELENS'	£25-30

Mack (American)
52001	96	'JERSEY CITY' CF pumper	£15-20
52002	96	'LIONEL CITY' CF pumper	£15-20
52003	97	'CITY of NAPA' CF pumper	£15-20
52004	98	'St MARY'S' CF pumper	£15-20
52005	97	'LODI' CF pumper	£12-15
52101	97	'LONG BEACH' ladder	£20-25
52102	99	'MILWAUKEE' CF ladder	£25-30
52103	00	'ALLENTOWN' CF ladder	£25-30
52401	97	'ELKRIDGE' B pumper	£15-20
52402	97	'LIONEL CITY' B pumper	£15-20
52403	99	'CORPUS CHRISTI' B pump.	£15-20
52601	96	'MALVERN' B pumper	£15-20
52602	96	'GETTYSBURG' B pumper	£15-20
52603	97	'LAMPETER' B pumper	£15-20
52701	96	'CHICAGO' B, ladder	£25-30
52702	97	'WILKES-BARRE' B, ladder	£25-30
53001	00	'MILWAUKEE, B, ladder	£30-35
53602	99	'CHICAGO' B wrecker	£20-25
53802	01	'SAN FRANSICO' CF ladder	£40-50
98450	95	'CHICAGO' B pumper	£15-20
98451	95	'BERWICK' CF pumper	£15-20
98484	94	'CHICAGO' CF pumper	£15-20
98485	95	'NEPTUNE' CF pumper	£15-20
98486	95	'PAXTONIA' B pumper	£15-20

Mini-Van (British)
97337	95	'FAWLEY REFINERY'	£15-20

Morris 1000 (British)
96854	95	'MORRIS MOTORS' Pickup	£10-12

Seagrave
50501	01	'COLUMBUS' Pumper	£26-32
50502	01	'TAMPA Fl.' Pumper	£26-32

Simon Snorkel (British)
32001	97	'CHESHIRE'	£25-30
97392	94	'WEST GLAMORGAN'	£25-30
97399	95	'CLEVELAND'	£25-30

Thames Trader (British)
30307	97	Police Control Unit	£15-20

Volkswagen (American)
98475	95	Fire Marshall Van	£10-15

White (American)
98452	95	Tanker, 'VOLUNTEER'	£15-20

Steam Vehicles ('Vintage Glory' and 'Dibnah's Choice')

Foden
20202	01	'OPENSHAW BREWERY'	£30-40
80201	99	'TATE & LYLE', with tilt	£30-40
80202	99	'BISHOP & SONS' flatbed	£30-40
80203	00	'J. ASHWORTH' dropside	£22-26
80204	99	'IND COOPE' tanker	£30-40
80205	99	'PICKFORDS' dropside	£30-40
80206	00	'GUINNESS' dropside, barrels	£24-28

Fowler
20101	00	'NORMAN E. BOX' + cylinder load on low-load trailer	£45-50
20103	02	'FRED HARRIS' showmans	£40-45
80101	99	'ANDERTON & ROWLANDS' 'The Lion'	£45-50
80102	99	'PICKFORDS' 'Talisman' plus cylinder load on trailer	£50-60
80103	99	'King Carnival II'	£40-50
80104	99	'NORMAN E. BOX' 'Atlas'	£35-40
80105	99	'WHARTON' 'Supreme'	£40-45
80106	99	'EASTNOR' 'Titan'	£35-40
80107	00	'Super Lion' Millennium Edition, Chrome plated	£60-70

80108	00	'Wolverhampton Wanderer'	£40-45
80109	00	'Lafayette', 'War Dept.'	£30-35
80110	00	Onward' + Caravan	£40-45
80111	00	'Super Lion' Stump Cutter	£30-35
80112	00	'MARSTONS', 'Duke of York' Crane Engine	£35-40
80113	00	'WILKINSON' 'The Great North' Crane and Log Trailer	£45-50

Garrett
20301	01	'The Mighty Atom' showmans	£30-35
20302	01	'War Department.', with trailer	£40-50
20303	01	'FRED HARRIS' 'Horses'	£30-35
22402	00	'Princess Royal' Tractor on trailer pulled by Bedford TK	£60-65
80301	00	'Bunty' road tractor	£25-30
80302	00	'Consuelo Allen', roller	£25-30
80303	00	'Little Billy', showmans	£25-30
80304	00	'The Baroness', 10-ton roller	£25-30
80305	00	'WYNNS' + trailers + logs	£55-60
80306	00	'Lord George', showmans	£25-30
80307	00	'ANKER VALLEY' 'Victor' tractor, trailer and load	£40-45

80308	00	'Princess Maud' showmans	£25-30
80309	00	'Mr. Potter' road tractor	£25-30

Sentinel
20001	00	'TARMAC' dropside + trailer	£30-35
80001	99	'TATE & LYLE' dropside	£30-35
80002	99	'PAUL Bros.', with trailer	£35-40
80003	99	'SHEPHERD NEAME', tilt	£30-35
80005	99	'BLUE CIRCLE' platform	£30-35
80006	99	'McMULLEN' dropside	£30-35
80007	00	'UNITED AFRICA' platform lorry, load and trailer	£30-35
80008	00	'MORRIS' + trailer, oil drums	£30-35
80009	00	'CHARRINGTONS' dropside + trailer and coal sacks	£30-35
80010	00	'GUINNESS' flatbed, chains	£24-28

Miscellaneous
20401	01	'FRED HARRIS' Gallopers. Internally lit, hand turned diecast model that can be motorised	£80-110

'Collection Heritage'

The 'Collection Heritage' series of models was introduced in 1997 specifically for the French market. A very limited number were available in the UK through specialist dealers.

AMX Military Tank
66701 99 Dépanneur ('bulldozer-tank') **£20-25**

Bedford Trucks
11402 01 'PINDER' Kangaroo Trailer........**£35-40**

Berliet Trucks and Tankers
70001 97 'CHAMBOURCY' tanker **£35-40**
70101 97 'PINDER' circus elephants **£35-40**
70201 97 'PINDER' human cannon **£35-40**
70202 01 'MICHELIN' GLR8 box van **£30-35**
70203 01 'HENRI WALBAUM' **£40-45**
70204 01 'BERGER' GLR8.....................**£35-40**
70205 01 'PORTSEIGNE' GLR8.............**£35-40**
70206 01 'STAG' with Safi Roller............**£50-55**
70301 97 'PINDER' artic. horse-box **£35-45**
70401 97 'PINDER' heavy recovery........**£35-40**
70402 99 'BOURGEY' heavy recovery......**£35-40**
70403 00 'MICHELIN' GLR Wrecker.......**£25-30**
73001 97 'L'ALSACIENNE BISCUITS' ...**£35-40**
73002 97 'BANANIA' box van **£35-40**
73003 99 'GRINGOIRE' box van **£20-25**
73004 99 'ORANGINA' box van **£20-25**
73005 99 'ROQUEFORT' lorry **£30-35**
73007 01 'BERGER' box van **£30-35**
73101 97 'VINI-PRIX' beer lorry **£35-40**
73201 97 'SHELL' GLR8 rigid tanker **£35-40**
73301 97 'PINDER' circus 'Luton' van.....**£35-40**
73401 97 'PINDER' box van and trailer.....**£50-60**
73501 98 'COLMAR' GLR8 fire ladder.....**£45-50**
73601 99 'LU' TLR with covered trailer ...**£40-45**
73602 99 'AMORA MOUTARDE' GLR8 .**£35-40**
73801 98 GLR8 military covered wagon **£35-40**

Bernard Trucks and Vans
72001 97 'DANONE' van **£35-40**
72002 97 'CALBERSON-FLAGEUL' **£35-40**
72003 97 'LUSTUCRU' egg lorry **£35-40**
72004 97 'PINDER' large box van **£35-40**
72005 99 'SAINT-MARC' box van **£35-40**
72006 99 'CHOCOLAT MENIER' van **£35-40**
72007 99 'RICQLES' large box van **£35-40**
72008 99 'AIGUEBELLE' lorry **£35-40**
72011 01 'BERGER' box van **£30-35**
72012 01 'DELICES' **£30-35**

Citroën Type 55 Trucks
74001 98 Military canvas-back lorry..........**£35-40**
74101 98 'La VACHE SERIEUSE'............**£35-40**
74102 99 'MICHELIN' box van **£35-40**

74103 99 'CHAMBOURCY' **£35-40**
74201 98 'BOURGEY' low-loader **£35-40**
74301 99 'PINDER' truck + trailer **£35-40**
74401 98 'MULHOUSE' fire ladder **£45-50**
74402 99 Electro fire ventilator **£35-40**
74403 99 'VITTEL' Fire Escape **£35-40**
74601 98 'DYNAVIA' Fruehauf tanker **£35-40**
74602 99 'SHELL' Fruehauf tanker **£35-40**
74701 99 'GINI' drinks lorry **£35-40**
74702 01 'BERGER' bottles and crates **£35-40**
74801 99 'CITROEN' Fruehauf trailer **£35-40**

Daimler Double-deck Bus
35202 97 'PINDER' living quarters............**£35-40**

Diamond-T Tractor Units
55102 99 Military tank transporter **£55-60**
55105 01 'STAG' with Road Roller...........**£55-60**
55303 99 'BOURGEY' generator load **£70-80**
55401 98 'PINDER' circus box trailer **£60-65**
55602 98 'De LORNE' fire wrecker **£60-65**
55607 99 'RENAULT' wrecker.................**£60-65**

Land-Rover
07201 97 'PINDER' public address **£15-20**
07412 99 'Alpes Maritime' fire vehicle **£12-15**
07415 99 'ARDENNES' fire vehicle **£12-15**
70503 00 'MICHELIN' + trailer **£20-25**

Peugeot Vans
70610 01 'POSTES' **£12-16**
70611 01 'ORANGINA' **£12-16**
70612 01 'BRANDT' **£12-16**
70613 01 'Caisson de Recompression'........**£12-16**
70614 01 'CHENARD & WALCKER' **£12-16**
70615 01 'MICHELIN' **£12-16**
70616 01 'MONTEL de GELAT' **£12-16**
70617 01 'POULAIN' **£12-16**

Renault Trucks and Vans
70510 01 'BERGER' high roof **£12-16**
70511 01 'CHAMBOURCY' **£12-16**
70512 01 'MICHELIN' high roof **£12-16**
70513 00 'LAMPES CLAUDES' **£12-16**
70514 01 'RENAULT SERVICE' **£12-16**
70515 01 'VALENTINE' **£12-16**
70516 01 'BAROCLEM' **£12-16**
70517 01 'SCHNEIDER' **£12-16**
70902 01 'MICHELIN' JL20+trailer **£35-45**
70903 01 'PINDER' JL20 ticket trailer........**£35-45**
70904 01 'DUNLOP' + Fruehauf trailer **£40-45**
70905 01 'WAGNER & BONNEFOIS' **£35-40**
70906 01 'SAINT-GOBAIN' tanker **£40-45**
71001 97 'MICHELIN' covered lorry.........**£20-25**
71003 99 Military covered lorry **£20-25**
71004 99 'REGIE RENAULT' promo **£20-25**

71005 00 'MICHELIN' canvas back...........**£18-22**
71007 01 'CALBERSON' **£18-22**
71008 01 'PERE la GROLLE' **£20-25**
71101 97 'Du MESNIL' lemonade lorry.....**£20-25**
71102 99 'RENAULT' oil drum lorry **£20-25**
71104 99 'ORANGINA' drinks lorry **£20-25**
71105 99 'VICHY ETAT' Renault promo....**NGPP**
71201 97 'TOTAL' fuel tanker **£20-25**
71202 97 'PINDER' circus fuel tanker **£20-25**
71203 98 'VAR' fire service water tanker....**£20-25**
71204 99 'ESSO' tanker **£20-25**
71206 99 'SHELL' Renault promo..............**NGPP**
71301 97 'PERRIER' box van **£20-25**
71401 97 'VALENTINE' box van...............**£20-25**
71402 97 'PINDER' mobile kitchen **£20-25**
71403 99 'CALBERSON' box van **£20-25**
71405 98 'SIC' soft drinks box van **£20-25**
71406 99 'PSCHITT' box van **£20-25**
71407 99 'RENAULT Services' promo........**NGPP**

Saviem Trucks and Tankers
70901 99 'Meaux, Seine & Marne' ladder..**£40-45**
71106 99 'PERRIER' drinks lorry **£20-25**
71408 99 'CIRAGE ABEILLE' lorry **£20-25**
71409 99 'NESCAFE' **£20-25**
71501 99 'MICHELIN' van **£35-40**
71502 99 'SUCHARD MILKA' **£35-40**
71503 01 no details ....
71504 01 no details ....
71505 01 no details ....
71601 99 'RENAULT' farm lorry **£35-40**
71701 99 'CALBERSON' cable drums **£35-40**
71801 99 'BP ENERGOL' tanker **£35-40**
71802 01 no details ....

Scammell Highwayman Trucks
16801 97 'PINDER' generator truck and
            animal trailers **£60-65**

Simca Cargo
72901 99 'SIMCA' platform + crates ....
72902 99 'RIPOLIN' covered lorry ....
72903 99 'VILLEROY & BOCH' ....
72904 99 'AZUR' tanker ....
72905 00 'MICHELIN' flatbed + tyres **£18-22**
72914 01 'SNCF' box trailer **£20-25**
72915 01 'PINDER ON ICE' **£20-25**
72917 01 'PINDER' 'Viande/Sellerie' **£35-40**

Unic Vehicles
72801 99 'CALBERSON' semi-trailer **£20-25**
72802 99 'PINDER CIRCUS' van **£20-25**
72803 99 'PHILIPS' van **£20-25**
72805 01 'BIC' **£20-25**
72916 01 'POMPES GUINARD' fire **£20-25**

'Motoring Memories'

A range of 'budget' models introduced in 1998 using mostly re-worked 'Cameos' castings. Note that some reference numbers refer to more than one model because those models came in a trade 'assortment pack'.

Austin A35 Saloon
67201 98 Black...................................**£3-5**

Austin A35 Van
61209 98 'CADBURYS DAIRY MILK' **£3-5**
67301 98 'AUSTIN SERVICE'.....................**£3-5**

Ford Capri Mk.I
67701 98 red/black................................**£3-5**

Ford Cortina Mk.III
67801 98 yellow/black.............................**£3-5**

Ford Escort Mk.I
67001 98 light blue................................**£3-5**

Ford Escort Van
61209 98 'CADBURYS FLAKE' **£3-5**
61210 98 'A.A. ROAD SERVICE' **£3-5**
61212 98 'ROYAL MAIL'..........................**£3-5**
61213 98 'FORD'.....................................**£3-5**
67101 98 'FORD' **£3-5**

Ford model 'T' Van
?   98 'BRANNIGANS' on-pack offer......**£3-5**

Land-Rover
61209 98 'CADBURYS WHOLE NUT' **£3-5**
61210 98 'A.A. PATROL SERVICE' **£3-5**
61212 98 'ROYAL MAIL'..........................**£3-5**

Mini
61211 98 'Mr BEAN' **£3-5**
68001
98   Racing green and white **£3-5**

Morris 1000 Van
61209 98 'CADBURYS FRUIT & NUT' **£3-5**
61210 98 'A.A. ROAD SERVICE' **£3-5**
61212 98 'ROYAL MAIL'..........................**£3-5**

Volkswagen Beetle
67901 98 Yellow **£3-5**

Assortments
'Cameos' castings loosely based on Ford Model 'T', Chevrolet, 'Bullnose' Morris and Leyland subjects in 'themed' packs of four.
61201 98 'ROYAL MAIL' **£3-5**
61203 98 'EDDIE STOBART' **£3-5**
61205 98 'CADBURY' 'Archive'..................**£3-5**
61206 98 'CADBURY' 'Modern' **£3-5**
61207 98 'PICKFORDS' **£3-5**
61208 98 'GOLDEN OLDIES' **£3-5**

In 1998, Corgi put together a range of 'budget' models (using stock castings and components) to encourage collecting by children.

Aircraft
59701	98	Hughes 'POLICE' Helicopter	**£4-5**
59901	98	'CONCORDE'	**£4-5**

Ambulance
86401	01	'WEST COUNTRY'	not produced

BMW 525
57801	98	'HAMPSHIRE POLICE'	**£4-5**

Ford Cargo Box Van
59601	98	'EDDIE STOBART'	**£6-7**

Ford Escort Van
58301	98	'PONY EXPRESS'	**£4-5**
58302	98	'POWERGEN'	**£4-5**
58303	98	'A.A.' Service Van	**£4-5**
58304	98	'EDDIE STOBART'	**£4-5**

Ford Transit
58103	98	'OMEGA EXPRESS'	**£4-5**
58104	98	'NATIONAL POWER'	**£4-5**
58105	98	'TARMAC'	**£4-5**
58106	98	'A.A.' Service Van	**£4-5**
58108	98	'AUTOGLASS'	**£4-5**
58109	98	'SECURICOR'	**£4-5**
58111	98	'Cadbury's CURLYWURLY'	**£4-5**
58112	98	'EDDIE STOBART' Mini-Bus	**£4-5**
58115	99	'GREEN FLAG' Service Van	**£4-5**
58201	98	'BADGER BROS' Wrecker	**£4-5**
58202	98	'A.A.' Wrecker	**£4-5**
58701	98	'HIGHWAY SERVICES' tipper	**£4-5**
81701	01	'MICHELIN'	**£2-3**
81702	01	'BRITISH TELECOM'	**£2-3**
81703	01	'The AA'	**£2-3**

Fork Lift Truck
56701	99	'City Forklift Services'	**£4-5**

James Bond vehicles (1:64)
99651	99	'Dr. No' Sunbeam Alpine	**£3-4**
99652	99	'Thunderball' Aston-Martin DB5	**£3-4**
99653	99	'Goldfinger' Ford Mustang	**£3-4**
99654	99	'You Only Live Twice' Toyota	**£3-4**
99655	99	'O.H.M.S.S.' Mercury Cougar	**£3-4**
99657	99	'Spy Who Loved Me' Lotus	**£3-4**
99658	99	'Living Daylights' Aston-Martin	**£3-4**
99659	99	'Goldeneye' Aston-Martin DB5	**£3-4**
99660	99	'Dr. No' Aston-Martin	**£3-4**
99661	99	'Goldfinger' Aston-Martin	**£3-4**
99662	99	'For Your Eyes Only' Lotus	**£3-4**
99725	99	'Diamonds are Forever' Mach I	**£3-4**

Land-Rover
57902	98	'ROYAL MAIL' Post Bus	**£4-5**
57903	98	'Army' camouflage	**£4-5**

Legends of Speed
BENTLEY
00201	00	Racing Car, Green, '1'	**£4-5**

BUGATTI
00202	00	Racing Car, Blue, '3'	**£4-5**

MERCEDES-BENZ
00203	00	Racing Car, Silver, '6'	**£4-5**

Leyland Terrier
56502	99	'EDDIE STOBART' box van	**£4-5**

Mazda vehicles
57201	99	'FIRE CHIEF'	**£4-5**

Mercedes vehicles
58402	98	'EDDIE STOBART' 207D van	**£4-5**
58402	98	'LONDON ZOO' 207D van	**£4-5**
58501	98	'PIONEER' 6-w cement mixer	**£4-5**

Mini
04420	98	'CADBURY'S MINI-EGGS'	**£4-5**

Miscellaneous
58601	98	'City Cleansing' Refuse Truck	**£6-7**
58901	98	'Tripod Crest' Street Sweeper	**£6-7**
59001	98	'DoT' Snow Plough	**£6-7**

Novelty Advertising Vehicles
57501	98	'CADBURY'S CREME EGG'	**£1-2**

Plaxton Coach
32601	98	'BLUEBIRD'	**£6-7**
32602	98	'NATIONAL EXPRESS'	**£6-7**
84101	01	'BUS EIREANN'	**£6-7**

Porsche 944
57701	98	'POLICE'	**£4-5**

Range Rover
57601	98	'METROPOLITAN POLICE'	**£4-5**
82801	01	'GARDA' (Irish)	**£4-5**

Raygo Roller
86001	01	'WIMPEY' ('London Scene')	**£6-7**

Routemaster Bus
32301	98	'LT', 'London Standard'	**£4-5**
32303	98	'Cadbury's DOUBLE-DECKER'	**£4-5**
32402	98	'CITY TOUR'	**£4-5**
32403	98	'LT', 'SIGHTSEEING'	**£4-5**
82301	01	'LONDON' ('London Scene')	**£5-6**
82302	01	'DUBLIN GREEN'	**£5-6**
82303	01	'GUIDE FRIDAY', 'Dublin Tour'	**£5-6**

Scania Trucks
59503	98	'EDDIE STOBART' c/side	**£9-10**
60011	99	'EDDIE STOBART' 3-pc set	**£22-26**

'Steady Eddie'
59401	98	'Steady Eddie'	**£2-3**
59402	98	'Oliver Overdrive'	**£2-3**
59403	98	'Loretta Lorry'	**£2-3**
59404	98	'Jock the Tartan Tanker'	**£2-3**
59406	98	'Steady Eddie' and story book	**£5-6**
59407	98	'Steady Eddie', story book, Car Wash and Play Mat	**£8-10**
59408	99	'Rich Van Rental'	**£2-3**
59409	99	'Angie Ambulance'	**£2-3**
59410	99	'Steady Eddie' with hard hat	**£2-3**
59411	99	'Steady Eddie' with woolly hat	**£2-3**

Superhaulers
59504	98	'EDDIE STOBART' Volvo	**£8-11**
59514	99	'CADBURY' Volvo tanker	**£8-11**
59515	99	'TATE & LYLE' ERF tanker	**£8-11**
56519	99	'Cadbury's Bike Boost' Volvo	**£8-11**
59501	98	'CRUNCHIE' ERF c/side	**£8-11**
59502	98	'EDDIE STOBART' c/side	**£8-11**
86601	01	'CASTROL HONDA' Scania	**£9-12**
86602	01	'ESSO' Scania tanker	**£9-12**
86801	01	'DUCATI' ERF transporter	**£9-12**
86901	01	'LAWSON' Renault transporter	**£9-12**
86902	01	'SHELL' Renault tanker	**£9-12**
87001	01	'EDDIE STOBART' DAF c/side	**£9-12**
87002	01	'DUKES' DAF curtainside	**£9-12**
?	01	'BEAMISH GRAYSTON'	**?**

Taxi
58002	98	'COMPUTER CAB' FX4	**£4-5**

Volvo Fire Engine
86301	01	'IRISH FIRE BRIGADE'	**£6-7**

Sets of toys
59101	98	Range Rover and Caravan	**£11-13**
60001	98	'Mounted Police' Set (Land-Rover, horsebox, mounted policeman	**£9-11**
60003	98	'LONDON' Set: Routemaster bus, Taxi and mounted policeman	**£9-11**
60004	98	'ELLERDALE' Set (Land-Rover, Horsebox, horse	**£9-11**
60006	98	'Kenya Safari Rally' (Land-Rover, Trailer with Mini '53'	**£18-20**
60007	98	3-piece 'Cadbury' set includes: 'Freddo', 'Crunchie' and 'Buttons' Curtainside Trucks, plus a playmat	**£22-25**
?	99	'Chad Valley' Motorway Play Set: a 'Woolworths' Superhauler, Plaxton Coach, Range Rover Police, 'AA' Wrecker, Porsche and BMW	**NGPP**
?	99	'Toys 'R' Us Recovery' set: 'AA' Wrecker plus Mini Saloon	**NGPP**

New issues

275

Accessories and Kits
31804 97 Bus Depot £7-9

AEC Regal half-cab Coaches
33201 96 'FINGLANDS', football fans......£15-18
97020 92 'WYE VALLEY' £15-20
97021 95 'MacBRAYNES' £30-35
97180 91 'GREY-GREEN' £15-20
97181 91 'TIMPSONS' £15-20
97184 91 'SHEFFIELD' £15-20
97185 92 'WEST RIDING' £15-20
97186 92 'GREY CARS' £15-20
97187 92 'HANSON' £15-20
97189 91 'OXFORD' £15-20
97190 91 'LEDGARD' £15-20
97191 91 'ROSSLYN MOTORS' £15-20
97193 92 'CARNEYS' £15-20
97194 92 'HARDINGS' £15-20
97196 93 'STANLEY FIELD' £15-20
97197 93 'WESTERN WELSH' £15-20
98161 93 'EASTERN COUNTIES' £15-20
98162 93 'WALLACE ARNOLD' £15-20

AEC Regal IV Single-Deck Bus
97018 95 'DUNDEE' £12-15

AEC Regent Double-Deck Buses
41/1 90 'BARTONS' (see GS D41/1) ....GSP
47/1 90 'BEANO' (see GS D47/1)...............GSP
599 87 'T. S. B' £20-25
599/1 86 'WISK' £20-25
599/1 89 'WESTERN' £12-15
599/2 87 'WOODHAMS SCOOTERS' £15-20
599/3 87 'HUNTLEY & PALMERS'.........£15-20
599/4 88 'GLASGOW' £18-25
599/5 88 'RHONDDA' £15-20
599/6 89 'MORECAMBE' £15-20
599/7 89 'BRADFORD' £15-20
599/8 89 'HANTS & DORSET',
          (see Gift Set D4/1)..................GSP
599/9 90 'WESTERN' £12-15
599/10 90 'BRIGHTON & HOVE' £12-15
599/11 90 'DUBLIN' £8-10
599/12 90 'BATTLE OF BRITAIN' £10-12
599/13 90 'HALIFAX'..............................£10-12
634 86 'MAPLES'................................£10-12
643 86 'NEWCASTLE ALE'.................£10-12
96980 91 'STEVENSONS'.......................£10-12
96983 91 'LIVERPOOL'..........................£10-12
? 91 'ROCHDALE'...........................£10-12
97001 93 'P.M.T.', 'Stoke' £10-12
97002 93 'SHEFFIELD'..........................£10-12
97003 93 'WEST BRIDGEFORD' £10-12
97062 91 'OXFORD' (re-run) £10-12
       93 'OXFORD' (re-run) £10-12
? 93 'CORGI', club model £10-12

AEC Reliance Buses
97130 95 'OXFORD' £10-12
97900 95 'DEVON GENERAL' £10-12

AEC Routemaster Buses
25901 01 'METROLINE' 'Aldwych' £20-25
35001 96 RM 5 'LT', red..........................£30-35
35002 96 RM 664 'LT' £20-25
35004 97 RM 1933 'LT' £20-25
35003 96 'GEORGE SHILLIBEER'.........£20-25
35006 97 'LIVERPOOL' ('Beatles')..........£20-25
35007 98 RM 1818 'LT' Tottenham £20-25
35007H 98 'HAMLEYS' £30-35
35010 00 'The Queen Mother's Century' ..£20-25
35101 97 RM 94 'LT SIGHTSEEING' £20-25
35102 00 'London Coaches' open top........£20-25
36006 97 RM 254 'LT' £20-25

Albion Valiant Duple Coach
33302 00 'WESTERN SMT' (PE) £40-45

American Buses (Modern)
GM 4502, 4507

54007 96 GM4502, 'LIONEL CITY' £25-30
54103 96 GM4507, 'LIONEL CITY' £25-30
GM 5301
54301 96 'NEW YORK' £25-30
54302 96 'LIONEL CITY TRANSIT' £25-30
54401 96 'LIONEL CITY BUS' £25-30
54402 96 'GREYHOUND LINES' £25-30
54404 97 'LIONEL CITY TRANSIT' £25-30
54501 96 'SAN DIEGO' £25-30
54502 96 'PENNSYLVANIA R-ROAD' ...£25-30
54504 97 'SANTA MONICA' £25-30
54601 96 'D. C. TRANSIT' £25-30
54602 96 'CHICAGO TRANSIT'.............£25-30
54605 97 'READING LINES' £25-30
GM 5302
54303 98 'TRAILWAYS' £25-30
GM 5303
54303 97 Greyhound 'NEW YORK
          WORLD FAIR' £25-30
MCI buses
53403 01 'COACH USA' £30-35
98421 95 MCI Demo Bus.........................£25-30
98422 95 'PETER PAN' £25-30
98427 95 'BIRTHDAY BUS' £25-30
98431 95 Bank version of 98427.............£50-75
98432 95 Bank version of 98421.............£50-75
98650 95 'CALIFORNIA' £25-30
98651 95 'THRASHER Bros.'
          not issued ....NPP
98652 95 'SEA WORLD' £25-30
98653 95 Bank version of 98652.............£25-30
98654 95 Bank version of 98651.............£25-30
98655 95 Bank version of 98650.............£25-30

American Buses (Vintage)
GM 4502 - 4515
54001 96 4506, 'SURFACE
          TRANSPORTATION' £20-25
54002 96 4506, 'MADISON AVENUE' £20-25
54003 96 4505, 'St. LOUIS' £20-25
54004 96 4507, 'NEW YORK' £20-25
54005 96 4502, 'PUBLIC SERVICE' £20-25
54006 96 4507, 'WABASH RLY' £20-25
54008 97 4502, 'SAN FRANCISCO' £20-25
54009 97 4507, 'NEW ENGLAND' £20-25
54010 97 4505, 'CHICAGO MC' £20-25
54011 97 4507, 'LIONEL CITY' £20-25
54101 96 4509, 'GREYHOUND' £20-25
54102 95 4509, 'RED ARROW' £20-25
54104 97 4509, 'PEERLESS' £20-25
54105 00 4507, 'TEXACO' crew bus £22-28
54106 97 4509, 'NEW HAVEN' £20-25
54202 98 4515, 'SEATTLE' £20-25
54203 00 4515, 'PHILADAELPHIA' £20-25
54306 00 'GOLDEN GATE', 'fishbowl' ...£25-30
54401 96 'LIONEL', 'fishbowl' body.........£20-25
GM 5300
54304 99 'LOS ANGELS MTA' £28-32
54308 01 'NEW YORK' 'fishbowl' £30-35
54309 01 'GRAY COACH' 'fishbowl' £30-35
54506 98 'PEORIA' 'Hazardous' £28-32
GM 5306
54507 98 'LIBERTY LINES' £28-32
STREET CARS
55001 97 (PTC) 'PHILADELPHIA' £28-32
55010 97 (PCC) 'TORONTO' £28-32
55004 97 (PTC) 'LIONEL CITY' £28-32
55005 98 (PCC) 'CINCINNATI' £28-32
55007 98 (PCC) 'LOS ANGELES' £28-32
55008 98 (PCC) 'BOSTON' £28-32
55009 99 (PCC) 'WASHINGTON DC' £28-32
55013 00 (PCC) 'PITTSBURGH' £25-30
55014 00 (PCC) 'MINNEAPOLIS' £25-30
55018 01 (PCC) 'PITTSBURGH' £30-35
TD 4502
97635 96 'LOS ANGELES' £28-32
98600 96 'PACIFIC GREYHOUND' £28-32
98601 96 'PACIFIC ELECTRIC'...............£28-32
TD 4505, 4506 and 4507
98602 96 TD4505, 'GREYHOUND' £28-32

98603 96 TD4506, 'DETROIT DSR' £28-32
98604 96 TD4507, 'FIFTH AVE. Co.'.......£28-32
98741 95 Greyhound,
          'SAN FRANCISCO' £28-32
YC 743, (YC = Yellow Coach)
53901 96 'UNION PACIFIC' £25-30
53902 96 'LIONEL BUS LINES' £25-30
53903 97 'EASTERN MICHIGAN' £25-30
53904 96 'LIONEL CITY BUS LINES'.....£25-30
53906 99 'GREYHOUND' 'Kansas' £25-30
53907 97 'BALTIMORE and OHIO' £25-30
98460 94 Greyhound 'WORLDS FAIR' £25-30
98461 94 Greyhound
          'BATTLE of BRITAIN' £25-30
98462 94 Greyhound 'CHICAGO' £25-30
98462 94 Greyhound 'ATLANTA' £25-30
98464 94 'BURLINGTON' 'whale-line' ...£25-30
98465 94 'BURLINGTON' 'pin-stripe' £25-30
98467 95 'NEW JERSEY' £25-30
98468 95 'CHAMPLAIN' £25-30
98469 95 Greyhound 'LOS ANGELES' £25-30
98470 95 'SILVERSIDE' £25-30
98471 95 'BATTLE of BRITAIN' £25-30
98472 95 'W.A.C.' £25-30
98473 95 'WAVES' £25-30

Bedford 'OB' Coaches
949/1 87 'NORFOLKS',
          small 'Ipswich' £50-60
       87 large 'Ipswich' £40-50
949/2 78 'ROYAL BLUE',
          small 'Exeter' £80-90
       87 large 'Exeter' £50-60
949/3 87 'ALEXANDER BLUEBIRD' £35-40
949/4 87 'GREY CARS' £20-25
949/5 87 'CROSVILLE' £25-30
949/6 87 'SOUTHDOWN' £100-125
949/7 87 'EASTERN COUNTIES' £25-35
949/8 88 'SOUTH MIDLAND' £25-35
949/9 88 'PREMIER', blue bonnet £25-30
          without blue bonnet £50-75
949/10 88 'HIGHLAND' ....GSP
949/11 88 'EAST YORKSHIRE' £20-25
949/12 89 'CLASSIC COACH' £20-25
949/13 89 'HANTS & SUSSEX' £25-30
949/14 89 'WALLACE ARNOLD' £20-25
949/15 89 'MACBRAYNES' £40-45
949/16 89 'HANTS & DORSET',
          see Set D41/1 ....GSP
949/17 90 'GREENSLADES' £10-15
949/18 90 'DEVON GENERAL' £15-20
949/19 90 'SOUTHERN VECTIS' £15-20
949/22 90 'RAF COACH', see Set D35/1 ....GSP
949/22 90 'BOULTONS' £15-20
949/23 90 'HOWARDS TOURS' £15-20
949/24 90 'SOUTHERN NATIONAL'........£15-20
949/25 90 'EASTERN NATIONAL' £15-20
949/26 90 'WEST YORKSHIRE' £15-20
949/27 90 'BRITISH Rlys', 'Melstead' £20-25
949/28 90 'YORK FAIR', see Set Q55/1 ....GSP
949/29 90 'BARTON'S', Set D41/1 ....GSP
949/30 90 'WESTERN NATIONAL' £18-20
949/31 91 'BRITISH Rlys', 'Bristol' £18-20
949/32 90 'CORGI ON THE MOVE',
          see Set D82/1 ....GSP
949/33 90 'STANDERWICK', Set Q57/1 ....GSP
33801 95 'PEARCE & CRUMP'
          'The Titfield Thunderbolt' £15-20
33802 98 'MALTA', 'Melueha' £18-22
33803 98 'BRITISH RAILWAYS' £22-25
33804 99 'GUINNESS' £22-25
97075 92 'SOUTH WALES' £12-15
97100 91 'ISLE OF MAN TOURS' £12-15
97101 91 'SCILLY ISLES' £12-15
97102 91 'SKILLS of NOTTINGHAM' £10-15
97104 91 'BRONTE' £15-20
97105 92 'FELIX' £15-20
97106 92 'BIBBYS' £15-20
97107 92 'MURGATROYD'.....................£15-20
97108 92 'GRANVILLE TOURS' £15-20

97109	93	'WHITTAKERS TOURS'	£15-20
97111	93	'MEREDITH'	£15-20
97113	93	'WARBURTONS'	£15-20
97115	93	'SEAGULL COACHES'	£10-15
97437	95	'MALTA'	£30-35
98163	93	'GREY-GREEN'	£15-20
98164	93	'EDINBURGH'	£15-20
no ref	92	'SMITH'S COACHES'	
		(only 3 made)	NGPP

Bedford 'Val' Coach

35301	97	'YELLOWAYS'	£22-25
35302	97	'Magical Mystery Tour'	£22-25
35303	97	'SELNEC'	£22-25
35305	98	'WALLACE ARNOLD'	£22-25
36502	99	'The Italian Job'	see Gift Set 36502

Bristol 'K' type Bus

97853	95	'BRISTOL TRAMWAYS'	£20-25
97857	95	'LONDON TRANSPORT'	£25-30
97875	95	'CARDIFF 75th'	£20-25

Burlingham 'Seagull' Coach

34101	96	'RIBBLESDALE'	£15-20
97170	93	'WOODS'	£15-20
97171	93	'NEATH CARDIFF'	£20-25
97172	93	'STRATFORD BLUE'	£30-40
97173	93	'RIBBLE'	£30-35
97174	93	'YELLOWAY'	£30-35
97175	93	'DON EVERALL'	£15-20
97176	93	'KING ALFRED'	£15-20
97177	93	'NORTHERN ROADWAYS'	£15-20
97178	95	'COLISEUM COACHES'	£15-20
97179	95	'BANFIELD'S COACHES'	£15-20
97340	95	'TRENT'	£15-20
97342	95	'WEST COAST'	£15-20

Daimler 'CW' Bus

(see also French 'Collection Heritage')

36201	96	'GREEN LINE'	£18-22
97336	96	'GLASGOW'	£18-22
97820	94	'WEST BROMWICH'	£20-25
97822	94	'DERBY CORPORATION'	£20-25
97827	94	'SHEFFIELD'	£20-25
97829	95	'DOUGLAS'	£20-25

Daimler Duple Coach

97821	94	'SWAN'	£12-18
97823	94	'BLUE BUS SERVICES'	£12-18
97825	94	'BURWELL & DISTRICT'	£12-18
97830	95	'SCOUT'	£12-18

Daimler Fleetline Bus

97824	94	'BIRMINGHAM'	£25-30
97826	94	'MANCHESTER'	£25-30
97828	95	'ROCHDALE',	
		'Guernsey Tomatoes'	£25-30
	96	'Corgi Heritage Centre'	£40-50

Guy Arab Double-Deck Bus

34301	97	'SWINDON'	£20-25
97198	92	'SOUTHDOWN'	£30-40
97199	92	'BIRKENHEAD'	£20-25
97201	93	'BIRMINGHAM'	£30-35
97202	93	'MAIDSTONE'	£20-25
97203	93	'LONDON TRANSPORT'	£25-30
97204	93	'COVENTRY'	£20-25
97205	93	'BOURNEMOUTH'	£20-25
97206	93	'NORTHERN GENERAL'	£20-25
97208	93	'YORKSHIRE'	£20-25
97209	93	'WALSALL'	£20-25
97310	93	'SOUTHAMPTON'	£20-25
97311	94	'MIDLAND RED'	£20-25
97312	94	'WOLVERHAMPTON'	£20-25
97313	94	'PAISLEY & DISTRICT'	£20-25
97314	96	'OXFORD'	£20-25
97315	95	'LT' wartime livery	£20-25

Karrier 'W' type Trolley-Bus

34701	95	'NOTTINGHAM CITY'	£25-30
34703	97	'DERBY CORPORATION'	£25-30
97316	95	'IPSWICH'	£25-30
97870	94	'NEWCASTLE'	£25-30
97871	95	'BRADFORD'	£25-30

Leyland Atlantean Buses

33501	96	'GUIDE FRIDAY', open top	£25-30
97230	94	'RIBBLE', 'Gay Hostess'	£25-30
97231	94	'HULL'	£25-30
97232	95	'WALLASEY'	£25-30
97233	95	'DEVON GENERAL', open	£25-30
97341	95	'MAIDSTONE'	£25-30

Leyland Olympian Bus

34801	96	'WESTERN WELSH'	£12-15

Leyland Tiger Bus and Coach

34901	97	'MANCHESTER'	£20-25
97192	92	'RIBBLE'	£20-25
97210	93	'MAYPOLE'	£15-20
97211	93	'BARTON'S'	£15-20
97212	93	'ELLEN SMITH'	£15-20
97213	93	'RED & WHITE'	£15-20
97214	94	'SKILL'S 75th'	£15-20

97216	94	'THE DELAINE'	£15-20
97363	96	'EDINBURGH'	£15-20
97364	95	'NORTH WESTERN'	£15-20
97810	95	'LEICESTER'	£15-20

Sunbeam 'W' type Trolley-Bus

34702	96	'ASHTON under LYME'	£25-30
97800	94	'READING'	£25-30
97780?	95	'MAIDSTONE''	£25-30

Thornycroft Double-Deck Bus

1st type: 4 top-rail supports
2nd type: 8 top-rail supports

858	86	'SANDEMANS', 1st/2nd	£12-15
858/1	87	'NATIONAL MOTOR MUSEUM',	
		red/white 2nd type	£12-15
		red cab canopy	£20-25
858/2	87	'CHARLIE CHAPLIN'	£12-15
858/3	87	'PALM TOFFEE'	£12-15
858/4	87	'IDRIS SODA WATER'	£12-15
858/5	87	'The TIMES'	£12-15
858/6	87	'L. & N.W.R.'	£12-15
858/7	88	'OAKEYS KNIFE POLISH'	£12-15
858/8	88	Military Bus, Kay's Set C88	GSP
858/9	88	'BAXTERS', Kay's Set C89	GSP
858/10	88	'SCHWEPPES', BP promo	£10-12
858/11	88	'GREAT EASTERN Rly'	£20-25
884	86	'BEER IS BEST', 1st type	£12-15
885	86	'THOMAS TILLING', 1st	£20-25
		same but 2nd type	£15-20
888	86	'GRANT'S, cert.,1st type	£15-20
		2nd type	£20-25
975	86	'ALLENBURYS'	£12-15
25001	01	'BRITISH LEGION' 80 years	£15-20
96985	92	'EAST SURREY'	£12-15
96986	93	'BRIGHTON & HOVE'	£12-15
96987	93	'SCHWEPPES'	£12-15
96988	93	'BEAMISH'	£12-15
96989	95	'GENERAL' (Corgi direct)	£10-12
96991	95	'SHEFFIELD' (Corgi direct)	£10-12
96992	95	'NORFOLK'S' (Corgi direct)	£10-12
96993	95	'YELLOWAYS' (Corgi direct)	£10-12
96994	95	'S. WALES' (Corgi direct)	£10-12

Corgi Classics Military Models

See also 'Collection Heritage' and 'Aviation Archive' sections.

Armoured Car

69901	98	Saladin	see Set 69901

Bedford MK Truck

69902	99	Canvas back truck + 25lb gun	£35-40

Berliet Truck

73801	98	GLR8 military covered wagon	£35-40

Citroën 55 Truck

74001	98	Canvas back truck	£35-40

Diamond-T

55601	98	'USAF' wrecker	£20-25

Jeep

50103	01	M151 Recoiless Rifle, trailer	£18-22
50105	01	M151 'USAF'	£14-16

Land-Rover

07302	98	British Army, olive green	£10-12
57903	98	'Army' camouflage	£6-9
07501	99	'British Army' LR with trailer	£20-25

M35 Truck

50204	01	A1 2.5ton truck, 'USMC'	£28-32

Tanks

50303	01	M48 A3 Patton Tank 'US Army'	£30-35
51101	01	M113 ACAV 'US Army'	£30-35
66501	98	Tiger Mk.I Tank	£15-20
66601	98	King Tiger Heavy Tank	£15-20
69901	98	Centurion Tank	see Set 69901

Thornycroft

C858/8	88	Military Bus, Kay's Set C88	GSP

'Tramlines' and 'Tramway Classics'

Corgi Tramlines were introduced in 1988 and were presented in 'window' display boxes with a printed diorama and a grey plastic road track base. These tram models are designed to fit 'OO' gauge model railway track, but note that since actual tram tracks are usually of a narrower gauge than standard railway tracks, the scale of Corgi model trams is not 1:76. However, in 1999, the range was renamed 'Tramway Classics' with the scale stated as 1:72. Models of the famous 'balloon' trams of Blackpool were introduced in 1997 – see the 'Original Omnibus' listings for details.

Double-Deck Trams
(closed top, closed platforms)

37/1		'PENNY POST', special box	**£15-20**
993/1	89	'PORTSMOUTH'	**£15-20**
993/2	89	'DOVER'	**£15-20**
993/3	91	'COVENTRY'	**£15-20**
25201	01	'BELFAST' 'Malone Rd'	**£15-20**
25202	01	'LONDON' '68'	**£15-20**
25203	01	'LIVERPOOL' 'Lower Lane'	**£15-20**
25204	01	'BOLTON' 'Horwich'	**£15-20**
25205	01	'NOTTINGHAM' 'Market Pl'	**£15-20**
36701	01	'SUNDERLAND' 'Roker'	**£15-20**
36702	?	'DUNDEE'	**£15-20**
36704	99	'LONDON TRANSPORT'	**£15-20**
36705	99	'EDINBURGH CITY'	**£15-20**
36706	99	'SHEFFIELD' 'Crookes'	**£15-20**
36707	99	'LEEDS' 'Yeadon'	**£15-20**
36708	99	'L.T.' 'Ilford Broadway'	**£15-20**
36709	00	'Queen Mother's Century'	**£15-20**
36710	00	'SUNDERLAND' 'Rover'	**£15-20**
36711	00	'BIRMINGHAM' 'Lodge Rd'	**£15-20**
36712	00	'Queen Mother's Century'	**£15-20**
97262	93	'BLACKPOOL'	**£15-20**
97264	92	'CARDIFF'	**£15-20**
97265	92	'BELFAST'	**£15-20**
97273	94	'BLACKPOOL'	**£15-20**
97285	92	'LEICESTER'	**£15-20**
97286	92	'SUNDERLAND'	**£15-20**
97287	92	'NOTTINGHAM'	**£15-20**
97288	92	'SHEFFIELD'	**£15-20**
97293	92	'NEWCASTLE EVENING C'	**£15-20**
97294		'BIRMINGHAM'	**£15-20**
97296	92	'LIVERPOOL'	**£15-20**
98154	95	'DOVER'	**£15-20**

Double-Deck Trams
(closed-top, open platforms)

992/1	88	'LEEDS CITY'	**£15-20**
992/2	88	'GLASGOW'	**£15-20**
992/3	88	'L.C.C.'	**£15-20**
992/4	88	'BLACKPOOL'	**GSP**
992/5	88	'BRADFORD'	**£30-35**
992/6	89	'SOUTHAMPTON'	**£15-20**
992/7	89	'BIRMINGHAM'	**£40-45**
992/8	90	'LONDON TRANSPORT'	**£15-20**
992/9	91	'SOUTH SHIELDS'	see 97261
25205	01	'NOTTINGHAM'	**£15-20**
36801	01	'GLASGOW'	**£15-20**
36802	01	'LEEDS'	**£15-20**
97260	91	'BIRKENHEAD'	**£15-20**
97261	91	'SOUTH SHIELDS'	**£15-20**
97267	94	'GRIMSBY'	**£15-20**
97268	94	'L.C.C.'	**£15-20**
97270	94	'BOLTON / ACDO'	**£15-20**
98152	93	'GLASGOW'	**£15-20**
98153	93	'LONDON'	**£15-20**
98154	93	'DOVER'	**£15-20**

Double-Deck Trams
(open-top, open platforms)

991/1	88	'L.C.C.'	**£30-35**
991/2	88	'BLACKPOOL'	**£15-20**
991/3	89	'BATH ELECTRIC'	**£15-20**
991/4	89	'BOURNEMOUTH'	**£15-20**
991/5	89	'BURTON & ASHBY'	**£15-20**
991/6	90	'CROYDON'	**£15-20**
991/7	90	'GARDEN FESTIVAL'	**£15-20**
991/8	90	'LLANDUDNO'	see 97242
25201	01	'BELFAST'	**£15-20**

36601	96	'WALLASEY'	**£15-20**
36602	96	'LEICESTER'	**£15-20**
36603	96	'WEST HARTLEPOOL'	**£15-20**
36604	00	'CROYDON CELEBRATION'	**£15-20**
36801	96	'GLASGOW'	**£15-20**
97240	91	'LOWESTOFT'	**£15-20**
97241	91	'SOUTH METROPOLITAN'	**£15-20**
97242	90	'LLANDUDNO'	**£15-20**
97265	95	'BELFAST'	**£15-20**
97266	95	'PAISLEY & DISTRICT'	**£15-20**
97268	95	'LONDON COUNTY'	**£15-20**
97269	95	'PLYMOUTH'	**£15-20**
97365	95	'BLACKPOOL TOWER'	**£15-20**
97290	92	'HULL'	**£15-20**
97291	92	'SOUTH SHIELDS'	**£15-20**
97365	96	'BLACKPOOL TOWER'	**£15-20**
98150	93	'LOWESTOFT'	**£15-20**
98151	93	'SOUTH METROPOLITAN'	**£15-20**

Single-Deck Trams (open platforms)

990/1	88	'SOUTHAMPTON'	**£18-22**
990/2	88	'SHEFFIELD'	**£18-22**
990/3	89	'DERBY'	**£18-22**
990/4	89	'WOLVERHAMPTON'	**£18-22**
990/5	90	'MAIDSTONE'	**£18-22**
36901	96	'BLACKPOOL'	**£18-22**
36902	00	'DARLINGTON' 'Theatre'	**£15-20**
97263	94	'ASHTON-UNDER-LYNE'	**£15-20**

Single-Deck Trams (closed platforms)

36903	00	'BLACKPOOL' 'Fleetwood'	**£15-20**

Promotional Trams

?	93	'BRITISH TRAM CO.' newspaper promotionals: 'Hull', 'Nottingham', 'Newcastle', 'Leicester', 'Sunderland', 'Sheffield', 'South Shields'; each: **£20-25**

A page from Corgi's 2001 catalogue showing the 'New Mini' models

Ref	Intro	Model name, details	MPR

Car makes are listed alphabetically.
Model references are listed numerically.

Gift Set models are listed here individually
only if they have a different reference number
from the set that contains them. The Classics
Gift Sets listing includes additional details.

See also 'Corgi Classics TV and Film
Favourites' and Corgi 'Toys' 1998-2001.

Most models in this range are in a scale of
1:43. Exceptions include the 1:36 Minis and
1:18 MGs and are clearly indicated.

MPR = Market price range
GSP = Gift Set price   NPP = No price possible
NGPP = No guide price at present

Austin-Healey

733/1	90	hard-top, red/white	£10-15
733/2	90	hard-top, Kay's Set D53/1	GSP
734/1	90	open, blue, (99050)	£10-15
735/1	90	soft-top, green/grey	£10-15
02401	96	soft-top, Primrose/black	£10-15
02501	96	open, Ivory/black	£10-15
96200	91	hard-top, turquoise/white	£10-15
96220	91	open, pale blue/cream	£10-15
96240	91	open, yellow	£10-15
99050	93	open, blue, (D734/1)	£10-15
99051	91	soft-top, dark green/grey	£10-15
?	96	open, chrome	£40-50
?	96	soft-top, chrome	£40-50

Chevrolet Bel-Air
(see also under 'Fire Service Vehicles')

532	94	blue or black	£10-15
582/2	89	pale blue	£10-15
	89	black / white	£10-15
96570	92	gold, 'Millionth'	£10-15
?	92	pale blue	£10-15
?	94	blue or gold	£10-15
97396	94	'HIGHWAY PATROL'	£10-15

The 'Donnington Collection'

97373	96	Hesketh 308, James Hunt	£10-12
97374	96	Surtees TS9, John Surtees	£10-12
97375	96	Shadow DN1, Jackie Oliver	£10-12
97376	96	Ferrari 312B, Mario Andretti	£10-12
97377	96	Lotus 74D, Emerson Fittipaldi	£10-12
97378	96	Surtees TS9B, Mike Hailwood	£10-12

Ferrari 250

739/1	90	250 GTO Sport, red, '151'	£10-15
740/1	90	250 GTO Road, red, (96320)	£10-15
02601	?	yellow	£10-15
96320	90	re-run of D740/1	£10-15
98124	93	250 GT Road, red	£10-15

Ford Cortina (and Lotus-Cortina)

708/1	89	Lotus Cortina, white/green	£10-15
	89	Lotus Cortina, see Set D53/1	GSP
708/2	89	Ford, maroon	£10-15
708/3	89	Lotus, Monaco red	£10-15
708/4	89	Lotus, aqua blue	£10-15
708/5	89	Rally car, see Set D16/1	GSP
708/6	90	'POLICE', white	£10-15
708/7	90	Ford, black	£10-15
708/8	90	Ford, spruce green	£10-15
01301	97	red	£10-15
01302	99	1966 RAC Rally, Jim Clark	£15-20
96500	92	'POLICE', (re-issued D708/6)	£10-15
96501	94	Ford, French blue	£10-15

96502	?	Rally car, 'Corgi Rally'	£10-15
96760	91	Rally car, 'J. Whitmore'	£10-15
96763	92	Rally car, 'Roger Clark'	£10-15
96764	92	Rally car, 'Jim Clark'	£10-15
98130	93	Lotus, white/green	£10-15
98165	95	'LT' 'Radio Control'	£10-15
98266	94	chrome-plated, plinth, certificate (1000)	£40-50

Ford Popular Saloon

701/1	88	grey-blue	£10-15
701/3	89	black	£10-15
701/5	89	fawn	£10-15
701/6	89	Rally car, see Set D16/1	GSP
701/7	89	pale green	£10-15
701/8	90	Newark grey	£10-15
701/9	90	Winchester blue	£10-15
01401	97	white	£10-15
01402	98	black	£10-15
96481	94	sage green	£10-15
98132	93	black	£10-15
98132	93	re-run of C701/3	£10-15
98264	93	chrome-plated, plinth, certificate (1000)	£40-50

Ford Sierra Cosworth

59301	97	'SAFARI RALLY'	£8-10
96012	94	'SPENDER'	£10-12

Ford Thunderbird

810/2	94	black	£10-12

Ford Zephyr Saloon

710/1	89	red	£10-15
710/2	89	blue	£10-15
710/3	89	Monaco red	£10-15
710/4	89	Regency grey	£10-15
710/5	89	'POLICE', black	£10-15
710/6	90	maroon	£10-15
710/7	90	Pompadour blue	£10-15
?	?	Linden green	£10-15
96721	91	Rally car, 'Anne Hall'	£10-15
98133	?	re-run of D710/3	£10-15

Ford Zodiac Saloon

709/1	89	maroon / grey	£10-15
709/2	89	two-tone blue	£10-15
709/3	89	yellow / white	£10-15
709/4	89	red / white	£10-15
709/5	89	Rally car, see Set D16/1	GSP
709/6	90	black / blue	£10-15
709/7	90	two-tone green	£10-15
709/8	90	Ermine white / grey	£10-15
	90	grey / yellow (very few made)	NGPP
01601	97	turquoise / white	£10-15
01602	99	yellow / white	£10-15
98135	93	re-run of D709/3	£10-15
?	96	chrome-plated, certificate	£40-50

Jaguar 'E'-type

02701	96	open, dark green	£10-15
02702	98	open, Opalescent Maroon	£10-15
02801	96	soft-top, black	£10-15
02802	01	Gold-plated	
96042	91	open, cream / black	£10-15
96043	91	open, black, cream interior	£10-15
96080	92	open, red	£10-15
96081	92	open, primrose, red interior	£10-15
96082	92	soft-top, gold, 'K. Baker'	£10-15
98120	93	soft-top, British racing green	£10-15
98121	93	open, silver-blue	£10-15
?	96	open, chrome-plated	£40-50
?	96	soft-top, chrome-plated	£40-50

Jaguar Mk.II Saloon

700/1	88	red	£10-15
700/3	88	black, certificate (7,000)	£10-15

700/4	89	Opalescent Golden Sand	£10-15
700/5	89	green	£10-15
700/6	89	metallic blue	£10-15
700/7	89	metallic grey	£10-15
700/8	89	silver-blue (96560)	£10-15
700/9	90	willow green	£10-15
700/11	90	Rally car, see Kay's Set D53/1	GSP
706/1	88	'POLICE', black	£10-15
706/2	89	Police car, Kay's Set D75/1	GSP
01801	96	'BUSTER', red	£10-15
01802	97	Opalescent Bronze	£10-15
01804	98	British Racing Green	£10-15
01805	99	'40th Anniversary' gold-plated	£20-25
96680	91	Rally car, 'Stirling Moss'	£10-15
96681	91	Rally car, 'John Coombes'	£10-15
96682	91	'Inspector Morse'	£90-100
96683	94	white	£10-15
96685	95	'Staffordshire Police'	£10-15
97702/a	92	dark red, plinth	GSP
98131	93	silver-blue (as in Set 97700/a)	£10-15
98263	93	chrome-plated, plinth, certificate (1,000)	£40-50

Jaguar XK120

02901	96	open, British Racing Green	£10-15
02902	98	open, Lavender Grey	£10-15
02903	98	'50th', gold-plated	£15-20
03001	96	soft-top, Gunmetal Grey	£10-15
96040	91	open, white	£10-15
96041	91	open, British Racing Green	£10-15
96044	91	soft-top, maroon, white top	£10-15
96060	91	open, black, white top	£10-15
98900	94	open, chrome-plated	£40-50

Mercedes-Benz 300sl

03401	96	open, pale green	£10-15
03501	96	soft-top, black	£10-15
96410	93	open, red, cream seats	£10-15
96411	93	open, dark grey, red seats	£10-15
96415	93	soft-top, ivory, black top	£10-15
96416	93	soft-top, silver, black top	£10-15

MGA

730/1	90	hard-top, silver/black	£10-15
730/2	90	hard-top, Kays Set D53/1	GSP
731/1	90	open, British Racing Green	£10-15
732/1	90	soft-top, red / black (99048)	£10-15
03101	98	Alamo Beige	£10-15
03201	96	soft-top, Iris blue	£10-15
03301	96	open, Orient red	£10-15
96140	91	hard-top, red, rack	£10-15
96160	91	open, black, rack	£10-15
96180	91	soft-top, white / grey, rack	£10-15
99046	93	hard-top, silver / black	£10-15
99048	93	soft-top, red / black (D732/1)	£10-15
?	96	open, chrome-plated	£40-50
?	96	soft-top, chrome-plated	£40-50

MGB 1:18 scale

45201	96	soft-top, Primrose Yellow	£20-25
95103	95	open, Tartan Red	£20-25
95104	95	open, Old English White	£20-25
95106	95	open, British Racing Green, limited edition 15,000	£25-30

MGF 1:18 scale

46601	96	open, Amaranth (purple)	£20-25
46602	99	open, British Racing Green	£20-25
46603	99	open, Signal Red	£20-25
46702	97	'JAPAN RACING'	£20-25
46703	00	'Rover Team Spirit'	
95100	96	Diamond White	£20-25
95101	95	hard-top, Flame Red	£20-25
95102	95	open, British Racing Green	£20-25
95105	95	open, Metallic Charcoal, plinth	£25-30
---	95	'Press Drive '95'. Gift to journalists	NGPP

Mini Saloon (Rally Minis) 1:36

04401	96	'VIKING TYRES'	**£10-12**
04402	96	'CORGI CLASSICS'	**£10-12**
04403	96	'Mr. BEAN' (see 96011)	**£15-20**
04404	96	'GISLAVED'	**£10-12**
04405	97	'CORGI 40th Anniv.'	**£10-12**
04406	97	'Tony Dron', 1966 Monte Carlo	**£15-20**
04407	97	'Crellin / Hopkirk' 1994 Monte Carlo Rally	**£15-20**
04408	97	'Dyson / Bird', 1966 Monte Carlo Rally	**£15-20**
04409	97	Mini Equinox	**£10-15**
04410	98	Union Jack Mini, red	**£15-20**
04411	97	'Kenya Safari' (with mud)	**£12-15**
04412	98	Charcoal and Chequers Mini	**£10-12**
04413	98	Union Jack Mini, BRG	**£15-20**
04414	97	Nurburgring Mini	**£90-110**
04415	97	Eddie Stobart Mini	**£15-20**
04416	98	Chequers (Blue) Mini	**£15-20**
04417	98	'HSS 40th', 'Network Q'	**£10-12**
04418	98	'Monte Carlo Rally', '87'	**£15-20**
04419	98	'Mr BEAN'S Mini'	**£10-12**
04420	98	'Cadbury's Mini Egg'	**£5-7**
04421	98	'Safari Mini' (without mud)	**£15-20**
04422	98	'D.Paveley/A.Bull' '97 MCR'	**£10-12**
04423	98	'Geoff Taylor' 'Mighty Minis'	**£10-12**
04424	98	'British Gas' '94 RAC Rally'	**£10-12**
04425	99	'Horiba' '98 Spanish Rally'	**£10-12**
04426	99	'Mintex Rally'	**£10-12**
04427	99	'Plant Bros' '97 RAC Rally'	**£10-12**
04428	99	'Steven King' 'Mighty Minis'	**£120-140**
04429	99	'John Kirby' '24'	**£10-12**
04430	00	'Peter Crewes' '7'	**£10-12**
04431	00	'Sam Roach' '79'	**£10-12**
04432	00	'Nigel Ainge' 'Mighty Minis'	**£15-20**
04433	99	'Green Team' 'Network Q'	**£10-12**
04434	99	'Neil Burgess' '88'	**£10-12**
04435	00	'Plant Bros. Millennium Mini'	**£35-40**
04436	00	'Chris Hunter' 'Mighty Minis'	**£15-20**
04437	00	'Stewart Jenner' '76'	**£10-12**
04439	00	'Tony Ragona' '26'	**£10-12**
04440	00	Psychedelic Mini	**£15-20**
04441	00	'The Italian Job' Minis, each with driver figure and pile of 'gold' bars:	
04441		'The Italian Job' Mini, Red	**£15-17**
04441		'The Italian Job' Mini, White	**£15-17**
04441		'The Italian Job' Mini, Blue	**£15-17**
	NB	(See also Classics Gift Sets section for 'The Italian Job' sets)	
04442	?	?	?
04443	00	'Collect 2000' Mini	**£35-40**
04444	01	'jungle.com' (Plant Bros.)	**£10-12**
04501	99	'40th', gold-plated	**£30-35**
04502	99	Dark Mulberry Red	**£10-15**
04503	99	Old English White	**£10-15**
04504	99	Island Blue	**£10-15**
04505	00	'John Cooper Mini 40', BRG	**£30-35**
04506	00	'Terry Colley' '40' (Magazine)	**£10-12**
04507	00	'John Cooper', Red / White	**£15-20**
04508	00	'Union Jack Mini' (Harrods)	**£20-25**
04509	01	Red / Grey, 'End of the Road'	**£15-20**
05505	99	'Frizzell Insurance', 'CSMA'	**GSP**
05506	99	'The Italian Job' Set (3)	**GSP**
82201	01	'Knightsbridge', Gold	**£10-12**
82202	01	'Steve Ball' '3'	**£10-12**
82203	01	'Christopher Huck' '41'	**£10-12**

82204	01	'Plant Bros.' 'Manx Rally'	**£10-12**
82204	01	'M. Plant' limited edition	**£40-50**
82205	01	'Classic Edition', Amaranth	**£10-12**
82206	01	'Mini 40', Dark Mulberry Red	**£10-12**
82207	01	'Mini 40', Old English White	**£10-12**
82208	01	'Mini 40', Island Blue	**£10-12**
82209	01	'Mini 40', Rover Cooper LE	**£10-12**
82210	01	Gold (painted) Express Gifts	**£15-20**
82211	01	'Peter Baldwin', 'Mini Miglia'	**£10-12**
82212	01	'Dave Braggins', 'Mini 7'	**£10-12**
94415	?	'NEON', Metallic Blue	**£8-10**
96011	?	'Mr. BEAN' (as 04403)	**£10-12**

Mini-Cooper 1:43 scale

36502	99	'The Italian Job'	see Set 36502
94140	92	Red / White, 'Monte Carlo'	**£10-12**
94141	92	Black / White, RN '7'	**£10-12**
98136	93	Almond Green / White	**£10-12**
98137	93	Black and 'wickerwork'	**£10-12**
98138	94	British Racing Green / White	**£10-12**
98139	94	Red / White	**£10-12**
98141	95	'LIVERPOOL POLICE'	**£10-12**

Mini 40 (BMW Mini/Cooper)

86501	01	Mini-Cooper, Red / White	**£10-12**
86502	01	Mini-Cooper, Silver / Black	**£10-12**
86503	01	Mini-Cooper, Black / White	**£10-12**
86504	01	Mini-Cooper, Dakar Yellow	**£10-12**
86505	01	Mini-Cooper, Flamenco Orange	**£10-12**
86506	01	Cooper, British Racing Green	**£10-12**

Morris Minor 1000 Convertible

02001	97	Smoke Grey	**£10-12**
96750	94	Snowberry White, closed	**£10-12**
96751	94	Clipper Blue, open	**£10-12**
96752	94	Porcelain Green, closed	**£10-12**
96753	94	Frilford Grey, open	**£10-12**
96754	94	Highway Yellow, open	**£10-12**
96755	95	Rose Taupe, closed	**£10-12**
96757	95	dark blue, in 'Lovejoy' box	**£10-12**
96765	95	Almond Green, open	**£10-12**
96766	95	Turquoise, closed	**£10-12**
97345	?	black, open	**£10-12**
?	96	chrome-plated	**£40-50**

Morris Minor 1000 Saloon

702/1	88	'BSM', black	**£15-20**
702/2	88	dark blue	**£10-12**
702/4	89	lilac, 'Millionth Minor'	**£10-12**
702/5	89	maroon, grey grille surround	**£10-12**
	89	with maroon grille surround	**£10-12**
702/6	90	Almond Green (see 98134)	**£10-12**
702/7	90	Ivory	**£10-12**
702/8	90	Clipper Blue	**£10-12**
702/9	90	Sage Green (79137), not issued	NPP
703/1	88	Police 'Panda' Car, separate or integral hubs, thin end of sign attached to roof, no mirror or wiper detail on windscreen, thick quarterlights	**£15-20**
	88	integral hubs, detailed windscreen, thick end of sign attached to roof, thin quarterlights	**£15-20**
01901	97	Rose Taupe	**£10-12**
01903	98	Almond Green	**£10-12**
02002	98	'50th', gold-plated	**£15-20**
96740	91	Rally car, 'Pat Moss', cream	**£10-12**

96741	92	'Himalayan Rally', dark blue	**£10-12**
96742	93	Rally car, 'London to Peking'	**£10-12**
96744	94	'Police', 'AMP 339H'	**£10-12**
	94	'Police', 'BDA 327H'	**£10-12**
96745	94	black, red stripe	**£10-12**
96746	94	Rally car, RN '323'	**£10-12**
96756	94	'Bristol Omnibus'	**£10-12**
96758	95	'Some Mothers Do 'Ave 'Em'	**£10-12**
96759	94	'Merthyr Tydfil Police'	**£10-12**
98134	93	Almond Green (D702/6)	**£10-12**
98262	93	chrome-plated, plinth, direct mail (1,000)	**£40-50**

Morris Minor 1000 Traveller

02201	97	Clipper Blue	**£10-12**
02202	99	Maroon	**£10-12**
96870	94	Almond Green	**£10-12**
96871	94	black	**£10-12**
96873	94	'Edinburgh Police'	**£10-12**
96874	94	Old English White	**£10-12**
97343	95	'Bomb Disposal'	**£10-12**
?	96	Corgi Collector Club	**£10-12**

Porsche 356

741/1	90	hard-top, red / black	**£10-12**
742/1	90	open, white / black	**£10-12**
743/1	90	soft-top, black / red	**£10-12**
03701	96	soft-top, white	**£10-12**
03801	96	open, red	**£10-12**
96360	91	open, blue / black	**£10-12**
98122	93	soft-top, all black	**£10-12**
98123	93	open, silver / black	**£10-12**

Range Rover

57606	99	Metallic Gold, '30th Anniv.'	**£10-12**

Saab 96 Saloon

711/1	90	dark red (99045)	**£10-12**
711/2	90	light blue	**£10-12**
712/1	90	Rally car, 'Erik Carlsson'	**£10-12**
01701	99	red	**£10-12**
96662	91	Rally car, 'Pat Moss'	**£10-12**
99045	93	dark red (D711/1)	**£10-12**

Triumph TR3a

736/1	90	hard-top, red / black	**£10-12**
737/1	90	open, pale blue (99053)	**£10-12**
738/1	90	soft-top, cream/black (99054)	**£10-12**
03901	98	British Racing Green	**£10-12**
04001	96	soft-top, Sebring White	**£10-12**
04101	96	open, black	**£10-12**
96300	91	soft-top, red / black, rack	**£10-12**
99052	91	hard-top, red / black	**£10-12**
99053	90	open, pale blue (D737/1)	**£10-12**
99054	93	soft-top, cream/black (D738/1)	**£10-12**
?	96	open, chrome-plated	**£40-50**
?	96	soft-top, chrome	**£40-50**

VW Caravanette and Camper

984/1	90	Caravanette	see 96940
06701	98	Camper, red / white	**£10-12**
06801	97	Ochre / white	**£10-12**
06901	97	Red / white	**£10-12**
96940	92	Caravanette, red/grey	**£10-12**
96941	91	Caravanette, grey/white	**£10-12**
97040	91	Camper, green/white	**£10-12**

Collectors notes

Models and accessories in the 'Aviation Archive' range were initially made to a scale of 1:144. In 2000, a scale of 1:72 was introduced (mainly for smaller, older, military aircraft and similar) plus a small range of Helicopters in 1:48 scale for the American market. In 2001, larger passenger aircraft models were supplied with model boarding steps.

Accessories and Kits (1:144)
31805	99	Aircraft Hangar kit	£8-12
31806	99	WWII Control Tower kit	£8-12

Avro Lancaster (1:144)
47301	98	'Battle of Britain Memorial'	£25-30
47301A	98	500 only, sold on board a real Lancaster, signed by Sqd Ldr	£40-50
47302	98	'RAF Coastal Command'	£25-30
47303	99	'Royal Canadian Air Force'	£25-30
47401	98	'TRANS-CANADA'	£25-30
49501	99	'Battle of Britain'	see Set 49501

Avro Lancaster (1:72)
32601	01	'467 Squadron'	£80-90
32602	01	'Mickey the Moocher'	see Set 32602
32603	01	'KMB' (VC)	£25-30

Avro Lancaster (1:144)
47304	01	'Operation Chastise'	£35-40
47306	00	'Mickey the Moocher'	£35-40

Avro Vulcan (1:144)
31201	01	'XM600' '617 Squadron'	£35-40
48301	99	'RAF' '44 Squadron'	£35-40
48302	99	'RAF' 'Dambusters Sqdn'	£40-45
48303	99	'RAF' 'First and Last'	£35-40
48304	00	'XM655' 'IX Squadron'	£35-40

Avro York (1:144)
30101	01	'RAF Transport Command'	£35-40
47202	98	'BOAC'	£25-30
47203	98	'DAN-AIR LONDON'	£25-30
47204	99	'RAF' 'King's Flight'	£25-30

Boeing 707 (1:144)
32901	01	'VC-137C' 'AIR FORCE ONE'	£40-50
32902	01	'TRANS-WORLD' 'N18709'	£40-50
32903	01	'BRITISH AIRWAYS'	£40-50
32904	01	'BRANIFF' + steps	£40-50
32905	01	'BOAC' + steps	£40-50
32906	01	'PAN AM' + steps	£40-50

Boeing B-17 Flying Fortress (1:144)
31101	01	'RAF' '214 Squadron'	£25-30
31102	01	'Memphis Belle'	£25-30
31103	01	'414 Sqdn' ' Yankee Doodle'	£25-30
48201	99	'USAF' 'Bit o' Lace'	£25-30
48203	99	'RAF' 'Coastal Command'	£25-30
48204	99	'USAAF' 'Memphis Belle'	£25-30
48205	00	'U' 'Sentimental Journey'	£25-30
49502	99	'USAF' 'Sally-B'	see Set 49502
?	99	'Sally-B Society' special	£40-50

Boeing B-29 Superfortress (1:144)
31801	01	'USAAF' 'Esso Express'	£35-40
31802	01	'Hawg Wild' (Duxford)	£35-40
48901	00	'Enola Gay'	£35-40

Boeing Stratocruiser (1:144)
31001	01	'NORTHWEST' 'N74601'	£30-35
48102	99	'ILLINOIS AIR GUARD' HC	£30-35
48103	99	'DELAWARE AIR GUARD'	£30-35
48104	00	'MATS' C-97A Stratofreighter	£30-35
48105	99	'BOAC'	£30-35

Bristol Britannia (1:144)
31501	01	'BRITANNIA' 'G-ANBF'	£30-35
31502	01	'Team Spirit' 'Boscombe Down'	£30-35
31503	01	'BKS' + steps	£30-35
31504	01	'CUNARD EAGLE' + steps	£30-35
48601	00	'LAKER AIRWAYS'	£30-35
48602	00	'BOAC' 'G-AOVB'	£30-35
48603	00	'MONARCH' 'G-AOVH'	£30-35

De Havilland Comet (1:144)
31401	01	'Royal Aircraft Establishment'	£35-40
31402	01	'UNITED ARAB' + steps	£35-40
48501	99	'BEA' 'G-APMA'	£30-35
48502	99	'DAN-AIR' 'G-APDB'	£30-35
48503	99	'RAF Transport Command'	£30-35
48504	00	'BOAC' 'G-APDD'	£35-40
48505	00	'A&AEE Boscombe Down'	£35-40

De Havilland Mosquito (1:72)
32801	01	BIV-FHS, 'DK333'	£30-35
32802	01	FB-VI 'VSP'	£30-35

Douglas DC-3 (1:144)
30001	01	'CONTINENTAL' 'N25673'	£20-25
30002	01	'US Navy' (with skis)	£20-25
47104	98	'BEA'	£20-25
47105	98	'EASTERN AIRLINES'	£20-25
47107	98	'AIR ATLANTIQUE'	£20-25
47108	99	'KLM'	£20-25
47109	99	'LUFTHANSA'	£20-25
47110	99	'AIR FRANCE'	£20-25

Douglas C-47 Skytrain (1:144)
47112	99	'USAF' 'Electronic Warfare'	£20-25

English Electric Lightning (1:72)
32301	01	'The Tigers' Aerobatic Team	£25-30
32302	01	'RAF No.19 Sqdn', Aug.1973	£25-30
32303	01	'226 OCU' F1	£25-30
49401	01	'56 Sqdn' 'Firebirds' 1962	£25-30

Handley-Page Victor (1:144)
31601	01	'XL-189' 'Falklands'	£35-40
31602	01	'XL-231' 'Lusty Lindy'	£35-40
48701	01	?	£35-40
48702	01	?	£35-40
48703	01	?	£35-40

Harrier and Sea Harrier (1:72)
32401	01	'Falklands' 'XZ997'	£25-30
32402	01	'Royal Navy' 'XZ450'	£25-30
32403	01	'US Marine Corps.' AV-8A	£25-30
32404	01	'Daily Mail Air Race 1969'	£25-30
32405	01	'899 Sqdn.' '50th Anniversary'	£25-30

Hawker Hunter (1:72)
32701	01	'Blue Diamonds' Mk.6	£25-30
32702	01	'RAF Brawdy' Aug. 1979	£25-30
32703	01	'Defence Research Agency'	£25-30
32704	01	'43 Sqdn.' 'Fighting Cocks'	£25-30
49801	01	'79 Sqdn' 'XG228'	£25-30
49802	01	?	£25-30
49803	01	?	£25-30

Hawker Hurricane (1:72)
32001	01	'174 Sqdn' 'BE421'	£25-30
32002	01	'Night Fighter'	£25-30
32602	01	'LF-363'	see Set 32602
49101	01	'RAF' 'Sqdn Ldr Townsend'	£25-30
49102	00	'Sqdn Ldr Stanford Tuck'	£25-30
49104	01	'87 Sqdn' 'Fl Lt R.Gleed'	£25-30
49501	99	'Battle of Britain'	see Set 49501

Hawker Hurricane (1:144)
49503	00	'LF363 '56F'	see Set 49503

Helicopters (1:48)
50401	01	'US Army Vietnam'	£35-40
50402	01	'Los Angeles City Fire Dept.'	£35-40
50403	01	'MUSMC' Frog Gunship	£35-40
50405	01	'Medevac' 'US Army'	£35-40
51202	01	Bell Cobra, 'USMC'	£35-40

Lockheed Constellation (1:144)
30401	01	'BOAC' 'G-ALAL'	£30-35
30402	01	'USAF' 'Columbine'	£30-35
47501	98	'TWA'	£30-35
47502	98	'QANTAS' 'Inaugural 50th'	£30-35
47503	98	'AIR INDIA'	£30-35
47505	98	'BRANIFF AIRWAYS'	£30-35
47506	98	'USAF'	£30-35
47507	99	'EASTERN AIRLINES'	£30-35
47508	99	'PAN AM'	£30-35
47509	99	'MATS' '48-609'	£30-35
?????	98	'KLM'	£30-35

Lockheed Hercules (1:144)
31301	01	'US Navy' 'Op'n Deep-Freeze'	£30-35
31303	01	'RAAF'	£30-35
48401	99	'RAF' air re-fueller	£30-35
48402	99	'US Navy' 'Blue Angels'	£30-35
48403	99	'RAF' 'Hephaeston'	£30-35
48404	99	'U.S. COAST GUARD'	£30-35
48405	00	'RAF' 'Desert Storm'	

M-D Phantom F-4 (1:72)
32201	01	'VF-111' 'Sundowners'	£30-35
32202	01	'RAF'	£30-35

Messerschmitt Bf109E (1:72)
32101	01	'Wespen Geschwader'	£20-25
32102	01	'Helmut Wick'	£20-25
49201	01	'UDET' 'Hpt Hans von Hahn'	£20-25
49202	00	'Schlageter' 'Adolf Galland'	£20-25
49205	01	'UDET' 'Olt Franz von Werra'	£20-25
49505	00	'Battle of Britain'	see Set No. 49505

Mitsubishi Zero (1:72)
33101	01	'IJN' 'Pearl Harbor'	£20-25
33102	01	'251st' 'Nishizawa'	£20-25

N.A. P-51D Mustang (1:72)
32201	01	'Old Crow'	£20-25
32202	01	'Hun Hunter from Texas'	£20-25
32203	01	'100th FS' 'Bunnie'	£20-25
49301	00	'Big Beautiful Doll' 'Landers'	£20-25
49302	00	'Charles 'Chuck' Yeager'	£20-25
49502	99	'Big Beautiful Doll'	see Set 49502

N.A. P-51D Mustang (1:144)
49504	00	'Old Crow' '357th'	see Set 49504

Short Sunderland Flying Boat (1:144)
31701	01	'RAF'	£30-35
48801	99	'RAF' 'Coastal Command'	£30-35
48802	99	'BOAC' 'Hythe Class'	£30-35
48803	99	'RAAF' 'No.10 Sqdn'	£30-35
48804	99	'RAAF' '461 Sqdn Plymouth'	£30-35

Supermarine Spitfire (1:144)
49503	00	AB910 '222 Natal Sqdn'	see Set 49503

Supermarine Spitfire (1:72)
31901	01	'276 Air-Sea Rescue Sqdn'	£20-25
31902	01	Mk.V desert camouflage	£20-25
31903	01	'Sqdn. Leader Zumbach'	£20-25
32602	01	'Mk.IIa-P7350'	see Set 32602
49001	01	'RAF' 'Flt Ltn Adolf Malan'	£20-25
49002	00	'Wing Co. Douglas Bader'	£20-25
49004	01	'603 Sqdn.' 'Flg Off Carbury'	£20-25
49005	01	'KIWI' 'Plt Off Alan Deere'	£20-25
49501	99	'Battle of Britain'	see Set No. 49501
49505	00	'Battle of Britain'	see Set No. 49505

Republic P-47 Thunderbolt (1:144)
49502	99	'No Guts, No Glory'	see Set 49502
49504	00	'56th Fighter Group'	see Set 49504

Vickers Viscount (1:144)
30501	01	'AER LINGUS' 800 'EI-AOE'	£30-35
30502	01	'UNITED' 700 'N7440'	£30-35

30503	01	'BRITISH AIR FERRIES' 800 ...	**£30-35**
30504	01	'NORTHEAST' + steps..............	**£30-35**
30505	01	'CAPITAL AIRLINES' + steps...	**£30-35**
47601	99	'BEA' 700 'G-ALWF'	**£25-30**
47602	99	'PARCELFORCE'	**£25-30**
47603	99	'CONTINENTAL'	**£25-30**
47604	99	'LUFTHANSA'	**£25-30**
46705	00	'BRITISH EAGLE' 'G-AOCC' ..	**£25-30**
47606	99	'VIRGIN ATLANTIC'	**£25-30**
47607	00	'BEA' 800 'G-AOHH'	**£25-30**

Vought Corsair (1:72)

33001	01	'Daphne C.' 'USAAF'	**£18-22**
33002	01	'White 29' 'USAAF'	**£18-22**

'Aviation Archive' sets

32602 01 **'Battle of Britain Memorial Flight'**: Avro Lancaster 'Mickey the Moocher', Spitfire P7350 and Hurricane LF363 ....**£130-150**

49501 99 **'Battle of Britain Memorial Flight'**: Avro Lancaster, Spitfire and Hurricane + badges **£60-70**

49502 99 'USAF' B17 'Sally-B', Mustang 'Big Beautiful Doll' and Thunderbolt 'No Guts, No Glory' **£45-50**

49503 00 **'Battle of Britain Memorial Flight'**: Spitfire AB910 '222 Natal Sqdn' and Hurricane LF363 '56F' **£20-25**

49504 00 **'Little Friends Set'**: 'Old Crow' Mustang, '56th Group' Thunderbolt............**£15-20**

49505 00 **'Battle of Britain Dog Fight Set'** Spitfire '609 Sqdn' and ME109e 'Uffz Hohenseldt' **£40-45**

49506 00 **'Confederate Airforce Set'**: BB29 'Fifi', Mustang, Thunderbolt **£50-55**

No. 32405 Hawker Harrier is one of the range of 1:72 scale Aviation Archive models from Corgi. It is finished in the '50th Anniversary' livery of '899 Squadron'.

A page from Corgi's 2001 catalogue showing some of the current 'TV & Film Favourites'

Austin 1300 Estate
00802 00 'FAWLTY TOWERS' + figure....**£12-15**

'Beatles' Collection
05401 97 'YELLOW SUBMARINE' **£25-30**
05403 99 'YELLOW SUBMARINE'
plus 54mm white-metal
figures of the Fab Four **£30-35**
05706 97 Bedford CA graffiti van.............**£15-20**
22301 97 AEC advertising lorry.............**£20-25**
35006 97 AEC Routemaster, 'Penny Lane' **£25-30**
35302 97 Bedford Val coach, 'MAGICAL
MYSTERY TOUR', 1:50 .....**£20-25**
42403 00 Bedford Val coach, 'MAGICAL
MYSTERY TOUR', 1:72 ....
58003 97 Taxi with Rita Meter Maid **£14-18**

Bedford 'MK' Truck
18901 98 'Soldier, Soldier' + figures **£20-25**

Bedford 'OB' Box Van
18501 01 'Dad's Army' + Hodges figure....**£18-22**

Bentley
00101 99 'The AVENGERS', 1:43 ....**£15-20**

Buick Regal
57403 99 'KOJAK', 1:36, + figure **£14-18**

Chitty-Chitty-Bang-Bang
05301 99 Re-issue, driver figure only **£20-25**
98751 90 Re-issue, all 4 figures **£100-120**

DeLorean
05501 01 'BACK TO THE FUTURE'
plus Doc Brown figure **£14-18**

Dodge Charger
05301 01 'The DUKES of HAZZARD'
+ Bo and Luke Duke figures **£14-18**

Ford Capri
57401 99 'PROFESSIONALS', + figures...**£14-18**

Ford Sierra Cosworth
96012 96 'SPENDER' **£9-12**

Ford Torino
57402 99 'STARSKY & HUTCH', figures.**£14-18**

Ford Thunderbird
39901 99 'ELVIS', pink, 1:36, figure..........**£15-20**
39902 00 'MARILYN MONROE', figure ....

Ford Zephyr 6
00502 00 'Z-CARS' 'Police' **£10-12**

Jaguar Mk.II
01801 97 'BUSTER' **£10-12**
01803 99 'INSPECTOR MORSE', 1:36 .....**£14-18**
01806 01 'Insp. MORSE', with diorama...**£20-25**
96682 96 'INSPECTOR MORSE' **£60-80**

Jaguar XJS
57404 00 'Return of The Saint' + figure.......**£9-12**
57405 00 'The NEW AVENGERS'
with Mike Gambit figure **£9-12**

Land-Rover
07104 98 'DAKTARI' + lion and chimp **£15-20**

Mini and Mini-Cooper
04441 00 'The Italian Job' Mini, Red **£15-17**
04441 00 'The Italian Job' Mini, White......**£15-17**
04441 00 'The Italian Job' Mini, Blue.......**£15-17**
04403 ?   'Mr. BEAN' (see 96011) **£10-12**
04419 99 'Mr. BEAN', 1:36 ....**£10-12**
05506 98 'The Italian Job'................see Set 05506
36502 99 'The Italian Job'................see Set 36502
96011 ?   'Mr. BEAN' (as 04403)...............**£10-12**

Morris 1000 Convertible
96757 95 dark blue, in 'Lovejoy' box...........**£9-12**

Morris 1000 Saloon
96758 95 'Some Mothers Do 'Ave 'Em' **£9-12**

Pontiac
05601 01 'KNIGHTRIDER' + figure **£10-15**

Range Rover
57604 00 'The NEW AVENGERS'
with John Steed figure **£9-12**

Reliant Regal Van
05201 99 'TROTTERS' ('dirty' version)......**£8-12**

Rover V8
01901 01 'Lock, Stock and Two
Smoking Barrels' + figure **£10-15**

Thornycroft Van
09002 01 'Dad's Army' + Cpl Jones figure **£18-22**

James Bond vehicles

ASTON-MARTIN DB5
04201 97 1:43, gold, with Oddjob. Films
'Goldfinger' / 'Thunderball' **£15-20**
04202 99 1:43, gold-plated, 'Goldfinger'
35th anniversary **£18-22**
04301 97 1:36, 'Goldeneye' **£10-12**
04302 97 1:36, re-issue, silver....................**£10-12**
04303 99 1:36, black/red box, 600 only ..**£200-300**
96445 97 1:36, 30th Anniversary,
gold plated **£90-100**
96655 96 1:43, silver, replica box **£30-40**
96656 96 1:43, gold plated **£50-60**
96657 96 1:36, 'Goldeneye', silver **£10-12**
ASTON-MARTIN V8
04801 01 1:36, 'The Living Daylights' **£10-12**

BMW Z3
04901 01 1:36, 'Goldeneye' **£10-12**

BMW Z8
05001 01 1:36, 'The World is Not Enough'**£10-12**
99105 01 Same plus Diorama.....................**£25-30**

BMW 750i
05101 01 1:36, 'Tomorrow Never Dies' **£10-12**

CITROEN 2cv
65301 99 'For Your Eyes Only', 1:36 ....**£15-20**
65301 01 Same but in revised packaging....**£10-12**

FERRARI 355
92978 96 Red, in film 'Goldeneye' **£10-15**

GYROCOPTER
04601 01 1:36, 'You Only Live Twice'......**£10-12**

HELICOPTER
65501 99 1:43, 'The Spy Who Loved Me' .**£15-20**

LOTUS ESPRIT
65001 97 1:36, 'The Spy Who Loved Me' .**£15-20**
65002 01 1:36, 'The Spy Who Loved Me' .**£10-12**
04701 01 1:36, 'For Your Eyes Only' **£10-12**

MERCEDES-BENZ SALOON
05701 01 1:43, 'Octopussy' **£10-12**

MOON BUGGY
65201 97 'Diamonds Are Forever'.............**£15-20**

MUSTANG MACH I
02101 01 1:43, 'Diamonds Are Forever' **£10-12**

SPACE SHUTTLE
65401 99 'Moonraker' **£15-20**
?   01 'Moonraker' **£10-12**

TOYOTA 2000GT
65101 97 1:43, 'You Only Live Twice' **£15-20**
65102 01 1:43, 'You Only Live Twice' **£10-12**

SPECIAL '007' SET
99106 01 4-piece Set in film canister:
BMW Z8, Aston-Martins DB5
and Volante + Lotus Esprit **£40-50**

Miscellaneous
50902 01 'The GREEN HORNET' **£10-15**
52405 01 'MONKEEMOBILE' **£10-12**
87501 01 'Charlie's Angels' Van...............**£10-12**
87502 01 'The A-TEAM' + 'BA' figure........**£10-15**

The 'Green Hornet's 'Black Beauty' in Corgi's 'TV & Film Favourites' range.

Corgi Classics Gift Sets

Ref	Intro	Set name	Contents	Market Price Range
D4/1	1989	'Transport of the Early 50s'	'HANTS & DORSET' OB Coach + Routemaster, dark green/cream, 4,800	£35-40
D7/1	1989	'ROYAL MAIL'	Bedford OB Box Van plus Morris Minor Van in Post Office Red, 4,600	£40-50
D9/1	1989	'SHELL 1910-1940'	Grattan's set: Thornycroft Box Van and AEC Cabover Tanker, 4,400	£20-25
D13/1	1989	'Police Vans'	Two Morris Minor Vans: 'DOG SECTION' and 'GATESHEAD', 4,500	£40-50
D14/1	1989	'DANDY & BEANO'	Two Bedford CA Vans: 'DANDY' (yellow) and 'BEANO' (blue), 4,400	£35-45
D15/1	1989	'GPO Telephones'	AEC Cabover and Morris Minor vans in olive-green GPO livery, 4,400	£25-30
D16/1	1989	'RALLYING WITH FORD'	Zodiac (yellow/white, '21'), Zephyr (red, '29'), Popular ('139'), 3,400	£25-35
D17/1	1989	'SHELL 1950-1960'	Bedford OB Box Van and OB Pantechnicon, 5,000	£25-30
D19/1	1989	'SHELL 1910-1940'	AEC Cabover Tanker and Thornycroft Van	£20-25
D23/1	1989	Ford Popular Vans	Grattan's set. 3 vans: 'Fraser Cook', 'Lewis East' and 'Signsmith', 5,000	£30-35
D35/1	1990	'Battle of Britain'	Bedford OB Coach, Morris Minor Van, Ford Zephyr, 13,000	£25-30
D36/1	1990	'Racing Zephyrs'	Three Ford Zephyrs: white ('47'), yellow ('117'), black ('97'), 8,000	£20-25
D37/1	1990	'PENNY POST' Tram	Red/black fully closed tram, '150th Anniversary', 'Penny Black' design	£20-25
D41/1	1990	'BARTONS TRANSPORT'	Red Bedford OB Coach and red/cream AEC double-decker, 12,000	£20-25
D46/1	1990	'Vehicles of '50s & '60s'	Maroon/cream OB Box and Morris 'J' vans 'British Railways', 13,00	£20-25
D47/1	1990	'BEANO 1990'	AEC Bus 'Bash Street Kids' and Morris 'J' Van 'Minnie the Minx', 15,000	£15-20
C49	1986	'Transport of The 30s'	'The TIMES' Thornycroft Bus and Ford Model 'T' Van, 8,900	£15-20
C50	1987	'Transport of The 30s'	'London Markets' set of three Ford Model 'T' Vans: 'Smithfield', 'Covent Garden' and 'Billingsgate', 5,000 (no cert.)	£15-20
D51/1	1991	'GREENE KING'	Kay's set: AEC Cabover Tanker and Thornycroft Truck, 4,900	£20-25
D52/1	1990	'CHARRINGTONS'	Kay's set: AEC Cabover Tanker and Thornycroft Truck, 5,000	£20-25
D53/1	1990	'Rally' Set	Kay's set: Jaguar Mk.II, Ford Cortina, Austin-Healey, MGA, 4,500	£25-30
D54/1	1990	'Utilities' Set (4 vans)	Kay's set: Bedford CA 'Gas', Ford Popular, Morris Minor, Morris 'J', 5,000	£30-35
Q55/1	1990	'YORK FAIR'	Bedford OB Coach and OB Pantechnicon, '225 Years', 5,300	£25-30
Q57/1	1990	'Northern Collection'	OB Coach 'Standerwick' and OB Pantechnicon 'Slumberland', 4,900	£25-30
C67/1	1991	'Systeme Rally'	Export set	£10-15
C67/2	1991	'Peugeot Rally'	Export set	£10-15
D67/1	1990	'UNITED DAIRIES'	AEC Cabover van (orange) and AEC Tanker (white), 7,500	£15-20
C68	1987	'Transport of The 30s'	Kay's mail-order set: Thornycroft and Ford Model 'T' vans, 5,000	£30-35
C69	1987	'Transport of The 30s'	Mail-order set: Thornycroft and Ford 'T' vans 'BRYANT & MAY', 10,000	£15-18
D71/1	1989	'Ford Model 'T' Set	Kay's mail-order set: 'SOMERLITE' and 'TEXACO' tankers with 'A1 SAUCE' and 'APS MEDICINES' vans, 2,500	£20-25
D72/1	1989	'Minor & Popular Vans'	Kay's set: Morris vans 'RINGTON'S TEA' and 'FRY'S COCOA' plus Ford Popular vans COLMAN'S MUSTARD' and BOWYER'S SAUSAGES', 3,400	£25-30
D74/1	1989	'PICKFORDS'	Kay's set: OB Pantechnicon, Ford Popular van and Morris Minor van, 3,500	£65-80
D75/1	1989	'Police Cars'	Kay's set: Jaguar Mk.II, 'PANDA' Morris Minor and Ford Zephyr, 3,100	£40-45
D82/1	1990	'CORGI ON THE MOVE'	OB Coach and Pantechnicon, Corgi club set, personal certificates	£20-25
C88	1988	'Military' Gift Set	Kay's set: Thornycroft Bus and Ford Model 'T' Van, 6,000	£20-25
C89	1988	'60 Years Transport'	Kay's set: Thornycroft Bus 'BAXTERS', OB Coach 'HIGHLAND' and Tram 'FORD for VALUE', 3,100	£140-160
C90	1988	'Ford Model T Utility' Set	Kay's set: Ford vans 'ROYAL LAUNDRY' and 'SUNLIGHT', 8,600	£10-12
C91	1989	'Morris Minor Vans'	Grattan's set: 'GRATTAN'S', 'MITCHELL'S', 'TELEGRAPH & ARGUS', 5,000	£45-55
D94/1	1990	'WHITBREAD'	Bedford OB Box Van and Ford Model 'T' Van, 5,800	£20-25
05505	1998	'CSMA 75th Anniversary'	Civil Service Motoring Association set: Ford Capri, Jaguar XK120, 'Bullnose' Morris Van, Mini-Cooper Rally Car, plinth, certificate (5,000)	£35-40
05506	1999	'The Italian Job'	Red, White and Blue Mini-Coopers in special packaging. See also Set 36502	£25-30
05508	2001	'Mini Se7en Racing Club' Set	Featuring the two 1999 Mini Se7en and Mini-Miglia Championship winning cars in a diorama	NGPP
06203	1997	'EXPRESS POST'	Mini Vans set	£9-12
08002	1997	'Royal Mail and Express Post'	Set of two Mini-Vans	£20-25
08004	1997	'HAMPSHIRE POLICE' Set	Bedford S.C.U. and Morris 1000 Van	£25-30
08005	1997	'STOCKPORT POLICE' Set	Mini-Van and Morris 1000 Saloon	£20-25
08006	1997	'STOCKPORT POLICE' Set	Mini-Van and Morris 1000 Saloon	£20-25
08008	2000	'GUINNESS' Set	Bedford CA Van 'Red Heart' and Mini-Van 'Imported' with leprachaun, globe and bottle on roof	£20-25
16601	1997	'PICKFORDS' Set	Scammell Highwayman ballast-tractor and Land-Rover LWB	£65-75
17701	1997	'PICKFORDS' Set	Two Scammell Constructors with a 24 wheel low-loader	£85-95
31001	1996	'SHAP FELL'	Leyland articulated flatbed and Atkinson flatbed in 'BRS' livery	£20-25
31002	1997	'NATIONAL BENZOLE' Set	Foden tanker and Morris 'J' van	£35-40
31003	1997	'CHRIS MILLER Ltd'	AEC Ergomatic articulated low-loader with a Scammell Crane unit	£35-40
31004	1997	'WYNN'S'	Scammell articulated low-loader and Bedford 'S' tractor unit	£40-45
31005	1997	'SHELL-BP'	Bedford 'S' articulated tanker and a Land-Rover LWB	£35-40
31006	1997	'WYNN'S	Ford Thames Trader dropside and Morris 1000 Van	£40-45
31008	1998	'WIMPEY'	Bedford 'S' Low-loader with Priestman Luffing Shovel, plus Thames Trader Tipper	£35-40
31009	1998	'WYNN'S' 'Oriana' Set	Two Diamond-T Tractors, girder trailer + 'Oriana' boiler + Scammell Tractor	£90-100
31013	1999	'A.L.E.' Set	Two Scammel Contractors, Nicholas bogie units and a gas pressure vessel	£80-90
31014	2000	'SUNTER Bros. Set'	Diamond-T Ballast Tractor + Nicolas Bogies and Vessel Load; Guy Invincible Platform + pipes	£85-95
31701	1996	'EDDIE STOBART'	Foden flatbed lorry and a Mini Van in Stobart livery	£25-35
31702	1996	'SADDLER'S'	ERF box van / trailer with VW van advertising 'Saddler's Famous Fun Fair'	£30-45

31703	1996	**'CHIPPERFIELD'S**		
		BENGAL TIGERS' ....Thames Trader van, Morris 1000 van, Land-Rover, AEC fire appliance **£50-65**
31704	1997	**'EDDIE STOBART'** ....Thames Trader articulated platform lorry and a Morris 1000 Van **£35-40**
33001	1994	**'Routemasters Around Britain'** ....Barrhead, Bournemouth, The Delaine, London Transport (route '30') **£20-25**
36501	1997	**'BARTONS'** ....Burlingham Seagull Coach and Morris Minor Traveller **£25-30**
36502	1999	**'The Italian Job'** ....Three 1:43 Mini Coopers plus a Bedford VAL Coach. See also Set 05506 ....**£30-35**
37003	2000	**'The Sate Landau'**...............................Marking the 'Queen Mother's Century'. Set contains: the State Landau, 4 horses, 2 riders,
		figures of the Queen Mother and Prince Charles. Model mounted on wooden plinth **£65-75**
59563	2000	**'GUINNESS Past and Present' Set** ....1:64 scale Renault Premium Curtainside and Leyland Comet Flatbed with load **£25-30**
59564	2000	**'GUINNESS Past and Present' Set** ....1:64 scale Scania Tanker and Karrier Dropside with load **£25-30**
59565	2000	**'GUINNESS Past and Present' Set** ....1:64 scale Volvo Rigid Curtainside and Commer Flatbed with crates and barrels **£15-20**
69901	1998	**'Military' Set**.......................................Saladin Armoured Car and Centurion Tank **£35-40**
76901	2001	**'EDDIE STOBART' Anniversary Set**.......Five modern tractor units mounted on a wooden plinth, celebrating Stobart's '30th Anniversary' .**£130-160**
91356	1994	**'EDDIE STOBART' Gift Set** ....Superhaulers (Transit Van, Box Van), Juniors plus figures..**£15-20**
93715	1992	**3-piece Mini Set** ....Red, silver and green Minis sold only by Woolworths **£30-35**
96445	1993	**'GOLDFINGER' Set** ....30th anniversary of 'Goldfinger', James Bond's Aston-Martin **£90-100**
96990	1992	**AEC Bus Set** ....Yellow/dark blue AEC Bus and OB Coach, 'AEC' logos **£15-20**
96995	1992	**'IAN ALLAN' Set** ....Red AEC Bus and green/white Bedford CA Van **£15-18**
97049	1994	**'YELLOWSTONE PARK'**......................Ford Model 'T' tanker and a Ford Model 'T' car...**£12-15**
97050	1993	**'REGENT BUS' Set** ....Two open-top buses, white/red and cream/blue **£16-18**
97051	1993	**'INVICTAWAY' Set** ....Dark blue Metrobus and cream/green Plaxton Coach...**£16-18**
97052	1994	**'DEVON GENERAL'** ....Guy Arab and Leyland Atlantean double-deck buses **£35-40**
97053	1994	**'YORK BROTHERS'** ....AEC Regal and Burlingham Seagull coaches **£25-35**
97061	1991	**'COVENTRY' Bus Set** ....AEC double-decker 'VERNONS' and Bedford OB Coach in maroon **£15-20**
97063	1991	**'YELLOWAYS' Set**................................Yellow/orange Bedford OB Coach and AEC Regal Coach **£25-35**
97064	1993	**'BLACKPOOL' Bus Set**..........................AEC 'Travel Card', Metrobus 'Roller Coaster', Plaxton 'Seagull' **£20-25**
97065	1993	**'STAGECOACH' Set** ....Routemaster, Metrobus 'Perth Panther' and Plaxton 'Bluebird' **£20-25**
97066	1993	**'Routemasters In Exile'** ....Scotland: Kelvin, Clydesdale, Perth, Strathtay **£20-25**
97067	1993	**'Routemasters In Exile'** ....Midlands: K & M Gagg, East Midlands, Confidence, United Counties **£20-25**
97068	1994	**'Routemasters In Exile'** ....North: Burnley/Pendle, Manchester, East Yorkshire, Carlisle **£20-25**
97069	1993	**'WHITTLES'**...Burlingham Seagull and AEC Regal coaches, dark blue and red **£25-35**
97070	1992	**'SILVER SERVICE'** ....AEC Regal and Bedford OB coaches in silver and blue **£25-35**
97071	1992	**'DEVON' Bus Set** ....AEC double decker in red/white and AEC Regal coach in cream/green **£25-30**
97072	1992	**'GOSPORT & FAREHAM'** ....AEC double decker and AEC Regal coach, green 'Provincial' livery **£25-30**
97074	1994	**'Routemasters In Exile'** ....South: Southampton, Kentish, Capital, Southend **£20-25**
97075	1992	**'SOUTH WALES'** ....AEC Regal coach in maroon/red and OB coach in cream/red.....................................**£20-25**
97076	1992	**'W. ALEXANDER'** ....Red Guy Arab double decker and blue Leyland Tiger **£30-35**
97077	1992	**'EAST LANCASHIRE'** ....Guy Arab in red/black and Leyland Tiger in dark green **£30-35**
97078	1993	**'CORKILLS'** ....Two Bedford coaches, 'de Vanenburg', 'Hotel Kasteel', Dutch **£20-25**
97079	1993	**'PREMIER'** ....Premier's 70th Anniversary set (Tiger and OB) **£25-35**
97200	1991	**'BRS' Set** ....Kay's set: green/black Bedford OB Box and Morris 'J' Vans, 5,000 ....**£20-25**
97331	1992	**La France Set** ....'SOUTH RIVER' (closed) and 'SCOTTDALE' (open) fire appliances **£30-35**
97351	1992	**AEC Ladder Set** ....AEC Ladder Truck and Bedford CA Van 'Bristol'. Not issued ....**NPP**
97391	1992	**AEC Pumper Set** ....AEC Fire Engine and Bedford CA Van 'Bristol'. Not issued ....**NPP**
97541	1991	**'ROYAL MAIL VANS'**............................Three Royal Mail Morris Minor vans **£25-30**
97680	1991	**'30 Years of the 'E' type'** ....Off-white open and red closed 'E'-type Jaguars **£15-20**
97681	1991	**'STIRLING'S CHOICE'** ....Austin-Healey (silver, '7') and Jaguar XK120 (green, open) **£15-20**
97690	1991	**'FERRARI' Set** ....Kay's set of 3: light green ('15'), dark blue ('5'), light grey ('10'), 5,000 ....**£20-25**
97695	1992	**'ABINGDON' Set** ....Morris 'J' van 'BMC', MGA (white, '324'), MGA (red, '38') **£30-35**
97697	1993	**'Leicestershire and Rutland Police'** ....Morris 1000 Van and Jaguar Mk.II, both in white with 'POLICE' markings **£15-20**
97698	1993	**'METROPOLITAN POLICE'** ....Bedford OB Coach and Morris 1000 Saloon **£20-25**
97700	1991	**'Jaguar Through the Years'** ....'E'-type (black, '110'), XK120 (open, white), Jaguar Mk.II (light blue) **£30-35**
?	1991	**'JAGUAR XK120'** ....GUS set: cream ('65'), white ('166'), green ('64'), 5,000 ....**£18-22**
97701	1991	**'RACING 'E'-TYPES'** ....Grey/black ('170'), red/black ('108'), 7,500 ....**£15-20**
97702	1992	**'JAGUAR COLLECTION'** ....A maroon Mk.II, a green XK120, and a red 'E'-type, wooden plinth..............................**£30-35**
97703	1993	**'RAC RALLY'** ....Three Jaguar XK120s: green ('64'), cream ('65'), white ('166') **£25-30**
97706	1993	**'FIRST TIME OUT'** ....Three Jaguar XK120s: blue ('6'), white ('7'), red ('8') **£25-30**
97708	1993	**'TOUR de FRANCE'** ....Jaguar Mk.II ('82'), Ferrari GTO ('165'), Mini-Cooper ('8') **£20-25**
97709	1993	**'ALPINE RALLY'** ....Ford Cortina ('29'), Austin-Healey ('95'), Mini-Cooper ('38') **£30-35**
97712	1992	**'MONTE CARLO MINI'** ....Three red/white Minis, racing numbers '32', '57', and '177' **£30-35**
97713	1992	**'THE ITALIAN JOB'** ....Three Minis from the film - red, white, blue **£30-35**
97714	1994	**'D-DAY' Set** ....Ford Popular, Bedford OB van, Morris 'J' van and an open-top Tram **£35-40**
97721	1994	**'DURHAM POLICE'** ....Mini-Cooper and Jaguar Mk.II police cars **£20-25**
97722	1994	**'SOUTH GLAMORGAN POLICE'** ....Morris 1000 Van and MGA hard-top in police livery...**£20-25**
97730	1992	**'AUSTIN-HEALEY' Set** ....Three competition models: green ('18'), red ('76'), blue ('414') **£20-25**
97735	1992	**'CUMBRIAN' Set** ....Bedford OB Van plus Morris 'J' Van in red and white **£15-20**
97740	1991	**'The TIMES' Gift Set** ....Morris Minor Van and Bedford CA Van **£15-18**
97741	1991	**'ISLAND TRANSPORT'** ....Two Bedford OB Coaches in 'J.M.T.' and 'PIONEER' liveries **£15-20**
97742	1991	**'JOHN SMITHS'** ....Thornycroft Beer Lorry and AEC Cabover Tanker **£18-22**

97746	1991	'TOYMASTER'	Bedford CA van and 'Corgi' Morris 'J' van (Toymaster shops only)	£15-20
97747	1991	'WEBSTERS'	AEC Cabover Tanker and Thornycroft Beer Lorry	£18-22
97749	1991	'BRITISH RAIL'	Ford Popular Van and Bedford CA Van in maroon/cream	£15-20
97750	1992	'EAST KENT'	Bedford OB Coach and AEC Regal Coach in dark red livery	£20-25
97751	1992	'BASS' Brewery Set	Kay's set: Thornycroft Truck and Ford Model 'T' Van	£18-22
97752	1992	'RUDDLES'	Bedford OB Box Van and Thornycroft Beer Lorry	£18-22
97753	1992	'TERRYS of YORK'	Thornycroft Box Van and Ford Model 'T' Van	£18-22
97754	1993	'LMS RAILWAY'	AEC Cabover Van and Thornycroft Van in 'LMS' livery	£25-30
97755	1992	'WHITBREAD 250th'	Anniversary set with AEC Cabover Tanker and Thornycroft Beer Lorry	£12-15
97765	1993	'STRATHBLAIR'	Bedford OB Coach 'Wiles' and Morris 'J' Van 'Forbes'	£25-30
97781	1993	'TATE & LYLE'	Foden Tanker and Bedford OB Box Van	£40-50
97851	1996	'CROSVILLE'	Original Omnibus set containing a Bristol 'K' and a Bristol 'L'	£20-25
98759	1991	'DANDY' Set	Morris 'J' Van and Bedford CA Van	£20-25
98960	1992	'BEANO' Set	Morris 1000 Van 'Biffo' and Morris 'J' Van 'Beryl the Peril'	£20-25
98965	1993	'EAGLE' Set	Volkswagen Van and Bedford CA Van	£15-20
98970	1992	'X-MEN' Set	Bedford Van plus Morris 'J' Van	£15-20
98972	1992	'SPIDERMAN'	Morris 'J' Van and Morris 1000 Van	£20-25
98973	1992	'CAPTAIN AMERICA'	Volkswagen Van and Ford Popular Van	£15-20
99106	2001	'Definitive Bond Film Canister Set'	Aston-Martins DB5 and V8, BMW Z-8 and Lotus Esprit, all in a replica film canister. (60 only)	NGPP
99929	1992	MGA Set	Two chromed MGAs (1,000)	£45-55
032/A/96041		'Classic British Sports Car Collection'	Eight cars on wood plinth: 96041, 96060, 96160, 96180, 96220, 96300, 99051, 99053. Originally a Sunday magazine direct-mail offer, then through Corgi Club.	£30-35
?	1993	'Premier Albanian' Set	Leyland Tiger and Bedford OB Coaches with 'Premier' logo	£15-20
?	?	'Connoisseur Collection'	2 'E'-type Jaguars, chrome, plinth, 5,000, direct mail	£45-55

Collectors notes

Corgi 'OOC' 42402 Leyland Leopard / Plaxton Panorama in 'Southdown' livery.
Model introduced in the 'third quarter' range of 2001.

Corgi 'Original Omnibus Company'

Ref Intro Model MPR

'OOC' models are made to 'OO' scale (1:76).

IMPORTANT NOTE: Following the sale of 'OOC' to 'Corgi Classics Ltd' in 1996, a new numbering system was introduced. The first 3 digits in each reference now indicate the type of vehicle modelled while the remaining 2 digits are an issue number. As from January 2001, 'OOC' model numbers are preceded by the letters 'OM' in Corgi literature. Also, some earlier references are being re-used – therefore, please be aware of apparent duplication of numbers (years of issue are clearly shown).

Accessories and Kits

44901 97 Bus Station buildings....**£10-12**
44901 01 Digbeth Coach Station..**£14-16**
44902 99 Victoria Coach Station..**£14-16**
44903 01 Marton Depot..............**£14-16**
44904 00 Southdown Depot..........**£14-16**
95400 97 Bus Garage kit..............**£10-12**

AEC single-deck bus

45701 01 'L.T.'..............................**£18-22**
45702 01 'BRADFORD'..............**£18-22**
45704 01 'L.T.' (Country Area)...**£18-22**
97095 95 'MACBRAYNES'..........GSP
97096 95 'EDINBURGH'...............GSP

AEC Regent II

40401 96 'KINGSTON'...............**£10-13**
40401 01 'SOUTH WALES'.........**£14-16**
40402 96 'NEWCASTLE'.............**£10-13**
40403 96 'EASTBOURNE'..........**£10-13**
40404 96 'BRIGHTON' bus ticket promotion.......**£130-160**
40405 97 'GRIMSBY'..................**£10-13**
40406 97 'CITY of OXFORD'....**£10-13**
97 Same but red roof.........**£45-55**
40407 98 'KOWLOON M.B.'.....**£90-100**
40408 98 'KOWLOON M.B.'......**£45-55**
40409 98 'ABERDEEN' promo...**£18-22**
40410 99 'WIDNES'...................**£14-16**
40411 99 'MORECAMBE'..........**£14-16**
97097 95 'TYNEMOUTH'..............GSP
97814 96 'L. T.'............................**£14-16**

AEC Regent V

41001 96 'ABERDEEN'..............**£10-13**
41002 96 'HEBBLE'....................**£10-13**
41003 99 'DEVON GENERAL'..**£18-22**
97943 96 'DOUGLAS'.................**£10-13**

AEC Reliance

40202 96 'BEA'..............................**£10-12**
42402 01 'SHEFFIELD'...............**£16-18**
45002 96 'CITY of OXFORD'........GSP
97130 94 'OXFORD'....................**£10-12**
97902 96 'PMT'..............................**£10-12**
97904 96 'LEICESTER CITY'....**£10-12**

Bedford 'OB' coach

42501 96 'ROYAL BLUE'............**£35-45**
96 Same but high seats.......**£60-70**
42502 96 'TROSSACHS'.............**£14-16**
96 Same but high seats.....**£18-22**
42503 97 'HANTS & DORSET'..**£18-22**
42504 97 'CROSVILLE'..............**£10-13**
42505 97 'MALTA'.........................**£10-13**
42506 98 'VISTA COACH'..........**£10-13**
42601 96 'MacBRAYNES'..........**£20-30**
96 Same but high seats......**£60-70**
42601 01 'MALTA'.......................**£14-16**
42602 96 'MOUNTAIN GOAT'..**£10-13**
42602 01 'BIBBY'S Ingleton'......**£16-18**
42603 97 'Hants & Sussex' 60th..**£10-13**
42604 98 'GREY GREEN'...........**£10-13**
42605 98 'SEAGULL'....................**£10-13**
42606 98 'GUINNESS'..................**£11-14**
42607 98 'SOUTHDOWN'............**£11-14**
42608 99 'YELLOWAY'..............**£12-16**
42609 99 'BRITISH RAIL'...........**£12-16**
42610 00 'Alexander' 'Gordon'...**£18-22**
42611 00 'EDINBURGH'.............**£12-16**
42612 00 'ALEXANDER'............**£28-32**

Bedford Val coach

42403 01 'KING ALFRED'..........**£16-18**

BET Federation bus

40201 96 'MIDLAND' black top.**£18-22**
40201 01 'SOUTHDOWN'..........**£20-25**
40202 00 'BEA'...........................**£10-13**
40202 01 'MIDLAND RED'.........**£14-16**
40203 97 'EAST KENT'...............**£10-13**
40205 99 'BALLYKISSANGEL'.**£10-13**
91730 99 'OXFORD' trad............**£10-13**
97835 99 'RIBBLE'......................**£10-13**
97900 98 'DEVON GENERAL'..**£10-13**
97901 99 'MIDLAND' 'Gaydon'.**£10-13**
97902 99 'PMT'............................**£10-13**
97903 00 'LOUGH SWILLY'......**£10-13**
97904 00 'LEICESTER'...............**£10-13**
97905 00 'SAFEWAY'...................**£10-13**

Blackpool trams

BLACKPOOL BALLOON TRAM

43501 97 1960s livery....................**£14-18**
43501 01 'THWAITES'...................**£18-24**
43502 97 Wartime...........................**£14-18**
43502 01 'VALHALLA'...................**£20-25**
43503 97 1930s version...................**£14-18**
43503 01 'ODEON'........................**£20-25**
43504 98 'ILLUMINATIONS'.......**£15-18**
43505 98 1960s, re-run of 43501....**£14-18**
43506 98 1934 version....................**£14-18**
43507 98 'EMPIRE POOLS'..........**£14-18**
43508 98 'WALL'S ICE CREAM'..**£17-20**
43509 98 'NORTH PIER', 1990s....**£14-18**
43510 98 '100 Years' re-run 43506.**£20-30**
43511 98 'St John's Tower', 43509 **£20-30**
43512 99 'PONTINS'.......................**£18-22**
43513 99 1980s livery....................**£15-20**
43514 99 'Pasaje del Terror'...........**£15-20**
43515 00 'MICHELIN'.....................**£18-22**
43516 00 'GOOSEBUMPS'............**£18-22**

BLACKPOOL BRUSH RAILCOACH

44001 98 Original livery.................**£15-18**
44001 01 'BRITISH LEGION'.....**£20-25**
44002 98 1998 plain livery.............**£15-18**
44002 01 'TERROR TRAIN'........**£18-22**
44003 98 'ALLINSON'..................issued ?
44003 01 'SANDCASTLE'..........**£18-22**
44004 00 'BLACKPOOL ZOO'..**£16-20**
44005 00 Wartime finish..............**£16-20**
44006 00 'HOT ICE'......................**£16-20**

BMMO C5 coach

45501 01 'Midland Red' CM.......**£16-20**
45502 01 'Lichfield Speedway'....**£16-20**
45503 01 'Midland Red' C5........**£16-20**
45504 01 'Midland Express'........**£16-20**
45505 01 'Midland Red' C5a.......**£16-20**

BMMO D9 bus

45601 01 'Midland Red'.............**£16-20**
45602 01 'L.T.' open top..............**£16-20**
45603 01 'WEST MIDLANDS'...**£16-20**
45604 01 'Midland Red'.............**£16-20**

Bova Futura coach

45301 99 'Wilts & Dorset'...........**£14-18**
45301 01 'PAUL S. WINSON'.....**£16-20**
45302 99 'JOHNSONS'...............**£14-18**
45302 01 'EUROLINES'.............**£16-20**
45303 99 'FLIGHTS'....................**£14-18**
45303 01 'ANDERSONS'...........**£16-20**
45304 00 'FORESTDALE'..........**£14-18**
45304 01 'WOODS TRAVEL'....**£16-20**
45305 01 'Nat EXPRESS'..........**£16-20**

Bristol 'K' bus

40701 96 'UNITED COUNTIES' **£10-13**
40702 99 Plain green/cream.........**£12-16**
40703 99 'PREMIER TRAVEL'..**£14-16**
97851 96 'HANTS & DORSET'..**£14-16**
97854 96 'WESTERN National'..**£10-13**
97856 96 'WEST YORKSHIRE'.**£10-13**
97857 96 'LT TRANSPORTER'..**£10-13**
97858 96 'CALEDONIAN'.........**£10-13**
97859 96 'BRISTOL'...................**£10-13**

Bristol 'L' single deck

40501 96 'L.T.'.............................**£10-13**
40502 99 Plain red/cream.............**£12-16**
97850 95 'MERTHYR TYDFIL'.**£12-13**
97852 95 'MAIDSTONE'............**£10-13**
97855 94 'UNITED'......................**£10-13**
97860 96 'BATH TRAMWAYS'..**£10-13**
97867 96 'NORTH WESTERN'..**£10-13**
97868 96 'EASTERN Counties'..**£10-13**
97869 96 'LINCOLNSHIRE'.......**£10-13**

Burlingham Seagull

40301 96 'WAL. ARNOLD'........**£18-22**
40301 01 'FLIGHTS'...................**£14-18**
40302 96 'PMT'..........................**£10-13**
40302 01 'STRATFORD BLUE'...........
40303 96 'SILVER STAR'...........**£10-13**
40304 96 'BOULTON'S' bus ticket promotion....**£35-45**
40305 97 'Yelloway', 'Torquay'...**£35-45**
97 Same but 'Rochdale'...**£10-13**
40306 97 'HAPPIWAYS'.............**£10-13**
40307 98 'NEATH & CARDIFF'.**£10-13**
40308 97 'RIBBLE', 'Coventry'..**£10-13**
40309 98 'SEAGULL'..................**£10-13**

Dennis Dart

42801 97 'KINGFISHER'............**£10-13**
42802 97 'Eastern National'.........**£10-13**
42803 97 'HK CITYSHUTTLE'..**£10-13**
42804 97 'STEVENSONS'..........**£10-13**
42805 97 'PLYMOUTH'..............**£10-13**
42806 97 'LONDON LINES'......**£10-13**
42807 97 'THE BEE LINE'.........**£10-13**
42808 98 'KOWLOON'...............**£10-13**
42809 98 'VFM', 'South Shields' **£11-14**
42810 98 'ORPINGTON'............**£11-14**
42811 98 'BUSWAYS'................**£11-14**
42812 98 'BREWERS', 'RAF'....**£11-14**
42813 98 'ABERDEEN' promo....**£18-22**
42814 99 'NEW LANTAO'.........**£14-16**

DENNIS DART Super Low Floor

44701 99 'CITYBUS'...................**£20-30**
44702 99 'AIRLINKS'..................**£14-18**
44703 99 'LONDON UNITED'...**£14-18**
44705 99 'BARTON'....................**£14-18**
44706 00 'PLYMOUTH'..............**£14-18**
44707 00 'BUS EIREANN'.........**£14-18**

Guy Arab bus

43905 01 'WESTERN SMT'........**£14-16**
43906 99 'SOUTHDOWN'..........**£25-35**
43921 00 'L.T.'.............................**£14-16**

Guy Victory

44301 01 'KMB 1982 - 1999'......**£40-50**
44801 99 'CHINA MOTOR'........**£18-22**
44802 99 'KMB 1979 - 1980'......**£40-50**
44803 99 'KMB Recruitment'......**£18-22**
44804 00 'KMB 1981 - 1983'......**£35-45**
44805 00 'Goodbye LV'..............**£35-45**
44806 00 'CMB LV1'...................**£40-50**

Leyland Atlantean

44601 99 'Hong Kong Citybus'...**£20-30**
44602 99 'SINGAPORE'............**£18-22**
44603 99 'Citybus Network 26'...**£18-22**

Leyland Leopard

40201 96 'MIDLAND RED'........**£12-15**
40202 01 'MIDLAND RED'..................?
40205 97 'BALLYKISSANGEL'.**£10-12**
42402 01 'SOUTHDOWN'..................?
42402 01 'NATIONAL'...............**£16-18**
42404 01 'MIDLAND RED'........**£16-18**
97835 96 'RIBBLE'....................**£10-12**
97901 96 'MIDLAND RED'........**£18-20**
97903 94 'LOUGH SWILLY'......**£10-12**
97905 95 'SAFEWAY'................**£10-12**

Leyland Lynx

43101 97 'WEST MIDLANDS'...**£14-16**
43102 97 'WYCOMBE BUS'......**£10-13**
43103 97 'CITYLINE', Mk.I.......**£10-13**
43104 97 'NOTTINGHAM'.........**£10-13**
43105 97 'YORKSHIRE', Mk.I...**£10-13**
43106 98 'LONDON UNITED'...**£11-14**
43107 98 'STAGECOACH'.........**£11-14**
43108 98 'BEELINE', Mk.I.........**£11-14**
43109 98 'CROSVILLE', Mk.I....**£11-14**
43110 98 'UNITED', Mk.II..........**£11-14**
43111 98 'CARDIFF', Mk.II........**£11-14**
43112 98 'RED & WHITE'..........**£11-14**
43113 98 'BRIGHTON & Hove' .**£11-14**
43114 98 'FISHWICK & SONS' .**£11-14**
43115 98 'PMT Inter-Urban'........**£12-16**
43116 98 'MAIDSTONE'............**£11-14**
43117 99 'WEST MIDLANDS'...**£14-16**

Leyland Olympian

43001 97 'WEAR BUSES'..........**£10-13**
43002 96 'CROSVILLE'..............**£22-28**
43003 97 'GATESHEAD'............**£10-13**
43004 97 'KEIGHLEY'................**£10-13**
97 Same but line variation.**£35-45**
43005 97 'STAGECOACH'.........**£22-28**
43006 97 'N.W. BEE LINE'.........**£10-13**
43007 98 'GO COASTLINE'.......**£11-14**
43008 98 'BLACKPOOL'............**£11-14**
43009 98 'UNITED COUNTIES' **£11-14**
43010 98 'PMT'..........................**£12-16**
43011 99 'Yorks. RIDER'............**£12-16**
43012 99 'OCEAN PARK'..........**£22-28**
43013 99 'RIBBLE NBC'............**£14-16**
43014 00 'Southern VECTIS'......**£25-35**

Leyland Olympian 3-axle

43201 97 'KOWLOON' standard **£70-80**
43202 97 'KOWLOON RAILWAY' 10th Anniv'y livery.....**£35-45**
'10th Anniv'y' o/print .**£70-80**
43203 97 'KMB', 'Handover'.......**£45-55**
43204 97 'Citybus','Reunific'n' ..**£35-45**
43205 97 'CITYBUS' (Standard).**£18-22**
43206 97 'CMB' (Standard).........**£18-22**
43207 97 'KMB', 'Reunification' **£22-28**
43208 98 'LONG WIN BUS Co.' **£18-22**
43209 98 Promotional pack..........NGPP
43210 98 'CMB','Reunification' .**£35-45**
43211 98 'NEW WORLD'...........**£55-65**
43212 98 'NEW WORLD'...........**£40-50**
43213 98 'NEW WORLD'...........**£40-50**
43214 98 'CAPITAL CITYBUS' .**£18-22**
43215 98 'Year of the Tiger'......**£80-100**
43216 98 'CMB' Airport Bus........**£30-40**
43217 98 'Stagecoach H.K.'.........**£18-22**
43218 98 'KCRC' original livery.**£30-40**
43219 99 'Singapore Superbus'....**£18-22**
43220 99 'KMB' std (new issue) .**£30-40**
43221 99 'Year of the Rabbit'......**£40-50**
43222 99 'KMB' 'Dragon Boat' ..**£18-22**
43223 00 'Friends of KMB'.........**£18-22**
43224 00 'KMB' '50th'..................**£18-22**
43225 00 'Year of the Dragon'.....**£35-40**
43226 00 'Year of the Dragon'.....**£35-45**

Leyland PD1, PD2, PD3

40801 96 'HANTS & DORSET'..**£10-13**
40802 96 'CROSVILLE', PD1....**£10-13**
40901 96 'CHESTERFIELD'.......**£10-13**
40902 96 'A1 SERVICE', PD2....**£10-13**
40903 97 'LYTHAM St ANNES' **£18-22**
40904 99 'WALSALL'..................**£12-16**
41101 96 'MANCHESTER'.........**£10-13**
41102 97 'PORTSMOUTH'.........**£18-22**
41103 98 'BLACKPOOL', PD2....**£11-14**
41104 99 'PLYMOUTH', PD2.....**£13-15**
41201 96 'CARDIFF', PD2a........**£10-13**
41202 00 'BLACKPOOL' PD2a ..**£12-16**
41203 00 'BLACKPOOL'............**£15-20**
97837 96 'NORTH WESTERN' ..**£10-13**
97839 96 'EASTERN Counties' ..**£10-13**
97941 96 'St. HELENS', PD2a....**£10-13**
97944 96 'NEWCASTLE', PD2 ..**£10-13**
97945 96 'RIBBLE', PD2............**£10-13**

Leyland PD3 'Queen Mary'

41901 00 'SOUTHDOWN'..........**£22-28**
41901 01 'WEARDALE'..............**£14-16**
41902 00 'SOUTHDOWN'..........**£22-28**
41902 01 'W. ARNOLD' open.....**£14-18**

41903 00 'N.C.B.' £22-28
41903 01 'London Pride' open £15-18
41904 00 'CMB' red/cream £40-50
41904 01 'OK Motor Services' £15-20
41905 00 'London Country' £22-28
41906 00 'London Country' Club £25-30
41907 00 'LANCASTER' £14-18
41908 01 'KMB' blue/cream £14-18
41909 01 'SOUTHDOWN' £18-22
41910 01 'A1 SERVICES' £14-18
42001 00 'SOUTHDOWN' open £25-35
42002 01 'LALLY'S' £14-18

Leyland PS1 single-deck

40601 96 'WESTERN WELSH' £10-13
40601 01 'SOUTHDOWN' £50-70
40602 97 'ISLE of MAN' £10-13
97836 96 'EAST YORKSHIRE' £10-13
97838 96 'BIRCH BROTHERS' £10-13

MAN/Volgren 3-axle bus

45401 01 'Year of the Snake £25-30
45402 01 'CITYBUS' (HK) £25-30

MCW Orion

40901 01 'NOTTINGHAM' £16-20

Metrobus

45101 99 'Yorkshire RIDER' £14-16
45101 01 'STEVENSONS' £14-18
45102 00 'L.T.' (General) £14-18
45102 01 'GENERAL' £16-20
45103 00 'L.T.' dual-door £14-16
45103 01 'STRATHCLYDE' £14-18
45104 00 'EAST KENT' £14-16
45104 01 'L.T.' 'Cobham 2001' £50-70
45105 00 'L.T.' £14-16
45105 01 'COVENTRY' £16-20
45106 00 'Gt MANCHESTER' £14-16
45107 00 'KMB' £20-30
45107 01 'W.M.P.T.E.' £16-20
45108 00 'L.T.' £14-16
45109 00 'Stagecoach East Kent' £14-16

Neoplan Cityliner

44201 98 'PARRYS' £16-18
44201 01 'OAK HALL' £18-22
44202 99 'HALLMARK' £18-22
44203 99 'HARRIS COACHES' £16-20
44204 99 'SUPREME' £16-20
44204 01 'The King's Ferry' £16-20
44205 99 'Z-CARS of Bristol' £16-20

Optare Delta

42901 97 'GATESHEAD' £10-13
42902 96 'NORTHUMBRIA' £25-35
42903 97 'BLACKPOOL' £18-22
42904 97 'TRENT' £14-16
42905 97 'P. M. T.', 'Hanley' £10-13
42906 97 'CROSVILLE' £10-13
97 Missing route number £14-16
42907 98 'EDINBURGH' £11-14
42908 98 'EAST LONDON' £11-14
42909 98 'WESTLINK' £11-14
42910 98 'FYLDE BLUE' £12-16
42911 98 'BARTONS' £12-16
42912 99 'S. W. TRAINS' £12-16

Optare Solo

44101 99 'WILTS. & DORSET' £40-50
44101 01 'BLACKPOOL' £15-20
44102 99 'Go WEAR' £14-16
44103 99 'First LEEDS' £14-16
44105 00 'Travel LONDON' £14-16
44106 00 'MK METRO' £14-16
44107 00 'NATIONAL TRUST' £20-30
44108 00 'Wilts & Dorset' promo £14-18
44109 00 'WEST MIDLANDS' £15-20

Palatine II

43601 98 'BLACKPOOL' £11-14
43601 01 'HARRIS BUS' £15-17
43602 98 'CITY LINE', 'Centre' £11-14
43603 98 'GLASGOW' £11-14
43604 98 'UXBRIDGE BUSES' £20-30
43605 98 'CAPITAL CITYBUS' £18-22
43606 99 'NORTHUMBRIA' £12-16
43607 99 'EAST YORKSHIRE' £12-16
43608 99 'BADGERLINE' £12-16
43609 99 'Go COASTLINE' £14-16
43610 99 'NORTHUMBRIA' £14-16
43611 99 'MTL NORTH' £20-25
43612 00 'NOTTINGHAM' £14-16
43613 00 'ORPINGTON' '50' £18-22
43614 00 'First CITYLINE' £14-18

Plaxton Beaver

43401 98 'Eastern National' £10-13
43402 98 'MANCHESTER' £10-13
43403 98 'Corgi Collector Club' £18-22
43404 98 'PMT' £10-13
43405 98 'MERRY HILL' £10-13
43406 98 'TRENT BUSES' £10-13
43407 99 'ARRIVA MEDWAY' £12-14
43408 99 'MIDLAND RED' £12-14
43409 99 'TRENT BUSES' £12-14
43410 99 'MIDLAND Mainline' £12-16
43411 00 'SHEFFIELD' £14-16
43412 00 'First GLASGOW' £14-16
43413 00 'First CALDERLINE' £14-16

Plaxton Excalibur

43302 01 'HARRY SHAW' £14-18
43801 98 'WAL. ARNOLD' £12-16
43802 98 'ULSTERBUS' £12-16
43803 98 'OXFORD Citylink' £14-16
43804 98 'SHEARINGS' £12-16
43805 99 'FLIGHTS COACH' £12-16
43806 99 'VIRGIN RAIL' £14-18

Plaxton Panorama

42401 99 'BLACK & WHITE' £14-18
42401 01 'HIGHLAND' £14-18
42402 99 'SOUTHDOWN' £14-18
42402 01 'SHEFFIELD' £14-18
42403 00 'Magical Mystery' £14-18
42403 01 'KING ALFRED' £14-18
42404 00 'S'down' (M.Collector) £25-35
42405 00 'YELLOWAYS' £14-18
42406 00 'TIMPSON' £14-18

Plaxton Premiere

43301 98 'OXFORD Citylink' £18-22
43301 01 'WAL. ARNOLD' £16-20
43302 98 'EXPRESS SHUTTLE' £14-16
43302 01 'HARRY SHAW' £14-18
43303 98 'FLIGHTLINK' £12-16
43304 98 'BUS EIRANN' £12-16
43305 98 'Stagecoach Western' £12-16
43306 98 'NAT. EXPRESS' £12-16
43307 98 'EPSOM COACHES' £12-16
43308 98 'SKILLS' £12-16
43309 98 'BRIGHTON & Hove' £14-16
43310 98 'FIFE SCOTTISH' £14-16
43311 98 'BASSETT' £14-16
43312 99 'SILVERDALE' £14-18
43313 98 'PLYMOUTH CITY' £14-16
43314 99 'SOUTHEND' £14-18
43315 99 'GNER', 'Railink' £14-18
43316 00 'Scottish Citylink' £14-18
43317 00 'JETLINK' £18-22
43318 00 'N.E. Remembrance' £14-18
43319 00 'National Holidays' £18-22
43320 00 'ROBINSONS' £14-18

Trident 3-axle

44301 98 'KMB', red stripes £60-70
44302 98 'HK CITYBUS' £25-30
44303 98 'KMB', (no stripes) £45-55
44401 99 'NEW WORLD' £100-150
44402 00 'New World WISH' £40-50
44403 00 'KMB' cartoon bus £18-22
44405 00 'LONG WIN' £35-45
44406 00 'GREENER BUS' £35-40

TRIDENT 3-axle DUPLE METSEC

44501 99 'CITYFLYER' A21 £30-40
44502 99 'Cityflyer' A11 (UK) £18-22
44502 99 'Cityflyer' A11 (HK) £50-60
44503 99 'Cityflyer' extra tampo £30-40
44504 00 'CITYBUS' £18-22
44505 00 'New World' '100th' £40-50
44506 00 'KMB' 'Millennium' £30-40
44507 00 'www.citybus' £18-22
44508 00 Chrome plated £20-30
44509 00 'CITYBUS' '10th' £20-30
44510 00 'Year of the Dragon' £20-30
44511 00 'Citybus KMB' £40-50
44512 00 'Citybus Millennium' £20-30
44513 01 'GREENER BUS' £20-30

Q1 Trolley Bus

(+ AEC 3-axle and BUT 9641T buses)

43701 98 'L.T.', 'Fulwell Depot' £20-30
43701 01 'BELFAST' £14-18
43702 98 'BELFAST' £12-16
43702 01 'CARDIFF' £14-18
43703 98 'GLASGOW' £12-16
43704 98 'CARDIFF' £12-16
43705 98 'NEWCASTLE' £12-16
43706 99 'CARDIFF' £12-16
43707 99 'GLASGOW' £12-16
43708 99 'L.T.', route '603' £12-16
99 'L.T.', route '602' £20-30
43709 99 'Glasgow' 'Beatties' £20-30
43710 00 Chrome plated £18-22
43711 00 'HUDDERSFIELD' £14-18
43712 00 'L.T.' £20-30
43713 00 'NOTTINGHAM' £14-18
43714 00 'READING' £14-18

Van Hool Alizee

42701 96 'SHEARINGS' £18-22
96 with seat variation £55-65
42701 01 'Go WHIPPET' £14-16
42702 96 'NAT. EXPRESS' £30-40
42703 97 'BUS EIREANN' £30-40
42704 97 'Wallace ARNOLD' £22-28
42705 97 'OK TRAVEL' £10-13
42706 97 'BAKERS DOLPHIN' £10-13
42707 97 'CITYBUS', HK £10-13
97 w. Chinese no. plates £60-70
42708 97 'BLUEBIRD' £30-40
42709 97 'EAVESWAY' £10-13
42710 97 'RAILAIR', Heathrow £10-13
42711 97 'SPEEDLINK' £10-13
42712 97 'SHEARINGS' 2nd £10-13
42713 98 'CLARKES' £11-14
42714 98 'EUROLINES' £11-14
42715 98 'SHEARINGS', '500th' £11-14
42716 98 'SCOT. CITYLINK' £11-14
42717 98 'LEGER TRAVEL' £18-22
42718 98 'SEAGULL' £11-14
42719 98 'EAST KENT' £11-14
42720 98 'EAVESWAY' £11-14
42721 98 'ROBINSONS' £11-14
42722 98 'KINGS FERRY' £12-15
42723 98 'SEAGULL' £12-15
42724 98 'ELLEN SMITH' £12-15
42725 99 'WESTERN National' £12-15
42726 99 'SHEARINGS' £14-16
42727 99 'LEWIS' '70th' £14-16
42728 00 'PARKS' £14-16
42729 00 'BRITISH AIRWAYS' £14-16

Utility buses

AEC

43904 99 'LEICESTER' £14-16
43911 00 'Leicester' 'OOC Club' NGPP
43915 00 'EDINBURGH' £14-16

BRISTOL

43902 99 'Souhern VECTIS' £14-16
43912 00 'CHATHAM' £14-16

DAIMLER

43902 01 'L.T.' £14-16
43905 99 'GREENLINE' £14-16
43907 01 'MAIDSTONE' £14-16
43908 99 'GLASGOW' £14-16
43909 99 'SHEFFIELD' £14-16
43914 00 'CHESTER' £14-16
43916 00 'LYTHAM St ANNES' £14-16
43917 00 'YELLOWAY' £14-16
43919 00 'SOUTHPORT' £14-16

GUY

43901 99 'OXFORD' £14-16
43901 01 'LLANDUDNO' £14-18
43903 01 'BRADFORD' wartime £14-16
43907 99 'LT' (Model Collector) £30-40
43910 00 'BIRMINGHAM' £14-16
43913 00 'ALEXANDER' £14-16
43919 00 'SOUTHAMPTON' £14-16
43920 00 'DERBY' £14-16
43921 00 'L.T.' £14-16

LEYLAND

43903 99 'L.T.' £14-16

Weymann trolley buses

40101 96 'MAIDSTONE' £18-22
40102 96 'HASTINGS' £18-22
40103 97 'WALSALL' £12-15
40104 97 'Bradford','Thornbury' £10-13
40105 98 same, but 'Coronation' £10-13
40106 98 'MAIDSTONE' £18-22
40107 99 'BRIGHTON / HOVE' £18-22
97811 96 'NOTTS and DERBY' £14-16
97813 96 'BRIGHTON' £14-16

Miscellaneous

AEC Tower Wagons / Repair Lorries

41501 98 'MACBRAYNES' £10-13
42101 96 'BRIGHTON' £18-22
42102 97 'LT', green £25-35
42103 98 'LT', red £10-13

Bristol Tower Wagon

42301 96 'MAIDSTONE' £14-16

Guy Tower Wagons / Repair Lorries

41601 96 'BOURNEMOUTH' £10-13
41602 97 'SOUTHDOWN' £35-45
42201 97 'BIRMINGHAM' £10-13

Leyland Breakdown Wagon

41801 97 'RIBBLE' £10-13

'OOC' Gift Sets

45001	96	'DORSET DELIGHTS'	Weymann Trolleybus ('Bournemouth') and Bristol 'L' ('Wilts & Dorset') plus a bus terminus kit	£20-30
45002	96	'VARSITY'	AEC Reliance coach ('Oxford') and Burlingham Seagull coach ('Premier') plus a bus terminal kit	£20-30
45003	97	'STAGECOACH'	with figures	£20-30
45004	98	'CHINA MB OLYMPIAN STORY'		£50-70
45005	00	'EAST MEETS WEST'	Citybus and Stagecoach	£40-60
45006	00	'CITYBUS NETWORK 26'		£40-50
45007	01	'CITYBUS OCEAN PARK'	Hong Kong 'Ocean Park' set containing a Victory and a Leyland Olympian Bus	£35-45
97055	94	'THAMES VALLEY'	Bristol 'K' and a Bristol 'L'	£20-30
97056	94	'CROSVILLE'		£20-30
97057	95	'SOUTHDOWN'	Leyland PS1/ECW and Leyland Leopard	£20-30
97095	95	'LANCASHIRE HOLIDAY'	Leyland PD2 ('Bolton'), AEC Orion ('Macbraynes') and a kit	£20-30
97096	95	'CAPITAL & HIGHLANDS'	Leyland PD2 and AEC/MCW Orion ('Edinburgh'), terminus kit	£20-30
97097	95	'BRIDGES & SPIRES'	AEC Regent II and Bristol 'L' ('Tynemouth') and a terminus kit	£20-30

Corgi Super Juniors and Superhaulers

See also Corgi 'Toys' range 1998 – 2001

FORD D SERIES TRUCK (1970-75)
2002 Car Transporter, White cab,
 Blue lower, Red deck **£20-25**
 Red cab, White deck **£40-50**
2003 Low Loader, Blue.............**£20-25**
2004 'CORGI' Removals Van,
 Red cab, Silver trailer....**£40-50**
 Light Blue cab **£40-50**
2007 Low Loader, Red cab,
 Blue trailer with Orange
 Junior digger load.............**£25-35**
2012 Low Loader, Military
 Green with US vehicle ....NGPP

FORD D SERIES SETS (1970-76)
3003 Car Transporter Set, White
 or Red cab, 5 Juniors........**£40-50**
3011 Low Loader Set, Red cab,
 plus 6 Juniors **£50-60**
3024 Low Loader Set, Blue cab,
 Yellow deck (1976),
 6 Juniors **£50-60**
3025 Car Transporter Set, Yellow
 cab, Orange deck (1976),
 5 Juniors **£30-35**

MACK TRUCKS (issued 1971-75)
2006 'ESSO' Tanker, White.......**£10-15**
2010 'EXXON' Tanker, White ..**£20-25**
2011 'US' Army Tanker,
 Military Green body.........**£20-25**
2027 'RYDER RENTALS',
 Yellow cab + box trailer....**£10-15**

MERCEDES TRACTOR UNITS, CAR TRANSPORTER (issued 1976)
2014/15 White cab and deck,
 Blue chassis **£20-25**
2015 White cab, Yellow deck,
 Red chassis **£20-25**
N.B. Car Transporter Sets 3023,
 3015, 3105 ....**£30-35**

MERCEDES TANKERS (1983-84)
Market Price Range – as shown
otherwise **£10-15**. Liveries issued:
1130 'CORGI CHEMCO',
 Red or White cab ....
1130 'SHELL' Yellow or White cab .....
1166 'GUINNESS' ....
1167 'DUCKHAMS' ....
1167 '7 UP' **£20-30**

MERCEDES BOX TRAILERS (issued 1978-85)
Market Price Range as shown otherwise
£10-15. Liveries issued:
1111 'SAFEWAY' **£15-20**
1129 'ASG SPEDITION' ....
1129 'CORGI' Black or White cab........
1131 'CHRISTIAN SALVESON'........
1137 'SOUKS SUPERMARKET'
 (Saudi issue) **£25-30**
1139 'HALLS FOOD' ....
1144 'ROYAL MAIL PARCELS' ....
1145 'YORKIE' ....
1146 'DUNLOP' ....
1166 'ARIA DAIRY' ....
1175 'INTERNATIONAL
 Distributors Meeting' **£70-80**
1175 'TI RALEIGH' ....
1176 'ZANUSSI' ....
1177 'WEETABIX' ....
1178 'MAYNARDS' ....
1202 'PICKFORDS HOMESPEED'
 ....**£70-80**
2028 'GERVALS DANONE' ....
2020 'BIRDS EYE' ....
--- 'B. H. S.' **£20-30**
--- 'CARTERS LEMONADE
 LINER' **£25-35**

MERCEDES SETS
1200 'DUCKHAMS' & 'GUINNESS'

Tanker plus 3 Scammells ..**£40-50**
1403 'CORGI CHEMCO',
 plus Junior Van **£25-30**
3128 'DUCKHAMS' & 'YORKIE',
 plus 10 Juniors **£40-50**

SCAMMELL 4x2 LANDTRAIN TRACTOR UNITS TANKERS (1985)
1141 'SHELL',
 Yellow or Orange cab.......**£10-12**
1185 'DUCKHAMS' **£10-12**

SCAMMELL BOX TRAILERS (84)
Market Price Range as shown otherwise
£10-12. Liveries issued:
1144 'ROYAL MAIL PARCELS' ....
1145 'YORKIE' Yellow or Red cab ....
1175 'ZANUSSI' **£35-45**
1177 'WEETABIX' ....
1186 'LUCAS CAV FILTERS'..**£15-20**
1186 'LUCAS GB TRUCK
 RACING' **£15-20**
1186 'McVITIES' Blue or Orange cab .
 'NORMANS SUPERMARKET
 ....**£20-25**
 'T.I. RALEIGH'..........................

SCAMMELL 4x2 SETS
1200 Contains: 1177 RALEIGH,
 1177 WEETABIX and
 1186 McVITIES **£23-45**
N.B. See also 'Corgitronic' section.

SCAMMELL 6x4 LANDTRAIN TRACTOR UNIT
J3700 Car Transporter 'COCA COLA
 RACE TEAM' (US issue).**£30-40**

SCAMMELL BOX TRAILERS (issued 1986-92)
Market Price Range as shown otherwise
£8-15. Liveries issued:
52/2 'CORNING' ....
1246 'COCA COLA' (UK issue)
 Grey shadow on wavy line ....
1246 'DR PEPPER'.........................
1246/1 'YORKIE' ....
1246/6 'FRANCOIS AVRIL' **£20-25**
1246/8 'FAO SCHWARTZ' **£20-25**
1247 'BF GOODRICH' ....
3300c 'COCA COLA' (US issue)
 No Grey shadow on White
 wavy line on trailer...........**£20-25**
71500 '7 UP' ....
91320 'WEETABIX' ....
 'HERSHEY'S CHOCOLATE',
 Purple or Dark Brown cab..........

SCAMMELL FLATBED TRAILER (issued 1986)
1220/1 Red cab and flatbed with load
 (also 'BP' offer model) **£7-10**

VOLVO F12 'Globetrotter' TRACTOR UNIT
Three cab types: Type 1: cast marker
lights with or without airfoil; Type 2:
Cast air horns and marker lights; Type
3: cast marker lights, chrome air horns

VOLVO CAR TRANSPORTERS (1984-92)
1193 Red cab, White deck,
 Red chassis **£7-10**
1222 Red, Blue or Yellow cab ...**£7-10**
91380 Red or White cab..............**£7-10**

CAR TRANSPORTER SETS (84-92)

Tractor units issued with Red, Blue,
White or Yellow cabs...................**£10-15**

VOLVO TANKERS (issued 1986-92)
Market Price Range as shown otherwise
£8-12. Liveries issued:
1250/2 'NOROL' ....
1250/3 'POLO' ....
1264 'BP' White cab ....
1265 'BP' Green cab
 (New Zealand issue)........**£15-20**
1265/4 'NESTE' ....
91341 'BP' Green with White
 cab roof, 'BURMAH' ...**£75-100**
91355 'TESCO'.........................
 'SHELL' Red or Yellow cab .....
 'DUCKHAMS',
 Yellow or Blue cab.................
 'GULF' White or Silver cab .....
1250 & 1265/1/2 'TEXACO', Red or
 White cab. Tanker Set issued
 1987/88 'TEXACO' **£12-15**

VOLVO BOX TRAILERS (1985-89)
Market Price Range as shown otherwise
£8-12. Liveries issued:
V20 'COCA COLA' 1000 only,
 British Home Stores **£30-40**
1188 'ROYAL MAIL PARCELS' ....
1194 'LEE COOPER' ....
1196 'HOTPOINT' ....
1197 'ASG SPEDITION' ....
1206 'HILLARDS',
 (2,500 certificated) **£40-50**
1211 'RILEYS' ....
1212 'TNT OVERNITE' **£80-90**
1212 'BRITISH HOME STORES' ....
1217 'KAYS' ....
1224 'CADBURY'S FLAKE' ....
1225 'BILSPEDITION' **£20-25**
1227 'BEEFEATER' **£25-35**
1231 'WIMPY' Red or White cab .....
1231 'LO COST' ....
1231 'KAYS' ....
1231 'MARS' ....
1231 'MARS' Brown or Black cab .....
1231 'McCAIN' ....
1231 'ROYAL MAIL DATAPOST' ......
1231 'ROYAL MAIL Parcelforce' .....
1231 'SAFEWAY' ....
1231/1 'WEETABIX' ....
1231/5 'WOOLWORTHS' ....
1231/6 'TESCO' ....
1231/13 'GAMINO' ....
1231/18 'GATEWAY' ....
1231/19 'MARABOU CHOCOLATE'..
1231/23 'FRIZZY PAZZY' ....
1231/22 'STEIFF' ....
1231/29 'INTERMARCHE' **£20-25**
1231/31 'FREIA CHOCOLATE' ....
1231/37 'SAS CARGO' **£20-25**
1232 'BOSCH PLATINUM' .**£20-25**
1233 'CADBURYS DAIRY MILK' .
1245 'FUJI FILM' ....
1248 'CARTERS LEMONADE
 LINER' **£15-20**
91300 'ORANGINA' ....
91301 'SNICKERS' **£20-25**
91310 'HULA HOOPS' ....
91350/5 'EDDIE STOBART' ....
 'YORKIE' ....
 'BRITISH TELECOM' ....
 'FEDERAL EXPRESS' ....

VOLVO BOX TRAILER SETS
Each contains 2 Superhaulers plus
matching Juniors. Issued 1987-94.
Market Price Range **£6-9**.
V37 'EDDIE STOBART'
 Superhauler plus Transit Van.......
C43 'TOYMASTER'
 Superhauler + 2 Juniors.....**£25-35**
C43 'WEETABIX' Superhauler
 plus Routemaster & Junior ....
J3167 'WIMPY' & 'WEETABIX' ....

J3167/4 'WHITE ARROW' ....
J3167/6 'KAYS'.........................
J3184 'ROYAL MAIL DESPATCH' ..
J3186 'ROYAL MAIL DATAPOST'...
J3189 'BRITISH TELECOM' ....

CORGI CLASSICS - VOLVO BOX TRAILERS (issued 1993-94)
Market Price Range **£7-10**.
98100 'SWIFT SERVICE'.................
98101 'AMTRAK'.........................
98102 'UNITED TRANSPORT' ....
98103 'P7O FERRYMASTERS'.........
98304 'CHRISTIAN SALVESON' ......
98305 'EXEL LOGISTICS'.............
98306 'DODDS TRANSPORT' ....
98307 'LYNX PARCELS'.................

SEDDON-ATKINSON 400 SERIES TRACTOR UNITS
3171 Car Transporter
 'GLOBETROTTER'
 (Saudi Arabia issue) **£15-20**

SEDDON-ATKINSON TANKERS (issued 1987-92)
Market Price Range as shown,
otherwise **£8-12**.
1251/1 'BOC CENTENARY' ....
1251/2 'ROLO' ....
1264/1 'CADBURYS'.............**£75-100**
1264/1 'BP'.........................
1264/2 'ELF'.........................

SEDDON-ATKINSON BOX TRAILERS (issued 1987-92)
Market Price Range as shown,
otherwise **£7-10**.
SA4 'GATEWAY' **£35-40**
1238 'ROYAL MAIL PARCELS' ....
1238/1 'McCAIN'.........................
1238/2 'CADBURYS FLAKE' ....
1238/3 'SECURICOR' ....
1238/3 'SILENTNIGHT' ....
1238/4 'RADIO 1 ROADSHOW' ....
1238/6 'ROYAL MAIL DATAPOST' ..
1238/7 'FEDERAL EXPRESS' ....
1238/9 'CADBURYS CHOCOLATE' .
1238/10 'LYNX' ....
1238/11 'MARS' ....
1238/12 'WIMPY' ....
1238/13 'CADBURYS WISPA' ....
1238/14 'ROYAL MAIL
 PARCELFORCE',
 Red shadowing.....................
91310 'SMARTIES'.........................
91420 'PERRIER' ....
91422 'ROYAL MAIL
 PARCELFORCE',
 Grey shadowing ....
91424 'ASDA'.........................
91430 'KIT-KAT'.........................

SEDDON ATKINSON SETS (88-91)
Market Price Range **£15-20**.
3087 'WIMPY' Superhauler
 plus 2 Juniors ....
3167 'WIMPY' Superhauler
 plus 4 Juniors ....
3184 'ROYAL MAIL DESPATCH
 CENTRE' Superhauler
 plus 4 Juniors.............................
92625 'ROYAL MAIL
 PARCELFORCE',
 2 Superhaulers plus 2 Juniors....
 'SECURICOR' No details .NGPP

KENWORTH T600 & T800 AERODYNE TRACTOR UNITS (issued 1993-94)
Single models are certificated. Sold as
Race Image Collectibles in the USA.

Super Juniors and Superhaulers

91385	'VALVOLINE' **£10-15**		
81388	'QUAKER STATE' **£10-15**	plus Drag car	
91389	'HAVOLINE' **£25-30**	98518 'OLDSMOBILE' ....NGPP	
91390	'PLASTIKOTE' **£25-30**	98519 'SUPER CLEAN' ....NGPP	
91591	'LOTUS' RACE SET,	98521 'SLICK 50' ....NGPP	
	Superhauler plus 2	**FORD AEROMAX TRACTOR**	
	Juniors etc **£15-20**	**UNITS (issued 1994)**	
93016	'FUJI FILM' RACE SET,	Single models certificated. Sold as Race	
	Superhauler plus	Image Collectibles in the USA.	
	4 Juniors etc **£20-25**	91391 'CITGO' ....NGPP	
98404	'RAYBESTOS'.............NGPP	98400 'MAXWELL HOUSE'...NGPP	
98405	'DUPONT' ....NGPP	98401 'MOTORCRAFT	
98511	'VALVOLINE' ....NGPP	LAKE SPEED' ....NGPP	
98516	'WESTERN AUTO'	98520 'MOTORCRAFT	
		BOB GLIDDEN' ....NGPP	

CORGI/KIKO TOYS BRAZIL
Kiko Toys manufactured models for the South American market using Corgi Junior components in 1985/6.

KK1	Low Loader with Junior digger, White cab **£30-40**	
KK2	'ATLANTIC OIL', White/Blue Tanker **£30-40**	
KK3	'SATURNO' (ZANUSSI), Black cab/trailer **£30-40**	

RECOMMENDED READING

'CORGI SUPER JUNIOR and SUPERHAULER GUIDE' provides full details plus pictures of all the variations compiled by Andy and Pat Browning, 3 Waterside Terrace, Ninn Lane, Great Chart, Ashford, Kent, TN23 3DD. Tel: (01233) 643461.

NB All the profits from this publication go to a childrens charity.

Corgi Toys Miscellaneous Modern Commercials Issues

Ford Escort 55 Vans

Market Price Range £8-15

Type 1:
Black plastic rear bumper (pre-'86)
Type 2:
Metal rear bumper (mid-'86 to '89)
Type 3:
New one-piece moulded body (without opening rear doors) from 1989.
Assume models to be Type 1 unless shown otherwise. The models feature a metal body with a plastic chassis and wheels. They have amber side and tail lights, opening rear doors (types 1 and 2) and beige (types 1,2,3) or black (2 & 3) interiors. White or brown interiors sometimes appear with type 1.
Model types shown in brackets.

Liveries issued:

C496 'ROYAL MAIL' (1, 2 & 3)	C499 'BRITISH TELECOM' (1)	C561 'WAITROSE' ....
C496/2 'POLICE' (2 & 3)	C503 'DUNLOP' (2).............................	C562 'GAMLEYS' ....
C496/3 'BRITISH GAS' (2)	C503/7 'TELEVERKET' (2)	C563 'McVITIES' ....
C496/4 'BRITISH AIRWAYS' (2)	C504 'JOHN LEWIS' (2)	C564 'TELEVERKET' ....
C496/5 'NOTRUF' (2)	C512 'BOLTON EVE. NEWS' (2)........	C577 'PLESSEY' ....
C496/9 'BRITISH TELECOM' (2)	C514 'CHUBB'	C578 'BEATTIES' ....
C496/15 'HOOVER'	C514 'DIGBY'S' Light or Dark Blue	C584 'MANCHESTER Eve. News' ......
C496/16 'B.B.C.' (2)	C515 'NEW'	C621 'POLICE' ....
C496/17 'FORD' (2)	C532 'RAC'	C626 'CHUBB FIRE' ....
C496/18 'BRITISH GAS' (2 & 3).........	C534 'PIZZA SERVICE'	C632 'KAYS' (2) ....
C496/19 'BRITISH TELECOM' (3)	C537 'AA'	91610 'AA' (3) ....
C496/20 'UNIGATE' (3)	C543 'TELEVERKET'	91611 'RAC' (3) ....
C496/24 'PTT TELECOM' (3).............	C549 'HOTPOINT'	91612 'ROYAL MAIL' (3) ....
C497 'RADIO RENTALS' (2)	C557 'FIRE SALVAGE'	91620 'YORKSHIRE GAS' (3).............
C498 'BRITISH GAS' (1)	C559 'JAGO AUTOMOTIVE'	91984 'AUTO FEDERATION' (3)........
	C560 'WILTSHIRE FIRE'	

Ford Transit Vans

Issued 1987-92. See also under 'Emergency Vehicles'. **Market Price Range £5-10**

656/1 'RAC'	656/12 'KTAS'	C656/28 'Nottingham	656 'FIRE SERVICE'...............	91647 'POLITI' (Denmark).......
656/3 'AMBULANCE'	656/16 'BUNDESPOST'	Ambulance'	656 'KAYS'	91647 'POLIS' (Swiss)...........
656/4 'FORD'; 656/5 'AA'.......	656/18 'FALCK SERVICE'	656/29 'CENTRE PARCS'	656 'AMBULANSE' (Norway)	91657 'BELGIAN
656/7 'POSTBIL'		656/30 'CENTRE PARKS'........	656 'AMBULANSSI' (Finland)	RED CROSS' ....
656/8 'POLISSI'	C656/21 'LYNX'	656/31 'UNICHEM'	91640 'S. WALES POLICE'	
656/9 'POLIS'	C656/22 'POLICE'	656/33 'McDOUGALL ROSE'.	91642 'FALKEN' (Denmark)......	

Scania Box Vans

Scania Box Vans Issued 1983-88. Market Price Range £5-10
NB. Seddon Atkinson and Vovlo Trucks are included in the Superhauler listings.

1123 'KOHLER'	1146 'RYDER'	1183 'GLASSENHETER'	1251/2 'ROLO' ....
1132 'SWEDISH POST'	1148 'SECURICOR'	1183 'BROSSARD'........................	1264 'ELF' Tanker ....
1132 'DANZAS'	1150 'BRITISH SUGAR'	1238 'McCAIN'	? 'BRS TRUCK RENTALS' ....
1133 Tipper Truck	1151 'HONDA'	1238 'CADBURY'S'	
1134 'LANTMANNEN'	1182 'SUZUKI'	1238 'SECURICOR'	
1134 'CORGI'	1183 'ADIDAS'	1251 'B.O.C'	

Mercedes 207-D Vans

Issued 1984 – 1989. Market Price Range – all £5-10.

C516 'BMX SERVICE'........	C576 'PARCELINE'.............
C535 'ATHLON'	C576 'LEKER OG
C539 'GROUP 4'	HOBBY' ....
C548 'SECURITAS'	C576 'OVERNITE TNT' .....
C554 'ROYAL MAIL'	C576/10 'C.R. SMITH' ....
564 'PTT'	C588 'CURTIS HOLT' ....
568 'B.F. GOODRICH'	C630 'KAYS' ....
576 'PEPSI'	C631 'BLUE ARROW' ....
C576/2	C670 'PARCELFORCE' ....
'PORSCHE RACING'	

Ford Cargo Box Vans

Issued 1985 - 1986; all £5-10

1190 'THORNTONS' ....
1190 'EVER READY' ....
1192 'LUCAS' ....
1228 'The NEW LEWIS'S' ....
1249 'WHITES BAZAAR' ....
? 'ARNOTTS BISCUITS', Australian issue.......NGPP

Corgi Truckers

A series of 1:76 scale models introduced in 1989; all £8-12

C1300/1	MAN Container 'YORKIE', Yellow/Blue.................
C1301/1	MAN Tanker 'BP', White, Yellow/Green design ......
C1301/2	MAN Tanker 'MOBIL', Beige, Blue/Red logo ....
C1302/1	MAN Tipper, All Orange ....
C1303/1	Ford Cargo Container, 'SCHWEPPES' ....
C1302/2	Ford Cargo Container, '7 UP' ....
C1304/1	Ford Cargo Tanker, 'DUCKHAMS OILS' ....
C1304/2	Ford Cargo Tanker, 'SHELL' ....
C1305/1	Ford Cargo Tipper, Grey/Green/Silver body ....
C1305/2	Ford Tipper, Red/Silver body..............................

Corgi Cameos

A range of low cost models, which were first issued in 1990 as 'The Village Cameo Collection' and individually sold through retail outlets. In addition they were also used as promotional models. In 1992 Corgi Direct became responsible for sales, and the models have been marketed in sets of ten via press and TV publicity campaigns and have been released in a wide variety of colour shades and promotional logos.
At this stage it is impossible to provide price guidance for either the individual models or the sets, some of which are limited editions of 10,000 pieces. The following provides a basic collectors' listing.

The Editor is indebted to George Hatt author of 'The Corgi Classics Collectors Guide' for providing much invaluable information. George's Guide contains a detailed listing of 'Corgi Cameo' models, colours and variations and collectors are strongly advised to obtain a copy. Send to:
Digby's Publications, 16 Horse Road, Hilperton, Trowbridge, Wiltshire, BA14 7PE.
Tel: (01255) 768821.

Saloon Cars   (2nd colour indicates roof colour)

CITROEN 2cv
Cream/Brown ....
Blue/Grey,
    'KELLOGGS' logo on some..
Green/Grey ....
Dark Red/Black,
    'CADBURYS' logo ....

Bright Red/Black ....
Yellow/Grey ....

MINI COOPER
Blue, Grey, White, Red
    or Yellow ....
Cream (2nd Corgi Convention) .

Dark Green,
    (Cadbury 'Sixties' Set)..........
Light Green ....
Red/White, 'FINA PETROL' ....
Purple/White,
    (Cadburys 'Sixties' Set) ....

MORRIS MINOR
Blue, Brown, Pink or White ......
Green,
    'KELLOGGS' logo on some...
Green,
    (Cadburys 'Sixties' Set)..........

VOLKSWAGEN BEETLE
Beige, Blue or Maroon ....
Orange,
    (Cadburys 'Sixties' Set)..........
Dark Orange...............................
Off-White or Yellow with or
    without 'KELLOGGS' logo ....

Commercial Vehicles

A.E.C. CABOVER VAN
'ANGLO PAK' - 'FINA' Set 3...
'BOUNTY' - Chocolate Set ......
'CADBURY'S - CO-OP Set ....
'CADBURY'S - Set 97426.......
'CADBURY'S - Set 97436 ......
'CAMWALL' ....
'CARTER PATERSON' ....
'CHARRINGTONS'.................
'COLMANS MUSTARD'........
'CRUNCHIE' - Set 97435.......
'Drummer Dyes' - 'FINA' Set...
'DUNLOP TYRES' ....
'FYFFES' ....
'G.W.R. PARCELS'................
'JOHN KNIGHT' - 'FINA' Set.
'LIFEBUOY' - 'Unilever' Set
    (10,000)..............................
'MARS' - Choc. Set (10,000)....
'MERRY CHRISTMAS' Set
    (20,000) ....
'METROPOLITAN
    RAILWAY' - Set 97833 ....
'OMO' - 'Unilever' Set
    (10,000)..............................
'Peek Freans' - 'FINA' Set 2.....
'PICKFORDS' ....
'ROYAL MAIL' Set ....
'Seth Wilkinson' - Set C26.......
'STABILO SCHWAN',
    German promotional..............
'THE HOLLY & THE IVY'.....
'J. WARD' ....
'WHITBREAD TROPHY' Set..
'3rd Div.' - D-Day Set (10,000)
'12th Corps' - D-Day Set
    (10,000) ....

BEDFORD BUS
'B.E.A.' ....
'B.O.A.C.'.................................
'BLUEBIRD' ....
'BOURNEVILLE' - Set 97435 .
'CLASSIC CARS'.....................
'CROSVILLE' ....
'Devon General' - 'FINA' Set 1
'DOROTHY HOLBROOK' ......
'EASTERN NATIONAL' -
    'FINA' Set 3, with/without
    '3934' fleet No. ....
'FIRE DEPT' 3 - 'FINA' Set 2..
'GUARDS ARMOURED
    Div.' D-Day Set (10,000) ..
'HEINZ BEANS' ....
'KIT-KAT'- Choc. Set(10,000)..
'LUX' - Unilever Set (10,000) ..
'OSRAM LAMPS' ....
'QUALITY STREET'
    - Set (10,000) ....
'RAPID ROAD' ....
'RIVER VALLEY' ....
'SILENT NIGHT'
    - Christmas Set (20,000) ......
'SOUTHERN Rly' - Set 97833 .
'STELLA ARTOIS'
    - Whitbread Set (10,000)......
'VIM' - Unilever Set (10,000)....
'WHITBREAD' Set (10,000)....
'34th TANK BRIGADE'
    D-Day Set (10,000) ....

FORD Model 'T' VAN
'AERO' - Choc. Set (10,000)....
'BLACK MAGIC' Set (10,000)
'CADBURY'S ROSES'
    - Set 97436 ....

'CADBURY'S The
    CHOCOLATE'On Pack Offer..
'COMMANDO BRIGADE'
    D-Day Set (10,000)...........
'CORGI' - Set 97426................
'CORGI' - Gaydon Show ....
'CHUPA CHIPS'.......................
'CITY AND SUBURBAN'........
'G. DAVID' - 'FINA' Set 3 ......
'DULUX PAINT' ....
'DONCASTER MUSEUM' ......
'FRESHBAKE' ....
'GRATTANS' - Set C26...........
'HUDSONS SOAP'
    - Unilever Set (10,000)........
'JOHNNIE WALKER'
    (Gold or Maroon jacket)......
'KING OF THE ROAD' ....
'KLEENEZE' ....
'KELLOGGS' ....
'L.N.E.R.' - Set 97833.............
'LANDBRO' - 'FINA' Set 3 .....
'L.M.S.' ....
'LONDON MAIL' ....
'LIPTONS TEA' ....
'MACKESON STOUT'
    - Whitbread Set (10,000)......
'MURPHY'S IRISH STOUT'
    - Whitbread Set (10,000).....
'NAT. GARDEN FESTIVAL'....
'NOEL' - Christmas Set
    (20,000) ....
'PERSIL' - Unilever Set
    (10,000) ....
'PICKFORDS' Set....................
'PRINCES SPREAD' ....
'RIPLEY CO-OP' Set................
'ROBERTSON' ....
'ROYAL MAIL' Set ....
'SEASONS GREETINGS'

    - Christmas Set (20,000) ......
'Smiths Crisps' - 'FINA' Set 2..
'THE SKETCH' - 'FINA' Set 1
'WEBSTERS' ....
'YULETIDE GREETINGS'
    - Christmas Set (20,000) ......
'ZEBRA POLISH' ....
'2nd Army' D-Day Set (10,000)

ROYAL FAMILY Issues
H.R.H. The Queen ....
H.R.H. Prince Phillip ....
H.R.H. Prince Charles..............
H.R.H. Lady Diana ....

MORRIS TANKER
'W. BUTLER' - 'FINA' Set 3 ...
'CADBURY'S' - Set 97426.......
'CADBURY'S' - Set 97436 ......
'CARLESS CAPEL' ....
'CHRISTMAS CHEER'
    - Christmas Set (20,000) .....
'CHRISTMAS WISHES'
    - Christmas Set (20,000) .....
'CO-OP' - Ripley 'Co-op' Set...
'CORNISH CREAM' ....
'DOUBLE DIAMOND' ....
'ELF PETROL' ....
'FINA PETROL' - Sets 1 or 2...
'FLOWERS FINE ALE'
    - Whitbread Set (10,000).....
'FOSTERS LAGER' ....
'Galaxy' - Choc. Set (10,000) ...
'HEINEKEN LAGER'
    - Whitbread Set (10,000).....
'KNIGHTS CASTILE',
    - Unilever Set (10,000).........
'MILKY WAY' Chocolate Set
    (10,000) ....
'RINSO' Unilever Set (10,000).

'SHELL' ....
'SOMERLITE OIL' ....
'7th or 79th ARMOURED
    Div.' D-Day Set (10,000)....

MORRIS PICK-UP TRUCK
'B.B' - 'FINA' Set 3 ....
'BEACH GROUPS'
    D-Day Set (10,000) ....
'BODDINGTONS'
    - Whitbread Set (10,000)......
'CADBURY'S DRINKING
    CHOCOLATE' - Ripley
    'Co-op' Set...........................
'CADBURY'S FRUIT & NUT'
    - Set 97435 ....
'CHARLES WELLS' ....
'Ferrocrete' - 'FINA' Set 2 ....
'GAYMERS CIDER' ....
'G.W.R.' - Set 97833 ....
'HARRY FIRTH' - Set C26 ......
'Milky Bar' Choc. Set (10,000)..
'MORRIS COMMERCIALS' ...
'ROLO' - Choc. Set (10,000) ...
'PEACE ON EARTH'
    - Christmas Set (20,000) ......
'J. SMITH' ....
'SUNLIGHT SOAP'
    - Unilever Set (10,000).........
'SURF' ....
'SUTTONS SEEDS'..................
'THORLEY'S - 'FINA' Set 1....
'WELSH BITTER'
    - Whitbread Set (10,000)......

**CHIPPERFIELDS CIRCUS
SET (1996)**
56901 Set of 10 vehicles in
blue/red 'Chipperfields' livery...

Corgi Toys 'Cars of the `50s' series   Scale 1:36

C801 82 **1957 Ford Thunderbird**, White/Tan,
            Cream/Orange or Cream/Black £15-25
C802 82 **Mercedes 300 SL**, Burgundy or
            Silver body, with suspension.............£15-25
            Red body, no suspension £15-25
C803 83 **1952 Jaguar XK120 Sports**,
            Red body/Black hood.......................£15-25
C803/1 83 **1952 Jaguar XK120 Rally**,
            Cream/Grey RN '56'........£15-25
            White body, rally number '56' £15-25
C804 83 **Jaguar 'Coupé des Alpes'**,
            Cream/Grey RN '56' or '414'......£15-25
            Same but with rear wheel 'spats' £15-25
C805 83 **1956 Mercedes 300SC**,
            Black body, Tan hood.......................£15-25
    84   Maroon body £15-25
    86   Beige body and hood........................£15-25
    87   Grey (Black hood), export model £15-25

C806 83 **1956 Mercedes 300SL**,
            Black body, Grey/Black hood £15-25
    86   Black/Green body, Beige seats.........£15-25
    86   Red, (Cream interior), export model .£15-25
    86   Blue body £15-25
C810 83 **1952 Ford Thunderbird**,
            White body £15-25
    84   Pink body.......................................£15-25
    87   Red body..£15-25
            Cream body, Orange roof £15-25
            Black/White, Red/White interior......£15-25
C811 84 **1954 Mercedes SL**, Silver body £15-25
    86   Red body..£15-25
    87   Grey body, export model...................£15-25
C812 85 **1953 MG TF**, Green/Tan seats........£15-25
C813 85 **1955 MG TF**, Red/Black.................£15-25
    87   Cream/Red, export model £15-25
C814 85 **1952 Rolls-Royce Silver Dawn**,
            Red/Black £15-25

    86   White/Beige......................................£15-25
    86   Silver/Black, export model...............£15-25
C815 85 **1954 Bentley 'R' type**,
            Black or Cream body £15-25
    86   Dark Blue and Light Blue body £15-25
    86   Cream/Brown, export model.............£15-25
            White body, Black roof £15-25
C816 85 **1956 Jaguar XK120**,
            Red body, Black tonneau, '56'.........£15-25
            Red body, Cream hardtop.................£15-25
C819 85 **1949 Jaguar XK120**,
            White body, Black hood, '7'.............£15-25
C825 85 **1957 Chevrolet Bel Air**,
            Red body, White roof and flash £15-25
    87   Black/White, export model £15-25
C869 86 **MG TF Racing Car**, Royal Blue
            body, Beige seats, RN '113'..............£15-25
C870 86 **Jaguar XK120**, Green body, Yellow
            seats, RN '6', export model £15-25

26612 Plaxton Paramount 3500 SOUTHERN VECTIS ☐

To add to the holiday atmosphere Southern Vectis used this stylish livery to good effect on its Paramount coaches. Fleet number 320, registered TJI 7520 this Leyland coach features the Island logo on the rear and a Sun Island destination on the front.

15301 Leyland National MKII Long 2 Door LOTHIAN ☐

The first release of this version of the National is in the distinctive Edinburgh colours of maroon and white of Lothian Buses. Fleet number 148 registered B148 KSF is on route 13 to Blackhall.

25807 Daimler DMS WILTS & DORSET ☐

Wilts & Dorset is always popular with collectors and this latest addition to our model fleet in the attractive modern livery features fleet number 4912, registered OJD 190R on route 164 to West Howe.

27305 (99638) Leyland TD1 Crosville L.M.S. Gilbow Railway Series

In the rich maroon of Crosville's railway fleet, number 359 registered FM 5887 displays destination route boards in the upper and lower window, in service to Heswell and Pensby.

15712 Plaxton Panorama Elite III SOUTH WALES ☐

Continuing to build our South Wales Transport fleet, the very distinctive livery used on this Panorama creates a completely new look for this vehicle. Our first Panorama for some time captures fleet number 188 registered LHU 661L, on the express route X1 to Swansea.

26203 Guy Arab I Utility Bus SWINDON CORPORATION ☐

The Guy Utility bus has a special association with Swindon and our model features the twin of the first production Guy Utility vehicle. Registered CWV 375, fleet number 48 remained in service until 1962 and featured in its latter life it is on route to Stratton X Road with adverts for Arkells Beer and Vernons Pools.

27504 Wright Scania Axcess KENTISH BUS ☐

To accompany our last months RML but in the revised colour scheme our Wright Axcess looks very smart. Carrying route branding for the 480 service Dartford to Gravesend our model registered N252 BKK is heading for Dartford Temple Hill.

25807SB Daimler DMS WILTS & DORSET (SHOWBUS MODEL) ☐

Similar to the standard release model but on route 131 to Corfe Mullen, the Showbus Rally version is produced in low volume to advertise and support this years' Showbus Rally, which this year takes place on Sunday 23rd September at Duxford.

Exclusive First Editions advertising for part of their 2001 'third quarter' range.

Exclusive First Editions

Exclusive First Editions were introduced in 1989 and are made to a constant scale of 1:76 ('00' gauge). If a model is listed separately but is only available in a set then 'GSP' (Gift Set Price) is shown and reference to the Gift Sets section will give the price for the set.

'LT' or 'L.T.' = 'London Transport'
'LC' or 'L.C.' = 'London Country'
'GL' = 'Greenline'

MPR = Market Price Range
GSP = Gift Set price
NGPP = no guide price at present

Buses, Coaches, Trams

Ref	Intro	Model	MPR
AEC Duple half-cab coach			
25301	98	'EAST YORKSHIRE'	£11-13
25302	99	'GREY-GREEN'	£11-13
AEC Regal single-deck buses			
20501	96	'HOWES'	£11-13
20502	96	'SOUTH WALES': 'Furnace'	£11-13
-- DL	98	'Morfa'	£11-13
20503	98	'BRITISH RAILWAYS'	£11-13
20701	96	'TRENT', 'Nottingham'	£11-13
20702	96	'TIMPSON'S'	£11-13
20703	96	'SOUTH WALES'	£11-13
20704	97	'S.U.T.', 'Switzerland'	£11-13
AEC Regent double-deck buses			
'London Transport' fleetname			
10101	89	'DURACELL', 'RT 981'	£20-25
	89	Same, but 'RT 206', also in GS 99901	£20-25
10104	90	'SCHWEPPES', red, also in Gift Set 99901	£20-25
10105	90	'TATE & LYLE', in GS 19901	£20-25
10106	90	'RANK HOVIS', in GS 19902	£20-25
-- DL	93	'RANK HOVIS'	£20-25
10107	90	'DULUX', red, 'RT 33'	£20-25
10109	90	'BIRDS', 'RT 4572'	£20-25
10110	91	'TAYLOR WOODROW' 'RT 4331'	£20-25
		and in Gift Set 19904	GSP
-- DL	94	Deluxe version	£20-25
10111	91	'BARCLAYS'	£20-25
10112	91	'VERNONS'	£20-25
10115			not issued
10116	92	'AIR FRANCE'	£20-25
10121	95	'LT', part printed	£20-25
C -- a	95	'LT', 'ALLSORTS'	£20-25
C -- b	95	'LT', 'St ALBANS 95'	£25-30
C -- c	95	'LT', 'BAXTERS'	£20-25
C -- d	96	'BROMLEY'	£20-25
C -- e	96	'AUSTRIAN ALPINE'	£20-25
C -- f	96	'RAMBLERS'	£20-25
C --x1	96	'ALLSORTS' 'Xmas', 'LLU613'	£20-25
C --x2	96	'Xmas', 'KYY877'	£20-25
10122	?	'SRT', 'Woman's Own'	£30-40
10124	97	'SRT 29', route '34'	£25-30
10127	95	'DULUX', 'RT3148'	GS99921
	96	'RT Special'	£25-30
10128	?	'Cobham Ramblers'	GS99920
'London Transport' RT with 'roof-box'			
16401	94	'NAT. SAVINGS'.in GS 99908	
16402	94	'RT 602', green, '301'	£40-50
c16402	94	'Save St Albans'	£35-40
16403	94	'RT 260', route '185'	£25-30
16404	95	'VERNONS', '158'	£25-30
16405	99	'LT' Anniversary	£35-40
'London Country' fleetname			
10103	90	'BIRDS EYE', singly and in Gift Set 99901	£20-30
10123	97	'Hertford' 'RT 3752'	£25-30
C10123sv		'Severn Valley Rly'	£25-30
C -- a	97	'Ramblers Assoc'	£25-30
C -- b	97	'Bromley Pageant'	£20-25
C -- s	97	'Sutton Utd' 'RT1095'	£25-30
'Greenline' fleetname			
10102	90	'BUXTED', 'RT 981'	£20-30
10117	92	'EFE CLUB 92', 'RT 3254'	£100-120

Ref	Intro	Model	MPR
10125	91	'Walthamstow'	GS 99914
Provincial operators			
10108	90	'NORTHERN'	£20-25
10113	91	'DUNDEE'	£20-25
10113b	91	Same, reversed blinds	£70-80
10114	92	'BRADFORD'	£20-25
10118	93	'St HELENS'	£20-25
10119	94	'HULL', route '25'	£20-25
10120	94	'ENSIGNBUS'	£20-25
AEC Regent V (Orion)			
19701	95	'SHEFFIELD'	£11-13
19702	95	'DEVON GENERAL'	£20-25
19703	95	'ST HELENS'	£11-13
-- DL	96	Same but subs. offer	£50-60
19704	95	'SOUTH WALES'	£11-13
19705	95	'SAMUEL LEDGARD'	£11-13
19706	96	'HEBBLE'	£11-13
-- DL	96	'HEBBLE', 'Bradford'	£11-13
19707	96	'WEST YORKSHIRE'	£11-13
-- DL	97	Same but deluxe	£11-13
19708	96	'OXFORD'	£25-30
c19708		Same but 'Classic Bus'	£30-40
Commissioned models			
C10101		'Austrian Airlines', 'RT 981'	£280-300
		'RT 206'	NGPP
C10101b		'Bromley Pageant '92', 'RT 206'	NGPP
C10104		'Austrian Airlines', 'RT 206'	£280-300
C10104b		'Bromley Pageant '92', 'RT 206'	£25-30
		'RT 858'	£25-30
C10111		'Austrian Airlines', 'RT 206'	£280-300
C10110		'London Toy & Model Club'	£18-22
C10110/03		'PSV Circle '92'	Set of 3
C101001		'Pearl Assurance'	£50-55
C101002a		'Birmingham': route '130'	£45-50
C101002b		route '108'	£90-100
C101003a		Green (with yellow band), 'RT3254', route '50'	£480-500
C101003b		Green (no yellow band), 'RT3254', route '50'	£50-60
C101003c		Red, 'RT3254', rt '50'	£60-70
C101003d		Green, 'Allsorts 10th'	£80-100
C101004a		'Star Group': 'LT' legal lettering	£100-120
C101004b		with no legal lettering	£80-100
C101004c		with yellow band	£70-80
C101005		'Beatties', 'RT 1044'	£25-30
C101006		'Fisherman's Friend'	£25-30
C101007a		'Midland Red', 'Evening Despatch'	£20-25
C101007b		'EFE 1'	£20-25
C101007c		'Fence Club'	£80-100
C101008		'Coventry'	£55-60
C101009		'Glasgow'	£55-60
C101010		'Devon General'	£120-140
C102001		'Devon General'	£75-100
AEC Regent open top buses			
-	90	'EFE 2', 'Birmingham', with certificate.	£12-15
-	90	'COLMANS'	£30-35
-	90	'SOUTHERN VECTIS', 'See the Island'	£100-120
10201	89	'EASTBOURNE'	£12-16
10202	89	'GREAT YARMOUTH' 'Caister'	£12-16
10203	90	'Coronation'	£20-25
10204	91	'LT', 'Typhoo'	£25-30

Ref	Intro	Model	MPR
C102001		'Southern Vectis'	£90-100
C102002		'LT', 'Colmans'	£30-35
C102003		'Birmingham', 'EFE 2'	£20-25
---		'LT', 'London Toy and Model Museum'	£30-35
AEC Reliance - see Harrington coaches			
AEC RF buses			
23201	98	'GREENLINE', in GS 99917	GSP
23202	98	'GREENLINE' '725'	£25-30
23203	99	'L.C.', 'Staines'	£16-20
23301	97	'L.T. Country Service': 'Woldingham'	£25-30
c23301a		'Ramblers Assoc.'	£80-100
23302	97	'L.T.', 'Passingford Bridge'	£40-45
23303	97	'L.C.', 'East Grinstead'	£25-30
23304	97	'L.T.', 'Weybridge Stn'	£25-30
23305	97	'GL', 'High Wycombe'	£30-35
23306	98	'BEA', 'Airside Coach'	£11-13
23307	97	'METROBUS'	£11-13
23308	98	'L.T.', 'Golders Green'	£30-40
23309	98	'L.T.', 'Claygate'	£25-30
23310	98	'L.C.', 'Welwyn'	£25-30
-- DL	99	'London Country'	£50-60
23311	00	'LT' route '20B'	£25-30
c23311a		'LT Museum' '227'	£40-50
23312	00	'BLUE TRIANGLE'	£16-20
AEC Routemaster buses			
'London Transport' fleetname			
15601a	93	'BOAC', 'RM 2110'	£20-25
15601b	93	'BOAC', 'RM 1910'	£20-25
15602a	93	'OVALTINE' 'RM 2103'	£20-25
15602b	93	'OVALTINE', 'RM 1818'	£20-25
15602c	93	'LT','RM 40'/'RM 966'	£70-80
c15602	93	'BEATTIES'	£15-18
c15602	93	'BRITISH DIECAST MODEL TOYS CATALOGUE'. Deluxe promotional only available with 5th Edition Catalogue. Red body, yellow posters	£20-25
c15602b	95	'BROMLEY PAGEANT', 'RM 2103'	£25-30
c15602c	98	'ASTON MANOR'	£20-25
15605a	93	'EVENING STANDARD', 'RM 1018', route '16'	£20-25
15605b	93	'RM 1277', route '73'	£20-25
c15605a	94	'I.A.P.H', 'RM 1277'	£70-80
c15605b	94	'BROMLEY PAGEANT', red, 'RM 1018'	£25-30
c15605c	94	'Louis Dreyfus'	£30-35
c15605d	94	'Aston Manor', 'RM 158' route '159'	£30-35
15608a	93	'PICKFORDS', 'RM 1768'	£25-30
15608b	93	'RM 966'	£80-90
c15608hw		'TYPHOO', 1994 USA model, 'House of Windsor'	£80-90
c15608dl	94	'TYPHOO', LT Museum	£45-55
c15608dl2		'Aston Manor', '2b'	£45-55
15608e	94	'IAN ALLAN 500th'	£80-90
15608f	94	'LT', 'Manchester Museum'	£60-70
15610	94	'DALTONS'	£20-25
c15610	95	'BRITISH AIRWAYS'	£40-50
c15610s	?	'SUTTON Utd'	£20-25
15612	93	'FARES FAIR'	£20-25
		same but in GS99908	GSP

Ref	Intro	Model	MPR
15614	94	'BEA', 'RM 996'	£20-25
15614	94	'RM 40 YEARS'	£15-20
15616	95	'TRUMANS' '291'	£20-25
c15618a	?	'LT Red Buses 500th'	£60-70
15619	?	'LT Forest Ranger'	GS99911
15620	?	'South London'	GS99911
c15620a	98	'BROMLEY PAGEANT', route '146' (&'159')	£70-80
c15620b	98	route '146' only	£25-30
15621	97	'British Railways'	£20-25
15622	97	'Forest Hill' '1336'	£20-25
15623	98	'LT', 'Victoria'	£20-25
15628	00	'LT' 'RM2000'	in GS99921
15628a	00	'LT Museum' 'Acton'	£40-50
AEC Routemaster RML			
25501	98	'LT', in GS 99917	GSP
25502	98	'LT', in GS 99917	GSP
25503	98	'Stoke Newington'	£11-13
c25503	98	'Ramblers Association'	£30-35
25504	99	'LT', 'Metroline'	£11-13
25505	99	'East Ham', '15'	£11-13
c25505	99	'Aston Manor 1999'	£20-25
c25505a		'Cobham 1999'	£20-25
c25505b		'North Weald 1999'	£20-25
c25505c		'Bromley Pageant '99'	£20-25
c25505d		'BEATTIES' special	£50-60
25507	99	'LT' 'Dartford', green	£16-20
c25507a		'LT' 'Ramblers', green	£20-25
25508	00	'LC' in GS 99919	GSP
25509	00	'LT', green	£16-20
25509a	00	'LT', 'Amersham Run'	£40-50
25510	00	'London United'	£16-20
Provincial operators, etc.			
15602	98	'ASTON MANOR'	£25-30
15603	93	'BLACK PRINCE'	£18-20
15604	93	'SOUTHEND'	£20-25
- - -dl	93	'SOUTHEND', '1'	£20-25
15606	93	'EAST YORKSHIRE': no ads, '808'	£20-25
15606a	95	same but 'Beatties'	£20-25
15607	93	'CLYDESIDE'	£20-25
- - -dl	94	'Clydeside' 'Model and Collectors Mart'	£20-25
15609	93	'MANSFIELD'	£20-25
- - -dl	94	same but in Set 99910	GSP
15611	93	'BURNLEY & PENDLE' '180'	£20-25
- - -dl	94	same, in GS 99910, '186'	GSP
15613	94	'BLACKPOOL', '527'	£20-25
15615dl	95	'United Counties'	£20-25
15617	95	'EAST LONDON': 'RM1527'	£25-30
c15617a	95	Route '8'	£25-30
c15617b	95	Route '15'	£25-30
c15619a	98	'COBHAM'	£25-30
c15619b	98	'NORTH WEALD'	£20-25
15624	98	'G.M. BUSES'	£20-25
15625	98	'HALIFAX'	£20-25
15626	99	'ENSIGNBUS'	£20-25
15626a	99	'ASTON MANOR'	£20-25
15627	99	'DELAINE'	£20-25
15627a	99	'DELAINE'	£13-15
15629	99	'SOUTHAMPTON'	£14-16
25504	99	'METROLINE', (RML)	£9-12
AEC Routemaster open buses			
17801	95	'LONDON COACHES'	£11-13
c17801	97	'North Weald Rally'	£12-16
17802	95	'LONDON PLUS'	£11-13
c17803		'THE BIG BUS Co.'	£12-16
17901	94	'London Sightseeing'	£11-13
17902	94	'London', 'Metroline'	£11-13

AEC Routemaster RCL coach
25601 98 'GREENLINE':
'Forest Hill' £30-40
c25601 'Ramblers'.....................£25-30
25602 99 'L. COUNTRY' £16-20
c25602a 'Sutton United' £16-20
c25602b 'LC' 'Oasis Ramblers'.£16-20
25603 99 'GREENLINE' £16-20
25603a 00 'Ramblers Holidays' £40-50
25604 00 'Original Sightseeing'..£16-20
25605 00 'BLUE TRIANGLE' ..£16-20

AEC STL
27801 01 'London Transport' £12-15
27802 01 'Greenline' £12-15

Alexander 'A'-type Atlantean/Fleetline
23501 97 'EDINBURGH' £11-13
23502 97 'BOURNEMOUTH' £25-30
23504 ? 'H. K. CITYBUS' £20-25
23701 97 'TRENT', 'Derby'.........£11-13
23702 97 'EAST YORKSHIRE' £11-13
23703 98 'BRADFORD' 'Leeds'...£11-13
23704 98 'HALIFAX' £11-13
23705 99 'SELNEC', 'Jericho'......£11-13
23706 99 'BURY', 'Walmersley'...£11-13
23801 97 'GLASGOW' £11-13
23802 99 'FISHWICK & SONS'...£11-13
24201 97 'MIDLAND RED':
'Colliery' (Showbus)....£25-30
24201sb 'Duxford' (Showbus)...£30-40
24202 97 'E. YORKSHIRE' £11-13
24401 98 'L.T.', 'Sightseeing' £11-13
24402 00 'BOURNEMOUTH' £12-14
-- DL 00 'B'mouth LT Museum' ..£50-60
24501 97 'NEWCASTLE'...........£16-20

Alexander 'Y'-type bus/coach
22501 97 'PREMIER' £11-13
22502 97 'P. M. T.' £11-13
22503 97 'S. M. T.' £40-50
22504 97 'STRATFORD BLUE'..£11-13
22505 97 'VENTURE' £11-13
22506 97 'Midland Red' 'NBC'...£11-13
22507 98 'WEST RIDING' £11-13
22508 98 'CROSVILLE' £11-13
22509 98 'EAST YORKSHIRE' ..£11-13
22510 98 'SHEFFIELD CITY'....£11-13
22701 97 'NORTH WESTERN' ...£11-13
22702 97 'YORKS. TRACTION' ..£11-13
22703 97 'ROAD CAR' £11-13
22704 97 'HIGHLAND' £11-13
22705 98 'LOTHIAN' £11-13
22706 98 'LANCASTER' £11-13
-- DL 00 'LANCASTER' £12-14
22707 98 'E. SCOTTISH' £11-13
22708 99 'ULSTERBUS' £11-13
22709 99 'MAIDSTONE' £11-13
22710 00 'Stagecoach Western'...£11-13
22711 00 'South YORKSHIRE'...£12-15
22712 00 'CLYDESIDE' £12-15

Alexander buses (various)
22701 96 'NORTH WESTERN'...£10-12
22702 97 'YORKS. TRACTION' £10-12
22703 97 'ROAD CAR', 'Louth'..£10-12

Bedford OB coaches
20101 95 'Southern VECTIS' £20-25
20102 95 'ROYAL BLUE' £16-20
20103 95 'SOUTHDOWN' .in GS 99910
20104 95 'GREY CARS' £11-13
20105 95 'EASTERN COUNTIES'
................£11-13
20106 96 'PREMIER TRAVEL' ...£11-13
20107 96 'Premier WATFORD' ...£11-13
20108 96 'SOUTH MIDLANDS'.£11-13
20109 96 'EAST YORKSHIRE' ...£11-13
20110 96 'BERE REGIS' £11-13
20111 96 'GREY-GREEN':
'Clacton' £11-13
-- DL 96 'Littlewoods'..........£16-20
20112 96 'WEST YORKSHIRE' ..£11-13
20113 96 'Sheffield United Tours'£11-13
20114 96 'WILTS & DORSET'...£11-13
-- DL 98 same but 'Pewsey'......£11-13
20115 96 'YELLOWAYS' £11-13
20116 96 'BARTON' £11-13

20117 96 'EAST KENT' £18-20
20118 96 'BRITISH RAILWAYS':
'FWO 615-1229W' £20-25
20119 97 'HWO 881-1203W' £12-15
20120 97 'W. NATIONAL' £20-25
20121 98 'DEVON GENERAL' £20-25
20121 99 'SKILL'S', 'Filey' £11-13
20124 99 'Midland GENERAL' ...£11-13
20125 01 'EDINBURGH' £12-15

Bedford SB coaches
18701 95 'ORANGE LUXURY' ..£11-13
18702 95 'GORWOODS' £11-13
18703 95 'GREY GREEN' £11-13
18704 95 'Southern VECTIS' £11-13
18705 95 'B.O.A.C.' £11-13
18706 95 'BARTON' £11-13
-- DL 95 'GS Littlewoods' £12-15
18707 95 'STEVENSONS' £11-13
18708 95 'McBRAYNES' £16-20
18709 95 'PREMIER', 'Watford'.£11-13
18710 96 'BERE REGIS' £11-13
18711 96 'BOLTON' £11-13
18712 99 'SKILL'S' £11-13

B.E.T. style single-deck buses
24301 97 'PREMIER TRAVEL' ...£11-13
24302 97 'MACBRAYNES' £11-13
24303 97 'DEVON GENERAL' ...£11-13
24304 97 'VENTURE' £11-13
24305 98 'SOUTHDOWN' .in GS 99915
24306 98 'MAIDSTONE'..........£25-30
24307 98 'NORTH WESTERN' ...£11-13
24308 98 'HIGHLAND' £11-13
24309 98 'EAST YORKSHIRE' ..£11-13
24310 98 'HALIFAX' £11-13
24311 98 'WESTERN WELSH' ...£11-13
24312 98 'CROSVILLE' £11-13
24313 98 'MANCHESTER' £11-13
-- DL 99 'Manchester Airport' ...£11-13
24314 98 'YORKS. TRACTION' ..£11-13
24315 99 'SALFORD CITY' £11-13
24316 00 'City of Oxford' ...in GS 99919
24317 00 'CITY OF CHESTER'...£11-13
24318 01 'TRENT' £11-13

BET Willowbrook
27101 99 'WEST MIDLANDS' ...£11-13
27102 00 'MIDLAND RED' £12-14

Bristol Lodekka buses
13901 92 'BRISTOL':
'Southmead' £20-25
13902 92 'BEATTIES'.............£20-25
13903 ....not issued
13904 ....not issued
13905 94 'EASTERN COUNTIES'
................£11-13
13906 94 'SOUTHERN VECTIS'£20-25
13907 95 'CUMBERLAND' £11-13
13908 95 'NOTTS & DERBY':
'Heanor' £11-13
-- DL 95 'B2' £11-13
13909 95 'CAMBUS':
'Warrington' £11-13
-- DL 96 'New Hospital', cert....£11-13
13910 97 'WESTERN National'...£20-25
13911 97 'CROSVILLE' £11-13
13912 ? 'HK Citybus'..........£20-25
13913 00 'E. National COACH' ..£12-15
13914 01 'Central SCOTTISH' ...£14-16
14001 92 'BRIGHTON' £11-13
14002 93 'EASTERN National' ...£11-13
- -DL Same but Deluxe £18-22
c14002 'PSV Circle' £18-22
14003 93 'CROSVILLE' £11-13
- -DL 93 Same but Deluxe £18-22
14004 93 'CHELTENHAM' £11-13
c14004 'Classic Bus H Trust' ..£25-30
14005 93 'SOUTHDOWN' .in Set 99907
14006 93 'LINCOLNSHIRE' £11-13
-- DL 97 'BATH SERVICES' £40-50
14007 93 'THAMES VALLEY' ...£11-13
c14007 'BEATTIES'.............£20-25
14008 96 'MORRIS BROS' £11-13
14009 98 'HANTS & DORSET' ..£14-16
14010 99 'SOUTH WALES' £14-16
14101 92 'United' 'Darlington'...£14-16

14102 92 'United' 'BEATTIES' ...£14-16
14103 98 'BAXTER'S', 'Mull'....£14-16
14201 92 'Alexander Midland' £14-16
c14201 'Scottish Bus Museum'.£18-20
c14201a 'Heart of Pennines Run'£20-25
14202 93 'MIDLAND General'...£11-13
--- DL 93 'MIDLAND General'...£11-13

Bristol LS single deck buses
16301 93 'UNITED' £18-20
16302 93 'EASTERN NATIONAL'
................£18-20
16303 94 'THAMES VALLEY' ...£11-13
16304 94 'WESTERN NATIONAL'
................£18-20
16307 94 'WILTS & DORSET' ...£11-13
16308 94 'LINCOLNSHIRE' £11-13
16309 94 'GREENLINE' ....in GS 99909
16310 94 'EASTERN COUNTIES'
................£11-13
16311 95 'BRISTOL'..............£11-13
-- DL 96 'BATH SERVICES' £11-13
16312 96 'WILTS & DORSET:
'Andover' £18-20
-- DL 98 'Basingstoke' £11-13
16313 96 'SOUTHERN NATIONAL'
................£11-13
16314 96 'WEST YORKSHIRE' ..£11-13
16315 97 'SOUTHERN VECTIS'£11-13
16316 98 'EASTERN NATIONAL'
................£11-13
16317 99 'PROVINCIAL' £11-13
16317a 99 'Southsea Spectacular'..£14-18
16318 99 'Midland GENERAL' ...£11-13
-- DL 00 'Midland GENERAL' ...£12-15
16319 99 'RIBBLE' £11-13
16320 00 'HANTS & DORSET'...£12-15

Bristol MW coaches
16201 93 'GREYHOUND'.........£20-25
16202 93 'CROSVILLE' £20-25
16203 94 'ROYAL BLUE' £40-50
16204 94 'SOUTH MIDLAND'...£11-13
16205 94 'WILTS & DORSET'...£11-13
16206 94 'LINCOLNSHIRE' £11-13
16207 95 'EASTERN COUNTIES'
................£11-13
16208 95 'S. VECTIS' £11-13
16209 95 'UNITED' £11-13
16210 96 'ROYAL BLUE' £30-40
16211 96 'MORRIS BROS' £11-13
16212 96 'EASTERN SCOTTISH'
................£11-13
16213 00 'HANTS & DORSET' ..£12-15
16214 00 'RED & WHITE' £12-15

Bristol RE / RELL single deck buses
25001 98 'SOUTHERN NATIONAL'
................£11-13
-- DL 00 'SOUTHERN NATIONAL'
................£12-14
25002 99 'CUMBERLAND' £11-13
25003 99 'EASTERN NATIONAL'
................£11-13
25101 98 'UNITED' £11-13
25102 99 'PMT' £11-13
25103 00 'Southern VECTIS' £11-13
25201 98 'BADGERLINE' £11-13
25202 98 'TRENT', 'Matlock' £11-13
25203 98 'CROSVILLE' £11-13
-- DL 00 'BRISTOL OMNIBUS'£12-15
25204 98 'BRISTOL', 'Swindon' .£11-13
25205 99 'WILTS. & DORSET' ...£11-13
25206 99 'Western National' £11-13
25207 99 'SOUTHDOWN' £40-50
25208 00 'HASTINGS' £12-15

Bristol VR double-deck buses
18501 98 'SOUTHERN NATIONAL'
................£11-13
18502 98 'EASTERN COUNTIES'
................£11-13
18601 97 'SOUTH WALES' £11-13
18602 97 'WILTS & DORSET' ...£20-25
18603 97 'EAST YORKSHIRE' ..£11-13
18604 97 'CROSVILLE' £11-13
18605 99 'PROVINCIAL' £11-13
c18605 99 'SUTTON UFC'..........£15-18

18606 01 'CUMBERLAND' £16-20
20301 95 'EAST YORKSHIRE' ..£11-13
20302 96 'BRISTOL' £11-13
20303 96 'SOUTHDOWN' £25-30
20304 96 'MANCHESTER' £16-20
20305 96 'WEST YORKSHIRE' ..£11-13
-- DL 97 'YORK CITY', cert. £12-15
20306 99 'SELNEC CHESHIRE'..£11-13
-- DL 00 'SELNEC CHESHIRE' £12-15
20401 96 'BADGERLINE' £18-20
20402 96 'UNITED', 'Durham' ...£11-13
20403 96 'DEVON GENERAL' ...£11-13
20404 96 'EAST KENT' £11-13
20405 96 'NORTHERN' £11-13
20406 96 'CAMBUS' £11-13
-- SB 96 'CAMBUS', Showbus ..£18-20
20407 97 'Crosville' 'Cymru' £30-40
20408 97 'EASTERN COUNTIES'
................£30-40
20409 96 'Southern VECTIS' £25-30
20410 96 'SOUTHDOWN 75',
in set 99912............GSP
20411 97 'WESTERN NATIONAL'
................£40-50
20412 98 'EASTERN NATIONAL'
................£30-40
20413 97 'Great YARMOUTH' ...£11-13
20414 98 'HEDINGHAM' £11-13
20415 98 'BLUE BUS':
'Great Yarmouth' £11-13
-- SB 98 'Showbus' £14-16
20416 98 'MAIDSTONE' £11-13
20417 99 'Aldershot & Dist.' ..GS 99916
20418 98 'WAL. ARNOLD' £11-13
20419 99 'ENSIGNBUS' £11-13
20420 99 'United Tyne & Wear'..£11-13
20421 99 'WILTS & DORSET' ...£25-30
20422 00 'SOUTHERN NATIONAL'
................£12-15
20423 00 'UNITED COUNTIES' £12-15
20424 00 'MAYNES' £12-15
20425 00 'WILTS & DORSET' ...£25-30
20426 00 'Eastern National LT'....£12-15

Bristol Utility Bus
26501 99 'Maidstone & District'..£11-13
26502 00 'L.T.' £12-15

Bristol Windover coaches
20801 96 'THAMES VALLEY' ...£11-13
-- DL 98 'THAMES VALLEY' ...£11-13
20802 98 'NORTH WESTERN'...£11-13

Daimler CVG buses
19801 95 'MANCHESTER' £11-13
-- DL 96 'MANCHESTER',
Classic Bus magazine ..£35-40
19802 95 'PMT'................£11-13
19803 95 'DUNDEE'.............£11-13
- -DL Same but Deluxe £11-13
19804 95 'COVENTRY' £11-13
--- SB 95 Same but Showbus.....£25-30
19805 96 'WEST MIDLANDS' ...£11-13
-- DL 97 'Earlsdon', cert.........£11-13
19806 97 'HALIFAX' £11-13
19807 98 'LANCASHIRE' £11-13
19808 98 'WEST BROMWICH' ..£11-13
c19808 Same but 'Classic Bus' ..£15-18
19809 98 'SELNEC', 'Bolton' ...£11-13
19810 99 'LEEDS CITY' £11-13
19811 99 'DERBY', 'Shelton'.....£11-13

Daimler DMS buses
25701 99 'L. T.', 'Edgware Stn' ...£11-13
25702 99 'ENSIGNBUS' £16-20
25703 99 'S. YORKSHIRE' £11-13
25704 00 'CMB' £20-25
25705 00 'LT' £12-16
25705a 00 'LT' 'Cobham 2000' ...£20-25
25706 00 'LT', in GS 99918............GSP
25707 00 'Oxford Park & Ride'..£12-14
25708 00 'O.K. TRAVEL' ...in GS 99921
25708 99 'LT', 'Depot' £20-25
25709 00 'CITYBUS' ....NGPP
25801 99 'WEST MIDLANDS' ...£11-13
25802 99 'MIDLAND RED' £11-13
-- DL 99 'MIDLAND RED' £11-13
25803 99 'O.K. TRAVEL' £11-13

25804 00 'Western National' £11-13
25804SB same, but 'Showbus' ......NGPP
25805 00 'Hampshire Bus' £12-13
26101 00 'BIG BUS Co.' £16-20

Daimler Fleetline buses

18001 94 'BIRMINGHAM' £20-25
18002 95 'MANCHESTER' £11-13
18003 96 'BIRKENHEAD' £11-13
18004 ? 'K.M.B.' £70-80
18005 99 'DERBY' £11-13
18201 94 'London COUNTRY' ...£30-40
18202 94 'LT', 'XF2' ....in GS 99909
18203 ? 'LC', 'Blue Arrow' £11-13
25401 98 'BIRMINGHAM' £11-13
25402 99 'WELSH RHONDDA' ..£12-15
27401 01 'CMB' 'Training' £20-25

Daimler Utility Bus

26401 99 'MIDLAND RED' £11-13
26402 00 'GREENLINE' £25-30

Dennis Dart – see Plaxton Pointer

Guy Arab double deck buses

26201 99 'COVENTRY' £11-13
26202 00 'COLCHESTER' £12-15
26301 99 'L.T.', 'Wanstead' £20-25
26302 99 'BIRMINGHAM' £11-13
26303 99 'DEVON GENERAL' ...£14-16
26304 99 'BIRKENHEAD' £11-13
26305 00 'Midland GENERAL' ...£11-13
-- DL 00 'Midland GENERAL' ...£12-15
26306 00 'SOUTHDOWN' £20-25
26307 00 'LT' 'Cobham Ramblers' in GS 99920 ....GSP
26308 00 'Great YARMOUTH' ...£12-15

Harrington Cavalier coaches

11901 ....not issued
11902 91 'YELLOWAYS' £18-22
11903 92 'GREY-GREEN' £14-16
12101 91 'SOUTHDOWN' £25-30
12102 92 'EAST YORKS' £11-13
12103 92 'HEBBLE' £11-13
c12103 93 'PENNINE RALLY' £16-20
12104 92 'SURREY', in set 99906. .GSP
12105 92 'NEATH & CARDIFF' .£11-13
12106 93 'VALIANT' £11-13
-- DL 93 same but extra detail £11-13
12107 93 'SOUTHDOWN', in GS 99907. ....GSP
12108 94 'RIBBLE' £20-25
12109 94 'ROBIN HOOD' £11-13
12110 96 'FLIGHTS TRAVEL' £11-13
12111 98 'CHARLIE'S CARS' £11-13
12112 99 'WALLACE ARNOLD' £11-13
12113 00 'MAIDSTONE' £20-25

Harrington Grenadier coaches

12201 91 'BLACK & WHITE' £18-22
12202 92 'PREMIER' £11-13
12203 92 'BARTONS', set 99905 ...GSP
12204 92 'ORANGE LUXURY' ..£11-13
-- DL 92 'ORANGE LUXURY' ..£18-22
12301 91 'MAIDSTONE' £20-25
12302 92 'GREY CARS' £11-13
12303 92 'TIMPSONS', set 99906...GSP
12304 92 'SOUTHDOWN' £14-16
12305 93 'ELLEN SMITH', std. ..£11-13
-- DL Same but Deluxe £11-13
c12305 93 'Ribble Road Safety' £18-22
12306 93 'B.O.A.C.', std. £14-16
-- DL Same but Deluxe £14-16

Leeds Horsfield tram

13402 91 'TIZER' £18-22
13402b 91 same, brown chassis £60-70
13403 92 'JACOBS' £18-22
13404 99 'Leeds' wartime £18-22
13405 99 'SAFETY FIRST' £18-22
13406 99 'LEEDS' £18-22
14301 92 'YORKSHIRE POST' ..£14-16
14302 93 'WHITBREAD' £25-30
14303 94 'YORKSHIRE EVENING POST' £18-20
13404 95 'LEEDS', wartime £10-12
13405 97 'SAFETY FIRST' £10-12

Leyland Atlantean buses (see also Alexander and Daimler Fleetline)

16501 94 'RIBBLE' £35-40
16502 94 'WALLASEY' £35-40
16503 94 'DEVON GENERAL' ...£35-40
16504 94 'MAIDSTONE' £35-40
16505 94 'PLYMOUTH' £11-13
16506 94 'SHEFFIELD', 'Tetley' £11-13
16507 94 'GATESHEAD' £11-13
16508 94 'NORTHERN' £11-13
16509 95 'LEICESTER' '26' £11-13
16510 94 'BIRMINGHAM' £11-13
16511 95 'HULL', route '430' £11-13
16512 ? 'LIVERPOOL ......in GS 19907
16513 95 'SALFORD' £11-13
16514 95 'STEVENSONS': 'Walkden' £11-13
-- DL 98 'Burton' £11-13
16515 95 'TRENT', 'Sileby' £11-13
16516 95 'PORTSMOUTH': 'Eastney' £11-13
-- DL 97 'South Parade Pier' £20-25
16517 96 'GWR' £11-13
16518 96 'Liverpool', 'BOAC' £18-20
16519 97 'SCOUT', 'Burnley' £11-13
16520 00 'South YORKSHIRE' ...£11-14
16521 00 'Ribble White Lady' £25-30

18101 94 'LT XA13', 'BOAC' £40-50
18102 95 'LT XA9', route '24' £30-40
--- DL 95 'LT XA9', route 'P3' .£110-130
18103 96 'LEEDS CITY': 'Swinnow' £11-13
-- DL 98 'Bramley' £11-13
18104 97 'L. COUNTRY', 'XA' ..£25-30
18105 ? 'CHINA M. B.' £25-30
18106 ? 'CHINA M. B.' £25-30
18107 99 'STOCKTON' £11-13
18107dl 00 'STOCKTON' £12-15
18108 00 'LT', route '234' £12-15
18108a 00 'North Weald Rally' £15-18
18108b 00 'Ramblers Holidays' £20-25
18108c 00 'Bexley Pageant' £15-18
18109 00 'LEEDS' £12-15
24701 98 'MANCHESTER' £25-30
24702 98 'DEVON GENERAL' ...£25-30
24703 98 'PLYMOUTH' £11-13
24704 98 'SELNEC', 'Reddish' ...£11-13
24705 98 'LANCASTER' £11-13

Leyland Duple coaches

26801 99 'SKILL'S', 'York' £12-15
26802 99 'SCOUT' £11-13
26803 00 'RED & WHITE' £12-15

Leyland National single deckers

14401 92 'GREENLINE' £20-25
14402 92 'MANCHESTER' £11-13
14403 93 'UNITED', std. £11-13
-- DL Same but Deluxe £11-13
14404 98 'LONDON UNITED' £11-13
-- DL 00 'LONDON UNITED' £11-13
14601 94 'RIBBLE', short, Mk.I ..£30-35
14701 93 'McGILLS' £18-20
14901 97 'YORK CITY RIDER' ..£11-13
15001 ? 'SOUTHDOWN' .in GS 99912
15101 92 'HANTS & DORSET' ..£14-16
c15101b 93 Same but 'Beatties' £30-35
15102 93 'CROSVILLE': 'Woodside' £11-13
c15102a 93 same but Club model ..£11-13
c15102b 93 same but 'Beatties' £35-40
15103 93 'NORTHERN', std. £11-13
same but Deluxe £11-13
15104 93 'BRISTOL': 'Temple Meads' £20-25
--- DL 93 'Evening Post' £18-20
15105 99 'PROVINCIAL £11-13
-- DL 98 'Cheltenham Road' £10-12
15105a 00 'Southsea 2000' £16-20
15106 00 'Midland General' £11-13
16601 94 'LT', 'Kingston', '111' ..£30-35
16602 94 'EASTBOURNE' £11-13
16603 95 'ENSIGNBUS' £20-25
16604 99 'LT Metroline' ......in GS 99918
16701 94 'LT', route 'S6' £25-30
16901 93 'LT', route '513' ... in GS 9908
17201 94 'TRENT', 'Mickleover' ..£25-30
17202 94 'THAMESWAY' £11-13
17203 95 'YORKS. TERRIER' £11-13
-- DL 97 Same, 'Bradway', cert. ..£11-13
17204 97 'WILTS & DORSET' £11-13
17205 97 'MAIDSTONE' £20-25
17206 97 'MIDLAND RED' £11-13
17207 99 'Aldershot & Dist.' ..GS 99916
17208 98 'WESTERN NATIONAL' £11-13
17209 99 'J. FISHWICK' £11-13
17210 00 'BARTON BUSES' £11-13
17211 00 'PERTH PANTHER' £12-14
17301 95 'READING', Volvo £18-20
17302 01 'ISLE OF MAN' £12-15
17401 98 'BLUE BUS' £11-13
17501 99 'SOUTHERN NATIONAL' £11-13
17502 00 'South YORKSHIRE' ...£12-15
17503 01 'First MANCHESTER' £12-15

Leyland RTL double-deck buses

11101 90 'CONTRACTUS', in set 19903 ....£14-16
11102 90 'BOAT SHOW', In set 19903 ....£18-22
-- DL 90 'BOAT SHOW', (LT Museum only). £40-45
11103 90 'WILKINSON SWORD', singly and in set 19903 .£18-22
C11103a 92 'LT', 'PSV Circle' ....NGPP
C11103b 93 'LT', 'Bromley' £25-30
11104 90 'LOCKEYS', no ads £14-16
11105 91 'BRYLCREEM' £30-35
11106 91 'FISHERMANS FRIEND', 'RTL 285', special box £25-30
-- DL 93 Same but Deluxe £30-35
11107 92 'BARTON', in set 99905. .GSP
11108 92 'A1 SERVICE' £14-16
11109 95 'OK MOTOR' £14-16
11110 96 'Stevensons' 'Uttoxeter' (AEC radiator) £200-230
11110 96 same but Leyland rad ...£14-16
-- DL 98 'Anslow'+ Leyland rad .£14-16
11110 96 Same but AEC grille .£175-200
11111 ? 'WALSALL' £14-16
11112 00 'JERSEY M. T.' £14-16
22801 ? 'LT', 'Guernsey Toms', In set 99913 ....GSP
-- DL ? 'LT', 'Ireland by Rail' ...£65-75

Leyland STD double-deck buses

20201 96 'L.T.', route '38a' £35-40
20202 97 'L.T.', 'Typhoo' ...in GS 99913
-- DL 97 'L.T.', 'Rail & Sea' ...£110-130

Leyland TD1 buses

27201 00 'BOLTON' £11-13
27201a 00 Subscribers' model ....NGPP
27202 00 'BIRKENHEAD' £12-15
27202a 01 Subscribers' model ....NGPP
27203 00 'SHEFFIELD' £12-15
27204 00 'GLASGOW' £12-15
27205 00 'THAMES VALLEY' ...£12-15
-- SB 00 Same but 'Showbus' £12-15
27206 00 'LINCOLN CITY' £12-15
27301 01 'RIBBLE' £12-15
27302 01 'CROSVILLE' £12-15
27302 01 'Yorkshire Traction' £12-15
27303 01 'JERSEY' £12-15

Leyland Tiger buses and coaches

18301 94 'YORKS. WOOLLEN' .£12-15
18302 94 'SUNDERLAND' £11-13
18303 95 'BARTON', route '26' ..£12-15
18304 95 'Yorks. Woollen' wartime, (also in GS19906) £11-13
18305 95 'EAST MIDLANDS': 'Retford' £11-13
-- DL 97 'Clipstone' £11-13
18306 96 'WESTERN WELSH' ..£11-13
-- DL 96 Same but Deluxe £11-13
18401 94 'WEST RIDING' £11-13
18402 95 'LANCASHIRE' £11-13
18403 95 'COUNTY MOTORS' ..£11-13
18404 95 'DONCASTER': '11 Arksey' £11-13
c18404 'Ian Allan' £11-13
18405 95 'LINCOLNSHIRE': 'Grantham' £11-13
-- DL 97 'Mablethorpe' £11-13
18406 95 'O. K. M. S.' £11-13
c18406 'O. K. M. S.', 'Beatties' .£11-13
18407 96 'Yorks. TRACTION' £11-13
18408 99 'Fishwick & Sons' £12-15

Leyland PD1 Lowbridge

15801 93 'WIGAN' £11-13
15801 95 'Wigan', Club Model. ...£25-30
15802 93 'EAST KENT' £11-13
15803 95 'EAST MIDLAND' £11-13
-- DL 96 Same but Deluxe £11-13
15804 96 'SCOUT', 'Preston' £30-40

Leyland PD1 Highbridge

15901 93 'LEICESTER', std £11-13
-- DL Same but Deluxe £11-13
15902 94 'RIBBLE', 'Dulux' £25-30
15903 94 'Samuel LEDGARD' £11-13
15904 94 'CITY COACHES' £11-13
15905 95 'SALFORD CITY' £11-13
15906 99 'LANCASHIRE' £11-13
15907 00 'Lytham St Annes' £11-13
15907dl 00 same but Deluxe £12-15
15908 00 'WARRINGTON' £11-13
15909 00 'ISLE OF MAN' £12-15
15910 00 'SOUTHDOWN' £12-15

Leyland PD2 Lowbridge

16001 93 'Todmorden', 'LMS' £20-25
16002 93 'Todmorden', 'BR' £25-30
16003 94 'EAST KENT' £11-13
16004 94 'DEVON GENERAL' ...£25-30
16005 94 'MIDLAND RED' £14-16
16006 94 'WEST RIDING' £11-13
16007 95 'NORTH WESTERN' ...£11-13
-- DL 96 Same but Deluxe £11-13
16008 00 'SEAVIEW' £12-15

Leyland PD2 Highbridge

16101 93 'Wigan' £11-13
c16101 95 'Wigan', Club Model £18-20
16102 93 'LEICESTER CITY' £11-13
16103 94 'CROSVILLE' £25-30
16104 94 'LEEDS' £11-13
16105 94 'SHEFFIELD' £11-13
16106 94 'LIVERPOOL', in 19907 ..GSP
16107 95 'STRATFORD BLUE' ..£14-16
-- DL 99 'STRATFORD BLUE' ..£11-13
16108 ? 'SOUTHDOWN' .in GS 99910
16109 95 'PORTSMOUTH': 'Farlington' £11-13
-- DL 97 'Guildhall' £25-30
16110 96 'LIVERPOOL' £11-13
16111 96 'BIRMINGHAM' £11-13
c16111 96 'ASTON MANOR' £18-20
16112 97 'STOCKPORT' £11-13
16113 97 'KING ALFRED' £11-13
16114 98 'NEWCASTLE' £11-13
16115 98 'Great YARMOUTH' £11-13
c16115 99 'Great YARMOUTH' 'Classic Buss 1999' £15-18
16116 98 'CITY of EXETER' £11-13
16117 99 'HALIFAX' £11-13
16118 00 'FISHWICK & SONS' .£18-20

Leyland PD2/12

20001 95 'MAIDSTONE' £20-25
20002 95 'RIBBLE' £11-13
20003 96 'BOLTON' £11-13
-- DL 98 'Belmont' £11-13
20004 96 'SUNDERLAND': 'West Hartlepool' £11-13
-- DL 97 'Durham' £11-13
20005 96 'BIRKENHEAD' £11-13
20006 99 'CITY OF EXETER' £11-13
20007 01 'PLYMOUTH CITY' £12-15

Leyland TS8 single deck buses

18306
-- DL 99 'WESTERN WELSH' ..£10-12
18497 98 'YORKS. TRACTION' £10-12

Leyland Windover coaches

20901 96 'YORKS. TRACTION' £11-13
20902 97 'HEBBLE' £11-13
20903 ? 'SOUTHDOWN' ..in set 99915

Buses, Coaches, Trams

Mercedes-Benz Minibus and Hoppa
24801 98 'EASTERN NATIONAL' £11-13
24802 98 'WESTERN NATIONAL' £11-13
24803 98 'BADGERLINE' £11-13
24804 98 'BRISTOL' £11-13
24805 98 'MAIDSTONE' £11-13
24806 98 'THAMESWAY' £11-13
24807 99 'SCARBOROUGH' £11-13
24808 99 'First MANCHESTER'.£11-13
24809 00 'EASTERN COUNTIES' £12-15
24810 00 'DEVON GENERAL'.£12-15
24901 98 'BREWERS', 'Neath'.£11-13

Plaxton Panorama Elite coaches
15701 93 'SOUTH WEST NBC'.£11-13
15701dl and 15702dl: 'UNITED',
  94 (sold as a pair)...........£35-45
15702 93 'RIBBLE NBC' £11-13
15703 93 'EAST KENT', std.......£11-13
-- DL same but 'Skyways' £11-13
15704 93 'ABBOTTS', std. £11-13
-- DL Same but Deluxe £11-13
15705 93 'SHEFFIELD', std. £11-13
-- DL Same but Deluxe £11-13
15706 93 'BRISTOL', std. £11-13
-- DL Same but Deluxe £11-13
15707 93 'GREY GREEN', std. ...£11-13

-- DL Same but Deluxe £11-13
15708 94 'BARTONS'.................£18-20
15709 94 'SOUTHDOWN'..........£50-60
15710 98 'WAL. ARNOLD'.........£11-13
15711 00 'London Country' £12-14

Plaxton Paramount 3500 coaches
22701 00 'UNITED WELSH' £11-13
26610 99 'PREMIER'..................£11-13
26602 99 'GREY GREEN' £11-13
26603 99 'PLYMOUTH' £11-13
26604 00 'Greenline Invicta'......£13-16
-- DL 00 'Greenline Invicta'......£13-16
26605 00 'WAL. ARNOLD'........£12-15
26606 00 'SHEARINGS' £16-20
26607 00 'SKILLS' £12-15
26608 00 'BUS EIREANN'...........£12-15
26609 00 'Western National' £12-15
26610 01 'East Yorkshire' £12-15
26701 01 'United Welsh' £12-15
26702 01 'Caledonian Express'...£12-15

Plaxton Pointer / Dart single-deck buses
20601 96 'METROLINE' £25-30
20602 96 'BADGERLINE' £16-20
20603 96 'THAMESWAY':
  'Canvey' £11-13
-- DL 97 'Basildon' £11-13
20604 96 'YORKSHIRE TERRIER':
  'Darnall' £11-13

-- DL 97 'Crystal Peaks' £11-13
20605 96 'YORKS. TRACTION'.£11-13
20606 96 'BREWERS' £11-13
20607 96 'BRIGHTON BLUE'.£30-35
20608 96 'P.M.T.', 'Talke Pits'....£11-13
20609 97 'PLYMOUTH' £30-35
20610 96 'MANCHESTER' £11-13
20611 97 'WESTERN NATIONAL' £30-35
20612 97 'METROBUS' £11-13
20613 97 'EASTERN NATIONAL' £11-13
20614 97 'LEEDS CITYLINK'....£11-13
20615 97 'THAMESDOWN' £11-13
20616 97 'DOCKLANDS' £11-13
20617 97 'GREY-GREEN' £11-13
20618 9? 'MACAU' £18-20
20619 9? 'MAINLINE' Volvo.£20-25
20620 98 'MAIDSTONE' £11-13
20621 98 'LEA VALLEY' £11-13
20622 98 'ARRIVA' 'Cowie' £11-13
20623 98 'BLUE BUS' £11-13
-- DL 99 'BLUE BUS' £11-13
20624 99 'Arriva' 'Sth London'....£11-13
20625 99 'WARRINGTON' £11-13
20626 00 'MIDLAND RED' £11-13
20627 00 'DEVON GENERAL' ...£11-13

Plaxton Super Low Floor
26901 00 'New World Fruit'........£40-50

RCL Routemaster buses
25604 00 'SIGHTSEEING TOUR' ....
25605 01 'BLUE TRIANGLE' ....

RM Routemaster buses
15626 99 'ENSIGNBUS' ....
15627A 01 'THE DELAINE' ....
15629 00 'SOUTHAMPTON' ....

RML Routemaster buses
25509 00 'GREEN LONDON' ....

Reeves Burgess Mini-bus
25901 99 'BARTON' £11-13
25902 99 'NOTTINGHAM' £11-13

Wright Scania Axcess
27501 00 'LINCOLNSHIRE' £20-25
27502 01 'Eastern National' £12-15
27503 01 'Eastern Counties'
  'PARK & RIDE' £12-15

Wright Volvo Renown
27601 01 'Bus EIREANN' £12-15

?????
22401 00 'B.O.A.C.' £25-30

Commercial Vehicles

AEC Ergomatic trucks and tankers
13801 97 'MIDLAND RED' £9-12
21501 96 'PHILLIPS' £8-11
21602 96 'SHORE PORTERS'.£8-11
21604 98 'FEDERATION' £9-12
21802 99 'TRUMAN'S' £8-11
22101 96 'EXPRESS DAIRIES'..£8-11
22102 ? 'TAYFORTH
  McKINNON'.£8-11
22601 96 'SPIERS' £8-11
22602 97 'BRS' £11-13
22603 99 'WESTERN BRS' £11-13
22604 99 'TRUMANS' £11-13
23001 98 'B.R.S. BRISTOL'........£9-12
23101 97 'WOODCOCK' £9-12
26001 98 'B.R.S. LEEDS' £9-12

AEC articulated trucks
19501 94 'HOOVER' £8-11
19502 95 'PICKFORDS' £8-11
19503 96 'HITCHMANS' £8-11
19601 95 'B.R.S.' £12-15

AEC 6-wheel box vans
10501 89 'LONDON CARRIERS'£5-8
-- DL 91 Same but in Set 99903....GSP
10502 89 'START-RITE' £4-6
10503 90 'B.R.S.', 'Huddersfield' .£6-8
-- DL 91 'B.R.S.', Set 99903........GSP
-- 91 'B.R.S.', 'Club 91' £8-10
10504 90 'PEK PORK' £5-8
10505 90 'OXYDOL' £5-8
10506 91 'HOOVER' £12-15
10507 93 'RAYLEIGH'S' £12-15
10905dl 94 'WELCHS' £8-10
c105001 'FISHERMANS FRIEND'
  `89...................................£8-10

AEC 8-wheel box vans
11001 89 'CROFT SHERRY' £4-6
11002 89 'PICKFORDS' £8-10
-- DL 91 Same but in set 99903...GSP
11003 90 'TATE & LYLE',
  in set 19901..................GSP
11004 90 'RANK HOVIS',
  in set 19902. ....GSP
-- DL 93 'RANK HOVIS' £8-10
11005 90 'LACONS'.................£8-10
11006 91 'ROSES LIME JUICE' £8-10
11007 95 'BOUTS CARRIERS' ..£9-11
11008 ? 'BRS' ('BTC Ltd')......NGPP

AEC 6-wheel dropside wagons
10301 90 'FENLAND' £4-6

-- DL 91 Same + plastic 'load'..£8-10
10302 90 'CYRIL RIDGEON' £4-6
-- DL 91 Same + plastic 'load'...£8-10
10303 90 'J. D. LOWN' £4-6
-- DL 91 Same + plastic 'load'...£8-10
c103001 'FISHERMANS FRIEND'
  `89 ....£35-40

AEC 8-wheel dropside wagons
10604dl 92 'MOBILOIL'...........£11-13
10801 89 'BRITISH STEEL' £4-6
-- DL 92 Same + plastic 'load'...£8-10
10802 89 'WHITBREAD' £4-6
-- DL 91 Same + plastic 'load'...£8-10
10803 90 'MARLEY TILES'.........£11-13
10804 91 'MACREADYS' £5-7
-- DL 92 Same + plastic 'load'...£8-10
10805 91 'TAYLOR WOODROW',
  in GS 19904...................GSP
-- DL 93 Same; simply + 'load' ...£8-10
- DL2 93 'Model Collector' offer
  version £35-40
10806dl 92 'ROSES LIME' £8-10
11005dl 93 'LACONS' + 'load'.£11-13
c108001 90 'FISHERMANS FRIEND'
  ....£10-15

AEC 6-wheel flatbeds
10503dl 92 'B.R.S.' + 'load' £18-20
10701 89 'FURLONG Bros.' £4-6
-- DL 91 Same + plastic 'load'...£8-10
10702 89 'BLUE CIRCLE'.............£5-7
-- DL 91 Same + plastic 'load'...£8-10
10703 90 'WIMPEY' (yellow)......£5-7
  'WIMPEY' (red) £8-10
-- DL 92 Same + plastic 'load'...£8-10
10704dl 94 'J.D. LOWN' £11-13
10904dl 93 'RANK HOVIS' £11-13

AEC 8-wheel flatbeds
10401 89 'BATH & PORTLAND' .£4-6
--DL 91 Same but with 'load' ...£8-10
10402 89 'LONDON BRICK' £6-8
-- DL 91 Same but with 'load' ...£8-10

AEC 6-wheel tankers
10901 89 'HEYGATES' £4-6
10902 89 'LORD RAYLEIGHS' £4-6
10903 90 'L.P.G.',
  white round tank............£4-6
-- DL 93 'L.P.G.', silver oval tank,
  and in Set 99904........£8-10
10904 90 'RANK HOVIS',
  in Set 99902.................GSP

10905 90 'WELCHS' £5-7

AEC 8-wheel tankers
10601 89 'CENTURY OIL' £4-6
-- DL 91 Same but in Set 99904 ..GSP
10602 89 'J. & H. BUNN' £4-6
10603 90 'TATE & LYLE' ....Set 19901
10604 90 'MOBILGAS' £8-10
-- DL 91 Same but in Set 99904...GSP
10605 90 'REGENT' £12-15
10606dl 93 'WHITBREAD' £8-10

AEC 8-wheel tippers
12001 90 'WIMPEY' £8-10
12002 90 'TARMAC' £8-10
-- DL 92 Same + plastic 'load'...£15-18
12003 91 'TAYLOR WOODROW',
  in Set 19904.................GSP
-- DL 92 Same but with 'load' £8-10
12004 91 'KETTON' £11-13

Albion Ergomatic trucks
21603 97 'B.R.S.' £10-12
21801 96 'W.J. RICH & Sons'....£10-12
21802 97 'TRUMANS' £11-13

Atkinson articulated trucks
13001 91 'TSL' £11-13
13002 91 'SWIFTS' £11-13
13003 92 'MIDLAND CAR' £11-13
13004 93 'CLASSIC' £11-13
19301 95 'SUTTONS'.................£8-11
19302 95 'BOWKERS' £8-11
19303 96 'PARKINSONS' £8-11
19401 95 'FLOWERS' £8-11
19402 95 'TATE & LYLE' £8-11
19403 96 'MONKS' £8-11
19404 97 'KRAFT' £8-11
19405 99 'BRS Door to Door' ...£11-13

Atkinson rigid trucks and tankers
12501 92 'WELLS DRINKS' £18-22
12601 91 'McNICHOLAS' £6-8
-- DL 91 Same but with 'load' ...£8-10
12701 91 'CHARRINGTONS' ...£12-15
12801 92 'McPHEES' £35-40
12802 94 'SUTTONS'................£11-13
12803 96 'HENSHALL' £11-13
12901 91 'FYFFES' £12-15
13101 96 'DENTS' £8-11
13201 94 'SUTTONS'.................£8-11
13202 97 'M & B' £9-12
13203 97 'MACKESON' £9-12
13301 91 'St.ALBANS' £8-11

-- DL 93 Same + extra detail......£8-11
13501 98 'PICKFORDS' £10-12
13701 92 'FINA', tanker £25-30

Bedford TK articulated vehicles
22001 96 'SCHREIBER' £10-12
22002 97 'WAVY LINE' £10-12
22003 97 'V. G.' £10-12
22004 97 'VLADIVAR' £10-12
22201 96 'BRITISH RAILWAYS' £30-35
22202 96 'B.R.S.' £10-12
22203 97 'S. G. B.' £10-12
22204 97 'BRITISH RAIL' £10-12
22205 98 'BRITISH RAILWAYS',
  'Door to Door' £10-12
27001 00 'B.R.S.' transporter ...£10-12

Bedford TK rigid trucks
21201 96 'BLOXWICH' £10-12
21202 96 'B.R.S.' £10-12
21202 96 'VP WINE' £10-12
21701 97 'B.R.S.' £10-12
-- DL 97 'B.R.S.','Littlewoods' £12-15
21901 96 'BARTON' £10-12
21902 96 'COURAGE' £10-12
22901 97 'SOUTHERN BRS'....£10-12
22902 97 'SAINSBURY'S' £10-12
22904 97 'GOLDENLAY' £10-12
22905 97 'BIRDSEYE' £10-12
22906 97 'WAGON WHEELS' .£10-12
22908 98 'ROADLINE' £10-12
22909 99 'BRS RENTAL' £10-12
23101 97 'GREY-GREEN' £10-12
23401 97 'WHITBREAD' £12-15
23601 98 'GREY-GREEN' £10-12
23602 98 'PICKFORDS' £18-20
23603 98 'PICKFORDS' £10-12
23604 99 'CROSVILLE' £10-12
24101 97 'S. A. BRAINS' £10-12
24102 98 'GREENE KING' £10-12
24103 99 'WATNEYS' £10-12

Bedford TK Rigid and Trailer
24001 97 'MYER'S BEDS' £10-12
24002 98 'BRS PARCELS Ltd'.£10-12

Leyland Ergomatic trucks
21601 96 'HOLT LANE' £10-12
21602 96 'SHORE PORTERS' ...£10-12
22103 96 'R. WHITE'S' £10-12
22104 97 'TESCO'...................£10-12
22301 96 'MAJOR' £10-12
24601 98 'GUINNESS' £10-12

EFE Gift Sets

19901	1990	'TATE & LYLE' ....10105 AEC Bus, 11003 8-wheel Van, 10603 8-wheel Tanker **£40-45**

19901 1990 'TATE & LYLE' ....10105 AEC Bus, 11003 8-wheel Van, 10603 8-wheel Tanker **£40-45**
19902 1990 'RANK HOVIS' ....10106 AEC Bus, 11004 8-wheel Van, 10904 6-wheel Tanker **£30-35**
19903 1990 'The RTL Story' ....11101 'Boat Show', 11102 'Wilkinson', 11103 'Bott' **£30-40**
19904 1991 'TAYLOR WOODROW' ....10110 AEC Bus, 10806 8-wheel Dropside, 12003 8-wheel Tipper **£30-35**

19905 1994 'Routemaster' Set ....15609 and 15611 AEC Routemasters. 'Model Collector' magazine offer....................**£30-40**
19906 1995 'World War II' Set ....13404 Tram and 18304 Leyland Tiger....................**£30-35**
19907 1995 'Liverpool' Set....................16512 Atlantean and 16106 Leyland PD, only available from Ian Allan **£35-40**
19908 1997 'RM' Set ....15610 and 17802, only from Beatties....................**£30-35**
19909 1999 'Littlewoods Set' ....no details **£30-40**

99901 1990 'London Buses'....................10101 'Duracell', 10103 'Birdseye', 10104 'Schweppes'....................**£40-50**
99902 1990 'FISHERMANS FRIEND'..........10108 AEC Bus, 10507 6-wheel Van, 6 or 8 wheel Dropside Wagon.
    1st run....................in separate boxes (smooth base RT Bus and 6 wheel Dropside Wagon) **£40-50**
    2nd run....................in separate boxes (textured base RT Bus and 8 wheel Dropside Wagon) **£30-35**
    3rd run....................in one box, (textured base RT Bus and 8 wheel Dropside Wagon) **£30-35**

99903 1991 De Luxe 'Box Vans' Set..............10501 'London Carriers', plus 10503 'B.R.S.' & 11002 'Pickfords' **£35-40**
99904 1991 De Luxe 'Tankers' Set................'L.P.G.', 'CENTURY OIL', 'MOBILGAS'....................**£40-50**
99905 1992 'BARTONS TRANSPORT' ....Leyland RTL and Harrington Grenadier **£25-30**
99906 1992 'Harrington Coaches' ....Cavalier 'Surrey' and Grenadier 'Timpsons' ('Model Collector' offer)....................**£25-30**
c99906 1995 'Harrington Coaches' ....Cavalier 'Surrey' ('Surrey United') and Grenadier 'Timpsons' ('Crystal Palace')......**£30-40**
99907 1993 'SOUTHDOWN' 1....................Bristol Lodekka and Harrington Cavalier, ('Model Collector' offer) **£60-70**
99908 1993 'London Transport Museum' 1....16401 Regent, plus 16901 Leyland and 15612 AEC, (LT Museum exclusive)............**£60-70**
99909 1994 'London Transport Museum' 2....18202 Leyland Atlantean plus 16310 Bristol LS coach, (LT Museum exclusive)........**£80-90**

99910 1997 'SOUTHDOWN' 2....................Leyland PD, Bedford OB, ('Model Collector' offer) **£110-130**
99911 1994 'London Transport Museum' 3....'RM Set' with two Routemasters, (LT Museum exclusive) **£60-70**
99912 1997 'SOUTHDOWN' 3................Bristol VR and Leyland National, ('Model Collector' offer)....................**£80-90**
99913 1994 'London Transport Museum' 4....'London Leylands': a standard Leyland + 'roof-box' RTL, (LT Museum exclusive) ...**£60-70**
99914 199? 'London Transport Museum' 5....Two 'GREENLINE' buses, (LT Museum exclusive) **£90-110**
99915 199? 'SOUTHDOWN' 4....................24305 Leyland Tiger Cub and 20903 Tiger PS1. EFE subscribers only **£50-60**

99916 ? 'Aldershot & District' Set ....no details **£40-50**
99916a ? 'Aldershot & District' Set ....no details **£50-60**
99917 199? 'London Transport Museum' 6....Two 'RML' buses, (LT Museum exclusive) **£40-50**
99918 1999 'Beatties' Set....................A Daimler DMS and a Leyland National, only available from Beatties shops **£40-50**
99919 2000 'London Transport Museum' 7....Two 'London Connections'....................**£50-60**
99920 2000 'Ramblers' Gift Set....................no details **£40-50**
99921 2000 'Millennium' Set....................Models featuring the 'London Transport' Covent Garden Museum **£70-80**

Open Touring Cars

These models were issued as pairs in a single box and it is to this 'twin-pack' that the price range refers.

1991 11401 Triumph Roadster (Red)....................packed with ....11601 Triumph Vitesse (White)....................**£14-16**
1991 11402 Triumph Roadster (Black)....................packed with ....11602 Triumph Vitesse (Light Blue)....................**£8-10**
1992 11403 Triumph Roadster (Blue)....................packed with ....11603 Triumph Vitesse (Red)....................**£14-16**
1992 11404 Triumph Roadster (Dark Green) ....packed with ....11604 Triumph Vitesse (Dark Blue)....................**£8-10**

1991 11501 MG MGB (Dark Green)....................packed with ....11701 Austin-Healey Sprite (Yellow)....................**£14-16**
1991 11502 MG MGB (Red)....................packed with ....11702 Austin-Healey Sprite (White)....................**£8-10**
1992 11503 MG MGB (Orange)....................packed with ....11703 Austin-Healey Sprite (Green)....................**£8-10**
1992 11504 MG MGB (Black) ....packed with ....11704 Austin-Healey Sprite (Red)....................**£8-10**

Original box types

Standard issues of single models were originally packed in rigid card window boxes coloured grey, with black and red printing. Special boxes were made for certain promotional models.

White boxes (with black printing) were used initially for the 'FISHERMANS FRIEND' issues that were part of an 'on-pack offer' promotion, and a subsequent RT bus promotion was presented in a pale blue box.

Certain of the models were designated 'De Luxe' and acquired additional detail or plastic 'loads' of various kinds. Each was packed in a 'double blister-pack' designed to hang on display stand pegs or stand (untidily) on a shelf. The first of the Gift Sets ('Tate & Lyle') was designed to look like a book (even having 'Volume One' printed on its blue card covering). The inner container was plain white expanded polystyrene. Subsequently the 'Rank Hovis' set (designated 'Volume Two') had an inner container of improved appearance with a flock base and clear plastic covering

Current box types

Through the latter part of the 1990s, Standard issues were presented in black window boxes with light red printing. A similar box in royal blue was used for the De Luxe range, while standard commercial vehicles boxes were maroon. The Grocery Series had cream boxes and the Brewery Series had green boxes. Like the Gift Sets, current packing is being individually designed to be more appropriate to the contents.

Ships

10001 99 RMS 'TITANIC'
    The ill-fated liner...........**£18-22**
? 99 'OLYMPIC'
    ? **£18-22**
10005 00 'OLYMPIC'
    in 'Dazzle' finish **£18-22**
? 99 'BRITTANIA'
    Hospital Ship **£18-22**

Lledo 'Days-Gone'

One of the founders of Matchbox Toys, Jack Odell OBE formed the Lledo toy company in 1982 and the first six models made their appearance at Easter 1983. The range was called 'Models-of Days-Gone'. Lledo introduced the 'Premier Collection' and the 'Military Collection' in 1991 to offer greater choice, more detailed finish and improved appearance of certain models. They have 'DG' numbers and their own attractive packaging. The standard range is now known simply as 'Days-Gone'.

With increasing interest the range has expanded to over one hundred models and has generally represented vehicles made up to the 1940s. 'Days Gone Vanguards' introduced in 1993 enhanced and extended the range of interest into the 1950s and 1960s. From 1996, 'Vanguards' have become a separate range with its own

'VA' numbering reference. The 'Special Licensed' range (with appropriately branded packaging) arrived in 1997, as did 'Cargo Kings' - Volvo, Kenworth and Scania truck models in 1:76 scale.

Rationalisation of output means that some earlier models have been discontinued and are likely to increase in price. The scarcer models have been given individual price gradings. Expect to pay £4-£6 for common issues.

Where no price is shown, the Market Price Range is below £6.
NGPP = no price grading possible at present   NPP = no price possible
GSP = Model is part of a set, see Gift Sets section for the Gift Set Price
SBX = special box, (C)LE = (certificated) limited edition, FB = Fire Brigade

Ref	Intro	Model	MPR
		DG 1 Horse-Drawn Tram	
		Includes a set of figures: two lady passengers, a male passenger, a girl and the driver.	
000a	83	'WESTMINSTER' Green chassis, Orange seats, Yellow crest	**£15-25**
000b	83	Green chassis, Orange seats, Cream crest	**£10-15**
000c	83	Green chassis, Orange seats, White crest	
		(a,b,c) with no strengtheners on end panel or shafts	**£100-120**
		(a,b,c) with strengtheners on shafts but not end panels	**£20-30**
000d	87	Green chassis, Red seats, White crest	
001a	84	'MAIN STREET', Green/Grey	
002a	84	Brown/Cream	
003		Not allocated	
004a	84	'CRICH'	
005a	84	'DOWNTOWN', Cream, Green seats	
005b	87	Cream, Dark Green seats	
005c	88	Dark Green seats, no Gold in crest	
005d	92	Dark Green seats, reversed crest	
006a	90	'HERSHEY'	
		90 Model withdrawn, but re-run for DG1-005d and:	
007a	96	'DG Club' Summer Special	
		DG 2 Horse-Drawn Milk Float	
		Includes a set of cream plastic figures: a woman, a man, the driver and a dog.	
000a	83	'EXPRESS DAIRY'	
001a	84	'CHAMBOURCY'	
002		Not allocated	
003a	84	'CLIFFORD DAIRY'	
004a	84	'CELTIC DAIRY'	
		90 Model withdrawn.	
		DG 3 Horse-Drawn Van	
		Until 1985 a set of cream plastic figures was included - a woman, a boy and a driver.	
000a	83	'WINDMILL BAKERY', Yellow body,Cream shafts	
000b	84	Yellow body, Beige shafts	
001a	85	'COCA-COLA'	
002a	84	'FINE LADY BAKERIES'	
003a	84	'ROBERTSONS', Green/Yellow	
003a	87	re-run, darker green 'leaves'	
004a	84	'PEPPERIDGE FARM'	
005a	84	'STAFFS. COUNTY SHOW', Pale Green	
005b	84	Mint Green	**£5-7**
006a	84	'MATTHEW NORMAN'	
007a	85	'ROYAL MAIL', special box	
008a	84	'L.S.W.R.'	
009a	84	'HAMLEY'S TOYS', SBX	

Ref	Intro	Model	MPR
010a	85	'TRI-SUM POTATO CHIPS'	
011a	87	'LLEDO Worldwide CC'	**£5-7**
012a	88	'J. SPRATT', special box	
013a	90	'ROYAL MAIL', special box	
014a	92	'HARRODS', (Set HD1004)	GSP
015a	92	'GREAT EASTERN', (Set RSL4003)	GSP
016a	97	'DAYS GONE CLUB', 'Spring 97'	
		1990: Model withdrawn from standard production but casting remained available for use in sets.	
		DG 4 Horse-Drawn Omnibus	
		Cream plastic figures included: two ladies, a man, the driver and conductor, (no. '4' moulded into the surround).	
000a	83	'VICTORIA-KINGS CROSS', Red body, Green seats, 'LIPTONS' on Off-White panel	**£10-20**
000b		As 000a but pure White panel.	
000c		As 000a but White logo, Green panel	
000d	84	As 000c but Brown seats	
001a	84	'BOWERY to BROADWAY' Red body, Black wheels	
002a	84	'BOWERY to BROADWAY', Green body, Brown seats and wheels	
002b	84	Green body and seats, Brown wheels	
002c	84	Dark Green, Brown seats, Gold wheels	
002d	88	Mid-Green, Brown seats, Gold wheels	
003a	84	'PUTNEY'	
004a	85	'MASONS PANTRY'	
004b	85	with 'Mrs Beaton' on wrong sides	**£18-22**
005a	84	'PEARS', Red wheels	
005b	87	'PEARS', Black wheels	
006a	84	'MADAME TUSSAUDS' Red seats and wheels	
006b	87	Red seats, Black wheels	
007a	86	'HIGH CHAPARRAL'	
008a	84	'HAMLEYS TOYS', SBX	
009a	87	'BALMORAL TOURS', special box	
010a	88	'RADIO TIMES', 'A Million Copies' in special box	**£100-125**
010b	88	'RADIO TIMES', 'Thomas Tilling', SBX	
011a	88	'NEWS of the WORLD', special box	
012a	89	'COLMANS MUSTARD'	
013a	91	'STONES GINGER WINE'	
014a	92	'OXO'	
015a	93	'CO-OP TEA'	
016a	93	'FURNESS RAILWAY', (set RSL4003)	GSP
017a	94	'MADAME TUSSAUDS'	
018a	94	'HARRODS' (set HR 2002)	GSP
019a	95	'MANN'S BEER'	

Ref	Intro	Model	MPR
		DG 5 Shand-Mason Horse-Drawn Fire Engine	
		A set of three (dark blue) plastic firemen figures was included up to 1985 (and re-introduced in 1989 partially painted and affixed).	
000a	83	'LONDON', Red body, Black wheels	
000c	87	Gold wheels	**£65-80**
001a	83	'CHICAGO', Red body, Black wheels, Black horses	
001b	85	Gold wheels, Cream horses, (72 only)	**£65-80**
002a	83	'GUILDFORD', Green body, Gold wheels, Black boiler (288 made)	**£100-150**
002b	83	Green body, Gold boiler	
002c	84	Dark Green body, Gold boiler	
003a	84	'HONG KONG', White body, Red wheels, Red boiler (288 issued)	**£100-150**
003b	84	'HONG KONG', Gold boiler	
004a	84	'G.W.R.', Brown body, Brown wheels, Cream horses.	
004b	85	Gold wheels, wood plinth, special box	**£7-10**
004c	85	Gold wheels, Black horses	
005a	85	'LAKE CITY', Yellow body, Red wheels	
005b	87	Yellow body, Black wheels	
006a	84	'PHILADELPHIA'	
007a	84	'BIFBAC 2'	
008a	88	'LONDON EAST HAM', special box	
009a	89	'CARROW WORKS'	
010a	94	'METROPOLITAN F.B.' (Set FB1003)	GSP
		91 Model withdrawn from standard production but re-run for DG 5-010a, and:	
---		94 'THORNEY', 24k gold-plated. Only 12 produced for the 1994 International Lledo Show	NGPP
		DG 6 1920 Ford Model 'T' Van	
		Models 000-035 came with blue plastic figures: a policeman, man with starting-handle and dog, girl with teddy. There are 4 variations of baseplates: 1st (metal) 'DG6-DG', 2nd (metal) 'DG6-DG8', 3rd (metal) 'DG6-8', 4th (plastic) 'DG6-8-33'.	
000a	83	'OVALTINE', Orange body, with 1st baseplate	**£8-10**
		with 2nd or 3rd baseplate	
001a	83	'YORKSHIRE POST', (1st Lledo Code 1 Trade Special)	NGPP
002a	84	'COOKIE COACH Co', Yellow logo	
002b	84	'COOKIE COACH Co'	
003a	84	'BRITISH MEAT', Cream body, Brown chassis, Brown roof	**£7-10**
003b	84	Black chassis and roof **£10-15**	
004a	84	'AEROPLANE JELLY'	
005a	84	'BRITISH MEAT'	

Ref	Intro	Model	MPR
006	84	'MARCOL', with 'Red Dragon' on some	
007a	84	'POLICE AMBULANCE', CLE of 5000	**£30-40**
008a	84	'I.P.M.S.'	**£7-10**
009a	84	'LIVERPOOL GARDEN FESTIVAL'	
010a	84	'ILLINOIS TOYFAIR'	
011a	84	'STRETTON'	
012a	84	'YORKSHIRE EVENING POST'	
013a	84	'DAYS GONE CLUB', Black	**£7-10**
014a	84	'BRITISH BACON'	
015a	84	'HARRY RAMSDEN'	
016a	85	'OVALTINE 75th', Stone roof, special box	
016b	90	Tan roof, (000a re-run error)	
017a	84	'DAILY EXPRESS', (in CP1 Pack)	GSP
018a	85	'PERRIER JOUET'	
019a	85	'HOME ALES'	
020a	84	'COCA-COLA', 'At Soda Fountains'	
021a	84	'COCA-COLA', 'Every Bottle Sterilized'	
022a	84	'WONDERBREAD'	
023a	84	'RAILWAY EXPRESS', ('84 USA Pack)	GSP
024a	84	'KODAK'	
025a	84	'MARKS & SPENCER'	
026a	84	'MARCOL 2', Yellow body, printed rear doors	
027a	84	'PHILADELPHIA', Cream/Black	
028a	84	Red/Black	
029a	84	'YORKSHIRE BISCUITS'	
030a	84	'AUTOMODEL EXCHANGE'	
031a	84	'ECHO 100'	
032a	85	'STRETTON', Green chassis and roof	**£7-10**
033a	85	'BARCLAYS', Light Blue body, Cream chassis, Blue headboard letters	**£18-20**
033b	85	Cream headboard letters	
033c	90	with Black chassis and tyres	**£300-500**
034a	84	'MAGASIN du NORD', Dark Green, with White headboard lettering	**£30-40**
034b	84	Gold headboard lettering	
035a	84	'HAMLEYS' special box	
036	85	'AUSTRALIAN Collectors Club', Dark Beige body, Dark Brown chassis, Tan or Dk. Brown roof	**£7-10**
036c		Beige body, '85 Convention' (36 only)	**£750-1000**
037a	84	'MURPHYS CRISPS'	
038a	85	'WELLS DRINKS'	
039a	85	'WOODWARDS'	
040a	85	'LINDT', Pale Blue body, Blue roof	
040b		Pale Blue roof	**£30-40**
041a	85	'EVENING CHRONICLE'	
042a	86	'CWM DALE', White body, Blue chassis	
042b		Red chassis	**£7-10**

043a 85 'ROYAL MAIL', SBX ....
044a 85 'ALTON TOWERS', SBX ......
045a 85 'NORTHERN DAILY' ....
046a 86 'CADBURYS' ....
047a 86 'JOHN SMITHS' ....
048a 86 'BAY to BIRDWOOD RUN'..
049a 86 'HARDWARE JOURNAL', special box **£40-50**
050 **'TOY FAIR'.** Trade-only models, Red/Cream, in White promotional box:
050a 86 'TOY FAIR, '86, Harrogate' **£10-15**
050b 86 ''86, Harrowgate', (with 'w') **£60-75**
050c 87 ''87, Harrogate' **£10-15**
050d 88 ''88, Harrogate' **£10-15**
050e 89 ''89, Harrogate' **£10-15**
051a 86 'CADBURYS', SBX ....
052 Not allocated
053a 86 'TIZER' ....
054a 86 'COCA-COLA', special box ...
055a 86 'HERSHEYS', special box......
056a 87 'HEDGES & BUTLER' ....
057a 86 'CANADIAN TRAVEL & GIFT', 500 ....**£60-75**
058a 86 'COCA-COLA', SBX, Red hubs, Chrome radiator ....
058b 87 Brass hubs and radiator ....
059a 86 'CRAFT & HOBBY', 500, Canadian..............**£60-75**
060a 87 'BLACK VELVET' ....
061a 87 'FAIRY SOAP' ....
062a 87 'ROSE & CROWN' ....
063a 87 'Royal Flying Corps' ....GSP
064a 88 'HAMLEYS' ....
065a 88 'BUDWEISER', SBX ....
066a 88 'LLEDO WORLDWIDE C.C.', Green/Black ....
067a Not Allocated
068a 88 'GOLDEN SHRED' ....
069a 88 'CHARRINGTONS' ....
070a 88 'MILLBANK BOOKS' ....
071a 90 'H.M.V.' ....
072a 89 'SHELL PUMP SERVICE' .....
073a 89 'WALLS ICES' ....

074- 86 **Canadian models**, in 'maple leaf' boxes, as a set, ...**£40-45** later available singly:
074a 88 'ONTARIO' ....
075a 88 'YUKON' ....
076a 88 'N.W. TERRITORIES' ....
077a 88 'PRINCE EDWARD ISLE', wrong date ('1870') ....
077b 90 correct date ('1873') ...**£75-85**
078a 88 'NEWFOUNDLAND' ....
079a 88 'QUEBEC' ....
080a 88 'NOVA SCOTIA' ....
081a 88 'MANITOBA' ....
082a 88 'ALBERTA' ....
083a 88 'NEW BRUNSWICK' ....
084a 88 'BRITISH COLUMBIA' ....
085a 88 'SASKATCHEWAN' ....
086a 88 'CANADA' ....

087a 89 'SELFRIDGES', (in Set LS1004) ....GSP
088a 89 'AU BON MARCHE' ....
089a 89 'SCHNEIDERS' ....
090a 89 'WINCHESTER CLUB' ....
091a 89 'BRITANNIA FILM', (in 'Gold Set') ....GSP
092a 89 'NESTLES' ....
093a 89 'N.Y. MOORS', (in Set)...GSP
094a 89 'HAMLEYS '89', SBX ....
095a 90 '4711' ....
096a 90 'ROWNTREES COCOA' ....
097a 90 'JAEGER', Set LS2004 ...GSP
098a 90 'ROYAL MAIL' ....
099a 90 'HERSHEY', (USA) .....NGPP
100a 90 'DAYS GONE' Club Model, Burgundy and Black ....
101a 90 'ARNOTTS', ABL1003...GSP
102a 91 'DG Club', Blue/Green ....
103a 91 'JOSEPH LUCAS' ....
104a 91 'BLACKPOOL' ....
105a 91 'ZEBRA GRATE POLISH' ....
106a 92 'DAYS GONE' Club Model, Pale Metallic Green/Black .....
107a 92 'JAMESONS' ....
108a 92 'HOTEL COLUMBIA', (in Set HLL1003)
109a 93 'HUNTLEY & PALMERS' ....
110a 93 'MIDLAND' ....*
111a 93 'LANCS. & YORKS.' ....*
112a 93 'NORTH EASTERN' ....*
113a 93 'LMS' ....*
114a 93 'DAYS GONE' Club Model ...
115a 94 'Days Gone Club' 94..........
116a 94 'FLORIS TOILETRIES' ....
117a 94 'LONDON NW' ....
118a 94 'LONDON SW' ....
119a 94 'CAMBRIAN' ....
120a 94 'SOMERSET & DORSET' .....
121a 94 'RUPERT BEAR' ....
122a 95 'PEPSI-COLA' ....
123a 94 'NORMAN ROCKWELL' ......
124a 94 'AUSTRALIAN POST' (Australia)....................NGPP
125a 95 'ANTON BERG' ....
126a 95 'Caledonian Railway' ....**
127a 95 'Great Eastern Railway' ......**
128a 95 'North British Railway' ....**
129a 95 'Great Western Railway' .....**
130a 95 'HUIS TEN BOSCH', Burgundy, Japan ....NGPP
131a 95 'HUIS TEN BOSCH', Dark Blue, Japan ....NGPP
132a 95 'HUIS TEN BOSCH', Green, Japan ....NGPP
133a 95 'DG CLUB 95', SBX ....
134a 95 'HUIS TEN BOSCH', Mid-Green, Japan ....NGPP
135a 95 'HUIS TEN BOSCH', Royal Blue, Japan ....NGPP
136a 95 'STOCKHOLM OLYMPICS' .
137a 95 'Dr. PEPPER' ....
138a 96 'LEA & PERRINS' ....
139a 96 'SHELL 100 Years', SBX ....
140a 96 'DAYS GONE CLUB 96' ....
146a 97 'DAYS GONE CLUB 97' ....
147a 97 'SMITH'S CRISPS ....
148a 98 'COCKBURN'S PORT' ....
150a 98 'VAN HOUTEN' ....
--- 96 'BRITISH OLYMPIC SQUAD', plinth ....NGPP
153 99 'McVITIE & PRICE' ....
154 99 'COURVOISIER' ....
155 99 'WILD TURKEY' ....
156 99 'GRANT'S' ....
158 00 'SPAM' ....
159 00 'GLENFIDDICH' ....
160 00 'EDDIE STOBART' ....
162 01 'ENGLAND'S GLORY' ....
163 01 'YORKSHIRE TEA' ....
164 01 'CASTROL' ....
165 01 'BLACK BUSH' ....
166 01 'MACKINTOSH'S' ....

DG 7 1934 Ford Model 'A' Woody Wagon

Cream plastic figures of a woman with 3 poodles were discontinued after 005.

000a 84 'PATS POODLE PARLOUR' .
001a 84 'COCA-COLA' ....
002a 84 'FORD', (set GS1) ....GSP
002b 85 no headboard, sold singly.......
003a 84 'WEST POINT TOY SHOW'
004 84 'HAMLEYS', Chrome or Brass radiator, SBX ....
005a 85 'GODFREY DAVIS' ....
006a 86 'DELLA' ....
007a 86 'COMMONWEALTH GAMES' (in set) ....GSP
008a 88 'CASTROL OIL' ....
009a 90 'PASCALL SWEETS' ....
90 New baseplate introduced ('7-9-13-14-37').
1991: Model ceased production.

DG 8 1920 Ford Model 'T' Tanker

The same blue plastic figures included with DG 6 were provided with 000 to 004 inclusive.

000a 84 'ESSO', 'Inflamable' (only 1 'm') **£5-7**
000b 84 'Inflammable' (correct) ....
001a 84 'COCA-COLA' ....
002a 85 'CASTROL' ....
003a 84 'PHILADELPHIA', Red, Black roof ....
003b 85 White roof **£10-15**
004a 85 'PENNZOIL' ....
005a 85 'HOFMEISTER' ....
006a 86 'BLUE MOUNTAIN' ....
007a 87 'CROW CARRYING' ....
008a 86 'HERSHEYS', special box......
009a 87 'WATER WORKS' ....
010a 87 'ZEROLENE', (dealer promo, 3,000)..**£10-15**
011a 88 'SHELL FUEL OIL' ....
012a 88 'HOMEPRIDE' ....
013a 88 'DUCKHAMS OILS' ....
014a 89 'SHELL FRANCE' ....
015a 89 'BP MOTOR SPIRIT' ....
016a 89 'TEXACO' ....
017a 89 'ARMY WATER' ....GSP
018a 90 'PRATTS' ....
019a 91 'MOBILGAS' ....
020a 93 'RUSSIAN OIL' ....
023 99 'BP' ....

DG 9 1934 Ford Model 'A' Car

White plastic figures (two villains and seated policeman with gun) with 001a and b. The same figures (but in black), were with 001c and 002 to 004.

000a 84 'POLICE' Car, Mid Blue/Dark Blue....**£20-30**
000b 84 All Dark Blue, Cream seats....
000c 84 All Dark Blue, Black seats.....
001a 84 'NEW YORK - RIO' ....GSP
002a 84 'PHILADELPHIA FIRE' ....
003a 85 '15 MILLIONTH FORD' ....
1991: Model ceased production.

DG 10 1935 Dennis Coach

Cream plastic figures included (1984-85) were of: man leaning on bus-stop, man and woman with boy, young woman with dog.

000a 84 'BRIGHTON BELLE', Maroon body, Beige roof, Chrome radiator **£15-20**
000b Beige roof, Brass radiator ......
000c Cream roof, Brass radiator .....
001a 84 'TILLINGBOURNE' ....
002 87 'SILVER SERVICE', Silver or White 'Matlock' ......
003a 84 'SOUTHERN VECTIS', with Yellow logo ....
with White logo...........**£12-15**
004a 84 'SCHOOL BUS', with Chrome radiator **£7-10**
004b 84 with Brass radiator ....
004c 87 'OAKRIDGE SCHOOL' ....
005a 84 'POTTERIES', with Cream roof......................
005b 86 with Red roof **£15-18**
006a 85 'GWR', special box, '150th Anniversary' **£8-12**
007a 85 'BARTON' ....
008 86 'LONDON COUNTRY', Brass or Chrome radiator ....
008c 88 with Black chassis...**£150-200**
009a 84 'HAMLEYS', SBX **£5-8**
010 Not allocated
011 Not allocated
012a 85 'TARTAN' ....
013a 85 'TRAILWAYS' ....GSP
014a 85 'IMPERIAL AIRWAYS', with Blue roof........................
014b 87 with Red roof **£12-15**
015a 86 'REDBURNS' ....
016a 86 'COMMONWEALTH GAMES', (in set) ....GSP
017a 86 'HERSHEYS' ....
018a 88 'E.B. TAYLOR' ....
1989: New baseplate text: 'DG10-12-34-35'.
019a 89 'CITY of COVENTRY' ....
020a 90 'B.O.A.C.' ....
021a 91 'B.E.A.' ....
1992: DG10 production ceased.

DG 11 Horse-Drawn Van

Cream plastic figures (up till 1985): driver, woman with birdcage, girl with hoop, boy with bag and bulldog. Driver figure re-introduced in 1989, plus change in design of horses.

000a 84 'TURNBULL & Co' ....
001a 85 'ABELS' ....
002a 85 'BIG TOP CIRCUS' ....
003a 85 'Staffs. COUNTY SHOW' ......
004a 85 'ROYAL MAIL', SBX ....
005a 85 'WILLIAMS GRIFFIN' ....
006a 86 'MacCOSHAMS' ....
007a 86 'COCA-COLA', (Hartoy) GSP
008a 88 'BUDWEISER', SBX ....
009a 89 'LLEDO WORLDWIDE' ....
010a 88 'R.P. COOPER' ....
011a Not allocated
012a 89 'JAMES BROWN & SON' .....
013a 89 'ALBERT DALEY & Co' ....
014a 90 'MARKS & SPENCER', special box ....
015a 90 'ROYAL MAIL', SBX ....
016a 90 'ARNOTTS', (ABL1003) .GSP
017a 91 'ROBERT HEATON & SON'.
018a 91 'DG CLUB SUMMER '91' ....
019a 91 'SAINSBURYS' ....
020a 92 'HARRODS', (HD1002)..GSP
021a 92 'HAMLEYS', (in Set HAL1004) ....GSP
022a 93 'SCHWEPPES' ....
023a 93 'PEPSI-COLA', special box ....
024a 93 'GREAT NORTHERN', (Set RSL4003)................GSP
025a 94 'OXO TRENCH HEATER' ....
026a 95 'RUPERT', special box ....

DG 12 1934 Dennis Fire Engine

Chassis, baseplate, wheels and radiator as DG 10. Escape wheels not fitted to 000a, 001a, 003a 3. Blue plastic firemen included up to 1985.

000a 84 'LUCKHURST', Red/Green ...
000b 89 Red body and chassis ..**£10-15**
001a 85 'CARDIFF CITY' ....
002 Not allocated
003 85 'BERMUDA', Blue body, Cream or White floor ....
004a 86 'LCC' ....
005 86 'CHELMSFORD', Brass or Chrome radiator ....
006a 87 'AUXILIARY' ....
007a 87 'ESSEX COUNTY', Red/White ....
007b 90 with White 'ESSEX' ...**£40-50**
008a 87 'WARE FIRE SERVICE' ....
009a 87 'WINDSOR', special box........
010a 88 'GLASGOW' ....
011a 88 'BOSTON' ....
012a 89 'BIRMINGHAM' ....
1989: Baseplate with 'DG10-12-34-35' introduced.
013a 90 'BRADFORD' ....
014a 90 'HERSHEY', special box ....
014b 'HERSHEY', new shape **£35-40**
015a 91 'MANCHESTER' ....
016a 92 'WEST HAM' ....
017a 93 'VALLETTA', (MG1003)..GSP
018a 94 'HAMLEYS 94' ....
019a 94 'LONDON FIRE BRIGADE' .
021a 98 'HULL POLICE F.B.' ....
023 99 'GUILDFORD' ....
024 00 'LONDON F.B.' ....
025 01 'DEVON COUNTY' ....

DG 13 1934 Ford Model 'A' Van

Cream plastic figures up to 011: man

reading paper, newsboy, deliveryman.
000a 86 'CAMP COFFEE', SBX
001a 84 'EVENING NEWS'
002a 85 'TUCHER BEERS', SBX
003a 86 'MITRE 10', SBX **£20-25**
004a 84 'HAMLEYS', SBX
005a 85 'MICHELIN', (also in Set)
006a 85 'JERSEY Eve. POST' **£10-15**
007a 85 'MARY ANN' **£10-15**
008a 84 'ROYAL MAIL'
008b 92 'ROYAL MAIL', new longer body
009a 85 'COCA-COLA'
010a 85 'BASILDON BOND', with matt finish **£6-8**
010b 85 with gloss finish
011a 86 'RYDER'
012a 85 'COCA-COLA'
013a 85 'EVENING SENTINEL'
014a 85 'STROH'S'
015a 85 'ROYAL MAIL 350', SBX
016a 85 'FESTIVAL GARDENS'
017a 86 'ROBINSONS'
018a 88 'EVER READY'
019a 87 'H.P. SAUCE'
020a 86 'F.D.B.' (Danish) **£20-25**
021a 86 'COCA-COLA', Black chassis
021b Yellow chassis **£200-250**
022a 88 'J. LYONS'
023a 86 'HERSHEYS KISSES'
024a 86 'HERSHEYS'
025a 'ROYAL MAIL', SBX
026a 88 'HEINZ TOMATO SOUP'
027a 88 'CHARLES TATE'
028a 88 'EXCHANGE & MART'
029a 88 'ELIZABETH SHAW'
030a 89 'OXYDOL'
031a 89 'AQUASCUTUM', (in Set LS1004) GSP
032 Not allocated
033a 89 'ALLENBURYS'
034a 89 'EMPIRE', ('Gold Set') GSP
035a 89 'KLEENEX'
036a 91 'AUSTIN REED', (in Set LS2004) GSP
037a 89 'B.B.C.'
038a 89 'ARMY RECRUITMENT', (in Set BA1003) GSP
039a 90 'PERSIL'
040a 90 'MADAME TUSSAUDS'
041a 90 'MARKS & SPENCER', special box
042a 90 'ROYAL MAIL'
043a 90 'HERSHEYS', Silver and Brown, (US issue) NGPP
044a 90 'N.Y. MOORS' (Set 2) GSP
045a 90 'ARNOTTS',(ABL1003) GSP
1990: Baseplate with '7-9-13-14-37' introduced
046a 91 'ROSELLA'
047a 91 'CASTROL'
1991: Steering wheel and seats added to model.
048a 92 'HAMLEYS'
1992: Longer body introduced.
049a 92 'RINSO'
050a 92 'SOUTHERN RAILWAY', (in Set RSL2003) GSP
051a 92 'HARRODS', (HD1004) GSP
052a 92 'QANTAS', (QA1002) GSP
053a 92 'GODE', (Germany) **£25-30**
054a 92 'RAMA', (Germany) **£20-25**
055a 93 'GOLDEN SHRED'
056a 93 'PEPSI-COLA', special box
057a 93 'MARKS & SPENCER', (in Set MS2004) GSP
058a 93 'Grand Hotel Peking', (in Set HLL2003) GSP
059a 94 'CARLSBERG'
060a 94 'KODAK' (Mexico) **£30-40**
061a 94 'RUPERT BEAR', SBX
062a 94 'Dr. PEPPER', special box
063a 94 'NORMAN ROCKWELL', special box
064a 95 'RITTER SCHOKOLADE'
065a 95 '7-UP' (USA, SBX) NGPP
066a 95 'DAILY HERALD', (Set VE 1003) GSP
067a 95 'LOS ANGELES OLYMPIC GAMES'
068a 96 'WATERMANS PENS'
072a 97 'CHERRY BLOSSOM'
073a 97 'DG CLUB', 'Summer 97'
074a 98 'ROYAL MAIL', 'Air Mail'
075a 98 'HOLSTEN BIER'
076a 98 'TERRY'S'
--- 96 'BRITISH OLYMPIC SQUAD', plinth NGPP
077 99 'JEYES FLUID'
078 00 'BOVRIL'
079 00 'ROYAL MAIL'
080 01 'SUNLIGHT FLAKES'
081 01 'EDDIE STOBART'
082 01 'BLUE BIRD'
083 01 'VASELINE'
084 01 'GLENGOYNE'

DG 14 1934 Ford Model 'A' Car with Hood

Cream plastic figures (one US policeman and two firemen), were only issued with 000a/b and 001a.
000a 85 'SAN DIEGO', 'Fire Chief' in Gold with Black surround **£150-200**
000b 'Fire Chief' not in Gold with Black surround
001a 85 'TAXI'
002a 85 'ACME CLEANERS'
003a 86 'HAMLEYS', special box
004 86 'GRAND HOTEL', Brown with Cream or Beige
005 Not allocated.
006a 87 'STATE PENITENTIARY'
007a 88 'SAN DIEGO', (US version) NGPP
1990: Baseplate with '7-9-13-14-37' introduced.
008a 90 'RALEIGH CYCLES'
1991: DG14 production ceased.

DG 15 1932 AEC Regent Double-Deck Bus

The first 'Days Gone' model without the plastic figures. Lower seats were absent till 1989.
000 85 'HALLS WINE', Red/Black, Chrome or Brass radiator
001a 85 'COCA-COLA'
002a 85 'CASTLEMAINE XXXX', (in 3-bus Set) GSP
003a 85 'HAMLEYS', special box
004a 85 'LIVERPOOL GARDENS'
005 85 'CINZANO', Chrome or Brass radiator
006a 86 'EVENING ARGUS'
007a 86 'HALLS WINE', Pale Brown body **£30-35**
007b 86 bare metal body **£15-20**
007 86 (a & b) in wooden display case with plated components **£100-125**
008a 86 'ROYAL WEDDING' **£10-15**
009 87 'MADAME TUSSAUDS', Chrome or Brass radiator
010 86 'SWAN VESTAS'
011a 86 'COMMONWEALTH GAMES', (in Set) GSP
011b 87 with Brass radiator
012a 87 'HEINZ'
013a 87 'STRATFORD BLUE', SBX
014a 87 'TV TIMES'
015a 88 'HAMLEYS'
016a 88 'BIRMINGHAM MAIL'
017a 88 'GOLDEN WONDER'
018a 88 'LLEDO CLUB' **£10-15**
019a 89 'MAPLES'
020a 89 'TERRY'S GYM'
021a 89 'St. IVEL CHEESE'
022a 89 'HAMLEYS, special box
023a 90 'PALMOLIVE'
024a 90 'R.A.C.'
025 90 'POST EARLY FOR XMAS', Red or Cream seats, SBX
026a 90 'HERSHEYS', Beige and Brown, (US issue) NGPP
027a 90 'N.Y. MOORS', (Set 2) GSP
028a 92 'HARRODS', (HD1002) GSP
029a 93 'Mazawattee Tea'
030a 93 'Van HOUTENS COCOA'
031a 93 'D.G. CLUB' Autumn '93
032a 94 'LIBBYS PINEAPPLE'
033a 94 'HAMLEYS', HA 2002 GSP
034a 94 'GODE', (Germany) **£15-20**
035a 95 'PEARS SOAP'
036a 94 'HARRODS', (HR 2004) GSP
037a 97 'SCHWEPPES'
038a 98 'NESTLES'
039a 98 'SPILLERS SHAPES'
040 99 'LUCOZADE'
041 00 'Schweppes Lemon Squash'
042 01 'SCHWARTZ'

DG 16 1934 Dennis Parcels Van

Seats and steering wheel did not appear until 1991. Separate wheel/tyre units or composite wheels can be found.
000a 85 'MAYFLOWER'
001a 85 'ROYAL MAIL', SBX
002a 85 'CROFT ORIGINAL'
003a 86 'HAMLEYS', special box
004a 86 'TREBOR'
005a 86 'L.N.E.R.'
006a 86 'KIWI', Black hubs, Brass radiator
006b 87 Cream hubs, Chrome radiator
007a 85 'BUSHELLS'
008 Not allocated.
009a 87 'CADBURYS'
010a 87 'FYFFES'
011a 86 'COCA-COLA', special box
012a 86 'HERSHEYS GOODBAR', special box
013a 86 'HERSHEYS KRACKEL', Brass radiator, special box
013b 87 Chrome radiator, special box
014a 88 'PICKFORDS', Blue body
014b 89 Dark Blue body
015a 87 'LLEDO WORLDWIDE CC'
016a 88 'HAMLEYS'
017a 89 'ABELS'
018a 90 'MADAME TUSSAUDS'
019a 89 'ALLIED'
020a 89 'COSMOS'
021a 89 'GOODYEAR'
021b 90 same but White 'Goodyear'
022a 89 'HAMLEYS'
023a 90 'OXO'
024a 90 'ROYAL MAIL'
025a 90 'N.Y. MOORS', (Set 3) GSP
026a 91 'SCHWEPPES'
1991: Steering wheel/seats added.
027a 91 'ATORA FOR XMAS'
028a 91 'L.N.E.R.', (TPL1003) GSP
029a 91 'L.N.E.R.', (RSL1003) GSP
030a 91 'Y.M.C.A.', (HF1003) GSP
031a 92 'HUDSONS SOAP'
032a 93 'TUNNOCKS'
033a 93 'NAAFI', (Set DM1003) GSP
034a 93 'RAF Runway Control', (Set DML1003) GSP
035a 94 'KODAK'
036a 94 'BOVRIL'
037a 94 'RUPERT BEAR'
038a 94 'D.G. CLUB' Autumn '94
039a 95 'RUPERT BEAR', SBX
040 01 'TWININGS'

DG 17 1932 AEC Regal Single Deck Bus

000a 85 'SOUTHEND', with filler cap casting **£60-75**
000b without filler cap casting
000c 86 with Red roof, (1,000 only) **£25-35**
001a 85 'EUROTOURS',(in Set) GSP
002a 85 'CORPORATION'
003a 86 'HAMLEYS', SBX **£25-35**
004a 85 'LONDON TRANSPORT'
005a 86 'OXFORD (MORRELL'S)'
006a 86 'COMMONWEALTH GAMES', special box
007a 86 'STRATFORD BLUE', Chrome radiator
007b 87 Brass radiator **£6-9**
008a 87 'BURNLEY'
009a 86 'BIG TOP CIRCUS'
010a 87 'PENNINE'
011a 87 'RFC', (in Set) GSP
012a 88 'HAMLEYS'
1988: New roof (with 2 hoardings) introduced.
013a 88 'HANTS & DORSET'
014a 88 'SUTTONS'
015a 89 'ROYAL BLUE', Blue and Black
015b 89 Same but White background to headboard decal
016a 89 'COLCHESTER', Maroon
017a 88 'ROYAL NAVY', (in Set RN1003) GSP
018a 89 'N.Y. MOORS', (Set) GSP
019a 90 'RED & WHITE'
020a 91 'BUCKLAND OMNIBUS'
021a 92 'SOUTHERN VECTIS'
022a 92 'GREEN LINE'
022b 93 No fleet number on bonnet
022c 94 Silver print on side boards
023a 95 'SUNDERLAND'
024a 95 'US RED CROSS', (in Set VE 1003) GSP
026 99 'MACBRAYNES'
027 00 'SOUTHDOWN'

DG 18 1936 Packard Van

Steering wheel and seats did not appear on this model until 1991.
000 85 'AMBULANCE', Chrome or Brass radiator
001a 85 'AMERICAN AMBULANCE', as 000a but Red cross in circle
002a 86 'COMMONWEALTH GAMES', special box, with Chrome radiator **£6-8**
002b 87 Brass radiator, normal box
003a 86 'RAPID CASH'
004 86 'FIRESTONE', Chrome or Brass radiator
005 Not allocated
006 87 'WHITE STAR', Chrome or Brass radiator
007a 87 'COLMANS'
008a 87 'RFC', (in Set) GSP
009a 88 'PERRONI BIRRA'
010a 88 'NATIONAL WESTMINSTER' **£10-15**
011 88 'FOTORAMA', Chrome or Brass radiator
012a 90 'St. IVEL'
013a 89 'FORTNUM & MASON', (in Set LS1004) GSP
014a 89 'B & C FILMS', (in 'Gold' Set) GSP
015a 88 'St. MARY'S HOSPITAL', (Canadian charity) **£20-25**
016a 89 'LEYLAND PAINTS'
017a 89 'HAMLEYS', special box
018a 90 'ASPREY', (LS2004) GSP
019a 90 'DG CLUB', Autumn model
020a 91 'McVITIE & PRICE'
021a 92 'CAMP COFFEE'
022a 92 'St.JOHN AMBULANCE', in Set MG1003 GSP
023a 93 'FERODO'
024a 93 'IMPERIAL' (HLL2003) GSP
025a 94 'NORMAN ROCKWELL', special box
--- 86 'CAMPERDOWN' Australian hospital charity **£40-50**

DG 19 1931 Rolls-Royce Phantom II (Brewster)

Incorporates the DG 18 baseplate. It acquired a steering wheel in 1989.

000a 85 Burgundy ('TV Times')..........
001a 86 Yellow/Tan, Chrome radiator ..
001b 86 Yellow/Tan, Brass radiator ......
002a 86 'Basketweave', Beige/Cream, Grey tyres, Brass radiator........
002b 87 Grey tyres, Chrome radiator....
002c 87 Beige tyres, Brass radiator ......
003a 88 Metallic Grey/Black ....GSP
003b 88 Not mounted or drilled, (unofficial)....................**£7-10**
004a 87 Gold and White ....
005a 87 'Ruby Wedding', SBX............
006a 89 Dark Green/Black/Beige ....
007a 88 'Minder', Gold/White.............
008a 89 'Lledo Worldwide CC', Silver/Black ....
009a 89 'Army Staff Car', in Set BA1003 ....GSP
010a 92 Black/Ivory, Chrome radiator..
011a 92 Silver/Black, (for German market) ...**£20-25**
--- 85 All Cream, Chrome radiator, (108 only)......**£30-35**
1993: Model withdrawn.

DG 20 1936 Ford Stake Truck

Steering wheel and seats from 1991.

000a 86 'EAGLE ALES' ....
001a 86 'COCA-COLA', special box ...
001b 86 same but with Red barrels......
002 87 'STROH'S', Red/Black, Brass or Chrome radiator ....
003 86 'WHITBREAD', Brass or Chrome radiator ....
004a 86 'GOODRICH' ....
005a 88 'AULD SCOTCH GINGER' ..
006a 87 'UNIROYAL' ....
007a 88 'BUDWEISER', SBX ....
008a 88 'IND COOPE' ....
009a 89 'WATNEYS' ....
010a 89 'CALOR GAS' ....
011a 88 'ROYAL NAVY', (in Set RN1003) ....GSP
012a 90 'PIRELLI' ....
013a 90 'BRITISH OXYGEN' ....
014a 90 'HERSHEYS', US issue in special box ....NGPP
015a 90 'RAF', (in Set BB1003) ...GSP
016a 90 'WINN DIXIE' ....
017a 91 'DUNLOP TYRES'................
93 'DUNLOP TYRES', 'Brooklands Collection' ....
018a 91 'GOODYEAR TYRES' ....
019a 93 'McDOUGALLS' ....
020a 94 'NESTLES MILK' ....
021a 94 'Dr. PEPPER', special box ......
022a 95 'PENNZOIL' ....

DG 21 1934 Chevrolet Van

Plastic roof may have front headboard, front and lengthways headboards or none. Seats and steering wheel added in 1991, baseplate updated in 1992.

000a 86 'SHARPS', Chrome radiator...
000b 87 Yellow, Brass radiator ....
001a 86 'LLEDO WORLDWIDE CLUB', special box...............
001b 86 Maroon hubs, Black prototype logo......................
002a 86 'LEICESTER MERCURY' .....
003a 86 'HOSTESS CAKE' ....
004a 87 'Dr. PEPPER' ....
005a 86 'COCA-COLA', special box ...
006 Not allocated.
007a 88 'HAMLEYS' ....
008a 88 'BUDWEISER', SBX ....
009a 88 'BIRDS CUSTARD' ....
010a 88 'FARRAH'S TOFFEE' ....
011a 88 'VITA-WHEAT' ....
012a 89 'SIMPSONS', (LS1004) ..GSP

013a 89 'BENETTONS' ....
014a 89 'HERSHEYS KISSES' ....
015a 89 'CHERRY BLOSSOM' ....
016a 89 'MAJESTIC FILMS' ......GSP
017a 90 'TOYFAIR '90', ...**£9-12**
018a 90 'RECKITTS BLUE' ....
019a 90 'MARKS & SPENCER' ....
020a 90 'LIBERTY'S', (LS2004)..GSP
021a 90 'CLUB SUMMER '90' ....
022a 90 'SCOTTISH BLUEBELL', in Set BM1004 ....GSP
023a 90 'BRYANT & MAY', in Set BM1004 ....GSP
024a 90 'SWAN VESTAS', in Set BM1004 ....GSP
025a 90 'ENGLANDS GLORY', in Set BM1004 ....GSP
026a 91 'HAMLEYS' ....
027a 91 'EXIDE' ....
028a 91 'FAIRY SOAP' ....
029a 91 'BUSHELLS COFFEE' ....
030a 91 'US MARINES', (in Set PH1003)...............GSP
031a 92 'ELLIMANS' ....
032a 92 'MAGGI'S SOUP' ....
033a 91 'SCRIBBANS', (Trade special)..............NGPP
034a 92 'LMS & LNER', in Set RSL2003 ....GSP
035a 92 'GRAND HOTEL', in Set HLL1003 ....GSP
036a 92 'LNER Country', in Set RSL3003 ....GSP
037a 92 'HAMLEYS', in Set HAL1004 ....GSP
038a 93 'PEPSI-COLA', special box ....
039a 94 'ROSES LIME JUICE' ....
040a 94 'SPRENGEL', (German market) **£20-25**
041a 94 'HENDERSON', (Set MCL 1003) ....GSP
042a 94 'USA WORLD CUP' ....
043a 94 'NORMAN ROCKWELL' ......
044a 95 'NIVEA CREME OL' ....
045a 95 'RUPERT BEAR', SBX ....
046a 95 'DG GOLD CLUB', special box....................NGPP
047a 95 'Dr. PEPPER', special box ......
048a 96 'La VACHE QUI RIT' ....
050a 97 'BRYLCREEM' ....
051a 98 'TEACHER'S WHISKY'.........
052a 98 'EVER READY' ....
053 01 'LAPHROIG' ....

DG 22 1933 Packard Town Van

000a 86 'STAG WHISKY' ....
001a 86 'LORD TED' ....
002 87 'FLORISTS' ....
003a 87 'WHITMANS' ....
004a 87 'LLEDO WORLDWIDE CLUB', special box **£6-8**
005a 88 'HAMLEYS' ....
006a 88 'PIZZA EXPRESS' ....
007a 88 'BUDWEISER', SBX ....
008a 88 'TESCO'....................**£20-25**
009a 89 'SOHO DAIRIES', Black ....
009b 90 Same but Dark Brown............
010a 90 'HEINZ 57' ....
011a 91 'SHARPS TOFFEE' ....
012a 92 'PUNCH' ....
1993: Model withdrawn.

DG 23 1954 Scenicruiser

This was the first (and for many years, the only) 'Days Gone' model to feature window glazing.

000a 87 'GREYHOUND', Silver, pale windows, bare metal chassis **£10-15**
000b 87 dark windows, Silver chassis ..
000c 87 dark windows, Black chassis...
001a 87 'GOLDEN WEST' ....
002a 91 'BUFFALO' ....
1991: DG23 withdrawn.

DG 24 Rolls-Royce Playboy (Brewster)

The radiator component is the same as on DG 19.

000a 87 Yellow body, ('TV Times') .....
001a 87 Lilac body ....
001b 87 Dark Lilac body......................
002a 88 Metallic Grey body ....GSP
002b 88 Not mounted or drilled, (unofficial)....................**£7-10**
003a 87 Red and White, special box .....
004a 88 Metallic Green body ....
005a 89 Dark Green body ....
--- 89 24k Gold plated, on plinth, (110 made)..................NGPP
1991: Model withdrawn.

DG 25 1925 Rolls-Royce Silver Ghost (Barker)

Seats and steering wheel are a single plastic moulding.

000a 87 Dk.Blue/Black, ('TV Times')..
001a 87 Silver and Blue ....
002a 88 Metallic Grey ....GSP
002b 88 Not mounted or drilled, (unofficial)....................**£7-10**
003a 87 White / Black, (Cream seats) ..
003b 88 All White body, (White seats)..
004a 89 Blue/Black/Tan ....
005a 89 Dark Green body ....
1991: DG25 production ceased.

DG 26 1934 Chevrolet Bottle Delivery Truck

Baseplate, chassis and radiator as DG 21. Steering wheel / seats from 1991.

000a 87 'SCHWEPPES', Lemon, Red chassis **£12-16**
000b 87 Yellow body, Red chassis ....
000c 88 with Black chassis...**£150-200**
001a 87 'LLEDO WORLDWIDE CLUB.', White/Black.............
002 87 'COCA-COLA', Brass or Chrome radiator ....
003a 88 'BUDWEISER', SBX ....
004a 88 'BARR'S' ....
005a 88 'CORONA' ....
006a 88 'TIZER' ....
007a 89 'CANADA DRY', (illegible artwork)...................
007b 89 Legible rear, illegible side ......
007c 90 Legible rear and side ....
008a 90 'SCHWEPPES' ....
009a 91 'TENNENTS' ....
010a 92 'BASS' ....
011 92 'FYFFES', fleet no '6' at front or rear......
012a 93 'PEPSI-COLA', special box .....
013a 93 'PERRIER' ....
014a 93 'BROOKE BOND' ....
015a 94 'Dr. PEPPER', special box ......
016a 95 'BECK'S BEER' ....
017a 95 '7-UP', special box.................
018a 96 'TUBORG LAGER' ....

DG 27 1934 Mack Breakdown Truck

The steering wheel appeared on this model in 1991.

000a 87 'A1 RECOVERY' ....
001a 88 'HANKS AUTO' ....
002 Not allocated
003a 88 'MOBILOIL' (UK issue)........
004a 89 'MOBILOIL' (French) **£6-8**
005a 89 'ARTHUR DALEY' ....
006a 91 'U.S. ARMY', (US1003) .GSP
007a 92 'LONDON CC' ....
93 'B.A.R.C.', (in 'Brooklands Collection')........
1993: Model withdrawn.

DG 28 1934 Mack Canvas-back Truck

Chassis, plastic baseplate and radiator as DG 27. From 1991 the model was fitted with a steering wheel.

000 88 'TYPHOO' ....
001a 88 'TATE & LYLE' ....
002a 88 'LLEDO WORLDWIDE CLUB', special box.................
003 88 'HEINZ BEANS' ....
004a 89 'DUNLOP' ....
005 Not allocated.
006a 89 'ROYAL NAVY', in Set RN1003............GSP
007a 90 'STROH'S' ....
008a 89 'N.Y. MOORS', (Set).......GSP
009a 89 'COCA-COLA', (few released)..............**£400+**
010a 91 'GREENE KING' ....
011a 90 'RAF', (in RAF Set) ....GSP
012a 90 'WINN DIXIE', (US) ..**£20-25**
013a 91 'HAMLEYS', special box ....
014a 91 'L.N.E.R.', (TPL1003) .....GSP
015a 91 'L.M.S.', (RSL1003) ....GSP
016a 91 '8th ARMY', SBX ....
017a 91 'Quartermasters Corps', in Set USA1003 ....GSP
018a 91 'REVELL '91', US Trade special **£70-80**
019a 91 'Corps Truck', (PH1003) .GSP
020a 92 'G.W.R.', (RSL2003) ....GSP
021a 92 'HAMLEYS', special box ....
022a 91 'Motor Torpedo' in Set PH1003 ....GSP
023a 92 'WINCARNIS' ....
024a 92 'D.G. Club 91-92' ....
025a 92 'TOYFAIR '92', Trade Fair model........**£20-25**
026a 92 'ROYAL NAVY', in Set MG1003 ....GSP
027a 92 'US Marines',(GU1003) ..GSP
028a 92 'S.R. Express', in Set RSL3003 ....GSP
029a 93 'KAFFEE HAG' ....
030a 93 'RAF', Set DML1003 ....GSP
031a 93 'LLEDO SHOW' 1993 ....
032a 94 'SAINSBURY'S LAMB' ....
033a 95 'PEPSI-COLA' ....
034a 94 'Dr. PEPPER', special box ......
035a 95 'PERSIL' ....
1995: DG28 withdrawn from standard production.

DG 29 1942 Dodge 4x4

000a 88 'US Field Ambulance' ....
001a 89 'RAF Aircrew' ....
002a 91 'TEXACO' ....
003a 91 'US Army Ambulance', in Set USAL1003 ....GSP
004a 92 'Bomb Disposal', SBX ....
005a 92 'Marines', (GU1003)........GSP
006a 93 'Police Emergency' ....
007a 94 'SAN JOSE FIRE DEPT' ....
008a 94 'Canadian Army', (Set DDL 1003)..............GSP
009a 94 'US Army Signals', (Set DDU 1003)...........GSP
1994: DG29 withdrawn from standard production.

DG 30 1939 Chevrolet Panel Van

000a 88 'JOHN BULL TYRES' ....
001a 89 'FRY'S COCOA' ....
002a 89 'LIPTONS' ....
003a 89 'LLEDO WORLDWIDE CLUB', special box ....
004a 89 'HAMLEYS', SBX ....
005a 90 'SPRATTS' ....
006a 90 'BROOKE BOND' ....
007a 90 'HERSHEY', (US issue, special box) **£20-25**
008a 90 'RAF', Set BBL1004 ....GSP
009a 91 'NESTLES' ....
010a 91 'GOLDEN STREAM TEA' ....
011a 91 'Polish Army', SBX ....
012a 91 'Army Surgical Unit', in Set USA1003 ....GSP
013a 91 'US Navy', (PHL1003) ....GSP

014a 92 'STEPHENS INKS' ....
015a 93 'SHELL-BP' ....
016a 94 'RANSOMES
    LAWNMOWERS' ....
017a 94 'INDIAN', (MCL 1003) ..GSP
018a 95 '7-UP', special box ....
020a 97 'JACK DANIELS' ....

DG 31 Horse-Drawn Brewer's Dray

DG31 had DG 4/5/11 wheels, a dedicated driver figure and painted detail on the horses.
000a 88 'WHITBREAD' ....
001a 88 'EVERARDS', Red body,
    (Dealer Promotion) **£15-20**
002 89 'TAUNTON CIDER' ....
003 89 'GREENE KING',
    (reversed or correct tampo) ....
004a 89 'TRUMANS' ....
005a 91 'COURAGE ALES' ....
006a 92 'WORTHINGTON' ....
007a 93 'BASS' ....
008 94 'FULLERS ALES',
    (red or green bar), SBX..........

DG 32 1907 Rolls-Royce Silver Ghost

This model echoes the Odell design of the Lesney Y15-1 version of 1960 with its cast metal body, bonnet, chassis and windscreen.
000a 88 Silver body, Maroon seats ......
001a 89 Dark Green body, Beige seats .
002a 90 Metallic Green, Black seats ......
003a 90 'Gold-plate' effect ....NGPP
004a 91 Dark Red, Black seats ....
005a 92 Dark Blue, Black seats ....
006a 92 Bronze (Germany).......**£15-20**
007a 92 'Gold' (Germany) **£15-20**
008a 95 Gold-plated, (RPL 1003)..GSP
009a 96 Black ....
010 00 Beige / chrome ....

DG 33 1920 Ford Model 'T' Car

This model uses DG6 and 8 radiator, chassis, baseplate and wheels.
000a 89 Black body, chassis and roof ...
001a 89 'SINGER', Maroon seats ....
001b 89 'SINGER', Black seats............
002 Not allocated
003a 90 'HERSHEYS', SBX,
    (US issue) ....NGPP
004a 91 'GRAND HOTEL' ....
005a 92 'HOTEL PARIS',
    in Set HLL1003...............GSP
006a Gold body....................NGPP
007a 93 'PFAFF' ....
008a 94 'EXCHANGE & MART' ....
009a 94 'HUIS TEN BOSCH',
    Maroon, Japan...............NGPP
010a 94 'HUIS TEN BOSCH',
    Green, Japan...............NGPP
011a 94 'HUIS TEN BOSCH',
    Blue, Japan ....NGPP
012a 94 'HUIS TEN BOSCH',
    Cream, Japan ....NGPP
013a 95 'HUIS TEN BOSCH',
    Bright Blue, Japan........NGPP
014a 96 'ROWNTREES' ....
015a 96 'DG CLUB', Summer '96 ....

DG 34 1932 Dennis Delivery Van

Modified DG 10 with a roof-rack and with reduced seating section.
000a 89 'HOVIS' ....
001a 89 'SMEDLEYS' ....
002a 89 'HAMLEYS' ....
003a 90 'CHEDDAR CHEESE' ....
004a 90 'RAF', Set BBL1003 ....GSP
005a 91 'DG CLUB, 'Spring' ....
006a 92 'Wartime Library' ....
007a 94 'HARRODS',(HR 2004)..GSP
008a 98 'JIF LEMON JUICE' ....

1993: DG34 production ceased. Re-started in 1998.

DG 35 1932 Dennis Limousine

Another modification of DG 10, using the ladder component from DG 12 and a smaller roof-rack than DG 34.
000a 89 'EDINBURGH Fire Brigade'..
001a 90 'POST OFFICE
    TELEPHONES' ....
002a 90 'RAF', Set BB1003 ....GSP
003a 91 'SIGNALS HQ', SBX ....
004a 91 'N.F.S.', in Set HF1003....GSP
005a 92 'B.B.C. Wartime Outside
    Broadcasts' ....
1994: withdrawn from DG range.

DG 36 1939 Chevrolet Pick-up

Based on DG30 Panel Van. Oil-drums load introduced in 1992.
000a 89 'BUCK & HICKMAN' ....
001a 90 'CAKEBREAD & ROBEY' ...
002a 91 'AVON TYRES' ....
003a 91 'US Army Explosives',
    Set USAL1003 ....GSP
004a 92 'DUCKHAMS' ....
005a 93 'REDEX' ....
    93 'CASTROL', ('Brooklands')...
006a 94 'GODE' (German) **£15-20**
007a 94 'PENNZOIL' ....
008a 94 Service Truck,
    (Set DDB 1003) ....GSP
009a 94 'Dr. PEPPER', special box ......

DG 37 1932 Ford Model 'A' Panel Van

The model has a modified DG 9 body plus a plastic van upper body and roof section.
000a 90 'CANADIAN CLUB' ....
001a 90 'Mr. THERM' ....
002a 91 'USA POLICE' ....
003a 92 'DAYS GONE CLUB '92' ......
    1991: DG37 withdrawn from
    standard production.

DG 38 1925 Rolls-Royce Silver Ghost Saloon

Basically DG 25 + new roof moulding.
000a 89 Dark Green body, Gold lining .
    1990: DG38 withdrawn from
    standard production.

DG 39 1934 Mack Truck

Sack load. Steering wheel from 1991.
000a 90 'BLUE CIRCLE' ....
001a 91 'KETTON CEMENT' ....
002a 89 'GAS LIGHT & COKE' ....
003a 92 'PORTLAND CEMENT' ....
004a 92 Military Truck, SBX...............
    1993: DG39 withdrawn from
    standard production.

DG 40 1934 Mack Crane Truck

As DG 27 Breakdown Truck but with forward-facing crane.
000a 90 'TARMAC' ....
001a 91 'RICHARD COSTAIN' ....
002a 91 Ammunition Crane,
    in Set PH1003 ....GSP
003a 92 'US Navy', Set GU1003 ..GSP
004a 93 'RAF', in Set DM1003 ....GSP
    1992: DG40 withdrawn from
    standard production.

DG 41 1928 Karrier Trolley Bus

This Karrier 'E6' was the first model in the 'Premier Collection'.
000a 90 'ROBIN STARCH'.................
001a 90 'MARKS & SPENCER',
    special box ....

002a 91 'HAMLEYS', special box ....
003a 91 'BISTO' ....
004a 91 'BOVRIL' ....
005a 91 'N.Y. MOORS', in Set .....GSP
006a 92 'SAXA SALT' ....
007a 92 'SCHWEPPES' ....
008a 92 'HAMLEYS', HAL1004..GSP
009a 92 'SUNMAID RAISINS' ....
010a 94 'CROSSE & BLACKWELL'..
011a 94 'ROWNTREE' ....
012a 94 'HUIS TEN BOSCH',
    (Japan)..............................NGPP
013a 96 'COLMAN'S MUSTARD' .....
015a 98 'VENO'S' ....
016 99 'OXO' ....
017 00 'LT' 'TY-PHOO' ....
020 01 'CASTROL' ....

DG 42 1934 Mack Tanker

DG 27 with a tank replacing the original crane. Steering wheel from 1991.
000a 90 'NATIONAL BENZOLE' ....
001a 90 'RAF', Set BB1003 ....GSP
002a 91 'REGENT PETROL' ....
003a 91 'US Air Corps',
    in Set USAL1003 ....GSP
004a 91 'US Navy', (PHL1003)....GSP
005a 92 Water Tank, (EAL1003)...GSP
006a 92 'SHELL FUEL OIL',
    (German market) ....NGPP
    94 'SHELL FUEL OIL'
    ('Brooklands') ....
007a 93 'PENNZOIL' ....
008a 94 'TEXACO' ....
    1995: DG42 withdrawn from
    standard production.

DG 43 1931 Morris Van

Another in the 'Premier Collection' range of models.
000a 90 'WEETABIX' ....
001a 90 'CHIVERS JAMS' ....
002a 91 'HAMLEYS', special box ......
003a 91 'D.G. CLUB Winter 90/91'.....
004a 91 'AC SPARK PLUGS' ....
005a 91 'LNER', (TPL1003)............GSP
006a 91 'METROPOLITAN Rly',
    (Set RSL1003)...............GSP
007a 91 'BIRDS CUSTARD' ....
008a 91 '8th Army Ambulance', SBX..
009a 91 '91 Toyfair', Dealer
    promo, special box **£8-12**
009b 91 no locations on door.....NGPP
010a 91 'Cornwall Home Guard',
    (Set HF1003)...................GSP
011a 92 'HAMLEYS', special box .....
012a 92 'AMBROSIA' ....
013a 92 'ARNOTTS' ....
014a 92 'G.W.R.', (RSL3003) ....GSP
015a 92 'HARRODS', HD1004 ....GSP
016a 92 'SUNLICHT SEIFE',
    (German market) ....NGPP
017a 93 'TATE SUGARS' ....
018a 94 'BRANDS' ....
019a 94 'RUPERT BEAR', SBX ....
020a 95 'BRASSO METAL POLISH' .
021a 95 'RUPERT', (RUL 1003) ..GSP
022a 96 'THREE in ONE OIL' ....
026a 97 'GOLDEN SHRED' ....
027a 98 'HORLICK'S' ....
028a 98 'EXPRESS DAIRY' ....
?   99 'BOOTS' ....
031 00 'WHITE LABEL' ....
032 00 'EDDIE STOBART' ....
033 01 'KIWI BOOT POLISH' ....

DG 44 1937 Scammell Six-wheeler

Realistic 'heavy-duty' wheels distinguish this model in the 'Premier Collection' range.
000a 90 'BISTO' ....
001a 90 'TOBLERONE' ....
002a 91 'MARMITE' ....
003a 91 'FOX's GLACIER MINTS' .....

004a 91 'N. Y. MOORS', in Set ....GSP
005a 92 'ROWNTREES' ....
006a 92 'McMULLEN' ....
007a 92 'D.G. CLUB Spring '92' ....
008a 92 'British Army',
    Set EAL1003..................GSP
009a 93 'BERLINER KINDL',
    German market.............NGPP
010a 93 'TETLEYS FINE ALES' ....
011a 94 'HEINZ PICKLES' ....
012a 94 'CARNATION' ....
013a 94 'Command Caravan',
    in Set DDB 1003 ....GSP
014a 95 'KRONENBOURG' ....
015a 95 'RUPERT BEAR', SBX ....
016a 95 'VICTORY ALE',
    in VEL 1003 Set ....GSP
017a 95 'PEPSI-COLA', (US) ...NGPP
018a 96 'CASTLEMAINE XXXX' ....
019a 96 '7-UP' ....
020a 96 'BILLY SMART'S',
    in Circus Set CR 1003 ....GSP
022a 97 'QUALITY STREET' ....
023a 98 'BRILLO SOAP PADS' ....
024 97 'SHREDDED WHEAT' ....
025 99 'BELL'S' ....
029 00 'FISHER-RENWICK' ....
031 01 'WALTZER' ....
032 01 'BILLY SMART'S' ....
033 01 'WYNN'S'...............................

DG 45 1908 Rolls-Royce Silver Ghost Coupé

000a 92 Metallic Green ....
001a 91 Crimson body, Black seats ......
002a 93 White body ....
003a 94 'DG Journal', 'gold' ......NGPP
    1993: DG45 withdrawn from
    standard production.

DG 46 1930 Bentley 4½ litre

Reminiscent of Lesney Y5-1 with separate wings and spare wheel.
000a 91 British Racing Green ....
001a 91 Dark Blue body, No. '1' ....
002a 91 'Gold-plate' effect **£20-30**
003a 92 British Racing Green, '2' ....
004a 92 Cream body, No. '18' ....
005a 93 Maroon body, No. '10' ....
    93 British Racing Green body,
    No. '85' ('Brooklands').........
006a 94 Black ....
007a 95 Dark Green ....
008a 96 Blue, No. '3' ....

DG 47 1933 Austin Taxi

Introduced at the end of 1991 into the 'Premier Collection'.
000a 91 Dark Blue body ....
001a 92 Black body and wheels ....
002a 92 'HAMLEYS', (HA1002) .GSP
003a 92 'HAMLEYS',
    (in Set HAL1004) ....GSP
004a 93 Maroon body ....
005a 96 Dark Green ....
007a 97 Grey body and wheels ....
008a 97 'BOVRIL', Maroon / Black.....
009 00 Black ....

DG 48 1939 Chevrolet

000a 91 Cream and Dark Green ....
001a 91 'D.G. CLUB Autumn '91',
    Gold ....
002a 92 Cream and Maroon ....
003a 92 'British Army',
    in Set EAL1003..............GSP
004a 93 'YELLOW CABS' taxi ....

005a 93 'RAF', (Set DML1003)....GSP
006a 94 'HIGHWAY PATROL' ....
007a 94 'SHAEF', (DDL 1003) ..GSP
008a 94 'GHQ', (DDU 1003) ....GSP
009a 95 'BOOMERANG TAXIS' ....
010a 96 'F.D.N.Y. Fire Chief' ....

DG 49 1931 AEC Renown Double-Deck Bus

DG 15 and 17 radiator appear on this 6-wheeled bus in the 'Premier Collection'.

000a 91 'BOURN-VITA' ...
001a 91 'ROSES LIME JUICE' ...
002 92 'HAMLEYS', Black or Red chassis, SBX ...
003a 92 'MARTINI' ...
004a 92 'JANTZEN' ...
005a 92 'HAMLEYS', (HA1002) .GSP
006a 92 'D.G. CLUB 92' ...
007a 92 'HARRODS', (HD 1004) GSP
008a 92 'QANTAS', (QA1002) ...GSP
009a 93 'PEPSI-COLA', SBX ...
010a 93 'HAMLEYS', special box ...
011a 93 'LITTLEWOODS' ...
012a 93 'St. MICHAEL', in Set MS2004 ...GSP
013a 94 'HEINZ SPAGHETTI' ...
014a 94 'SWAN VESTAS' ...
015a 94 'HUIS TEN BOSCH', (Japan) ...NGPP
016a 95 'SHREDDED WHEAT' ...
017a 95 'VICTORY-MARS', in Set VE 1003 ...GSP
018a 95 'CEAD MILE FAILTE', special box ...
019a 96 'MADAME TUSSAUDS' ...
020a 98 'GOLDEN SHRED' ...
021a 98 'JAFFA ORANGES' ...
022 00 'GREEN LINE' ...
023 01 'FRY'S CHOCOLATE' ...

DG 50 1926 Morris Van

000a 92 'LYONS TEA' ...
001a 92 'BRYANT & MAY' ...
002a 93 'HAMLEYS' ...
003a 93 'H.M.V. - MILLERS' ...
004a 93 'DAYS GONE CLUB' ...
005a 93 'MARKS & SPENCER', in Set MS2004 ...GSP
006a 93 'RAFFLES', (HLL2003)..GSP
007a 94 'KODAK' (Mexico) ...**£30-40**
008a 94 'KIWI BOOT POLISH' ...
009a 94 'RUPERT BEAR' ...
010a 95 'PEPSI-COLA' ...
011a 94 'HARRODS', (HR 3002).GSP
012a 94 'NORMAN ROCKWELL', special box ...
013a 94 'AUSTRALIAN POST', (Australia) ...NGPP
014a 95 'SILVER KING' ...
015a 95 'GOLD CLUB' 3rd Ed. 24k gold-plated ...NGPP
016a 96 'TOM SMITH'S' ...
019a 97 'LYLE'S GOLDEN SYRUP' ..
020a 98 'LIPTON'S TEA' ...
021a 98 'GLENMORANGIE' ...
023a 98 'BEEFEATER DRY GIN' ...
024 99 'HELLMAN'S' ...
025 99 'GLENFIDDICH' ...
029 00 'HEINZ' ...
030 00 'BELLS' ...
035 01 'COCKBURN'S PORT' ...
036 01 'EDDIE STOBART' ...
037 01 'LAMB'S' ...
038 01 'HIS MASTER'S VOICE' ...
039 01 'HARVEY'S BRISTOL' ...
040 01 'PERSIL' ...
042 01 'THORNTON'S' ...
043 01 'The FAMOUS GROUSE' ...

DG 51 1934 Chevrolet Box Van

000a 92 'MADAME TUSSAUD'S' ...
001a 92 'STARTRITE' ...
002a 93 'HOVIS' ...
003a 93 'DAYS GONE CLUB' ...
004a 93 'MARKS & SPENCER', in Set MS2004 ...GSP
005a 94 'BUSHELL'S TEA' ...
006a 94 'ERDAL', (Germany)...**£15-20**
007a 94 Army Wireless Truck, in Set DDB 1003 ...GSP
008a 94 'NORMAN ROCKWELL' ...
009a 95 'HAMLEYS' ...
010a 95 'RUPERT BEAR', SBX ...
011a 95 'Dr. PEPPER', SBX ...
012a 96 'JOHNSON'S WAX' ...
014a 97 'CHIVER'S JELLIES' ...
015 99 'BARR'S IRN-BRU' ...

DG 52 1935 Morris Parcels Van

Introduced in to the 'Premier Range' in October 1992.

000a 92 'ROYAL MAIL' ...
001a 92 'PICKFORDS' ...
002a 93 'PEPSI-COLA', SBX ...
003a 93 'LNER PARCELS' ...
004a 93 '43rd Division' ...
005a 93 'DAYS GONE CLUB' ...
006a 93 '1993 TOYFAIR' ...
007a 93 'RAF', in Set DM1003 ...GSP
008a 94 'NEW YORK TOY FAIR' ...
009a 94 'KODAK FILMS', (Mexico) ...**£30-40**
009b 94 (general release) ...
010a 95 'HARRODS' (HR 2002)..GSP
011a 95 'HAMLEYS' ...
012a 95 'SAROTTI SCHOKOLADE' .
013a 95 'RUPERT BEAR', SBX ...
014a 95 'A.R.P.', Set VEL 1003 ...GSP
015a 96 'P. O. TELEPHONES', in Set POL 1003 ...GSP
018a 97 'McVITIE & PRICES' ...
019a 98 'GUERNSEY P. O.' ...
020a 98 'BLUE BIRD' ...
021 01 'FOX'S GLACIER MINTS' ...
022 01 'WHITWORTH' ...

DG 53 1926 Rolls-Royce Laudaulet

Introduced in 1992 as a Promotional. It was issued as a standard model in October of that year.

000a 92 'Days Gone Collector', 'Gold-plate' effect ...
001a 93 'Gold-plate' effect, 'Promotional' base ...NGPP
002a 95 Gold plated (RPL 1003)..GSP
1995: DG53 withdrawn from standard production; then:
003 00 Black/Silver ...?

DG 54 1929 Rolls-Royce 'D' back

This version appeared first as a Promotional (in May 1992).

000a 93 Blue body, Tan roof ...
001a 94 'Days Gone Collector', Vol.4, 'Gold' effect ...
002a 95 Gold plated (RPL 1003)..GSP
003a 95 'Gold' effect, Germany .NGPP

DG 55 Horse-Drawn Tanker

Introduced in 1992 and given a Days Gone number, this model has only been used for Promotional purposes.

DG 56 1934 Ford Model 'A' Van (Raised Roof)

Introduced in 1992 for promotional use.

000a 94 'D. G. Club', Winter 94 ...
001 99 'CHARRINGTONS' ...

DG 57 1939 Ford Tanker

000a 93 'SHELL-BP Aviation' ...
001a 94 'ESSO PETROLEUM' ...
003a 94 'USAF', Set DDU 1003...GSP
002a 95 'NAVY', DDL 1003 ...GSP
004a 95 'GULF GASOLINE' ...
005a 96 'CASTROL MOTOR OIL' ...

DG 58 1950 Morris 'Z' Van

The first in a new range of 1950s and 1960s model vehicles called 'Days Gone Vanguards'. It did not acquire cab window glazing until 1995.

000a 93 'P. O. TELEPHONES' ...
001a 93 'MALVERN WATER' ...
002 93 'MACKESONS STOUT' ...
003a 94 'ROYAL MAIL' ...
004a 94 'GILLETTE' ...
005a 94 'HAMLEYS' ...
006a 94 'PEPSI COLA' ...
007a 94 'D.G. CLUB', Spring 94 ...
008a 94 'D.G. GOLD CLUB', (Gold finish) ...NGPP
009a 95 'SINGER' ...
010a 95 'BRITISH RAILWAYS', in Set BRL 1003 ...GSP
011a not yet allocated.
012a 95 '7-UP' ...
013a 94 'HARRODS',(HR 2004)..GSP
014a 96 'A.A. Technical Service' ...
015a 97 'HEINZ BAKED BEANS' ...
017a 98 'NATIONAL BENZOLE' ...
018 99 'SMIRNOFF' ...
020 01 'GLENFIDDICH' ...

DG 59 1950 Bedford 30cwt Truck

The second of the original 'Days Gone Vanguards'. Cab window glazing appeared in 1995.

000a 93 'BIRDS CUSTARD' ...
001a 93 'CANADA DRY' ...
002a 93 'DUNLOPILLO' ...
003a 94 'PEPSI-COLA XMAS', SBX .
004a 94 'LUCOZADE' ...
005a 94 'BE-RO FLOUR' ...
006a 94 'HAMLEYS 94' ...
007a 94 'PEPSI-COLA' ...
008a 94 'WEET-BIX for HEALTH' ...
009a 94 '94 TOYFAIR' ...**£10-15**
010a 94 'NEW YORK TOYFAIR', USA ...**£100-125**
011a 95 'ARNOTTS BISCUITS' ...
012a 95 'OXYDOL' ...
013a 95 'BRITISH RAILWAYS', in Set BRL 1003 ...GSP
014a not yet allocated.
015a 95 'RUPERT', (RUL 1003) ..GSP
016a 95 '7-UP', special box ...
017a 95 'D.G. CLUB', Autumn 95 ...
018a 95 'London Olympic Games', special box ...NGPP
019a 96 'SHELL 100 Years' ...
022 97 'CAMPBELLS' ...
026a 97 'B.S.A. MOTOR CYCLES' ...
027a 98 'FISHERMAN'S FRIEND' ...
028 99 'HEINZ' ...
029 01 'EDDIE STOBART' ...

DG 60 1955 Dennis F8 Fire Engine

The third model in the Days Gone 'Vanguards' range. It did not have cab window glazing until 1995.

000a 93 'ESSEX' ...
001a 93 'DERBYSHIRE' ...
002a 93 'WESTERN AREA - OBAN'.
003a 94 'WEST SUSSEX F.B.' ...
004a 94 'NEW ZEALAND F.B. ...
005a 94 'LONDON, (FB 1003) ...GSP
006a 94 'Special Fire Service', in Set HR 3002 ...GSP
007a 95 'LONDON F.B.' ...
008a 95 'CIVIL DEFENCE CORPS' ...
009a 96 'MIDDLESEX F.B.' ...
011a 98 'CHESHIRE COUNTY' ...
012 99 'LANCASHIRE F.B.' ...
014 99 'SURREY' ...
015 00 'SUFFOLK COUNTY' ...
016 01 'WEST SUSSEX F.B.' ...

DG 61 1953 Pontiac Delivery Van

The fourth model in the Days Gone 'Vanguards' range.

000a 93 'Dr. PEPPER' ...
001a 93 'DETROIT POLICE' ...
002a 93 'MILWAUKEE' Ambulance ...
003a 94 'T.W.A.' ...
004a 94 'PEPSI COLA', SBX ...
005a 94 'EXCELSIOR', in Set MCL 1003 ...GSP
006a 94 'Dr. PEPPER', SBX ...
007a 95 'AGFA FILMS' ...
008a 95 '7-UP', (US, SBX) ...NGPP
1995: DG61 withdrawn from standard production.

DG 62 1935 Ford Articulated Tanker

Lledo's first articulated vehicle model.

000a 94 'REGENT PETROLEUM' ...
001a not yet allocated.
002a 95 'FINA PETROL' ...

DG 63 1950 Bedford 30cwt Delivery Van

Another in the Days Gone 'Vanguards' range. Early 1994 issues had no cab window glazing.

000a 94 'SAINSBURYS' ...
001a 94 'PENGUIN BOOKS' ...
002a 94 'OXO' ...
003a 94 'D.G. Club', Summer 94 ...
004a 95 'HAMLEYS' ...
005a 95 'CEREBOS SALT' ...
006a 95 'WALL'S SAUSAGES' ...
007a not yet allocated.
008a 95 'RUPERT', (RUL 1003) ..GSP
009a 95 'UK TRADE FAIR' ...**£10-15**
010a 95 'NEW YORK TRADE FAIR' ...**£100-125**
011a 95 'Dr. PEPPER', SBX ...
012a 96 'PERSIL' ...
016 97 'PEPSI-COLA' ...
017a 97 'RECKITT'S BLUE' ...
018a 98 'IMPERIAL LEATHER' ...
019 99 'TEACHER'S WHISKY' ...
020 99 'BLACK & WHITE' ...
021 99 'NEEDLERS' ...
023 00 'ROYAL MAIL' ...

DG 64 1950 Bedford Ambulance

Also in the Days Gone 'Vanguards' range. Some early 1994 issues did not have cab window glazing.

000a 94 'KENT COUNTY' ...
001a 94 'DURHAM COUNTY' ...
002a 95 'L.C.C. AMBULANCE' ...
003a 95 'FAMAGUSTA' ...
004a 95 'BRITISH RAILWAYS', in Set BRL 1003 ...GSP
005a 96 'P. O. TELEPHONES', Set POL 1003 ...GSP
008 00 'SALOP COUNTY' ...

DG 65 1960 Morris 1000 Traveller

The first car model in the original 'Vanguards' range and also the first Lledo model to be made to a quoted scale of 1:43. For further issues, please see number VA10 in the 'Vanguards' section.

000a 94 Green ...**£6-9**
001a 94 White ...**£6-9**
002a 95 Trafalgar Blue ...**£6-9**
003a 95 Smoke-Grey ...**£6-9**
004a 95 'Days Gone Journal', 'Gold-plated' effect ...NGPP

DG 66 1926 Dennis Delivery Van

000a 94 'CASTROL MOTOR OIL' ...
001a 94 'AUSTRALIAN POST', (Australia) ...NGPP
002a 94 'PEPSI COLA XMAS', special box ...

003a 95 'CAMPBELL'S SOUPS' ....
004a 95 'HARRODS', (HR2004)..GSP
005a 95 'D.G. CLUB, Winter 94-95',
    special box ....
006a 95 'PARIS OLYMPIC
    GAMES', special box ..NGPP
007a 95 'Dr. PEPPER', SBX ....
008a 96 'WHITBREAD' ....
009a 96 'SHELL 100 Years' ....
012a 97 'IMPERIAL AIRWAYS' ....
014a 98 'B.P. MOTOR SPIRIT' ....
017a 98 'GROLSCH' ....
018a 98 'ELIZABETH SHAW' ....
019 99 'CHIVERS & SONS Ltd'........
020 01 'ROYAL MAIL' ....
021 01 'LYONS'.............................
022 01 'HOMEPRIDE' ....

DG 67 1935 Ford Articulated Truck

000 94 'DUNLOP' ....
001a 94 'ROBERT BROS CIRCUS' ......
002a 95 'LYONS SWISS ROLLS' ......
003a 95 'D.G. CLUB' Summer '95,
    special box ....
004a 95 'Dr. PEPPER', SBX ....
005a 96 'PEPSI COLA' ....
006a 96 'SMITHS CRISPS'................
007a 96 'TOM ARNOLD'S
    CIRCUS, Set CR 1003....GSP
010a 97 'SERVIS'............................
011a 98 'JEYES' FLUID' ....

DG 68 1932 AEC Open-top Bus

The lower section casting from DG 15
given a new open upper deck.
000a 94 'RAF DUXFORD',
    (Lledo Show LE)............**£6-8**
001a 94 'D.G. CLUB', Summer '94........
002a 95 'SIGHTSEEING', SBX........
003a 95 'CROSVILLE' ....
004a 95 'Victory in Europe',
    in Set VEL 1003 ....GSP
005a 96 'STRATFORD BLUE' ....
006a 96 '7-UP' ....
008 01 'BOVRIL' ....

DG 69 1960 Morris 1000 Van

A popular subject in 1:43 scale.
000a 95 'EVER-READY' ....
001a 95 'CURRYS'............................
002a 95 'D.G. CLUB' Spring'95,
    special box ....
    1995: DG69 became VA 11.

DG 70 1939 Ford Canvas-back Truck

000a 95 'ANCHOR BEER' ....
001a 96 'N. C. B' ....
002a 96 'PEPSI COLA', SBX.............
003a 96 'SHELL 100 Years' ....
004a 96 'P. O. TELEPHONES',
    in Set POL 1003..............GSP
005a 96 'DG CLUB', Autumn '96 ....

DG 71 1959 Morris LD150 Van

A 1:50 scale 'D-G Vanguards' model.
000a 95 'KODAK'.............................
001a 95 'WORMWOOD SCRUBS'.......
002a 95 'H.P. SAUCE'......................
003a 95 'DUXFORD '95'.....................
004a 95 'MELBOURNE OLYMPIC
    GAMES',special box............
005a 96 'ROYAL MAIL' ....
006a 96 '7-UP', special box ....
007a 96 'PEPSI COLA', SBX.............
008a 96 'D. G. CLUB', Winter '96 ......
009a 96 'Sir Robert Fossett's Circus',
    in Set CR 1003 ....GSP
013a 97 'WHITBREAD' ....
014 97 '999', Limited Edition............

015a 98 'MOBILGAS'........................
016a 98 'POST OFFICE
    TELEGRAPH SERVICES' ....
017 99 'RAIL EXPRESS PARCELS' .
019 01 'BEEFEATER' ....

DG 72 1952 VW Beetle

'D-G Vanguards' VW in 1:43 scale.
000a 95 Blue......................................
001a 95 Pale Green ....
    1995: DG72 became VA12.

DG 73 1955 VW Kombi Van

A 'D-G Vanguards' 1:50 scale model.
000a 95 'CINZANO'...........................
001a 95 'BOSCH' ....
002a 95 'PEPSI COLA', Xmas
    special, Light Blue, SBX,
    LE 5,000......................NGPP
003a 95 'PEPSI COLA', Xmas
    special, White, packed
    in Pepsi 'can'.................NGPP
004a 96 'PEPSI COLA', SBX.............
005a 96 'GERMAN POST' ....
006a 96 'ESSO Paraffin' ....
007a 96 '7-UP', special box ....
008a 96 'UK TRADE FAIR 96'............
009a 96 'D. G. CLUB', Spring '96.......
013a 97 'MADAME TUSSAUD'S' ....
014a 98 'LAMBS NAVY RUM'...........
015 99 'ORANGINA' ....
016 99 'MICHELIN' ....

DG 74 1959 Austin '7' Mini

A 1:43 'D-G Vanguards' model.
000a 95 Pale Blue.............................
001a 95 Red.....................................
002a 95 'POLICE', White...................
    1995: DG74 withdrawn from
    the 'Days Gone' range. See
    the 'Vanguards' section for
    subsequent issues as VA 13.

DG 75 1957 Bristol Lodekka Bus

A 'Days Gone Vanguards' model, in the
'HO' scale of 1:87.
000a 95 'DULUX'..............................
001a 95 'WESTONS' ....
002a 95 'DG CLUB', Xmas '95 ....
003a 96 'TIZER', 'Fife' ....
005a 97 'POLO MINTS' ....
006 98 'TATE & LYLE' ....
008 99 'WHITE LABEL' ....
009 00 'PEARL ASSURANCE' ....

DG 76 Mercedes Bus

000a 96 'JAEGERMEISTER' ....
001a 96 'DG' Summer Special ....
002a 97 'SWISS POST' ....

DG 77 1937 Scammell Tanker

000a 96 'MOBILGAS - MOBILOIL' ...
001a 97 'I.C.I. CHEMICALS'..............
002 99 'NATIONAL BENZOLE' ....

DG 78 1939 Dodge Airflow

000a 96 'MOBILOIL' ....
001a 97 'TEXACO' ....

DG 79 1939 Ford Fire Engine

000a 96 'U.S.A.A.F.' ....
001a 97 'CHICAGO FIRE Dept.' ....
002a 98 'US NAVY FIRE Dept.' ....

DG 80 1937 Scammell Tractor

000a 96 'PICKFORDS'........................
003a 97 'BRITISH RAIL' ....

004a 97 'ROYAL MAIL' ....
005 99 'E. W. RUDD' ....
006 99 'TATE & LYLE' ....

DG 81 1935 Sentinel S6 Steam Wagon

000 99 'TARMAC LIMITED' ....

DG 82 1930 Ford Model 'A' Coupé

000a 97 Two-tone Grey.....................
001a 97 Brown and Beige ....

DG 83 Reo Van

000a 95 'ROME OLYMPIC GAMES' .

DG 84

DG 84 Not yet allocated

DG 85 1912 Renault Van

000a 97 'RENAULT' ....
001a 97 'MICHELIN' ....
002a 97 'ROYAL MAIL' ....
004a 98 'VAN HOUTEN'S COCOA' ...
006a 98 'BIRD'S POWDER' ....
010 00 'OXO FLUID BEEF' ....
011 00 'CHIVERS REGAL' ....
012 01 'EDDIE STOBART' ....
013 01 'STORK MARGARINE' ....
014 01 'SWAN VESTAS' ....
015 01 'PEARS' ....
016 01 'FAIRY SOAP' ....
017 01 'JAMESONS' ....
018 01 'NESTLE'S FRUIT & NUT' ..

DG 86 1955 VW Camper

000a 97 'FLOWER POWER' ....
001a 97 Red and Black ....

DG 87 1957 M.A.N. Van

000a 97 'HOLSTEN BIER' ....
001 97 'De KUYPER' ....
003 99 'JOHNNIE WALKER' ....

DG 88 1931 Sentinel 4-wheel Steam Wagon

000a 97 'WATNEYS' ....
001a 97 'McMULLEN & SONS' ....
005a 98 'TATE & LYLE'S' ....
006a 98 'BASS & Co.' ....
008 99 'J. SAINSBURY' ....
009 99 'J. J. HATFIELD' ....
010 99 'MORRIS & Co.' ....?
010 00 'ROYAL MAIL' ....

DG 89 Rolls-Royce Silver Cloud

000 00 White / Maroon ....

DG 90 1966 GMC Tanker

000a 98 'TEXACO' ....

DG 91 1930 Foden Steam Wagon

000a 98 'NEWQUAY STEAM
    BITTER' ....
001a 98 'PICKFORDS'........................
003 99 'FULLERS' ....
004 99 'WD' ....
005 99 'TATE & LYLE' ....
007 00 'EDDIE STOBART' ....
008 00 'BECK & POLLITZER' ....

DG 92, 93, 94, 95, 96

DG 92 Not yet allocated
DG 93 Not yet allocated

DG 94 Not yet allocated
DG 95 Not yet allocated
DG 96 Not yet allocated

DG 97 1934 Sentinel S4 Steam Wagon

000 99 'TETLEY FINE ALES' ....
003 99 'GLENDRONACH' ....

DG 98

DG 98 Not yet allocated

DG 99 1931 Sentinel 4-wheel Flatbed Steam Wagon

000 99 'McALPINE' ....
001 00 'CHARRINGTON'S' ....

DG 100 1937 Fordson 7v Truck

000 99 'E. & K. BENTON' ....
002 00 'Post Office Telephones' ....
003 00 'EDDIE STOBART' ....
005 01 'ROYAL MAIL' ....
006 01 'DETTOL' ....
007 01 'LUX' ....

DG 101 1931 Sentinel 6-wheel Steam Wagon

000 99 'McALPINE' ....
002 00 'WHITBREAD' ....

DG 102 Horse-Drawn Brewer's Dray

000 99 'Wm. YOUNGER' ....

DG 103 Sentinel S6 6-wheel Flatbed Steam Wagon

000 00 'LONDON BRICK' ....

DG 104, 105

DG 104 Not allocated
DG 105 Not allocated

DG 106 Sentinel Ballast Tractor

000 00 'G.W.R.' ....
001 01 'BISHOP & Sons' ....

DG 107

DG 107 Not yet allocated

DG 108 Dick Kerr Tram

000 01 'WHITBREAD'......................
002 01 'CROSSE & BLACKWELL' ..

DG 109 Dick Kerr Tram

000 01 'NESTLE'S MILK' ....
002 01 'SAXA SALT' ....

DG 110 Scammell Ballast Box with Drawbar Low-Loader

000 00 'PICKFORDS' (transformer) ..
001 01 'WIMPEY' (crane load) ....
002 01 'SUPERB JUNGLE' ....
003 01 'BILLY SMART'S' ....
004 01 'HILL of BOTLEY' (boat) .....

DG 111 Sentinel Ballast Tractor with Low-Loader Trailer

000 00 'SUNTER' (boiler load) ....
001 01 'WYNN'S' (propeller load) ....

DG 112 Scammell Tractor with Articulated Low-Loader	
000	00 'WYNN'S' (cylinder load)....?
001	00 'LMS' (crate load)..................
002	01 'BRS' (glass load) ....
003	01 'CHURCHILL DODGEMS' ...
004	01 'BILLY SMART'S' ....
005	01 'GPO' (cable drums) ....

DG 113 AEC Mammoth with Articulated Back Box	
000	01 'BILLY SMART'S' ....

DG 114 AEC Mammoth Ballast Box	
000	01 'BRITISH RAILWAYS' ....
001	01 'GLADIATOR' (generator).....
003	01 'BRS' 'Silvertown'................

DG 115 Sopwith Camel	
000	01 'Royal Flying Corps'..............
001	01 '10 (Naval) Sqdn, RNAS' ....

003	01 'Jan Oleislagers' ....
004	01 'Capt. Claude Emery'.............

DG 116 Fokker DR1 Triplane	
000	01 'Baron von Richthofen'..........
001	01 'Lt Fritz Kempfe' ....
003	01 'Lt Josef Jacobs' ....
004	01 'Jasta 18'..............................

DG 117 Tiger Moth Biplane	
000	01 'G-ACDC' (oldest flying) ......
001	01 'Post-war Training'.................
003	01 'RAF Training Scheme' ....
004	01 'University of London'...........

DG 118 Citroën 55 Van	
000	01 'DANONE'............................

DG 119 Citroën Type 'H' Van	
000	01 'MICHELIN' ....

DG 120 Berliet GLR Truck	
000	01 'PERRIER' ....

DG 121 Renault 1,000Kg Truck	
000	01 'RENAULT AUTOMOBILE' .

DG 122 Stearman Kaydet	
000	01 'USAAF Trainer' ....
001	01 'US Naval Trainer' ....
003	01 'C-GSDK' ....
004	01 '203 US Navy' ....

DG 123 AEC Mammoth Ballast Box + Low-Loader	
000	01 'SR' (cable drums load) ....
001	01 'WALTZERS' (fairground) .....
002	01 'BRITISH ARMY' (tank) ....

DG 124 AEC Mammoth with Articulated Low-Loader Trailer	
000	01 'LNER' (cylinder load) ....

DG 125 Burrell Showman's Steam Wagon	
000	01 'PRESTONS of POTTO' ....
001	01 'GOLDEN DRAGON' ....
003	01 'GASCOIGNE' ....

DG 126 Burrell Road Roller	
000	01 Road Roller............................
001	01 'RUSTON & HORNSBY' .....

DG 127 Morris Minor 1000 Van	
000	01 'LONDON HERB' ....
001	01 'POST OFFICE TELEPHONES'......................

'Special Licensed' series

Introduced in 1997 and presented in colourful boxes printed with 'brand' graphics appropriate to the model within. All are based on the equivalent 'Days-Gone' casting.

SL 3 HORSE-DRAWN DELIVERY VAN
000 98 'COCA-COLA' ....
001 99 'PEPSI-COLA', '5c' .....

SL 6 FORD Model 'T' VAN
003 97 'COCA-COLA' ....
005 98 'GUINNESS' ....

SL 7 1930 FORD Model 'A' WOODY WAGON
000 98 'COCA-COLA' ....
001 99 'PEPSI' (SLO 7) ....

SL 8 1920 FORD Model 'T' TANKER
000 99 'GUINNESS' ....

SL 13 FORD Model 'A' VAN
000 98 'COCA-COLA' ....
002 98 'CAMPBELL'S'...........
      99 'CAMPBELL'S'...........
003 99 'Ice-Cold PEPSI'.........

SL 17 1932 AEC REGAL BUS
002 99 '7-UP'...........................

SL 18 1936 PACKARD VAN
000 98 'COCA-COLA' ....

SL 21 CHEVROLET VAN
002 98 'COCA-COLA' ....
005 99 '7-UP'.......................
006 99 'My GUINNESS'.........

SL 23 1954 SCENICRUISER
000 97 'ROUTE 66'.................
001 98 'COCA-COLA' ....

SL 26 1928 CHEVROLET

DELIVERY VEHICLE
000 98 'COCA-COLA' ....
001 99 'PEPSI'.......................

SL 30 CHEVROLET VAN
000 98 'COCA-COLA Bottles'

SL 32 1907 ROLLS-ROYCE SILVER GHOST 40/50HP
000 97 Silver body, Green seats, Grey tyres..........
001 97 Black body, Red seats, Black tyres..............
002 97 Red/Silver, Black seats and tyres......................

SL 36 CHEV. PICK-UP
000 98 'COCA-COLA' ....

SL 37 FORD Model 'A' VAN
000 98 'COCA-COLA' ....

SL 43 1931 MORRIS VAN
000 97 'R. A. C.'.....................
001 98 'CAMPBELL'S'...........
002 99 'PEPSI-COLA' ....

SL 44 1937 SCAMMELL
000 98 'COCA-COLA' ....
003 99 'GUINNESS' ....

SL 46 1930 4½ Ltr BENTLEY
000 97 Brit. Racing Green, '6' .
001 97 Blue, '3' ....
002 97 Red, 8'........................
003 97 Yellow, 17'.................
004 98 Grey, 18'.....................
005 99 Black, '1' ....

SL 48 CHEVROLET CAR
000 97 'ROUTE 66'.................

001 98 'COCA-COLA' ....
002 99 'PEPSI-COLA' ....

SL 49 AEC RENOWN BUS
000 98 'JOIN THE R.A.C.' .....
001 98 'GUINNESS As Usual'

SL 50 1926 MORRIS VAN
000 97 'JOIN THE R.A.C.' ....
002 99 '7-UP'..........................

SL 51 CHEVROLET VAN
000 98 'COCA-COLA' ....
002 98 'CAMPBELL'S SOUP'
      99 'CAMPBELL'S SOUP'
003 98 'My GUINNESS'.........

SL 53 1926 ROLLS-ROYCE
000 97 Mushroom/Maroon, Cream tyres...............
002 98 Cream/Brown, Black tyres ....

SL 54 1929 ROLLS-ROYCE
000 97 White/Brown, Red wheels, Black tyres ......
001 97 Yellow and Black, Black wheels and tyres
005 98 Two-tone Green, Black tyres ....

SL 58 1950 MORRIS 'Z' VAN
001 99 '7-UP', 'Fresh Up'........

SL 59 BEDFORD TRUCK
000 97 'PG TIPS', 'Geoff' ....
001 97 'MINNIE THE MINX', 'BEANO'..................
005 98 'R.A.C.'........................
007 98 'GUINNESS' ....
009 99 'PEPSI'........................

? 99 'CAMPBELLS' ....

SL 63 1950 BEDFORD VAN
000 97 'PG TIPS', 'Shirley' .....
001 97 'DENNIS THE MENACE', 'BEANO' .
002 97 'R.A.C.'........................
004 98 'COCA-COLA' ....
007 99 'My GUINNESS'.........S

1926 DENNIS VAN
001 98 'COCA-COLA' ....
003 99 '7-UP', 'Lemon Soda' ..
004 99 'GUINNESS' ....

SL 67 1935 FORD ARTICULATED TRUCK
000 97 'DESPERATE DAN', 'DANDY'....................
002 98 'COCA-COLA' ....
005 99 '7-UP', 'Joyce Joliet' ....

SL 68 1932 AEC OPEN BUS
000 99 'PEPSI' (SLO 68) ....

SL 70 1939 FORD CANVAS-BACK TRUCK
000 97 'RAC' ....
001 98 'COCA-COLA' ....
005 99 'PEPSI-COLA' ....
006 99 '7-UP In Cans' ....

SL 71 MORRIS LD150 VAN
000 97 'PG TIPS', 'Kevin' ......
001 97 'BERYL THE PERIL', 'DANDY'..................
004 98 'R.A.C.' ....
005 98 'GUINNESS TIME' .....
006 99 'PEPSI-COLA' ....

SL 73 1955 VW KOMBI VAN

000 97 'PG TIPS', 'Samantha' .
001 98 'COCA-COLA' ....
005 99 'Had Your GUINNESS?' ....
? 99 'CAMPBELLS' ....

SL 78 DODGE AIRFLOW
000 97 'ROUTE 66'..................

SL 79 FORD FIRE ENGINE
000 97 'ROUTE 66', 'No. 4' ...

SL 85 1912 RENAULT VAN
000 98 'R.A.C.' ....
001 98 'BEEFSTEAK SOUP' ..
002 99 'A GUINNESS a Day' ..
008 99 'JOSEPH LUCAS'........

SL 88 1931 SENTINEL STEAM WAGON
000 97 'NEWTON & RIDLEY' ....
002 99 'GUINNESS' ....

SL 89 1959 ROLLS-ROYCE
000 98 Metallic Grey/Silver......
001 98 Black ....
002 99 Gold/Black ....

SL 92 BENTLEY 'S' SERIES
000 98 Maroon/Silver ....
001 99 Green/Silver ....

SL 93 DODGE VAN
000 99 '7-UP'.........................

Lledo Promotionals and 'View Vans'

Lledo Promotionals came into being in 1985. Using existing standard castings, they were originally produced in runs of as few as 500 and went direct to clients, not to normal retail outlets. Some earlier 'promotionals' were supplied with the 'Days Gone' logo on the baseplate (soon modified to read 'Lledo Promotional'). Runs of up to 1,000 units were finished with printed self-adhesive labels while runs of 1,000 or more warranted tampo printing. Many thousands of Promotionals have been produced and as a result it has proved impossible to provide meaningful price information for collectors.

View Vans and Souvenir Buses are a variation on the Promotional theme and include LP6, LP13, LP15, LP17 and LP21. They are printed with a standard 'camera' logo and supplied in a choice of three colours for each type. They are finished with photographic labels including stately homes, football teams, etc. The models are completed by a company independent of Lledo and are packed in distinctive 'dark gold' boxes. Values have yet to exceed the normal retail price of these souvenirs.

'Days-Gone' Gift Sets

Individual models contained in these sets are listed separately in the 'Days Gone' listings. This list indicates the content of specific sets and prices where available.

Set 1 96 **'Assorted' Set**....Buses DG15-035, DG41-011 and DG75-000 ....**£10-12**
Set 1 97 **'Assorted' Set**....Vans DG26-018, DG44-018 and DG66-008 ......**£10-12**
Set 2 96 **'Assorted' Set**....Vans DG6-125, DG13-064 and DG52-012 ....**£10-12**
Set 2 97 **'Assorted' Set**....Buses DG49-019, DG68-005 and DG76-000 ....**£10-12**
Set 3 96 **'Assorted' Set**....Vans DG21-044, DG43-020 and DG66-003 ......**£10-12**
Set 3 97 **'Assorted' Set**....Tankers DG57-005, DG77-000, DG78-000 ....**£10-12**
Set 4 96 **'Assorted' Set**....Tankers DG57-004 and DG67-000, plus VW Van DG73-001 ....**£10-12**
Set 4 97 **'Assorted' Set**....Vans DG6-138, DG21-048 and DG67-006 ....**£10-12**
Set 5 96 **'Assorted' Set**....Trucks DG26-016 and DG44-014, plus VW Van DG73-000 ....**£10-12**
Set 5 97 **'Assorted' Set**....Vans DG51-012 and DG63-012, plus Ford Model 'T' Car DG33-014 ....**£10-12**
Set 6 96 **'Assorted' Set**....Vans DG59-011 and DG67-002, plus Bristol Lodekka DG75-001 ....**£10-12**
Set 6 97 **'Assorted' Set**....Vans DG43-022, DG58-014 and DG73-006 ......**£10-12**

AB 1003 90 **Arnotts Biscuits Set** DG6-101a Ford T Van, DG11-016a Horse Drawn Removal Van, DG13-045a Ford Van................**£20-25**
AR 1002 01 **'The Showman's Collection'**: Burrell Showman's Engine and Carousel 'Golden Dragon ....
BA 1003 89 **British Army Collection** DG8-017a Tanker, DG13-038a Ford Van 'Recruitment', DG19-009a Staff Car......................**£20-25**
BB 1003 90 **RAF Ground Crew Support** DG20-015a Balloon Tender, DG35-002a RAF Riggers, DG42-001a Fuel Tanker **£15-20**
BBL 1003 90 **RAF Personnel Transport** DG28-011a Truck, DG30-008a Ambulance, DG34 004a Office (12,500) **£15-20**
BM 1004 90 **Bryant & May Set** Four DG21 vans: 022a 'Scottish Bluebell', 023a 'Bryant & May', 024a 'Swan Vestas', 025a 'Englands Glory'. (Limited Edition of 12,500) **£20-25**
? 86 **Commonwealth Games Set** DG7-007a Woody Wagon, DG10-016a Coach, DG15-011a AEC Bus.............................**£10-12**
BPL 1003 96 **British Motoring Classics** 24k gold plated Ford Anglia 105E, Mini-Minor and Morris 1000 Traveller.........................NGPP
BRL 1003 95 **British Railways Set** DG58-010a, 59-013a, 64-004a **£12-15**
BS 1002 01 **'Billy Smart's Big Top'**: AEC Mammoth Generator Lorry + 'Circus' Big Top......................
CC 1003 86 **Coca-Cola Set** DG6-058a Ford T Van, DG11-007a Horse Drawn Van, DG13-021a Ford Van...**£25-35**
CC 2003 87 **Coca-Cola Set** DG6-054a Ford T Van, DG21-005a Chevrolet, DG26-002a Chevrolet **£25-35**
CP 1 84 **Collector Pack** DG3-003a Robertsons, DG4-005a Pears Soap, DG6-017a Daily Express **£10-15**
CR 1003 96 **Classic Circus Collection** DG44 'Billy Smart's', DG67 'Tom Arnold's', DG71 'Fossett's' **£15-20**
DDB 1003 94 **British D-Day Set** DG36 Service Truck, DG51 Wireless Truck, and DG44 Command Caravan.................................**£12-15**
DDL 1003 94 **'D-DAY' Ltd. Ed. Set** DG29-008a, 48-007a, 57-002a **£12-15**
DDU 1003 94 **American D-Day Set** DG29 Signals Truck, DG48 GHQ Staff Car, DG57 Flight Refueller **£12-15**
DML 1003 93 **Dambusters Set** DG16-034a Control, DG28-030a RAF, DG48-005a RAF, (7,500)...**£12-15**
DM 1003 93 **Dambusters Set** DG16-033a NAAFI, DG40-004a RAF, DG52-007a RAF **£12-15**
EAL 1003 92 **El Alamein Set** DG42-005a Water, DG44-008a Army, DG48-003a Army, (12,500) **£12-15**
FB 1003 94 **London Fire Brigade** DG5-010a, 12-019a, 60-005a **£12-15**
GS 1 84 **Gift Set** DG6-023a Railway Express, DG7-002a Ford Sales, DG9-001a NY-Rio **£10-15**
GS 2 85 **Gift Set** DG6-033a Barclays, DG11-001a Abels, DG13-005a Michelin...**£15-20**
GS 3 85 **Bus Gift Set** DG10-013a Trailways, DG15-002a Castlemaine, DG17 001a Eurotour **£10-15**
GS 4 86 **Coca-Cola Set** DG6-058a Ford T Van, DG11-007a Woody Wagon, DG13-021a Ford Van **£20-25**
GS 5 86 **Hershey's Set** DG6-055a Ford T Van, DG13-023a Ford A Van, DG16-012a Dennis Van **£20-25**
GS 1004 89 **Golden Days Of Film** Early Film Industry vans in 'gold-plate': DG6-091a Britannia, DG13-034a Empire, DG18-014a B & C Films, DG21-016a Majestic (10,000) **£80-90**
GU 1003 92 **Guadalcanal Set** DG28-027a Marines, DG29-005a Marines, DG40-003a Navy **£10-13**
84 **Hamleys Set** DG3-009a, DG4-008a, DG6-035a, DG7-004a, DG10-009a, DG13-004a **£35-40**
HA 1002 92 **Hamleys London Set** DG47-002a Taxi and DG49-005a AEC Bus...**£8-12**
HA 2002 94 **Hamleys London Set** DG12-018a and DG15-033a **£8-12**
HAL 1004 92 **Hamleys Limited Edition Set** DG11-021a, DG21-037a, DG41-008a, DG47-003a, (5,000) **£15-20**
HD 1002 92 **Harrods Set** DG11-020a Van and DG15-028a AEC Bus....**£10-12**
HD 1004 92 **Harrods Set** DG3-014a, 13-051a, 43-015a, 49-007a **£12-18**
HF 1003 91 **The Home Front Set** DG16-030a YMCA, DG35-004a NFS, DG43-010a Cornwall...**£12-15**

HFL 1002 97 **Henry Ford Set** 'Bronzed' finish DG9 and DG33, plinth, clear acrylic box 'FORD', 7,500..**£12-15**
HLL 1003 92 **Hotel Labels Set** DG6-108a 'Colombia', DG21-035a 'de Paix', DG33-005a 'de Paris', 12,500................................**£12-15**
HLL 2003 93 **Hotel Labels Set** DG13-058a 'Grand', DG18-024a 'Imperial', DG50-006a 'Raffles', 7,500....................................**£12-15**
HR 2002 94 **Harrods Set** DG4-018a, DG52-010a **£10-12**
HR 3002 94 **Harrods Set** DG50-011a, DG60-006a **£10-12**
HR 2004 94 **Harrods Set** DG15-036a, 34-007a, 58-013a, 66-004a **£15-20**
LOS 8002 95 **'Souvenir of London'** 'LCC' Fire Engine and Ambulance **£8-12**
LOS10002 95 **'Souvenir of London'** Open top Bus 'See London' and Morris Z Van 'Royal Mail..**£8-12**
LOS11002 95 **'Souvenir of London'** Taxi and 'Madame Tussaud's' Bus **£8-12**
LP 1553 91 **Charles & Diana Set** Two Rolls-Royce models in special Purple box (not limited) **£10-15**
LS 1004 89 **London Stores Set No.1** Four different vans: DG6-087a Selfridges, DG13-031a Aquascutum, DG18-013a Fortnum & Mason, DG21-012a DAKS Simpson **£12-18**
LS 2004 90 **London Stores Set No.2** DG6-097a Jaeger, DG13-036a Austin Reed, DG18-018a Asprey, DG21-020a Liberty...........**£12-18**
LSL 1005 98 **Land Speed Legends Set** 5 record breakers: LP 4903, LP 5267, LP 5268, LP 5269, LP 5270....................................**£20-30**
MCL 1003 94 **Motorcycle Vans Set** DG21-041a, 30-017a, 61-005a **£12-15**
MG 1003 92 **Malta George Cross Set** DG12-017a Valletta, DG18-022a St John, DG28-026a Royal Navy..**£10-15**
MS 1004 90 **Marks & Spencer Set** DG11-014a, DG13-014a, DG21-019a, DG41-001a. (Also available singly) **£10-15**
MS 2004 93 **Marks & Spencer Set** DG13-057a, DG49-012a, DG50-005a, DG51-004a **£15-18**
NYMR1003 89 **North Yorks Moors Set 1** DG6-093a Cartage, DG17-018a NYM Railway, DG28-008a Parcels (7,500) **£15-18**
NYMR2003 90 **North Yorks Moors Set 2** DG13-044a, DG15-027a, DG16-025a, (6,500) **£15-18**
NYMR1002 91 **North Yorks Moors Set 3** DG41-005a Scarborough and DG44-004a NYMR, (6,500) **£10-12**
PA 1002 01 **'Pioneers of Aviation' 'Barnstorming Duo' Set**: Stearman Kaydet and Tiger Moth with 'wing-walker' figures.........
PA 2002 01 **'Pioneers of Aviation' 'Dog-fight Duo' Set**: Fokker DR1 (von Richthofen) + Sopwith Camel (Capt.Brown)......
PA 3002 01 **'Pioneers of Aviation' 'Wing-Walkers' Set**: Stearman Kaydet and Tiger Moth with 'wing-walker' figures.........
PA 4002 01 **'Pioneers of Aviation' Set**: Fokker DR1 Triplane and Sopwith Camel..
PHL 1003 91 **'Pearl Harbor' Set 1** DG28-019a Corps, DG30-013a Navy, DG42-004a Navy, (12,500) .**£10-15**
PH 1003 91 **'Pearl Harbor' Set 2** DG21-030a Marines, DG28-022a Torpedo, DG40-002a Crane **£10-15**
POL 1003 96 **Post Office Telephones Set** 52-015a, 64-005a, 70-004a......**£15-18**
QA 1002 92 **Qantas Set** DG13-052a Ford Van, and DG49-008a Bus.........**£8-12**
? 87 **RFC / RAF Set** DG6-063a and DG28-011a '216 Squadron', DG18-008a Ambulance...**£45-55**
RN 1003 88 **Royal Navy Set** DG17-017a 'Britannia', DG20-011a 'Rooke', DG28-006a 'Devonport' (10,000) **£35-45**
RPL 1003 95 **Gold Rolls-Royces Set** DG43-021a, 59-015a, 63-008a **£15-20**
RR 1003 88 **Rolls Royce Set** 19-003a, 24-002a, 25-002a, plinth, 7,500 ..**£30-35**
RR 2003 97 **Rolls Royce Set** DG32, DG53 and DG54.............................**£10-12**
RSL 1003 91 **Railway Express Parcels 1** DG16-029a LNER, DG28-015a LMS, DG43-006a Metropolitan, (12,500)...........**£10-15**
RSL 2003 91 **Railway Express Parcels 2** DG13-050a Southern, DG21-034a LMS/LNER and DG28-020a GWR, (10,000)...**£10-15**
RSL 3003 91 **Railway Express Parcels 3** DG21-036a LNER, DG28-028a Southern and DG43-014a GWR, (10,000) **£10-15**
RSL 4003 93 **Railway Road Vehicles of the 1900s** DG3-015a GER, DG4-016a Furness and DG11-024a GtNorthern, (7,500).......**£15-18**
RUL 1003 95 **'RUPERT 75th' Set** DG43-021a, 59-015a, 63-008a **£12-15**
TPL 1003 91 **LNER Parcels Vans** DG16-028a Dennis, DG28-014a Mack and DG43-005a Morris, (12,500) **£12-15**
USA 1003 91 **US Army Set 1** DG27-006a, DG28-017a and DG30-012a ..**£12-15**
USAL1003 91 **US Army Set 2** DG29-003a Ambulance, DG36-003a Pick-Up, DG42-003a Air Corps, (12,500) **£12-15**
VE 1003 95 **'VE-DAY' Set** DG13, DG17 and DG49 ....**£12-15**
VEL 1003 95 **'VE-DAY' Ltd. Ed. Set** DG44, DG52 and DG68................**£12-15**

Trade packs and display material

DGA 1012 00 **'Days-Gone' Assortment No.1** Retailer's pack of 12 boxed models
DGA 2012 00 **'Days-Gone' Assortment No.2** Retailer's pack of 12 boxed models
DGA 3012 01 **'Days-Gone' Assortment No.1** Retailer's pack of 12 boxed models.
DGA 4012 01 **'Days-Gone' Assortment No.2** Retailer's pack of 12 boxed models.
DGA 7012 01 **'Days-Gone' Assortment No.5** Retailer's pack of 12 boxed models.
DGA 8012 01 **'Days-Gone' Assortment No.6** Retailer's pack of 12 boxed models.
DGA 8013 01 **'Days-Gone' Assortment No.6** Retailer's pack of 12 boxed models.
DGCD 002 00 **'Days-Gone' Counter Display** A counter stand for 16 models ....
DSTEP00 01 **'Days-Gone' Stepped Display Unit** A counter stand for 8 models ..
DSHELF0001 **'Days-Gone' Shelf Strips** for shelf-edge information ....
DHEAD00 01 **'Days-Gone' Header Boards** for use with counter displays, etc ......

Miscellaneous Lledo products

'Fantastic Set-O-Wheels'

A series of models introduced in 1985 for the US toy market and distributed by Hartoy Inc. of Florida. They were blister-packed on card with the legend 'Made in England by Lledo (London) Ltd.' on most of the baseplates.

F1a	DG 6	'MALIBU OR BUST'	**£10-15**
F1b		same but 'Days Gone' baseplate	**£10-15**
F2a	DG 7	'TRI-STATE DEALER',	
		Yellow wheels	**£10-15**
F2b		Black wheels, 'DG' baseplate	**£10-15**
F3a	DG15	'LIQUID BUBBLE'	**£10-15**
F4a	DG10	'OAKRIDGE SCHOOL'	**£10-15**
F5a	DG12	'BOSTON FIRE Dept'	**£10-15**
F5b		with 'Days Gone' baseplate	**£10-15**
F6a	DG13	'JOLLY TIME'	**£10-15**
F6b		with 'Days Gone' baseplate	**£10-15**
F7a	DG14	'POLICE' Car	**£10-15**
F7b		with 'Days Gone' baseplate	**£10-15**
F7c		As F7a but 20-spoke wheels	**£10-15**
F8a	DG14	'SAN-DIEGO FIRE'	**£10-15**
F8b		As F8a but Brass grille	**£10-15**

'Marathons'

Introduced in 1987. Some also used as promotionals. Range discontinued in 1988. **MPR is £5 or less.**

M1a	01a	87	**Leyland Olympian Bus**,
			'LONDON PRIDE SIGHTSEEING',
			'PINDISPORTS', Blue body
M1a	01b	87	same but 'PINDISPORTS' in Red
M1a	02a	87	'LONDON ZOO'
M1a	03a	87	'PAN AM'
M2a	01a	87	**Setra Coach**, 'PAN AM'
M2a	02a	87	'AIR CANADA'
M2a	03a	87	'GHANA AIRWAYS'
M3a	01a	87	**Neoplan Spaceliner**,
			'ISLAND TOURS'
M3a	02a	87	'SPEEDLINK'
M3a	03a	87	'GATWICK FLIGHTLINE'
M4a	01a	88	**Leyland Rigid Truck**,
			'FEDERAL EXPRESS'
M5a	01a	88	**Leyland Tipper**, 'LECCA ARC'
M6a	01a	88	**Leyland Tanker**, 'SHELL'

'Land Speed Legends'

This range of model Land Speed Record Cars employs an 'LP' reference system but are not considered to be 'promotionals'. See also Set number LSL 1005.

LP 4903	'THRUST SSC', Andy Green
LP 5267	'BLUEBIRD', Sir Malcolm Campbell
LP 5268	'THRUST 2', Richard Noble
LP 5269	'RAILTON MOBIL SPECIAL', John Cobb
LP 5270	'SONIC 1', Craig Breedlove

'London's Burning'

A small range of emergency vehicles based on the ITV drama series set in 'a London fire station'. Special packaging.

LP 5219	(DG5) Shand-Mason Fire Engine
LP 5220	(DG12) Dennis Fire Engine
LP 5221	(DG27) Mack Breakdown Truck
LP 5222	(DG60) Dennis F8 Fire Engine
LP 5223	(DG64) Bedford Ambulance
LP 5224	(PM105) Ford Transit

Edocar ('Old-Timer' Series)

Made in 1986 for Edor BV (Fred Beheer BV), in the Netherlands and sold there under the name 'EDOCAR'. The baseplates all have the wording 'EDOCAR - Made in England by Lledo' plus the model number. Some have original Days-Gone colours but have been left unprinted (without logos). All but A7 have only Black tyres. The 'double window' boxes were made and printed in Holland.

A1a	DG 8	Tanker (unprinted),	
		Red/Black/Yellow	**£10-15**
A1b		'ESSO BLUE', Blue/White	**£10-15**
A2a	DG 12	Dennis Fire Engine, Red body,	
		White floor	**£10-15**
A2b		Red body, Black floor	**£10-15**
A3	DG 14	Taxi, Yellow / Black	**£10-15**
A4a	DG 16	'HUMBROL', Chrome grille	**£10-15**
A4b		with Brass grille	**£10-15**
A5	DG 17	AEC Single Deck Bus, White,	
		(box states 'AEC Double Decker Bus')	**£10-15**
A6a	DG 18	Packard 'Ambulance',	
		Chrome grille	**£10-15**
A6b		Brass grille	**£10-15**
A7	DG 19	Rolls Royce Phantom, Silver/Black,	
		Black or Cream tyres	**£10-15**
A8	DG 21	'EDOCAR'	**£12-18**

American '500' series

A range of six Days Gone models were marketed in the USA in plain colour finishes and with no printed logos or liveries. In each case the standard reference number carried the suffix '500'.

DG14	Ford Model 'A', Yellow / Black	**£20-25**
DG22	Packard Town Van, Black / Red	**£20-25**
DG30	Chevrolet Van, Red / Black	**£20-25**
DG33	Ford Model 'T', Black	**£20-25**
DG36	Chevy Pick-Up, Green	**£20-25**
DG37	Ford Model 'A' Van, Blue	**£20-25**

Lledo Display Cases

CC 0015	Wall Display Case. Wooden 'pigeon-hole' style case to contain 15 models	NGPP
CD 0002	Counter Display Case. Injection moulded and flock-covered, to contain 24 models, headboard	NGPP
WD 0001	Wall Display Case. Injection moulded and flock-covered, to contain 20 models, headboard	NGPP
WD 0002	'Queen' Display Case. Glass front, 8 glass shelves in addition to base, to contain 54 models	NGPP
WD 0003	'Standard' Display Case. Glass front, 3 glass shelves in addition to base, to contain 28 models	NGPP
WD 0004	'King' Display Case. Glass front, 11 glass shelves in addition to base, to contain 72 models	NGPP
WD 0017	Wall Display Case. Flock-covered plastic in green or black, to contain 20 models	NGPP
BG 2004	Perpetual Calendar. Holds one model plus reel of adhesive tape	NGPP

'The London Experience'

The musicals of Sir Andrew Lloyd-Webber feature in this range of London bus models based on the DG75 Bristol Lodekka casting. Special packaging.

LP 5142	'CATS'
LP 5143	'Phantom of the Opera'
LP 5144	'Starlight Express'
LP 5145	'Jesus Christ, Superstar'

The 'Grey' Series

Finished in neutral Grey and left unprinted for use as samples of promotionals by sales representatives (mainly in the USA). Only 144 sets of models were produced (in 1986) and all except DG7, DG11 and DG14 have 'Days Gone' baseplates. Beware fakes.

DG 2	86	Horse-Drawn Milk Float	**£8-12**
DG 3	86	Horse-Drawn Delivery Van	**£8-12**
DG 4	86	Horse-Drawn Omnibus	**£8-12**
DG 5	86	Horse-Drawn Fire Engine	**£8-12**
DG 6	86	Ford Model 'T' Van, White roof	**£8-12**
DG 7	86	Ford Woody Wagon,	
		'Lledo' and 'DG' baseplates	**£8-12**
DG 8	86	Ford 'T' Tanker, Green tank	**£8-12**
DG 10	86	Dennis Single Deck Bus	**£8-12**
DG 11	86	Horse-Drawn Large Van,	
		Cream horses, Blue roof,	
		'Lledo' and 'DG' baseplates	**£8-12**
DG 12	86	Fire Engine	**£8-12**
DG 13	86	Ford Model 'A' Van	**£8-12**
DG 14	86	Ford Model 'A' Car,	
		Cream wheels, roof and seats,	
		'Lledo' and 'DG' baseplates	**£8-12**
DG 15	86	AEC Double Deck Bus	**£8-12**
DG 16	86	Dennis Parcels Van	**£8-12**
DG 17	86	AEC Single Deck Bus	**£8-12**
DG 18	86	Packard Van	**£8-12**
DG 19	86	Rolls-Royce Phantom II	**£8-12**

'Cargo Carriers'

Introduced in 1999 to accompany the 'Cargo Kings' range. These versions of the 'Eurovan' have been introduced so far:

CC00 1000	'UPS' ('Universal Parcels Service')
CC00 1001	'PARCEL FORCE' ('Royal Mail')
CC00 1002	'TNT'
CC00 1003	'FEDEX' ('Federal Express')
CC00 1004	'LYNX'
CC00 1005	'SECURICOR EXPRESS'

'Cargo Kings'

Articulated truck models in 1:76 scale.

VOLVO ARTICULATED TRUCK

CK00 1000	98	'PARCEL FORCE'
CK00 1001	98	'P&O FERRYMASTERS'
CK00 1003	98	'CARLSBERG BEER'
CK00 1007	98	'THRUST SSC'
CK00 1008	98	'DUCATI 916 CORSE'
CK00 1009	98	'YORKIE'
CK00 1010	98	'SAINSBURY'S'
CK00 1011	99	'RNLI'
CK00 1016	99	'TNT'
CK00 1017	99	'BODDINGTONS'
CK00 1018	99	'TANGO'
CK00 1022	99	'REVE RACING'
CK00 1023	99	'GOODYEAR'
CK00 1024	99	'McCAINS'
CK00 1025	99	'GUINNESS'
CK00 1026	99	'JOHN SMITH'S'

KENWORTH ARTICULATED TRUCK

CK00 2005	98	'CARGO KINGS'
CK00 2006	98	'ICE WARRIORS'
CK00 2009	99	'PEPSI'
CK00 2010	99	'PEPSI'
CK00 2011	99	'7-UP'

'The Millennium Dome'

?	1999	Approximately 100mm in diameter, special 'Year 2000' packaging	**£10-15**

Lledo 'Vanguards'

Ref	Intro	Model	MPR

VA 1 FORD ANGLIA 105E
- 000 96 Navy Blue £7-10
- 001 96 Pale Green.....................£7-10
- 002 96 White / Maroon...............£7-10
- 008 97 Yellow £7-10
- 010 97 Maroon / Grey.................£7-10
- 011 96 Pale Blue £7-10
- 012 98 'POST OFFICE
  SUPPLIES' £7-10
- 014 99 White / Green..................£7-10
- 015 00 'Lancs. County Const'y'£7-10
- 016 01 White / Blue £7-10
- 017 01 Lime-Green / White £7-10

VA 2 VOLKSWAGEN CABRIOLET
- 000 96 Red £7-10
- 001 96 Pale Blue £7-10
- 002 97 Black £7-10

VA 3 AUSTIN A40 VAN
- 000 96 'RANSOMES' £7-10
- 001 96 'BRITISH RAILWAYS',
  see Set BR 1002...........GSP
- 002 96 'A. A.' £7-10
- 004 97 'H. M. V.' £7-10
- 006 97 'CUSSONS IMPERIAL
  LEATHER' £7-10
- 007 98 'BULMER'S CIDER'.......£7-10
- 010 99 'HEINZ 57' £7-10
- 011 99 'WHITBREAD
  CHANDY' £7-10
- 012 99 'J. LYONS' £7-10
- 013 99 'RALEIGH' £7-10
- 013 00 'BBC Television' £7-10
- 015 01 'CASTROL' £7-10

VA 4 FORD ANGLIA VAN 305E
- 000 96 'ROYAL MAIL' £7-10
- 001 96 'A. A.' £7-10
- 002 96 'HOTPOINT' £7-10
- 003 96 'P. O. TELEPHONES',
  see Set PO 1002..............GSP
- 005 97 'R. A. C.' £7-10
- 006 97 'BEA', 'Follow Me' £7-10
- 007 97 'LONDON
  TRANSPORT' £7-10
- 008 98 'ESSO AVIATION' £7-10
- 009 99 'NATIONAL
  BENZOLE' £7-10
- 010 99 'JORDANS' £7-10
- 012 01 'Ford Special Products' ..£7-10

VA 5 TRIUMPH HERALD
- 000 96 Red £7-10
- 001 96 'B.S.M.' £7-10
- 002 96 Yellow £7-10
- 003 96 Beige, Set HB 1002 ....GSP
- 005 97 Grey...............................£7-10
- 006 97 'THE MOTOR' £7-10
- 007 97 Red / White £7-10
- 008 98 White / Black £7-10
- 010 99 Two-tone Green £7-10
- 012 00 Two-tone Blue.................£7-10
- 013 01 Red / White £7-10

VA 6 FORD THAMES TRADER BOX VAN
- 000 96 'MARTINI' £7-10
- 001 96 'BIRDS EYE' £7-10
- 002 96 'PG TIPS'........................£7-10
- 004 97 'LUCOZADE' £7-10
- 005 97 'ATORA' £7-10
- 006 97 'SAINSBURY'S',
  certificated LE £7-10
- 008 99 'RALEIGH CYCLES',
  LE of 3,000 ....£7-10

VA 7 BEDFORD 'S' type TANKER
- 000 96 'REGENT' £7-10
- 001 96 'SHELL-BP' £7-10
- 003 97 'TOTAL' £7-10
- 004 97 'COURAGE', 5,000 ....£7-10
- 005 98 'MOBILGAS',
  LE of 5,000 ....£7-10
- 009 99 'CEMENT MARKETING',
  LE of 3,000 ....£7-10

VA 8 BEDFORD 'S' type VAN
- 000 96 'HEINZ 57' £7-10
- 001 96 'KODAK' £7-10
- 002 97 'SURF', 5,000 ....£7-10
- 004 97 'SAINSBURY'S',
  certificated LE £7-10
- 005 98 'MERRYDOWN
  CIDER', 5,000 ....£7-10
- 006 98 'POST OFFICE
  STORES', 5,000 ....£7-10
- 009 99 'POLICE', 3,000............£7-10
- 010 99 'SAINSBURY'S' £7-10

VA 9 FORD THAMES TRADER TANKER
- 000 96 'NORTH EASTERN
  GAS BOARD' £7-10
- 001 96 'CASTROL' £7-10
- 002 96 'CLEVELAND' £7-10

VA 10 MORRIS MINOR TRAVELLER
- 000 96 Black £7-10
- 001 96 Maroon £7-10
- 002 97 Green..............................£7-10
- 003 97 'COASTGUARD' £7-10
- 004 99 'RAF' £7-10
- 005 99 Cream £7-10
- 006 99 Red £7-10
- 007 00 Clipper Blue £7-10

VA 11 MORRIS MINOR VAN
- 000 96 'A. A. PATROL'...............£7-10
- 001 96 'BRITISH RAIL',
  see Set BR 1002............GSP
- 002 96 'OVALTINE'.....................£7-10
- 003 96 'P. O. TELEPHONES',
  see Set PO 1002............GSP
- 004 96 'SOUTHERN GAS'..........£7-10
- 004 00 'Met. Police Dogs'.........£7-10
- 005 97 'R. A. C.' £7-10
- 006 97 'ROYAL MAIL' £7-10
- 007 98 'CAFFYNS' £7-10
- 009 99 'SOUTHERN
  ELECTRICITY' £7-10
- 010 99 'MAC FISHERIES' £7-10
- 011 01 'EDDIE STOBART' £7-10
- 012 99 'BRS' £7-10
- 013 99 'COALITE'.......................£7-10
- 016 01 'EDDIE STOBART' £7-10
- 017 01 'HOOVER' £7-10

VA 12 VOLKSWAGEN BEETLE
- 000 96 Beige £7-10
- 001 96 Black £7-10
- 002 96 'POLIZEI' £7-10
- 003 97 'FEUERWEHR' £7-10

VA 13 AUSTIN 7 MINI
- 000 96 Green..............................£7-10
- 001 96 White £7-10
- 002 96 'POLICE' £7-10
- 003 97 Grey £7-10
- 006 01 Black £7-10

VA 14 MINI-VAN
- 000 97 'R.A.C.'...........................£7-10
- 001 97 'ROYAL MAIL' £7-10
- 002 97 'A.A. PATROL' £7-10
- 004 98 'DEWHURST' £7-10
- 007 99 'ROYAL NAVY' £7-10
- 008 99 'CABLE &
  WIRELESS' £7-10
- 009 99 'CASTROL' £7-10
- 011 99 'SOUTHERN
  ELECTRICITY' £7-10
- 012 99 'SOMERSET F.B.' £7-10
- 014 01 'Metropolitan Police'.......£7-10
- 015 01 'BRISTOL WATER' £7-10

VA 15 THAMES TRADER DROPSIDE LORRY
- 000 98 'MILK' £7-10
- 001 98 'TRUMAN'S', 5,000......£7-10
- 002 99 'GUINNESS' £7-10

VA 16 COMMER DROPSIDE LORRY
- 000 96 'CARLSBERG' £7-10
- 002 98 'WESTON'S CIDER',
  5,000 ....£7-10
- 004 99 'HOLTONS', 5,000.........£7-10
- 007 99 'H-K ELECTRICAL'.......£7-10
- 008 99 'JORDANS' £7-10
- 009 99 'GUINNESS' £7-10

VA 17 AUSTIN A35 VAN
- 000 97 'R.A.C.' £7-10
- 002 98 'BARKERS' £7-10
- 004 99 'SECURICOR' £7-10
- 005 00 'Wilts. Constabulary'......£7-10
- 006 01 'MEB' £7-10

VA 18 LEYLAND COMET BOX VAN
- 000 97 'EVER-READY' £7-10
- 002 98 'BASS', 5,000................£7-10
- 003 99 'TATE & LYLE',
  5,000 ....£7-10
- 004 99 'LOVELL'S', 3,000........£7-10

VA 19 ROVER P4
- 000 97 Maroon £7-10
- 001 97 Beige / Brown £7-10
- 002 98 Black £7-10
- 003 98 Green..............................£7-10
- 004 99 Blue / Grey £7-10
- 005 99 Grey / Burgundy £7-10
- 006 99 'POLICE' £7-10
- 007 99 Two-tone Green £7-10
- 008 00 Ivory / Medium Grey £7-10
- 011 01 'Round the World Rally' £7-10

VA 20 LEYLAND COMET TANKER
- 000 97 'POWER' £7-10
- 001 97 'NATIONAL
  BENZOLE' £7-10

VA 21 FORD POPULAR 100E
- 000 97 Yellow £7-10
- 002 97 Green..............................£7-10
- 003 98 Blue £7-10
- 004 99 Maroon £7-10
- 005 98 Grey £7-10
- 006 99 Sapphire Blue £7-10
- 007 00 Ivory / Hereford Green ...£7-10
- 008 01 Vulcan Grey/Maroon £7-10

VA 22 RELIANT REGAL
- 000 98 'ROYAL MAIL' £7-10
- 001 98 'A.A. PATROL' £7-10
- 002 99 'NOTTINGHAM
  WATER' £7-10
- 003 99 'Del Boy's' Reliant,
  grubby version,
  14,860 only £7-10
- --- 98 clean version,
  (LP4913) £7-10

VA 23 AUSTIN A35
- 000 98 Green..............................£7-10
- 001 99 Grey £7-10
- 002 99 Speedwell Blue £7-10
- 003 99 Black £7-10
- 004 00 Capri Blue £7-10
- 005 00 'Graham Hill' Rally Car £7-10
- 006 01 Old English White £7-10
- LP5395 (1999), Cream, '40th
  Anniversary Mini'...........£10-15

VA 24 KARRIER BOX VAN
- 000 98 'RAIL EXPRESS
  PARCELS' £7-10

VA 25 MINI-COOPER
- 000 98 Red/Black £7-10
- 002 99 Green / White £7-10
- 003 99 'Monte Carlo' £7-10
- 004 99 'Monte Carlo' £7-10

- 005 99 Cream £7-10
- 007 00 'Pat Moss' Rally Car £7-10
- 009 01 Fiesta Yellow/O.E.White £7-10

VA 26 HILLMAN IMP
- 000 98 Red £7-10
- 002 99 'COASTGUARD'...........£7-10
- 003 99 'FRASER RACING' £7-10
- 004 99 Green..............................£7-10
- 007 00 'Geo. Bevan' Race Car ..£7-10
- 008 00 Maroon £7-10
- 011 00 'Team Hartwell'...............£7-10

VA 27 ROVER P6 2000
- 000 99 Red £7-10
- 001 99 White Police car £7-10
- 002 99 Zircon Blue £7-10
- 003 99 Willow Green £7-10
- 004 99 'POLICE' £7-10
- 006 00 City Grey.........................£7-10
- 007 00 'West Midlands Police'...£7-10
- 008 00 'Roger Clark' Rally Car .£7-10
- 009 00 Tobacco Brown £7-10

VA 28 COMMER BOX VAN
- 000 98 'SHELL OIL' £7-10
- 001 98 'GREEN SHIELD
  STAMPS', 5,000...........£7-10

VA 29 LEYLAND COMET DROPSIDE LORRY
- 000 99 'BRS' £7-10
- 002 99 'ARMSTRONG' £7-10

VA 30 KARRIER BANTAM TANKER
- 000 99 'BUTLER FUELS' £7-10

VA 31 KARRIER DROPSIDE LORRY
- 001 99 'CORONA' £7-10

VA 33 FORD THAMES 300E VAN
- 000 99 'SINGER' £7-10
- 001 00 'BRYLCREEM' £7-10
- 002 00 'Maidstone & District' ...£7-10
- 003 01 'Evening Standard' £7-10

VA 34 FORD CAPRI 109E
- 000 99 Turquoise / White £7-10
- 002 99 Maroon / Grey.................£7-10
- 003 00 Savoy Black £7-10
- 004 00 Monaco Red / Ermine....£7-10
- 005 01 Ermine White £7-10

VA 35 FORD CLASSIC 109E
- 000 99 Lime Green / White £7-10
- 002 99 Yellow / White £7-10
- 003 00 Panama Yellow / White .£7-10

VA 36 COMMER FLATBED LORRY
- 000 99 'PICKFORDS' £7-10
- 001 99 'JOHN SMITH'S'..........£7-10

VA 37 LEYLAND COMET FLATBED
- 001 99 'JORDANS' £7-10

VA 38 VAUXHALL VICTOR F
- 000 00 Gypsy Red.......................£7-10
- 001 00 Primrose Yellow..............£7-10
- 002 99 Black £7-10
- 003 00 'Kenya Safari Rally' £7-10
- 004 00 Shantung Beige £7-10
- 005 01 Horizon Blue £7-10

VA 39 THAMES TRADER FLATBED
- 000 99 'TATE & LYLE' £7-10

VA 40 SINGER CHAMOIS
- 000 99 Polar White £7-10
- 001 00 Turquoise Blue Metallic .£7-10
- 002 00 'Coronation Rally' £7-10
- 003 00 Polar White £7-10

VA 41 FORD CORTINA Mk.II and Lotus Cortina
000 01 Ermine White / Black **£7-10**
001 01 'Hampshire Constab'y'....**£7-10**
002 01 'Roger Clark' **£7-10**
003 01 Lagoon Blue, '35th'........**£7-10**
004 01 'Thames Valley Police'....**£7-10**

VA 44 Austin A60 Cambridge
000 00 Cumulus Grey / White **£7-10**
001 00 'Sussex Police'................**£7-10**
002 00 Maroon / Grey.................**£7-10**
003 01 'Herts. Police' **£7-10**
004 01 Snowberry / Maroon **£7-10**

VA 45 Austin Allegro
000 00 Harvest Gold **£7-10**
001 00 'Metropolitan Police'.......**£7-10**
002 00 'BL' Works Rally Car **£7-10**
003 01 Blaze **£7-10**
004 01 Cosmic **£7-10**
005 01 'PATRICK MOTORS' **£7-10**

VA 46 Ford Zephyr 6 Mk.III
000 00 'West Riding Constab'y' .**£7-10**
002 00 Maroon **£7-10**
001 00 Goodwood Green............**£7-10**

VA 47 Triumph TR3a
000 00 Pale Yellow **£7-10**
001 01 Apple Green....................**£7-10**

VA 48 Morris 1300 Estate
000 00 Trafalgar Blue **£7-10**
001 00 Maroon............................**£7-10**

VA 49 Jaguar 'E'-type 3.8ltr Roadster
000 00 Cream **£7-10**
002 01 Carmen Red, '40th' **£7-10**

VA 50 MGA (open top)
000 00 Dove Grey.......................**£7-10**
002 01 Irish Blue........................**£7-10**

VA 51 Austin-Healey E-3000 Mk.II
000 00 Colorado Red / Ivory **£7-10**
001 01 British Racing Green and Old English White **£7-10**

VA 52 Ford Granada Mk.I and Ghia
000 00 Flame Red **£7-10**
001 01 Roman Bronze **£7-10**
002 01 Onyx Green (Black roof)**£7-10**

VA 53 Triumph Dolomite Sprint
000 00 Yellow / Black.................**£7-10**
001 00 'British Leyland' Rally ...**£7-10**
002 00 'West Yorks. Police' **£7-10**
003 01 'Broadspeed' **£7-10**
004 01 Brooklands Green **£7-10**
005 01 White **£7-10**

VA 54 Morris Oxford Series VI
000 00 Green..............................**£7-10**
001 01 Trafalgar Blue and Snowberry White **£7-10**

VA 55 Ford Consul 3000GT
000 00 'Lancashire Constab'y'...**£7-10**
001 00 'COYS Historic Rally' ...**£7-10**
002 01 Daytona Yellow...............**£7-10**
003 01 'West Yorkshire Police' .**£7-10**

VA 56 Austin 1300 Estate
000 00 Snowberry White **£7-10**
001 01 El Paso Blue....................**£7-10**

VA 57 Austin-Healey 3000 Mk.I
000 00 'Historic Rally' **£7-10**

VA 58 Morris Minor Convertible
000 00 Lilac 'Millionth' **£7-10**
001 01 Almond Green..................**£7-10**
002 01 Black (Maroon hood)......**£7-10**

VA 59 Jaguar XK120
001 01 Black **£7-10**

VA 60 Ford Zephyr 4 Mk.III
000 01 Lime Green **£7-10**
001 01 'Bomb Disposal Unit' **£7-10**
002 01 Monaco Red.....................**£7-10**

VA 62 Ford Popular Van
000 01 'Fordson Tractor Sales'...**£7-10**

VA 63 Morris Marina 1300 / 1800
000 01 Teal Blue **£7-10**
001 01 Harvest Gold **£7-10**
002 01 'Essex Police' **£7-10**

VA 64 Vauxhall Cresta & Velox PA
000 01 Dusk Rose/Lilac Haze **£7-10**
001 01 'Stockport Police' **£7-10**
002 01 Lime Yellow / Swan **£7-10**

VA 65 Rover 3500 V8
000 01 Almond **£7-10**
001 01 'Metropolitan Police'......**£7-10**
002 01 Monza Red **£7-10**
003 01 'Hampshire Constab'y' ...**£7-10**

VA 66 Ford Transit Mk.I Diesel
000 01 'P. O. TELEPHONES'....**£7-10**
002 01 'Lancs. Accident Police'.**£7-10**
001 01 'EVENING NEWS'........**£7-10**
003 01 'EDDIE STOBART' **£7-10**
005 01 'Cumbria Police'.............**£7-10**

VA 67 Triumph Spitfire Mk.II
000 01 Signal Red.......................**£7-10**
002 01 Conifer Green **£7-10**
003 01 Wedgewood Blue **£7-10**

VA 68 Hillman Minx IIIa
000 01 Ember Red / Cream **£7-10**
001 01 'Salford Police' **£7-10**

VA 80 Morris 1300 Estate
000 01 Trafalgar Blue **£7-10**

Vanguards 'Gold'

Introduced in 1998. 3,000 of each.

VG0030
12s Shelby Cobra 427s/c, silver ....
51r Shelby Cobra Daytona, red............
61r Jaguar 'E'-type, red roadster...........
62b Jaguar 'E'-type, blue coupé ....
73k Lotus Europa Special, black ....
VG0031
51g Caterham Super Seven, green........
51k Caterham Super Seven, black ....

'Custom and Classic'

Though not intended for promotional use, this range of Volkswagen models employs an 'LP' reference system. Introduced in 1998.
See also DG 86 and VA 12.

VOLKSWAGEN BEETLE
LP 5255 99 Saloon, red / cream............
LP 5256 98 Saloon, blue / cream............
LP 5257 98 Saloon, yellow ....
LP 5362 99 Saloon with oval rear window, lime green ....
LP 5570 99 With oval window, 'Run to the Sun' ....
LP 5573 99 Open, 'Run to the Sun' .....

VOLKSWAGEN VAN and CAMPER
LP 5258 98 Van, black, 'Aircooled' .....
LP 5259 98 Van, light blue with 'surfer' motif .....
LP 5361 99 Van, 'LOTTERMANN'....
LP 5368 99 1955 Camper Van, lemon / white............
LP 5571 99 Van, 'Run to the Sun' ....
LP 5572 99 Van, 'Run to the Sun' ....

Vanguards Gift Sets

AU 1002 97 **'AUSTIN SALES / SERVICE'** VA3 Austin A40 Van with VA17 Austin A35 Van, 5,000...**£12-15**

BA 1002 96 **'RACING ANGLIAS' Set** VA1-003 and VA1-004 'Broadspeed' Ford Anglias, numbers '6' and '7' **£12-15**

BO 1002 99 **'BOOTS the CHEMIST' Set** VA29 Leyland Comet and VA7 Bedford 'S' Tanker, 3,000.................................**£15-20**

BPL 1003 96 'British Motoring Classics' 24k gold plated Ford Anglia 105E, Mini-Minor and Morris 1000 Traveller ....NGPP

BR 1002 96 **'BRITISH RAILWAYS' Set** VA3 Austin A40 Van (Maroon), and VA11 Morris Minor Van (Yellow), 5,000 .....**£12-15**

CL 1002 99 **'CLASSIC and CAPRI' Set** VA34 Ford Capri 109E and VA35 Ford Classic 109E, 5,000...............................**£12-15**

HB 1002 96 **'HEARTBEAT COLLECTION'** Dr Kate Rowan's Triumph Herald and the Ashfordley Police Anglia 105E....**£12-15**

HB 2002 97 **'HEARTBEAT COLLECTION'** Ashfordley Police Ford Anglia 100E and Mini-Van, 5,000..............................**£12-15**

JOR 1002 99 **'JORDANS' Lorry Set** Commer Dropside VA 16008 and Leyland Comet Flatbed VA 37001..................**£15-20**

KT 1002 98 **'KEN THOMAS'** 'Coronation Café' VA16 Commer Dropside and VA8 Bedford 'S', 5,000..........................**£12-15**

MC 1002 99 **'MONTE CARLO MINIS'** VA25003 and VA25004 Monte Carlo Mini-Coopers **£12-15**

MS 1002 98 **'MACKESON DISPLAY SERVICE'** VA17 Austin A35 Van and VA3 Austin A40 Van, 5,000...............**£12-15**

PC 1002 97 **'POLICE PANDA CARS' Set** VA1 Ford Anglia and VA13 Mini Minor Panda Cars in Blue/White, 5,000...........**£12-15**

PO 1002 96 **'P. O. TELEPHONES' Set** VA4 Ford Anglia Van and VA11 Morris Minor Van, 5,000.................................**£15-20**

PO 2002 98 **'POST OFFICE TELEPHONES'** VA14 Minivan and VA11 Morris 1000 Van, 5,000....................................**£12-15**

PP 1002 00 **'PINKY & PERKY' POLICE SET** Two VA 26 Hillman Imps, 'Dumbartonshire Police'............**£12-15**

RP 1002 99 **'POLICE' Set** Featuring the two Rover Police Cars VA19006 and VA 27004.......................................**£12-15**

RS 1002 97 **'BRITISH ROAD SERVICES'** VA6 Thames Trader Box Van and VA8 Bedford Box Van, 5,000.......................**£15-20**

ST 1002 99 **'St ANDREWS AMBULANCE'** VA14 Minivan and VA11 Morris Minor Van, 2,000..................................**£15-20**

WV 1002 97 **'WHITBREAD SERVICE'** VA3 Austin A40 Van and VA4 Ford Anglia 305E Van, 5,000............................**£12-15**

'Snapshots in Time' (Vanguards models in a cold-cast diorama)
BD 1002 00 **'Guinness' Diorama**, Austin A40 Van and Ford Anglia 305E Van ...
CD 1002 00 **'Earls Court' Diorama**, Rover 100 at the 1960 Motor Show ....
GD 1002 01 **'Royal Mail' Diorama** ....
PD 1002 00 **'Renfrew & Bute Constabulary'** Jaguar XK120 and Rover P6...
PD 2002 01 **'Annual Inspection' Diorama** ....
PD 3002 01 **'No.10' Diorama**, Rover 3500 V8 ....
RD 1002 00 **'Brands Hatch Diorama'** with two racing Ford Classic 109Es.........
RD 2001 01 **'Mini-Cooper' Diorama** ....
RD 3002 01 **'Racing' Diorama**, Ford Anglia and Hillman Imp ....
VA 0413 01 **'RAC' Set**, Ford Anglia with accessories ....
VA 1416 01 **'Royal Mail' Set**, Minivan with accessories ....
VA 6604 01 **'Telecommunications' Set**, Ford Transit Van with accessories ....
VA 6606 01 **'Nottingshire Police Motorway Unit'**, Ford Transit + accessories ..

Oxford Die-Cast

Designed primarily for promotional use, Oxford Die-Cast models were introduced in late 1993. Occupying the Swansea factory previously used by Corgi, the company has specialised in true Limited Edition production runs. Early in 1998, production moved to a new, purpose-built factory at Neath.

The company has formed the Oxford Die-Cast Club. Members get their own newsletter and catalogue, and a free club model produced to a limit equal to the number of club members at the time. 'Normal' production is available only via the club at £4-95 per model (£5-95 in the few cases of 'sporting' models where royalties are involved). The only other source of models is through the purchase of the product being promoted. There are also occasionally, special club models for members.

The Editor would like express his thanks to Dennis Bone of Oxford Die-Cast for his assistance in compiling this listing which usefully shows production quantities rather than prices. Club details from:
The Oxford Die-Cast Club, PO Box 519, Berkhamstead, Herts., HP4 1YR, England. Telephone (01442) 879996, Fax: (01442) 877703, website: oxforddiecast.co.uk

Abbreviations
NC = not certificated   NYP = not yet produced
As part of the reference number: **g** = gold wheels,   **h** = Hamley's model
t = Ford Model 'T',   **x** or **y** = base plate colour changes
A = Australian distribution,   **D** = German distribution,   **E** = Spanish distribution
F = French distribution,   **N** = Dutch distribution,   **U** = United States distribution

Morris ('Bullnose') Van

Ref	Intro	Model	Made (x1,000)	Ref	Intro	Model	Made (x1,000)	Ref	Intro	Model	Made (x1,000)
001	93	'CHESHAM Utd F.C.'	2	036 g	94	'PETERBOROUGH UNITED F.C.'	1.1	080	96	'GLIDER BISCUITS'	16
001g	93	'CHESHAM Utd F.C.', 'Sportsman's Dinner'	0.5	037 g	94	'BIRMINGHAM CITY F.C.'	1.2	081	96	'BENSONS CRISPS' original logo	12
002	94	'PRINCES'	5	038 g	94	'CITY LINK'	3	082	96	Same but modern logo	12
003	93	'LO-SALT'	10	039	94	'RMS TITANIC'	2	083	96	'CARR-DAY-MARTIN'	4.5
003 g	94	'LO-SALT'	2	040 g	95	'CUTTY SARK'	2	084	96	'SWANSEA JACK' certificate and booklet	5
004 g		'QUALITY STREET'	1.3	041 g	94	'SKIPS'	1.1	085 g	96	'VIMTO'	16
005	93	'ODC'	5	042 g	95	'JOHN WEST'	60	086	96	'ROYAL BUCKS LAUNDRY', special cert	5
005 g	93	'ODC', UK launch	1	043 g	94	'LONDON GAS'	2.5	087	96	'KENNETH WOLSTENHOLME'	20
006 g	94	'ODC', New York Premium Exhibition	7.5	044 g	94	'GAS LIGHT & COKE COMPANY'	2.5	088 g	96	'BRYNMILL SCHOOL'	2.5
007	94	'LION PEPPER'	4	045 g	95	'BOSTIK'	5	089 g	96	'STREAMLINE JAM'	25
007 g	94	'LION PEPPER'	7.5	046 g	95	'SODA CRYSTALS' (black roof and base, see 069g)	12.5	090 g	96	'MANOR HOUSE HOSPITAL'	5
008	94	'TREX'	12					091 g	96	'SELLOTAPE'	5.5
008 g	94	'TREX'	5	047 g	95	'STANLEY TOOLS'	2.5	092 g	96	'SPICERS' (Sellotape)	2.5
008 x	94	'TREX', grey base	5	048 g	95	'STOCKLEY'S'	2.5	093 g	96	'Sellotape-VIKING'	2.5
008 y	94	'TREX', blue base	5	049	95	'SUNBLEST'. Double offer with 050G	35	094 g	96	'DUDLEY' (Sellotape)	2.5
009	94	'JORDANS'	1					095 g	96	'HEART of BRITAIN'	5.5
009 g	94	Same but gold wheels	50	050 g	95	'SUNBLEST', '50 Golden Years'. Double offer with 049	35	096gh	96	'HAMLEYS'	5
009 x	94	Same but grey base	20					097 g	96	'SCO-FRO/ICELAND'	7.5
010 g	94	'Beds. FESTIVAL'	10	051 g	95	'IMPERIAL BITTER'. First 500 models NC	2.5	098gU	96	'THORSEN TOOLS'	2.5
011 g	93	'FOTORAMA'	10	052 g	95	'KING HENRY Grammar School 45th Anniversary'	1	099 g	96	'MACAW Kwiksave'	2.9
012 g	94	'MACARONI'	5	053	95	'SHEFFIELD STEELERS'	1	100	97	'KEN JONES'	1.25
013	94	'EVANS VANODINE 75th Anniversary'	1.25	054 g	95	'STORK' 75th Anniversary	25	101 g	96	'PG TIPS', certificate with product, no certs	10 ... 40
		note: 400 out of the 1,250 were made with gold wheels.		055 g	96	'BEN SHAWS'	15	102 g	96	'Wallace Whiskey'	2.5
				056 g	95	'PORKINSON'	7,500	103 U	96	'AGH', (attorneys)	1
014 g	94	'OUTSPAN', offered with model 004	25	057 g	95	'CHARTRIDGE PARK'	1	104	97	'Harry Ramsden's'	2.6
015	94	'PLASTI-KOTE', 2,300 made with chrome wheels, 700 with black wheels	3	058	95	'Notts. Parking Services'	2	105 g	97	'SELLOTAPE'	5
				059	95	'DOUWE EGBERTS'	1	106 g	97	'JOHN WEST'	38
016	94	'CHEQUERS INN'	5	059 g	95	'DOUWE EGBERTS'	2.5	107	97	'LYONS', (Eire only), with certificate	4.6
017	94	'TESCO MILK'	25	061 g	95	'COLDSTREAM'	2			uncertificated	8
017 g	94	'TESCO MILK'	3	062 g	95	'BULMERS'	10	108 g	97	'LUTON F.C.'	2.6
018 g	94	'LEYLAND AUTO'	2.5	063 g	95	'MELTONIAN'	1	109	97	'COLCHESTER FC'	2.5
019 g	94	'SCOTTISH ISLAND'	2.5	064 g	95	'MILLWALL F.C.'	1.25	110 g	97	'TITANIC'	5.1
020 g	94	'ODC', Xmas '94	2	065	95	'CHARLTON ATHLETIC F.C.'	1.25	111	97	'SIMON TAYLOR',	2.5
021	---		NYP	066 g	95	'BUDGENS', (milk)	15	112	97	'Centenary School'	1.25
022	94	'Welsh Tourist Board' 1994 Eisteddfod	4	067 g	95	'RED LION'	5	113 g	97	'BOOTHS'	15
022 g	94	Same but gold wheels	1	068 g	95	'DUBLIN CRYSTAL'	10	114	97	'HELP the AGED'	40
023 g	94	'MANCHESTER UNITED F.C.'	10	069 g	95	'SODA CRYSTALS', 2nd (046g red roof and base)	20	115 g	97	'SCOPE'	40
024	---		NYP	070 g	96	'DIAL-A-BEAR'	10	116	97	'PACE'	5
025	94	'ASTON VILLA'	7.5	071	96	'FORCE WHEAT'	17.5	117 g	97	'TULLAMORE'	15
026gU	94	'ZEB'S COOKIES'	2.5	072 g	96	'ACDO'	18	118 g	97	'YORK CITY F.C.'	2
027 g	94	'BLACKBURN ROVERS F.C.'	5	073 g	95	'OXFORD DIE-CAST', Collectors Gazette	40	119 g	97	'PORTSMOUTH F. C.'	1.2
028 g	94	'BONE BROS'	2	074 g	95	'CHESHAM BUILDING SOCIETY', 150th	15	120 g	97	'AUTOMOBILIA'	1,2
029 g	94	'CHESHAM Utd F.C.'	1	075 g	96	'KILMEADEN'(Eire)	7	121	97	'NATIONAL GRID'	1.75
030 g	94	'GOLDEN SHRED'. First few NC	3.5	076 g	96	'CO-OP '99' TEA'	90	122gU	97	'GRANTS FARM'	25
				077 g	96	'CO-OP BISCUITS'	90	123 g	97	'BOOKER'	4
031	94	'QPR F.C.'	1.2	078	96	'CO-OP TEA', 'English and Scottish'	90	124 g	97	'SCOTCH WHISKEY'	10
032	94	'DERBY COUNTY'	1.2	079 g	96	'DUERR'S'	15	125 g	97	The PUZZLER'	10
033	94	'BARNET F.C.'	1.2					126 g	97	'WALKERS TOFFEE'	8
033 g	94	'BARNET F.C.'	2.5					127 g	97	'New Zealand Lamb'	6
034	94	'BRISTOL ROVERS'	1.2					128gU	97	'DAYS INN' 2nd	10
035 g	94	'ARSENAL F.C.'	2					129	97	'SAFFRON WALDEN LAUNDRY'	1.5

Ref	Intro	Model		Ref	Intro	Model		Ref	Intro	Model
129 g	97	Same but gold wheels 1.1		163	99	'BLYTHESWOOD' 3.5		197 g	00	'NAIROBI COFFEE' 5
130	98	'J. SAINSBURY' 28		164 g	99	'CROSSWORD' 8		198 g	00	'DICKINSON & MORRIS' 5
131 g	98	'BOLTON Eve. NEWS' 25		165 g	99	'SIMPSON' 3		199 g	00	'DUBLINER' 3
132 g	98	'ELECTRICITY' 1.1		166 u	99	'KOUNTRY FRESH' 20		200 g	00	'ODC PLATINUM 2000' 1.3
133	98	'BUCKS EXAMINER' 2.5		167 g	99	'FRANK COOPER' 7.5		201	00	'WILKIN & SONS' 2
134	97	'ODC', Xmas 97 10		168gU	99	'DAYS INN' 2nd 5		202 g	00	'JENNINGS ALE' 2.5
135 g	98	'MICHAEL BUTLER' 2.5		169 g	99	'METRO Technologies' 1		203 g	00	'HALES CAKES' 2
136 g	98	'CHAMPION' 15		170 g	99	'PLASTIC PADDING' 2		204 g	00	'WIRRAL GLOBE' 2
137 g	98	'LYTHAM St ANNES EXPRESS' 1.5		171	99	'TURF Cigarettes' 2		205	00	'RHS WISLEY' 28
				172gU	99	'ELKS' 2		206	00	'MERRYTHOUGHT' 1
138 g	98	'MICHELIN' 5		173 g	99	'CELTIC MANOR' 2		207 g	00	'SUNDAY POST 75' 7.5
139 g	98	'DANEPAK' 45		174	99	'DAILY EXPRESS' 20		208 g	00	'Queen Mother 100' 2.5
140 g	98	'HORLICKS FARM' 20		175	99	'MAGNOLIA PARK' 1.8		209 g	00	'CANCER RESEARCH' 15
141	98	'OSCARS' 2.5		176 g	99	'CHIVERS MARMALADE' ...29		210gU	00	'NEW YORK POST' 1
142 g	98	'BRAINS FAGGOTS' 10		177	99	'DAILY EXPRESS' 2nd.......12		211g	01	'NEWARK Advertiser' 2
143 g	98	'Geo. ADAMS' 10		178 g	99	'Prince Charles' 20		212g	01	'MOTHER'S PRIDE' 1
144gA	98	'JOHN WEST' 20		179	99	'HOBSON & Sons' 2.5		213	01	'BARCLAYS' 1
145 g	98	'Ht. of MIDLOTHIAN' 5		180	99	'WESSEX PICTURES' 2.5		214	01	'ELKS' 1
146 g	98	'BOVRIL' 48		181		....nyp				
147 g	98	'O.D.C. NEATH' 2.6		182 g	99	'LANCASHIRE EVENING POST' 2.5				
148 g	98	'J.S. ARMS' 2.5								
149 g	98	'FASHION FABRICS' 1		183	00	'EVO-STIK' 3				

Cigarette Collection (all members only)

CIG1	00	'TURF'	2
CIG2	00	'PLAYERS'	2
CIG3	00	'SENIOR SERVICE'	2
CIG8	00	'CAPSTAN'	2
CIG11	00	'KENSITAS'	2
CIG12	00	'ARK ROYAL'	2
CIG14	01	'RED & WHITE'	....2.5

Continued first column:

150 g	98	'DAILY RECORD'	8
151 g	98	'SOREEN'	12
152gU	98	'GRANT'S'	20
153gU	98	'COLONIAL'	15
154gU	98	'KROGER'	20
155	98	'SHELDON'	55
156	98	'Prince Charles 50th'	4
157 g	98	'TESCO'	12
158 g	98	'B.I.B.I.C.'	....2.5
159 g	98	'St DALFOUR'	6
160 g	98	'RADIO TIMES'	70
161 g	99	'PASCOE'S'	3
162 g	99	'LIVERPOOL ECHO'	3

Continued second column:

184	00	'BRITISH LEGION'	75
185 g	00	'COUNTRY GARDEN'	6
186			....nyp
187 sD	00	'CASTROL'	7
188 g	00	'FISHERMANS FRIEND'	3
189 g	00	'THORNTONS'	...50.5
190 g	00	'GLEN MORANGIE'	5
191	00	'LONDON CLEANING'	....2.5
192	00	'FRAY BENTOS'	4
193	00	'DAILY TELEGRAPH'	8
194	00	'CUMBERLAND PENCILS'	....5.5
195	00	'ODC US / UK SALES'	1
196 D	00	'BARCLAYS'	....1.5

Comic Cuts

CC2	00	'TIGER'	....1.5

Corner Shop (all members only)

CS6	01	'BRISTOWS' (members only)	....0.8

Ford Model 'T' Van

Ref	Intro	Model	Made (x1,000)		Ref	Intro	Model	Made (x1,000)		Ref	Intro	Model	Made (x1,000)
01 tg	95	'OXFORD DIE-CAST', gold base 2.5			060tgU	97	'GEC MARCONI' 1.25			128 t	00	'SHOOTING STAR' 2
02 tg	95	'WYCOMBE WANDERERS' 1.25			061 tg	97	'WALKERS TOFFEE' 8			129 t	00	'ORMO' 2
03 tg	95	'ARSENAL F.C.' 1.25			067tg	98	'DAILY RECORD' 8			130tgU	00	'NEW YORK POST' 1
04 tg	95	'PURA OIL' 10			068tg	98	'SOREEN' 12.5			132t	01	'BETTWS COMMUNITY LINK' 1
05 tg	95	'BUDGENS MILK' 15			069tgU	98	'GRANT'S FARM' 20					
08 tg	95	'ODC', Xmas '95 6			070tgU	98	'COLONIAL' 15			133t	01	'BETTWS in BLOOM' 1
09 tg	96	'KINGSMILL' 27.5			071 t	98	'SHELDONS' 4			134t	01	'SHELDONS' 8
011tgU	96	'SIMPSON' 7.5			075 t	98	'TESCO' 12			135tg	01	'British Legion 2000' 15
012tg	96	'PLASTI-KOTE' 18			077tg	98	'PHARMACY LIVE' 2.5			136t	01	'RHYS COAL' 1
016tg	96	'WD-40' 32			078tg	98	'RADIO TIMES' 70			137t	01	'BALLANTINES' 12
021 t	96	'CO-OP PELAW' 16			081tg	99	'PASCOE'S' 3			138t	01	'CHESHAM DAIRIES' 1
026tg	96	'CARR-DAY-MARTIN' 4.5			082tg	99	'LIVERPOOL ECHO' 3					
027tg	96	'VIMTO' 16			089tU	99	'KOUNTRY FRESH' 3.5					
030tg	96	'COUNTRY LIFE' 60			091tg	99	'TAKE A PUZZLE' 8					
032th	96	'HAMLEYS' 5			092 t	99	'DIECAST COLLECTOR' 5					
034tg	96	'EPICURE' 15										
035tg	96	'THE GAZETTE' 2.5			094tg	99	'LOCTITE' 2					
036 t	96	'AMBULANCE', WWI 2.6			096 t	99	'LONGACRES' 3.5					
038tg	96	'PG TIPS', certificate ....10 to the trade 40			097 t	99	'STOCKHAM' 1					
					098 t	99	'TOMLINSON' 2.6					
039tg	96	'PG SCOTTISH BLEND', with certificate ....4.5 promotional 8			099 t	99	'CELTIC MANOR' 2					
					100 t	99	'DAILY EXPRESS' 15					
040 t	97	HERALD TRIBUNE 2.5			102tgU	99	'KROGER' 30					
042tg	97	'WATERFORD CRYSTAL' 5.2			105tgU	99	'DAYS INN' (2nd) 5			**Cigarette Collection** (all members only)		
					106tg	99	'CHIVERS ROSES MARMALADE' 29			CIG4	00	'LUCKY STRIKE' 2.5
044tg	97	'MANOR HOUSE' 6.1								CIG6	00	'CRAVEN 'A' 2
045tg	97	'TITANIC' 5.1			108 t	99	'Edward & Sophie' 20			CIG10	00	'BLACK CAT' 2
047tgU	97	'NEW YORKER CHEESE' lhd 2.6			112 t	99	'EVO-STIK' 3			?	01	'NAVY BLUE' ....?
					113t	99	'BRAZIL'S', (members only)........1.5					
049tgU	97	'DAYS INN' 15			113tS	99	'BRAZIL'S' Exhibition model 0.5			**Corner Shop** (all members only)		
050 t	97	'RNIB' 40			114tg	00	'BRITISH LEGION' 75			CS2	00	'DIP' 2
051tg	97	'HEARING DOGS' 40			115tU	00	'TENDER TWIST BREAD' 50			CS5	00	'LYONS COFFEE' 0.8
053tg	97	'WIMPEY' 10			117tg	00	'CUTTY SARK' 1					
055tg	97	'HOLLAND'S Pies.................7.5			119tg	00	'LUCKY STRIKE' 2.5			**Comic Cuts**		
056 t	97	'SIEBE AUTO' 1.05			121t	00	'DAILY TELEGRAPH' 20			CC4	01	'RADIO FUN' 1.2
					125 t	00	'CHELSEA' 28					
					126 t	00	'SUNDAY POST' 7.5					
					127 t	00	'St John's Ambulance' 1.75					

Ford Model 'T' Tanker

013 t	96	'CO-OP COCOA'	90
028 tg	96	'VIMTO'	16
057 t	97	'BENZINE', WW 1	....2.6
084tU	99	'THINK SAFETY'	....1.3
086tU	99	'PURITY'	9
104tU	99	'GULDENS'	....2.5
111tgU	99	'CITGO'	25
120tg	00	'ODC' Xmas 1999	...15.5

Oxford Die-Cast

Ford Model 'T' Pick-Up Truck

Ref	Intro	Model	Made (x1,000)	Ref	Intro	Model	Made (x1,000)	Ref	Intro	Model	Made (x1,000)
05 tg	95	'BUDGENS', milk	15	037 tg	96	'BLACKFRIARS'	3	083tU	99	'ZEP' oil can (grey top)	6
06 tg	95	'SODA CRYSTALS'	20	041 tg	97	'JOHN WEST'	38	085tgU	99	'SWANER'	1.25
07 tg	95	'LAGAN'	5	043 t	97	'WATERFORD CRYSTAL'	5.2	087tU	99	'PURITY'	9
010 tg	96	'KINGSMILL'	27.5	046 t	97	'ARMY PROVISIONS'	2.6	088tgU	99	'GOLD KIST'	9
014 tg	96	'CO-OP MILK'	90	048 tg	97	'E. H. BOOTH & Co'	15	090tU	99	'ZEP' oil can (yellow top)	6
015 t	96	'CO-OP FLOUR'	90	052 t	97	'SINGLE SERVICE'	5	093tgU	99	'DAYS INN'	5
017 t	---		NYP	054 tg	97	'SODA CRYSTAL',(4th)	25	095tg	99	'LOCTITE'	5
018 t	96	'E. L. RHYS', coal	25	058 tg	97	'PERCY DALTON'	5	101tU	99	'KROGER'	30
019 tg	96	'FRESH MILK', (Co-op '99' Tea milkman deliveries promo)	40	059tgU	97	'GRANTS FARM'	25	103tU	99	'GRANTS FARM'	27
020 t	96	'WOODGATE DAIRIES'	2	062 t	97	'B2', 'US', WW1	2.6	107tg	99	'CHIVERS ARISTOCRAT'	29
022 t	96	'CO-OP COAL'	16	063 t	98	'J. SAINSBURY'	28	109tU	99	'COLONIAL BREAD'	20
023 t	---		NYP	064 t	98	'J. SAINSBURY'	28	110tU	99	'RAINBO BREAD'	15
024 t	96	'CHIVERS', Eire	1.2	065 t	98	'CHESHAM DAIRIES'	2.5	116tU	00	'TENDER TWISTS'	50
024 tg	96	Same but gold wheels	6.5	066tg	98	'Mr BRAINS'	20	118tU	00	'FIRESTONE'	10.5
025 tg	96	'DUERRS', jam jar	15	072 t	98	'HUMBROL'	6	122tDU	00	'MAC & CHEESE'	12
029 tg	96	'ODC', Xmas '96	9.2	073tgU	98	'SUPERFRESH'	15	123tgE	00	'BIMBO'	65
031 t	96	'COUNTRY LIFE'	8	074tU	98	'KROGER'	28	124 t	00	'KERRYGOLD'	45
033 th	96	'HAMLEYS'	5	076 t	98	'I.L.P.H.'	1	131tgU	00	'NEW YORK POST'	1
				080 t	99	'PASCOE'S'	3				

Ford Model 'A'

Ref	Intro	Model	Made (x1,000)	Ref	Intro	Model	Made (x1,000)	Ref	Intro	Model	Made (x1,000)
A1g	00	'ODC' launch model	2.5	A12gU	00	'KROGER'	1	**Cigarette Collection** (all members only)			
A2	00	'DAILY TELEGRAPH'	20	A13g	00	'ROYSTON CROW'	1.5	CIG5	00	'GOLD FLAKE'	2
A3			nyp	A14	00	'NEWS CHRONICLE'	1	CIG7	00	'WOODBINE'	2
A4			nyp	A15g	00	'DUERRS'	15	CIG9	00	'PARK DRIVE'	2
A5g	00	'SODA CRYSTAL'	14	A16g	00	'ODC Xmas 2000'	16	CIG15	01	'BLACK & WHITE'	2.5
A6g	00	'DAILY SKETCH'	1.25	A17g	01	'Royal British Legion'	15	CIG16	01	'ANCHOR'	2
A7	00	'Cavalcade of Steam'	2.5	A18g	01	'TEACHERS'	10				
A8	00	'ROYAL Hort. Soc'	50	A19g	01	'Barnsley Chronicle'	2.5	**Corner Shop** (all members only)			
A9	00	'SUNDAY POST 1945'	7.5	A20	01	'DERST BAKERY'	10	CS1	00	'TUNIS DATES'	2.5
A10g	00	'SUTTON TRUST'	1					CS3	00	'LIPTONS'	1.5
A11g	00	'BRISTOL ROVERS'	0.8					CS7	01	'HARPIC'	1

AEC (and Renault) Bus

Ref	Intro	Model	Made (x1,000)	Ref	Intro	Model	Made (x1,000)	Ref	Intro	Model	Made (x1,000)
B1	96	'ODC London'	4	B27	97	'NOTTINGHAM'	2.5	B53U	99	'RAINBO BREAD'	15
BR2	96	'ODC Paris' (as Renault)	4	B28	97	'MANOR HOUSE' (3rd)	5.3	B54	00	'LANCASHIRE EVENING POST'	2.5
B3	96	'JOHN WEST'	50	B29	97	'ELIZABETH II - PHILIP' (50 years)	5	B55	00	'BRITISH LEGION'	75
B4	96	'KINGS HEAD'	7.5	B30	97	'BUDGENS MILK'	7.5	B56	00	'W.H. SMITH' / 'DIECAST COLLECTOR'	7.5
B5	96	'BEAULIEU'	5	B31	98	'J. SAINSBURY'	28	B57	00	'DAILY TELEGRAPH'	20
B6	96	'FOTORAMA'	8	B32	97	'DUBLIN CRYSTAL', (2nd), Eire	5	B58	00	'NOTTINGHAM'	1.5
B7	96	'CO-OP'	16	B33	97	'Victory' WWI	3.2	B59	00	'NEW ZEALAND LAMB'	6
B8	96	'VIMTO'	16	B34	98	'BEAMISH'	5	B60	00	'DIECAST COLLECTOR' finished in white	4
B9	96	'SODA CRYSTAL'	19	B35	98	'TULLAMORE' (Eire)	25	B61	00	As B60 but in red	4
B10	96	'OUTSPAN'	20	B36	98	'NOTT's FOREST F. C.'	5	B62	00	'CHELSEA FLOWER SHOW'	28
B11	96	'STREAMLINE'	25	B37	98	'BABBACOME'	2.6	B63	00	'CAVALCADE of STEAM'	2
B12	96	'HEART of BRITAIN'	5.5	B38	98	'BOVRIL'	48	B64	00	'LANGHAM HILTON'	2
B13	96	'OLE BILL' Bus	2.6	B39	98	'SOREEN'	12.5	B65	00	'SUNDAY POST'	7.5
B14	96	'COUNTRY LIFE'	8	B40U	98	'DAYS INN'	10	B66	00	'CRYSTAL PALACE FC'	1.25
B15 h	96	'HAMLEYS'	10	B41	98	'Bolton Evening News'	5	B67U	00	'GEORGIA FARM'	3
B16	97	'Bekonscot Village'	4	B42	98	'TESCO'	12	B68	00	'NOTTINGHAM TOPPER'	2.5
B17	96	'WALLACE WHISKEY'	4	B43	98	'RADIO TIMES'	40	B69	00	'GURKHA RIFLES'	1.8
B18	97	'PG TIPS'	8	B44	99	'PASCOE'S'	3	B70	01	'Royal British Legion'	15
B19	97	'OAKEY'	4.2	B45	99	'SENT to COVENTRY'	1.5	B71	01	'BRADITE PAINTS'	1
B20	97	'WATERFORD CRYSTAL' (Eire)	6.2	B46	99	'LOCTITE'	2	B72	01	'LUTON TOWN'	1.25
B21N	97	'INTERNATIONAL MEDICAL' Holland	2.6	B47	99	'CELTIC MANOR'	2	B73	01	'MANOR HOUSE'	1
B22	97	'ARSENAL F.C.'	2.5	B48	99	'SUNDAY EXPRESS'	15	B74	01	'WATERFORD CRYSTAL'	1
B23	97	'E. H. BOOTH & Co'	15	B49U	99	'GRANTS FARM'	27				
B24	97	'RNLI'	40	B50	99	'CHIVERS'	29				
B25	97	'NSPCC'	40	B51	99	'Queen Elizabeth and Prince Philip'	20				
BR26F	97	'HERALD TRIBUNE' (as Renault)	2.5	B52U	99	'COLONIAL BREAD'	20				

Ref	Intro	Model	Made (x1,000)	Ref	Intro	Model	Made (x1,000)	Ref	Intro	Model	Made (x1,000)

Chevrolet Pick-Up

Ref	Intro	Model	Made (x1,000)
C001	97	'ODC' launch model	5
C002	98	'NORBERT DENTRESSANGLE'	6
C003u	98	'DAYS INN'	10
C004u	98	'U.S. NAVY'	3
C005	98	'FREMLINS'	10
C006	98	'TESCO'	12
C007	98	'DIECAST COLLECTOR'	12
C008	98	'ODC' Xmas 98	14
C009	99	'RADIO TIMES'	70
C010	99	'BRAKSPEAR'	1.5
C011	99	'BRONCHO BILL'	5
C012	99	'WATERFORD CRYSTAL'	3.5
C013U	99	'BERGEN Eve RECORD'	3.5
C014	99	'ALCOA'	2
C015U	99	'KOUNTRY FRESH'	3.5
C016	99	'AYLWARD & SONS'	2
C017	99	'MARCEL' (circus)	5
C018	99	'TEN PENNY ALE'	2
C019	99	'CELTIC MANOR'	2
C020	99	'DAILY EXPRESS'	15
C021	99	'IMPERIAL ALE' (members only)	2
C022U	99	'GRANTS FARM'	27
C023	99	'TURTLE WAX'	5
C024	99	'EXPRESS' (Edward & Sophie)	35
C025U	99	'KROGER PICKLES'	24
C026	99	'VICTORIA BITTER' (members)	2
C027U	99	'COLONIAL'	20
C028U	99	'RAINBO'	15
C029	00	'MARSH BREWERY' (members)	2
C030	00	'US ARMY' (members only)	2
C031U	00	'GEORGIA FARM'	3
C032	00	'BRITISH LEGION'	95
C033	00	'DESERT FORCE'	1.5
C034	00	'CAINS BREWERY'	2.5
C035	00	'DAILY TELEGRAPH'	30
C036	00	'RHYS COAL' (members only)	2.5
C037U	00	'INSTANT RICE'	9.5
C038	00	'L.N.E.R.' (members only)	1.5
C039	00	'MILLINGTONS'	1.5
C040D	00	'KUPPERS'	1.5
C041	00	'Imperial Force' (members only)	2.5
C042D	00	'KUPPERS'	1.3
C043	00	'RHS LINDLEY LIBRARY'	28
C044	00	'AMERICANA 2000'	2.5
C045	00	'SUNDAY POST 1980'	18
C046U	00	'KOUNTRY FRESH'	1.5
C047	00	'BRAINS BREWERY'	2
C048	00	'ODC PLATINUM MEMBER'	2.5
C049U	01	'NEW YORK POST'	2.5
C050	01	'SHELDONS'	8
C051	01	'ROYAL BRITISH LEGION'	25
C052	01	'YORKSHIRE POST'	2.5
C053	01	'DERST BAKERY'	10

Comic Cuts

Ref	Intro	Model	Made (x1,000)
CC1	00	'EAGLE'	1.5

Corner Shop (members only)

Ref	Intro	Model	Made (x1,000)
CS4	00	'HOME & COLONIAL'	0.8

Routemaster Bus

Ref	Intro	Model	Made (x1,000)
RM1	99	'NOTTINGHAM'	2.5
RM2	99	Notts County 'ENERGY'	2
RM3	99	'EAST YORKSHIRE'	2
RM4	99	'Sent to COVENTRY'	1.5
RM5	99	'STARDROPS'	2
RM6	99	'GREENLINE'	3
RM7	99	'NORTHERN BUS'	3
RM8U	99	'DAYS INN'	3
RM9	99	'L.T.' training bus	3.5
RM10	99	'LONDON COUNTRY'	3
RM11	99	'DAWSONS'	1
RM12	00	'SOUTH WALES'	3
RM13	00	'HALIFAX'	3
RM14	00	'NEW ZEALAND LAMB'	6
RM15	00	'KD TRANSPORT'	2
RM16	00	'LT Last Tram' (members only)	2
RM17	00	'Cavalcade of Steam'	2
RM18D	00	'BRANTHO-KORRUX'	1
RM19	00	'DAWSON RENTALS'	1.05
RM20	00	'ASTRAZENECA'	1.45
RM21	00	'BRITISH AIRWAYS' (members)	2
RM22	00	'HAMILTON QUARTER'	2
RM23	00	'KENTISH BUS' (members only)	1.5
RM24	01	'BEEFEATER'	12
RM25	01	'BEA'	2
RM26	01	'SILVER JUBILEE'	2.5
RM27	01	'FORESTER'	1.5
RM28	01	'JOB OPPORTUNITIES'	3.5

Sets of models

Ref	Intro	Model	Made (x1,000)
1	96	'World Cup Set' (12)	20
2	96	'Broncho Bill's Circus' (6)	5.25
3	98	'London Bus Set' (2)	6
4	99	'Home Guard Set' (4)	3.5
5	99	'Coventry Bus Set' (2)	2
6	00	'Dunkirk Set' (4)	1.5
7	00	'Battle of Britain' (4)	1.5
8	00	'Smoker's Set' (4)	1

Mini Classics Collections (sets of 3):

Ref	Intro	Model	Made (x1,000)
1	99	'Southern Collection'	2.6
2	99	'North West Collection'	5
3	99	'LMS Collection'	5
4	99	'Scottish Collection'	5
5	00	'Butlins Collection'	2
6	00	'Luton Town FC Collection'	2
7	00	'Malta Collection'	1
8	00	'J. Arthur Rank Collection'	1
9	00	'Railway Deliveries'	2
10	00	'G.W.R.'	2
11	00	'Southern'	2
12	00	'L.N.E.R.'	2
13	00	'British Rail'	2

'Sporting Heroes'

'SPORTING HEROES' range models have optional certificate which is signed personally by the named celebrity. £5-95 each with certificate £4-95 without.

Ref	Intro	Model	Made (x1,000)
SH1g	95	John Emburey	5
SH2g	98	Geoff Boycott OBE, England	5
SH3g	97	Gordon Banks OBE, Stoke	5
SH4	97	Geoff Boycott OBE, Yorks	5
SH5	98	Sir Stanley Matthews	4
SH6g	97	Gavin Hastings, Scotland	5
SH7g	97	Rob Andrew, England	5
SH8g	97	Ieuan Evans, Wales	5
SH9g	96	Nigel Winterburn	1.1
SH10g	97	Nick Popplewell	5
SH11g	99	Sir Henry Cooper OBE KSG	3
SH12g	00	Bob Champion MBE	2.5

'Mobiles' (Novelty Advertising Vehicles)

Ref	Intro	Model	Made (x1,000)
MO1	93	'OUTSPAN Oranges'	NC
MO2	96	'OUTSPAN Grapefruit'	NC

Cubs

All uncertificated.

Ref	Intro	Model	Made (x1,000)
Cub1	99	'MALTA'	?
Cub2	99	'MALTA' ('Valetta')	?
Cub?G	99	'PADDY'S WHISKY'	?
Cub?R	99	'PADDY'S WHISKY'	?

Milk Floats

Ref	Intro	Model	Made (x1,000)
D1	01	'DAIRY CREST'	?
D2	01	'ARLA'	?
D3	01	'MILLENIUM'	?
D4	01	'EXPRESS'	?

Consruction vehicles

Ref	Intro	Model	Made (x1,000)
A40D	01	'VOLVO' articulated hauler	?
18C	01	'CLEVELAND FIRE' Volvo BM materials loader	?

Display Cases

Wooden cabinets (in a variety of finishes) with 'Oxford Die-Cast' logo on front.

Ref		Description
OD1	24x16 in. , vertical, 7 shelves	
OD1a	24x16 in. , horizontal, 5 shelves	
OD2	32x22 in. , vertical, 11 shelves	
OD2a	32x22 in. , horizontal, 7 shelves	

Collectors notes

Minor Manufacturers

Many toys and models exist about which we know very little. The 1940s in particular saw a proliferation of small manufacturers (often only a one-man operation in a North London shed). In this post-wartime period the established manufacturers were engaged in an export drive that meant shortages of products at home. Not surprisingly, enterprising ex-servicemen and others turned their hands to toy production on a scale that they could manage. Their range was small (sometimes only one product) and they were often in business for only a year or two.

One outcome of this is that some toys and models discovered in attics or at swapmeets present us with a puzzle. Who made the item? When were they in production? Where was the maker's workshop? Very often there is no information at all on the product or simply a statement to the fact that it was 'Made in England'. Identification is sometimes diffcult – but is it impossible?

Since the 8th Edition was published, some very interesting additional information has been obtained and we are delighted to be able to pass on the details below. However, we do still require your help, so if you have any information on any of the manufacturers listed below, please write to: The Editor, Swapmeet Publications, PO Box 47, Felixstowe, Suffolk, IP11 9HE.

Arbur	**Condon**	**John Hill & Co.**	**Mafwo**	**Tal Developments**
Baxtoys	**W.H.Cornelius**	**Jolly Roger**	**Millbo**	**Teddy Toys**
Betal	**Denzil Skinner**	**Kenbo**	**Millbro**	**Industries**
BMC	**Eaglewall Plastics**	**Kenbro**	**Model Toys**	**Toby**
Bren L Toys	**Empro**	**Kemlow**	**Moultoys Ltd**	**Toy Products**
Castle Art	**Gaiety**	**Kitmaster**	**Salco**	**Trent Products**
Cherilea	**Goody Toys**	**Knight**	**Slikka**	**Wardie**
City Toys	**Johillco**	**Louis Marx**	**Sundaw**	

ARBUR PRODUCTS   BREN L TOYS   TOBY   JOLLY ROGER

John Hill & Co.
i) **Roman Gladiator Set**: Gold Chariot and Charioteer, 2 horses, 5 Centurion Gladiators + Officer in pale cream toga. Boxed**£125-150**
ii) **Roman Chariot**: Gold Chariot with 2 horses and Gold Charioteer...........................**£80-100**

Brimtoy (diecast issues)
1948-50 **Vauxhall Saloon**. Yellow body, Silver trim, cast wheels, plain card box with model picture..**£100-150**

Sundaw Products (c1950)
H130 **Single-deck Motor Bus**. Red body, 'TRANSPORT SERVICES' logo, rubber wheels. Red/white end-flap box with picture...**£250-350**
H131 **Double-deck Motor Bus**. Green body, 'TRANSPORT SERVICES' logo, rubber wheels. Green/white end-flap box with model picture **£400-600**
NB Similar models were sold by Vectis Auctions Ltd in December 2000 for **£180** (H130) and **£600** (H131). (See pictures in the 'Miscellaneous Models' colour section.)

True-to-Type Models (similar in size to
Matchbox Miniatures; all have unpainted cast wheels)
i) **Cable-Layer Truck**. Green truck, Grey/Cream cable drum......................**£25-35**
ii) **Tip Cart Truck**. Red body and tipper **£25-35**
iii) **Excavator Truck**. Green body, Blue back........................**£25-35**
NB The three models listed above were sold by Vectis Auctions Ltd in 2000 for **£800**!

Kemlow
Made in the 1950s by Kemlow's Diecasting Products Ltd., Wood Green, London. Their distributors were B.J. Ward Ltd. (trading as 'Wardie Products'). Products included:
'PICKFORDS' Removal Van, 1:60 ....
Articulated Timber Truck, 1:50.................
Farm Tractor and Trailer, 1:60...................
Caravan. 1:43......................................
Ford Zephyr Mk.I, 1:43 ....
Thornycroft Mighty Antar, 1:43 and 1:60...
Flat Truck, 1:50 ....
Armoured Car, 1:60 ....
Field Gun, 1:60 ....

Kemlow 'PICKFORDS' Van

Jolly Roger
Made c1946/7 by Tremo Mouldings, Cardiff. Boxed models include:
Maserati...
Plymouth Saloon (see main picture above)...

Bradcars (c1950-55)
Bradshaws Model Products. 1:75 scale.
One-piece castings, no interiors.
Boxed models include:
Austin A30, **Riley 1.5 litre**, **Austin 7**, **Morris 6**.

Gaiety Toys (late 1940s)
Castle Art Products Ltd., Birmingham.
Models in boxes are rare. Products known:
Morgan 3-wheel Sports Car, 4.75in. long....
Racing Car, single driver, 5in. long..............
Racing Car, driver/co-driver, 4in. long.........
Racing Car, single driver, 3.25in. long..........
Fire Engine...
Models are painted various colours, often chromed.

Set of Petrol Pumps marked 'A Wardie Product'.
(Photo: Peter Brighty)

Abbreviations

A

A.E.C.	Associated Equipment Company
AA	Anti-aircraft
A.A.	Automobile Association
ABC-TV	Associated British Cinemas (Television)
A.F.S.	Auxiliary Fire Service
AG	Amber glass
AMC	American Motor Corporation
APC	Armoured Personnel Carrier
ATV	Associated Television

B

BA	British Airways
BAC	British Airways Corporation
BB	Black base
BBC	British Broadcasting Corporation
BEA	British European Airways
BFPO	British Forces Post Office
BG	Blue glass
bhp	brake horsepower
BLMC	British Leyland Motor Corporation
BMC	British Motor Corporation
BMW	Bayrische Motoren-Werke
B.O.A.C.	British Overseas Airways
BP	British Petroleum
BPT	Black plastic tyres
BPW	Black plastic wheels
BR	British Railways
BRM	British Racing Motors
BRS	British Road Services
B.S.M.	British School of Motoring
BW	Black wheels

C

CA	A type of Bedford van
CF	A type of Bedford van
CG	Clear glass
CLE	Certificated Limited Edition
cv	chevaux-vapeur (a measure of power; translated into English, it literally means 'horse-steams')
C.W.S.	Co-operative Wholesale Society
cwt.	hundred-weight

D

DCMT	Die Casting Machine Tools
DG	(Lledo) Days Gone
DH	De Havilland
Dk.	Dark (shade of colour)
DTB	'Dinky Toys' on base
DUKW	An amphibious military vehicle developed by General Motors in WWII. The letters are not initials or an abbreviation but simply part of an early drawing office reference.

E

E	East
EEC	European Economic Community
E.F.E.	Exclusive First Editions
e.g.	exempli gratia (= 'for example')
EMI	Electrical & Musical Industries
ER	Elizabetha Regina, (E II R, Queen Elizabeth II)
ERF	Edwin Richard Foden
Est.	Established (or estimate/d)

F

Fiat	(or FIAT) Fabbrica Italiana Automobile Torino
fig(s)	figure(s)

G

GB	Green box, or Grey base
G.B.	Great Britain
GBT	Globe-Trotter
GER	Great Eastern Railway
GG	Green glass
GMC	General Motors Corporation
GP	Grand Prix
GPO	General Post Office
GPW	Grey plastic wheels
GR	Georgius Rex
GS	Gift Set
GSP	Gift Set price
GTO	Gran Turismo Omologato
GTV	Gran Turismo Veloce
GUS	Great Universal Stores
GWR	Great Western Railway

H

HM	His/Her Majesty
HMAC	His Majesty's Armoured Car
HMS	His/Her Majesty's Ship
H.M.V.	'His Masters Voice'
hp	horse-power
H.W.M.	Hersham & Walton Motors

I

IBM	International Business Machines
ICI	Imperial Chemical Industries
INTER	(or INTL) International
I.O.M.	Isle of Man

J

JB	James Bond
JCB	Joseph C. Bamford
J.M.T.	Jersey Motor Transport

K

K.D.F.	Kraft durch Freude
K.L.G.	Kenelm Lee Guinness
K.L.M.	Koninklijke Luchtvaart Maatschappij NV (Dutch airline)

L

L.A.P.D.	Los Angeles Police Department
LE	Limited Edition
LM	Le Mans
LMS	London Midland & Scottish Railway
LNER	London & North Eastern Railway
LNWR	London & North Western Railway
LP	Lledo Promotional
LT	London Transport
Lt.	Light (shade of colour)
Ltd.	Limited Liability Company
LWB	Long wheel-base

M

MB	Matchbox
Met.	Metallic
MG	Make of car, ('Morris Garages')
MGA, MGB, MGC	types of MG car
M.I.C.A.	Matchbox International Collectors Association
mm.	millimetres
MOY	Models of Yesteryear
MPR	Market Price Range
MW	Metal wheels

N

N	North
NAAFI	Navy, Army & Air Force Institutes
N.A.S.A.	National Aeronautics & Space Administration
NB	nota bene ('mark well')
NCL	National Carriers Limited
NCO	Non-Commissioned Officer
NCP	National Car Parks
NEC	National Exhibition Centre
NGPP	No guide price at present
nhp	(or n.h.p.) nominal horsepower
No.	Number
NPP	No price possible
NS	(or n/s) Nearside
NSPCC	National Society for the Prevention of Cruelty to Children

O

OPO	On-pack offer
OG	Orange glass
OS	(or o/s) Offside

P

PB	Propeller blade(s)
PG	Purple glass
PLC	Public Limited Company
P.M.G	Post Master General (Australia)
PO	Post Office
PRM	Promotional model
PSV	Public service vehicle
P.T.T.	Postes-Telephones-Telegraphes

R

RAC	Royal Automobile Club
RAF	Royal Air Force
R.C.M.P.	Royal Canadian Mounted Police
RHD	Right-hand drive
RM	Routemaster (bus)
RN(s)	Racing or Rally number(s)
RNLI	Royal National Life-boat Institution

S

S	South
SB	Silver base
SBRW	Solid black rubber wheels
SBX	Special box
S.F.F.D.	San Francisco Fire Department
S.F.P.D.	San Francisco Police Dept.
SPW	Silver plastic wheels
SR	Southern Railway
St.	Saint or Street
STP	Scientifically-Treated Petroleum
SWB	Short wheel-base
SWRW	Solid white rubber wheels

T

TC	Twin carburettors
TDF	Tour de France
TK	Type of Bedford truck
TP	Twin Pack
TS	'Touring Secours'
TT	Two-tone (or Tourist Trophy)
TV	Television
TWA	Trans-World Airlines

U

UB	Unboxed, or Unpainted base
UK	United Kingdom
UN	United Nations
US	United States (of America)
USA	United States of America
USAAF	United States Army Air Force
USAF	United States Air Force
USS	United Space Starship
UW	Unpainted wheels

V

VW	Volkswagen

W

W	West
WB	Window box, or White base
WW	Wide wheels

Y

YB	Yellow box, or Yellow base
YMCA	Young Men's Christian Association

Swapmeet Publications Reader Service

9th Edition
'British Diecast Model Toys Catalogue'
Reader Survey

Whether you are a collector or trader, we would greatly value your views on this new Edition and would ask you to kindly complete and return this questionnaire.

We hope to publish the results of this survey, and for the three most constructive and helpful replies that we receive, we shall be giving a year's **free subscription** to the collecting magazine or newspaper of their choice. If necessary, do please use a photocopy of this form or a separate sheet of paper for your response. Thank you.

1   What do you like MOST about the Catalogue? _____

_____

2   What do you like LEAST about the Catalogue? _____

_____

3   What improvements or additions would you like to see? _____

_____

4   Would you like the Catalogue to be published yearly or every two years?

_____

If you have model information not currently included in the Catalogue – do please send it to us. Your costs will be fully refunded.

Name and Address (BLOCK CAPITALS, please) _____

_____

_____

Kindly send your response to:
Swapmeet Publications, PO Box 47, Felixstowe, Suffolk, IP11 7LP.

Sale and Purchase Record

Date	Models bought or sold	Price

Sale and Purchase Record

Date	Models bought or sold	Price

Guide to Advertisers

Official Company Acknowledgements

The names 'CORGI TOYS', 'CARS OF THE '50s', 'CORGITRONICS', 'CORGIMATICS', 'HUSKY', 'JUNIORS', 'ROCKETS' and 'CAMEOS' are all acknowledged as trademarks of Corgi Classics Ltd.
The names 'CORGI CLASSICS', 'ORIGINAL OMNIBUS COMPANY', 'TRAMLINES', 'TRAMWAY CLASSICS', 'VINTAGE GLORY', 'DIBNAH'S CHOICE' and 'AVIATION ARCHIVE' are acknowledged as trademarks of Corgi Classics Ltd.
The names 'LLEDO', 'MODELS OF DAYS-GONE', 'DAYS-GONE', 'VANGUARDS' and 'MARATHONS' are acknowledged as trademarks of Corgi Classics Ltd.

'EXCLUSIVE FIRST EDITIONS' is acknowledged as a trademark of Gilbow (Holdings) Ltd.
'BRITAINS' is acknowledged as the trademark of Britains Ltd.
The name 'OXFORD DIE-CAST' is acknowledged as the trademark of Oxford Die-Cast Ltd., Aylesbury, Bucks.
The name 'TRI-ANG' is acknowledged as a trademark of Hornby Hobbies Ltd., Margate, Kent.
The names 'MATCHBOX', 'MATCHBOX COLLECTIBLES', 'MODELS of YESTERYEAR', 'DINKY TOYS' and 'SUPERFAST' are acknowledged as trademarks of Mattel Inc. USA.

Edition 3 of 'British Model Trains Catalogue' will be available in the Autumn of 2002